34th EUROPEAN SYMPOSIUM ON COMPUTER AIDED PROCESS ENGINEERING / 15th INTERNATIONAL SYMPOSIUM ON PROCESS SYSTEMS ENGINEERING

VOLUME 3

COMPUTER-AIDED CHEMICAL ENGINEERING, 53

34th EUROPEAN SYMPOSIUM ON COMPUTER AIDED PROCESS ENGINEERING / 15th INTERNATIONAL SYMPOSIUM ON PROCESS SYSTEMS ENGINEERING

VOLUME 3

Edited by

Flavio Manenti
*"Giulio Natta" Department of Chemistry, Materials and Chemical Engineering,
Polytechnic University of Milan, Milan, Italy*

Gintaras V. Reklaitis
*Davidson School of Chemical Engineering, Purdue University,
West Lafayette, Indiana, United States*

ELSEVIER

Amsterdam – Boston – Heidelberg – London – New York – Oxford
Paris – San Diego – San Francisco – Singapore – Sydney – Tokyo

Elsevier
Radarweg 29, PO Box 211, 1000 AE Amsterdam, Netherlands
The Boulevard, Langford Lane, Kidlington, Oxford OX5 1GB, UK
50 Hampshire Street, 5th Floor, Cambridge, MA 02139, USA

Notices
Knowledge and best practice in this field are constantly changing. As new research and experience
broaden our understanding, changes in research methods, professional practices, or medical treatment
may become necessary.

Practitioners and researchers must always rely on their own experience and knowledge in evaluating
and using any information, methods, compounds, or experiments described herein. In using such
information or methods they should be mindful of their own safety and the safety of others, including
parties for whom they have a professional responsibility.

To the fullest extent of the law, neither the Publisher nor the authors, contributors, or editors, assume
any liability for any injury and/or damage to persons or property as a matter of products liability,
negligence or otherwise, or from any use or operation of any methods, products, instructions, or ideas
contained in the material herein.

British Library Cataloguing in Publication Data
A catalogue record for this book is available from the British Library

Library of Congress Cataloging-in-Publication Data
A catalog record for this book is available from the Library of Congress

ISBN (Volume 3): 978-0-443-33899-1
ISBN (Set) :   978-0-443-28824-1
ISSN: 1570-7946

For information on all Elsevier publications visit our
website at https://www.elsevier.com/

  Working together
to grow libraries in
developing countries

www.elsevier.com • www.bookaid.org

Publisher: Candice Janco
Acquisition Editor: Anita Koch
Editorial Project Manager: Lena Sparks
Production Project Manager: Paul Prasad Chandramohan
Designer: Mark Rogers

Typeset by STRAIVE

Contents

Flavio Manenti, Gintaras V. Reklaitis (Eds.), Proceedings of the 34th European Symposium on Computer Aided Process Engineering / 15th International Symposium on Process Systems Engineering (ESCAPE34/PSE24), June 2-6, 2024, Florence, Italy

Learning based Adaptive Robust Control of a Precipitation Process

Sandesh Hiremath,[a] Mikhail Kakanov,[a] Andreas Voigt,[b] Kai Sundmacher,[b] Naim Bajcinca[a]

[a]*Department of Mechanical and Process Engineering, RPTU Kaiserslautern, Gottlieb Daimler-Straße 42, 67663 Kaiserslautern, Germany.*
[b]*Faculty of Process and Systems Engineering Institute of Process Engineering Universitätsplatz 2, 39106 Magdeburg, Germany.*
sandesh.hiremath@rptu.de

Abstract

In this work we propose a novel learning-based controller for the control of a batch-type precipitation process involving a carbonate substance. The controller utilizes a stochastic state space model for predicting the process dynamics. The prediction model is based on population balance equation and particle growth kinetics. The model also accounts for stochastic factors, process uncertainties and model imperfections. The controller is designed via a predictive stochastic control formulation and is implemented in a learnable manner. For this we propose a novel architecture where in both the prediction model Φ and control synthesis model Λ are implemented using a deep neural network (DNN) based on which we incorporate joint training of Λ and Φ via transfer-learning technique. Finally, we perform simulations and demonstrate the superior robustness to stochastic disturbances and improved adaptivity to the varying process dynamics.

Keywords: Stochastic PDE control, Learning-based control, Process control.

1. Introduction

Solving global climate change problem requires innovative strategies for reducing greenhouse gas emissions, particularly the permanent sequestration of carbon dioxide. Carbon mineralization, proposed in 1990 (Seifritz, 1990), offers a way to store CO2 as stable and eco-friendly carbonates, establishing a leakage-free method for its disposal. Calcium and magnesium, among abundant alkaline earth metals, stand out for carbonate formation (Goff et al., 1998). Natural minerals and industrial waste streams like cement, coal ash, and steelmaking slag serve as viable feedstocks (Sanna et al., 2014). Chemical processes often involve macroscopic and microscopic phenomena, impacting material properties. Specifically, within carbonate precipitation, precise particle size distribution (PSD) control is pivotal for optimizing throughput and sustainability of carbon capture and storage. Control methodologies for chemical systems range from PDEs, molecular dynamics, and Monte-Carlo models to integro-differential equations like population balances. The field has seen significant advancements in nonlinear PDEs, leading to robust controllers (Armaou et al., 2006). Control strategies now encompass particulate and fluid dynamic systems (Rajagopalan et al., 2019) with approaches to distributed parameter systems like passivity-based (Ydstie, 2002) and predictive control (Chen et al., 2019). These classical control methods face challenges in handling noisy perturbations and lack real-time autonomy due to the necessity of frequent system re-identification, thus impeding production throughput. Furthermore, the static/dynamic optimization formulations limit adaptability and learning from data, unlike their statistical counterpart.

The success of machine learning, especially deep neural networks (DNNs) has revolutionized solution techniques across all domains of research and applications, in particular also for the control of particulate processes. The Deep-Q-Network (DQN) technique is an example of this approach (Mnih et al., 2013), which has been successfully applied in various industrial contexts, including optimizing multi-stage precipitation processes for zinc product purity (Chen et al., 2020). Similarly, for the control of mobile robots' learnable predictive controllers are also popularly used (Hiremath. et al., 2023); (Hiremath. et al., 2022). Although DNN-based methods have limitations concerning explainability and risk quantification, hybrid methods such as model-based RL and physics informed approaches have emerged (Rudy et al., 2017); (Raissi, 2018) to alleviate some of these limitations. Altogether, DNN-based techniques offer innovative solutions to tough challenges in the autonomous control of particulate processes and promises generalized control strategies and high autonomy.

This work presents a novel control method of a precipitation process robust to noise and adaptive to the variability of process dynamics. We employ stochastic partial differential equations (SPDEs) for modeling the evolution of PSD and stochastic optimal control problems (SOCPs) for control synthesis. Both the models are implemented using DNNs. Specifically, a Gated Recurrent Unit (GRU) architecture is employed for control synthesis, while a UNet architecture for the prediction of the process dynamics. The two are combined via transfer-learning technique to obtain a learnable, adaptive and robust controller (LARC). The structure of this article includes a formal problem formulation (Section 2) detailing process modeling (Section 2.1) and predictive control (Section 2.2). We discuss the design concepts of the learning-based control system in Section 3 and in Section 4 presents insights from numerical simulations. Finally, in Section 5 we summarize the findings and provide concluding remarks.

2. Problem formulation

2.1. Process modelling

This work focuses on controlling the precipitation of a carbonate (such as $CaCO_3$, $MgCO_3$) from an aqueous solution containing corresponding ions (such as Ca^{+2} or Mg^{+2}), carbon dioxide (CO_2), and seed particles. The operating conditions of the reactor tank such as pH, temperature, and pressure, influence the kinetics of the ions that eventually leads to the carbonate formation. We model the precipitation process using a coupled system of ordinary and partial differential equations. For the sake of simplicity and also to align with experimental settings, we neglect nucleation and disregard thermodynamic influences like temperature and pressure. Based on this we employ a population balance equation (PBE) to describe the evolution of particle size distribution (PSD) and couple it with the evolution of ion concentration, modeled using ODEs. Let $f: R^+ \times R^+ \to R^+$ represent the PSD of carbonate particles, where $f(t,x)$ denotes particle density at time $t \geq 0$ and size $x > 0$. Similarly, letting $c: R^+ \to R^+$ be the ion concentration in the solution the simplified precipitation model reads

$$\frac{\partial f}{\partial t}(t,x) = \frac{1}{\tau_t}\left(f_0(x) - f(t,x)\right) - G(t)\frac{\partial f}{\partial x}(t,x), \text{ for } t,x > 0, \text{ and } f(0,x) = f_0, f(t,0) = \frac{b(t)}{G(t)}$$

$$dc_t = \left(\frac{-c_t}{\tau_t} - \rho k_v G(t)M(t)\right)dt + \sigma c_t dW_t, \text{ for t} > 0, \text{ and } c(0) = c_0 \qquad (1)$$

$$G(t) = k_g\left(\frac{c(t)}{c_{sat}} - 1\right)^{1.5}, M(t) = \int_0^\infty x^2 f(t,x)dx, b(t) = \rho k_b\left(\frac{c(t)}{c_{sat}} - 1\right)^{2.5} M(t).$$

As mentioned above, $f(t,x) \propto 1/m^4$ represents the PSD of carbonate, where $x \propto \mu m$ denotes particle size. $c(t) \propto mol/l$ signifies the ion concentration, $G(t) \propto m/s$ is the growth rate of the carbonate particles, and $M(t) \propto 1/m$ is the second moment of $f(t, x)$, indicating particle surface area. $\tau(t) \propto min$ denotes residence time for the ion particles in aqueous state. Additionally, $\rho \propto mol/m^3$ represents density, $c_{sat} \propto mol/l$ is the saturation constant, $k_g \propto \mu m/s$ is the growth rate coefficient, and $k_v = 1$ is the particle shape coefficient. The concentration equation incorporates state-dependent stochastic noise, modeled by standard Brownian motion W_t, capturing thermodynamic fluctuations and ion concentration impurities. This coupling with the PBE, in general, results in SPDE which we compactly write (1) as an abstract Cauchy problem

$$dX_t = [A(X_t, U_t; \theta)X_t + H(X_t, U_t; \theta)]dt + X_t^T \Sigma_t dW_t, \text{for } t > 0, \text{and } X(0) = X_0$$

$$A(X_t, U_t; \theta) = \begin{pmatrix} -G(t)\partial_x - U_t & 0 \\ 0 & -U_t \end{pmatrix}, \ H_t := \begin{pmatrix} U_t f_0 \\ -\rho k_v G(t) M(t) \end{pmatrix}, \ U_t = \frac{1}{\tau(t)} \tag{2}$$

$$X_t := [f_t, c_t]^T, \Sigma_t := \begin{pmatrix} 0 & 0 \\ 0 & \sigma_t \end{pmatrix}, \theta := [k_v, k_g, k_b, \rho, c_{sat}]^T$$

Here A denotes an unbounded nonlinear operator whose domain adheres to the boundary conditions, H_t denotes the nonlinear reaction terms, θ denotes the vector of process parameters, and U_t denotes the control.

2.2. Predictive control formulation

The control method is based on the stochastic optimal control problem (SOCP) formulation. This entails the use of a suitable objective function J which reads

$$J(x, U; \theta, X) = E\left[\int_0^T \alpha_u |u_s|_2^2 ds + \alpha_T |X_T - Y_T|_2^2 | X_0 = x\right], \alpha_u := 0.01, \alpha_T := 1.$$

Based on this the optimal control policy U^* is obtained as a solution to the SOCP

$$U^* = argmin_{U \in \mathcal{U}} \ J(x, U; \theta, Y), \text{s.t. (2) holds.} \tag{3}$$

Thus, obtained policy U^* can be viewed as a mapping $(x, \theta, Y) \mapsto U^*$ which in turn defines an optimal control law denoted as $U^* = \pi^*(x, \theta, Y)$.

3. DNN Implementation

We solve the above SOCP (3) in a generalized manner by leveraging the universal approximation power of DNNs. Thus, we focus on constructing an approximate $\Lambda(\xi)$ for the optimal control law $\pi^*(\xi)$. Based on this Λ is implemented as a DNN whose parameters are represented by $\lambda \in R^l$. Thus $\lambda \mapsto \Lambda(\xi; \lambda)$ represents a parameterized estimator and the optimal parameter $\hat{\lambda}$ is obtained by optimizing (training) it over a suitable dataset $\mathcal{X}$. This leads to the following statistical problem (SP)

$$\widehat{\lambda^M} = \arg\min_{\lambda \in R^l} \frac{1}{M} \sum_{k=1}^M \sum_{i=1}^N |\widehat{U_{t_i}^k}|_2^2 + |\Phi_{t_N} - Y_{t_N}^k|_2^2 + \max\left(0, \text{mode}\left(\widehat{f_{t_i}^k}\right) - \text{mode}(f_{t_i}^k)\right). \tag{4}$$

Here Φ is another DNN, with parameters $\varphi \in R^p$, that serves as a model for predicting the dynamics of the process for a given input $\zeta := (x, \theta, U)$. Similarly, the map $\zeta \mapsto \Phi(\zeta)$ is obtained by statistically optimizing over $\mathcal{Y}$, which leads to the following SP

$$\widehat{\varphi^M} = \arg\min_{\varphi \in R^p} \frac{1}{M} \sum_{k=1}^M \sum_{i=1}^N |\widehat{X_{t_i}^k} - X_{t_i}^k|_2^2 + |\text{mode}\left(\widehat{f_{t_i}^k}\right) - \text{mode}(f_{t_i}^k)|_2^2. \tag{5}$$

Using Φ as the predictor while training Λ offers several advantages: (i) flexibility in coping with process variability, (ii) expediting controller training by avoiding explicit process dynamics solving, and (iii) enables adaptation to measured data. The combined networks $\Lambda(\Phi)$ create a learning-based robust and adaptive controller called as LARC. Since the lab setup and experimentations are still in progress, we circumvent the bottleneck of data unavailability by synthetically generating the datasets $\mathcal{Y}$ and $\mathcal{X}$ for training the Φ and Λ networks respectively. To this end, the parameters are obtained by uniformly sampling from intervals defined in Table 1 and the reference process dynamics is obtained by numerical integration of (2). Altogether $\mathcal{X}$ and $\mathcal{Y}$ are composed of $M = 15K$ samples each, which was then split into train, test and validation sets in the ratio $3 : 1: 1$, resulting in $9K$ samples for training and $3K$ samples for testing and validation each.

Table 1: *Variable interval bounds*

Variable	Min	Max	Unit	Variable	Min	Max	Unit
τ	10	500	min	x	0	1	μm
ρ	0.01	0.05	g/cm^3	c_0	0.00125	0.05	mol/l
k_g	1	15	$\mu m/s$	μ_0	0.2	0.8	μm
c_{sat}	$1e^{-05}$	$2e^{-05}$	mol/l	k_b	0	0	1

The Φ network predicts PSD $\widehat{f}_t$ and ion concentration $\widehat{c}_t$ in the joint space $[0, Time] \times [0, Size]$. Due to the effective multiscale design of the UNet, Φ is implemented as per that architecture, with 27 layers resulting in $17M$ trainable parameters. The Λ network, designed for sequential predictions, utilizes a stacked GRU-based architecture with 2 stacked layers resulting in 156 trainable parameters. The training sequence involves training Φ first and subsequently using it for training Λ.

Figure 1: *Training and validation plots for $\Lambda(\Phi)$ (left), MAE values for adaptability (middle) test for Φ and $\widehat{\Phi}$ and robustness (right) tests for $\Lambda(\Phi)$ and $\Lambda(\widehat{\Phi})$.*

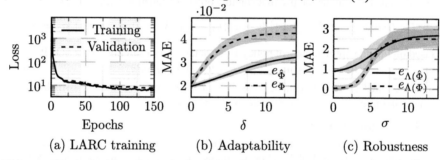

(a) LARC training   (b) Adaptability   (c) Robustness

This constitutes the idea of transfer-learning where pre-trained process network $\widehat{\Phi}$ is jointly re-trained with the Λ network. This approach on the one hand enables to obtain a more adaptive and robust control architecture and on the other hand facilitates online/active closed-loop learning on live data. After 150 epochs the joint training is resulted in a good reduction in the loss functional. Furthermore, a similar loss reduction on the validation-set (as shown in Figure 1(a)) signifies minimal over-fitting. With this we obtain a trained controller $\Lambda(\Phi)$ which we shall use to perform closed loop simulations and also evaluate its robustness and adaptiveness behaviour.

4. Numerical Simulations

In this section, numerical experiments are conducted to study the adaptiveness and robustness property of the LARC model $\Lambda(\Phi)$. For testing the adaptiveness, the Φ model is fed with a noisy parameter $\tilde{\theta}_t$ obtained as a noisy perturbation of the nominal value θ_t. More specifically, $\tilde{\theta}_t = \theta_t(1 + \delta z)$ for $R^d \ni z \sim \mathcal{N}(0,1)$, with d being the dimension of θ_t. Letting f_T denote the reference PSD obtained via numerical integration of (2) with θ_t as the parameter and letting $\widehat{f}_T(\delta)$ denote the prediction of Φ using $\tilde{\theta}_t$, we define the mean absolute error (MAE) $e_\Phi(\delta) := \frac{1}{b}\sum_{k=1}^{b}\left|f_T^k - \widehat{f}_T^k(\delta)\right|$ with batch size $b = 100$. Based on this we compute $e_\Phi(\delta)$ and $e_{\widehat{\Phi}}(\delta)$ for increasing values of δ using retuned and the initial trained process models Φ and $\hat{\Phi}$ respectively. The obtained values are plotted in Figure. 1(b) based on which we see that both models are fairly robust to perturbations in the parameter with deviation in the order of 10^{-2}. Furthermore, we see that the retuned model (dashed line) is quicker in adapting to large perturbations. Based on this we can infer that the transfer-learnt Φ model is relatively more adaptive compared to $\hat{\Phi}$. Next, we performed a robustness experiment with the controller network $\Lambda(\Phi)$ where we sequentially fed the controller with perturbed feedback $\widetilde{X_t} = \left[\widetilde{f_t}, \widetilde{c_t}\right]^{\mathsf{T}}$ obtained from a numerically simulated process with an increasing intensity of the process noise parameter $\sigma_t = \sigma$. This corresponds to a closed-loop simulation with a noisy simulated process model which we ran for 200 time steps with sampling time $t_s = 0.1\text{min}$. Based on this we computed the MAE $e_{\Lambda(\Phi)}(\sigma) := \sum_{k=1}^{b}\left|\widehat{f_T^k}(\sigma) - \overline{f_T^k}\right|$, of the final controlled PSD $\widehat{f_T}(\sigma)$ from the prescribed target PSD $\overline{f_T}$ on the test dataset with batch size $b = 100$. The errors so obtained for increasing values of σ are as shown in Figure. 1(c). From the plot we see that even with 2 fold increase in the noise intensity, $e_{\Lambda}(\sigma)$ was within the tolerable threshold of ≤ 0.05. Furthermore, in comparison to $e_{\Lambda(\hat{\Phi})}$ (i.e. the MAE obtained for Λ trained with fixed process network $\hat{\Phi}$) we see that $e_{\Lambda(\Phi)}$ is relatively negligible for small σ values and also shows faster saturation to increasing σ values. This further indicates that the higher adaptability of Φ enables more robust behavior of $\Lambda(\Phi)$. Altogether, from Figure. 1(b), (c) we can infer that $\Lambda(\Phi)$ is an adaptive and robust controller. Finally, we used the $\Lambda(\Phi)$ for the control of simulated precipitation process with default noise intensity of $\sigma = 0.1$ and for a given fixed initial and target PSD f_0 and $\overline{f_T}$ respectively. We performed six sequential batch operations with each batch running for 100 steps with sampling time $t_s = 0.1\text{min}$. The results of the simulation are as shown in Figure. 2. Based on this we see that $\Lambda(\Phi)$ was able to drive the initial PSD (dashed curve) of the simulated process (dark solid curve) to the target (dotted curve) in roughly 60mins even in the presence of moderate intensity of noise. Altogether, this indicates that the LARC model performs well in simulation and is ready for real closed loop testing.

Figure 2: *Batch control of precipitation process*

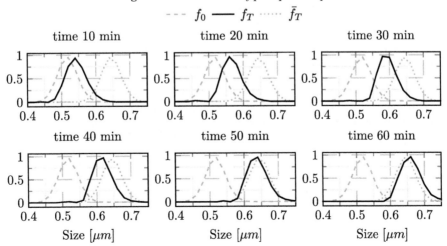

5. Conclusions

In this work, we have introduced a novel learning-based adaptive and robust controller (LARC) $\Lambda(\Phi)$ for the task of controlling a simplified precipitation model by utilizing the approximation power of DNN architectures, UNet for prediction and GRU for control synthesis. The numerical experiments indicate that the Φ model not only provides accurate predictions of PSD and ion concentration but is also adaptive to varying process parameters. The ability of $\Lambda(\Phi)$ to drive the system from an initial distribution to a predefined target, even in presence of moderate amount of noise, highlights its practical efficacy. Furthermore, the retuning of the Φ model while training the Λ network offers a more synchronized behavior wherein the retuned Φ offers better adaptivity. Additionally, the use of Φ as the prediction model facilitates active online/active learning based on live measurement data. Based on these, some of the planned work for the near future involves (i) incorporating measured data in the training, (ii) adapting the process model for pH-based control and also accounting for dynamic effects of temperature and pressure.

Acknowledgement: Funded by the Deutsche Forschungsgemeinschaft (DFG, German Research Foundation) - Priority Programme SPP2364 - Autonomous Processes in Particle Technology – project number 504852622.

References

A. Armaou, M. A. Demetriou, 2006. Optimal actuator/sensor placement for linear parabolic PDEs using spatial H2 norm. Chemical Engineering Science 61 (22), 7351–7367.

A. K. Rajagopalan, S. Bötschi, M. Morari, M. Mazzotti, 2019. Feedback Control for the Size and Shape Evolution of Needle-like Crystals in Suspension. III. Wet Milling. Crystal Growth and Design 19 (5), 2845–2861.

A. Sanna, M. Uibu, G. Caramanna, R. Kuusik, M. M. Maroto-Valer, 2014. A review of mineral carbonation technologies to sequester CO 2. Chem. Soc. Rev. 43 (23), 8049–8080.

B. Ydstie, 2002. Passivity based control via the second law. Computers & Chemical Engineering 26 (7), 1037–1048.

D. Shi, N. H. El-Farra, M. Li, P. Mhaskar, P. D. Christofides, 2006. Predictive control of particle size distribution in particulate processes. Chemical Engineering Science 61 (1), 268–281.

F. Goff, K. S. Lackner, 1998. Carbon Dioxide Sequestering Using Ultramafic Rocks. Environmental Geosciences 5 (3), 89–102.

M. Raissi, 2018. Deep hidden physics models: Deep learning of nonlinear partial differential equations. The Journal of Machine Learning Research 19 (1), 932–955.

N. Chen, J. Dai, X. Zhou, Q. Yang, W. Gui, 2019. Distributed Model Predictive Control of Iron Precipitation Process by Goethite Based on Dual Iterative Method. International Journal of Control, Automation and Systems 17 (5), 1233–1245.

N. Chen, S. Luo, J. Dai, B. Luo, W. Gui, 2020. Optimal Control of Iron-Removal Systems Based on Off-Policy Reinforcement Learning. IEEE Access 8, 149730–149740.

S. A. Hiremath, P. Gummadi, A. Tika, P. Rama, N. Bajcinca, 2023. Learning based interpretable end-to-end control using camera images. In: Proceedings of the 20th International Conference on Informatics in Control, Automation and Robotics - Volume 1: ICINCO. INSTICC, SciTePress, pp. 474–484

S. A. Hiremath, N. Bajcinca, 2022. DNN based learning algorithm for state constrained stochastic control of a 2d cartpole system. In: 2022 European Control Conference (ECC). IEEE.

S. H. Rudy, S. L. Brunton, J. L. Proctor, J. N. Kutz, 2017. Data-driven discovery of partial differential equations. Science Advances 3 (4).

V. Mnih, K. Kavukcuoglu, D. Silver, A. Graves, I. Antonoglou, D. Wierstra, M. Riedmiller, 2013. Playing atari with deep reinforcement learning.

W. Seifritz, 1990. CO2 disposal by means of silicates. Nature 345 (6275), 486–486.

Flavio Manenti, Gintaras V. Reklaitis (Eds.), Proceedings of the 34th European Symposium on Computer Aided Process Engineering / 15th International Symposium on Process Systems Engineering (ESCAPE34/PSE24), June 2-6, 2024, Florence, Italy

Q-Learning & Economic NL-MPC for Continuous Biomass Fermentation

Tom Vinestock[a], Hak-Keung Lam[a], Mark Taylor[b], Miao Guo[a]*

[a]*Department of Engineering, King's College London, London, WC2R 2LS, UK*
[b]*Marlow Ingredients, Station Road, Stokesley, TS9 7AB, UK*
miao.guo@kcl.ac.uk

Abstract

An economic optimal control problem for biomass fermentation is presented. Building on this, this work contributes a performance comparison between Q-Learning and non-linear model predictive control (MPC) as applied to a simulated biomass fermentation system. Two different scenarios are considered. In the first scenario, it is assumed an accurate model is available. In the second scenario, it is assumed there is parametric mismatch between the model and the true plant. In the second scenario, a simple transfer learning approach is used to improve the performance of the Q-Learning controller, while parameter estimation is used to aid the MPC. Trajectories and performance indicators are presented for both controllers and for both scenarios. It is found that Q-Learning out-performs MPC in the first scenario. In the second scenario, transfer learning is found to significantly improve the performance of the Q-Learning, and to outperform a comparison controller combining MPC with moving horizon estimation (MHE).

Keywords: Fermentation, MPC, Q-Learning, Transfer Learning, Mismatch

1. Background

Fermentation is an important industrial process, used in the production of food, bio-chemicals, and pharmaceuticals. Fermentation of microbial protein in bioreactors offers an efficient means of converting carbohydrate-based substrates into high protein outputs and is more environmentally sustainable than traditional animal-based protein production across a wide-range of metrics (Good Food Institute 2021). However, maximising the performance of these fermentations through process control is complex (Chai et al. 2022), as the process is non-linear and uncertain, with time-varying behaviour.

Within fermentation, a distinction can be made between biomass fermentation, in which the desired product is microbial biomass, and precision fermentation, in which the desired product is a (primary or secondary) metabolite. Previous works on fermentation process control have tended to focus on precision fermentation, such as continuous fermentation of biofuels (Mohd et al. 2016), and batch fermentation of pharmaceuticals (Ashoori et al. 2009), with a relative lack of work on control of continuous biomass fermentation. More particularly, there has been little comparison of reinforcement learning (RL)-based and model predictive control (MPC) methods in continuous biomass fermentation.

Whereas in precision fermentation, particularly to produce high-value pharmaceuticals, efficiency and productivity are arguably secondary considerations, in continuous biomass fermentation, such as to produce dietary proteins, efficiency and productivity are the key performance indicators, as the mass-specific value of the output is lower. Increasing production capacity and improving process efficiency are therefore an important industry challenge for microbial protein manufacturers. The cost-sensitivity of biomass fermentation to produce protein as a commodity for feed or food motivates interest in developing and applying economic, rather than trajectory-following, control approaches.

2. Research Objectives

The research objective is to investigate and compare economic control methods suitable for continuous biomass fermentation. This is a non-linear control problem with an economic objective. In this work, building on Nguang et al. (1998), an optimal control problem for maximising biomass production is formulated for the case of a well-mixed reactor with a single growth-limiting substrate.

The control objective was to maximise the biomass output during a 200-hour window, from a defined, low-biomass concentration starting condition. This reflects industrial practice, in which continuous fermentations are subject to regular re-starts, to avoid problems such as genetic drift. A secondary consideration, the substrate utilization efficiency, was not formally included in the control objective. However, efficiency rates for the different control methods are also reported, as they would also be of interest to an industrial process operator.

Two different cases are considered. In the first case, which is a simpler, more idealized scenario, it is assumed an accurate model of the plant is available. In the second case, which is intended to better reflect the real-world complexities of the control problem, the parameters of the plant are only known approximately, resulting in parametric model-plant mismatch.

3. Methodology

3.1. System Description

We consider a fixed volume system, with Monod growth kinetics and a single growth-limiting substrate. The state-space is of dimension two (biomass concentration and substrate concentration) and the action space of dimension one (dilution rate). The inlet substrate concentration is considered fixed. This system is described in Equation 1, with values used for the constants also stated. To simulate this system numerically, the SciPy ODEint function was used to integrate the system equations.

$$\dot{X} = \mu(S)\,X - DX \tag{1a}$$

$$\dot{S} = D(S_{in} - S) - \frac{\mu(S)}{Y_X}\,X \tag{1b}$$

$$\mu = \mu_{max}\frac{S}{K_S + S} \tag{1c}$$

S = Substrate Concentration, g/L; X = Biomass Concentration, g/L
D = Dilution Rate, /h; K_s = 0.45 g/L Monod Half Saturation Constant
μ_{max} = 0.15 /h, Maximum Growth Rate; Y_x = 0.5 g/g, Yield Coefficient

3.2. Control Methods

The performance of two different control methods, namely economic non-linear model predictive control (NL-MPC), and Q-Learning (QL), was evaluated, initially in the zero-mismatch case, and then in the parametric mismatch case. The control objective in both cases is to maximise the total biomass output over a defined period of time (see Equation 2a), subject to the system dynamics set out in Equation 1.

Non-linear model predictive control (NL-MPC) is an often-employed method which formulates the discrete-time, continuous-action, continuous-state control problem as a non-linear program (NLP). However, the "curse of dimensionality" can present problems when the timescale associated with the best strategy is long relative to the process time; the number of steps ahead the MPC considers, known as the control horizon, determines the dimension of the optimisation problem solved at each step.

QL is a simple reinforcement learning technique, for discrete-state, discrete-action, discrete-time systems, in which a sequence of immediate rewards is used to estimate the long-term pay-off of each state-action pair, with these values stored in a table (see Equation 2cii). The trade-off between long- and short-term interests is controlled by the discount factor, γ. After convergence, the QL agent will usually choose the action with the highest payoff, but during training random actions will be taken more often to explore the system dynamics. For a detailed explanation of the QL algorithm, see Watkins and Dayan (1992).

The objective function used for the MPC was the sum of 3 terms, as defined in Equation 2b: total biomass output during the horizon window, a terminal state bonus, and an actuation switching cost. The Euler method was used to discretise the system dynamics for use in the MPC control problem. This defined a non-linear program (NLP). IPOPT (Wächter & Biegler 2006), a local NLP solver, was used to solve the MPC optimisation problem, through the Pyomo (Hart 2011) interface. The performance of the MPC depends on the control horizon, the control timestep, and on the weighting terms used to reduce actuation switching and to promote long-termism (terminal state weight). Both of these terms were added to improve performance.

The reward used for the Q-Learning was biomass output in one timestep, as defined in Equation 2ci. The exploration rate, ε, used in the QL was linearly decremented from the initial rate to the minimum rate. The SciPy ODEint function was used to integrate the system equations in all cases. The results for MPC and QL are both for the best parameters identified through grid search.

$$D^*(t) = \underset{D(t)}{\mathrm{argmax}} \int_0^{T_{end}} X(t)\, D(t)\, dt \tag{2a}$$

$$\max_{D_{\{1:H\}}} \Sigma_{i=1}^{H}(D_i X_i) - w_{switch}\Sigma_{i=1}^{H-1}(D_{i+1} - D_i)^2 + w_{terminal}X_H \tag{2b}$$

$$r_i = D_i X_i \tag{2ci}$$

$$Q'(X_i, S_i, D_i) = (1 - \alpha)Q(X_i, S_i, D_i) + \alpha(r_i + \gamma \max_D Q(X_{i+1}, S_{i+1}, D_{i+1})) \tag{2cii}$$

We then consider the case in which there is mismatch between the model and the true process. MPC is, as its name suggests, a model-based technique. RL is a model-free approach. However, because RL requires many interactions to learn how to control a system well, in practice a numerical model of the target process is required for process control applications, with the model used to train the reinforcement learning agent. Some degree of mismatch between model and plant is inevitable in most systems. Therefore, it is important to consider the impact of mismatch on control systems, and to think about how this mismatch can be accommodated.

In the QL controller, mismatch is addressed using a simple transfer learning (TL) approach. First, the agent is pre-trained on a model over a large number of episodes of 200 h each, split into control timesteps of 2 h. Then the agent is re-trained on the true process during a single "live" run, by increasing the exploration rate, in this case from 0.01 to 0.1. In the MPC, potential mismatch is addressed by parameter estimation, with parameters continually re-estimated using Moving Horizon Estimation, based on (noisy) simulated sensor readings.

4. Results

4.1. Performance in the Case of Zero-Mismatch

QL can outperform MPC if the discretization used is sufficiently fine. This is primarily because of the duration of the fermentation, which means that the MPC is too short-sighted; extending the MPC horizon further causes the solver to be frustrated by local minima. The equivalent parameter in QL, the discount factor, was set so a reward in 200 h time was valued half as much as a reward now. Discretising each state and action variable into 40 levels allowed the performance of the Q-Learning controller to outperform the MPC. The difference in performance between MPC and Q-Learning was relatively small. However, the highest performance configuration of Q-Learning tested consistently outperformed the highest performance configuration of MPC. The parameters used for MPC can be seen in Table 1, and those used for the Q-Learning can be seen in Table 2. The range of outputs for Q-Learning over 10 iterations of training from scratch was [302.9, 307.8] g/L over 200 h, whereas the output of the MPC was 302.54 g/L. Similarly, the range of substrate efficiencies for the Q-Learning was [87.4, 88.6] %, whereas the MPC efficiency was 83.9 %. State, input, and output trajectories for the two control systems can be seen in Figure 2.

Table 1: Best MPC Controller Configuration in case of Known Plant Parameters

Control Timestep, $\Delta t = 2$ h	Control Horizon = 44 h	Terminal Weight = 1E-4	Switch Weight =1E-7

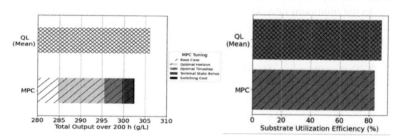

Figure 1: Total Outputs and Substrate Utilization Efficiency for Q-Learning and MPC, with Zero-Mismatch. In the output chart, the impact of the MPC tuning on performance is shown.

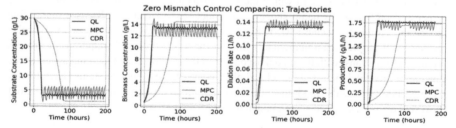

Figure 2: State, Input and Output Trajectories of QL and MPC controlled system, with constant dilution rate (CDR) for reference. Dilution Rate and Productivity plots for QL and MPC have been smoothed with a window of 20 hours.

Table 2: Best Q-Learning Controller Configuration in case of Known Plant Parameters

Control Timestep, $\Delta t = 2$ h	Initial Exploration Rate, $\varepsilon_0 = 0.5$	Final Exploration Rate, $\varepsilon_0 = 0.01$	Learning Rate, $\alpha = 0.3125$
Discount Factor, $\gamma = $ exp(-Δt ln(2)/Duration)	Number of Discrete Action Levels = 40	Number of Discrete State Levels per State Variable = 40	Training Episodes = 128,000

4.2. Transfer Learning

Slight parametric mismatch was applied, by increasing the value of the maximum growth rate, μ_{max}, used in the model from 0.15 to 0.2. Five QL parameters were varied to identify a QL system that performed well when applied to a mismatched system: number of states, number of actions, control timestep, re-training learning rate and re-training exploration rate. The optimum retraining initial exploration rate was 0.1, compared to 0.5 and 0.01 at the start and end, respectively, of pretraining. Better TL results were obtained when the number of state levels (per variable) and actions was reduced to 9 and 18 from 40 and 40, respectively. Increasing the number of learning opportunities during re-training by reducing the control timestep from 2 h to 1 h also improved performance. Both of these later changes come at the expense of performance in a system without mismatch (see Figure 3), which failed to match the performance of the MPC with true parameters. Note that the simpler QL system with true parameters underperforms relative to the MPC system with true parameters.

Using optimal hyperparameters for performance on the target system during the first fermentation episode saw the performance of the RL controller, as measured by output, drop less than 1% when it was pre-trained on a system with a 33% higher maximum growth rate, relative to training on a system without mismatch. Indeed, the QL with TL approach outperformed the optimisation-based approach combining MPC and moving horizon estimation (MHE) for state and parameter estimation in both output and efficiency (see Figure 3). In practice, the re-training hyper-parameters couldn't be optimised for the target system, but heuristics could be used to estimate the most appropriate re-training hyper-parameters as a function of the scale of the suspected mismatch between the training system and the target system. State, input, and output trajectories for the QL with TL system during its single episode of retraining can be seen in Figure 4.

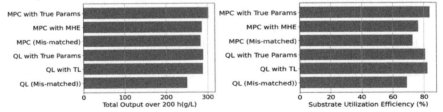

Figure 3: Total Outputs and Substrate Utilization Efficiency for QL and MPC, with slight parametric mismatch.

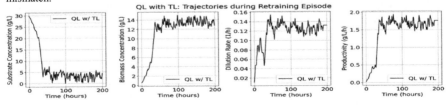

Figure 4: State, Input and Output Trajectories of QL with TL during its retraining episode.

5. Conclusions & Future Work

While QL has been viewed with skepticism by the control community, it is nonetheless a simple control approach that can offer good performance, with QL outperforming a more complex MPC scheme in this application. It should be noted that once the QL controller has been trained and the exploration rate has been reduced to a small value, it is very similar to an explicit MPC controller. As with explicit MPC, for QL the computational effort is concentrated prior to deployment, with considerable training costs, but few online computational costs.

Simple transfer learning can facilitate the rapid adaptation of QL to moderate parametric mismatch. However, there are some trade-offs between designing a small QL system that is quick to adapt to a new system, with mismatch relative to its training system, and maximising the performance of the QL system once it has fully adapted, which may require more complexity. More sophisticated QL schemes that avoid the need to discretize the state and action space could help address this problem, although it is to some extent fundamental.

Future research could investigate RL-MPC hybrids or broaden the controlled variables to include dissolved oxygen, temperature, pH and nitrogen concentration. Additionally, the control systems will be implemented in a real-world setting. This will likely lead to consideration of the effects of non-parametric mismatch. Beyond this, potential future areas of research include high fidelity process simulation for fermentation, application of control approaches to co-culture fermentation systems, and using metabolic modelling, such as flux balance analysis, to derive insights into the control system design.

References

A. Ashoori, B. Moshiri, A. Khaki-Sedigh, and M. R. Bakhtiari, 2009, "Optimal control of a nonlinear fed-batch fermentation process using model predictive approach", *Journal of Process Control*, vol. 19, issue 7, pp. 1162–1173.

W. Y. Chai, K. T. K. Teo, M. K. Tan, and H. J. Tham, 2022, "Fermentation process control and optimization", *Chemical Engineering & Technology*, vol. 45, issue 10, pp. 1731–1747.

B. Dahhou, G. Roux, and G. Chamilothoris, 1992, "Modelling and adaptive predictive control of a continuous fermentation process", *Appl. Math. Model.*, vol. 16, issue 10, pp 545-552.

Good Food Institute, 2021 "Fermentation: State of the industry report."

Hart, W. E., Watson, J. P., and Woodruff, D. L., 2011, "Pyomo: modeling and solving mathematical programs in Python", *Math. Program. Comput.*, vol. 3, issue 3, pp. 219-260.

N. Mohd and N. Aziz, 2016, "Performance and robustness evaluation of nonlinear autoregressive with exogenous input model predictive control in controlling industrial fermentation process", *Journal of Cleaner Production*, vol. 136, issue 11, pp. 42–50.

S. K. Nguang and X. D. Chen, 1998, "Simple procedure for operating a class of continuous fermentation processes at the optimal steady state productivity", *Biochemical Engineering Journal*, vol. 1, issue 1, pp. 131-136.

A. Wächter and L. T. Biegler, 2006, "On the Implementation of a Primal-Dual Interior Point Filter Line Search Algorithm for Large-Scale Nonlinear Programming", *Mathematical Programming* 106(1), pp. 25-57.

Watkins, C.J. and Dayan, P., 1992, "Technical Note: Q-Learning", *Machine Learning*, vol. 8, pp. 279–292.

Flavio Manenti, Gintaras V. Reklaitis (Eds.), Proceedings of the 34th European Symposium on Computer Aided Process Engineering / 15th International Symposium on Process Systems Engineering (ESCAPE34/PSE24), June 2-6, 2024, Florence, Italy

Development of an inferential control system of hydrogen concentration of exhaust gas in fuel cell systems

Taisei Izawa[a], Sanghong Kim[a*], Miyuki Matsumoto[a], Shigeki Hasegawa[b,c], Motoaki Kawase[b]

[a]Department of Applied Physics and Chemical Engineering, Tokyo University of Agriculture and Technology, Tokyo 184-8588, Japan
[b]Department of Chemical Engineering, Kyoto University, Kyoto 615-8510, Japan
[c]Hydrogen Fundamental Development Div., Hydrogen Factory, Toyota Motor Corporation, Aichi, 471-8571, Japan
Corresponding Author's E-mail:sanghong@go.tuat.ac.jp

Abstract

Although controlling the H_2 mole fraction in exhaust gas is important to ensure the safety of FC system because H_2 gas has high explosion risk, there are few papers on it. In addition, it is difficult to measure the H_2 mole fraction in real FC systems. Therefore, a PLS model for predicting the H_2 mole fraction and a control system for manipulating the air flow rate at the air bypass valve are newly developed. The increase in power consumption with the implementation of the control system was calculated using a comprehensive FC system simulator. As a result, the H_2 mole fraction was kept below the legal limits with an average increase in power consumption by 25 %.

Keywords: Inferential control; Soft sensor; Fuel cells; Hydrogen; Exhaust gas

1. Introduction

Fuel cells (FC), which do not emit CO_2 when generating electric power, are attracting attention as one solution to environmental problems. FC vehicles such as "MIRAI" and "SORA," and household FC systems such as "ENE FARM" have been commercialized. The development of FC systems requires advanced technology and a lot of cost and time, and more efficient development is necessary to make FC systems much more widespread. The introduction of model-based development (MBD) is expected to solve these problems [1] [2]. This will increase the speed of development of a variety of product FC systems. To promote the widespread use of these products, it is also important to ensure that developed FC systems meet the international standards established in 2013 [3]. In this standard, to prevent H_2 explosion, the H_2 mole fraction in exhaust gas must be lower than 0.08 instantaneously and 0.04 averaged over 3 seconds. To meet these standards, a system to control the H_2 mole fraction in exhaust gas and a hydrogen sensor are required. However, the response speed of the current hydrogen sensors is low. Leonardi *et al.* developed a dual sensor with a Co-doped SnO_2 layer that has a response time of shorter than 14 s for 0–100% hydrogen concentration and a MO_x layer that has a response time of shorter than 3 s for 2,000 ppm of H_2 [4]. Although this sensor is simple, inexpensive, and has a wide sensing range, further improvement in response time is needed to comply with legal limits on H_2 mole fraction. Therefore, this study developed an inferential control system to keep the H_2 mole fraction in exhaust gas below the legal limits and a soft sensor to predict the H_2 mole fraction.

2. Method

2.1. Soft sensor for H_2 mole fraction

FC-DynaMo is a dynamic simulator developed based on the FC system of Toyota's MIRAI, which calculates the temperature, pressure, flow rate, and gas composition inside the FC system based on the set points of net power $P_{net,set}$ [kW], ambient pressure, ambient temperature, and wind speed. Net power is the difference between the gross power of the FC system and the power consumption of the auxiliary systems.

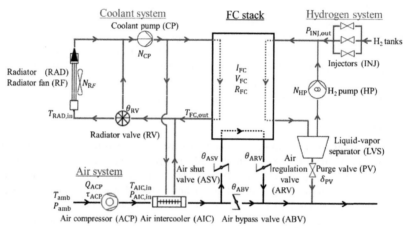

Figure 1 Schematic diagram of the FC system

Table 1 Variables used to develop the soft sensor

No.	Variables	Explanation	Cases 1-1 to 1-3	Cases 1-4 to 1-6
1	T_{amb}	Ambient temperature [°C]	–	–
2	P_{amb}	Ambient pressure [kPa]	–	–
3	I_{FC}	FC stack current [A]	✓	✓
4	V_{FC}	FC stack voltage [V]	✓	✓
5	R_{FC}	FC stack resistance [Ω]	✓	✓
6	$P_{INJ,out}$	Total pressure at INJ outlet [kPa]	✓	✓
7	N_{HP}	Rotational speed of HP [rpm]	✓	✓
8	δ_{PV}	PV state (0: close / 1: open) [-]	✓	✓
9	Q_{ACP}	Volumetric air flow rate at ACP [NL/min]	✓	✓
10	τ_{ACP}	Motor torque of ACP [N m]	✓	-
11	$T_{AIC,in}$	Temperature at AIC inlet [°C]	✓	-
12	$P_{AIC,in}$	Total pressure at AIC inlet [kPa]	✓	✓
13	θ_{ASV}	Opening angle of ASV [degree]	✓	-
14	θ_{ARV}	Opening angle of ARV [degree]	–	-
15	θ_{ABV}	Opening angle of ABV [degree]	–	-
16	$T_{RAD,in}$	Temperature at RAD inlet [°C]	✓	-
17	N_{CP}	Rotational speed of CP [rpm]	✓	-
18	N_{RF}	Rotational speed of RF [rpm]	✓	-
19	θ_{RV}	Opening ratio of RV [%]	✓	-
20	$T_{FC,out}$	Temperature of coolant at FC outlet [°C]	✓	-

Figure 1 shows a schematic of the FC system, and the definition of the variables is listed in Table 1. In the FC system, a mixture of gas from the FC anode and FC cathode outlets is discharged as exhaust gas. Since the H_2 in exhaust gas is mainly from the FC anode outlet, a soft sensor was developed to predict the H_2 mole fraction in the liquid-vapor separator (LVS).

The procedure of soft sensor design is as follows: firstly, model construction data and model validation data were generated. To generate model construction data, $P_{net,set}$ was set to 0 to 100 kW with the change rate of -100 kW/s to 100 kW/s to cover the wide range of operation as shown in Figure 2 (a). $P_{net,set}$ of model validation data was set for various conditions as shown in Figure 2 (b).

Secondly, input variables of a PLS model were selected from Table 1. Figure 1 shows the location of each sensor. In Cases 1-1 to 1-3 and 1-4 to 1-6, different sets of input variables were used.

Thirdly, the delay time between change of input and that of output was determined by considering process dynamics. Figure 3 shows the difference between static and dynamic models. The static model uses only current values of inputs $x_1 = \{x_{11}, \ldots, x_{1M}\}$ when predicting y_1. In a dynamic model, in addition to current values, past values of input variables are used to predict output variables. For example, $\{x_3, \ldots, x_N\} = \{x_{31}, \ldots, x_{3M}, \ldots, x_{N1}, \ldots, x_{NM}\}$ are used to predict y_N. In this study, the time delay of the input variables was determined based on space time of the LVS. Table 2 shows space time of LVS for each net power setpoint. The space time depends on $P_{net,set}$ and gas flow rate into LVS.

Finally, the PLS model was constructed under 6 conditions with different sets of input variables and delay time.

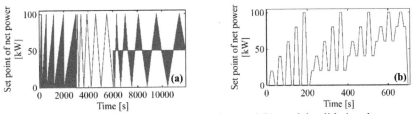

Figure 2 $P_{net,set}$ for (a) model construction data and (b) model validation data

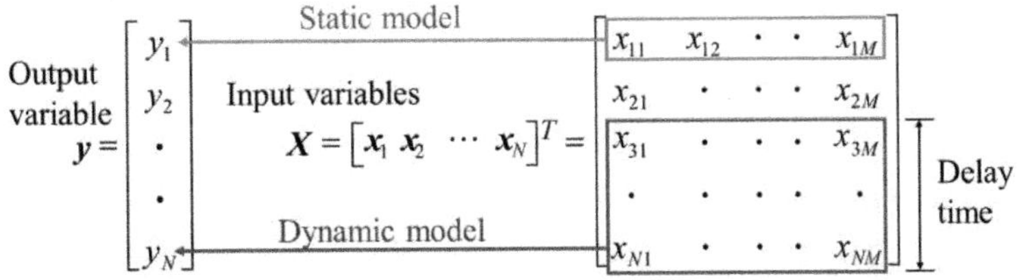

Figure 3 Static model and dynamic model

Table 2 Space time of LVS for $P_{net,set}$

$P_{net,set}$ [kW]	Temperature at LVS [℃]	Total pressure at LVS [kPa]	Molar flow rate into LVS [mol/s]	Space time of LVS [s]
1	45	108	0.04	0.6
100	104	228	0.38	0.1

2.2. Control system for H₂ mole fraction in exhaust gas

Figure 4 shows an overview of the developed control system. H_2 mole fraction at FC cathode outlet $x_{H_2,cFC,out}$ [-], molar flow rate of gas at FC cathode outlet $\dot{n}_{cFC,out}$ [mol/s], set point of molar concentration of H_2 in exhaust gas $x_{H_2,exh,set}$ [-], molar flow rate of gas at PV outlet $\dot{n}_{HEV,out}$ [mol/s] and the predicted value of H_2 mole fraction by the soft sensor at PV outlet $\hat{x}_{H_2,PV}$ [-] are input to the controller of volumetric flow rate at ABV $Q_{ABV,set}$. In the air system, the air is taken from outside the FC system by an ACP and sent to the FC stack to supply the oxygen for power generation. The controller of ABV manipulates the air flow rate which directly goes to the outside of the FC system. The developed controller controls the H_2 mole fraction in exhaust gas $x_{H_2,exh}$ [-] by manipulating the air flow rate through ABV. $Q_{ABV,set}$ is calculated as follows.

1. Receive the inputs: $x_{H_2,cFC,out}$, $\hat{x}_{H_2,PV}$, $\dot{n}_{cFC,out}$, $\dot{n}_{PV}$, and $x_{H_2,exh,set}$.
2. Calculate the molar flow rate of air in exhaust gas $\dot{n}_{0,exh}$ [mol/s] and the predicted H_2 mole fraction in exhaust gas $\hat{x}_{0,H_2,exh}$ [-] of by Eqs. (1) and (2) assuming the molar flow rate of air at ABV is 0 mol/s.

$$\dot{n}_{0,exh} = \dot{n}_{cFC,out} + \dot{n}_{PV} \qquad (1)$$

$$\hat{x}_{0,H_2,exh} = \frac{x_{H_2,cFC,out}\,\dot{n}_{cFC,out} + \hat{x}_{H_2,PV}\,\dot{n}_{PV}}{\dot{n}_{0,exh}} \qquad (2)$$

3. Calculate the set point of molar flow rate of air in ABV $\dot{n}_{ABV,set}$ [mol/s] by Eq. (4) so that predicted H_2 mole fraction in exhaust gas $\hat{x}_{H_2,exh}$ is equal to its set point $x_{H_2,exh,set}$.

$$\hat{x}_{H_2,exh} = \frac{\hat{x}_{0,H_2,exh}\,\dot{n}_{0,exh}}{\dot{n}_{0,exh} + \dot{n}_{ABV}} \qquad (3)$$

$$\dot{n}_{ABV,set} = \frac{\hat{x}_{0,H_2,exh} - x_{H_2,exh,set}}{x_{H_2,exh,set}}\,\dot{n}_{0,exh} \qquad (4)$$

4. Convert $\dot{n}_{ABV,set}$ calculated in step 3 to $Q_{ABV,set}$ by using the ideal gas law.

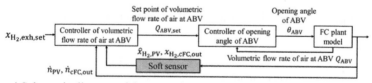

Figure 4 Schematic diagram of the control system

3. Results and discussions

3.1. Soft sensor of H₂ mole fraction

Table 3 shows the mean absolute error (MAE) and the mean absolute relative error (MARE) of the PLS models for Cases 1-1 to 1-6. Different input variables were used in Cases 1-1 to 1-3 and Cases 1-3 to 1-6, as shown in Table 1. The number of latent variables used in the PLS model was set to 5. Prediction accuracy was improved when variables in the coolant system were used in addition to those in the FC stack, air system, and hydrogen system, and when input variables with the time delay were used. Figure 5 shows the prediction result of Case 1-3, in which the prediction accuracy was best.

Table 3 Prediction result of the soft sensor of H_2 mole fraction

Case	Delay time [s]	MAE [-]	MARE [%]
1-1	0.0	0.049	10.3
1-2	0.1	0.045	9.8
1-3	0.6	0.045	9.7
1-4	0.0	0.084	18.6
1-5	0.1	0.076	17.7
1-6	0.6	0.077	17.9

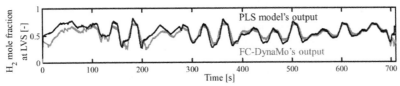

Figure 5 Prediction result of H_2 mole fraction at LVS in Case 1-3

3.2. Control system of H_2 mole fraction in exhaust gas

To determine the optimal $x_{H_2,exh,set}$ and to check the increased power consumption when a controller is introduced into the FC system, calculations were performed using FC-DynaMo under the conditions in Table 4. In Case 2-1, neither the soft sensor nor the control system was used. In Case 2-2, it was assumed that an ideal hydrogen sensor exists. The results of Cases 2-2 and 2-3 are compared by the additional power.

Table 5 shows the calculation result of the H_2 mole fraction in exhaust gas in Case 2-1. The violation rates in Table 5 indicate the percentage of time when $x_{H_2,exh}$ exceeded the legal limit relative to the simulation time. Legal limits were violated when $P_{net,set}$ was 1, 2, 3, and 10 kW, and not violated in the other values of $P_{net,set}$.

Table 4 Calculation conditions

Calculation conditions	Unit	Case 2-1	Case 2-2-	Case 2-3
Initial value of H_2 mole fraction at the FC anode	-	0.99	0.99	0.99
Initial value of temperature of the air and gas in hydrogen system	°C	55	55	55
Initial value of temperature of the coolant	°C	25	25	25
$P_{net,set}$	kW	1 to 100	1 to 100	1 to 100
With/without controller (0: without / 1: with)	-	0	1	1
With/without soft sensor (0: without / 1: with)	-	0	0	1
$x_{H_2,exh,set}$	-	-	0.015 to 0.035	0.015 to 0.035

Table 5 Violation rate and power consumption at ACP

Case	$P_{net,set}$ [kW]	Violation rate of the instantaneous value [%]	Violation rate of 3-sec. average [%]	Power consumption at ACP [W]
2-1-1	1	100	100	81.1
2-1-2	2	100	100	85.1
2-1-3	3	100	100	88.1
2-1-4	4	0	0	90.9
2-1-5	5	0	0	93.7
2-1-6	10	0	100	107.4

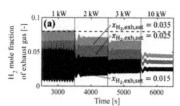 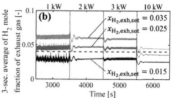

Figure 6 Control results of (a) instantaneous H_2 mole fraction and (b) 3-sec. average H_2 mole fraction in exhaust gas

Table 6 Comparison of additional power due to control system implementation of ideal sensor and developed soft sensor

$P_{net,set}$ [kW]	Additional power [W] / relative power consumption to those in Table 5 [-]		Average of $x_{H_2,exh}$ [-]	
	Case 2-2	Case 2-3	Case 2-2	Case 2-3
1	17.7 / 1.22	11.5 / 1.14	0.030	0.032
2	22.1 / 1.26	23.2 / 1.27	0.030	0.030
3	21.5 / 1.24	27.1 / 1.31	0.029	0.028
10	17.8 / 1.17	28.2 / 1.26	0.030	0.025

Figure 6 shows $x_{H_2,exh}$ when $P_{net,set}$ was 1, 2, 3, and 10 kW in Case 2-3 and relative rate of power consumption to those in Table 5. In Figure 6, legal limits: the instantaneous value of 0.08 and the 3-second average value of 0.04 are displayed with a dotted line. From Figure 6 (a) and (b), it was found that the violation rate becomes 0 when $x_{H_2\,exh,set} = 0.015$. Table 6 shows the additional power consumption in Case 2-2 with $x_{H_2,exh\,set} = 0.030$ and Case 2-3 with $x_{H_2,set} = 0.015$. The developed control system was able to keep x_{H_2} below the legal limit with an average increase in power consumption of 22.5 W. The control system also consumes an average of 2.7 W more power than the controller with an ideal sensor. 2.7 W is not significant in FC systems; thus, the accuracy of the developed soft sensor is high enough.

4. Conclusions

The soft sensor with MAE of 0.045 and MARE of 9.7 % was successfully developed. The control system using the developed soft sensor was able to keep the H_2 mole fraction in exhaust gas below the legal limits. An average increase in power consumption of air compressor was 22.5 W, from 81.1-107 to 92.6-136 W, with set point of H_2 mole fraction in exhaust gas at 0.015. These results show that a control system that meets the regulation on H_2 mole fraction in exhaust gas can be created without the need to develop a new hydrogen sensor having a high response time.

References

1. S. Hasegawa *et al.*, "Model-based development of fuel cell stack and system controllers," PSE 2021+, Jun. 19–23 (2022).
2. S. Hasegawa *et al.*, "Modeling of the dynamic behavior of an integrated fuel cell system including fuel cell stack, air system, hydrogen system, and cooling system," ECS Trans., 109, 9 (2022).
3. United nations, "Global technical regulation on hydrogen and fuel cell vehicle, " ECE Trans, 180, Add.13 (2013)
4. S. G. Leonardi *et al.*, "Development of a hydrogen dual sensor for fuel cell applications," Hydrogen Energy, 43, 11896–11902 (2018).

Flavio Manenti, Gintaras V. Reklaitis (Eds.), Proceedings of the 34th European Symposium on Computer Aided Process Engineering / 15th International Symposium on Process Systems Engineering (ESCAPE34/PSE24), June 2-6, 2024, Florence, Italy

Advancing Liquid Level Recognition: A Combined Deep Learning and Pixel Manipulation Approach

Borui Yang[a], Jinsong Zhao[a,b*]

[a]*State Key Laboratory of Chemical Engineering, Department of Chemical Engineering, Tsinghua University, Beijing 100084, China*
[b]*Beijing Key Laboratory of Industrial Big Data System and Application, Tsinghua University, Beijing 100084, China*
jinsongzhao@tsinghua.edu.cn

Abstract

In the process industry of chemical engineering, process monitoring and safety are of utmost importance, especially for accurate monitoring of liquid levels. In recent years, with the ongoing deployment of IoT (Internet of Things) devices, a myriad of computer-vision (CV) based measurement methods have emerged. However, these methods are mainly applicable to laboratory conditions with cylindrical level gauges, which turned out to be delicate and limited in real-world scenarios. To address these challenges, this paper proposed a novel framework that combines deep learning with pixel manipulation techniques, focusing on the more challenging circular-observation-window liquid level gauges (LLGs). The deep learning part utilized the Mask R-CNN framework to identify and extract the regions of interest (RoI) through supervised learning, followed by the recognition of liquid level by pixel manipulation method. The proposed framework effectively integrates the robustness of deep learning and the reliability of traditional methods, achieving high accuracy under complex conditions. If integrated into real-time process monitoring systems, it could further enhance the timeliness, reliability and safety of chemical process monitoring.

Keywords: liquid level recognition, deep learning, pixel manipulation, circle Hough transform.

1. Introduction

In the chemical industry, process monitoring and safety issues are of paramount importance. With the ongoing deployment of IoT devices in chemical scenarios, image acquisition equipment and corresponding supporting systems are gradually becoming one of the key nodes in the whole monitoring workflow. In chemical engineering processes, the liquid level is a crucial parameter as well. Many devices in chemical processes have strict limitations for liquid level, where a change may be an indicator of some unusual incidents. The measurement techniques of it are mostly hardware-based, such as optical, thermal capacity, and buoyancy level meters, which are relatively much more complex to deploy and maintain. Moreover, there are LLGs specially designed for manually reading, which are commonly found in smaller devices, for instance, oil tanks and fans, facilitated with transparent windows for viewing the level and colour of the liquid.

LLGs that require manual reading can be roughly categorized into 2 types: those with readout and without. The solution of the first one is quite simple: use YOLO-based model for Region of Interest (RoI) detection (Zou et al., 2021) and CNN-based (Zou et al., 2022) or RNN-based model (Zhang et al., 2022) for recognition of digits on the screen or dial.

However, in this paper we mainly focused on the alternative category, where the researches have been remaining rudimentary and undeveloped.

Thus, an extensive literature research was done, whose result shows that current CV-based methods for liquid level recognition have certain limitations. H. Zhu (2009) utilized a Sobel-operator-based algorithm to measure the liquid level inside the transparent infusion bottle. L. Peng et al. (2019) employed ArUco tag to localize the RoI and binarization method to recognize the liquid level in a cylindrical gauge. The studies all share some common characteristics: images are predominantly collected under lab-conditions and particularly designed for cylindrical level gauges, which may make their methods more vulnerable in practical conditions.

Motivated by the above, our paper proposes a novel method for liquid level recognition. We select a type of circular-observation-window LLG as the subject, whose recognition problem turn out to be a much more challenging and complicated one due to the strong disturbance of the images collected. The level recognition work is divided into two stages: level gauge area detection/segmentation and level recognition. The Mask R-CNN framework proposed by K. He et al. (2017) is introduced for level gauge region identification to find out the where the level gauge is and crop it to a smaller size to facilitate the subsequent level recognition stage. Subsequently, the level recognition based on Hough circle transform and pixel manipulation is conducted in the smaller image after cropping and then the liquid level is obtained and thus can be further fed into the control system. This liquid level recognition method combines the robustness of the deep learning method with the reliability of the traditional method: the neural network part is good at robustly recognizing the features of the level gauge window region, while the pixel operation part ensures the reliability of further liquid level recognition work.

2. Methodology

2.1. Mask R-CNN

The Mask R-CNN is a strong modification of Faster R-CNN framework, whose main purpose lies in predicting segmentation on RoI. The traditional Faster R-CNN (S. Ren et al., 2015) framework has two outputs for each candidate object, namely, a class label and a bounding box. The Mask R-CNN is comprised of three different blocks (S. Zhang et al., 2022): feature extraction backbone, region proposal network and result inference branches. It adds an extra branch that can predict the mask of the object, which turned out to be more suitable for the gauge region segmentation job. All these blocks are built based on neural networks (especially CNNs), which is tested to be effective in learning complicated image features.

2.2. Pixel Manipulation

2.2.1. Pre-processing of image

In general, in the pre-processing part CV-based method employed includes grayscale conversion, blurring, dilation and erosion. The images captured by industrial cameras are often in the RGB format, in which each channel contains different features. Grayscale conversion integrating the information from all channels by merging the channels into one, laying a foundation for subsequent processes. Blurring is achieved by convolving the image with a low-pass filter kernel, which is primarily employed to rule out the high-frequency noises in images, aiding in keeping the edge detection part from malfunction. Dilation and erosion are used to expand and contract the boundaries of objects respectively in an image.

2.2.2. Edge Detection: Canny method

Edge detection is another crucial part in computer vision, aiming at identify the contour lines and feature boundaries. Canny method is widely accepted as a superb edge detection approach in industrial usages, which has been included in OpenCV library.

2.2.3. Circle Hough Transform

Circle Hough Transform (CHT) is a feature extraction method utilized to detect circles in grayscale images. The mechanism of CHT is basically to construct an accumulator space $(a, b, r) \in R^3$ for circles. For each pixel on $circle\ (a, b, r)$, it adds a vote on the value on the accumulator space whose index is (a, b, r). After all the edge points have voted in the accumulator space, circles with more votes would standout and could be further filtered by setting the min distance between circles and min votes of each circle, etc.

3. The proposed method

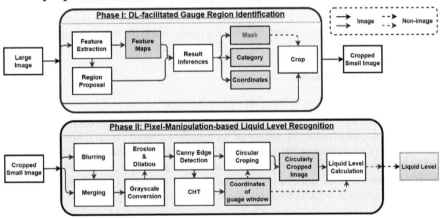

Fig. 1. Diagram of proposed framework (Solid-line arrows: image transference, dashed-line arrows: non-image (Parameter transfer, etc.) transference)

3.1. Phase I: DL-facilitated Gauge Region Identification

The proposed liquid level recognition framework is shown in the Fig. 1. In the phase I, an image is fed into the Mask R-CNN and got the mask of circular viewing-window as the output. According to the position of the mask, the original large-sized image is cropped into smaller-sized one, which is suitable for the liquid level recognition part.

3.2. Phase II: Pixel-Manipulation-based Liquid Level Recognition

Table. 1. Pseudo-code of algorithms (End For is omitted for clarity)

	Algorithm: Circular Cropping and Liquid Level Calculation
1:	**Circular Cropping**: Input: tuple $(img[height, width], (a, b, r))$
2:	$for\ i\ in\ range(0, height)$:
3:	$for\ j\ in\ range(0, width)$:
4:	$if\ (i - a)^2 + (j - b)^2 \geq (r - \alpha)^2\ then\ do\ img[i, j] = 0$
5:	$return\ img$
6:	**Liquid Level Calculation**: Input: tuple $(img_{circle}, (a, b, r), t = 0)$
7:	$for\ i\ in\ range(0, height)$:
8:	$for\ j\ in\ range(0, width)$:
9:	$if\ img_{circle} > 0\ do\ t = i$
10:	$Liquid\ Level = (b + r - t)/(2 \times r)$

In the Phase II, the cropped image undergoes blurring, merging, grayscale conversion, erosion, dilation, Canny edge detection in sequence, and the after-canny image is then supplied into the CHT algorithm, with the coordinates of circular viewing-window as the output tuple (a, b, r), of which the unit is pixel. The canny image is cropped conforming to the algorithm shown in Table.1. Subsequently, using the coordinates of the circle and the circularly cropped canny image, schematic diagram is shown in Fig. 2, and the level is calculated according to Table. 1.

Fig. 2. Schematic diagram of level recognition part (Left: blurred with predicted circular gauge area depicted. Middle: cropping with the pixels inside the circle remaining. Right: cropped image.)

4. Results and discussion

4.1. Phase I: DL-facilitated Gauge Region Identification

In our study, the backbone is set to ResNet50 (K. He et al, 2016) for its outstanding result. The dataset is comprised of 74 images of oil gauges, captured via an iPhone11 camera, from a total of 12 different wind turbines. The dataset is separated in to train set and test set in a ratio of 51: 23 (~ 2:1) The resolution of large images is 4032×3024. Data Augmentation tricks are not employed due to the fact that some of the images are taken from the same gauge, which could be considered as manually augmented.

$$diameter\ MAE = \frac{1}{N} \times \sum(d_{predicted} - d_{truth}) \qquad (1)$$

As for the evaluation criterions, we adopted diameter mean absolute error (MAE) (Eq. (1)) and Intersection over ground truth (IoGT) as measures of size and mask accuracy respectively. We evaluated the model on the test set and the metrics are satisfactory, which indicates that the gauge regions are excellently identified (IoGT~0.99, 99% of the pixels are correctly masked). Metrics are arranged in Table. 2 left.

Table. 2. Detection results and recognition results respectively, from left to right.

Name	Result (N=23)	Datasets	N	MRE	Error	Shape
diameter MAE	11.16 pixels	Daytime	15	-0.619%	6.4%	(1000,1000)
IoGT	0.9881	Night	10	-1.609%	9.6%	(600, 600)

4.2. Phase II: Pixel-Manipulation-based Liquid Level Recognition

Through the gauge area recognition part, the images are cropped into a smaller size and be supplied into Phase II. We employed 15 pictures taken in the daytime and 10 pictures at night to evaluate the effectiveness of the level recognition algorithm. There are 10 different gauges in the day-time dataset and 2 in the night-time. For the reason that this is a prediction problem, we employed range of error and mean relative error (MRE) as the evaluation indicator. Results are summarized in Table. 2 right.

In practical applications, we conducted fine-tuning of the hyperparameters through evaluation. The best preforming configuration is: kernel size of erosion: (10,10), canny higher_thres=95, lower_thres=20. This yields to more accurate and stable results in the recognition process of images of higher resolution and much more noises. Different cropping size is applied for data acquired during daytime and night is designed as a test for the robustness of the method.

Fig. 3. Robust recognition results under severe conditions. (Horizontal lines depict the oil levels)

Our research indicates that the method proposed can provide with a considerably stable measurement of the liquid level, with the range of error limited to 10%. Moreover, the measured level is quite close to the ground truth except for a slight negative bias. However, the negative bias is relatively small, which eloquently attested the method's efficacy and accuracy. The bias could be stemming from an unlevel shooting angle of image collector, which was done intentionally for elevation in robustness but simultaneously leads to distortion of the circular view-window and thus consequently gives rise to the inaccurate recognition. The bias could be easily corrected in industrial situations, where the installation spots and angles of cameras is standardized.

The test samples span a vast range in terms of but not limited to oil colour, RoI location, surrounding environment, and deliberate disturbances are introduced to assess the method's stability, as shown in Fig. 3. It is evident that the method remains stable under conditions of significant interference and adapts exceptionally well to situations of intense noise, light colour of oil where is hard to identify the liquid-gas interface, and obscure viewing window, etc. In constructing the model, we found that the blurring, erosion and dilation layers are crucial for improve the robustness of liquid recognition. Additionally, the sequence of these layers cannot get exchanged, altering it fails to progressively remove sharp noise in the image.

4.3. Alternative approach: Colour-attention mechanism

In addition to that, we have discovered a method that highlights the liquid-level-related features and suppresses attention to other irrelevant details, which we call it a colour-attention mechanism. The three channels, namely RGB, typically contain different information, in other words, different attentions emphasizing different objects in the image, which is quite similar to the concept of attention in Transformer (Vaswani, 2017). Therefore, a colour-attention mechanism can be designed, which could be built based on traditional blocks or neural networks that can process information from different channels, thereby enhancing features related to the liquid level while negating the impact of irrelevant features. Below is a preliminary experimental result: by filtering and doing simple operations on different channels, critical parts for liquid level recognition could be highlighted. And after several rounds of erosion and dilation, clear liquid level features are obtained, as shown in Fig. 4d.

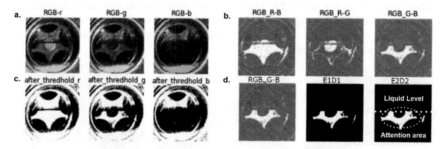

Fig. 4. Different treatment to an oil level gauge. (a. different channels of the image, b. subtraction of channels, c. binarization, d. erosion & dilation on image G minus B)

5. Conclusion

In this paper, we propose a liquid level recognition framework for circular-observation-window LLGs that combines Mask R-CNN and Pixel Manipulation techniques. This framework demonstrates high accuracy in recognition and performs effectively on images with significant interference. We also introduce the concept of colour-attention, which extracts information from different colour channels in conjunction to more effectively eliminate noise in images. In the future, we aim to further focus on the colour attention framework and develop a universal liquid level recognition framework, thereby better serving process monitoring and safety in the chemical industry.

References

K. He, G. Gkioxari, P. Dollár and R. Girshick, 2017, Mask R-CNN, IEEE International
    Conference on Computer Vision (ICCV), Venice, Italy, 2980-2988.
K. He, X. Zhang, S. Ren and J. Sun, 2016, Deep residual learning for image recognition,
    Proceedings of the IEEE conference on computer vision and pattern recognition, 770-778.
H. Ma and L. Peng, 2019, Vision based liquid level detection and bubble area segmentation in
    liquor distillation, IEEE International Conference on Imaging Systems and Techniques, 1-6.
S. Ren, K. He, R. Girshick and J. Sun, 2015, Faster r-cnn: Towards real-time object detection
    with region proposal networks, Advances in neural information processing systems, 28.
A. Vaswani, N. Shazeer, N. Parmar, J. Uszkoreit, L. Jones, A. Gomez and I. Polosukhin, 2017,
    Attention is all you need, Advances in neural information processing systems, 30.
J. Zhang, W. Liu, S. Xu and X. Zhang, 2022, Key point localization and recurrent neural network
    based water meter reading recognition, Displays, 74, 102222.
S. Zhang, X. Liang, X. Huang, K. Wang and T. Qiu, 2022, Precise and fast microdroplet size
    distribution measurement using deep learning, Chemical Engineering Science, 247, 116926.
H. Zhu, 2009, New algorithm of liquid level of infusion bottle based on image processing,
    International Conference on Information Engineering and Computer Science, IEEE,1-4.
F. Zou, Z. Shi, Z. Gan, L. Liao and J. Xu, 2021, Water meter reading recognition based on
    lightweight CNN, International Conference on Frontiers of Electronics, Information and
    Computation Technologies, 1-6.
L. Zou, L. Xu, Y. Liang, L. Chen, J.Yin and N. Xu, 2021, Robust water meter reading recognition
    method for complex scenes, Procedia Computer Science, 183, 46-52.

Flavio Manenti, Gintaras V. Reklaitis (Eds.), Proceedings of the 34th European Symposium on Computer Aided Process Engineering / 15th International Symposium on Process Systems Engineering (ESCAPE34/PSE24), June 2-6, 2024, Florence, Italy

Inventory Strategies for Optimizing Resiliency and Sustainability in Pharmaceutical Supply Chains – A Simulation-Optimization Approach

Catarina M. Marques[a*], Ana Carolina Silva[a], Jorge Pinho de Sousa[a,b]

[a]*INESC TEC, Rua Dr. Roberto Frias, Portugal*
[b]*Faculdade de Engenharia da Universidade do Porto, Rua Dr. Roberto Frias, Porto, Portugal*
catarina.m.marques@inesctec.pt

Abstract

In this work a hybrid simulation-optimization approach is presented to support decision-making towards improved resiliency and sustainability in pharmaceutical supply chain (PSC) operations. In a first step, a simulation model is used to assess the PSC performance under a set of disruptive scenarios to select the best inventory-based strategy for enhanced resiliency. Disruptions addressed in this work are mainly related to unpredicted medium-term production stoppages due to unexpected high-impact events such as accidents in production and transportation, or natural disasters. In a second step, a multi-objective mixed integer linear programming (MO-MILP) model is developed to optimize the selected inventory-based strategy regarding the economic, social, and environmental dimensions. In particular, the social and environmental aspects are introduced by anticipating the expected waste generation of close to expire medicines, redirecting them into a donation scheme. The proposed approach is applied to a representative PSC, with preliminary results showing the relevance of this tool for decision-makers to assess the trade-offs associated to the economic and social dimensions, as well as their impacts on waste generation.

Keywords: closed-loop supply chain, optimization, simulation, resiliency, sustainability.

1. Introduction

The pharmaceutical sector comprises a global industry responsible for the development, manufacturing, and distribution of medicines worldwide. Similarly to any other sector, the pressures to become cost-efficient had led to distribution networks highly globalized and complex, imposing significant managerial challenges, particularly in dealing with uncertainty.

With disruptive events becoming ever more frequent and severe, key vulnerabilities also become more significant, with any unpredicted changes resulting in substantial economic and social losses. Ensuring resilient operations across the entire pharmaceutical value chain is, therefore, not only a critical management concern, but also a core social responsibility (Tat & Heydari, 2021). Resilience, defined by Fahimnia and Jabbarzadeh (2016) as the ability to withstand and recover from disturbances, still remains elusive despite ongoing efforts to improve supply chain networks. Organizations, striving to react more effectively to uncertainties, often resort to strategies involving operational redundancies, such as holding extra inventory or dual sourcing (Pavlov et al., 2019). Inventory-based strategies are among the most common approaches used in practice, and are particularly interesting in pharmaceutical contexts as the continuous supply of products needs to be guaranteed in a long-run perspective (Lücker et al., 2019). These initiatives, however, come along with key trade-offs regarding the impact on the supply chain sustainability performance. Building up extra inventory is not only costly, but also environmental impactful through extra resource consumption and higher waste generation (Pavlov et al., 2019). Understanding and quantifying these trade-offs are crucial to define effective strategies that are both resilient and sustainable (Roostaie et al., 2019).

Despite some recent notable works (Ivanov, 2018; Zahiri et al., 2017), the join consideration of these two aspects, although critical, is still a key research challenge, particularly in the pharmaceutical industry.

The focus of this work lies, therefore, on the interface between resiliency and sustainability by exploring the right balance between risk mitigating inventory strategies and the PSC environmental and social performances.

A decision-support tool is proposed integrating a simulation model developed in an author's previous work (Silva et al., 2022) and a new Multi-Objective Mixed Integer Linear Programming (MO-MILP) model to achieve optimal supply chain management for enhanced resiliency and sustainability operations.

2. The Problem

A generic 3-echelon supply chain is considered in this work, as depicted in Figure 1. The network structure is composed by primary and secondary manufacturers, donation centres and markets.

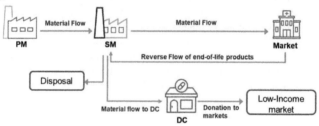

Figure 1 – Supply Chain network structure

Material flows from the Primary Manufacturers (PM) that are responsible for the production of the Active Pharmaceutical Ingredient (API) to the Secondary Manufacturers (SM), where the API product will be converted into the final drug product (FP) to be distributed to final markets through health providers such as hospitals and pharmacies, and finally, Donation Centres (DC) responsible for supplying low-income markets with donated material. It is assumed that the company adopts a donation policy and carries out social responsibility initiatives, redirecting unused risk mitigating inventory to these initiatives.

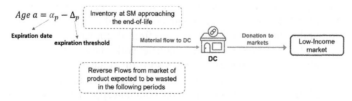

Figure 2 – Material flows to donations centres and low-income markets.

Therefore, donations have two distinct sources, as depicted in Figure 2: one related to the inventory product at the SM, approaching its end-of-life date; and the other one related to the product amounts recovered from the market, that are expected to be wasted in the upcoming time periods. In both cases, a threshold value is defined as the period of time in which no longer will it be possible to deliver the product to the market within its expiration date. Moreover, in the case of material from the reverse flows, it is also considered that a defined percentage of products reaching the market close to the threshold value, are expected to be wasted in the following periods. Therefore, in both situations, the expected waste generation is anticipated and avoided by redirecting it to markets in need.

The main goal of the proposed approach is, therefore, to optimize capacity and distribution planning decisions, including product recovery and donation flows, that minimize costs and waste, and maximize the social benefit, considering inventory-based resilient strategies.

3. Proposed Methodology

3.1. Solution Approach

The aim of this work is to build a hybrid simulation-optimization decision-support tool to both enhance resiliency and sustainability of global pharmaceutical supply chains. The proposed methodology extends the authors previous work (Silva et al., 2022), in which a simulation model was developed to assess the PSC performance under a set of disruptive scenarios and considering different inventory-based strategies, to improve resiliency and flexibility. In order to fully capture the complexity of the PSC, the simulation model was developed integrating three simulation paradigms.

While System Dynamics was used to model the high-level behaviour of the PSC, Agent-Based Simulation and Discrete Event Simulation were used to model the individual performance of each entity and the associated production processes (Silva et al., 2022).

In this work, an optimization model is developed to be integrated with the simulation approach (Figure 3), aiming to optimize the previously selected inventory-based strategy towards enhanced sustainability regarding the economic, environmental, and social dimensions.

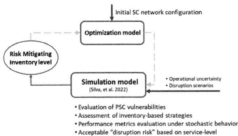

Figure 3 - Proposed hybrid simulation-optimization approach.

As shown in Figure 3, the simulation model is used to simulate several disruption scenarios, identify vulnerabilities in the PSC and proactively define target-specific strategies based on extra inventory to ensure a defined "acceptable" level of resiliency in terms of service level. The inventory level that best performs in terms of resiliency will be selected as an input parameter to the optimization model. As these strategies are both economically and environmentally costly, the optimization model will be instrumental in achieving the best trade-offs between the excess inventory, required to perform resiliently, and the optimal capacity, inventory, and production planning decisions, required to perform sustainably.

3.2. Mathematical Model

A bi-objective Mixed Integer Linear Programming (MILP) model is proposed in this work, encompassing strategic-tactical decisions related with capacity management, and production and inventory planning. The main decision variables include: (*i*) product allocation to facilities X_{pi} ($X_{pi} = 1$ if product p is assigned to facility i; $= 0$, otherwise); (*ii*) production quantities of each product p, with age a, in each factory i and time period t (Q_{pit}^{API}, Q_{piat}^{FP}); (*iii*) inventory levels of both types of products, explicitly considering the product age a for the FP (S_{pit}^{API}, S_{piat}^{FP}); (*iv*) product direct and reverse flows between the allowable entities ($F_{p(i,i')t}^{API}$, $F_{p(i,i')at}^{FP}$, $RF_{p(i,i')at}^{FP}$); (*v*) donation amounts ($D_{p(i,i')at}^{FP}$); (*vi*) amount of waste generated at secondary manufacturers and final markets due to product expiration (W_{piat}^{SM}, W_{piat}^{M}); (*vii*) amount of lost sales (L_{pit}); and (*viii*) number of new production lines installed in factory i and time period t (PL_{it}). It is worth to notice that the age-based inventory, production, and distribution management is only accounted for the final products (FP).

Two objective functions are considered: the *Profit*; and a social metric denoted here as *Social Benefit*, based on donation initiatives. The *Profit* is given by the difference between the incomes from product sales and the overall costs related to production, storage, distribution, donation, waste generated, lost sales, and investment in new production capacity. The second objective function (Eq. (1)) – *Social Benefit* – is given by the amount of product that is donated, considering two key social aspects: i) the affordability index of each market (ω_{pi}), and ii) the essential medicines index for each product and market (ξ_{pi}). The former is related to the economic ability of a specific region to purchase medicines, and the latter to the products importance to each market based on incidence of specific diseases. In this way, the social benefit is expected to be greater, by directing donations to the neediest regions and most critical products.

$$\max SocialBenefit = \sum_{p \in P} \sum_{i' \in Z^{DM}} \sum_{i \in I^M} \sum_{a \in A} \sum_{t \in T} D_{p(i',i)at} \times (1 - \omega_{pi}) \times \xi_{pi} \tag{1}$$

The main constraints of the model account for: (*i*) production allocation; (*ii*) resource and material balances at primary and secondary manufacturers, and donation centers; (*iii*) production and storage capacities; (*iv*) flows of products between all entities, according to the allowed connections; (*v*) age-based inventory levels; (*vi*) production quantities at primary and secondary manufacturers; (*vii*) possible production capacity expansions; and, finally, (*viii*) demand constraints defining the production and donation requirements.

4. Case study and preliminary results

4.1. Case study

To demonstrate the applicability of the proposed approach, a small instance of a global PSC was considered, including: 2 primary manufacturers (North America and Asia); 5 secondary manufacturers (North America, South America, Europe, Asia, and Africa); 5 global markets (North America, South America, Europe, Asia, and Africa); and 9 donation centres (distributed across Africa, Asia, and south America). Two final products are modelled, requiring each a specific API produced in the primary manufacturing facilities. Product recoveries from the market are based on the "age" at the moment of delivery to the market, considering that the older the product, the more likely it is to be wasted.

4.2. Results

Following the integrated approach depicted in Figure 3, the first step is to determine the risk mitigating inventory level for enhanced SC resiliency through the simulation model previously developed (Silva et al., 2022). Based on these results, the extra inventory level was defined as being 40% of market deliveries. For this value, a service loss of 9% was obtained immediately after a disruption, reaching the value of only 4% after recovering.

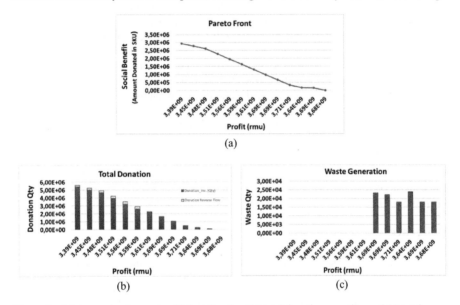

(a)

(b)   (c)

Figure 4 – (a) Approximate pareto efficient frontier, (b) total donation quantity, and (c) total waste generated for each pareto optimal solution.

Considering this inventory level, the bi-objective MILP model was solved by the ε-constraint method with the *Profit* as the primary objective function. Figure 4(a) represents the pareto efficient frontier; and Figure 4(b) and Figure 4 (c) show the main results regarding total donation amounts and waste generation respectively, for the different pareto optimal solutions. The preliminary results show that when profit is prioritized, as expected, some waste is generated, almost entirely due to market deliveries close to expiration. In this case, the model seems to follow a First Expired, First Out (FEFO) approach to manage the age-based inventory at the secondary manufacturers. On the other hand, when the social benefit objective is prioritized, the waste generated becomes zero at a certain point and the product donations increase. It is interesting to note that when increasing the importance of social benefit, the inventory management changes from FEFO to a strategy more similar to Last Expired, First Out (LEFO). This is due to the extra transportation costs associated to the reverse flows from market to the donation centres. Therefore, the model favours the "close to expire" products to take place still in the secondary manufacturers leading to an increase in donations directly from the SM instead of from the market.

5. Conclusions and Future Work

This paper presents an innovative hybrid simulation-optimization approach to tackle both resiliency and sustainability aspects in PSC operations. While simulation, under different disruptive scenarios, is able to select the inventory policy that best performs in terms of resiliency, optimization is used to refine this policy and determine optimal production and distribution plans for improved sustainable operations. Preliminary results show the potential of this approach in understanding the relevant trade-offs between resiliency and sustainability, and how to exploit them to raise a positive social and environmental impact. In fact, the developed methodology proved to be instrumental for decision-support regarding enhanced supply chain resiliency and sustainability. Moreover, a clear trade-off between the economic and social dimensions was observed, as well as their impact on waste generation. Future work will focus on extending the pharmaceutical supply chain to a 4-echelon structure to include the wholesalers as key players in a foreseen collaborative approach considering more refined donation schemes. Additionally, the developed models are expected to be improved to accommodate other resilient-driven strategies such as dual sourcing or dynamic capacity management. Finally, although these results are promising, some challenges still need to be further addressed regarding the interaction between simulation and optimization.

Acknowledgement

This work is partially financed by National Funds through the FCT - Fundação para a Ciência e a Tecnologia, I.P. (Portuguese Foundation for Science and Technology) within the project FuturePharma, with reference PTDC/EME-SIS/6019/2020.

References

Fahimnia, B., & Jabbarzadeh, A. (2016). Marrying supply chain sustainability and resilience: A match made in heaven. Transportation research part e: logistics transportation review, 91, 306-324. doi:doi.org/10.1016/j.tre.2016.02.007

Ivanov, D. (2018). Revealing interfaces of supply chain resilience and sustainability: a simulation study. International Journal of Production Research, 56(10), 3507-3523. doi:doi.org/10.1080/00207543.2017.1343507

Lücker, F., Seifert, R., & Biçer, I. (2019). Roles of inventory and reserve capacity in mitigating supply chain disruption risk. International Journal of Production Research 57(4), 1238-1249. doi:doi.org/10.1080/00207543.2018.1504173

Pavlov, A., Ivanov, D., Pavlov, D., & Slinko, A. (2019). Optimization of network redundancy and contingency planning in sustainable and resilient supply chain resource management under conditions of structural dynamics. Annals of Operations Research, 1-30. doi:doi.org/10.1007/s10479-019-03182-6

Roostaie, S., Nawari, N., & Kibert, C. (2019). Integrated sustainability and resilience assessment framework: From theory to practice. Journal of Cleaner Production, 232, 1158-1166.

Silva, A., Sousa, J., & Marques, C. (2022). Supply Chain Resiliency in the Pharmaceutical Industry–a Simulation-Based Approach. Paper presented at the 5th European International Conference on Industrial Engineering and Operations Management.

Tat, R., & Heydari, J. J. J. o. C. P. (2021). Avoiding medicine wastes: Introducing a sustainable approach in the pharmaceutical supply chain. 320, 128698.

Zahiri, B., Zhuang, J., & Mohammadi, M. (2017). Toward an integrated sustainable-resilient supply chain: A pharmaceutical case study. Transportation research part e: logistics transportation review, 103, 109-142.

Flavio Manenti, Gintaras V. Reklaitis (Eds.), Proceedings of the 34th European Symposium on Computer Aided Process Engineering / 15th International Symposium on Process Systems Engineering (ESCAPE34/PSE24), June 2-6, 2024, Florence, Italy

Big Data Analytics for Advanced Fault Detection in Wastewater Treatment Plants

Morteza Zadkarami[a,b], Krist V. Gernaey[*,b], Ali Akbar Safavi[a], Pedram Ramin[b]

[a]*School of Electrical and Computer Engineering, Shiraz University, Iran*
[b]*Process and Systems Engineering Center (PROSYS), Department of Chemical and Biochemical Engineering, Technical University of Denmark (DTU), Denmark*

kvg@kt.dtu.dk

Abstract

Fault detection in wastewater treatment plants (WWTPs) presents difficult challenges, highlighted by the nonlinear, nonstationary nature of operations and the varying fault intensities that often are neglected. While big data analytics promise transformative results, they come with their own challenges in process monitoring such as handling vast datasets, ensuring real-time responsiveness, and coping with imbalanced data distributions. With our 609-days simulation of the Benchmark Simulation Model 2 (BSM2), yielding datasets as expansive as 876,960 samples for each of the 31 measurements considered here, the inherent issues become more obvious. To address this challenging process monitoring problem, our research introduces a novel fault detection framework, handling both imbalanced data distribution and big data complications. The core of this framework includes two critical components. The first one is a wavelet-based feature analyzer which utilizes the wavelet energy and entropy information for each measurement to extract the most valuable and critical features. The other element is the enhanced neural network classifier which deals with imbalanced data distribution. This classifier partitions the data into multiple segments, subsequently determining the BSM2 operational condition (i.e. normal or fault) for each distinct segment. The proposed detection framework has demonstrated the capability to accurately identify the operational condition of the large-scale BSM2 dataset, achieving a False Alarm Rate (FAR) of less than 10%. The promising results obtained from this framework can facilitate future research on developing digital twins for WWTPs.

Keywords: Wastewater Treatment Plants (WWTPs), Process Monitoring, Big Data Analytics, Imbalanced Classification, Wavelet Analysis

1. Introduction

Wastewater Treatment Plants (WWTPs) play a key role in managing reclaimed water by removing nitrogen and organic matter. Therefore, it is important to develop fault detection systems for these plants to prevent harmful substances from being released into the environment. WWTPs include a series of biological, physical, and chemical reactions, leading to a plant-wide system inheriting nonlinear, nonstationary, auto- and cross-correlated characteristics (Liu et al., 2023).

Every fault detection approach possesses unique advantages and shortcomings. Therefore, the choice of a suitable fault detection framework depends on the specific case study and the considered objectives. Univariate fault detection approaches are among the most popular techniques applied on WWTPs because of the simple and straightforward nature. Sánchez-Fernández et al., (2018) adopted a modified version of the Exponentially Weighted Moving Average (EWMA) to detect various abnormalities including sensor faults, alkalinity variation, and pipe leaks. Multivariate fault detection methods, particularly based on Principal Component Analysis (PCA), are reported to be near 40% of the published fault detection studies on WWTPs (Liu et al., 2023). Ramin et al. (2021) implemented dynamic PCA on a WWTP containing process and instrument (i.e. sensor and/or actuator) faults. The study showed that the proposed dynamic PCA had promising precision. Kazemi et al., (2021) detected faults in an anaerobic digestion system by initially designing a soft sensor model for the Volatile Fatty Acids (VFA) based on influent and effluent characteristics. Once the VFA soft sensor task is established, the fault detection assessment was carried out using univariate and multivariate approaches. Despite the fact that fault detection approaches based on univariate and multivariate concepts are easy to implement, investigate and evaluate, they are mostly based on a Gaussian assumption which can lead to restrictions in practice since data typically do not follow a symmetric unimodal Gaussian distribution. To overcome the aforementioned issue, Zadkarami et al., (2023) suggested to employ discriminative classifications. Thus, these data-hungry models require big data sets to gain assuring results.

Thanks to the advancements in technology, data collection, storage, and processing can be done easily and rapidly, allowing us to reap the benefits of big data sets. The correct term of big data is a controversial topic in the literature since for different applications in the real world the definition varies. Nevertheless, based on a recent study (Gandomi and Haider, 2015), a dataset can be recognized as big data if it has at least one of the 5V characteristics as follows: Volume (i.e., large amount of data samples), Velocity (i.e., high rate of incoming data),Veracity (i.e., the data contains significant uncertainty and noise), Variety (i.e., the dataset is constructed by smaller datasets from different types and formats), Variability (i.e., the degree of complexity the data possesses, e.g. whether it contains noticeable fluctuations and peaks). In this study, big data analytics are necessary since there is a large quantity of data samples (i.e. 876,960), and the data also includes noise effects and rapid changes throughout the data pattern. Although big data can boost the modelling performance to a large degree, it comes with its own challenges including redundancy, curse of dimensionality, and high computational requirement.

In this paper, a novel fault detection framework is designed for a WWTP based on the Benchmark Simulation Model 2 (BSM2) considering big data aspects. To reflect the real-world application, the duration of faulty conditions is considerably shorter than the normal operation. This is affirmative for both process and instrument fault scenarios. Therefore, this research work deals with imbalanced big data collected from a highly sophisticated biochemical system. To address the data complexity, two main steps are introduced. First, a wavelet-based feature extraction structure is utilized which finds the best wavelet approximation and wavelet detail feature combinations to be inserted to a Multi-Layer Perceptron Neural Network (MLPNN) classifier. Since the imbalanced data (availability of more normal conditions) tend to be reflected in imbalanced MLPNN training, the second stage is to design a window-based classifier modification algorithm to put more emphasis on the smaller class (here the faulty conditions).

The rest of this paper is organized as follows: Section 2 describes the case study. The proposed fault detection methodology is thoroughly explained in Section 3. The obtained results along with discussions are presented in Section 4. Finally, Section 5 concludes the research.

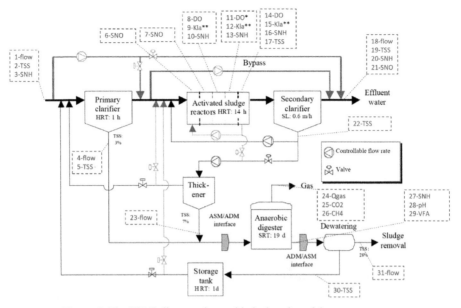

Figure 1. The BSM2 diagram along with the location of the measurements

2. The Case Study

Jeppsson et al. (2007) reported a full description of the BSM2, which is the most complete model of a practical WWTP. The BSM2 was extended with the capability to consider uncertainty and noise. In this study, an updated BSM2 model (Ramin et al. (2021)) was used which is designed for monitoring and fault detection purposes. The model was simulated for 609 days with a sampling time of 1 minute for 31 measurements, resulting in a sampling size of 876,960 for each measurement. To extract data from BSM2, different locations were selected, considering process parameters that are relatively easy-to-measure in those locations (Figure 1). The simulation is implemented on two fault scenarios including a process and an instrument fault. The simulation for the sludge bulking phenomenon, which falls into the process fault category, contains 822,765 (93.82%) normal condition data points and 54,195 (6.18%) faulty data points, resulting in an imbalance ratio (number of normal data / number of faulty data) of 15.18. On the other hand, the instrument fault representing an abnormality in the aerated reactors regarding the airflow has an imbalance ratio of 15.57 and contains 824,048 (93.97%) normal condition data points and 52,912 (6.03%) faulty data points.

3. The Fault Detection Framework

To address the big data and imbalanced data distribution issue, a novel fault detection framework is introduced. After normalizing each measurement to zero mean and unit variance, they pass through the designed feature analysis approach (Figure 2). The extracted features are then inserted into the developed classification architecture for decision making. For further details on wavelet analysis, one may refer to the research by Pourahmadi-Nakhli and Safavi (2011). Afterwards, the feature sets are inserted into an MLPNN classifier with two hidden layers respectively containing 25 and 15 neurons with sigmoid activation functions. The stopping criteria for this network is either the error reaches less than 0.01 or the iteration number exceeds 200.

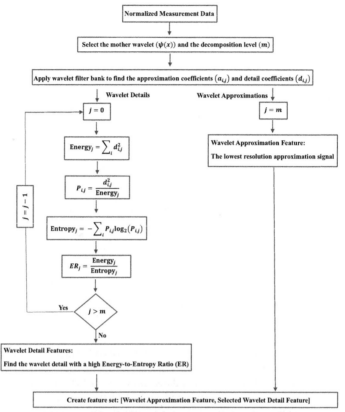

Figure 2. The designed feature extraction flowchart

Since the MLPNN, like most of the typical discriminative classifiers, tends to provide misleading results for imbalanced data distributions, a window-based classification correction structure (Algorithm 1) is designed. The main purpose of Algorithm 1 is to pay more attention to the smaller class (Faulty class) in each segment and modify the collected initial results from the MLPNN. The main idea behind Algorithm 1 is that the working operational changes for both process and actuator faults are assumed to be considerably slow. Therefore, if for a specific period of time a certain number of faults occur, one may choose to assume that the whole time period can be assigned as faulty conditions.

4. Results and Discussion

The last stage in every fault detection classification method is to assess the outcome labels using the confusion matrix (see Figure 3).

		Estimation	
		Normal	**Fault**
Actual	**Normal**	True Positive (TP)	Missed Detect (MD)
	Fault	False Alaram (FA)	True Negative (TN)

Figure 3. The Confusion Matrix

In the literature, the following criteria obtained from the confusion matrix are frequently employed (Susan and Kumar, 2021):

$$Missed\ Detection\ Rate\ (MDR) = MD/(MD + TP) \tag{1}$$

$$False\ Alaram\ Rate\ (FAR) = FA/(FA + TN) \tag{2}$$

$$Accuracy\ (ACC) = (TP + TN)/(TP + TN + FA + MD) \tag{3}$$

$$Recall = True\ Positive\ Rate\ (TPR) = 1 - MDR \tag{4}$$

$$True\ Negative\ Rate\ (TNR) = 1 - FAR \tag{5}$$

$$G_{mean} = \sqrt{TNR \times TPR} \tag{6}$$

For an ideal case, Eqs. (1-2) would be zero, while Eqs. (3-6) equals to unity. Table 1 shows the obtained fault detection results for different fault types along with considering various window sizes. It is obvious from Table 1 that for an imbalanced data distribution, such as this case study, exclusively investigating the accuracy, precision, and recall factors are not considered as reasonable criteria since they do not undertake the FAR explicitly in their calculations. On the contrary, G_{mean} provides plausible assessment. By examining the calculated G_{mean} index for each scenario, it is clear that the developed classifier correction structure can handle the imbalanced nature of the classes to a certain extent. Furthermore, in our study, the window size of 6 hours (360 samples) led to the most superior performance in detecting process and instrument faults. In fact, a promising FAR of approximately 4% and 10% for respectively the process fault and the instrument fault was obtained.

Table 1. Different fault detection results based on their correction window size

Fault Type	Window Size	MDR	FAR	Precision	Recall	Gmean	ACC	Time (sec.)
Process Fault	--	0.0021	0.3755	0.9758	0.9979	0.7894	0.9748	1889
	3 hours	0.0012	0.058	0.9961	0.9988	0.9699	0.9953	318
	6 hours	0.0017	0.0365	0.9975	0.9983	0.98	0.9961	326
	12 hours	0.0057	0.0425	0.9971	0.9943	0.9757	0.992	303
Instrument Fault	--	0.0013	0.5404	0.9664	0.9987	0.6774	0.9661	1605
	3 hours	0.0064	0.1036	0.9933	0.9936	0.9437	0.9877	276
	6 hours	0.0105	0.0927	0.994	0.9895	0.9475	0.9845	289
	12 hours	0.0087	0.1483	0.9904	0.9913	0.9188	0.9828	320

Only a few studies have conducted fault detection for the BSM2. Sánchez-Fernández et al., (2018) considered 140 measurements, many of which were inaccessible or redundant. Kazemi et al., (2021) focused only on faults in the anaerobic digestion unit, not the entire system. Ramin et al. (2021) suggested more realistic measurements and used dynamic PCA to examine their benchmark, achieving a precision index of 0.704 for process faults and 0.888 for instrumentation faults. However, the accuracy was unsatisfactory, with 0.651 for process faults and 0.432 for instrumentation faults. This study improves the BSM2 design of Ramin et al. (2021), making it more practical and challenging. The performance evaluation indicates that the new fault detection approach effectively handles the complexities and difficulties associated with the BSM2.

Algorithm 1. The windowed-based classifier correction algorithm
1. Select a window size
2. Get the labels from the MLPNN classifier output for the current window
3. Select a threshold
4. **If** 'the number of labels classified as faulty' > threshold
Set the whole labels of that window as faulty condition
else
Set the whole labels of that window as Normal condition
5. Record the updated condition labelling for that window
6. **If** 'the number of collected data' = 876,960 samples (609 simulation days)
Set the modified output labels as the final decision condition
else
Move to the next window and go to step 2
7. Validation

5. Conclusion

This research study introduced a novel fault detection framework for wastewater treatment plants based on the BSM2, addressing challenges of big data and imbalanced data distribution. The framework utilized a wavelet-based feature analyzer and an enhanced classifier. It was tested for both process and instrument faults individually, achieving a FAR of less than 10% in the optimum case. Future studies can be carried out in terms of simultaneous fault sources or investigating other approaches to address the imbalanced data nature of such systems.

References

A. Gandomi, M. Haider, 2015. Beyond the hype: Big data concepts, methods, and analytics. Int J Inf Manage, 35, 137–144.

A. Sánchez-Fernández, F.J. Baldán, G.I. Sainz-Palmero, J.M. Benítez, M.J. Fuente, 2018. Fault detection based on time series modeling and multivariate statistical process control. Chemometrics and Intelligent Laboratory Systems, 182, 57–69.

M. Pourahmadi-Nakhli, A.A. Safavi, 2011. Path characteristic frequency-based fault locating in radial distribution systems using wavelets and neural networks. IEEE Transactions on Power Delivery, 26, 772–781.

M. Zadkarami, A.A. Safavi, K.V. Gernaey, P. Ramin, O A. Prado-Rubio, 2023. Designing a fault detection classifier framework for an industrial dynamic ultrafiltration membrane process using wavelet-based feature analysis Process Safety and Environmental Protection, 174, 1-19.

P. Kazemi, C. Bengoa, J.P. Steyer, J. Giralt, 2021. Data-driven techniques for fault detection in anaerobic digestion process. Process Safety and Environmental Protection, 146, 905–915.

P. Ramin, X. Flores-Alsina, S. Olivier, N. Topalian, U. Jeppsson, K.V. Gernaey, 2021. Fault detection in a benchmark simulation model for wastewater treatment plants. Computer Aided Chemical Engineering, 49, 1363-1368.

S. Susan, A. Kumar, 2021. The balancing trick: Optimized sampling of imbalanced datasets—A brief survey of the recent State of the Art. Engineering Reports.

U. Jeppsson, M.N. Pons, I. Nopens, J. Alex, J.B. Copp, K.V. Gernaey, C. Rosen, J.P. Steyer, P.A. Vanrolleghem, 2007. Benchmark simulation model no 2: General protocol and exploratory case studies. Water Science and Technology, 56, 67–78.

Y. Liu, P. Ramin, X. Flores-Alsina, K.V. Gernaey, 2023. Transforming data into actionable knowledge for fault detection, diagnosis and prognosis in urban wastewater systems with AI techniques: A mini-review. Process Safety and Environmental Protection, 172, 501–512.

Flavio Manenti, Gintaras V. Reklaitis (Eds.), Proceedings of the 34th European Symposium on Computer Aided Process Engineering / 15th International Symposium on Process Systems Engineering (ESCAPE34/PSE24), June 2-6, 2024, Florence, Italy

Multiphase compartment modelling and systems identification of a U-loop reactor for continuous single cell protein production

Johan Le Nepvou De Carfort[a], Tiago Pinto[b], Ulrich Krühne[a*]

[a]*PROSYS, Department of Chemical and Biochemical Engineering, Technical University of Denmark, Sølvtofts Plads Building 228A, Kongens Lyngby, Denmark*
[b]*R&D Department, UNIBIO A/S, Roskilde, Denmark*
ulkr@kt.dtu.dk

Abstract

In this study, a multiphase compartment model for U-loop bioreactors is proposed and applied to a 5.5 $[m^3]$ pilot scale U-loop. The developed compartment model that includes the material balance of multiple compounds in the gas and liquid phases as well as interfacial mass transfer is coupled with the microbial biokinetics to simulate the fermentation process. The model inputs and outputs are identified in terms of control systems, and the model is linearized around industrially relevant operating conditions. The linearized system is identified in terms of relative gain and a linear state-space model is fitted.

Keywords: Compartment model, Multiphase, Bioreactor, Process control.

1. Introduction

Single Cell Protein (SCP) stands as a promising alternative to traditional protein sources to meet the growing global demand for sustainable and high-quality proteins. With a growing world population and increasing environmental concern, the exploration of alternative protein sources has gained significant attention. SCP offers an attractive solution, using cheap and available energy and carbon sources, and having a relatively low environmental footprint compared to traditional protein sources (animal, vegetal) [1]. It has been shown that SCP can be produced through the fermentation of *Methylococcus Capsulatus*, using methane as the main carbon source [2]. Although SCP has the potential to be used as a more sustainable protein source, the manufacturing of such proteins presents some engineering challenges related to the complex metabolism of methanotrophic microorganisms [3], and the high heat and mass transfer demand, that cannot be reached using conventional bioreactors [2]. Recent work has provided insight into the complex reaction kinetics through the study of cometabolic processes and full genome scale metabolic model of the microorganism [4,5], and it has been shown that U-loop bioreactors can be used to overcome the heat and mass transfer limitations [6,7]. The operation of continuous large-scale productions is, however, limited by the complex process dynamics arising from the inhomogeneous process conditions in a U-loop reactor. This study presents a dynamic numerical model of *Methylococcus Capsulatus* cultivation in a U-loop reactor, including a reduced biokinetic model of the microorganism and a gas-liquid hydrodynamic model of a U-loop. The purpose is to use the combined model to simulate the complex process dynamics and understand how to maintain the desired operating conditions during continuous production.

2. Materials & Methods

2.1. Biological Model

The applied biological model is a simplified Monod type kinetic model describing the growth rate accounting for the substrate limitations. The production and consumption rates of products and substrates determined from the reaction yields. The overall reaction is described in eq. (1), and the microbial specific growth rate mu in eq. (2).

$$CH_4 + 1.453O_2 + 0.1NH_4^+ \rightarrow 0.52\,X + 0.48\,CO_2 \tag{1}$$

$$\mu = \mu_{max}\left(\frac{CH_4}{K_{s,CH_4}+CH_4}\right)\left(\frac{O_2}{K_{s,O_2}+O_2}\right)\left(\frac{NH_3}{K_{s,NH_3}+NH_3}\right) \tag{2}$$

The volumetric rates of formation of the different species involved in the reaction can be expressed as shown in eq. (3). The model parameters are summarized in Table 1.

$$r_X = \mu X; \quad r_{CH_4} = -r_X Y_{XS}; \quad r_{O_2} = r_S Y_{SO}; \quad r_{CO_2} = -r_S Y_{SCO_2}; \quad r_{NH_3} = r_S Y_{SNH_3} \tag{3}$$

Table 1: Biokinetic model parameters

Parameter	Value	Unit
μ_{max}	0.37	$[h^{-1}]$
K_{s,CH_4}	9.6e-6	$[kg/m^3]$
K_{s,O_2}	2.09e-5	$[kg/m^3]$
K_{s,NH_3}	5.274e-4	$[kg/m^3]$
Y_{XS}	0.651	$[gCH_4/gX]$
Y_{SO}	1.995	$[gO_2/gCH_4]$
Y_{SCO_2}	2.099	$[gCO_2/gCH_4]$
Y_{SNH_3}	0.106	$[gNH_3/gCH_4]$

2.2. Compartment Modelling

Compartment models are a way of representing volumes as discretized regions with known volumes and exchange flow rates. The compartment models can be used to carry out dynamic simulations of the mixing between compartments. The purpose is to include the gas-liquid hydrodynamics and the inhomogeneous conditions of the U-loop reactors to the final model. To this extent, a multiphase compartment mode including interfacial mass transfer is required. A simplified sketch of a U-loop reactor is shown in figure 1 (a). The top tank (or degassing tank) is considered as a single compartment, and the loop section is discretized along the length (assuming plug flow). Gas and liquid inlets are located in the down-going leg, and the outlets are all located in the top tank. The pressure profile in the loop is determined from the height, as well as the contribution from the pump and pressure release valve. For each compartment, a mass balance of the gas and liquid phases is performed to solve for the gas and liquid composition. The volume fraction of each phase in each compartment is determined based on the relative volumetric flowrates of gas and liquid entering the compartment and the assumed superficial gas velocity according to eq. (4). The respective volume fractions are then determined by solving the system of equations (5).

$$U_s = U_g - U_l \tag{4}$$

$$\begin{cases} \dfrac{Q_{liq}}{A_{cross}\alpha_{liq}} = \dfrac{Q_{gas}}{A_{cross}\alpha_{gas}} - U_s \\ \alpha_{liq} + \alpha_{gas} = 1 \end{cases} \tag{5}$$

Where Q_{liq} and Q_{gas} are respectively the liquid and gas volumetric flow rates, A_{cross} is the cross sectional area of the loop section, U_s is the superficial gas velocity and α_{liq} and α_{gas} are the liquid and gas volume fractions, respectively. The bulk liquid phase is assumed to be in steady-state, so the total mass balance in compartment n can be expressed as shown in eq. (6). The specie material balance for component i in the liquid phase is expressed as eq. (7) including a reaction term and a mass transfer term. The material balance in the gas phase in compartment n (eq. (9)) is expressed as function of the gas residence time τ in each compartment, corresponding to the gas velocity U_g divided by the length of the compartment n, h_n (eq. (8)). It is assumed that no reactions are taking place in the gas phase.

$$Q_{liq,in} = Q_{liq,out} \tag{6}$$

$$\frac{dc_n^i}{dt} = \left(Q_{liq,n-1}C_{n-1}^i - Q_{liq,n}C_n^i \right)\left(\frac{1}{V_{liq,n}} \right) + r_n^i + iTR_n \tag{7}$$

$$\tau_n = \frac{U_g}{h_n} = \frac{U_s+U_l}{h_n} = \frac{U_s+\left(\frac{Q_{liq,n}}{A_{cross}\alpha_{liq,n}} \right)}{h_n} \tag{8}$$

$$\frac{dN_n^i}{dt} = \left(N_{n-1}^i \tau_{n-1} \right) - \left(\frac{iTR_n V_{liq,n}}{M_i} \right) - \left(N_n^i \tau_n \right) \tag{9}$$

Where C_n^i is the liquid concentration of component i in compartment n, and N_n^i the molar amount of component i in compartment n, r_n^i is the volumetric rate of formation of

Figure 1: (a) Sketch of the pilot-scale U-loop (grey arrows show the direction of the flow in the loop), (b) Sketch of the multiphase compartment model of the U-loop.

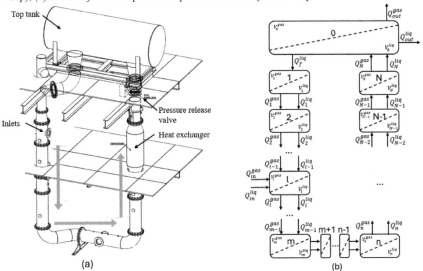

(a)

(b)

component i in compartment n, and iTR_n is the interfacial mass transfer rate of component i in compartment n. The biomass is assumed to stay in the liquid phase; therefore the mass transfer term is set to zero. Static pressure is assumed to be the main contributor to the overall pressure profile in the loop, so the pressure is set by the height of the liquid added to the pressure created by the pump and valve located respectively at the beginning and at the end of the loop. The pressure in the top tank is assumed atmospheric. The pressure drop along the loop due to friction with the pipe wall is assumed negligible, however, the pressure drop related to the static mixers located in the loop are added manually based on the position, size, and pressure drop of each mixer. A constant temperature of 30°C is assumed throughout the reactor. The interfacial mass transfer rates are expressed in eq. (10) according to the Film Theory [8].

$$iTR_n = k_L a_n \left(C_n^{i,*} - C_n^i \right) \tag{10}$$

Where $k_L a_n$ is the volumetric mass transfer coefficient in compartment n, and $C_n^{i,*}$ the saturation concentration of component i in compartment n. The $k_L a$ is assumed constant throughout the loop, more advanced models may be implemented in further work. The saturation concentration of each component is expressed in eq. (11) and the Henrys coefficients H_i according to [9].

$$C_n^{i,*} = H_i P_n^i \tag{11}$$

Where P_n^i is the partial pressure of component i in compartment n, based on the relative amount of component i in the gas phase, and the total pressure in compartment n. The resulting system of ordinary differential equations (one balance equation for each component for each compartment for each phase, excluding the biomass balance equation in the gas phase) is solved in Python using the *solve_ivp()* function from the *scipy.integrate* library, with the LSODA solver. Initial conditions are reported in table 2.

Table 2: Initial conditions for the numerical model.

Component	Initial value	Unit
X	20	$[g/m^3]$
$CH_{4,liq}$; $CH_{4,gas}$	70 ; 0.1	$[g/m^3]$; [mol]
$O_{2,liq}$; $O_{2,gas}$	1e-3 ; 7e-3	$[g/m^3]$; [mol]
$NH_{3,liq}$; $NH_{3,gas}$	1 ; 3e-3	$[g/m^3]$; [mol]
$CO_{2,liq}$; $CO_{2,gas}$	1e-5 ; 1e-8	$[g/m^3]$; [mol]

The multiphase compartment model is constructed for a 5.5 $[m^3]$ pilot-scale U-loop, with a liquid height of 6 $[m]$ and a loop pipe diameter of 0.4 $[m]$. The system is discretized into 51 compartments (1 for the top-tank, and 50 for the loop).

2.3. Systems Identification

Based on the main actuators, and the key process conditions to control, a list of 6 inputs and 6 outputs is identified and reported in table 3. The nominal input values are taken from industrial operating conditions. At first, a simulation with the given initial condition is performed over 200 h simulation time, to determine the steady-state output values. The local steady-state sensitivity of the outputs to changes in the inputs is quantified using the Monte Carlo approach. A set of 5000 input values are randomly sampled from normal distributions around the nominal value with standard deviation of 5%. For each set of input values, the steady-state responses of the model are evaluated. Finally, a linear model is fitted on the generated input/output data, normalized relative to the nominal values.

Table 3: Inputs and outputs considered in the systems identification.

	#	Symbol	Nominal Value	Unit
Inputs				
Gas inlet flowrates	Input 1	$Q_{in}^{CH_4}$	6.033e-3	$[Nm^3/s]$
	Input 2	Q_{in}^{air}	1.666e-3	$[Nm^3/s]$
	Input 3	$Q_{in}^{O_2}$	7.083e-3	$[Nm^3/s]$
	Input 4	$Q_{in}^{NH_3}$	3.333e-4	$[Nm^3/s]$
Liquid inlet flowrate	Input 5	Q_{in}^{liq}	1.000e-4	$[m^3/s]$
Liquid circulation rate	Input 6	Q_f^{liq}	1.256e-1	$[m^3/s]$
Outputs				
Liquid concentrations in the top-tank	Output 1	C_0^X	1.763e+1	$[g/L]$
	Output 2	$C_0^{NH_3}$	8.243e-6	$[g/L]$
	Output 3	$C_0^{O_2}$	3.417e-2	$[g/L]$
Offgas component flowrates	Output 4	$Q_{out}^{CO_2}$	1.599e-3	$[Nm^3/s]$
	Output 5	$Q_{out}^{CH_4}$	2.676e-3	$[Nm^3/s]$
	Output 6	$Q_{out}^{O_2}$	2.558e-3	$[Nm^3/s]$

3. Results and Discussion

The nominal steady-state output values are reported in table 3. The standardized regression coefficients are represented in figure 2. In can be noted that the NH_3 inlet flowrate has the largest impact om the model outputs. The magnitude of the regression coefficients can be used to pair the inputs to the outputs in a control structure. The numerical model is used to determine the coefficients for a linear state-space model around the nominal operating point. Perturbations in the inputs and the states allow for quantification of the linear model coefficients in the matrices A, B and C (eq. (12)).

$$\begin{cases} \dot{x} = Ax + Bu \\ y = Cx \end{cases} \tag{12}$$

Where x is the normalized state vector, $\dot{x}$ is the derivative of the normalized state vector, u is the normalised input vector and y the normalized output vector. For the investigated system, the total of 459 states made the computation of the observability and controllability matrices infeasible computationally. The implementation of a reduced order state space model (with less states) e.g. using the eigen value realization algorithm [10], the balanced truncation or the balanced proper orthogonal decomposition [11] method could allow for the computation of the observability and controllability matrices. Although the pressure is taken into account for calculating the solubility of the gaseous compounds, further work will focus on implementing more advanced models for the $k_L a$, to account for the changing bubble sizes and mass transfer coefficient k_L along the loop.

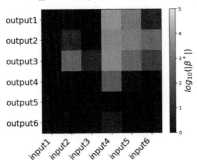

Figure 2: Standardized regression coefficient (log10 of the absolute value)

4. Conclusions

The proposed multiphase compartment model was used to simulate the *Methylococcus Capsulatus* fermentation for single cell protein production. The coupling of the microbial biokinetic model with the gas-liquid hydrodynamic model made it possible to simulate the effects of mass transfer and mixing limitations on biological growth. Industrially relevant inputs and outputs are identified, and the numerical model was linearized around nominal operating conditions. The linear model may be used in further work to develop and tune control systems and model-based monitoring for the fermentation process. Monitoring and control are key to maintaining desired process conditions, making continuous production possible. Optimal control is also crucial for reproducibility of the process and ensuring "Quality by Control".

References

1. Kim, S. W., Less, J. F., Wang, L., Yan, T., Kiron, V., Kaushik, S. J., & Lei, X. G. (2019). Meeting Global Feed Protein Demand: Challenge, Opportunity, and Strategy
2. Nielsen, J., & Villadsen, J. (2011). Bioreaction engineering principles Third Edition. *Reactions*, *25*(9).
3. Lieven, C., Herrgård, M. J., & Sonnenschein, N. (2018). Microbial Methylotrophic Metabolism: Recent Metabolic Modeling Efforts and Their Applications In Industrial Biotechnology. *Biotechnology Journal*, *13*(8). https://doi.org/10.1002/BIOT.201800011
4. Petersen, L. A. H., Lieven, C., Nandy, S. K., Villadsen, J., Jørgensen, S. B., Christensen, I., & Gernaey, K. v. (2019). Dynamic investigation and modeling of the nitrogen cometabolism in Methylococcus capsulatus (Bath). *Biotechnology and Bioengineering*, *116*(11), 2884–2895. https://doi.org/10.1002/BIT.27113
5. Lieven, C., Petersen, L. A. H., Jørgensen, S. B., Gernaey, K. v., Herrgard, M. J., & Sonnenschein, N. (2018). A Genome-Scale Metabolic Model for Methylococcus capsulatus (Bath) Suggests Reduced Efficiency Electron Transfer to the Particulate Methane Monooxygenase. *Frontiers in Microbiology*, *9*, 415473. https://doi.org/10.3389/FMICB.2018.02947/BIBTEX
6. Larsen, E. B. (2007). U-SHAPE AND/OR NOZZLE-U-LOOP FERMENTOR AND METHOD OF CARRYING OUT A FERMENTATION PROCESS. In *European Patent Office*.
7. Petersen, L. A. H., Villadsen, J., Jørgensen, S. B., & Gernaey, K. v. (2017). Mixing and mass transfer in a pilot scale U-loop bioreactor. *Biotechnology and Bioengineering*, *114*(2). https://doi.org/10.1002/bit.26084
8. Titchener-Hooker, N. (1995). Bioprocess Engineering Principles (by Pauline M. Doran). *TRENDS IN BIOTECHNOLOGY*, *13*(1).
9. Sander, R. (2015). Compilation of Henry's law constants (version 4.0) for water as solvent. *Atmos. Chem. Phys*, *15*, 4399–4981. https://doi.org/10.5194/acp-15-4399-2015
10. Juang, J. N., & Pappa, R. S. (1985). An eigensystem realization algorithm for modal parameter identification and model reduction. *Journal of Guidance, Control, and Dynamics*, *8*(5). https://doi.org/10.2514/3.20031
11. Willcox, K., & Peraire, J. (2002). Balanced Model Reduction via the Proper Orthogonal Decomposition. *AIAA JOURNAL*, *40*(11).

Flavio Manenti, Gintaras V. Reklaitis (Eds.), Proceedings of the 34th European Symposium on Computer Aided Process Engineering / 15th International Symposium on Process Systems Engineering (ESCAPE34/PSE24), June 2-6, 2024, Florence, Italy

Predicting the coagulation potential of waste lubricant oil (WLO) using multiblock machine learning of NIR and MIR spectroscopy

Rúben Gariso,[a] Tiago J.Rato,[a] Margarida J. Quina,[a] , Licínio Ferreira,[a] Marco S. Reis,[a,*]

[a]University of Coimbra, CIEPQPF, Department of Chemical Engineering, Rua Sílvio Lima, Pólo II – Pinhal de Marrocos, 3030-790 Coimbra, Portugal
*e-mail: marco@eq.uc.pt

Abstract

Waste lubricant oils (WLO) pose sustainability challenges, necessitating efficient and reliable methods for their treatment. Regeneration is the preferable approach, but WLOs can coagulate in the equipment, causing plant shutdowns for cleaning and maintenance. To avoid this situation, an alkaline treatment is currently used to assess the WLO coagulation potential prior to regeneration. However, this procedure is time-consuming and subjective, as it involves a visual assessment by the analyst. To overcome these limitations, alternative methods that minimize subjectivity and reduce analysis time are needed. To this end, a rapid and reliable method for predicting the coagulation potential of WLOs through multiblock machine learning analysis of near-infrared (NIR) and mid-infrared (MIR) spectroscopy data is introduced in this article. The classification models employ a combination of Partial Least Squares for Discriminant Analysis (PLS-DA) and the Bayesian linear classifier. The models' performance was optimized via extensive search using the AutoML framework called SS-DAC. More specifically, 1755 combinations of preprocessing, block scaling, and modeling methodologies were tested. By automating this process, a comprehensive and accurate prediction of WLO coagulation potential was achieved. The best NIR single-block model presented a classification accuracy of 0.53, while the best MIR single-block model had an accuracy of 0.88. In turn, the best multiblock model combining the NIR and MIR spectra had an accuracy of 0.94. This improvement is linked to an increase in the correct classification of WLOs that do not coagulate, whose miss-classification is the most critical. Thus, our findings reveal that the combined use of NIR and MIR spectra significantly improves the prediction of the coagulation potential of WLOs compared to the use of NIR or MIR alone, namely for the cases where the misclassification is more detrimental.

Keywords: Waste lubricating oil, Multiblock analysis, PLS, Classification.

1. Introduction

Waste lubricant oil (WLO) is a hazardous waste that can cause significant environmental damage if improperly managed. Regeneration is the priority process regarding the waste management hierarchy in the EU. In Portugal, the entire supply chain for the regeneration of WLO is carried out by Sogilub. The goal of regeneration is to obtain base oil again (the main component of virgin lubricant oil) from WLO. However, regeneration is only feasible if the WLO does not coagulate during processing. Otherwise, the process must be stopped for cleaning and subsequent disposal of the entire production. To minimize this risk, the coagulation potential of WLOs is currently assessed through a laboratory analysis using an alkaline treatment. However, this laboratory test is time-consuming, has some safety risks, and is subjective, depending on the analyst's visual interpretation of the results. As an alternative, a process analytical technology (PAT)-based classifier opens the potential to significantly expedite sample processing and enhance the safety and testing capacity of laboratories.

The present work aims to develop a classifier to predict the coagulation potential using a combination of mid-infrared (MIR) and near-infrared (NIR) spectroscopy. The two information sources were combined using multiblock analysis. A variety of PLS-based approaches were developed to handle multiblock data, such as Concatenated PLS, Hierarchical PLS (Wold et al., 1987), multiblock PLS (Wangen and Kowalski, 1989) and Sequential Orthogonalised PLS (Næs et al., 2020). A review of these methodologies can be found in (Campos et al., 2017). In this work, we employ the Concatenated PLS approach, which consists of concatenating all blocks into a single augmented matrix. Afterwards, the standard PLS is applied.

The rest of this article is organized as follows. In Section 2, the methodology is described, including the pre-processing techniques, block scaling, and modeling methodologies. Afterward, in Section 3, the results are presented. Finally, a summary of the conclusions is provided in Section 4.

2. Methodology

The proposed multiblock methodology is composed of three levels to be optimized: (i) spectra preprocessing; (ii) block scaling (iii); and modeling methodology. A simplified diagram of the workflow of the methodology is presented in Figure 1. To find the best combination of levels we resorted to the SS-DAC framework (Rato and Reis, 2019).

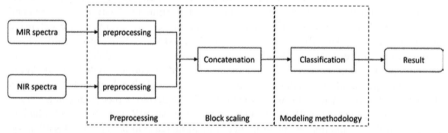

Figure 1 Diagram of the proposed methodology and its three levels to be optimized (spectra preprocessing, block scaling, and modeling methodology).

2.1. Level 1: Spectral preprocessing

The first optimization level of the proposed methodology regards the preprocessing of the spectral data to mitigate potential artifacts that may arise due to unintended interactions between light and the sample under examination. In this work, the focus is directed toward three prominent categories of preprocessing techniques:

- Standard Normal Variate (SNV) (Geladi et al., 1985);
- Multiplicative Scatter Correction (MSC) (Barker and Rayens, 2003);
- Savitzky-Golay differentiation (SGD) (Savitzky and Golay, 1964).

Different combinations of these preprocessing techniques, as well as different parameterizations of SGD (identified as SGD-{derivative order}-{window size}-{polynomial order}) were examined (see Table 1), leading to nine distinct pre-processing variations. Furthermore, it is considered that each data block may have a different preprocessing.

2.2. Level 2: Block scaling

After preprocessing each data block, in the second optimization level, each data block is scaled to ensure that its variability is properly represented within the model.

Block scaling approaches can be generalized by the following equation:

$$\mathbf{X}_{b\ scaled} = (1/K_b) \cdot \mathbf{X}_b \tag{1}$$

where $\mathbf{X}_b$ represents the original data block, indexed by b (for $b = 1, ..., B$), K_b is a block-scaling factor, and $\mathbf{X}_{b\ scaled}$ is the scaled data block.

The block-scaling factors, K_b, are determined using the techniques outlined in Table 1. These techniques can be grouped into two categories:

- Block Scaling (BS) methods, which only consider the number of variables within the block;
- Block Variance Scaling (BVS) methods, which consider the standard deviation of each block.

For detailed formulas and further information, please refer to the work of (Campos and Reis, 2020). After block-scaling, the blocks are concatenated and fed to a modeling methodology.

2.3. Level 3: Modeling methodology

The third and final optimization level of the proposed methodology concerns the fitting of a classification model using the concatenated data blocks. The primary technique employed to fit the models was partial least squares (PLS) for discriminant analysis (DA) (Barker and Rayens, 2003). In the current implementation of PLS-DA, the response variable is an indicator variable that codifies the WLO class (*coagulate* or *does-not-coagulate*) and a PLS-based method is used to extract the latent variables with higher discriminative power. Afterward, the extracted latent variables are fed to the Bayesian Linear Classifier (Hastie et al., 2009) to obtain the final model.

In this study, the full spectra PLS as well as two interval-based extensions of PLS (Nørgaard et al., 2000) were considered to extract the most relevant features:

- PLS (Wold et al., 2001);
- Forward interval PLS (FiPLS) (Xiaobo et al., 2007);
- Backward interval PLS (BiPLS) (Xiaobo et al., 2007).

3. Results

In this study, a total of 107 WLO samples were collected. The WLO coagulation potential was determined through a coagulation test using an alkaline treatment with KOH. Based on the result of this analysis, the samples are classified into *coagulate* or *does-not-coagulate* by the laboratory analyst. Furthermore, the NIR (2530 wavenumbers in the range of 7000 to 3950 cm^{-1}) and MIR (1814 wavenumbers in the range of 4000 to 500 cm^{-1}) spectra of each sample were also collected in triplicate. For the BiPLS and FiPLS-based models, each block was divided into 15 equal intervals.

To evaluate the impact of combining two blocks of information, the SS-DAC framework was used over multiple combinations of preprocessing techniques, block scaling, and modeling methodologies, leading to 1701 multiblock model combinations. Furthermore, the single-block model scenarios were also considered as benchmark, leading to an additional 54 single-block models. Overall, a grand total of 1755 models were tested. These models were labeled using the following nomenclature (see Table 1): {modeling methodology}-{data block}-{MIR preprocessing technique}-{NIR preprocessing technique}-{block scaling technique}.

In the first stage of SS-DAC the raw dataset was randomly split into a training dataset with 80 % of the samples and a test dataset with the remaining 20 % of the samples, maintaining balanced datasets. Furthermore, replicates of the same sample were attributed to the same dataset. The models were then trained on the training dataset using Monte Carlo Cross-Validation (MCCV) for tuning the model's hyperparameters (*i.e.*, the number of retained latent variables, and intervals in the models). Afterward, in the second stage of SS-DAC, the models' performance was assessed on the test dataset using the accuracy (H) as the key performance indicator (KPI):

$$H = \frac{TP + TN}{n} \tag{2}$$

where TP is the number of true positives, TN is the number of true negatives and n is the number of samples in the test dataset. The accuracy varies from 0 to 1, where higher values relate to better classification capabilities.

In the third stage of SS-DAC the models were compared against each other using the Wilcoxon signed-rank test (Wilcoxon, 1945). For each comparison, if a model has a statistically significant higher accuracy against another model it receives a *victory* and if there is no statistically significant difference in accuracy it receives a *tie*. A score is then computed by summing the number of victoried and ties of each model. Models with higher scores (*i.e.*, high count of victories and ties) are deemed to have consistently higher accuracy. The scores for the top 50 models are presented in Figure 2, ranked from highest to lowest performance. For this case, the maximum score a model can achieve is 1754, representing a victory against all other models. For reference, the models' accuracy on the test dataset was also computed.

Table 1 Summary of the data blocks and optimization levels considered in this study. The model's nomenclature is as follows: {modeling methodology}-{data block}-{MIR preprocessing technique}-{NIR preprocessing technique}-{block scaling technique}.

Data block	Optimization levels		
	Modeling methodology	Spectral preprocessing	Block scaling
Only MIR [A]	PLS [P]	Not used [0]	Not used [0]
Only NIR [B]	FiPLS [F]	Mean centering [1]	No Scaling [I]
MIR&NIR [C] *	BiPLS [B]	SNV [2]	Soft BS [II]
		MSC [3]	Hard BS [III]
		SGD-1-7-2 [4]	Super Hard BS [IV]
		SGD-1-15-2 [5]	Soft BVS [V]
		SGD-2-9-2 [6]	Hard BVS [VI]
		SNV-SGD-1-7-2 [7]	Super Hard BVS [VII]
		SNV-SGD 1-15-2 [8]	
		SNV-SGD 2-9-2 [9]	

* The model is free to select between both data blocks. Depending on the intervals selected by the model the data block is subclassified into: C11 if both blocks are selected; C10 if only the MIR block is selected; C01 if only the NIR block is selected.

Predicting the coagulation potential of waste lubricant oils (WLO) using multiblock machine learning of NIR and MIR spectroscopy

1847

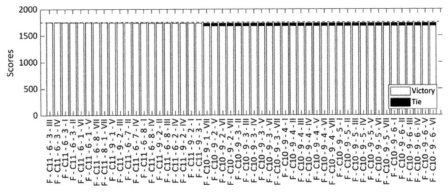

Figure 2 Score of the top 50 models using the SS-DAC framework. The model's nomenclature is as follows (see Table 1): {modeling methodology}-{data block}-{MIR preprocessing technique}-{NIR preprocessing technique}-{block scaling technique}.The dashed horizontal line represents the maximum score value (1754).

Regarding the single-block models, the best model using only the MIR spectra (F-C10-9-1-VII) was ranked in position #21, with an accuracy of 0.88 (with a partial accuracy of 0.78 for the WLO samples that coagulate and 1.00 for the WLO samples that do-not-coagulate), while the best model using only the NIR spectra (B-B-0-4-0) was ranked in position #1708 with an accuracy of 0.56 (with a partial accuracy of 0.44 for the WLO samples that coagulate and 0.67 for the WLO samples that do not coagulate).

As for the multiblock models, it was verified that, due to the interval selection of FiPLS, 478 out of 567 FiPLS-based multiblock models only used the MIR block. Thus, they are, in effect, equivalent to their single-block counterparts, and their performance is independent of the scaling and preprocessing of the NIR block. This also implies a performance tie when compared against each other, which is visible in Figure 2 for models in positions #21 (F-C10-9-1-VII) to #50 (F-C10-9-6-VI). The same situation also happens for models with smaller scores (not shown). Nevertheless, the NIR block is still informative when combined with the MIR block as shown on the top four models. These models share a similar structure, being based on FiPLS and SGD for the MIR block and MSC for the NIR block, with block scaling having a small impact on performance. The best model (F-C11-6-3-III) achieved a global accuracy of 0.94 (and a partial accuracy of 0.89 for the WLO samples that *coagulate* and 1.00 for the WLOs that *do-not-coagulate*), which represents an improvement of 6.82 % against the best MIR single-block model.

The top models frequently selected the [734.4 - 966], [1668 - 1900] cm^{-1} intervals from the MIR spectra, and the [4951 - 5150] cm^{-1} interval from the NIR spectra. The interval that appears more predominantly ([1668 - 1900] cm^{-1}) is thought to be related to the presence of esters (Weyer, 2012) in the WLO, a result that was also obtained in (Pinheiro et al., 2017).

4. Conclusions

Among the single-block models, those using the NIR spectra presented the worst performances as even the best NIR single-block model only had an accuracy of 0.56. In turn, the MIR single-block models proved to be more informative, achieving an accuracy of 0.88. The best performance was attained by multiblock models combining FiPLS with variations of SGD. The best multiblock model had an accuracy of 0.94, which represents an improvement of 6.82 % against the best single-block model. For this case, block scaling had a lesser impact on performance since FiPLS tended to select intervals solely from the MIR spectra. Nevertheless, a few intervals from the NIR spectra were also selected by the multiblock models. Thus, it is concluded that incorporating MIR and NIR spectral information significantly enhances the predictive capability of the models. The top models also point to the presence of esters as the most critical factor for WLO coagulation, thus providing crucial insights into the coagulation phenomenon.

Acknowledgments

The authors gratefully acknowledge the financial support of SOGILUB – Sociedade de Gestão Integrada de Óleos Lubrificantes Usados, Lda. The authors also acknowledge the support from the Chemical Process Engineering and Forest Products Research Centre (CIEPQPF), which is financed by national funds from FCT/MCTES (reference UIDB/EQU/00102/2020).

References

M. Barker, W. Rayens, 2003, Partial Least Squares for Discrimination, Journal of Chemometrics, 17, 166–173.

M. Campos, M. Reis, 2020, Data Preprocessing for Multiblock Modelling – A Systematization with New Methods, Chemometrics and Intelligent Laboratory Systems, 199, 103959.

M.P. Campos, R. Sousa, A.C. Pereira, M.S. Reis, 2017, Advanced Predictive Methods for Wine Age Prediction: Part II – A Comparison Study of Multiblock Regression Approaches, Talanta, 171, 132–142.

P. Geladi, D. MacDougall, H. Martens, 1985, Linearization and Scatter-Correction for Near-Infrared Reflectance Spectra of Meat, Applied Spectroscopy, 39, 491–500.

T. Hastie, R. Tibshirani, J. Friedman, 2009, The Elements of Statistical Learning: Data Mining, Inference, and Prediction, 2nd ed, Springer, New York, NY.

T. Næs, R. Romano, O. Tomic, I. Måge, A. Smilde, K.H. Liland, 2020, Sequential and Orthogonalized PLS (SO-PLS) Regression for Path Analysis: Order of Blocks and Relations between Effects, Journal of Chemometrics, e3243.

L. Nørgaard, A. Saudland, J. Wagner, J.P. Nielsen, L. Munck, S.B. Engelsen, 2000, Interval Partial Least-Squares Regression (iPLS): A Comparative Chemometric Study with an Example from Near-Infrared Spectroscopy.

C. Pinheiro, V. Ascensão, M. Reis, M. Quina, L. Gando-Ferreira, 2017, A Data-Driven Approach for the Study of Coagulation Phenomena in Waste Lubricant Oils and Its Relevance in Alkaline Regeneration Treatments, Science of The Total Environment, 599–600, 2054–2064.

T.J. Rato, M.S. Reis, 2019, SS-DAC: A Systematic Framework for Selecting the Best Modeling Approach and Pre-Processing for Spectroscopic Data, Computers & Chemical Engineering, 128, 437–449.

A. Savitzky, M.J.E. Golay, 1964, Smoothing and Differentiation of Data by Simplified Least Squares Procedures, Analytical Chemistry, 36, 1627–1639.

L.E. Wangen, B.R. Kowalski, 1989, A multiblock partial least squares algorithm for investigating complex chemical systems, Journal of Chemometrics, 3, 3–20.

J.W.J. Weyer Lois, 2012, Practical Guide and Spectral Atlas for Interpretive Near-Infrared Spectroscopy, 2nd ed, CRC Press, Boca Raton.

F. Wilcoxon, 1945, Individual Comparisons by Ranking Methods, Biometrics Bulletin, 1, 80–83.

S. Wold, S. Hellberg, T. Lundstedt, M. Sjostrom, H. Wold, 1987, PLS Modeling with Latent Variables in Two or More Dimensions, Frankfurt am Main.

S. Wold, M. Sjöström, L. Eriksson, 2001, PLS-Regression: A Basic Tool of Chemometrics, Chemometrics and Intelligent Laboratory Systems, 58, 109–130.

Z. Xiaobo, Z. Jiewen, H. Xingyi, L. Yanxiao, 2007, Use of FT-NIR Spectrometry in Non-Invasive Measurements of Soluble Solid Contents (SSC) of "Fuji" Apple Based on Different PLS Models, Chemometrics and Intelligent Laboratory Systems, 87, 43–51.

Flavio Manenti, Gintaras V. Reklaitis (Eds.), Proceedings of the 34th European Symposium on Computer Aided Process Engineering / 15th International Symposium on Process Systems Engineering (ESCAPE34/PSE24), June 2-6, 2024, Florence, Italy

Multi-Source Transfer Learning for Chemical Process Fault Diagnosis with Multi-Channel Feature Extraction

Ruoshi Qin[a], Jinsong Zhao[a,b,*]

[a] *State Key Laboratory of Chemical Engineering, Department of Chemical Engineering, Tsinghua University, Beijing 100084, China*
[b] *Beijing Key Laboratory of Industrial Big Data System and Application, Tsinghua University, Beijing 100084, China*
jinsongzhao@tsinghua.edu.cn

Abstract

In recent times, there has been a rising preference for employing deep learning models in intelligent chemical process fault diagnosis. However, a considerable portion of the established methodologies operate on the premise that both training and testing data stem from identical feature distributions, which proves inaccurate in real-world scenarios characterized by multiple working conditions. In order to facilitate the preservation of domain-specific characteristics and the extraction of common features across both domains simultaneously, a novel domain adaptation deep network with multi-channel feature extraction is proposed in this research. The model employing a Transformer-CNN-based feature extractor and a domain adaptation module with polynomial kernel-induced maximum mean discrepancy is expected to achieve accurate anomaly diagnosis from diverse working conditions in one process and similar processes. Experiments on the Tennessee Eastman process and an industrial case of fluid catalytic cracking prove the effectiveness and advancement of the proposed method.

Keywords: Fault diagnosis, Transfer learning, Domain adaptation, Multi-channel feature extraction, Tennessee Eastman process, Fluid catalytic cracking.

1. Introduction

Intelligent fault diagnosis techniques assume a pivotal role in process monitoring to ensure manufacturing safety. In recent years, many scholars have made great achievements in the field of fault diagnosis application with the development of deep learning. However, the current application of deep learning in chemical process fault diagnosis relies on two critical assumptions that sufficient abnormal data is labeled for model training and the test dataset is identically distributed as the training dataset. In most practical situations, faulty samples in chemical processes are scarce and the distributions of data from different working conditions or multiple similar facilities are distinct (Bi et al., 2022). While transfer learning presents a promising avenue for the transfer of knowledge across diverse domains (Qin et al., 2022), it is worth noting that published studies that focused on the scenario of multimode and multi-source transfer learning are still rare. Merely transferring all source samples to a shared feature space and utilizing the cross-domain common features for fault diagnosis cannot guarantee high classification accuracy (Xiao et al., 2022).

The latest studies reveal that a domain adaptation deep network can be specially designed in a multi-channel form to learn the domain-invariant features more effectively. Lu (2023) designed a multi-view and multi-level network (MMNet) for rotating machinery fault diagnosis. Zhu (2023) launched the Transformer-convolutional neural network (TrCNN) based multi-scale distribution alignment network to extract deep diagnostic information and align the characteristics from various aspects. But they are all limited to the simulation situation and hard to apply in real industry.

In this paper, a novel multi-source domain adaptation deep network with multi-channel feature extraction is proposed to increase the generalization ability of the fault diagnostic model. The multi-source domain adaptation network (MSDAN) employs a Transformer-CNN-based multi-channel architecture to achieve the extraction of the common features across domains and the specific features in respective domains. The domain-specific information inherent within samples that have been deemed unsuitable for transfer is proficiently attenuated to facilitate exacting classification. A multi-source domain adaptation module based on polynomial kernel-induced maximum mean discrepancy (PK-MMD) is introduced to accomplish distribution adaptation among the source and target domains. The domain-invariant learned features are utilized for fault classification evaluated by a relation score from the query sample and the template ones.

The remaining parts of the article are arranged as follows. In the upcoming section, the proposed method MSDAN is established with the basic theory of Transformer-CNN model and PK-MMD algorithm. Section 3 elaborates on the experiments on the lab simulation and the real plant and compares the results among different popular transfer learning models. The conclusion and outlook of this article are drawn in Section 4.

2. Multi-Source Domain Adaptation Network

2.1. Transformer-CNN Model

A standard Transformer consists of an encoder and a decoder, both sharing a similar design featuring multi-headed attention layers, feed-forward network layers, residual connections, and normalization layers. The pivotal multi-head attention mechanism facilitates effective interaction between the dual parts. CNN operates as a multi-layer feed-forward neural network, systematically extracting features through the arrangement of convolutional layers and pooling layers. It culminates with a fully connected layer to amalgamate local information and with a classifier like Softmax to accomplish categorization. By connecting Transformer in tandem with CNN to form the backbone network of the feature extractor, the diagnostic model can better extract the multiscale features of time-series data. The overall architecture borrows the module arrangement from relation network, and each module contains two branches indicated as source branch and cross-domain branch, which process the input normal and faulty samples respectively.

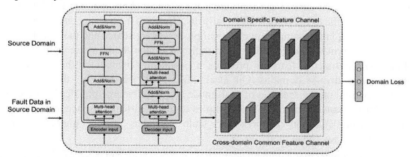

Fig.1. Transformer-CNN model structure for source domain.

2.2. Polynomial Kernel-induced Maximum Mean Discrepancy

Maximum mean discrepancy (MMD) is a widely used method to assess how transferable features differ in their distribution. Specifically, these features are initially transformed into a Reproduced Kernel Hilbert Space (RKHS), within which the average distance between these features is considered as the metric indicating their distribution discrepancy. Gaussian kernels are commonly utilized to induce RKHS for estimating MMD. However, there are notable shortcomings associated with diagnosis models that employ Gaussian kernel-induced MMD (GK-MMD). Firstly, GK-MMD relies on the mean distance but ignores high-order moments. This limitation hinders the accurate assessment of distribution discrepancy in transferable features. Secondly, the high time complexity of GK-MMD demands significant computation resources during the model training. Lastly, the transfer performance of GK-MMD-based models is highly sensitive to the Gaussian kernel parameters, impeding convergence to an optimal point during the distribution adaptation process.

In order to overcome the identified weaknesses, a refined distance metric that uses polynomial kernels to induce MMD instead of Gaussian kernels is expressly crafted. Polynomial kernel-induced MMD (PK-MMD) not only computes the weighted sum of order-wise moment distances but also possesses the ability to adjust kernel parameters, offering potential solutions to address a range of diverse transfer learning tasks.

Give the function of polynomial kernels as

$$k(\boldsymbol{x}, \boldsymbol{y}) = (a\boldsymbol{x}^{\mathrm{T}}\boldsymbol{y} + b)^c, \qquad c = 1, 2, \cdots \qquad (1)$$

where the output of polynomial kernels is determined by the slope a, the intercept b, and the order c.

By means of the binomial theorem, the empirical estimation of PK-MMD can be calculated by

$$D_{\mathcal{H}}^2(X, Y) = \sum_{k=0}^{c} \binom{c}{k} a^k b^{c-k} \left\| E_{X \sim p}(\boldsymbol{x})_k - E_{Y \sim q}(\boldsymbol{y})_k \right\|_{\mathcal{H}}^2 \qquad (2)$$

$$\left\| E_{X \sim p}(\boldsymbol{x})_k - E_{Y \sim q}(\boldsymbol{y})_k \right\|_{\mathcal{H}}^2 = \sum_{q=0}^{k} \binom{k}{q} \left(\boldsymbol{\vartheta}_q^{\mathrm{T}} \cdot \boldsymbol{\mu}_{k-q} \right) \qquad (3)$$

Under the condition $c = 1$, the expression given in (2) symbolizes the distance between the means, explicitly denoting the first moment of the provided datasets X and Y. And when $c > 1$, the formula is construed as a weighted summation of distances, encompassing the order-wise central moments within these datasets. The coefficients, represented by the slope a and the intercept b, serve as weights to balance the influences of both low-order and high-order moments in dataset pairs. A higher value for the slope a diminishes the impact of high-order moments on the distribution discrepancy observed between paired datasets.

2.3. MSDAN-based fault diagnosis framework

The framework of the proposed MSDAN-based fault diagnosis method is shown in Fig.2. In this domain adaptation deep network, the adjustment of network weights aims to enhance the network's classification performance. Consequently, samples unsuitable for domain adaptation exert reduced influence. Effective feature extraction occurs only from samples conducive to aligning the source and target domains. To extract both cross-domain common features and domain-specific features, multiple similar isolated network channels are designed in MSDAN. In each source channel, the dual branches share the same weights. The cross-domain common feature channel aims at extracting the common features via domain adaptation, while the domain-specific feature channel extracts the discriminant features facilitating both fault classification and domain classification. PK-MMD-based domain adaptation is utilized to acquire shared features across both the source and target domains. The model design utilizes historical data from chemical processes. Leveraging transferred knowledge, the diagnosis network oversees the online process and provides the fault classification outcome.

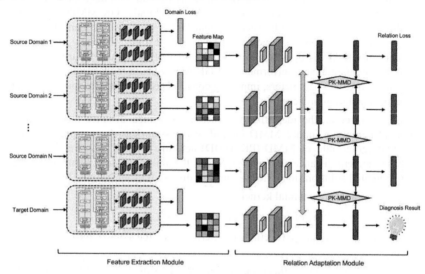

Fig.2. Architecture of MSDAN.

3. Case Studies

In this section, the benchmark Tennessee Eastman process (TEP) and the industrial fluid catalytic cracking (FCC) are applied to evaluate the performance of the proposed model.

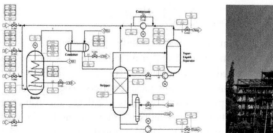

Fig.3. P&ID of TEP.   Fig.4. Scene of FCC case.

3.1. TEP

The TEP holds widespread usage in tasks related to monitoring chemical processes. Its unit operations encompass a reactor, condenser, recycle compressor, vapor-liquid separator, and stripper. This study builds upon the revised version of TEP as outlined in Bathelt (2015) at http://depts.washington.edu/control/LARRY/TE/download.html. The simulation involves 12 process-manipulated variables and 30 continuous process measurements. 19 fault types and 5 steady-state operating modes are introduced in this research to explore the multimode fault diagnosis performance. The selection of fault types and operational conditions mirrors prior published work, and the datasets are prepared in alignment with Wu (2020).

To explore the generalizability of deep transfer learning methods, the model trained for the source mode has to be applied to the new target mode. Note that there is no label information in all target domain data. Compared with the other transfer learning models (Qin et al., 2023), such as joint adaptation networks along with CNN (JAN-CNN) and dynamic adversarial adaptation network (DAAN), the proposed method achieves better domain alignment and higher classification accuracy in most scenarios. In particular, the more information from different source domains is imported for training, the more accurate unsupervised fault diagnosis is achieved.

Table 1. Unsupervised fault diagnosis performance of TEP.

(a) JAN-CNN

	$D_s(0)$	$D_s(1)$	$D_s(2)$	$D_s(4)$	$D_s(5)$	$D_s(0+1)$	$D_s(0+1+2)$	$D_s(0+1+2+4)$
$D_t(0)$	-	96.0%	96.4%	91.1%	97.6%	-	-	-
$D_t(1)$	95.6%	-	**95.9%**	90.8%	96.4%	-	-	-
$D_t(2)$	93.5%	95.6%	-	89.6%	**97.3%**	95.8%	-	-
$D_t(4)$	**88.8%**	89.7%	88.2%	-	90.6%	**91.2%**	92.4%	-
$D_t(5)$	93.9%	95.8%	97.3%	86.9%	-	95.9%	97.8%	96.5%

(b) DAAN

	$D_s(0)$	$D_s(1)$	$D_s(2)$	$D_s(4)$	$D_s(5)$	$D_s(0+1)$	$D_s(0+1+2)$	$D_s(0+1+2+4)$
$D_t(0)$	-	**97.2%**	96.8%	92.5%	97.3%	-	-	-
$D_t(1)$	96.6%	-	**95.9%**	93.9%	96.7%	-	-	-
$D_t(2)$	95.5%	96.1%	-	**92.0%**	97.2%	96.9%	-	-
$D_t(4)$	87.2%	**91.7%**	90.4%	-	91.1%	90.8%	93.0%	-
$D_t(5)$	94.7%	96.0%	97.3%	88.4%	-	96.2%	97.8%	97.2%

(c) MSDAN

	$D_s(0)$	$D_s(1)$	$D_s(2)$	$D_s(4)$	$D_s(5)$	$D_s(0+1)$	$D_s(0+1+2)$	$D_s(0+1+2+4)$
$D_t(0)$	-	96.7%	**97.1%**	93.8%	**98.2%**	-	-	-
$D_t(1)$	**97.1%**	-	95.6%	**94.0%**	97.6%	-	-	-
$D_t(2)$	**96.6%**	**96.8%**	-	91.5%	97.3%	**98.1%**	-	-
$D_t(4)$	86.4%	91.5%	90.3%	-	**93.3%**	90.0%	**93.5%**	-
$D_t(5)$	**95.2%**	**96.9%**	**97.7%**	91.0%	-	**97.2%**	**98.3%**	**98.4%**

Table 2. Unsupervised fault diagnosis summary of TEP.

	JAN-CNN	DAAN	MSDAN
Average accuracy rate	93.7%	94.5%	**95.0%**

3.2. FCC

Fluid catalytic cracking (FCC) is a pivotal process within the petroleum refining industry used to convert high-molecular-weight hydrocarbons into valuable gasoline, diesel, and other lighter fractions. Key components of the fluid catalytic cracking process include feedstock pre-treatment, reaction in the fluidized bed, mixture separation, catalyst regeneration, and product recovery. In this study, the process data from a large chemical plant in southeastern China is collected for nearly two years. The plant owns two FCC units with similar but not identical processes. The separation sections in these two sets are highlighted in this experiment because they have over eighty key alarm variables.

On the basis of the experience in the above tests, the two sets of devices are respectively set up as source or target domains for transfer learning. A total of ten common faults are selected as classification criteria, including high-temperature alarm at the top of the tower, low-level alarm at the bottom of the tower, and abnormal feed flow rate. The training dataset includes a handful of labeled fault data from the source mode and solely one batch of unlabeled fault data from the target mode. This configuration is utilized to conduct unsupervised anomaly diagnosis tasks, aimed at validating the effectiveness of the model. The brief results are shown below which confirm the advantages of MSDAN again.

Table 3. Unsupervised fault diagnosis performance of FCC.

	JAN-CNN	DAAN	MSDAN
$\mathcal{D}_s(\text{set } A) \rightarrow \mathcal{D}_t(\text{set } B)$	76.4%	83.5%	**88.2%**
$\mathcal{D}_s(\text{set } B) \rightarrow \mathcal{D}_t(\text{set } A)$	69.8%	72.9%	**81.0%**

4. Conclusions

In the present work, a multi-source domain adaptation network is proposed for cross-domain fault diagnosis in chemical processes. This advanced transfer learning method applies a more efficient multi-channel feature extractor which combines the strengths of Transformer and CNN. The multi-source domain adaptation with PK-MMD is superior to other widely-used adaptation techniques. The fault diagnosis results presented in this paper prove that this model can apply the diagnosis knowledge learned from different working conditions of one process and even similar processes in the real industry. This exploration will promote the practical application of deep transfer learning in chemical process fault diagnosis. Ongoing efforts are underway to improve this model, focusing on reducing reliance on labeled data from the source domain and tapping its potential for more industrial process tasks.

Acknowledgments

The authors gratefully acknowledge support from the National Science and Technology Innovation 2030 Major Project of the Ministry of Science and Technology of China (2018AAA0101605) and the National Natural Science Foundation of China (21878171, 62003004).

References

A. Bathelt, N.L. Ricker, M. Jelali, 2015, Revision of the Tennessee Eastman Process Model, *IFAC-PapersOnLine*, 48, 8, 309-314.

X. Bi, R. Qin, D. Wu, S. Zheng, J. Zhao, 2022, One step forward for smart chemical process fault detection and diagnosis, *Computers and Chemical Engineering*, 164, 107884.

N. Lu, Z. Cui, H. Hu, T. Yin, 2023, Multi-view and Multi-level network for fault diagnosis accommodating feature transferability, *Expert Systems with Applications*, 213, 119057.

R. Qin, J. Zhao, 2022, Adaptive multiscale convolutional neural network model for chemical process fault diagnosis, *Chinese Journal of Chemical Engineering*, 50, 398-411.

R. Qin, J. Zhao, 2023, Cross-domain Fault Diagnosis for Chemical Processes through Dynamic Adversarial Adaptation Network, *Computer Aided Chemical Engineering*, 52, 867-873.

H. Wu, J. Zhao, 2020, Fault detection and diagnosis based on transfer learning for multimode chemical processes, *Computers and Chemical Engineering*, 135, 106731.

H. Xiao, H. Ogai, W. Wang, 2022, Multi-Channel Domain Adaptation Deep Transfer Learning for Bridge Structure Damage Diagnosis, *IEEJ Transactions on Electrical and Electronic Engineering*, 17, 11, 1637-1647.

B. Yang, Y. Lei, F. Jia, N. Li, Z. Du, 2020, A Polynomial Kernel Induced Distance Metric to Improve Deep Transfer Learning for Fault Diagnosis of Machines, *IEEE Transactions on Industrial Electronics*, 67, 11, 9747-9757.

Q. Zhu, Y. Qian, N. Zhang, Y. He, Y. Xu, 2023, Multi-scale Transformer-CNN domain adaptation network for complex processes fault diagnosis, *Journal of Process Control*, 130, 103069.

Flavio Manenti, Gintaras V. Reklaitis (Eds.), Proceedings of the 34th European Symposium on Computer Aided Process Engineering / 15th International Symposium on Process Systems Engineering (ESCAPE34/PSE24), June 2-6, 2024, Florence, Italy

Continuous-time Formulation of Integrated Crude Scheduling and Planning Operations for Petrochemical Sites

Lifeng Zhang,[a] Congqin Ge,[b] Yuxuan Xu,[b] Zhihong Yuan[b*]

[a]*Centre for Process Systems Engineering, Department of Chemical Engineering, Imperial College London, South Kensington Campus, London, SW7 2AZ, United Kingdom*
[b]*Department of Chemical Engineering, Tsinghua University, Beijing, 100084, China*
Corresponding authors: zhihongyuan@mail.tsinghua.edu.cn

Abstract

This paper focuses on the optimization of integrated crude scheduling and refinery planning problems. Instead of using continuous time in crude scheduling and discrete time in refinery planning, a unified single-grid continuous time formulation is applied to both two parts of the problem. The Resource-Task-Network (RTN) is implemented in the crude scheduling problem to formulate the logical operational constraints. A mixed-integer linear programming (MILP) formulation is proposed. Compared to the common formulation of integration continuous time and discrete time, the proposed formulation reveals flexibility in adapting the total periods, which provides a balance to the objective and the accuracy of operations. Also, the RTN formulation avoids complicated constraints, showing a reduction in the model scale.

Keywords: Scheduling, Planning, Petrochemical, Continuous-time.

1. Introduction

Although the optimization in crude scheduling and refinery planning has been fully investigated individually over the past decades, the overall enterprise-wide optimization remains a big challenge. For the crude scheduling problem, several formulations were studied deeply, such as the State-Task-Network (STN) (Kondili et al., 1993) and the Resource-Task-Network (RTN) (Pantelides, 1994). This problem often aims to optimize the operation sequence between vessels and tanks. Thus, the time formulation plays an important role. The discrete-time simplifies the mathematical modelling while expanding the model scale. On the other hand, the continuous time could specify an accurate time point to assign the operations but more complicated logical constraints are derived. For the refinery planning problem, usually, the discrete-time formulation is implemented since the problem aims to obtain optimal planning on processing and selling over a certain time. Recently, the integrated problem of scheduling and planning has gradually drawn the attention of academics. Mouret et al (2011) investigated the integration of refinery planning and crude scheduling. A Lagrangian decomposition algorithm was applied to such large-scale problems. Further, the algorithm was used to solve the integrated scheduling and planning problem for an ethylene plant (Wang et al., 2016) and for the refinery plant (Yang et al., 2020). Continuous time and discrete time are used for scheduling and planning respectively in all these works. Even though the introduction of different time scales could capture the nature of decision-making for these two processes, the integration between continuous and discrete time formulations may add complexity to this model as extra constraints are needed to ensure the insistent. Therefore, in this paper, the unified continuous time formulation is applied to the integrated crude scheduling and refinery planning problem and a mixed-integer linear programming formulation is then obtained. The RTN is implemented to the crude scheduling to denote the logical constraints.

2. Problem statement

The integrated problem can be illustrated in Fig.1 shows. Usually, the crude oils are carried by marine vessels (MV) and arrive at a certain time. The crude in the vessel is then unloaded from the vessel and kept in the storage tanks (ST). The vessels may need to wait due to the availability of the dock station or STs. The crudes are stored in specific tanks. The crude oils are then transferred and blended in the following charging tank (CT) to meet the specification requirements before being processed in the crude distillation unit (CDU). The CDU is the core processing unit which separates the crudes into several streams in both crude scheduling and refinery planning. The CDU is required to operate continuously. These streams are then further processed, such as hydrotreating, cracking and reforming in the refinery units. The refinery units operate the processes at the same time as CDU. After that, final products can be obtained by blending the respective streams into corresponding pooling. The demands of all the products should be met for the entire time horizon.

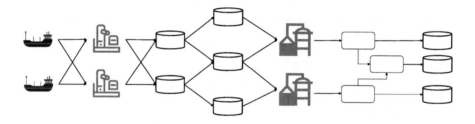

Figure.1. Illustration of the integrated crude scheduling and refinery planning process.

Thus, to formulate the mathematical formulation, the following assumptions are given:
1. The time horizon for optimization is specified;
2. The vessels with arriving time, and total crude oils carried are known in advance;
3. The inventory cost, transferring cost, processing cost for each tank and operation units are given;
4. The quality specifications on the crudes and products are given;
5. The demands of final products need to be satisfied during the time horizon;
6. Fixed yield constants and linear blending are assumed for this problem.

With the assumptions above, the goal of the optimization is to minimize the total cost over the specific time horizon under the demand and capacity constraints by assigning the operations, such as unloading and transferring to the optimal time point.

3. Mathematical formulation

In this section, the main constraints for the continuous-time RTN crude scheduling and refinery planning mode are proposed. The constraints can be divided into time constraints, logical constraints, scheduling constraints and planning constraints.

3.1. Time constraints

Given $n \in \{1, 2, \ldots, N\}$ continuous time slot, the start time T_n and duration time ΔT_n for each slot n should be determined by Eqs. (1) and (2) over the time horizon H.

$$T_1 = 0 \tag{1}$$

$$T_n = T_{n-1} + \Delta T_{n-1} \quad \forall n \in N \tag{2}$$

$$\sum_{n=1}^{N} \Delta T_n = H \tag{3}$$

3.2. Marine vessel operation constraints

The marine vessel is the start of the crude scheduling. Given the arrival time of each vessel in the set MV, the crude is then unloaded to the respective ST. The constraints for the vessels are shown as follows:

$$\sum_{n=1}^{N} y_{n,mv}^{be} = 1 \quad \forall mv \in MV \tag{4}$$

$$\sum_{n=1}^{N} y_{n,mv}^{fi} = 1 \quad \forall mv \in MV \tag{5}$$

$$R_{n,mv} = R_{n-1,mv} - y_{n,mv}^{be} + y_{n,mv}^{fi} \quad \forall n \in N, mv \in MV \tag{6}$$

$$F_{n,mv} \leq F_{mv}^{max} T_n + M \cdot R_{n,mv} \quad \forall n \in N, mv \in MV \tag{7}$$

$$F_{n,mv} \geq F_{mv}^{min} T_n - M \cdot R_{n,mv} \quad \forall n \in N, mv \in MV \tag{8}$$

$$\sum_{n=1}^{N} F_{n,mv} = I_{mv}^{0} \quad \forall mv \in MV \tag{9}$$

In Eqs. (4) and (5), the binary variable $y_{n,mv}^{be}$ and $y_{n,mv}^{fi}$ are used to denote the starting and finishing of the unloading operation for mv. Each vessel should start and finish unloading once during the time horizon. A binary variable $R_{n,mv}$ is defined to represent the equipment resource. It indicates the vessel is not unloading at time slot n if $R_{n,mv} = 1$. Eq. (6) shows the logical relationship of the equipment resource. In Eqs. (7) – (9), the volume of transferred crude in time slot n is constrained by equipment resource R and total inventory I_{mv}^{0}.

3.3. Storage tank operation constraints

The STs are used to store the crudes before transferring them to the charging tanks. The constraints are shown in Eqs. (10) – (13), including the equipment resource, transferred crudes, and inventory constraints.

$$R_{n,st} = R_{n,st}^{total} - \sum_{mv \in MV} (1 - R_{n,mv}) - y_{n,st,ct} \quad \forall n \in N, st \in ST, ct \in CT \tag{10}$$

$$F_{n,st,ct} \leq F_{st,ct}^{max} T_n + M(1 - y_{n,st,ct}) \quad \forall n \in N, st \in ST, ct \in CT \tag{11}$$

$$F_{n,st,ct} \geq F_{st,ct}^{min} T_n - M\left(1 - y_{n,ct,st}\right) \forall n \in N, st \in ST, ct \in CT \tag{12}$$

$$I_{n,st} \leq I_{n-1,st} + \sum_{mv \in MV} F_{n,mv} - \sum_{ct \in CT} F_{n,st,ct} \quad \forall n \in N, st \in ST \tag{13}$$

Eq. (10) denotes the equipment resource constraint. By adding bounds on variable $R_{n,st}$, the logical constraints which prevent importing and exporting materials simultaneously are imposed. Similarly, the constraints on the transferred materials are defined with Eqs. (11) – (12), while the inventory balance is shown in Eq. (13).

3.4. Charging tank operation constraints

The charging tank $ct \in CT$ receives the crudes from ST to meet the quality requirements. The blended crudes are later transferred to CDUs for further processing. Here, the constraints of CT are simplified as follows:

$$R_{n,ct} = R_{n,ct}^{total} - y_{n,st,ct} - y_{n,ct,cd} \quad \forall n \in N, st \in ST, ct \in CT, cd \in CD \tag{14}$$

$$F_{n,ct,cd} \leq F_{ct,cd}^{max} T_n + M\left(1 - y_{n,ct,cd}\right) \forall n \in N, ct \in CT, cd \in CD \tag{15}$$

$$F_{n,ct,cd} \geq F_{ct,cd}^{min} T_n + M\left(1 - y_{n,ct,cd}\right) \forall n \in N, ct \in CT, cd \in CD \tag{16}$$

$$I_{n,ct} \leq I_{n-1,ct} + \sum_{st \in ST} F_{n,st,ct} - \sum_{cd \in CD} F_{n,ct,cd} \quad \forall n \in N, ct \in CT \tag{17}$$

$$I_{n,c,ct} = I_{n-1,c,ct} + \sum_{st \in ST^c} F_{n,c,ct} - \sum_{cd \in CD} F_{n,c,ct,cd} \quad \forall n \in N, c \in C, ct \in CT \tag{18}$$

$$I_{n,ct} = \sum_{c \in C} I_{n,c,ct} \quad \forall n \in N, ct \in CT \tag{19}$$

$$\left[I_{n-1,c,ct}^{y_{n,ct,cd}} = I_{n-1,ct} \gamma_c \ \forall c \in C \right] \forall n \in N, ct \in CT, cd \in CD, \tag{20}$$

Same as the ST, the constraints on CT consist of equipment resources and transferred amounts. Eq. (17) denotes the total inventory balance in the tank ct while as crudes are blended in the tanks, the inventory of each crude $c \in C$ is further defined with Eq. (18) and the relationship is imposed by Eq. (19). Then the Eq. (20) represents when a certain charging tank ct is transferring to a CDU, the fraction of each crude $c \in C$ should satisfy a certain composition requirement.

3.5. Refinery planning constraints

After blending in the charging tanks, the crudes are then processed in the refinery units, starting with the CDUs. For each unit, the yields of the outlet flows are assumed as constants. Then the constraints for all the refinery units are presented as follows:

$$D_{n,cd}^{min} \leq F_{n,cd}^{in} = \sum_{ct \in CT} F_{n,ct,cd} \leq D_{n,cd}^{max} \quad \forall n \in N, cd \in CD \tag{21}$$

$$F_{n,u,s}^{out} = \sum_{s' \in S^{in}} F_{n,u,s'}^{in} \alpha_{u,s} \quad \forall n \in N, u \in U, s \in S^u \tag{22}$$

$$C_u^{min} \leq \sum_{s' \in S^{in}} F_{n,u,s'}^{in} \leq C_u^{max} \quad \forall n \in N, u \in U \tag{23}$$

$$D_p^{min} \leq F_p = \sum_{n \in N} \sum_{u \in U, s \in S^p} F_{n,u,s}^{out} \leq D_p^{max} \quad \forall p \in P \tag{24}$$

$$E_o^{min} \sum_{u \in U, s \in S^p} F_{n,u,s}^{out} \leq \sum_{u \in U, s \in S^p} F_{n,u,s}^{out} E_{o,u,s} \leq E_o^{max} \sum_{u \in U, s \in S^p} F_{n,u,s}^{out}$$

$$\forall n \in N, p \in P, o \in O \tag{25}$$

In Eq. (21), the total crudes processed in CDUs should satisfy the demand. Then for each refinery unit $u \in U$, the inlet and outlet relationship are presented with Eq. (22) while the capacity constraints are denoted with Eq. (23). For each desired product $p \in P$, the demands should be met in Eq. (24) with constraints of product property $o \in O$ shown as Eq. (25).

3.6. Objective function

The objective function of this problem is to minimize the total cost, mainly the inventory cost and processing cost for each tank and unit, minus the income of final products. The expression of the final objective can be seen as follows:

$$min\ z = \sum_{n \in N, u \in U, s \in S^u} F_{n,u,s}^{in} \beta_u + \sum_{tk \in MV \cup ST \cup CT} I_{n,tk} \beta_{tk} - \sum_{n \in N, p \in P} \beta_p F_{n,p} \tag{26}$$

Here, the parameter β denotes the coefficients in general.

4. Case study

In this section, a case study is conducted with the proposed modelling framework. The integrated continuous-time scheduling and planning model (ICSP) is formulated as well as a traditional integrated continuous-time scheduling and discrete-time planning model (ICSDP) for comparison. The ICSDP model is adapted from the reference (Wang et al., 2016, 2014) which constructed the models based on the implementation of the continuous time slot in each discrete time slot. The material balance is imposed at the end of each discrete time period. All the models are built on pyomo (Bynum et al., 2021) on Windows11 using Intel(R) Xeon(R) Gold 6226R CPU @ 2.90GHz with 64GB of RAM and solved with CPLEX 22.1.1 Given the different number of time slots, the model scales and objectives are shown in Table. 1. as follows.

Table.1. Model statistics and objectives

	Continuous slots	Discrete slots	# of binary variables	# of continuous variables	# of constraints	Objective /$
	8		304	1,029	1,939	-4,004.25
	12		456	1,541	2,903	-9,813.85
ICSP	16	-	608	2,053	3,867	-13,357.00
	20		760	2,565	4,831	-15,584.21
	24		912	3,077	5,795	-17,079.30
	1		304	1,029	1,939	-336.42
ICSDP	2	8	448	1,365	2,779	-10,768.10
	3		592	1,701	3,619	-13,612.54

In this case study, a total of 8 days is used to represent the discrete time slots, assigning one day as a discrete single slot to refinery planning in ICSDP models. The total time slots in ICSDP would be the number of continuous time slots multiplied by the discrete time slots $N_{con} \times N_{dis}$. While in ICSP models, the continuous time slots are also applied to the refinery planning, which offers more flexibility in choosing different time slots for the problem. For each kind of model, a better objective can be obtained when increasing the number of time slots, generating a profit from \$4,004.25 to \$17,079.30. However, even if the same time slots are used for both ICSP and ICSDP models, for example, 8 continuous time slots for ICSP and 1 continuous time slot for ICSDP, the ICSP model could provide a much better profit of \$4,004.24 than the ICSDP at \$336.42. This can be attributed to that the discrete time slots in the ICSDP model restrict the duration of time slots. While using the continuous-time formulation, the better solution is obtained with the optimal length of each time slot, even though the model scales are the same for both models. In addition to that, the ICSP usually generates a larger model than the ICSDP, such as the models of 24 time slots. This could make the problem hard to solve, especially for a large process.

5. Conclusion

In this paper, a unified single-grid continuous time formulation is applied to the integrated crude scheduling and refinery planning problem. To model the complex logical constraints in crude scheduling, the RTN formulation is implemented to model these constraints with equipment resources. Compared to the traditional integrated continuous-time scheduling and discrete-time planning model, the proposed formulation could provide better objectives by making flexible duration of the time slots in the planning part, revealing advantages in application although the model scale becomes larger. Future work will focus on the multiple continuous time grids for complicated integrated problems.

References

Bynum, M.L., Hackebeil, G.A., Hart, W.E., Laird, C.D., Nicholson, B.L., Siirola, J.D., Watson, J.-P., Woodruff, D.L., 2021. Pyomo — Optimization Modeling in Python, Springer Optimization and Its Applications. Springer International Publishing, Cham. https://doi.org/10.1007/978-3-030-68928-5

Kondili, E., Pantelides, C.C., Sargent, R.W.H., 1993. A general algorithm for short-term scheduling of batch operations—I. MILP formulation. Comput. Chem. Eng. 17, 211–227. https://doi.org/10.1016/0098-1354(93)80015-F

Mouret, S., Grossmann, I.E., Pestiaux, P., 2011. A new Lagrangian decomposition approach applied to the integration of refinery planning and crude-oil scheduling. Comput. Chem. Eng. 35, 2750–2766. https://doi.org/10.1016/j.compchemeng.2011.03.026

Pantelides, C.C., 1994. Unified frameworks for optimal process planning and scheduling, in: Proceedings on the Second Conference on Foundations of Computer Aided Operations. pp. 253–274.

Wang, Z., Feng, Y., Rong, G., 2014. Synchronized Scheduling Approach of Ethylene Plant Production and Naphtha Oil Inventory Management. Ind. Eng. Chem. Res. 53, 6477–6499. https://doi.org/10.1021/ie500079w

Wang, Z., Li, Z., Feng, Y., Rong, G., 2016. Integrated short-term scheduling and production planning in an ethylene plant based on Lagrangian decomposition. Can. J. Chem. Eng. 94, 1723–1739. https://doi.org/10.1002/cjce.22544

Yang, H., Bernal, D.E., Franzoi, R.E., Engineer, F.G., Kwon, K., Lee, S., Grossmann, I.E., 2020. Integration of crude-oil scheduling and refinery planning by Lagrangean Decomposition. Comput. Chem. Eng. 138. https://doi.org/10.1016/j.compchemeng.2020.106812

Flavio Manenti, Gintaras V. Reklaitis (Eds.), Proceedings of the 34th European Symposium on Computer Aided Process Engineering / 15th International Symposium on Process Systems Engineering (ESCAPE34/PSE24), June 2-6, 2024, Florence, Italy

Implementation of Model Predictive Control into the Rigorous Simulator of the Fuel Cell System

Masanori Oshima [a], Sanghong Kim [b*], Shigeki Hasegawa [a, c], Ibuki Sakata [b], Ken-Ichiro Sotowa [a], Motoaki Kawase [a]

[a]*Department of Chemical Engineering, Kyoto University, Nishikyo-ku, Kyoto 615-8510, Japan*
[b]*Department of Applied Physics and Chemical Engineering, Tokyo University of Agriculture and Technology, Naka-cho, Koganei-city, Tokyo 184-8588, Japan*
[c]*Hydrogen Fundamental Development Div., Hydrogen Factory, Toyota Motor Corporation, Aichi, 471-8571, Japan*
sanghong@go.tuat.ac.jp

Abstract

Polymer electrolyte fuel cell (PEFC) is a developing technology with a potential to contribute to carbon neutrality. To expedite the development of PEFC, a rigorous simulator of an integrated PEFC system called FC-DynaMo was built by Hasegawa et al. FC-DynaMo allows us to evaluate the performance of the overall FC system based on the detailed specifications covering microscopic to macroscopic levels, such as catalyst activity, properties of proton exchange membrane (PEM), detailed dynamics of valves and pumps, and geometrical shapes of pipes. On the contrary, the simulation results of the optimal operation of FC-DynaMo will clearly show a requirement for each specification that provides a solid guideline for the development of each part of the system. However, the operation of FC-DynaMo using simple rule-based and proportional-integral (PI) control algorithms of the default control system is far from the optimal operation. In this paper, the default control method in FC-DynaMo is replaced by model predictive control (MPC), one of the optimal control methods. The MPC system reduced the offset to approximately zero and the settling time by 86.0 seconds. At the same time, the overheating of the cell was suppressed by the constraint on the coolant temperature at the cell outlet. Such an operation slows down degradation of the membrane and leads to save the lifespan of the PEM.

Keywords: Polymer electrolyte fuel cell (PEFC), Model predictive control (MPC), Rigorous simulation.

1. Introduction

Hydrogen has been paid attention to as a replacement for fossil fuels to realize a carbon-neutral society. Polymer electrolyte fuel cell (PEFC), a technology for power generation using hydrogen, can potentially reduce a large amount of carbon dioxide released into the atmosphere considerably.

The power generation system using PEFC comprises many parts, and many researchers and engineers have developed them to improve the overall power-generation performance. In most cases, each part is developed separately since integrated assessment of all the parts takes much cost. To successfully develop PEFC using this strategy, a solid requirement for every part is essential. However, determining such a requirement is nearly impossible when considering only a limited number of parts. It is necessary to take the overall system into consideration.

To achieve this, a simulator of an integrated PEFC system, FC-DynaMo, has been developed by Hasegawa et al. (2021 and 2022a). The target system of FC-DynaMo consists of the general components: the FC stack, the auxiliary systems for H_2 supply, air supply, and cooling, and the electric power system. Moreover, FC-DynaMo was validated with the extensive experimental data obtained using a state-of-the-art fuel cell electric vehicle (FCEV), 2nd-generation MIRAI (Takahashi & Kaneko, 2021). Hence, it reproduces the dynamics of the overall power generation system of the FCEV in a wide operating range.

In FC-DynaMo, simple control methods, such as proportional-integral (PI) control and on-off control, are used for setpoint tracking of the net power generated in the FC system (Hasegawa et al., 2022b). However, such a control system is not suitable for the simulator since the behaviour of FC systems is highly complex (Yang et al., 2022). FC-DynaMo also reproduces the complexity; it exhibits nonlinear dynamics and has 675 state variables and 11 input variables. Hence, considerable improvement in control performance is expected by replacing the existing control methods with more advanced control methods, such as model predictive control (MPC) (Morari & H. Lee, 1999).

There are no less than 255 papers on implementing MPC into the FC system in simulation according to the keyword search using "fuel cell," "model predictive control," and "simulation" as keywords on Web of Science on September 6th, 2023. However, the simulation models in such papers targeted fewer components than FC-DynaMo, and most of them have not been validated using the data obtained from the actual FC system, as shown in the following examples. The model by Goshtasbi & Ersal (2020) lacks several components, including H_2 recycle flow, and the total number of states in the model is one-seventeenth of that of FC-DynaMo. Panos et al. (2012) ignored the dynamics of auxiliary components, such as valves and pumps, though they are included in FC-DynaMo. Vrlić et al. (2021) built a simulation model of an FC system based on the data obtained using an actual FCEV. However, the auxiliary systems are not considered in their simulation model. Hence, FC-DynaMo is more rigorous and inclusive than the simulation models considered in these papers. Implementing MPC into FC-DynaMo is expected to provide deeper insights into the optimal operation of the highly complex FC system.

In this research, the default control system of FC-DynaMo is replaced by an MPC system. The MPC system uses the true process model as the prediction model. Moreover, a constraint on the coolant temperature at the cell outlet was considered to prevent the overheating of the cell. The performance of the MPC system is validated in a simulation case study.

2. Process model

The process of interest in FC-DynaMo is shown in Figure 1. The air from the atmosphere is compressed and cooled down before it is supplied into the cell. All the compressed air is supplied to the cathode of the cell when the air bypass valve is completely closed; otherwise, some portion of air is directly emitted to the atmosphere with the purged H_2 and the air from the cathode outlet. This reduces the H_2 concentration of the emitted gas. H_2 is supplied to the anode through the three injectors. The electrochemical reaction between H_2 and O_2 occurs in the stack, and the coolant system removes the generated heat.

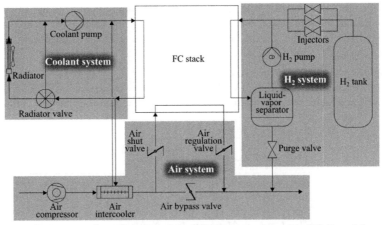

Figure 1: The process flow diagram of the FC plant considered in FC-DynaMo.

Table 1: The definition of the input variables $\boldsymbol{u}$ of the FC plant model.

Variables	Corresponding element in $\boldsymbol{u}$
Hydrogen pump rotational speed [rpm]	u_1
Air compressor motor torque [N m]	u_2
Air regulation valve opening [-]	u_3
Air bypass valve opening [-]	u_4
Air shut valve opening [-]	u_5
Three-way valve opening in the coolant system [-]	u_6
Radiator fan rotational speed [rpm]	u_7
Water pump rotational speed [rpm]	u_8
FC stack current [A]	u_9
The number of open hydrogen injectors [-]	u_{10}
Hydrogen purge valve state [-]	u_{11}

The unreacted H_2 is separated from the water generated in the stack using the liquid-vapor separator. The gas from the liquid-vapor separator is recycled to the inlet of the anode.

The plant model of FC-DynaMo is a nonlinear state-space model, that is,

$$x(t + \Delta t_{\mathrm{PL}}) = F\big(x(t), u(t), d(t)\big), \qquad y(t) = g\big(x(t)\big), \tag{1}$$

where Δt_{PL} is the sampling period of the plant model: 16 ms. The states, output, inputs, and measured disturbances are expressed as x, y, u, and d, respectively. The output y is the net power of the FC system, which is given by subtracting the power consumed in the auxiliary systems from the gross power generated in the FC stack. The definition of all the elements of the input vector u is listed in Table 1. The state vector x has 675 elements, such as the coolant temperature $T_{c,\mathrm{out}}$ at the outlet of the cathode and the cell voltage.

3. Control methods

3.1. Method 1: Existing control method

In FC-DynaMo, proportional-integral (PI) control and on-off control are mainly used in a cascade structure, as in Figure 2. The control objective is the setpoint tracking of the net power y. Primary controller C_1 determines the setpoint x'_{set} of the sub-state variables x'

using PI control and heuristic rule-based control. The definition of x' is shown in Table 2. Note that all the elements of the sub-state vector x' are included in the state vector x. In the secondary controller C_2, the manipulated variables u are determined from x'_{set} and x' by PI and on-off controllers.

3.2. Method 2: Model predictive control method

To improve the overall performance of the system, MPC is introduced. MPC optimizes the current and future u every control periods. The outline of the optimization problem is

$$P1: \quad \min_{\{u(t_0+i\Delta t_{\text{MPC}})\}_{i=0}^{N_C-1}} J = \sum_{t=t_0+\Delta t_{\text{MPC}}}^{t_0+N_P\Delta t_{\text{MPC}}} \left(y(t) - y_{\text{ref}}(t|\gamma)\right)^2 \tag{2}$$

subject to

$$T_{\text{c,out}}(t) < 95\,^{\circ}\text{C}, \quad t = t_0 + \Delta t_{\text{MPC}}, \cdots, t_0 + N_P\Delta t_{\text{MPC}}, \tag{3}$$

where Δt_{MPC} is $5\Delta t_{\text{PL}} = 0.080$ ms, N_P and N_C are positive integers such that $N_P \geq N_C$, and t_0 is the current time. The variable y_{ref} in Eq. (2) is reference trajectory defined as

$$y_{\text{ref}}(t|\gamma) = (1 - \gamma^{t-t_0})y(t_0) + \gamma^{t-t_0}y_{\text{set}}(t), \tag{4}$$

where $\gamma \in [0,1)$ is a parameter that determines the response speed of MPC. In Eq. (3), the upper limit constraint of $T_{\text{c,out}}$ is introduced to prevent the temperature in the cell from rising above 95 °C.

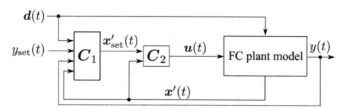

Figure 2: The default control system of FC-DynaMo.

Table 2: The definition of the sub-state vector x'.

Variables	Corresponding element in x'
Pressure at FC cathode inlet [kPa]	x'_1
Air flowrate to FC cathode inlet [NL/min]	x'_2
Air flowrate to air compressor [NL/min]	x'_3
Air flowrate at air bypass valve [NL/min]	x'_4
H$_2$ partial pressure at FC anode outlet [kPa]	x'_5
H$_2$ flowrate at hydrogen pump [NL/min]	x'_6
Injector outlet pressure [kPa]	x'_7
Liquid-water volume in liquid-vapor separator [m^3]	x'_8
FC cathode inlet coolant temperature [°C]	x'_9
FC cathode outlet coolant temperature [°C]	x'_{10}

However, the optimization problem P1 is mixed-integer programming, which requires a high computational burden to be solved because u_{10} and u_{11} are discrete variables. To solve this, P1 is modified as follows. An additional constraint, that is,

$$[u_{10}(t), u_{11}(t)]^\top = C_{\text{on/off}}\left(u_9(t), x'_{\text{set},7}(t), d(t), x(t)\right) \tag{5}$$

is introduced, where $x'_{\text{set},7}$ is the setpoint of the injector outlet pressure x'_7, and $C_{\text{on/off}}$ is the on-off controller of the method 1. Moreover, the discrete optimized variables u_{10} and u_{11} are replaced with $x'_{\text{set},7}$. Therefore, the modified optimization problem P2 is

$$\text{P2:} \qquad \min_{\left\{[u_1(t_0+i\Delta t_{\text{MPC}}),\cdots,u_9(t_0+i\Delta t_{\text{MPC}}),x'_{\text{set},7}(t_0+i\Delta t_{\text{MPC}})]^\top\right\}_{i=0}^{N_C-1}} J \tag{6}$$

     subject to   Eqs. (3) and (5).

In the actual implementation of MPC into FC-DynaMo, the problem P2, instead of P1, is solved to obtain $\{u_m\}_{m=1}^9$ and $x'_{\text{set},7}$. Then, u_{10} and u_{11} are calculated using Eq. (5).

4. Simulation case study

The methods 1 and 2 were compared in the setpoint change simulation of y. The controller parameters in the method 1 were set equal to their default values. In the method 2, N_P, N_C and γ were set to 100, 1, and 0.852. The value of y_{set} was changed stepwise from 0 to 95 kW at $t = 10$ s. The simulation results are shown in Figure 3. At $t = 200$ s, y was equal to y_{set} in the method 2 but below y_{set} in the method 1. Offset in y occurred only in the method 1 of the existing control method. The reason for this was further studied by introducing method 3. In the method 3, only the inner control loop of the existing control method is used without changing the parameters of C_2, and x'_{set} was set to $x'(200)$ in the method 2 of MPC. The simulation result of the method 3 is shown in Figure 3, as well. Figure 3 shows that the method 3 eliminated offset. Thus, the default control method can also provide offset-free operation without using the outer controller C_1.

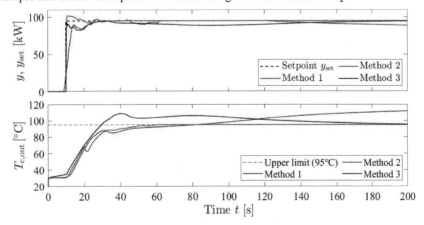

Figure 3: Time series plots of the net power y and the coolant temperature $T_{\text{c,out}}$ at the cathode outlet of the cell.

However, the result of the method 3 was still different from that of the method 2 using MPC. The settling time of the method 3 was 86.0 s longer than that of the method 2; the former and latter were 145.6 s and 59.6 s, respectively. Note that the range of y, within which the system was regarded as settled, was set to 95 $\pm$2.5 kW.

The benefits of MPC in the method 2 are attributed to the constraint on $T_{c,out}$. In both the methods 1 and 3, $T_{c,out}$ became higher than 95 °C, and the overheating of the cell that decreases the power-generation performance of the cell occurs. Therefore, MPC provided the best setpoint-tracking performance of y.

5. Conclusions

The MPC system was newly implemented into FC-DynaMo, the most rigorous simulator of the integrated PEFC system as far as the authors know. The MPC system was compared with the two control methods: the default control method and the modified default control method, where the state variables are controlled to the steady-state values realized by MPC with a part of the default control method. The upper constraint of the coolant temperature at the cell outlet of MPC prevented the decrease in the power generation performance by overheating in the cell, which occurred in the other two methods. As a result, the proposed MPC system provided the best performance in terms of the offset and the settling time.

References

A. Goshtasbi & T. Ersal. 2020. Degradation-conscious Control for Enhanced Lifetime of Automotive Polymer Electrolyte Membrane Fuel Cells. Journal of Power Sources, 457, 227996.

S. Hasegawa, Y. Ikogi, S. Kim, M. Kageyama, & M. Kawase. 2022. Modeling of the Dynamic Behavior of an Integrated Fuel Cell System Including Fuel Cell Stack, Air System, Hydrogen System, and Cooling System. ECS Transactions, 109(9), 15–70.

S. Hasegawa, M. Kimata, Y. Ikogi, M. Kageyama, M. Kawase, & S. Kim. 2021. Modeling of Fuel Cell Stack for High-Speed Computation and Implementation to Integrated System Model. ECS Transactions, 104(8), 3–26.

S. Hasegawa, Y. Miyamoto, S. Kim, Y. Ikogi, M. Kageyama, & M. Kawase. 2022. Model-Based Development of Fuel Cell Stack and System Controllers. Computer Aided Chemical Engineering, 49, 1123–1128.

M. Morari & J. H. Lee. 1999. Model Predictive Control: Past, Present and Future. Computers & Chemical Engineering, 23(4–5), 667–682.

C. Panos, K. I. Kouramas, M. C. Georgiadis, & E. N. Pistikopoulos. 2012. Modelling and Explicit Model Predictive Control for PEM Fuel Cell Systems. Chemical Engineering Science, 67(1), 15–25.

T. Takahashi & Y. Kaneko. 2021. Development of New Fuel Cell System. EVTeC 2021, 20214292.

M. Vrlić, D. Ritzberger, & S. Jakubek. 2021. Model-Predictive-Control-Based Reference Governor for Fuel Cells in Automotive Application Compared with Performance from a Real Vehicle. Energies, 14(8), 2206.

B. Yang, J. Li, Y. Li, Z. Guo, K. Zeng, H. Shu, P. Cao, & Y. Ren. 2022. A Critical Survey of Proton Exchange Membrane Fuel Cell System Control: Summaries, Advances, and Perspectives. International Journal of Hydrogen Energy, 47(17), 9986–10020.

Flavio Manenti, Gintaras V. Reklaitis (Eds.), Proceedings of the 34th European Symposium on Computer Aided Process Engineering / 15th International Symposium on Process Systems Engineering (ESCAPE34/PSE24), June 2-6, 2024, Florence, Italy

Neural Ordinary Differential Equations Auto-Encoder for Fault Detection in Process Systems

Umang Goswami,[a] Jyoti Rani,[a] Hariprasad Kodamana[a,b]

aDepartment of Chemical Engineering, Indian Institute of Technology, Delhi-110016, India
bYardi School of Artificial Intelligence, Indian Institute of Technology, Delhi-110016, India
kodamana@iitd.ac.in

Abstract

With the advent of Industry 4.0, there has been a paradigm shift in the operations of the manufacturing and industrial sectors. The fourth Industrial revolution has compelled the industries to integrate Machine Learning with its core processes. Over the years, data-driven approaches have been a key contributor to the smooth functioning of a process plant. In the proposed work, Neural ordinary differential equations Auto-encoder being a special class of neural networks are utilized for fault detection. The proposed methodology consists of a neural network coupled with an ordinary differential equation solver. The neural network is used to parameterize the derivatives of the hidden states and results in a continuous transformation of the states. For time series processes, the methodology proves to be of greater use because of its inherent ability of extrapolating the values for a particular time step. The proposed methodology was validated for the Tennessee Estman process and yielded better results when compared to the different deep learning-based models used for time series predictions in LSTM and its variants, and machine learning framework such as Dynamic Principal Component Analysis (DPCA).

Keywords: Fault Detection, Neural ordinary differential equations Auto-Encoder, fault detection, Tennessee Eastman Process.

1. Introduction

The incorporation of Machine Learning into traditional methods has significantly enhanced the efficiency of the chemical process industries. This advancement has not only financially benefited manufacturing units but also emphasized the importance of health and safety for individuals, contributing to the seamless operation of process units. Machine Learning and Deep Learning techniques introduce data-driven strategies to address the challenges of non-linearity and non-Gaussian patterns in time-series data (Goswami et al, 2023). This adaptable approach ensures smoother operation of process systems and aids in identifying any deviations from normal patterns during plant operations.

Traditional neural network methodologies such as Auto-encoder, LSTM networks and Machine learning techniques such as the Principal Component Analysis (PCA) and Dynamic Principal Component Analysis (DPCA) have been extensively used by the researchers to identify the faults present in the process systems at their point of occurrence. This has also led to other algorithms based on graphs (Goswami et al, 2023), and forward-forward algorithms (Kumar et al, 2023) to step in to the domain of fault detection. The methods vary from each other and bring their own inherent characteristics to make the process run free of hindrances. Taking into account the work done by previous researchers, we have formulated a novel fault detection framework which instead of the traditional neural networks utilizes the Neural Ordinary Differential Equation Auto-encoder (NODEAE) at its core. Neural Ordinary Differential Equations (NODEs) are a special type of neural network framework which continuously parameterizes the hidden states of the neural network by deploying a differential equation solver. This parametrization of the hidden states helps NODE operate in a continuous depth manner which distinguishes it from the state-of-the art neural networks (Chen et al, 2018). Conceptually, NODEAE is an extension to the residual networks which take input and its transformation to the next layer. This brings in a continuity to the data transformation. NODEs leverage this idea and couple it with the differential equation solver to obtain the value at the subsequent time steps. NODEs are trained with adjoint sensitivity method providing them the ability of adaptive evaluation and viewing the overall neural network as an ordinary differential equation and the output obtained at the end is the solution of the ordinary differential equation. The schematic of the proposed workflow is shown in Figure 1.

The proposed study is structured as follows: NODEAE is discussed in detail in Section 2. The fault detection framework is defined in section 3 and Section 4 holds the results and discussions of the proposed study followed by conclusion in Section 5.

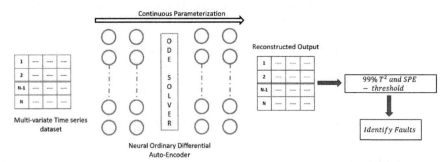

Figure 1: A schematic of the proposed workflow.

2. Neural Ordinary Differential Equation Auto-Encoder (NODEAE)

2.1. Mathematical Formulation

Throughout various industries, particularly in chemical processing, neural network-based algorithms have become integral tools for detecting faults and are applied in other fields as well. Neural networks are composed of interconnected models, featuring neurons organized into hidden layers. Here, the input is processed by being multiplied with the network's weights, yielding specific outputs. Building on traditional neural networks, residual networks introduce an innovation where not only the input is processed, but also its transformed version is carried forward to subsequent layers. This method, where input and its transformation are continuously added, forms a continuous function that closely aligns with numerical solutions similar to those derived from Euler's method.

An advanced development in this area is the integration of traditional neural networks with differential equation solvers. In NODEs, the derivatives produced by the network's hidden states are dynamically shaped by the differential equation solver. This integration allows for flexibility in choosing different differential solvers based on the application, including Euler's method, the Runge-Kutta method, and the VODE solver. The choice of solver enables neural networks to effectively predict outcomes at various time steps. This predictive capability is particularly useful for data interpolation and extrapolation at specific points, enhancing the network's applicability and accuracy in complex modelling scenarios.

Residual Networks as discussed above form a base to the formation of the proposed NODEAE. Equation (1) throws light on the working of the encoder section of the proposed NODEAE method, where an input *k(t)* at time *t* is along with its transformation in $f(k_t, w_t)$ is used calculate the output at the next time-step.

$$k_{t+1} = k(t) + f(k_t, w_t) \tag{1}$$

On adding, infinite number of layers to the network, the step size become infinitesimally small and thus can be modelled in continuous time domain as shown in equation (2), where w represents the weights of the network and $\frac{dk(t)}{dt}$ represents the change of network activations k with respect to time t.

$$\frac{dk(t)}{dt} = f(k(t), t, w) \tag{2}$$

In the forward pass of the proposed model, the output $k(T)$ can be calculated by solving equation (3), where T is equivalent to the number of discrete layers in a traditional neural network.

$$k(T) = k(0) + \int_{t=0}^{T} \frac{dk(t)}{dt} \tag{3}$$

On solving the forward pass equations, the latent features are extracted and are fed to the decoder section of the network, which contains couple of hidden layers to transform the output. There are certain challenges also associated when operating with the differential equation solvers, as it is difficult to solve the second order differential equation during backpropagation as it incurs a memory cost and also induces some numerical errors. The loss function L as shown in equation (4) is resultant formulation of the solution of the ODE solver.

$$L(k(t_1)) = L(ODESolve(k(t_0), f, t_0, t_1, w)) \tag{4}$$

To optimize the loss function, we need its derivative with respect to the neural network parameters or weights. We also need to understand how the loss gradient value changes at each time instant and this quantity is called the adjoint, which can be seen in equation (5) and (6).

$$a(t) = -\frac{\partial L}{\partial k(t)} \tag{5}$$

On substituting the loss value in equation (4), we can obtain adjoint value as shown in equation (6).

$$\frac{\partial a(t)}{\partial t} = -\frac{a(t)^T \partial f(k(t), t, w)}{dk} \tag{6}$$

Once the adjoint is known, we can compute $k(t)$ backwards in time starting from the final value of time. This is done in order to compute the loss derivative with respect to the neural network parameters. With the help of adjoint, now a single ode solver can be called and a single vector is considered which is formed by the concatenation of adjoint, partial derivatives and the original state. Equation (7) shows the loss value with respect to the parameters and utilizes both the original state and the adjoint function.

$$\frac{\partial L}{\partial w} = - \int_{t_1}^{t_0} a(t)^T \frac{df(k(t), t, w)}{dw} dt \tag{7}$$

The vector Jacobian products obtained in equations (6) and (7) can be used to evaluate the final output in the dynamic space.

1.1. Fault Detection Framework

The fault detection framework of the proposed methodology consists of two major steps; the initial step being the offline modelling and the next step being online monitoring. In the offline modelling, the model is trained on a Normal Operating Range (NOR) of the process data to ensure that the model is able to capture all the patterns of the fault-free data. The detailed steps of the Offline Modelling are as follows:

1. Consider a multi-variate time-series process data of dimension $n \times m$, where n represents the number of time-steps and m represent the number of process parameters/variables.
2. Once, the data is obtained it can be normalized by any of the normalization techniques. In our case, we have used the Standard Scaler technique.
3. The scaled data is then passed through the model, where the encoder section of the network captures the training data and a differential equation solver is utilised to continuously parameterize the hidden states.
4. Once the model is trained, the T^2 and SPE statistics are calculated for the fault free region applying 99% as the fault tolerant limit. The 99% is chosen as the cut-off to reduce the number of false alarms during a process.

Similar, to the Offline modelling, the online monitoring steps, where the faults are identified are described below:

1. Consider, a new normalized sample during the course of a process.
2. The proposed NODEAE model is then applied to test the new sample.
3. If the new sample exceeds the fault tolerant limit of 99%, the sample is marked as faulty, otherised it is marked as normal.

2. Validation Experiments

2.1. Tennessee Eastman Process Dataset

The Tennessee Eastman Process dataset serves as a benchmark validation tool for testing fault detection methods in process control. It represents a simulated industrial process that is intricate in nature, featuring four feed streams with variable concentrations. Key components of the process include a reactor unit, condenser, compressor, and a stripping section. This simulated setup is detailed across 22 distinct datasets, where one dataset is designated as fault-free and the rest represent various types of faults. The Tennessee Eastman Process data is characterized by a diverse range of fault conditions, including step changes, random variations, sticking, slow drifts, unknown, and constant valve positions. In total, the dataset encompasses 52 variables, of which 41 are process measurements, capturing the operational state of the process, and 11 are control or manipulated variables, used to adjust the process conditions.

2.2. Experimental Validation

The NODEAE module consists of an encoder and a decoder as discussed in Section 2. In the encoder section, we considered 52 neurons at the input, followed by 27 at the second hidden layer, followed by a Euler ODE solver, and 8 neurons in the latent space. The decoder section then consists of 27 neurons followed by 52 neurons at the output layer.

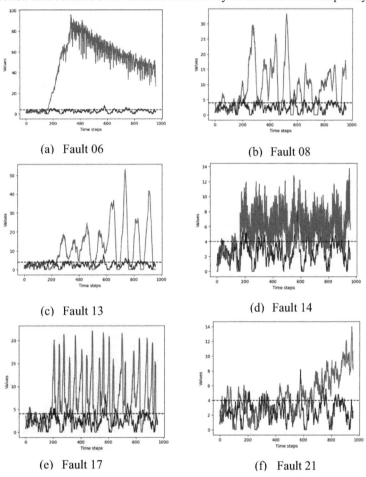

(a) Fault 06

(b) Fault 08

(c) Fault 13

(d) Fault 14

(e) Fault 17

(f) Fault 21

Figure 2: Different types of faults reconstructed through the proposed methodology.

The proposed methodology was validated on various types of faults. For our analysis, we utilised various faults such as Fault 06 (step type), fault 08 (Random Variation), fault 13 (sticking), fault 14 (slow drift), fault 17 (Unknown) and fault 21 (constant value position). Our methodology was able to demarcate various types of faults as shown in Figure 2. The red curve shows the fault behaviour of different types of faults, whereas the blue curve gives an idea about the Normal Operating Region of the Tennessee Eastman data.

On comapring the proposed methodology, with its machine and deep learning counterparts based on the T^2 and SPE statistics it was found that the the average Missed

Detection Rate (MDR) and False Alarm Rate (FAR) turned out to be the lowest for the proposed methodolgy because of its intrinsic quality to continuously parameterize the hidden state and exploring time depth domain. Table 1 gives a clear indication of the same.

Table 1: Comparison of Proposed Methodology with Baselines based on average values of faults.

Methodology	Missed Detection Rate (MDR)	False Alarm Rate (FAR)
LSTM	0.25	0.40
LSTM-AE	0.12	0.28
DPCA	0.30	0.35
NODEAE	**0.02**	**0.10**

3. Conclusions

The NODEAE approach integrates conventional neural network frameworks with ordinary differential equation solvers, transforming the discrete hidden layers typically found in neural networks into a continuous time-domain representation. This enables the model to interpolate and extrapolate effectively across different time steps. Applied to fault detection in Euclidean spaces, the NODEAE methodology was rigorously tested using the well-established Tennessee Eastman dataset, encompassing a range of fault scenarios. When compared with similar models, the NODEAE demonstrated superior performance, evidenced by its notably lower Missed Detection Rate (MDR) and False Alarm Rate (FAR) values.

References

Goswami, U., Rani, J., Kumar, D., Kodamana, H., & Ramteke, M. (2023). Energy Out-of-distribution Based Fault Detection of Multivariate Time-series Data. In *Computer Aided Chemical Engineering* (Vol. 52, pp. 1885-1890). Elsevier.

Goswami, U., Rani, J., Kodamana, H., Kumar, S., & Tamboli, P. K. (2023). Fault detection and isolation of multi-variate time series data using spectral weighted graph auto-encoders. *Journal of the Franklin Institute*, *360*(10), 6783-6803.

Kumar, D., Goswami, U., Kodamana, H., Ramteke, M., & Tamboli, P. K. (2023). Variance-capturing forward-forward autoencoder (VFFAE): A forward learning neural network for fault detection and isolation of process data. *Process Safety and Environmental Protection*, *178*, 176-194.

Chen, R. T., Rubanova, Y., Bettencourt, J., & Duvenaud, D. K. (2018). Neural ordinary differential equations. *Advances in neural information processing systems*, *31*

Flavio Manenti, Gintaras V. Reklaitis (Eds.), Proceedings of the 34th European Symposium on Computer Aided Process Engineering / 15th International Symposium on Process Systems Engineering (ESCAPE34/PSE24), June 2-6, 2024, Florence, Italy

A complete pipeline for the fusion of multiple heterogeneous redundant sources

Marco S. Reis[a,*], Eugeniu Strelet[a], Ivan Castillo[b], You Peng[b], Swee-Teng Chin[b]

aUniv Coimbra, CIEPQPF, Department of Chemical Engineering, Rua Sílvio Lima, Pólo II – Pinhal de Marrocos, 3030-790 Coimbra, Portugal
bThe Dow Chemical Company, Lake Jackson, USA
* marco@eq.uc.pt

Abstract

In the present context, there is an abundance and diversity of cost-effective measurement systems and data collection methods. These are often able to provide multiple estimates for a given target quantity, property, or key performance indicator (KPI). Such estimates can originate from various sources and have different levels of quality, such as high-quality laboratory measurements, medium-quality online analytical devices, and low-quality IoT readings or soft sensor estimates. While the different sources contain redundant information about the variable of interest, they differ in the acquisition rate, modality, and quality (i.e., uncertainty). Dealing with these multiple aspects simultaneously can be a complex task, usually addressed case-by-case. This paper introduces an integrated data fusion pipeline capable of accommodating the heterogeneity of data from various sources while assessing and monitoring their quality. It is designed to be scalable and adaptable to the diversity of solutions available today and in the foreseeable future. The proposed approach is rigorously tested and compared against other single-source and multi-source estimation alternatives, in a real industrial system that showcases both its flexibility and state-of-the-art estimation accuracy.

Keywords: Regularized Bayesian fusion, information quality, redundant sources.

1. Introduction

Modern industrial processes are characterized by the availability of multiple sources of information, each with its own modality, associated quality, and sampling rate (Becerra et al., 2021). Integrating all these heterogeneous data sources into a coherent analysis pipeline poses significant challenges (El Faouzi, 1997). For instance, the implementation of machine learning (ML) models often faces difficulties in the face of missing information, independently of the underlying mechanism (multirate sampling, missing observations/blocks at random, etc.). A common solution is employing data imputation schemes, but these approaches need to be selected and fine-tuned case-by-case, increasing the complexity of the analysis pipeline, as well as the risk of introducing artifacts in data during the imputation operations. Furthermore, some of the existing approaches compromise the expected smoothness of the target variable profile over time (Gutiérrez et al., 2022; Qin, 2014). Therefore, an alternative methodology should be adopted, that is scalable to multiple sources and naturally embraces the raw nature of industrial data, and in particular the dimensions referred to above (multimodality, diverse quality, irregular sampling).

A prevalent situation often found in industrial settings, is the existence of high-quality/low-frequency data (e.g., laboratory measurements of the quality parameters, usually by applying standard reference methods), co-existing with medium-quality/medium-frequency measurements obtained from online instrumental methods (such as inferential models based on process analytics technology (PAT) soft sensors), and low-quality/high-frequency data, derived from process data (such as sensor readings of temperature, pressure, flow, located in the process streams and units) (Qin, 2014). However, when integrating such multiple sources of information, one often finds unstable and uneven estimates of the target variable, instead of smoothly time-varying predictions, as expected from the inertial effects created by the large units and phenomena taking place therein. This can be attributed to the different quality of the sources available and the asynchronous pattern of collected data. The sensor fusion pipeline proposed in this work also overcomes this problem in the case of redundant sources. Let us start by clarifying the meaning of this terminology.

The nature of the several information sources with respect to a target response can be classified as (i) redundant, (ii) cooperative, or (iii) complementary, depending on the superposition of the predictive information each one carries regarding the target response. Complementary sources offer distinct pieces of information that are relevant to explain the variability of the response. Cooperative sources provide partially overlapping information that reinforces each other, but also contain some unique components that are not shared and are relevant for prediction of the response. Finally, redundant sources provide independent estimates of the same underlying phenomenon (Castanedo, 2013). Existing data fusion methods often tacitly assume a given relationship for the sources, or use fusion algorithms based on black box modeling, such as deep learning (DL) (Gao et al., 2020), without explicitly considering the inherent relationships between the sources. This can lead to sub-optimal fusion results that hinder the full exploitation of data in industrial applications.

In this paper, a flexible pipeline is proposed that combines all redundant sources of information about a given target property of interest, taking into account their associated quality (which is first estimated and then monitored), and accommodating different sampling rates and modalities, in order to produce updated estimates with the expected smoothness level, compatible with the process dominant dynamic mode.

2. Proposed data fusion pipeline: EVE-RegBF-MEMS

To effectively combine redundant information sources, a pipeline was assembled that consists of the following main steps. First, (i) the redundancy assumption is rigorously assessed. Afterward, (ii) the quality of the sources is estimated using EVE (Error Variance Estimation). Then, (iii) a new fusion method, RegBF, is applied, that takes into account such quality assessment. Finally, to secure the reliability of the fused data (and ultimately, of the whole fusion process), the quality of the sources is monitored over time (iv), using the MEMS methodology (Mutual Error Monitoring of Sources). This method identifies and flags any potential faulty or inconsistent source of information.

2.1. Classification of the sources

The first step is devoted to verifying if all the sources are of the redundant type. For such, a methodology was developed, that compares the predictive subspaces of the sources and assesses if they overlap (and are therefore redundant) or not (see Figure 1). In brief terms, we compute the projections of the reference source measurements onto the two sources under analysis, say i and j ($P_{ref/i}$ and $P_{ref/j}$, respectively), and calculate the angle, γ, between such projections: if $\gamma \sim 90°$, then i and j are complementary; if γ is close to γ_{red}, they are redundant, where γ_{red} is a redundancy parameter determined by Monte Carlo simulation. A statistical hypothesis test was also devised to support this decision (based on the bootstrap).

2.2. Assessing the sources' quality

The Error Variance Estimation (EVE) method estimates the error variance of different sources based on the differences calculated between them. EVE assumes that the variations of the sources result from the additive effect of state variability and independent Gaussian noise, $\varepsilon_s \sim$ i.i.d. $\mathcal{N}(0, \sigma_s)$. The EVE method consists of the following steps: (i) computing the variance for all possible combinations of paired differences between sources, (ii) formulating the system of equations for the observed variances of the paired differences, where the individual noise variances are the unknown parameters, and (iii) solving this system of equations using constrained weighted least squares (WLS). This process yields the individual error variance for each source. It is important to note that the EVE method requires at least three sources to be effective. With fewer than three sources, the system of equations is underdetermined.

2.3. Regularized Bayesian fusion (RegBF)

RegBF (Figure 2) is a new fusion method that leverages the availability of different sources at time t_k and the corresponding estimated uncertainties provided by EVE (and dynamically updated), to produce an improved estimate of the target response at t_k. The methodology shares some similarity with Bayesian fusion but imposes an additional regularization constraint for the successive estimates that controls their fluctuation or volatility over time. This regularization implies that information from $t_{k-1} < t_k$ is considered for the purposes of obtaining the estimate at t_k. Upon suitable tuning, the regularization has the effect of smoothing out the fused estimate to the expected dynamic behavior of the process. In other words, the regularization constraint provides an additional degree of freedom to align the estimation framework with the intrinsic dynamics of the system.

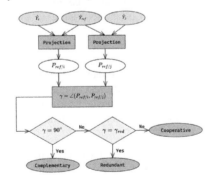

Figure 1 – Classification of the sources.

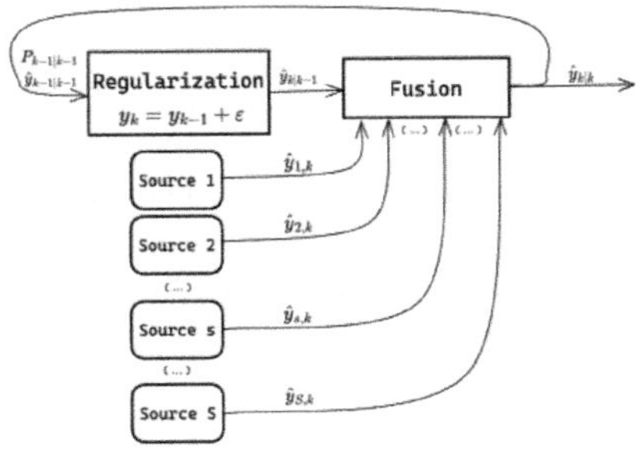

Figure 2 – Regularized Bayesian Fusion (RegBF).

2.4. Monitoring the sources' quality

The quality of the sources is monitored via a developed approach called mutual error monitoring of sources (MEMS). The main assumptions of the MEMS are that the probability of simultaneous failure of two or more sources is low in comparison to individual failures, and the source's uncertainty is stable under normal operating conditions (NOCs). MEMS is based on the mutual errors between the sources. Exponentially weighted moving average (EWMA) control charts are used to monitor the paired errors. A key performance indicator (KPI) for each source is determined by counting the number of OOC situations where each source is involved. A KPI=0 means a flowless source, whereas one with a high KPI indicates potential problems, possibly needing maintenance intervention.

3. Wastewater treatment plant (WWTP) case study

The proposed fusion pipeline was tested with a real case study. Data was gathered from a Dow Chemical Company wastewater treatment plant (WWTP) where a toxic substance should be eliminated from the effluent. The WWTP's essential processing stages are depicted in Figure 3, encompassing a settling unit, a flotation unit, and a filtering unit. The critical phase for toxin removal occurs within the flotation unit, where additives are introduced into the water stream to create flocculates containing the toxin. Subsequently, these flocculates are separated and removed, resulting in a clarified liquid stream that is finally released into the environment.

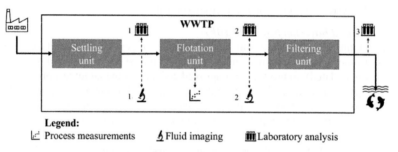

Figure 3 - Schematic representation of the wastewater treatment plant.

Operating a WWTP poses significant challenges stemming from the intricate, dynamic nature of biological processes and the characteristics of the data collected. One notable challenge is that the quality parameters of interest are often accessible at lower frequencies compared to the acquisition rates of the installed process sensors. This can significantly reduce the effectiveness of process management and decision-making. Furthermore, first principles models are not available to describe the system with enough accuracy or have too many unknown or unreliably estimated parameters. On the other hand, available data originates from various sources, arriving at different frequencies, and exhibiting distinct structures and varying quality levels. While these sources are complex to handle, they represent the only viable source of information to use for managing and optimizing WWTP operations.

In this case study, multimodal data were gathered from multiple locations within the WWTP, including images, process sensor readings, and laboratory measurements (as illustrated in Figure 3). These data sources were used to develop three soft sensors through Random Forest (RF) regression: (i) RF Pro flotation utilizes process data from the flotation unit, (ii) RF FI flotation leverages image data from the flotation unit, and (iii) RF FI settling relies on image data from the settling unit. All three soft sensors are designed to predict toxin levels at sampling point 2 (Strelet et al., 2021).

The primary objective of this case study is to achieve accurate toxin level predictions at sampling point 2 in real-time, despite the irregular nature of the information sources and their diverse quality. Due to confidentiality reasons, all data from this case study was previously normalized. This does not affect the conclusions but just protects the confidentiality nature of the information.

4. Results and discussion

Initially, we confirmed that all information sources within the WWTP were redundant. Figure 4 illustrates one such situation for two sources, namely RF Pro and RF FI flotation. Similar outcomes were observed for the other pairs of sources.

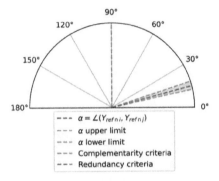

Figure 4 – Classification of sources: RF Pro flotation vs RF FI flotation.

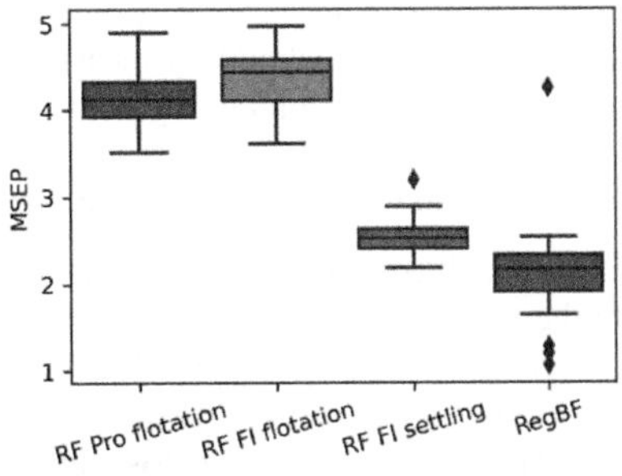

Figure 5 – Accuracy of the soft sensors (RF Pro flotation, RF FI flotation, and RF FI settling) in the test dataset.

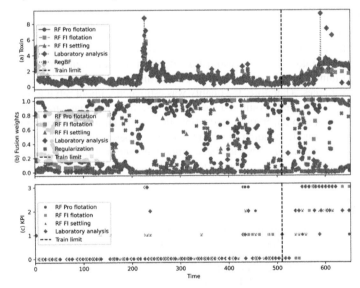

Figure 6 – Time series of RegBF and MEMS results.

The RegBF approach was applied using the outcomes of the EVE method for estimating source uncertainties within a time window spanning 14 units of time. The prediction performance under test conditions of the individual sources and RegBF is presented in Figure 5. Given the unavailability of the true toxin values in this industrial case, the performance was assessed using laboratory measurements as a reference source, as it exhibited the lowest uncertainty ($\widehat{\sigma}^2_{ref} = 0.062$) (consequently, this source does not appear in Figure 5).

The analysis of the performance results indicates that RegBF outperforms the information sources based on soft sensors, owing to the several advantageous properties of RegBF. Notably, the fusion weights are dynamically updated through the EVE method (Figure 6 (b)). Additionally, the regularization parameter is dynamically updated based on the stability or changes in the toxin level. Specifically, a higher rate of changes in toxin state leads to a lower regularization weight. This aspect played an important role during the test period where the laboratory measurements presented several spikes in the toxin level (see Figure 6 (a)), contrasting with the remaining sources that were more stable. Importantly, all sources were treated in exactly the same way, without conferring any special status to the reference measurements.

This approach contributes to a stable performance even in a faulty region that coincides with the test domain. As observed in Figure 6 (c), the KPI obtained via MEMS for that region frequently ranks high for all sources when compared to the training domain. This suggests a reduced reliability of these models in the test domain, possibly due to extrapolation issues. In fact, a closer analysis revealed a notable shift between the test and training domains. Given that three out of the four sources are soft sensors, this shift can potentially impact their performance. Furthermore, it is essential to acknowledge that laboratory measurements are also not entirely error-free.

5. Conclusions

A new fusion pipeline for redundant sources was proposed and validated. It efficiently integrates diverse sources characterized by differing modalities, acquisition frequencies, and data quality, into an accurate estimation. It is worth emphasizing that, similar to any fusion algorithm, the performance of RegBF is intricately tied to the quality of the information sources. Therefore, the quality was estimated without relying on a reference source, using EVE, and monitored using MEMS, further enhancing the stability of RegBF. In addition to uncertainty estimation, the quality monitoring enabled by MEMS contributes to our understanding of when the sources operate under normal conditions or may be undergoing failure. Due to space limitations, the method descriptions provided here are necessarily concise, but more details will be provided in the follow-up publications.

References

Becerra, M. A., Tobón, C., Castro-Ospina, A. E., & Peluffo-Ordóñez, D. H. (2021). Information Quality Assessment for Data Fusion Systems. Data, 6(6), 60. https://doi.org/10.3390/data6060060

Castanedo, F. (2013). A Review of Data Fusion Techniques. The Scientific World Journal, 2013, 1–19. https://doi.org/10.1155/2013/704504

El Faouzi, N.-E. (1997). Heterogeneous Data Source Fusion for Impedance Indicators. IFAC Proceedings Volumes, 30(8), 1307–1312. https://doi.org/10.1016/s1474-6670(17)44002-x

Gao, J., Li, P., Li, P., Chen, Z., Chen, Z., & Zhang, J. (2020). A Survey on Deep Learning for Multimodal Data Fusion. Neural Computation, 32(5), 829–864. https://doi.org/10.1162/neco_a_01273

Gutiérrez, R., Rampérez, V., Paggi, H., Lara, J. A., & Soriano, J. (2022). On the use of information fusion techniques to improve information quality: Taxonomy, opportunities and challenges. Information Fusion, 78, 102–137. https://doi.org/10.1016/j.inffus.2021.09.017

Qin, S. J. (2014). Process data analytics in the era of big data. AIChE Journal, 60(9), 3092–3100. https://doi.org/10.1002/aic.14523

Flavio Manenti, Gintaras V. Reklaitis (Eds.), Proceedings of the 34th European Symposium on Computer Aided Process Engineering / 15th International Symposium on Process Systems Engineering (ESCAPE34/PSE24), June 2-6, 2024, Florence, Italy

Optimal Operation of Vapor-recompressed Middle Vessel Batch Distillation

Surendra Beniwal, Sujit Jogwar*

Department of Chemical Engineering, Indian Institute of Technology Bombay, Mumbai-400076, India
jogwar@iitb.ac.in

Abstract

This article focuses on the optimal operation of an energy-integrated batch distillation configuration. The vapour-recompressed middle vessel batch distillation (VR-MVBD) employs a heat pump system wherein the latent heat available with the top vapour is utilized to vaporize the reboiler liquid. The optimal operation policy is formulated through the maximization of an operational performance index which combines separation and energy efficiency. Specifically, a dynamic optimization problem is solved by exploiting the various degrees of freedom, such as the initial feed distribution and trajectories of vapor and reflux flows. A reduced model governing the dynamics of the VR-MVBD column is employed for better computational efficiency. Lastly, the effectiveness of the proposed approach is demonstrated using a simulation case study of cyclo-hexane, n-heptane, and toluene separation. It is shown that the proposed optimal operation policy doubles the performance index of the system as compared to the base case.

Keywords: Batch distillation, energy-integration, heat pump, dynamic optimization

1. Introduction

Batch distillation, due to operational flexibility and low capital investment, is one of the most preferred separation processes in the chemical industry. However, it also encounters several challenges like long batch time and low energy efficiency. In recent years, effective utilization of energy in batch distillation has been the focus of research activity. To this end, numerous energy-integrated batch distillation configurations have been proposed, such as vapor-recompressed batch distillation (VRBD) (Johri et al., 2011), heat-integrated batch distillation (Nakaiwa et al., 2003), middle vessel batch distillation (MVBD) (Hasebe et al., 1992) and batch divided wall columns (Jana, 2016). Subsequently, Babu et al. (2012) integrated the MVBD and VRBD schemes to propose a vapor-recompressed middle vessel batch distillation (VR-MVBD) configuration to further improve energy efficiency of batch distillation. In VR-MVBD, the overhead vapor is thermally coupled with the reboiler using a heat pump. In order to generate a favorable thermal driving force, a compressor is employed to raise the condensation temperature of the top vapor above the bubble point of the bottom liquid.

In the context of VRBD, Parhi et al. (2019) developed an optimal reflux policy using a multi-objective optimization framework and demonstrated substantial reduction in energy consumption and CO_2 emission. Similarly, Vibhute and Jogwar (2020) obtained an optimal operation policy for a VRBD column using dynamic optimization and closed-loop control. Along similar lines, for a MVBD configuration (without vapor recompression), it has been shown that significant performance improvement can be achieved through dynamic optimization by balancing separation and energy efficiency

(Beniwal and Jogwar, 2023). In the case of VR-MVBD, additional interactions due to vapor recompression add a new dimension to this trade-off as the savings due to energy integration are also dependent on the top and bottom composition profiles and thus the extent of separation. However, the existing study on VR-MVBD by Babu et al. (2012) considers constant reboiler duty and vessel holdup throughout the batch and results in suboptimal performance (as demonstrated in this paper). Motivated by this, the present work focuses on the optimal operation of a VR-MVBD configuration by manipulating input variables, such as initial feed distribution and trajectories of vapor and reflux flows. To quantify performance of the column, an economic performance index is defined to capture separation and energy efficiency. Thereafter, a dynamic optimization problem is solved to maximize this performance index by utilizing the available degrees of freedom. The rest of the paper is organized as follows. Section 2

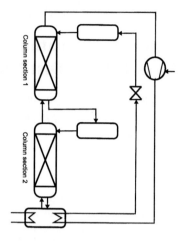

Figure 1: Vapor-recompressed middle vessel batch distillation (VR-MVBD) configuration

describes the considered system and presents the governing dynamic equations. The next section focuses on the formulation of the dynamic optimization problem. In section 4, a case study involving the separation of a mixture consisting of cyclo-hexane, n-heptane, and toluene is presented to illustrate the effectiveness of the proposed approach.

2. VR-MVBD configuration

As shown in Figure 1, this configuration consists of two column sections and three vessels for the separation of a ternary mixture. The vapor leaving the top of column section 1 is compressed using a compressor to increase its dew point temperature. The latent heat of this compressed vapor is utilized in the reboiler (bottom vessel) to generate vapor required for separation. The rest of the heat requirements are met via an auxiliary reboiler. The condensate leaving the reboiler-condenser is throttled and sent to the distillate vessel. Fresh feed can be introduced through any/all of the vessels. The VR-MVBD column is operated under total reflux, and the three products, based on their relative volatility, accumulate in the distillate, middle, and bottom vessel. The batch ends when the products in all three vessels reach their desired purity specification. For simplicity, let us consider constant holdup on each tray and constant relative volatility throughout the column. Accordingly, Eq. (1) captures the dynamics of this system.

$$\text{distillate vessel:} \quad \frac{dM_D}{dt} = V - R_1, \quad \frac{d(M_D x_{D,j})}{dt} = V y_{1,j} - R_1 x_{D,j}$$

$$\text{column section 1:} \frac{d(M_t x_{i,j})}{dt} = R_1\left(x_{(i-1),j} - x_{i,j}\right) + V\left(y_{(i+1),j} - y_{i,j}\right)$$

$$\text{middle vessel:} \quad \frac{dM_M}{dt} = R_1 - R_2, \quad \frac{d(M_M x_{M,j})}{dt} = R_1 x_{N_{T1},j} - R_2 x_{M,j}$$

$$\text{column section 2:} \frac{d(M_t x_{i,j})}{dt} = R_2\left(x_{(i-1),j} - x_{i,j}\right) + V\left(y_{(i+1),j} - y_{i,j}\right)$$

$$(1)$$

$$\text{bottom vessel:} \quad \frac{dM_B}{dt} = R_2 - V, \quad \frac{d(M_B x_{B,j})}{dt} = R_2 x_{N_{T2},j} - V y_{B,j}$$

where M, x, and y represent molar holdup, liquid phase mol fraction, and vapor phase mol fraction, respectively. V, R_1, and R_2 represent the vapor flow rate and reflux flow rates from the distillate and middle vessel, respectively. Subscripts D, M, and B refer to the distillate vessel, middle vessel, and bottom vessel, respectively. Subscripts t, i, and j denote tray, stage number (from the top of the column), and component j, respectively. Subscripts N_{T1} and N_{T2} refer to the last stage of column section 1 and 2, respectively. The vapor and liquid phase mole fractions are related to each other through the vapor-liquid equilibrium relationship and stage efficiency definition. Specifically, at i^{th} stage,

$$y_{i,j,eqm} = \frac{\alpha_j x_{i,j,eqm}}{\sum_j^3 \alpha_j x_{i,j,eqm}}, \qquad \eta_{i,j} = \frac{y_{i,j} - y_{i+1,j}}{y_{i,j,eqm} - y_{i+1,j}} \tag{2}$$

where α represents the relative volatility, the subscript eqm represents the equilibrium value, and η represents Murphree tray efficiency.

During the operation, the overhead vapor and the bottom vessel liquid get enriched in the more volatile and less volatile components, respectively. Therefore, to maintain a constant thermal driving force between the bubble point temperature of the reboiler liquid (T_B) and the dew point temperature of the compressed vapor ($T_{C,dew}$), the compressor is operated at variable speed. The required compression ratio (CR) and the corresponding compressor power (W) are estimated using the following equations.

$$CR = \left[\frac{T_{C,dew}}{T_T}\right]^{\left(\frac{\mu}{\mu-1}\right)}, \qquad W = \frac{V\mu R T_T}{\eta_{comp}(\mu-1)}\left[\left[\frac{P_{TC}}{P_T}\right]^{\left(\frac{\mu}{\mu-1}\right)} - 1\right] \tag{3}$$

where T_T, μ, and η_{comp} represent the temperature of the overhead vapor, specific heat ratio, and isentropic efficiency of the compressor, respectively. P_{TC} and P_C represent outlet and inlet pressure, respectively. Subsequently, the auxiliary reboiler duty is computed using the following equation.

$$Q_{aux} = V\left(\lambda_{T_B} - \lambda_{T_{c,dew}} - C_P\left(T_{c,actual} - T_{c,dew}\right)\right) \tag{4}$$

where λ and C_P represent latent heat and specific heat capacity, respectively.

3. Optimal operation

Optimization of an energy-integrated distillation configuration attempts to achieve desired separation with minimum energy consumption. Thus, to generate an optimal operating policy, it is essential to include both production and energy consumption for performance quantification. Accordingly, an overall performance index (OPI) is defined as the ratio of the value of the separated products to the cost of energy consumed during separation. The OPI can be computed using the following expression:

$$OPI = \frac{\sum_{i=1}^3 (C_i * M_i(t_{batch}))}{\int_0^{t_{batch}} [C_{Q1} Q_{aux}(t) + C_{Q2} W(t)] dt} \tag{5}$$

where M_i and t_{batch} represent i^{th} vessel holdup and batch processing time, respectively. C_i, C_{Q1}, and C_{Q2} represent the value of the product collected in the ith vessel, cost of the auxiliary reboiler duty and cost of the compressor duty, respectively.

The optimal operation problem involves obtaining the trajectory of input variables to maximize a performance index while incorporating practical constraints. Therefore, a dynamic problem is formulated to obtain the optimal operating policy for the VR-MVBD configuration. Maximization of OPI is considered as an objective function. The decision variables (u) are the trajectory of vapor flow rate (V), and reflux flow rates from distillate and middle vessel (R_1 and R_2). A piecewise constant input policy is considered. As the tray holdup is very small as compared to a vessel holdup, the dynamic system given by Eq. (1) is stiff. Singular perturbations are used to derive non-stiff realization of these dynamic equations and the corresponding DAE system is used during dynamic optimization (Beniwal and Jogwar, 2023). This reduces the number of dynamic variables as well as allows for using a larger time step for discretization. The corresponding dynamic optimization problem is given as follows.

$$\max_{V(t),R1(t),R2(t)} OPI$$

Subject to: Reduced dynamic model for VR-MVBD

$\quad\quad$ Input bounds: $\quad u_{min} \leq u(t) \leq u_{max}$

$\quad\quad$ Input move constraints: $\Delta u_{min} \leq \Delta u(t) \leq \Delta u_{max}$ $\quad\quad\quad\quad$ (6)

$\quad\quad$ Vessel holdup constraints: $M_{min} \leq M(t) \leq M_{max}$

$\quad\quad$ Purity constraints $\forall$ products: $x(t_{batch}) \geq x_{desired}$

$\quad\quad$ Feasible composition constraints: $0 \leq x(t) \leq 1, \quad 0 \leq y(t) \leq 1$

4. Case study

Let us now illustrate this framework with an example system of cyclo-hexane, n-heptane, and toluene separation. The base case design is considered from literature (Babu et al., 2012) and slightly modified to obtain 99% purity for all the three products. The VR-MVBD column consists of total 74 trays ($N_{T1} = 41$, $N_{T2} = 33$) to process 50 kmol fresh feed (F) with composition (z_{F1}) of (0.1, 0.6, 0.3). Initial feed is distributed to all the three vessels in proportion to the composition (denoted as proportional feed distribution). The volatility values are $\alpha_1 = 2.4575$, $\alpha_2 = 1.431$ and $\alpha_3 = 1$. At the base case, the column is operated under the constant vessel holdup with a fixed vapor flow rate of 0.58 kmol/min, and the corresponding batch time is 816 minutes. A two-stage compressor system with equal pressure ratio is employed to maintain the required compression ratio. The OPI value for the base case operation is 23.31. The relative error between the reduced and full model for product composition in distillate, middle, and bottom vessel is 1.97%, 1.10% and 2.33%, respectively.

The optimization problem given by Eq. (6) is solved using the CasADi (Andersson et al., 2019) framework in MATLAB version R2022a. Implicit Euler method, with a time step of 1 min, is used to discretize the dynamic equations. The maximum and minimum value for each optimization variable is taken as 0.5 kmol/min and 1 kmol/min, respectively. Their change at any time step is restricted to ± 0.05 kmol/min. The vessel holdups are constrained between 1.1 kmol and 45 kmol, respectively. Lastly, cost of each product, hot utility and compressor power are taken as 15 rcu/mol, 2.3 rcu/MJ and 7.0 rcu/MJ, respectively (rcu refers to relative cost unit).

Figure 2(a) shows the variation of component holdup for each vessel. Two distinct phases for holdup redistribution can be observed. Specifically, in the first phase of the operation, both the column sections are utilized to perform a relatively difficult separation between n-heptane and toluene, leading to an increase in the concentration of cyclo-hexane and n-heptane in the distillate vessel and the concentration of toluene in the bottom vessel. Subsequently, in the second phase of operation, final product purity specifications in all the vessels are achieved by transferring the partial holdup of the distillate vessel, enriched in n-heptane, to the middle vessel. The OPI value for this policy is 49.11 and corresponds to an increase of 111% from the base case.

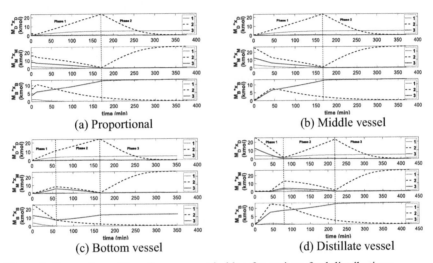

(a) Proportional   (b) Middle vessel

(c) Bottom vessel   (d) Distillate vessel

Figure 2: Dynamic profiles of component holdup for various feed distributions

Subsequently, three other initial feed distribution scenarios, bottom vessel feed (conventional batch rectifier), middle vessel feed and distillate vessel feed (inverted configuration), are considered. In the case of middle vessel feed, the variation of component holdup follows similar trend to the previous case. However, as the corresponding top and bottom compositions are different, the temperature lift required in this case is slightly higher than the previous case (see Figure 3) leading to an increase in compression power. The optimal OPI value for this case is 48.95, a small decrease of 0.3% from proportional feed distribution. When the initial feed charged to the bottom vessel, there are three distinct phases of holdup redistribution as shown in Figure 2(c). The

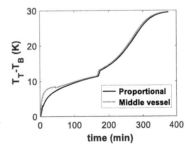

Figure 3: Dynamic profile for required temperature lift

additional phase at the start of the operation includes the distribution of material to all the vessels and temporarily storing component 3, vaporized along with components 1 and 2, in the middle vessel. In phase 2, component 3 from the middle vessel is transferred back to the bottom vessel, and the distillate vessel gets enriched in components 1 and 2. Final purity specifications are achieved in all the vessels with material redistribution during phase 3. The OPI for this policy is 48.12, a reduction of 2% from the proportional feed distribution due to the extra step of holdup transfer. Similarly, feed charged to the distillate vessel also results in three operational phases and gives an optimal OPI of 45.87.

Lastly, in order to investigate the effect of feed composition, two other feed conditions – equimolar (z_{F2}) and lean middle component (z_{F3}) – are considered. The corresponding optimal OPI values for each of the feed locations are reported in Table 1. It can be seen that the proportional feed distribution results in the best performance irrespective of the feed composition. This is in contrast with the normal MVBD case wherein feed to the middle vessel resulted in the best performance (Beniwal and Jogwar, 2023). This signifies the impact of coupling between energy consumption and extent of separation due to energy integration.

Table 1: Optimal OPI values for various feed composition and location

Feed location	Proportional	Distillate	Middle	Bottom
z_{F1} (0.1,0.6,0.3)	49.11	45.87	48.95	48.12
z_{F2} (0.33,0.33,0.33)	46.67	44.23	45.51	46.06
z_{F3} (0.40,0.25,0.35)	51.46	49.81	49.81	50.06

5. Conclusions

In this paper, optimal operation policy is formulated for an energy-integrated VR-MVBD system. An economic performance index (OPI) is defined to include separation and energy efficiency. It is shown that the optimal redistribution of vessel holdup results in significant performance (OPI) improvement over the base case scenario considered in previous literature. For the case study of cyclo-hexane/n-heptane/toluene separation, irrespective of the feed composition, the proportional feed distribution results in the best performance.

References

J. Andersson, J. Gillis, G. Horn, J.B. Rawlings and M. Diehl, 2019, CasADi: a software framework for nonlinear optimization and optimal control, Math. Program. Comput., 11(1):1–36.

G. U. B. Babu, R. Aditya, and A. K. Jana, 2012, Economic feasibility of a novel energy efficient middle vessel batch distillation to reduce energy use, Energy, 45(1):626–633.

S. Beniwal and S. S. Jogwar, 2023, Middle vessel batch distillation: Performance quantification, model reduction and optimal operation, AIChE J., submitted for publication.

S. Hasebe, B. B. Abdul Aziz, I. Hashimoto, and T. Watanabe, 1992, Optimal Design and Operation of Complex Batch Distillation Column, IFAC Proceedings Volumes, 25(24):177–182.

A. K. Jana, 2016, A new divided-wall heat integrated distillation column (hidic) for batch processing: Feasibility and analysis, Appl. Energy, 172:199–206.

K. Johri, G.U.B. Babu and A.K. Jana, 2011, Performance investigation of a variable speed vapor recompression reactive batch rectifier, AIChE J., 57: 3238-3242.

M. Nakaiwa, K. Huang, A. Endo, T. Ohmori, T. Akiya, and T. Takamatsu, 2003, Internally heat-integrated distillation columns: a review, Chem. Eng. Res. Des., 81(1):162–177.

S. S. Parhi, G.P. Rangaiah, and A.K. Jana, 2019, Mixed-Integer dynamic optimization of conventional and vapor recompressed batch distillation for economic and environmental objectives, Chem. Eng. Res. Des., 154:70–85.

M. M. Vibhute and S. S. Jogwar, 2020, Optimal operation and tracking control of vapor-recompressed batch distillation. AIChE Journal, 66(12):5–8.

Flavio Manenti, Gintaras V. Reklaitis (Eds.), Proceedings of the 34th European Symposium on Computer Aided Process Engineering / 15th International Symposium on Process Systems Engineering (ESCAPE34/PSE24), June 2-6, 2024, Florence, Italy

Heterogenous electrolysis plants as enabler of efficient and flexible Power-to-X value chains

Michael Mock[a]*, Isabell Viedt[a], Hannes Lange[a], Leon Urbas[a]

aTU Dresden, Chair of Process Control System and Process Systems Engineering Group, Helmholtzstr. 14, 01069 Dresden, Germany
E-Mail: michael.mock@tu-dresden.de Abstract

Abstract

The Power-to-Ammonia (PtA) value chain is an important enabler of sector coupling and integration of renewable energy in the process industry. The PtA pathway typically uses 90-96 % of the incoming fluctuating energy to produce green hydrogen using electrolyzer systems [1]. Hence to optimize the energy efficiency, flexibility, adaptability to fluctuating energy and cost of the PtA process, the correct choice of electrolysis technology is important. Each electrolysis technology has certain advantages and disadvantages in handling a fluctuating energy input [2]. The use of modular and heterogenous electrolysis systems, consisting of different types and sizes of electrolyzers, can utilize these advantages while counteracting the disadvantages. The project eModule researches a possible transfer of modular plant concepts, defined in the VDI/VDE/NAMUR 2776 standard for the process industry, to enable a fast, efficient, and flexible scale-up of electrolyzer systems.

For that purpose, this paper evaluates different modular electrolyzer configurations in a flexible PtA value chain. A monolithic electrolyzer configuration, consisting of electrolyzers of same size and technology, is simulated and used as a benchmark. Different heterogenous plant configurations and corresponding process control strategies for energy integration are created and simulated in MATLAB/Simulink. Metrics for energy efficiency, flexibility, and adaptability to fluctuating energy input are defined and compared. It is shown that the use of modular heterogenous electrolyzer systems enable a more efficient green hydrogen and ammonia production, while making the system more flexible and adaptable to a fluctuating energy input. The advantages of using modular heterogenous electrolyzer configurations in the PtA value chain are quantified, and upcoming techno-economic evaluations can show the economic potential of such plants.

Keywords: Power-to-X (PtX), Power-to-Ammonia (PtA), Heterogenous electrolysis, Co-simulation, Modular plants

1. Motivation

In the efforts to counteract climate change, the production of low-emission hydrogen has emerged as a key technology. This can enable sector coupling, increase energy security, and support the decarbonization of process chains that cannot be electrified. For the chemical process industry, the production of green hydrogen by coupling renewable energy with water electrolysis systems enables the direct integration of fluctuating energy into value chains, currently depending on fossil fuels. One example of such a value chain is the global ammonia production, having used around 60 % of the 53 Mt of industrial hydrogen in 2022, based mostly on fossil fuels [3].

To improve the alternative production route of the Power-to-Ammonia (PtA) value chain, electrolysis systems for green hydrogen production must become more efficient and flexible. Around 90 – 96 % of incoming fluctuating energy in the PtA process are typically consumed during the production of green hydrogen [1]. Improvements to the electrolysis systems therefore have a major impact on the overall consumption of the process chain. The use of the modular plant concepts, defined in the VDI 2776 and VDI/VDE/NAMUR 2658 standard for the process industry, might offer advantages for efficiency, flexibility, and adaptability to fluctuating energy. Project eModule researches the transfer of this concept for electrolysis systems. The different electrolysis technologies have certain advantages and disadvantages in handling a fluctuating energy input, which might be combined through use of modularization [2].

2. Methods

This paper researches the potential use of modular, heterogeneous electrolysis plants. Different electrolyzer configurations with identical nominal power input and varying technology combinations are proposed. The technologies under consideration are the alkaline electrolysis (AEL), the proton exchange membrane electrolysis (PEMEL) and the high temperature electrolysis (HTEL). Metrics for specific energy consumption, system efficiency and flexibility are defined to compare the heterogenous configurations and a benchmark configuration with a single electrolyzer technology. The resulting metrics are calculated and compared for two energy input scenarios. The potential of each heterogenous electrolyzer configuration for the use in a flexible PtA value chain is evaluated. Furthermore, the ability to follow the incoming energy fluctuations and the ability to provide the necessary hydrogen for a flexible ammonia synthesis loop is examined.

2.1. Heterogenous electrolyzer configurations in PtA value chains

The Power-to-Ammonia value chain is represented by a Haber-Bosch synthesis loop, connected to the electrolyzer configurations. An ammonia production of 5000 kg/h is set as a nominal production, which amounts to a necessary hydrogen feed of around 980 kg/h at nominal load. Furthermore the ammonia synthesis loop can be operated flexibly down to 20 % of nominal production capacity with a load change rate of 20 %/h [4]. To reach the necessary hydrogen production the electrolyzer configurations are set to an estimated necessary power of 55 MW. The distribution of this power to different technologies is approximated from work on hybrid electrolysis for green steel production and the resulting configurations are collected in Table 1 [5].

Table 1: Electrolyzer configurations with respective power per electrolyzer technology

	Unit	AEL	PEMEL	HTEL
Benchmark Configuration	*MW*	55	0	0
Configuration 1	*MW*	22	33	0
Configuration 2	*MW*	33	0	22
Configuration 3	*MW*	0	33	22

2.2. Definition of metrics

The energy efficiency of the different configurations for the simulated scenario can be defined by the specific energy consumption of the system in $kWh/Nm_{H_2}^3$, in Eq. (1):

$$E_{spec,sys} = \frac{P_{cons}}{V_{H_2,prod}} \tag{1}$$

with P_{cons} as the electrical power consumption in kWh and $V_{H_2,prod}$ as the produced hydrogen flow in Nm^3 over the simulated time.

Using the specific energy consumption, the system energy efficiency in % can be calculated in relation to the lower heating value of H_2 ($LHV_{H_2} = 3\ kWh/Nm^3$.), according to Eq. (2):

$$\eta_{sys} = 100\ \% \cdot \frac{LHV_{H_2}}{E_{spec,sys}} \tag{2}$$

Flexibility parameters of electrolyzer technologies, identified and collected by Lange et al., are used to calculate the Expected Unserved Flexible Energy ($EUFE$) of a portfolio of flexible energy resources, adapted from Gussain et al. [2, 6]. Further parameters for high temperature electrolysis have been adapted from Posdziech et al. [7]. The EUFE sums up the absolute difference between the wanted power input and the realizable power consumption of the system in kWh, according to Eq. (3).

$$EUFE = \int_{t_{start}}^{t_{end}} |P_{in} - P_{sys}| \tag{3}$$

3. Implementation

The defined configurations are simulated in MATLAB/Simulink using existing dynamic models. The models are based on available literature and evaluated by comparing the simulated output with given information on manufacturer data sheets. The efficiency metrics are calculated in MATLAB/Simulink, using the simulated energy consumption and hydrogen production. The implemented parameters used for the flexibility calculation are collected in Table 2. It is assumed, that the system is already heated and producing, so heat ramp-up and start-up times can be neglected.

Table 2: Flexibility parameters of electrolysis technologies adapted from [2, 7]

	Unit	AEL	PEMEL	HTEL
Load Flexibility	*%*	20 – 100	0 – 160	50 – 125
Load gradient, start-up	*%/s*	10	10	0,1
Load gradient shut-down	*%/s*	10	40,6	3

Within the technologies, all electrolyzers are operated at the same load, to prevent feed maldistribution. When a load change occurs, all available electrolyzers start-up with their respective load gradient. A hierarchical system has been implemented, designating which technology shall preferentially receive the power in case of partial load. HTEL is preferred to take most of the wanted load and to run as a base load. AEL is secondly favored, while PEMEL will be shut down first, if the entire capacity is not needed. Furthermore, if overcapacity is used, the system will automatically lower the load to nominal capacity, while other technologies ramp-up. This approach ensures that no electrolyzer remains in overcapacity for extended periods, contributing to a reduction in degradation.

Two energy input scenarios are simulated, shown in Figure 1. Scenario A changes the input in 15-minute steps in line with the resolution of available energy in the German energy market [8]. The power plateaus are selected in such a way that the following scenarios during the electrolyzer operation are covered, while the results are still comparable:

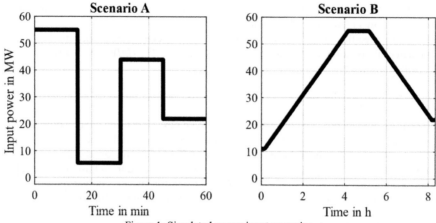

Figure 1: Simulated power input scenarios

- ❖ Ramp-up to full load & to partial load
- ❖ Ramp-down to achievable partial load & to unachievable partial load
- ❖ Ramp-up and ramp-down at $20\,\%/h$ to follow the load change rate of the ammonia synthesis loop (Scenario B)

4. Results

The achievable flexibility margins of the chosen scenarios are shown in Figure 2. The benchmark configuration and configuration 2 have limitations in their available power range due to the minimum load of the AEL and HTEL technologies. Configurations 1 and 3 can achieve the entire necessary load range and beyond due to the high range of the used PEMEL.

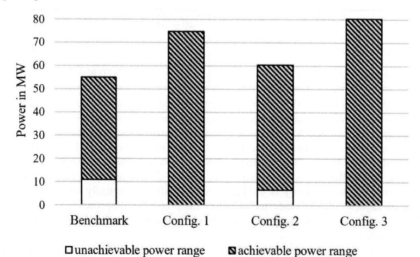

Figure 2: Flexibility margins with achievable and unachievable power ranges

The calculated efficiencies are compiled in Table 3, alongside the EUFE values corresponding to the simulated energy input scenarios. Configuration 2 has the highest efficiency at 72,46 % vs. LHV, followed by configuration 3 with 71.43 % vs. LHV. This is primarily attributed to the utilization of HTEL electrolyzers, which have a comparably low specific energy consumption if a high temperature feed is available. The benchmark configuration and configuration 1 also exhibit similar efficiencies, with 66,67 % vs. LHV for the benchmark and 65,8 % vs. LHV for configuration 1.

The EUFE values for scenario A vary strongly between the configurations. Configurations 1 and 3 show similar EUFE values at around 200 kWh, which are mainly contributed during initial start-up. The benchmark configuration and configuration 1 show much larger values. This is due to the unachievable partial load, which cannot be reached and therefore adds to the EUFE. Configuration 2 has the highest EUFE value at 5309 kWh, much larger than the rest. In comparison to the benchmark configuration, this happens because of the low ramp-up rate of the HTEL, which cannot be counteracted by the AEL. Configuration 3, which also must deal with the slow ramp-up of the HTEL, can reduce the EUFE value by using the PEMELs overload capacity to reach the necessary power quickly and reducing the input power of the PEMEL gradually, while the HTEL is still ramping up.

Scenario B shows similar and much lower EUFE values along all configurations. Configurations 2 and 3 share the same value, because no overload capacity is needed for the ramp-up rate of the ammonia synthesis loop and the lower load limit is always reached. The benchmark configuration and configuration 1 show slightly higher EUFE values. This is identified as a slight overshooting of the power consumption due to the high load change rates, compared to the HTEL in configurations 2 and 3. If the simulation and the control strategies are operated at a higher resolution, this value will further be reduced.

Table 3: Resulting efficiency metrics for the configurations and EUFE for input scenario A & B

	Unit	Benchmark	**Config. 1**	**Config. 2**	**Config. 3**
$E_{spec,sys}$	$\dfrac{kWh}{Nm^3_{H_2}}$	4,5	4,56	4,14	4,2
η_{sys}	%	66,67	65,8	72,46	71,43
EUFE A	kWh	1561	172	5309	243
EUFE B	kWh	172	121	67	67

In conclusion the combination of technologies can enhance the efficiency of electrolyzer systems while also providing a high range of flexibility. The right choice of technology and power distribution strategy is particularly important if a flexible system with sudden changes in energy input and low load operation is needed.

5. Discussion & Outlook

The presented results provide initial insights into the benefits of heterogeneous electrolysis systems for efficiency and flexibility of PtX value chains. However, further investigations are necessary to demonstrate the manageability of the overall system and the economic possibilities. Advanced metrics to demonstrate the flexibility of the overall system beyond energy consumption must be defined.

The defined scenarios and calculated flexibility margins in Figure 2 do not fully grasp the technological limitations and possibilities in their entirety yet. The use of HTEL electrolyzers is only feasible, if a high temperature feed is available. In case of the PtA process chain, process energy is available but the possible capacity of HTEL must be adjusted to the size of the ammonia synthesis loop.

Furthermore, overload capacity can be used in some electrolyzer systems but is often limited in frequency and duration to prevent degradation. Additionally, instead of controlling all electrolyzers in one technology with the same power input, single stack control can reduce the load range, by shutting down single electrolyzers instead of electrolyzer groups.

For upcoming work more sophisticated power control strategies and process control strategies of combined electrolyzer systems shall be developed, implemented, and tested. The initial setup and power distribution of heterogenous electrolyzer plants shall be optimized and include the available high temperature feed of follow-up processes. Beyond that, economic optimizations of electrolyzer systems shall be considered.

New methods and metrics to include the inherent dynamics of different electrolyzer technologies into the efficiency and flexibility calculation shall also be developed, implemented, and tested. The first steps of developing the necessary dynamic process models for all electrolyzer technologies are already on-going and suitable process control strategies for distributed electrolysis systems are in preparation.

Acknowledgments:
We would like to thank the German Federal Ministry of Education and Research and the project management organization Jülich for their financial support within the framework of the eModule research project (FKZ 03HY116A) of the H2Giga lead platform. Furthermore, the P2O-Lab of the Technical University of Dresden is thanked for its support.

References

[1] K. H. Rouwenhorst, A. G. Van der Ham, G. Mul, and S. R. Kersten, "Islanded ammonia power systems: Technology review & conceptual process design," *Renew. Sustain. Energy Rev.*, vol. 114, p. 109339, 2019.

[2] H. Lange, A. Klose, W. Lippmann, and L. Urbas, "Technical evaluation of the flexibility of water electrolysis systems to increase energy flexibility: A review," *Int. J. Hydrog. Energy*, vol. 48, no. 42, pp. 15771–15783, May 2023, doi: 10.1016/j.ijhydene.2023.01.044.

[3] I. International Energy Agency, "Global Hydrogen Review 2023," 2023, doi: https://www.iea.org/reports/global-hydrogen-review-2023.

[4] M. Mock, H. Lange, I. Viedt, K. R. Gopa, J. Mädler, and L. Urbas, "Dynamic operation for the effective use of green hydrogen in Power-to-X value chains," in *33rd European Symposium on Computer Aided Process Engineering*, vol. 52, A. C. Kokossis, M. C. Georgiadis, and E. Pistikopoulos, Eds., in Computer Aided Chemical Engineering, vol. 52. , Elsevier, 2023, pp. 1267–1272. doi: https://doi.org/10.1016/B978-0-443-15274-0.50202-X.

[5] Sunfire GmbH, "Hybrid Electrolysis for green steel production: Increasing efficiency in integrated steel works." Mar. 2022. [Online]. Available: https://dwv-info.de/them enbroschueren/hybrid-electrolysis-for-green-steel-production/

[6] D. Gusain, M. Cvetković, and P. Palensky, "Quantification of operational flexibility from a portfolio of flexible energy resources," *Int. J. Electr. Power Energy Syst.*, vol. 141, p. 107466, Oct. 2022, doi: 10.1016/j.ijepes.2021.107466.

[7] O. Posdziech, K. Schwarze, and J. Brabandt, "Efficient hydrogen production for industry and electricity storage via high-temperature electrolysis," *Int. J. Hydrog. Energy*, vol. 44, no. 35, pp. 19089–19101, Jul. 2019, doi: 10.1016/j.ijhydene.2018.05.169.

[8] "Stromerzeugung und -verbrauch in Deutschland - SMARD Strommarktdaten." [Online]. Available: https://www.smard.de/home

Flavio Manenti, Gintaras V. Reklaitis (Eds.), Proceedings of the 34th European Symposium on Computer Aided Process Engineering / 15th International Symposium on Process Systems Engineering (ESCAPE34/PSE24), June 2-6, 2024, Florence, Italy

Enabling Load-Flexible Ammonia Synthesis via Polytropic Fixed-Bed Reactors

Lukas Gottheil[a], Jens Bremer[a,*]

[a]*Clausthal University of Technology, Institute of Chemical and Electrochemical Process Engineering, Leibnizstrasse 17, 38678 Clausthal-Zellerfeld, Germany*
bremer@icvt.tu-clausthal.de

Abstract

Establishing an economically and technically viable Power-to-Ammonia process requires a reactor concept capable of operating in multiple steady-states, as well as between these states. In this work, we present a novel approach using polytropic fixed-bed reactors to enable load-flexible ammonia synthesis. Therefore, a dynamic pseudo-homogeneous reactor model, which considers the effects of real gas behavior and intraparticle mass transport limitations, is developed. Detailed dynamic simulation studies demonstrate that the proposed reactor concept is considerably less sensitive to disturbances compared to the conventional adiabatic multi-bed reactor. In fact, even under drastic load changes fast, smooth, and stable transitions among different steady-states were observed. It is also proven that the heat supplied via the cooling jacket adequately preheats the reactants in the first section of the reactor, making feed-effluent heat exchangers obsolete. The polytropic ammonia synthesis reactor can be operated over a remarkably wide load range, even at loads of only 10 %, while achieving high nitrogen conversions of at least 20 %.

Keywords: Ammonia, Polytropic Fixed-Bed Reactor, Load-Flexible Reactor Operation, Dynamic Reactor Simulation

1. Introduction

As the share of renewable energies is continuously increasing, the demand for global energy storage and energy transportation technologies is growing significantly. In this context, chemical-based energy storage via Power-to-X (P2X) processes is one of the most promising concepts for converting renewable energy. Among potential P2X fuels, ammonia stands out by its carbon-free nature, its ease of being liquefied compared to hydrogen and its industrial scale production process that has already been established for decades (Elishav et al., 2020). However, the use of electrolytically produced hydrogen as a reactant for ammonia synthesis introduces new challenges for the process. These mainly arise due to the intermittent nature of renewable energy supply leading to changing hydrogen flows from dynamically operated electrolyzer units. In order to avoid costly intermediate hydrogen storage, a concept for load-flexible ammonia synthesis is required. This implies an ammonia synthesis reactor capable of operating safely and efficiently on a wide load-range in multiple steady-states, including the transition between them.

Today, adiabatic quench-cooled multi-bed reactor systems with heat integration via feed-effluent heat exchangers (i.e. auto-thermal reactor concept) are widely used in industry for continuous steady-state ammonia synthesis. It is reported that this reactor type might operate at loads as low as 20 to 50 % of their nominal capacity (Fahr et al., 2023).

However, dynamic simulations have shown that this system is particularly sensitive to disturbances and can easily exhibit oscillatory behavior if perturbed. For instance, Morud and Skogestad (1998) demonstrated that a pressure drop of 25 % can lead to temperature oscillations with amplitudes of up to 200 °C. Rosbo et al. (2023) recently studied the stability and controllability of this reactor type based on dynamic simulations. Significant differences in the residence time of material and temperature waves as well as the external thermal feedback were identified as key factors causing instabilities. Advanced control strategies were proposed to significantly enhance process stability. Nevertheless, handling changing loads, in particular ramping the reactor from low to high loads, is still challenging and time consuming. Fahr et al. (2023) suggest increasing the dimensions of the feed-effluent heat exchanger to stabilize the reactor inlet temperature and to improve reactor stability.

It is well known that external thermal feedback, e.g. introduced by feed-effluent heat exchangers, can easily cause instabilities during transient transitions. One approach to reduce this issue is stabilizing the temperature profile inside the reactor by polytropic operation (e.g. via reactor wall cooling). With this method, it should be feasible to maintain almost constant reactor exit temperatures regardless of changing inlet conditions. Moreover, polytropic operation, especially in case of catalytic exothermic reactions, can generally be characterized by its improved dynamic behavior (Bremer et al., 2017) and a wider operating range (Bremer and Sundmacher, 2019), enhancing both stability and flexibility.

The aim of this work is to evaluate the feasibility of load-flexible ammonia synthesis via polytropic fixed-bed reactors. For this purpose, we present detailed simulation studies by employing a pseudo-homogenous reactor model, which particularly accounts for the dynamic behavior of ammonia synthesis. Especially the influence of key operational parameters and external heat transfer on the transient behavior (including stability) of the reactor is investigated and compared to the conventional multi-bed concept.

2. Dynamic Reactor Model

For the mathematical description of the polytropic fixed-bed reactor, a one-dimensional dynamic pseudo-homogeneous reactor model, adopted from Bremer and Sundmacher (2019), is used. Based on a differential volume element, mass balances (Eq. (1)), one for each species $i \in \{N_2, H_2, NH_3\}$, and an energy balance (Eq. (2)) are derived. It was decided to omit the implementation of the dynamic momentum balance to reduce computational effort and to improve stability of the applied numerical solver. Instead, pressure loss is described by Ergun equation (Eq. (3)), as friction typically dominates the dynamic momentum balance of a fixed-bed reactor. Changes in fluid velocity along the reactor axis are caused by mass conservation (Eq. (4)).

The density of the gas mixture ρ_{gas} is calculated according to Peng-Robinson equation of state. Activity-based kinetic models are chosen to describe the reaction rate. For the widely used magnetite-based iron catalyst, the kinetics of Dyson and Simon (1968) are applied. Additionally, a kinetic model provided by Rossetti et al. (2006) is available, to represent more active Ru-based catalysts. This model considers the inhibitory effect of hydrogen on the activity of Ru-based catalysts. In order to account for temperature-dependent intraparticle mass transport limitations within the pseudo-homogeneous model, an effectiveness factor η_{cat}, determined via the Thiele modulus, is included.

$$\varepsilon\rho_{\text{gas}}\frac{\partial w_i}{\partial t} = -\rho_{\text{gas}}v_z\frac{\partial w_i}{\partial z} - \frac{\partial(j_{z,i})}{\partial z} + \eta_{\text{cat}}\tilde{M}_iv_i(1-\varepsilon)r\,, \tag{1}$$

$$(\rho c_p)^{\text{eff}}\frac{\partial T}{\partial t} = -\rho_{\text{gas}}c_{p,\text{gas}}v_z\frac{\partial T}{\partial z} - \frac{\partial(\dot{q}_z)}{\partial z} + \eta_{\text{cat}}(1-\varepsilon)r(-\Delta h_r) - \frac{4}{d}k_{\text{w}}(T - T_{\text{cool}})\,, \tag{2}$$

$$\frac{\partial p}{\partial z} = v_z\frac{(1-\varepsilon)}{\varepsilon^3}\left(\frac{150(1-\varepsilon)\mu_{\text{gas}}}{d_p^2} + \frac{1.75\rho_{\text{gas}}}{d_p}v_z\right), \tag{3}$$

$$v_z = v_{z,\text{in}}\frac{\rho_{\text{gas,in}}}{\rho_{\text{gas}}}\,, \quad j_{z,i} = -\rho_{\text{gas}}\,\mathcal{D}_{z,i}\frac{\partial w_i}{\partial z}\,, \quad \dot{q}_z = -\Lambda_z\frac{\partial T}{\partial z}\,. \tag{4}$$

The effectiveness factor is calculated under the assumption that the diffusion of nitrogen within the catalyst pores is potentially rate limiting. The temperature of the cooling fluid is expected to be constant along the reactor. The heat transfer coefficient k_{W} incorporates heat transfer resistances of the catalytic bed, at the inner reactor wall, inside the wall between tube and shell, and at the wall in the cooling channel. Furthermore, the model features an optional feed-effluent heat exchanger to evaluate its influence on (polytropic) reactor dynamics. A simple NTU-ε approach as shown by Morud and Skogestad (1998) without consideration of process dynamics is used for modeling. The applied boundary conditions are given in Eq. (5). Initial conditions at $t = 0$ are set according to the dynamic case (e.g., disturbances, start-up, shut-down), respectively.

$$w_i|_{z=0} = w_{i,\text{in}}\,, $$
$$T|_{z=0} = T_{\text{in}}\,. \tag{5}$$

To solve the reactor model, the four PDEs (Eq. (1-2)) are transformed into ODEs by discretizing the axial domain via the finite volume method. This approach introduces numerical diffusion, which can be utilized to accurately represent the systems overall back-mixing intensity by choosing the correct number of finite volumes. To reflect the expected dispersion, about 400 finite volumes per meter of reactor length were found to be sufficient, as mass and energy-based Bodenstein numbers have similar dimensions with values of around 1800. Consequently, the dispersive fluxes $j_{z,i}$ and $\dot{q}_z$ in Eq. (1-2) are considered to be zero, and no additional boundary conditions are required. Most of the applied physical relationships and property calculations are explicitly stated and therefore do not appear as algebraic equations. The only implicit expression is the calculation of the reactor pressure (Eq. (3)). This results in a DAE system consisting of approximately 3200 differential states x and an additional 800 algebraic states z. The DAE system is implemented in MATLAB using the state-space representation (Eq. 6) to allow efficient computation. For integration we applied the IDAS solver from SUNDAILS suite. Depending on how much the state variables change during integration, CPU times between 2 and 20 s were achieved for a reactor simulation of about 2400 s.

$$\frac{d\mathbf{x}}{dt} = \mathbf{A}(\mathbf{x}(t), \mathbf{z}(t), \mathbf{u}(t)) \cdot \mathbf{x}(t) + \mathbf{f}(\mathbf{x}(t), \mathbf{z}(t), \mathbf{u}(t))\,, \quad \text{with } \mathbf{x}(t_0) = \mathbf{x_0}\,, $$
$$0 = \mathbf{C}(\mathbf{x}(t), \mathbf{z}(t), \mathbf{u}(t)) \cdot \mathbf{z}(t) + \mathbf{g}(\mathbf{x}(t), \mathbf{z}(t), \mathbf{u}(t))\,. \tag{6}$$

3. Computational Experiments on Load-Flexible Operation

In this study, a GHSV of 7500 h^{-1} was selected as a reference. The reactor feed is formed by a stoichiometric mixture of H$_2$ and N$_2$ at 150 bar. The polytropic reactor is filled with Fe-based catalyst particles. To evaluate our results with respect to an adiabatic multi-bed reactor, we conducted additional simulations as outlined by Morud and Skogestad (1998), with scaled reactor dimensions to match the reference GHSV.

3.1. Comparison of adiabatic multi-bed and novel polytropic reactor concept

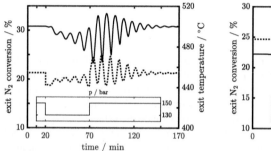 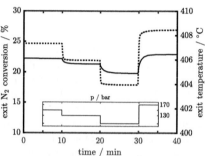

Figure 1: Dynamic simulations of an adiabatic multi-bed reactor (left) and a polytropic fixed-bed reactor (right) subjected to changing feed/reactor pressures (—— exit temperature, ···· exit N$_2$ conversion). In both concepts feed-effluent heat exchangers are considered and a Fe-based catalyst is utilized. Feed temperature is set to 200 °C and GHSV is 7500 h^{-1}.

Fig. 1 illustrates the dynamic responses of an adiabatic multi-bed reactor and a polytropic fixed-bed reactor to sudden pressure changes. The first pressure drop from 150 to 130 bar is identical for both reactor concepts. The feed temperature is set to 200 °C and a feed-effluent heat exchanger is considered in the simulations. In polytropic operation, the reactor is significantly less sensitive to disturbances related to pressure changes. Decreasing the pressure generally reduces the reaction rate and shifts the reaction equilibrium towards lower N$_2$ conversion. Consequently, under adiabatic conditions, the reactor temperature decreases since less heat is generated. As described by Rosbo et al. (2023), the external thermal feedback then may cause the formation of periodic temperature waves within the reactor. These waves can lead to instabilities during transition between operating points. In our simulations, we observed instabilities with amplitudes of up to 50 °C and maximum temperatures of 515 °C following a pressure drop of 20 bar (Fig. 1 (left)). In contrast, the exit temperature under polytropic operation is only marginally influenced even under significant larger pressure changes (Fig. 1 (right)). The heat transfer via the cooling jacket is sufficient to achieve an almost constant exit temperature, which prevents the external thermal feedback from negatively affecting the reactor stability. However, it should be mentioned that the hot-spot temperature may vary and potentially violate constraints concerning catalyst temperature. This aspect will be further addressed in the following section, utilizing local temperature profiles.

For both concepts, the N$_2$ conversion is strongly influenced by changing pressure, as the reaction kinetics are pressure dependent. Fig. 1 also shows that under reference conditions (t < 10 min), the polytropic concept achieves higher conversions of about 25 % than the adiabatic concept (21 %), as lower reactor temperatures towards the outlet are thermodynamically favorable.

An analysis of the provided time scales reveals that the polytropic reactor exhibits markedly faster dynamics, resulting in operating point transitions in less than ten minutes. This can be attributed largely to the external heat supply provided by the cooling jacket. In adiabatic operation, the thermal intertia has a noticeably more dominant influence on the energy balance, as heat is only supplied by convection and reaction.

3.2. Load-flexibility of the polytropic reactor concept

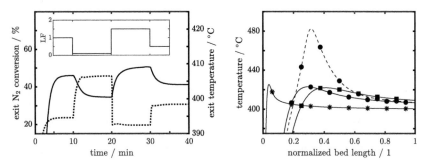

Figure 2: Dynamic simulation results for polytropic operation (left): Exit temperature (—) and exit N_2 conversion (·····) under changing loads (LF). Feed temperature is set to 20 °C, Fe-based catalyst is utilized and feed-effluent heat exchanger is deactivated. Corresponding steady-state axial temperature profiles (right): (*) LF = 0.1, (•) LF = 1 = 7500 h^{-1}, (■) LF = 1.5. For comparison one simulation utilizing a more active Ru-based catalyst (– –) is shown for LF = 1.

In polytropic operation, a sufficient amount of energy is transferred to the fluid mixture through the cooling jacket within the first reactor section. Therefore, the simulations shown in Fig. 2 were conducted with a reduced feed temperature of 20 °C and without feed-effluent heat exchangers. The calculated conversion is not affected by this and remains at approx. 25 % for the reference case (t < 10 min).

In Fig. 2 (left), rapid load changes (LF = load factor) in periods of about ten minutes are applied to the polytropic reactor. Despite significant changes, no oscillations in the temperature profile nor exit N_2 conversion can be observed during transitions. With increasing loads, exit temperatures are shifted to higher values as the position of the hot-spot moves towards the reactor outlet (Fig. 2 (right)). Both hot-spot and exit temperatures vary by at most 10 °C across the investigated load range and remain well below the critical temperature for catalyst deactivation. The exit N_2 conversion varies over a much wider range from 20 to 45 % as the residence time differs largely for these loads. By adjusting pressure and fluid velocity simultaneously to vary the load, it would be possible to narrow that range. In contrast to adiabatic reactors, the operating range of the polytropic reactor is predominantly constrained by economic considerations rather than stability concerns: At low loads, the space-time yield might be insufficient, while at high loads, the costs for reactant recycling (compression) rises significantly due to the low conversions.

The control scheme proposed by Rosbo et al. (2023) for an adiabatic multi-bed reactor allows the load to be incrementally increased by 10 % of the nominal capacity every ten minutes. As shown in the simulations, much more drastic load changes, i.e. 10 to 150 % at t = 20 min, can be realized safely and rapidly by polytropic reactor operation. This makes the polytropic reactor concept better suited for direct coupling with highly dynamic electrolyzer units.

Fig. 2 (right) also features an axial temperature profile for LF = 1 employing a more active Ru-based catalyst. The higher activity of the catalyst leads to increased hot-spot temperatures, which will increase even further at lower loads. However, the obtained temperatures can still be controlled, and if required, the coolant temperatures could be adjusted. In general, the coolant temperature serves as a crucial control and optimization parameter in the polytropic concept.

4. Conclusion

The presented results indicate that load-flexible ammonia synthesis via polytropic fixed-bed reactors is feasible. In particular, dynamic simulations between steady-states show smooth, safe, and rapid transitions, even for drastic load changes, such as ramping the reactor from 10 to 150 % load in less than 10 minutes. Compared to the conventional adiabatic multi-bed reactor increased N_2 conversions are achievable. Additionally, it has been found that the reactants are adequately preheated by polytropic operation, allowing significantly lower feed temperatures, and making feed-effluent heat exchangers obsolete. This study demonstrates that an efficient cooling concept can prevent potential instabilities and highlights further opportunities to optimize the reactor and its operation.

References

J. Bremer, K. H. G. Rätze, K. Sundmacher, 2017. CO2 Methanation: Optimal Start-Up Control of a Fixed-Bed Reactor for Power-to-Gas Applications. AIChE Journal 63 (1), 23-31.

J. Bremer, K. Sundmacher, 2019. Operating Range Extensions via Hot-Spot Control for Catalytic CO2 Methanation Reaction. Reaction Chemistry & Engineering 4, 1019.

D. C. Dyson, J.M. Simon 1968. Kineitc Expression with Diffusion Correction for Ammonia Synthesis on Industrial Catalyst. Industrial & Engineering Chemistry Researrch 7 (4), 605-610.

O. Elishav, B. M. Lis, E. M. Miller, D. J. Arent, A. Valera-Medina, A. G. Dana, G. E. Shter , G. S. Grader 2020. Progress and Prospective of Nitrogen-Based Alternative Fuels. Chemical Reviews 120, 5352-5436.

S. Fahr, M. Schiedeck, J. Schwarzhuber, S.Rehfeldt, A. Peschel, H. Klein, 2023. Design and Thermodynamic Analysis of a Large-Scale Ammonia Reactor for Increased Load Flexibility. Chemical Engineering Journal 471, 144612.

J. C. Morud, S. Skogestad, 1998. Analysis of Instability in an Industrial Ammonia Reactor. AIChE Journal 44 (4), 888-895.

J. W. Rosbo, T. K. S. Ritschel, S. Hørsholt, J. K. Huusom, J. B. Jørgensen, 2023. Flexible Operation, Optimisation and Stabilising Control of a Quench Cooled Ammonia Reactor for Power-to-Ammonia. Computers & Chemical Engineering 176, 108316.

I. Rossetti, N. Pernicone, F. Ferrero, L. Forni, 2006. Kinetic Study of Ammonia Synthesis on a Promoted Ru/C Catalyst. Industrial & Engineering Chemistry Research 45 (12), 4150-4155.

Flavio Manenti, Gintaras V. Reklaitis (Eds.), Proceedings of the 34th European Symposium on Computer Aided Process Engineering / 15th International Symposium on Process Systems Engineering (ESCAPE34/PSE24), June 2-6, 2024, Florence, Italy

Causal-assisted Sequence Segmentation and Its Soft Sensing Application for Multiphase Industrial Processes

Yimeng He,[a] Le Yao,[b] Xiangyin Kong,[a] Xinmin Zhang,[a,*] Zhihuan Song,[a] Manabu Kano[c]

[a] *The State Key Laboratory of Industrial Control Technology, College of Control Science and Engineering, Zhejiang University, Hangzhou 310027, China*
[b] *The School of Mathematics, Hangzhou Normal University, Hangzhou 311121, China*
[c] *Department of Systems Science, Kyoto University, Kyoto 606-8501, Japan*
xinminzhang@zju.edu.cn

Abstract

The multiphase characteristics of industrial processes pose challenges to industrial big data modeling. Conventional soft sensing models often overlook process dynamics and struggle to handle transient behaviours like phase transitions. To solve these problems, this article proposes a causal-assisted segmentation (CAS) model. The CAS model first uncovers the local dynamic characteristics of causal relationships among variables and splits the sequence according to the abrupt changes of causal mechanisms during phase transitions, where the consistency of causal mechanisms in the time dimension is examined by the proposed causal similarity. Then, the causal relationships in each phase are represented as a temporal causal graph (TCG). Furthermore, a soft sensing model called the temporal-causal graph convolutional network (TC-GCN) is established by transferring the time-extended data and the weighted adjacency matrix of the TCG to the graph convolutional layer. The effectiveness of the proposed CAS and TC-GCN models was verified through a penicillin fermentation process. Experimental results demonstrate that the breakpoints discovered by the CAS are consistent with the reaction mechanisms. Furthermore, the TC-GCN significantly improves the prediction accuracy.

Keywords: Multiphase process, causal discovery, soft sensor, time series segmentation, graph convolutional network.

1. Introduction

Many industrial processes exhibit multiphase characteristics, like some batch processes. Here, the multiphase characteristics indicate that due to the dynamic nature of processes or the influence of time-varying factors, relationships between variables or other process characteristics change even within a single operating batch (Yao and Gao, 2009). Some commonly used multivariate statistical control methods, such as principal component analysis (PCA) (Albazzaz and Wang, 2006), treat the data of one batch as a whole, ignoring the variations of process characteristics. This affects the monitoring and prediction capabilities of the models (Zhang et al., 2015).

To achieve a better understanding of multiphase processes, plenty of phase segmentation approaches have been proposed to segment the whole process into different phases. Especially, data-driven segmentation methods are widely applied to overcome the lack of process knowledge. Camacho et al. (2006) used slice PCA to extract variable correlation information, and then clustered the fragments. Wang et al. (2019) proposed a method that segments the sequence based on the predictive ability of the prediction model.

However, the models mentioned above all have certain limitations. For example, some models do not guarantee the continuity in the time dimension. Some do not consider the interpretability of the segmentation results. In other words, the methods that divide phases based on the process correlation information may lead to divisions that are not exactly the same as reaction phases. To solve these problems, the proposed casual-assisted segmentation (CAS) model combines causal discovery with predictive models, and segments the sequence by detecting the changes of causal mechanisms. It ensures continuity in the time dimension while enhancing the interpretability of the segmentation results. Additionally, the extracted temporal causal graph can be used to assist the development of the quality prediction model.

2. Preliminary of temporal causal discovery

This section introduces an original temporal causal discovery model, NTS-NOTEARS (Sun et al, 2023). It is used for the development of the proposed CAS model. NTS-NOTEARS consists of 1D convolutional neural networks (CNNs), which are designed to discover the instantaneous and lagged variable dependencies of multivariable time series. Suppose that the time series includes d variables, there are d CNNs jointly trained, where CNN_j predicts the expectation of the target variable x_j^t at each time stamp $t \geq K+1$, given the preceding and instantaneous input variables:

$$E[x_j^t \mid PA(x_j^t)] = CNN_j(\{x^{t-k} : 1 \leq k \leq K\}, x_{-j}^t) \tag{1}$$

where $PA(x_j^t)$ denotes the parents of x_j^t that are determined by the CNN weights (see next paragraph). Here K is the hyperparameter denoting the maximum time lag, so the input of CNN_j consists of all preceding variables up to the time stamp t-K (denoted as x^{t-k}) and all variables at the same time stamp t other than x_j (denoted as x_{-j}^t).

To estimate the dependency strength of the edge between x_i and x_j, the kernel weights of CNN_j are transformed to the elements of the weighted adjacency matrix W. Let $\phi_{i,j}^k$ represent the m kernel weights corresponding to the input x_i^k in CNN_j, the transform equation is as follows:

$$W_{ij}^k = \| \phi_{i,j}^k \|_{L^2} \text{ for } k=1,...,K+1 \tag{2}$$

3. Causal-assisted segmentation model

The proposed causal-assisted segmentation (CAS) model identifies the breakpoints where the phase changes. The CAS model uses the mentioned NTS-NOTEARS model to detect the time stamps where the preceding causal mechanisms no longer fit the current samples. For each phase, the causal mechanisms are extracted from the initial window of time, and the samples are deemed to be from a new phase if they are not predictable by using these causal mechanisms.

Specifically, there is a time series $X = [x_0, x_1, ..., x_T]$. The procedure of the CAS model for the phase division is as follows:

Step 1. *Initialization.* The samples in a time window of length h are used to discover the causal mechanisms of the p-th phase, which is denoted as $X^p = \{x_t^p\}, t = 1, 2, ..., h$ where $x_t^p = x_{b^{p-1}+t}$. b^{p-1} is the breakpoint between the $(p\text{-}1)$-th phase and the p-th phase, as well as the starting point of the p-th phase. X^p is normalized to have the zero mean and unit standard deviation, denoted as $\bar{X}^p$. The mean vector of X^p is denoted as μ_{train}^p.

Step 2. *Model Training.* The NTS-NOTEARS model is trained using the normalized window data $\bar{X}^p$. Through the training process, the temporal causal graph G^p and training loss L_{train}^p of the p-th phase can be obtained as follows:

$$L_{train}^p = \sqrt{\frac{1}{h-K} \sum_{t=K+1}^{h} \|\hat{x}_t^p - \bar{x}_t^p\|^2} \tag{3}$$

where $\hat{x}_t^p \in R^d$ is the predictive vector of $\bar{x}_t^p$, and each element of $\hat{x}_t^p$ is the predictive value obtained from the CNN mentioned in Eq. (1).

Step 3. *Phase Extension.* The CAS model extends the phase in the time step of w, until it finds the breakpoint where the CNNs of the NTS-NOTEARS are not able to predict the current samples. At the breakpoint, the former causal mechanisms are no longer able to adapt to the current samples and a new phase is supposed to start.

The similarity distance is defined to determine whether the current samples correspond to the former phase or not. The similarity distance includes the causal similarity distance and the stable similarity distance.

The causal similarity distance measures the difference in causal dependencies between the initial window and the current window, which is formulated as the testing loss for the current samples:

$$Dist_c^p = \sqrt{\frac{1}{n \cdot w} \sum_{t=1}^{n \cdot w} \|\hat{x}_t^{p-test} - \bar{x}_t^{p-test}\|^2} \tag{4}$$

where $X^{p-test} = \{x_t^{p-test}\}, x_t^{p-test} = x_{b^{p-1}+h+t}, t = 1, 2, ..., n \cdot w$ denotes the current samples, and n is the number of moving steps. $\bar{x}_t^{p-test}$ means the normalized current samples, and $\hat{x}_t^{p-test}$ denotes the predictive value of $\bar{x}_t^{p-test}$ from the NTS-NOTEARS model.

The stable similarity distance is used to evaluate the distance of stable states between the initial window and the current window, which is represented as the Manhattan distance between the mean vectors of the two data windows:

$$Dist_m^p = \| \mu_{train}^p - \mu_{test}^p \|_1 \tag{5}$$

where μ_{train}^p denotes the mean vector of X^p, and μ_{test}^p denotes the mean vector of X^{p-test}.

The similarity distance comprehensively considers $Dist_c^p$ and $Dist_m^p$. The coefficient ζ is set to balance the two items (generally, scaling the two distances to a similar range is recommended). Therefore, the similarity distance is formulated as follows:

$$Dist^p = Dist_c^p + Dist_m^p / \zeta \tag{6}$$

when $Dist^p$ is up to the threshold, the time stamp is regarded as the breakpoint between the $(p-1)$-th phase and the p-th phase, which is denoted as b^p. The threshold of $Dist^p$ is defined as follows:

$$Threshold^p = \alpha \cdot L^p_{train} + \beta \tag{7}$$

where $\alpha \cdot L^p_{train}$ indicates the limit of $Dist^p_c$, while β indicates the limit of $Dist^p_m$.

Step 4. *Repetition*. Step 1-3 are supposed to be repeated until the number of breakpoints reaches the maximum K_{max} or the length of the remaining sequence is less than the minimum L_{min}.

4. Temporal-causal graph convolutional network

Using the proposed CAS model, the time series is divided into different phases, and the temporal causal graph for each phase is obtained. To implement the quality prediction task, a new soft sensing model called temporal-causal graph convolutional network (TC-GCN) is constructed for each phase. The TC-GCN model integrates the temporal and spatial features by transferring the sequence data and the weighted adjacency matrix of the temporal causal graph to the graph convolutional (GC) layer.

In order to match the dimension of the temporal causal graph, the phase data is extended to $\tilde{X}^p \in R^{m \times ((K+1) \times d)}$, each sample $\tilde{x}^p_t$ consists of $\tilde{x}^p_{t-K}, \tilde{x}^p_{t-K+1}, ..., \tilde{x}^p_t$, and n is the number of samples in this phase.

The GC layer can be written as:

$$h^{GC} = D^{-0.5} A_p^{-0.5} D^{-0.5} \tilde{X}^p W^{GC}_{enc} \tag{8}$$

where A_p is the weighted adjacency matrix of the temporal causal graph G^p, W^{GC}_{enc} is the encoder parameter matrix which is obtained through the training. $D^{-0.5}$ is the matrix square root of D, and D is the degree matrix of the graph, given as follows:

$$D_{[i,i]} = \sum_j{}' A_{p[i,j]} \tag{9}$$

The input of the following multiple perceptron (MLP) is given as:

$$h_0 = h^{GC} + \tilde{X}_p W^{GC}_{res} \tag{10}$$

where W^{GC}_{res} is the trainable weight matrix.

5. Case study

In this section, the penicillin fed-batch fermentation process was used to validate the efficiency of the proposed CAS and TC-GCN models. The experiment was implemented on PenSim v2.0 platform. The total simulation time is 400 hours. The sample rate is 401 /h. The collected training and testing data both consist of 16000 samples. The two data sets are collected in two simulations in the normal state, with different setting values of the initial substrate concentrate (15.0 g/L and 14.5 g/L respectively). As the process knowledge, $0 \sim 45$ h is the stage of biomass accumulation. $45 \sim 400$ h belongs to the continuous penicillin production stage. The variable description of this process is listed in the Table 1. The dissolved oxygen concentration is taken as the quality variable. In the segmentation process, the initial window length h is set to 1000.

Table 1. The variable description of the fermentation process

Var.	Description	Var.	Description	Var.	Description
X1	Aeration rate	X6	Dissolved oxygen concentration	X11	PH
X2	Agitator power	X7	Biomass concentration	X12	Reactor temperature
X3	Substrate feed rate	X8	Penicillin concentration	X13	Generated heat
X4	Substrate feed temperature	X9	Culture medium volume	X14	Base flow rate
X5	Substrate concentrate	X10	CO_2 concentration	X15	Cold water flow rate

The maximum time lag K is set to 3. The number of the convolutional kernels m is set to 160. The coefficient ζ is 10. The two scale hyperparameters α and β are respectively 2 and 1.2. The CAS model segments the continuous 16000 testing samples into four phases: the obtained breakpoints are 1900, 2900, and 6000; the corresponding time stamps are respectively 47.5 h, 72.5 h, and 150 h. Figure 1 shows the segmentation results of three models: Gaussian mixture model (GMM) (Ariba et al., 2023), Greedy Gaussian segmentation (GGS) (Hallac et al., 2019), and the CAS model. As shown in Figure 1, compared with the true first phase-transition time stamp 40 h, the first breakpoints found by the three methods are 47.5 h (CAS), 53.6 h (GMM), and 53.6 h (GGS) respectively. It also can be seen that CAS clearly identifies the transition phase, which is located between the breakpoints 1900 and 2900, as shown by the solid line in Figure 1. However, the breakpoints found by GMM and GGS are more susceptible to the mean value.

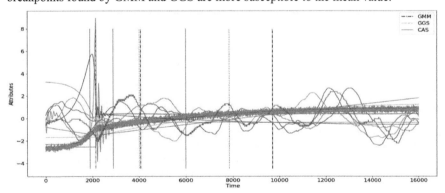

Figure 1. The segmentation results

After the segmentation, the TC-GCN models are established respectively using all the training data and the data in each divided phase. The numbers of hidden neurons in the two GC layers are 512 and 256 respectively. The numbers of hidden neurons for the multiple perceptron are 512 and 128 respectively. The batch size is 128. The learning rate is 0.001. The number of epochs is set to 2000. Table 2 displays the root mean square errors (RMSEs) of different models using various data sets. The TC-GCN models use adjacency matrices without weights, while the TC-GCN(W) models use the weighted adjacency matrices.

According to the results in Table 2, it can be seen that the soft sensing models trained using different phase data obtained lower RMSEs compared to training using all data. It indicates that the phase segmentation by CAS and the sample matching based on the similarity distance can improve the predictive accuracy of the soft sensing model. The results also display that the addition of adjacency matrices to the soft sensor model can enhance the predictive accuracy of testing samples at each phase, and the improvement is more significant when using weighted adjacency matrices.

Table 2. The RMSEs of different models using various data sets

	Using all the sequence data				Using the data in each divided phase		
\	MLP	TC-GCN	TC-GCN(W)	\	MLP	TC-GCN	TC-GCN(W)
Phase 1	0.174	0.148	0.168	Phase 1	0.148	0.100	**0.070**
Phase 2	0.219	0.266	0.306	Phase 2	0.223	0.202	**0.196**
Phase 3	0.151	0.185	0.164	Phase 3	0.118	0.089	**0.082**
Phase 4	0.143	0.127	0.105	Phase 4	0.034	0.027	**0.027**
Average	0.154	0.154	0.146	Average	0.096	0.076	**0.069**

6. Conclusion

In this work, a new phase segmentation model called causal-assisted segmentation (CAS) is first proposed, and then a temporal-causal graph convolutional network (TC-GCN) is designed for soft sensing modeling. The CAS model first discovers the local dynamic characteristics of causal relationships among variables and detects the breakpoints by identifying the abrupt changes of the causal mechanisms during phase transitions. The similarity distance is designed to measure the difference in the causal mechanisms of two different phases. For each phase, a TC-GCN model is established using the weighted adjacency matrix of the temporal causal graph. The verification experiments were conducted on the penicillin fermentation industrial process. The breakpoints found by the CAS are closer to the time stamps of phase transition. The designed TC-GCN model shows a significant improvement in prediction accuracy.

References

Y. Yao, F. Gao, 2009, A survey on multistage/multiphase statistical modeling methods for batch processes, Annual Reviews in Control, 33, 2, 172-183.

H. Albazzaz, X. Wang, 2006, Multivariate statistical batch process monitoring using dynamic independent component analysis, Computer aided chemical engineering, 21, 1341-1346.

X. Zhang, Y. Li, M. Kano, 2015, Quality prediction in complex batch processes with just-in-time learning model based on non-Gaussian dissimilarity measure, Industrial & Engineering Chemistry Research, 54, 31, 7694-7705.

J. Camacho, J. Picó, 2006, Multi-phase principal component analysis for batch processes modelling, Chemometrics and Intelligent Laboratory Systems, 81, 2, 127-136.

K. Wang, L. Rippon L, J. Chen, Z. Song, R.B. Gopaluni, 2019, Data-driven dynamic modeling and online monitoring for multiphase and multimode batch processes with uneven batch durations, Industrial & Engineering Chemistry Research, 58, 30, 13628-13641.

X. Sun, O. Schulte, G. Liu, P. Paupart, 2023, NTS-NOTEARS: Learning Nonparametric DBNs With Prior Knowledge, PMLR, 1942-1964.

H. Ariba, P. Vanabelle, S. Benaly, H. Thomas, C.R. André, G. Leonard, 2021, Application of data science to study fluorine losses in the phosphate industry, Computer Aided Chemical Engineering, 50, 1059-1065.

D. Hallac, P. Nystrup, S. Boyd, 2019, Greedy Gaussian segmentation of multivariate time series, Advances in Data Analysis and Classification, 13, 3, 727-751.

Flavio Manenti, Gintaras V. Reklaitis (Eds.), Proceedings of the 34th European Symposium on Computer Aided Process Engineering / 15th International Symposium on Process Systems Engineering (ESCAPE34/PSE24), June 2-6, 2024, Florence, Italy

CSVE: Enhancing Uncertainty Quantification in Industrial KPI Prediction

Yiran Ma,[a] Zhichao Chen,[a] Xinmin Zhang,[a,*] Zhihuan Song,[a] Manabu Kano,[b]

[a]*The State Key Laboratory of Industrial Control Technology, College of Control Science and Engineering, Zhejiang University, Hangzhou, 310027, China*
[b]*Department of Systems Science, Kyoto University, Kyoto 606-8501, Japan*
xinminzhang@zju.edu.cn

Abstract

Data-driven soft sensing technologies have been widely accepted to predict key performance indicators (KPI) automatically and accurately in industrial processes. Despite their utility, quantifying uncertainty—particularly epistemic uncertainty—is frequently neglected. This neglect is noteworthy, as uncertainty offers insights into prediction reliability, which is a crucial concern for industrial operators and engineers. Indeed, uncertainty quality serves as a critical criterion for determining whether it can be safely applied to real-world industrial processes. To address this gap, this work introduces calibrated Stein variational ensemble (CSVE), a method that integrates a formal Bayesian framework with the concept of ensemble. The proposed CSVE method yields calibrated probability density functions as predictions, offering both point predictions and natural uncertainty quantification. Furthermore, for the first time in the context of soft sensors, well-designed metrics are employed to assess uncertainty quality. The effectiveness of the proposed approach is validated through its application to a real-world industrial KPI prediction task. The results reveal that common methods such as bootstrap aggregation and parameter posterior inference methods can display miscalibrated uncertainty, posing reliability risks in industrial applications. In contrast, the proposed approach demonstrably mitigates these issues and enhances the quantification of uncertainty.

Keywords: Data-driven modeling, Industrial KPI prediction, Soft sensing, Uncertainty Calibration, Stein Variational Ensemble

1. Introduction

Predicting industrial key performance indicators (KPIs) accurately is important for contemporary industrial systems, especially in the realms that require relevant information for downstream tasks. Data-driven soft sensors, represented by discriminative models, have emerged as an innovative solution for predicting KPIs that are traditionally difficult to measure (Kano and Fujiwara, 2013; Zhang et al., 2023). Even though various discriminative models have achieved impressive accuracy in this field, they often neglect quantifying the uncertainty of predictions. The accurate quantification of uncertainty, especially epistemic uncertainty, is crucial in KPI prediction because uncertainty provides insights into the reliability of predictions, enabling more informed decision-making. Moreover, the discriminative models' limited robustness poses risks to safety-critical applications. This emphasizes the necessity of designing an excellent uncertainty quantification (UQ) method that can integrate with the numerous discriminative models developed for soft sensing.

Considering the lack of stochasticity in discriminative model parameters, bootstrap aggregation (Fortuna et al., 2009) and Monte Carlo (MC) dropout (Cao et al., 2023; Yang et al., 2022) were used in existing studies as straightforward methods to improve robustness or obtain predictive uncertainty. Bayesian Neural Networks (BNNs) based on variational inference (VI) can also be seen in some studies (Lee et al., 2021). However, the existing methods often have inadequate regularization or overly strong assumptions, leading to inadequate exploration in the parameter space. Relative research (Ashukha et al., 2021) has shown that the exploration of different modes in the posterior is crucial for good performance. Therefore, these traditional methods can display miscalibrated uncertainty, posing severe risks to safety-critical applications.

To address these problems, this study introduces the calibrated Stein variational ensemble (CSVE) as a new UQ method for soft sensors. The proposed method integrates a formal Bayesian framework with the concept of ensemble. Meanwhile, the importance of implementing uncertainty calibration for all UQ methods is emphasized. As a result, the proposed methodology yields calibrated probability density functions as predictions, offering better point predictions and better uncertainty quantification. The proposed approach is validated through comparative evaluations on a real-world KPI prediction task in an industrial process, demonstrating its effectiveness in improving epistemic uncertainty quantification.

2. Problem Formulation

Data-driven soft sensors are typically constructed and tested on the available historical datasets. However, since the real world is dynamic and variable, their performance may deteriorate gradually without being noticed. This means that relying solely on predictions from these soft sensor models may introduce risks into production processes. Therefore, generating additional information about the reliability of the predictions should be considered. To this end, quantifying uncertainty is a straightforward solution. Consequently, precise uncertainty quantification is as important as predictive accuracy for data-driven models.

Evaluating Uncertainty Quality. In this work, besides the negative log-likelihood (NLL) commonly used in Bayesian inference, other metrics that evaluate the uncertainty quality in the regression tasks are employed to assess the performance of the methods. According to (Naeini et al., 2015; Kuleshov et al., 2018; Levi et al., 2022), Expected Calibration Error (ECE) is used to evaluate the quality of credible intervals. Moreover, Expected Normalized Calibration Error (ENCE) (Levi et al., 2022), which is based on the idea that the predicted standard deviation should match the absolute error, is also used as an indicator of uncertainty quality.

3. Methodology

As mentioned before, the poor performance of existing UQ methods is caused by inadequate exploration of the parameter space. Stein Variational Gradient Descent (SVGD) (Liu and Wang, 2016), a representative of particle-based variational inference methods (ParVIs), was proposed to address this problem. Mathematically, SVGD simulates the gradient flow that minimizes the KL divergence in the Wasserstein space (Chen et al., 2018). Owing to the kernel used in SVGD, all the particles can affect each other. Therefore, the particles, following the dynamical system ruled by the gradient flow, can make a more comprehensive exploration of the parameter space. Considering this theoretical progress, this study proposes a new UQ method that integrates SVGD with uncertainty calibration to enhance the accuracy and uncertainty quality of industrial KPI predictions. The method proposed in this work is termed as calibrated Stein variational ensemble (CSVE), which comprises two parts: Stein variational ensemble (SVE) and interval-based uncertainty calibration. The details are as follows.

3.1. Stein Variational Ensemble

3.1.1. Base Model

The ensemble model is composed of multiple base models of the same structure. The principle of constructing the base models is the decomposition of aleatoric (data) uncertainty and epistemic (model) uncertainty. As the posterior approximation performed by SVGD is an estimate of model uncertainty, the data uncertainty should be captured by each base model separately. To guarantee the compatibility of the proposed method, an additional learnable parameter γ_t is added to each base model $\mathcal{M}_t$ to capture noise $\sigma_t^2 = e^{-\gamma_t}$ inherent in data, and the discriminative model adopted can remain unmodified. Therefore, each base model provides a probability density function (PDF) $p(y|\boldsymbol{x}_i, \theta_t)$ as its prediction. By aggregating the PDFs provided by the base models, a more comprehensive prediction of the KPI y can be obtained.

3.1.2. Update Rule

SVE is composed of T base models. The set of parameter vectors $\Theta = \{\theta_1, \theta_2, \dots, \theta_T\}$ of base models is regarded as the particles in the SVGD framework. In each iteration, the gradient $\nabla_\theta \log p(\theta)$ of each base model is first computed after a parallel forward pass. Subsequently, the parameter vectors can be updated simultaneously according to the SVGD update rule:

$$\theta^{\ell+1} \leftarrow \theta^\ell + \epsilon_\ell \hat{\phi}^*(\theta^\ell), \tag{1.}$$

where $\hat{\phi}^*(\cdot) = \mathbb{E}_{\theta \sim q}[\nabla_\theta \log p(\theta) k(\theta, \theta') + \nabla_\theta k(\theta, \theta')]$. The asymptotic convergence characteristic of SVGD guarantees that, over time, a set of particles will be obtained that effectively serve as representative samples of the parameter posterior.

3.2. Intervals-based Uncertainty Calibration

Trained Bayesian models require additional uncertainty calibration to fully leverage their capabilities in uncertainty quantification. After a Bayesian model has been trained using the training data, calibration should be carried out in accordance with its performance on an independent calibration set. Formally, a Bayesian regression model is well-calibrated (Kuleshov et al., 2018) if

$$\lim_{N \to \infty} \frac{1}{N} \sum_{i=1}^{N} \mathbb{I}\{y_i \le F_i^{-1}(p)\} = p, \tag{2.}$$

where $F_i^{-1}: (0,1) \to R$ denotes the inverse function of the cumulated density function (CDF), and $\mathbb{I}$ denotes the indicator function.

Given a calibration set $\mathcal{D}_{cali} = \{(\boldsymbol{x}_1, y_1), (\boldsymbol{x}_2, y_2), \dots, (\boldsymbol{x}_{N_{cali}}, y_{N_{cali}})\}$ independent of the training set, let $F_{x_i^{cali}}$ denote the predictive CDFs produced by an uncalibrated model. Then, pairs of PCDs are obtained via

$$\text{PCD}_j = F_{x_j^{cali}}^{-1}\left(y_j^{cali}\right),$$

$$\text{ECD}_j = \frac{1}{N_{cali}} \sum_{k} I\{\text{PCD}_k \le \text{PCD}_j\}. \tag{3.}$$

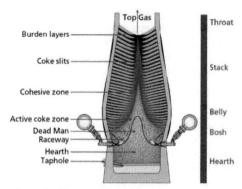

Figure 1 The schematic diagram of the blast furnace (Geerdes et al., 2020)

Subsequently, the calibration model R is fitted on the dataset $S_{cali} = \{(PCD_j, ECD_j) | j = 1, 2, \dots, N_{cali}\}$ such that $\tilde{F}_i = R \circ F_i$ is calibrated. Finally, the calibrated CDF $\tilde{F}_i$ is used to substitute the uncalibrated CDF F_i for making uncertainty-aware predictions.

4. Case Study: Results and Discussion

This section uses the Blast Furnace (BF) ironmaking process as a case study to evaluate the efficacy of the proposed methodology. The BF operates as a sophisticated moving-bed reactor, hosting a range of concurrent activities including complex chemical reactions, mass and heat transfer, alongside the flow of multiphase fluids. This dynamic environment is further detailed in Figure 1, which shows the internal structure of the BF divided into five distinct zones: Throat, Stack (or Shaft), Belly, Bosh, and Hearth. In this setting, raw materials gradually descend towards the lower sections of the furnace, counterbalanced by the upward movement of hot air. The end products of the blast furnace ironmaking process are hot metal and liquid slag, which mainly accumulate in the BF hearth. The extreme conditions prevalent within the BF preclude direct measurements of molten iron quality (Luo et al., 2023). Instead, the silicon content in the hot metal is employed as an indirect indicator of the molten iron quality. Under stable operational conditions, a high silicon content is indicative of excessive energy consumption due to increased temperatures, whereas a low silicon content suggests a disruption in standard reaction processes. Therefore, the precise and real-time estimation of the silicon content is crucial for maintaining the quality of the hot metal.

To construct the predictive model, time series data of 10000 samples were collected from the blast furnace ironmaking plant of Baosteel Group in China. The collected data was divided into a training set (64% of the entire dataset), a calibration set (16% of the entire dataset), and a test set (the remaining 20% of the entire dataset). Considering the time-series characteristic of the process data, it is not appropriate to shuffle the dataset. Therefore, the calibration set is selected as 3 small segments interspersed with the training

Figure 2 Calibration curves

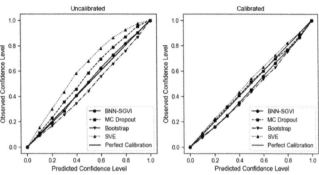

set. To predict the silicon content, 105 process variables, such as blast humidity, blast pressure, and gas flow rate, were selected as the secondary variables.

To validate the proposed CSVE, an MLP with the architecture of 105-128-128-128-1 is taken as an example. Bootstrap aggregation, MC dropout, and BNN-SGVI are adopted as baselines, with the same number of parameter samples $T = 20$.

4.1. Role of Calibration

The intervals-based uncertainty calibration is performed on all the baselines and CSVE. According to the calibration curves (Kuleshov et al., 2018) in Figure 2, it can be concluded that the uncertainty calibration procedure is effective for generating better credible intervals. As interval-based calibration is a simple post-processing method, it is believed that it should become a standard procedure for various UQ methods.

4.2. Metrics Evaluation

In this part, each method is applied to the uncertainty calibration procedure for fairness. The metrics evaluation results are reported in Table 1. CSVE is not only significantly superior in accuracy metrics (MSE, MAE, R2) compared to other methods but also exceeds in approximation quality (NLL), displaying strong point prediction and uncertainty quantification capabilities. As for calibration performance (ECE, ENCE), the proposed method gives competitive results. It is noteworthy that although MC dropout seems to be proficient in generating precise credible intervals of predictions, it still should not be the first choice for UQ considering its worst accuracy caused by dropout implementation and awful assumption of the posterior form.

Table 1 Metrics evaluation. * or ** marks the methods that our method significantly outperforms at a p-value < 0.05 or p-value < 0.01 via a paired samples t-test, respectively. Bolded results indicate the best in each metric. Underlined results indicate the second-best in each metric. The *standard deviation* is also reported, denoted by the figures to the right of ±.

Methods	Accuracy Metrics			Uncertainty Quality Metrics		
	MSE	MAE	R2	NLL	ECE	ENCE
BNN-SGVI (Cali.)	0.0710±0.013*	0.2074±0.023*	0.8971±0.019*	0.0492±0.063*	0.0430±0.023*	0.2070±0.114*
MC Dropout (Cali.)	0.0788±0.003**	0.2139±0.005**	0.8858±0.005**	0.1736±0.032**	**0.0107±0.004**	0.1038±0.020
Bootstrap (Cali.)	0.0695±0.005**	0.2036±0.008**	0.8994±0.007**	0.0347±0.030**	0.0383±0.012**	0.2429±0.048**
CSVE (ours)	**0.0587±0.009**	**0.1852±0.016**	**0.9150±0.013**	**-0.0140±0.023**	0.0243±0.009	**0.0962±0.030**

5. Conclusions

In this work, the necessity of improving the uncertainty quantification of soft sensing models in industrial KPI prediction is first emphasized. Then, a new uncertainty quantification method called CSVE is proposed. CSVE is designed based on SVGD and intervals-based uncertainty calibration. Like most deep ensemble methods, the proposed modeling framework can enhance existing differentiable soft sensor models without any modifications to the main model structure. In the case study on the blast furnace ironmaking process, it can be observed that both the uncertainty quality and accuracy metrics of the proposed method are improved due to the precise posterior approximation. Additionally, the experimental results also support the proposal of applying uncertainty calibration as a standard procedure for the UQ methods. Future work will validate the proposed methodology on different models, such as recurrent neural networks and Transformers.

References

Ashukha, A., Lyzhov, A., Molchanov, D., Vetrov, D., 2021, Pitfalls of In-Domain Uncertainty Estimation and Ensembling in Deep Learning.

Cao, L., Zhang, H., Meng, Z., Wang, X., 2023, A parallel GRU with dual-stage attention mechanism model integrating uncertainty quantification for probabilistic RUL prediction of wind turbine bearings. Reliability Engineering & System Safety, 235, 109197.

Chen, C., Zhang, R., Wang, W., Li, B., Chen, L., 2018, A Unified Particle-Optimization Framework for Scalable Bayesian Sampling.

Fortuna, L., Graziani, S., Xibilia, M.G., 2009, Comparison of Soft-Sensor Design Methods for Industrial Plants Using Small Data Sets. IEEE Transactions on Instrumentation and Measurement, 58, 2444–2451.

Geerdes, M., Chaigneau, R., Lingiardi, O., 2020, Modern Blast Furnace Ironmaking: An Introduction (Fourth Edition, 2020). IOS Press.

Kano, M., Fujiwara, K., 2013, Virtual Sensing Technology in Process Industries: Trends and Challenges Revealed by Recent Industrial Applications. Journal of Chemical Engineering of Japan, 46, 1–17.

Kuleshov, V., Fenner, N., Ermon, S., 2018, Accurate Uncertainties for Deep Learning Using Calibrated Regression, in: Proceedings of the 35th International Conference on Machine Learning. Presented at the International Conference on Machine Learning, PMLR, pp. 2796–2804.

Lee, M., Bae, J., Kim, S.B., 2021, Uncertainty-aware soft sensor using Bayesian recurrent neural networks. Advanced Engineering Informatics, 50, 101434.

Levi, D., Gispan, L., Giladi, N., Fetaya, E., 2022, Evaluating and Calibrating Uncertainty Prediction in Regression Tasks. Sensors 22, 5540.

Liu, Q., Wang, D., 2016. Stein Variational Gradient Descent: A General Purpose Bayesian Inference Algorithm, in: Advances in Neural Information Processing Systems. Curran Associates, Inc.

Luo, Y., Zhang, X., Kano, M., Deng, L., Yang, C., Song, Z., 2023, Data-driven soft sensors in blast furnace ironmaking: a survey. Frontiers of Information Technology & Electronic Engineering, 24, 327–354.

Naeini, M.P., Cooper, G., Hauskrecht, M., 2015, Obtaining Well Calibrated Probabilities Using Bayesian Binning. Proceedings of the AAAI Conference on Artificial Intelligence 29.

Yang, J., Peng, Y., Xie, J., Wang, P., 2022, Remaining Useful Life Prediction Method for Bearings Based on LSTM with Uncertainty Quantification. Sensors 22, 4549.

Zhang, X., He, B., Zhu, H., Song, Z., 2023, Information Complementary Fusion Stacked Autoencoders for Soft Sensor Applications in Multimode Industrial Processes. IEEE Transactions on Industrial Informatics, 1–11.

Flavio Manenti, Gintaras V. Reklaitis (Eds.), Proceedings of the 34th European Symposium on Computer Aided Process Engineering / 15th International Symposium on Process Systems Engineering (ESCAPE34/PSE24), June 2-6, 2024, Florence, Italy

Bilevel optimization of mixed-integer nonlinear integrated planning and scheduling problems using the DOMINO framework

Hasan Nikkhah,[a,b] Vassilis M. Charitopoulos,[c] Styliani Avraamidou,[d] Burcu Beykal[a,b]

[a]*Department of Chemical & Biomolecular Engineering, University of Connecticut, Storrs, CT, 06260, USA*
[b]*Center for Clean Energy Engineering, University of Connecticut, Storrs, CT, 06269, USA*
[c]*Department of Chemical Engineering, Sargent Centre for Process Systems Engineering, University College London, Torrington Place, London WC1E 7JE, UK*
[d]*Department of Chemical & Biological Engineering, University of Wisconsin-Madison, Madison WI, 53706, USA*
beykal@uconn.edu

Abstract

We study the solution of integrated planning and scheduling problems that are formulated as bilevel programming problems with mixed-integer nonlinear lower levels using data-driven optimization algorithms. Due to their inherent interdependence, multi-scale nature, and volatile market conditions, decision-making in such multi-level supply chain networks poses challenging task. Traditionally, these problems are addressed sequentially but, this approach often results in production schedules that are not feasible. Motivated by this, we formulate enterprise-wide decision-making problems with linear production planning and mixed-integer nonlinear scheduling level as a bilevel optimization problem. We solve the resulting integrated problem using the DOMINO framework which is a data-driven optimization strategy to handle general constrained bilevel optimization problems. We demonstrate our approach on case studies with varying complexities from crude oil scheduling using a continuous-time formulation to scheduling of continuous manufacturing processes using a traveling salesman problem formulation. The results show that DOMINO can address bilevel programming problems with high-dimensional mixed-integer nonlinear lower levels and can be applied to complex integrated enterprise-wide optimization problems, regardless of the lower-level formulation type.

Keywords: Data-driven optimization, mixed-integer nonlinear programming, bilevel programming, enterprise-wide optimization, production planning, scheduling.

1. Introduction

Production planning and scheduling are distinct decision-making levels within enterprise-wide optimization that operate over different timescales; nevertheless, they are intricately interconnected (Harjunkoski et al., 2014). This is because the targets set by the planning problem directly influence the scheduling decisions on the production level. While the planning functionality evaluates the market demand and establishes production goals accordingly, production scheduling determines the sequencing and allocation of tasks to specific production units based on the planning targets. In process industries, a prevalent approach to solving such integrated planning and scheduling problems involves a sequential tactic. This strategy entails solving the higher-level and longer-term planning problems first to establish the production targets for meeting the demands, followed by solving the shorter timescale scheduling problem to fulfill these targets. However, a significant drawback of this approach is that the decisions are taken without the accounting for the interdependence of the two problems, leading to over-optimistic decisions that may be realized in practice (Grossmann, 2005). This means that the planning decisions may result in schedules that cannot be feasibly executed within the capacity of the production units (Li and Ierapetritou, 2010). This challenge can be addressed by considering planning and scheduling problems simultaneously (Maravelias and Sung, 2009; Charitopoulos et al., 2018).

This intrinsic connection between planning and scheduling levels can be mathematically expressed using bilevel programming (Eq.1). Nevertheless, NP-hardness, nonconvexity, and discontinuity in bilevel programs lead to significant algorithmic challenges that are yet to be addressed (Beykal et al., 2021). One prevalent approach involves transforming bilevel formulations into a single-level formulation and subsequently treating it as a conventional optimization problem. As the optimality of the lower-level problem is a constraint on the upper problem, Karush-Kuhn-Tucker (KKT) optimality conditions can be used for the reformulation of general bilevel programs. Nonetheless, scheduling formulations at the lower-level problem that include mixed-integer variables prevent the use of KKT-based reformulation.

$$
\begin{aligned}
&\text{Min} \quad Planning\ Cost \\
&s.t. \quad Inventory\ \&\ Balance\ Equations \\
&\qquad \min \quad Scheduling/Production\ Cost \\
&\qquad s.t. \quad Scheduling\ Constraints
\end{aligned}
\tag{1}
$$

We have previously shown that such challenges can be resolved using data-driven optimization with the DOMINO framework and achieve near-optimal solutions for general constrained bilevel optimization problems with continuous linear, continuous nonlinear, mixed-integer linear, and integer nonlinear lower levels (Beykal et al., 2020; Beykal et al., 2021; Beykal et al., 2022). Expanding on our previous results, in this work, we study integrated planning and scheduling problems with mixed-integer nonlinear (MINLP) lower levels and investigate the effects of two different scheduling formulations, continuous-time and traveling salesman problem (TSP) on the overall bilevel optimization performance.

2. Methods

2.1. Planning and Scheduling Formulations

2.1.1. Scheduling of Crude Oil Refinery Operations (Continuous-time Formulation)

We use the crude oil unloading system formulation presented in Jia et al. (2003) which comprises several components, including marine vessels utilized for transporting crude oil, storage tanks, charging tanks to blend the crude oil, and crude oil distillation units (CDUs) where hydrocarbons are separated into downstream

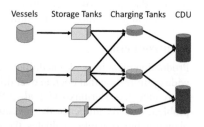

Figure 1. Superstructure of the oil flow network in the crude oil case study.

feedstocks (Fig. 1). When the marine vessels arrive at the refinery docks, the crude oil is unloaded from the vessels and transferred to the storage tanks. The crude oil in the storage tanks is then transferred to the charging tanks to produce the oil blend that is required by the crude oil distillation units. The objective of this scheduling problem is to minimize the total operating cost subject to capacity, flowrate, allocation, sequence, duration, and time horizon constraints, as well as the nonlinear component balance, and demand for oil blends from charging tanks which define the bilevel feasibility. This makes the lower-level scheduling an MINLP with 56 binary variables, 367 continuous variables, and 1112 constraints considering 4 event points. Detailed model equations and parameters can be provided upon request.

2.2.2. Scheduling of a Multiproduct CSTR Process (TSP-based Formulation)

In this example, we study the continuous methyl methacrylate polymerization process from Charitopoulos et al. (2017), where six different grades of polymers are produced via free-radical polymerization in an isothermal CSTR. The reactor is fed with the monomer, toluene (solvent), and azo-bis-isobutyronitrile (initiator) to carry out the polymerization reaction as shown in Fig. 2. The goal of the scheduling problem is to determine the optimal sequence of grade transitions among these six polymers that minimize the production cost (i.e., total

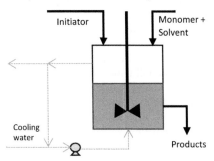

Figure 2. Multiproduct CSTR for scheduling different polymer grade production.

operational, raw material consumption cost during transition periods, and raw material cost) subject to allocation, sequencing, symmetry breaking, timing, and production constraints to satisfy the demand from the planning level (i.e., bilevel feasibility). Different than Eq. (1), in the bilevel integrated planning and scheduling formulation of this problem, the planning (leader) objective is taken as the maximization of the planning profit. The lower-level problem is an MINLP with 174 binary variables, 313 continuous variables, and 390 constraints. Detailed model equations and parameters can be found in Charitopoulos et al. (2017; 2018) .

2.2.3. The Planning Problem

The planning level of the crude oil operations case study minimizes the total inventory and scheduling operating cost over the entire time horizon T as shown by eq. (2).

$$Total\ Cost\ of\ Planning = \sum_{t}^{T} Inventory\ Cost^t + Operating\ Cost^t \qquad (2)$$

We assume that there is no backlog cost, but if negative inventories are encountered at any t period, the respective product inventory across the entire planning period is penalized by adding the minimum missing inventory to make it positive. The planning level is also subject to production target constraints retrieved from the scheduling level to ensure the products are being produced, and demand constraints where the production target P and the starting day inventory I^{t-1} should meet the product (s) demand D (Eq. 3).

$$D_s^t - P_s^t - I_s^{t-1} \leq 0 \quad \forall s,t \qquad (3)$$

Finally, the relative optimality gap of the scheduling level is imposed as a constraint on the planning level, where we used a tight relative optimality gap of 1E-6. For the multiproduct CSTR case study, we use the same inventory penalization approach, demand constraint, and lower-level optimality constraints. However, the objective function considers total planning profit instead of the planning cost.

2.2. Solution Strategy – The DOMINO Framework

We use the DOMINO framework (Beykal et al., 2020) to solve the resulting bilevel LP-MINLP integrated planning and scheduling model. This algorithm uses a data-driven optimization subroutine to sample the upper-level decision variables and solve the lower-level problems to global optimality at these sampling points using a deterministic global optimization solver. In this work, we use the DOMINO framework with the NOMAD algorithm that uses a progressive barrier constraint handling approach. To start the algorithm, a random initial point for the production targets for products is provided within the bounds of the decision variables. Then, scheduling problems are solved to global optimality for this point to retrieve the objective function value of the planning and the violations for the inventory, demand, production target, and optimality gap constraints. This information is then used by NOMAD to proceed with its algorithmic iterations of search and poll until it converges to a solution. We execute this algorithm 10 times for each case study, starting with a different random initial point. In the crude oil case study, we have three products that we assume the randomly generated demand for 7 days is known with an initial starting inventory of 10 units. We also assume the planning level is cyclical in nature, with the production target for the last day needing to fulfill the demand for that day and generate the inventory for the first day of the subsequent planning cycle. The planning problem has 18 decision variables, which DOMINO-NOMAD will determine and are subject to 43 grey-box constraints (i.e., scheduling constraints that involve planning variables, demand, and optimality gap constraints). For the multiproduct CSTR case study, we have 6 products with known demand for two weeks with an initial inventory of 10 units for each product. Therefore, this problem's data-driven complexity is 12 decision variables and 37 grey-box constraints. Both scheduling case studies are modeled in GAMS and solved with BARON (Sahinidis, 1996) at the lower level.

3. Results

The results with the best objective function value over the 10 random runs are presented in Figures 3 and 4 for the crude oil and the multiproduct CSTR studies, respectively. Figure 3 shows that, across the 7-day planning period, the demand for oil blends is met with the optimized production targets, and the production is satisfied with globally optimal schedules. We observe that the solution has a much higher production target on the first day for the oil blend 1, which is reserved as inventory to meet the higher demand on Day 2 of crude oil operations. For oil blend 2, we see that the demand is met by daily production, and the inventory levels are minimal throughout the planning horizon. This is because the storage and charging tank capacity in the crude oil blending system is high enough to process the required blends for the CDUs. Only for the last planning period do we see that the system produces more oil blends than demand. This is to ensure the planning is carried out in a cyclic fashion where the first-day inventory of the following planning week is produced on the last day of the previous planning period. Although not shown here, the oil blend 3 profiles show similar trends where demand is met, and scheduling levels are guaranteed globally optimal. These results indicate that DOMINO can solve highly complex enterprise-wide optimization problems with a bilevel feasibility guarantee subject to more than 1000 scheduling constraints.

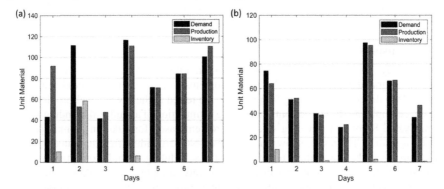

Figure 3. Demand, production, and inventory profiles for: (a) Oil blend 1 (b) Oil blend 2. Computational time to reach solution is 144 h (maximum wall time).

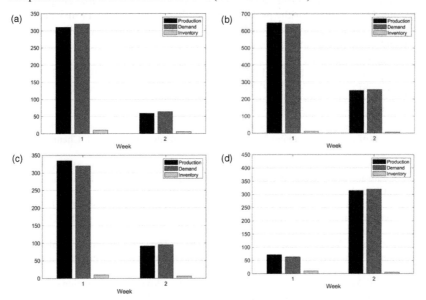

Figure 4. Demand, production, and inventory profiles for: (a) Polymer grade 1; (b) Polymer grade 2; Polymer grade 3; and Polymer grade 4. Computational time to reach solution is 44.13 h.

Likewise in Figure 4, we observe that the demands for different polymer grades are satisfied for the 2-week planning horizon with guaranteed optimal production schedules. Different than the crude oil operations results, we observe that some inventory is carried over within the planning period, yet still at minimal amounts. This is expected as the optimization algorithm minimizes the cost of overproducing and carrying over excess inventory. For the other two polymer grades not shown in Figure 4, we also observe the same trends where the demand is met over the 2-week planning horizon with globally optimal production schedules. When we look at the variability in the objective function value across the 10 random runs, we observe that the standard error is 0.0002. This shows that we consistently converge to the same solution even when the data-driven optimizer is initialized from different starting points. Overall, these two case studies demonstrate that our data-driven optimization approach is highly flexible and independent of any specific formulation, and it can address high dimensional integrated planning scheduling problems with a feasibility guarantee subject to MINLP complexity at the lower level.

4. Conclusions

In this study, we use the DOMINO framework and the NOMAD algorithm for solving bilevel integrated planning and scheduling problems with mixed-integer nonlinear lower levels. Two different scheduling formulations are tested at the lower-level problem with varying complexity. First, the continuous-time formulation of a crude oil blending system is analyzed. Second, a traveling salesman problem-based formulation of multiproduct CSTR is studied. The results show that DOMINO-NOMAD identifies guaranteed feasible solutions for both case studies, regardless of the scheduling formulation type. We have also shown that the algorithm can address highly complex and highly dimensional enterprise-wide optimization with scheduling problems subject to thousands of constraints. By explicitly incorporating the optimality gap at the planning level, we ensure that the bilevel feasibility is ensured by the data-driven optimizer, ultimately providing globally optimal schedules for the production level. In the future, we will investigate the performance of other data-driven optimizers and improve the efficiency of the algorithm for a computational speed-up.

Acknowledgments

Financial support from U.S. National Institutes of Health (NIH) grant P42 ES027704 and EPSRC grants EP/V051008/1 & EP/W003317/1 is gratefully acknowledged.

References

B. Beykal, S. Avraamidou, E.N. Pistikopoulos, 2021, Bi-level mixed-integer data-driven optimization of integrated planning and scheduling problems, Comput. Aid. Chem. Eng., 50, 1707-1713.

B. Beykal, S. Avraamidou, E.N. Pistikopoulos, 2022, Data-driven optimization of mixed-integer bi-level multi-follower integrated planning and scheduling problems under demand uncertainty. Comput. Chem. Eng., 156, 107551.

B. Beykal, S. Avraamidou, I.P.E. Pistikopoulos, M. Onel, E.N. Pistikopoulos, 2020, DOMINO: Data-driven optimization of bi-level mixed-integer nonlinear problems, J. Global Optim., 78, 1-36.

V.M. Charitopoulos, V. Dua, L.G. Papageorgiou, 2017, Traveling salesman problem-based integration of planning, scheduling, and optimal control for continuous processes, Ind. Eng. Chem. Res, 56(39), 11186-11205.

Charitopoulos, V. M., Papageorgiou, L. G., & Dua, V. (2019). Closed-loop integration of planning, scheduling and multi-parametric nonlinear control. Comput. Chem. Eng., 122, 172-192.

I.E. Grossmann, 2005, Enterprise-wide optimization: A new frontier in process systems engineering, AIChE J., 51(7), 1846-1857.

I. Harjunkoski, C.T. Maravelias, P. Bongers, P.M. Castro, S. Engell, I.E. Grossmann, J. Hooker, C. Méndez, G. Sand, J. Wassick, 2014, Scope for industrial applications of production scheduling models and solution methods, Comput. Chem. Eng., 62, 161-193.

N. V Sahinidis, 1996, BARON: A general purpose global optimization software package, J. Global Optim, 8, 201-205.

Z. Jia, M.G. Ierapetritou, J.D. Kelly, 2003, Refinery short-term scheduling using continuous time formulation: Crude-oil operations. Ind. Eng. Chem. Res. , 42(13), 3085-3097.

Z. Li, M.G. Ierapetritou, 2010, Production planning and scheduling integration through augmented Lagrangian optimization, Comput. Chem. Eng., 34(6), 996-1006.

C.T. Maravelias, C. Sung, 2009, Integration of production planning and scheduling: Overview, challenges and opportunities, Comput. Chem. Eng., 33(12), 1919-1930.

Flavio Manenti, Gintaras V. Reklaitis (Eds.), Proceedings of the 34th European Symposium on Computer Aided Process Engineering / 15th International Symposium on Process Systems Engineering (ESCAPE34/PSE24), June 2-6, 2024, Florence, Italy

A Real-Time Risk-Based Optimization Framework for Safe and Smart Operations

Austin Braniff[a], Sahithi Srijana Akundi[b,c,d], Yuanxing Liu[b,c,d], Faisal Khan[b,c], Efstratios N. Pistikopoulos[b,d], Yuhe Tian[a*]

[a] *Department of Chemical and Biomedical Engineering, West Virginia University, Morgantown, WV, United States*
[b] *Artie McFerrin Department of Chemical Engineering, Texas A&M University*
[c] *Mary Kay O'Connor Process Safety Center, Artie McFerrin Department of Chemical Engineering, Texas A&M University, College Station, TX, United States*
[d] *Texas A&M Energy Institute, Texas A&M University, College Station, TX, United States*

Abstract

We present a systematic framework for real-time risk-based optimization via multi-parametric programming. A dynamic risk indicator is utilized to monitor online process safety performance and provide model-based prediction of risk propagation, as a function of safety-critical process variables. Risk-based explicit/multi-parametric model predictive control is then developed to generate fit-for-purpose control strategies for proactive risk management. Given the probabilistic nature of risk, the controller design is extended to adapt a chance-constrained programming setting coupled with Bayesian inference for continuous risk updating along the rolling time horizon. A hierarchical dynamic optimization formulation is further developed to integrate risk control, operational optimization, and fault prognosis across multiple temporal scales in an integral but computationally efficient manner. If a potential fault is detected and cannot be prevented by adjusting operating actions, an alarm will be raised well ahead of time with the controller and optimizer continuously performing to attenuate the fault propagation speed and severity. The potential and efficacy of the proposed framework are demonstrated on three safety-critical case studies with increasing level of complexity: (i) Tank filling, (ii) Batch reactor at T2 Laboratories, and (iii) Cyber-physical hydrogen water electrolysis prototype.

Keywords: Process safety management, Dynamic risk assessment, Explicit model predictive control, Multi-parametric programming, Cyber-physical energy system

1. Introduction

The ongoing transition towards industrial digitalization and smart manufacturing have posed new challenges to chemical process safety management as plants become substantially more complex, dynamic, and integrated (Lee et al., 2019). Thus, it is essential to augment safety-critical decision making with systems-based real-time operation which can proactively reduce process safety losses. Oriented from process control perspective, several works have leveraged receding horizon estimation to detect faults at the early developing stage and predict its propagation (Ahooyi et al., 2016; Bhadriraju et al., 2021). Theoretical developments have also been made to characterize a set of state variables, e.g. Lyapunov level set (Wu et al., 2018) and pertinent systems theory (Venkidasalapathy and Kravaris, 2020), for guaranteed safe and stable operations under uncertainty. Despite these efforts, key research gaps remain on: (i) Lack of a mechanistic-based understanding and metric to quantify real-time process safety performance while considering nonlinear process variable interactions, dynamic control, and uncertainties, (ii) Lack of a systematic methodology to prognostically detect fault while automatedly determining the risk control and mitigation strategy to reduce failure probability, (iii) Lack of a cyber-physical prototype to implement and demonstrate the methods toward safe and smart manufacturing systems.

To address these challenges, in this work, we introduce a dynamic risk-based control and optimization framework via multi-parametric programming (mp-P). The remainder of this paper is structured as follows: Section 2 introduces the methodology framework integrating dynamic risk assessment, stochastic model predictive control, and operational optimization. Section 3 demonstrates the proposed approaches on three safety-critical case studies including the filling of a tank, the quality control of an exothermic batch reactor, and a proton exchange membrane water electrolysis cyber-physical prototype.

2. Dynamic Risk-based Control Optimization

In this section, we present a holistic methodology framework which tackles three major research questions: (i) How to integrate dynamic risk assessment and model predictive control? (ii) How to address the probabilistic nature of risk in the control scheme? and (iii) How to identify the optimal operating trajectory accounting for process control, fault prognosis, and operational optimization which may take place over multiple time scales?

2.1. Dynamic Risk-based Multi-Parametric Model Predictive Control (mp-MPC)

We first introduce the risk-based mp-MPC approach which sets the foundation for this framework. As shown in Fig. 1, a dynamic risk indicator (RI) is used to monitor online process safety considering fault probability and severity as a function of safety-critical process variables (x_t) deviation from nominal operating conditions (Bao et al., 2011). Risk-based MPC is then formulated which provides dual layers of risk management by incorporating: (i) safety-critical

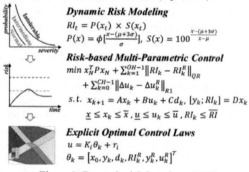

Dynamic Risk Modeling
$$RI_t = P(x_t) \times S(x_t)$$
$$P(x) = \phi\left[\frac{x-(\mu+3\sigma)}{\sigma}\right], \quad S(x) = 100^{\frac{x-(\mu+3\sigma)}{x-\mu}}$$

Risk-based Multi-Parametric Control
$$\min x_N^T P x_N + \sum_{k=1}^{OH-1}\left\|RI_k - RI_k^R\right\|_{QR}$$
$$+ \sum_{k=0}^{CH-1}\left\|\Delta u_k - \Delta u_k^R\right\|_{R1}$$
$$s.t. \ \ x_{k+1} = Ax_k + Bu_k + Cd_k, \ [y_k; RI_k] = Dx_k$$
$$\underline{x} \leq x_k \leq \overline{x}, \underline{u} \leq u_k \leq \overline{u}, RI_k \leq \overline{RI}$$

Explicit Optimal Control Laws
$$u = K_i\theta_k + r_i$$
$$\theta_k = \left[x_0, y_k, d_k, RI_k^R, y_k^R, u_k^R\right]^T$$

Figure 1: Dynamic risk-based mp-MPC.

variable bounds as path constraints, (ii) risk as output variable to be controlled based on multivariate process dynamics under uncertainty. The receding horizon estimation also enables model-based risk propagation forecast, leading to prognostic risk mitigation by the controller. The risk-based MPC is then re-formulated to a multi-parametric mixed-integer quadratic programming problem, from which optimal control laws can be obtained offline a priori as piecewise affine functions of process states, risks, disturbances, etc. (Ali et al., 2023) The mp-MPC offline computation capability offers unique advantages to generate a quantitative understanding on the impact on risk of disturbances and control action even before operating the process online. The risk controller can thus be tuned fitting the purpose to maximize the safe operating region against disturbances.

2.2. Stochastic Risk Control via Chance-Constrained Programming

Herein, we extend the above risk-based mp-MPC approach with considerations of the probabilistic nature of risk. We propose a novel stochastic risk control approach via chance-constrained programming (SRC-CCP) as shown in Fig. 2, which stands as a versatile and adaptive method to manage uncertainties within complex systems. This approach seamlessly integrates crucial elements. Firstly, it employs Receding Horizon

MPC, constantly adjusting control inputs by considering the system's changing dynamics. Secondly, it integrates dynamic probabilistic constraints, tactically embedding real-time risk management within the control framework to ensure the system operates within specified risk boundaries. Additionally, it includes a Bayesian update mechanism, dynamically adapting these risk thresholds based on current system observations. The probabilistic constraints are deterministically incorporated via chance-constrained programming. This holistic strategy emphasizes safety while allowing the system to flexibly optimize performance amidst uncertain conditions, an effective solution crafted for modern engineering challenges. The method approximates probabilistic constraints by converting them into deterministic forms, focusing specifically on normal distributions. For the constraint, $P(h(t) > h_{max}|t) \leq \epsilon_t$, a deterministic approximation is derived. $h(t)$ is a safety-critical process variable such as the tank liquid level adapted in Section 3.1. This involves calculating the inverse normal z-score ($z_t = \varphi^{-1}(\epsilon_t)$) using standard deviation (σ_t) and mean (μ_t) of the current probability distribution. The resultant formulation in Eq. 1 sets a threshold for $h(t)$ based on h_{max}, z-score, and standard deviation σ_t, aiding in risk management within predefined limits.

$$min_u \ J = x_N^T P x_N + \sum_{k=1}^{OH-1} \|(y_k - y_k^R)\|_{QR} + \sum_{k=0}^{CH-1} \|\Delta u_k - \Delta u_k^R\|_R + f(x(t))$$

$$s.t. \ x_{k+1} = Ax_k + Bu_k + C[d_k, De]$$

$$y_k = Dx_k$$

$$P[Event|x(t)] \leq \epsilon_t$$

$$\bar{x} \leq x \leq \underline{x} \qquad \bar{u} \leq u \leq \underline{u} \qquad \bar{y} \leq y \leq \underline{y}$$

Bayesian update:

$$P[Event|x(t+1)] = L(x(t)) * P[Event|x(t)]$$

Figure 2: SRC-CCP formulation.

$$h(t) > h_{max} + (z_t \sigma_t) \qquad (1)$$

2.3. Fault-Prognostic Control and Operational Optimization

We present another key aspect of this framework to simultaneously account for risk management, process control, and operational optimization which occur at distinct characteristic time scales. For example, there may exist a trade-off on the optimal batch time between reaching the end-point product quality (after hours or days) versus maintaining the operation at a low risk level (for every second or minute). To this purpose, a hierarchical control optimization formulation (Fig. 3) is developed coupling a short-term risk controller with a long-term economics and safety optimizer. The optimizer also provides a longer fault prognosis horizon, which can be chosen tailored to the process-specific operator response time, independent of the control output horizon estimation. The decision making of the controller and optimizer are fully integrated. Namely, the optimal operating trajectory determined by the optimizer at large time steps (e.g., for real-time optimization, end-point quality control) are used to continually update the set points of the controller. On the other hand, the optimizer is aware of the controller decisions by using the process

Control-aware Safety & Economics Optimizer

$$J^*(\theta) = min \sum WDe + Nu_T^R + M\,RI_T^R$$

$$s.t. \ x_{T+1} = \mathcal{A}x_T + \mathcal{B}u_T^R + C[d_T; De]$$

$$[y_T^R; RI_T^R] = \mathcal{D}x_T + \mathcal{E}u_T^R$$

$$\Theta = [x_0, d_T, De]^T$$

mp-QP Surrogate Model

$$min \sum \|\tilde{s}_{sm} - s_{sm=0}^R\|^2$$

$$s.t. \ x_{sm+1} = A\tilde{x}_{sm} + B\tilde{u}_{sm} + C[d_{sm}; De]$$

$$\tilde{s}_{sm} = [\tilde{y}_{sm}^R, \tilde{u}_{sm}^R]^T$$

Risk-aware mp-MPC

$$J^*(\theta) = min \sum_{k=0}^{NC} \|y_k - \bar{y}_k\|_{QR} + \|u_k - \bar{u}_k\|_R$$

$$s.t. \quad x_{k+1} = Ax_k + Bu_k \quad y_k = Cx_k$$

$$\theta = [x_0, RI_k, \bar{y}_k, \bar{u}_k]^T$$

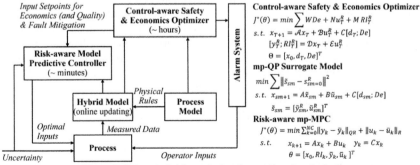

Figure 3: Integrated risk control and operational optimization.

model with closed-loop control laws. In certain cases, the difference between these two time spans may be significant, such as in process systems with very fast dynamics and/or requiring long forecasting horizon. A time-bridging surrogate model becomes essential to smoothly transition the operating decisions of the optimizer at large time steps to be achievable set points for the controller at smaller time steps. The mathematical formulations for the controller, optimizer, and surrogate modeling are provided in Fig. 3, which are all solved via mp-P to obtain optimal decisions offline a priori as explicit functions of process variables. This is a key advantage to ensure computational efficiency for multi-time-scale dynamic optimization. Another online real-time risk-based optimization strategy has also been developed, the detail of which can be found in Ali et al. (2023).

3. Illustrative Case Studies

3.1. Tank filling

The section implements SRC-CCP to manage a cylindrical storage tank system, which comprises a single inlet and outlet, storing a non-reactive, single-phase fluid. Central to this framework is the regulation of the safety-critical variable liquid level (h) in the tank at a setpoint (h_{sp}), facilitated by a control valve upstream of the tank. The remaining system variables and parameters include inlet volumetric flowrate (Q_{in}), outlet volumetric flowrate (Q_{out}), cylindrical cross-sectional area (A). The control formulation is presented in Eq. 2. The optimization objective revolves around minimizing a cost function that considers the deviation of the level from setpoint. This includes a probabilistic assessment for safety through Chance-Constrained Programming. Bayesian updating is employed to refine the estimation of level changes over time, utilizing a likelihood function that supports a higher probability towards minimizing the difference between the current level and the setpoint.

$$min_u \ J = \sum_{i=1}^{OH-1} \left(\left((h_i - h_{sp})^2 \right) + INLF(h_i, h_{sp}) \right) \quad (2a)$$

Bayesian Update:
$$P[\Delta h > 0|t+1] = L(h(t)) * P[\Delta h > 0|t] \text{ for t in T} \quad (2e)$$

$$\text{s.t.} \quad h(i+1) = \left(1 - \frac{k}{A}\right)h(i) + \left(\frac{1}{A}\right)Q_{in}(i) + \left(\frac{1}{A}\right)w(i) \quad (2b)$$

$$L(h(t)) = \frac{1}{\sqrt{2\pi}\sigma}\exp\left(-\frac{(h(t)-h_{sp})^2}{2\sigma^2}\right) \quad (2f)$$

$$0 \le h(i) \le h_{max} \quad (2c)$$

$$P(\Delta h > 0|t) \le \epsilon_t \quad (2d)$$

where Δh is the current state (tank level) of the system with respect to the boundary h_{max}. This constraint helps the user to set a threshold ϵ_t to the maximum risk allowed.

To evaluate the control efficacy, a closed-loop validation is performed and compared against the original open-loop tank level simulation (Fig. 4a). The results have showcased the remarkable stability of the tank level when employing Risk-informed Model Predictive Control via SRC-CCP. This approach consistently maintains the level within prescribed constraints, unlike the uncontrolled fluctuations in the open-loop scenario. While the tank levels remain within boundaries and close to reference value, the analysis focuses on the evolution of ϵ_t (acceptable risk level or maximum allowable probability of failure) in Fig. 4b. This trend indicates a deliberate strategy shift, integrating Chance-Constrained Programming to introduce a calculated margin for potential safety constraint violations. This prioritizes system performance over rigid adherence to safety constraints, allowing adaptability to changing conditions and disturbances. The gradual increase in ϵ_t reflects the sought balance between safety and performance optimization, highlighting the pivotal role of SRC-CCP in managing this delicate trade-off in dynamic environments.

3.2. T2 batch reactor

In what follows, we investigate a batch reactor adapted from the incident that occurred at T2 Laboratories in 2007. There are two exothermic reactions in this process. The main

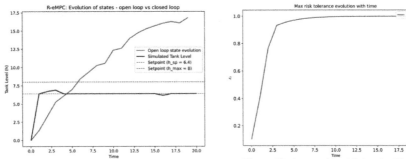

Figure 4a: Open-loop and close-loop tank level.   Figure 4b: Acceptable risk level with time.

reaction produces sodium methylcyclopentadiene as the desired product. Due to the very large pre-exponential factor, the side reaction rate increases significantly at high reactor temperatures and ultimately leads to uncontrollable thermal runaway. As such, reactor temperatures beyond 480K are defined as the high-risk region in which runaway has a higher probability to occur. Dynamic risk is computed as a function of real-time temperature deviations from its nominal value (460K). The manipulated variable for risk control is the heat transfer coefficient which is in a pseudo-linear relationship with cooling utility flowrate. The control optimization objectives are to: (i) Control the reactor at low risk level throughout the batch, (ii) Optimize the operation while reaching pre-specified endpoint product quality. Following Fig. 3, a short-term risk controller is designed with the control horizon as 5 min and output horizon as 10 min. A long-term quality optimizer is then formulated based on the closed-loop process dynamics forecasting the entire batch duration with an upper limit of 8 hours. We have firstly validated the effectiveness of the risk-aware controller to maintain the process at low risk level, without which open-loop operation will enter the high-risk region. Fig. 5 illustrates the integrated decision making with long-term quality optimizer. Fig. 5a presents the time profiles of reactant concentration at quality target specifications of 0.1, 0.05, and 0.01 mol/L. It can be inferred that our proposed methods are successful in meeting end-of-batch quality targets. By further examining the temperature trajectory in Fig. 5b, the optimizer adapts the maximum controllable risk (~ 470K) to meet end-product specifications efficiently and safely.

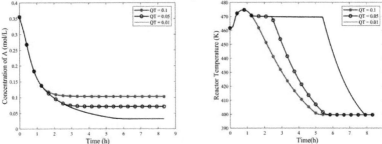

Figure 5a: Concentration under various quality targets.   Figure 5b: Temperature profiles.

3.3. PEM water electrolysis

Proton exchange membrane water electrolysis (PEMWE) is a key technology for green hydrogen production, while ensuring its safe and efficient operation remains a challenge. To achieve this, several key components have been investigated as part of the framework:

1. Lab-Scale Experimental Prototype: A lab-scale PEMWE experimental prototype is developed to gain a better understanding of the system behavior under different operating

conditions. The experimental configuration has four main units: (1) water supply, (2) electrolyzer, (3) power supply, and (4) data acquisition and control unit. As shown in Fig-

Figure 6: Experimental configuration of PEMWE system.

ure 6, the experimental setup situated on the left generates the vital data, which is then transmitted to the target computer on the right for monitoring and control in real-time. It provides a platform to test system performance with different control strategies.

2. Digital Twin: A digital twin, based on the physical laws governing the PEMWE system, is developed. The virtual replica allows for real-time monitoring and control. This provides valuable insights into PEMWE system dynamics to optimize its performance.

3. Multi-parametric Control Optimization: To obtain optimal control strategies, multi-parametric programming is used for explicit model predictive control while considering multiple parameters and constraints to maximize efficiency and minimize risk.

4. Integration of mpMPC-on-a-chip Controller: The above mpMPC algorithm is then integrated into a microcontroller. This advanced controller enables real-time monitoring and control of the hydrogen production process, ensuring optimal performance and safety.

5. Risk Identification and Process Safety Management: Risk identification and process safety management are also performed using the Hazard and Operability (HAZOP) method. This method systematically analyzes the PEMWE system to identify potential hazards and risks and implements appropriate measures to mitigate them. The integration of risk assessment and safety management aims to enhance the overall safety of PEMWE.

4. Concluding Remarks

This work has presented a framework for dynamic risk-based control and optimization via multi-parametric programming. Ongoing work is investigating error-tolerant risk control using robust MPC and cyber-physical systems integration.

5. Acknowledgement

The authors acknowledge financial support from NSF RETRO Project CBET-2312457, Department of Chemical and Biomedical Engineering at West Virginia University, Mary O'Connor Process Safety Centre and Energy Institute at Texas A&M University.

References

T. M. Ahooyi, M. Soroush, J. E. Arbogast, W. D. Seider, U. G. Oktem. (2016). Model-predictive safety system for proactive detection of operation hazards. AIChE J., 62(6), 2024-2042.

M. Ali, X. Cai, F. Khan, E. N. Pistikopoulos, Y. Tian. (2023). Dynamic risk-based process design and operational optimization via multi-parametric programming. Digital Chem. Eng., 7, 100096.

H. Bao, F. Khan, T. Iqbal, Y. Chang. (2011). Risk-based fault diagnosis and safety management for process systems. Process Saf. Prog., 30(1), 6-17.

B. Bhadriraju, J. S. I. Kwon, F. Khan. (2021). Risk-based fault prediction of chemical processes using operable adaptive sparse identification of systems (OASIS). Comput Chem Eng, 152, 107378.

J. Lee, I. Cameron, M. Hassall. (2019). Improving process safety: What roles for Digitalization and Industry 4.0?. Process Saf. Environ. Prot., 132, 325-339.

Z. Wu, H. Durand, P. D. Christofides. (2018). Safe economic model predictive control of nonlinear systems. Syst. Control. Lett., 118, 69-76.

J. Venkidasalapathy, C. Kravaris. (2020). Safety-centered process control design based on dynamic safe set. J. Loss Prev. Process Ind., 65, 104126.

Flavio Manenti, Gintaras V. Reklaitis (Eds.), Proceedings of the 34th European Symposium on Computer Aided Process Engineering / 15th International Symposium on Process Systems Engineering (ESCAPE34/PSE24), June 2-6, 2024, Florence, Italy

Flexible relaxation method for infeasibility diagnosis in the optimization model of natural gas pipeline network sales considering component self-consumption gas

Xiaozheng Chen [a], Siyi Mi [a], Jiaming Guo [a], Dingzhi Liu [b], Xiaoyong Gao [a*]

[a]*Department of Automation, China University of Petroleum, Beijing 102249, China*
[b]*PetroChina Planning and Engineering Institute, Beijing 100083, China*
x.gao@cup.edu.cn

Abstract

With the formation of the "One Network Across the Nation" pattern in China's natural gas industry, the analysis of pipeline flow and flow direction has become more complex. Conducting optimization analysis of natural gas pipeline network sales is crucial for the efficient operation of the pipeline network. However, natural gas sales optimization models still have challenges regarding flow boundaries and component self-consumption. Infeasible solutions often arise due to inappropriate boundary condition parameters, making the recovery of feasibility a key aspect in engineering applications. To address these challenges, a quadratic solving method is adopted to establish an optimization model for natural gas pipeline sales considering component self-consumption gas. Additionally, a flexible relaxation method is designed to detect contradictions and restore feasibility in the optimization model. Experiments show that using the GUROBI solver to model and solve actual natural gas sales cases, in the 221-node case, the traditional method of introducing 0-1 variable modeling takes 9.70 seconds, while the quadratic solving modeling method only takes 0.22 seconds, which greatly accelerates the solving speed. Meanwhile, the designed flexible relaxation method automatically locates the contradictory constraints of the infeasible model of natural gas pipeline network sales according to users' needs. It quickly restores the feasibility of the model by providing specific and reasonable modification suggestions.

Keywords: Natural gas pipeline network, model optimization, infeasibility diagnosis, feasibility restoration

1. Introduction

The formation of the "One Network Across the Nation" pattern realizes the safe transportation and free flow of oil and gas resources in China(Liu et al., 2023). It has also created a nationwide large-scale natural gas pipeline transmission system, leading to increased complexity in analyzing the flow and direction of the pipeline network. Constructing an optimization model for natural gas sales in the pipeline network can optimize the flow and sales structure of natural gas, thereby improving the overall sales efficiency of the gas pipeline network.

Due to the complex topology of the natural gas pipeline network system, the constructed optimization model for the gas pipeline network has numerous constraints and is large in scale (Liu et al., 2021). Contradictions between constraints in the model may lead to infeasibility. Therefore, it is crucial to perform contradiction detection on the optimization model for natural gas sales, providing results and modification suggestions that lead to model infeasibility. Algorithms such as additive filter algorithm and deletion filter algorithm have been proposed to find at least one irreducible infeasible set (IIS) in the infeasible model (Chinneck and Dravnieks, 1991; Chinneck, 1997). Boundary tightening techniques are utilized in the literature (Puranik et al., 2016; Puranik and Sahinidis, 2017) to eliminate infeasible and irrelevant constraints from the model and further identify IIS on the simplified model. However, the IIS search was time-consuming and did not provide effective modifications to the infeasible modeling of the natural gas pipeline network.

In this work, we designed a flexible relaxation method for infeasibility diagnosis for infeasible models. This method can provide modification suggestions that meet user requirements in natural gas pipeline networks, thereby effectively restoring the feasibility of the model. In addition, the natural gas pipeline network sales optimization model considering component flow self-consumption and flow boundary discontinuity is established by quadratic solving to speed up the model solving speed.

2. Model and Methods

2.1. Model description

According to the actual transportation path of natural gas in the pipeline network, the natural gas pipeline network sales optimization model can be simplified into five components: nodes, gas sources, pipelines, gas storages, gas storage tanks, and clients. The other four components are connected through nodes to form the natural gas value chain network topology (Zhang, 2022). The optimization model for natural gas sales aims to maximize benefits while satisfying the equations of flow balance conservation, upper and lower boundary constraints, and capacity constraints. For detailed model variables and constraint settings, see Liu et al. (2021).

2.2. Natural gas pipeline network flow interval segmentation model

The pipelines, gas storage tanks, and gas storages components in the natural gas pipeline network all have bidirectional flow characteristics. Forward flow variables and backward flow variables are set in the model to represent the vector form of the flow (using positive and negative signs to indicate direction) and scalar form (absolute value of flow) of the flow for these components. This approach helps eliminate the computational difficulties caused by the nonlinearity of the absolute value of component flow. Taking the pipeline component as an example, we can construct equation (1) and equation (2):

$$Q_p = q_{p,z} - q_{p,f} \tag{1}$$

$$|Q_p| = q_{p,z} + q_{p,f} \tag{2}$$

In which, the value ranges of the variables $q_{p,z}$ and $q_{p,f}$ are the forward flow interval and the backward flow interval of the pipeline, respectively. Eq. (1) represents the true flow rate of the pipeline with direction. The absolute value of the pipeline flow rate in Eq. (2) is used to calculate the cost term. When the forward and backward flow intervals of the pipeline are discontinuous on a one-dimensional numerical axis, the above equations need to be modified into Eq. (3) and Eq. (4):

$$Q_p = y \cdot q_{p,z}^{seg} - (1-y) \cdot q_{p,f}^{seg} \tag{3}$$

$$|Q_p| = y \cdot q_{p,z}^{seg} + (1-y) \cdot q_{p,f}^{seg} \tag{4}$$

In which, the superscript seg indicates that the pipeline is in a state of discontinuous flow intervals. By introducing binary variables y, the selection of positive and negative flow intervals in the pipeline is realized, accurately representing the segmented conditions of the pipeline flow intervals. This representation can also be applied to other components of the pipeline network where there are segmented flow intervals.

2.3. Quadratic solving model of natural gas pipeline network considering component self-consumption gas

Since the "13th Five-Year Plan", China has actively promoted the construction of natural gas pipeline networks, with a total of 4.6×10^4 kilometers of long-distance pipelines built. The total length of natural gas pipelines nationwide reaching 10.2×10^4 kilometers (Liu et al., 2021). With the formation of a large-scale national natural gas pipeline network, the self-consumption of components in the pipeline network cannot be ignored. When a component is not in use, there is no flow self-consumption of the component. However, when the component is in use, different flow directions of natural gas will produce flow self-consumption of different values.

Since the flow self-consumption of the component cannot be determined before solving, the traditional method introduces additional 0-1 variables for the component to choose whether to produce self-consumption or not. This method will cause a large number of bilinear terms in the model, which greatly reduces the speed of the model solving. The quadratic solving method proposed in this paper modifies the basic model according to the results of the first solution and selectively introduces flow self-consumption terms in the objective function and constraints.

Take the case of self-consumption gas generated by the gas storage component as an example. The gas storage produces self-consumption gas when natural gas flows in and out. According to the first solving result, the flow self-consumption model of the gas storage is modified:

1) If the natural gas inflow and outflow at the gas storage are both zero, indicating that the component is not in use and there is no flow self-consumption. Set the constraint:

$$q_{R,in} = q_{R,out} = 0 \tag{5}$$

In which $q_{R,in}$ is the inflow flow from the gas storage and $q_{R,out}$ is the outflow flow from the gas storage.

2) If the natural gas inflow or outflow at the gas storage is greater than 0, indicating that natural gas is flowing into the component and there is positive self-consumption. Need to correct constraints:

$$V_{R,min} - V_{R,init} + q_{R,c} + FW_{R,z} \leq q_{R,in} \leq V_{R,max} - V_{R,init} + q_{R,c} + FW_{R,z} \tag{6}$$

$$q_{R,in} > FW_{R,z} \tag{7}$$

$$R_{cost} = p_{R,in} \cdot q_{R,in} + GC_R \left[V_{R,init} + \left(q_{R,in} - q_{R,c} - FW_{R,z} \right)/2 \right] \tag{8}$$

In which $V_{R,init}, V_{R,min}$ and $V_{R,max}$ are respectively the initial storage capacity, minimum storage capacity and maximum storage capacity of the gas storage. $q_{R,c}$ is the fixed storage self-consumption of the gas storage. $FW_{R,z}$ is the forward flow self-consumption of the gas storage. R_{cost} is the cost item of the gas storage. $p_{R,in}$ is the unit cost of gas storage inflow flows. GC_R is the unit storage cost of the gas storage. Eq. (6) is the modified storage constraint, and Eq. (7) ensures that the flow of natural gas into the storage is greater than the flow self-consumption. The cost term in Eq. (8) includes the flow cost and the storage cost, where the storage cost is the product of the unit storage cost and the average of the natural gas volume before and after storage in the storage.

3) If the natural gas inflow or outflow at the gas storage is less than 0, indicating that natural gas is flowing out of the gas storage and there is reverse self-consumption. Need to correct constraints:

$$V_{R,init} - V_{R,max} - q_{R,c} - FW_{R,f} \leq q_{R,out} \leq V_{R,init} - V_{R,min} - q_{R,c} - FW_{R,f} \qquad (9)$$

$$q_{R,in} > FW_{R,f} \qquad (10)$$

$$R_{cost} = p_{R,out} \cdot q_{R,out} + GC_R[V_{R,init} - (q_{R,out} + q_{R,c} + FW_{R,f})/2] \qquad (11)$$

In which $p_{R,out}$ is the unit cost of gas storage outflow flows and $FW_{R,f}$ is the backward flow self-consumption of the gas storage. The meaning of the above equation is consistent with the presence of positive self-consumption. The components in the pipeline network successfully constructed a quadratic solving natural gas pipeline network model considering self-consumption through the above method.

2.4. Flexible relaxation method

In order to solve the problem of infeasibility of solving the natural gas pipeline network model, this paper designs the flexible relaxation method to give suitable correction suggestions for the users. Since the natural gas pipeline network model is a specific type of supply chain, it can be simplified to the linear programming problem see Formula (a) in Fig. 1. In step 1, the minimization of the sum of upper and lower bound constraint violations for each variable is represented by adding slack terms to the variables, yielding Formula (b). The positive violation terms in Formula (b) provide quantitative information about infeasibility (Jatty, 2023). In step 2, the violation term is combined with the objective function of the original model in the form of a large penalty coefficient to obtain the contradiction detection Formula (c) for the minimum violation relaxation. Formula (c) can either compute the optimal solution for the feasible model or give the correction information for the infeasible model. In order to make the correction information satisfy the actual situation of natural gas pipeline network business or be accepted by the

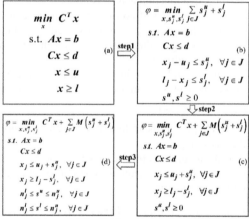

Figure 1. Flexibility relaxation method derivation process

users, the violation term in Formula (c) is further restricted in step 3 to obtain Formula (d) of the flexible relaxation method.

The flexibility of the flexible relaxation method is mainly reflected in the ability to obtain different corrections to the infeasible model according to the user's wishes or practical constraints, so that the model can be more correctly restored to feasibility. In addition, the relaxation method chooses to add violation terms to variables rather than constraints, so that the model can effectively give corrections on component variables. Moreover, the flexible relaxation method does not affect the solving results of the feasible model as the violation term of the model is zero at this time.

3. Results and Discussion

In this section, the quadratic solving method and the 0-1 solving method are used for the natural gas sales cases at 131-node and 221-node, respectively. Each node case contains data information for 18 years. All cases were solved using GUROBI (v 10.0.0) on an AMD Ryzen 7 5800H with Radeon Graphics, 3.20 GHz, RAM 16G PC. The final results of the solving are consistent. The comparison table of the solving time of two different node cases using different methods is shown in Figures 2 and 3. The quadratic solving method takes much less time than the 0-1 solving method from the chart.

In order to further analyze the differences between the two modeling methods. Table 1 provides a breakdown of the solution information for the two cases. The table includes the solving method, number of constraints, variables, and binary variables, total solution time for the 18-year period, as well as the minimum, maximum, and average time ratios. Each node case includes 18 time ratios, which are obtained by dividing the solution time of the 0-1 solving method by the solution time of the quadratic solving method.

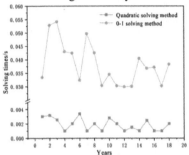 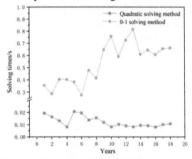

Figure2. Solution time of 131-node case   Figure3. Solution time of 221-node case

Table 1 shows that the number of binary variables and total variables in the model constructed using the 0-1 solving method is much larger than that of the quadratic solving method. The key advantage of the quadratic solving method in terms of solving speed lies in the reduction of binary variables. The time ratios in the table crystallize the speed advantage of the quadratic solving even more. In the 131-node and 221-node cases, the solving speed of the quadratic solving method is more than 20 times and 50 times faster than that of the 0-1 variable method, respectively. Additionally, it can be noted that because of the disparity in the number of 0-1 variables, the quadratic solving increases in the minimum, maximum, and average time ratios as the size of the node case increases. This indicates that the quadratic solving method has a greater advantage in solving speed for large-scale cases.

Table 1 Statistics of solution for various node scale cases

Case size	Solving mode	Constraints number	Vars number	0-1 Vars number	Solving time /s	Min time ratio	Max time ratio	Average time ratio
131-node	quadratic	917	786	0	0.034	9.57	49.46	24.60
	0-1	917	1310	393	0.689			
221-node	quadratic	1721	1469	10	0.220	14.11	100.09	52.09
	0-1	1645	2453	756	9.702			

To validate the effectiveness of the flexible relaxation method in restoring infeasible models to feasibility, a contradiction detection was performed on an infeasible case of 221-node for a specific year. Table 2 shows three modification options provided by the flexible relaxation method under different constraint conditions, which may consider pressure factors related to pipeline transportation or other practical business requirements. After the initial application of the minimum violation relaxation, the solution with the smallest modification was obtained for feasibility restoration. Subsequently, the flexible relaxation method provided additional modification options, where the modification amount of the model continued to increase, while the objective function value did not show a clear pattern of change.

Table 2 Contradiction detection information for the 221-node infeasible year case

Restrictions	Modify components	Direction	Bound	Modification	Modification amount	Objective function value
First solution	Gas storage 1	Input	Upper	1.33 to 1.45	0.12	36080.45
Gas storage 1 not adjustable	Gas storage 2	Output	Upper	0.28 to 0.40	0.24	36039.26
	Pipeline 651	Forward	Upper	0.28 to 0.40		
Pipeline 651 forward flow limit of 0.3	Gas storage 2	Input	Upper	0.28 to 0.30	0.32	36162.93
	Pipeline 556	Backward	Upper	0.00 to 0.10		
	Pipeline 731	Backward	Upper	0.00 to 0.10		
	Pipeline 806	Backward	Upper	0.00 to 0.10		

4. Conclusions

In this study, the segmented flow intervals of natural gas transported by pipe segments is considered by introducing 0-1 variables. Additionally, the actual impact of component self-consumption on optimization of gas transportation was addressed using the quadratic solving method. This method significantly improves the solving speed compared to the traditional method of introducing 0-1 variables. For infeasible problems in the natural gas pipeline network model, the flexible relaxation method provides multiple alternative modification options, giving users sufficient choice space to restore the model to feasibility.

References

D.Liu, Y.Zhang, Y.Liang, G.Li, S.Liu, J.Q.Ni, X.Liu, 2021, Construction and application of the optimization model of natural gas pipeline transmission based on "national one network", Petroleum and New Energy, 33(05), 64-70.

D.Liu, Y.Zhang, Y.Liang, 2023, A complete modeling method for nonlinear dynamic processes based on wiener structured neural network and wiener-hammerstein structured neural network, Control and Instruments in Chemical Industry, 50(05), 632-643+659.

J.W.Chinneck, E.W.Dravnieks, 1991, Locating minimal infeasible constraint sets in linear programs, ORSA Journal on Computing, 3(2), 157-168.

J.W.Chinneck, 1997, Finding a useful subset of constraints for analysis in an infeasible linear program, INFORMS Journal on Computing, 9(2), 164-174.

S.Jatty, N.Singh, I.E. Grossmann, L.S.dAssis, C.Galanopoulos, P.GarciaHerreros, B.Springub, N. Tran, 2023, Diagnosis of linear programming supply chain optimization models: Detecting infeasibilities and minimizing changes for new parameter value, COMPUTERS & CHEMICAL ENGINEERING, 171(1), 108-139.

Y.Puranik, N.V.Sahinidis, 2017, Deletion presolve for accelerating infeasibility diagnosis in optimization models, INFORMS Journal on Computing, 29(4), 754-766.

Y.Zhang, 2022, Modeling the optimization of natural gas supply and marketing plan based on value chain, China University of Petroleum(Beijing).

Y.Puranik, M.Kilinc, N.V.Sahinidis, T.Li, A.Gopalakrishnan, B.Besancon, T.Roba, 2016, Global optimization of an industrial gas network operation, AIChE Journal, 62(9), 3215-3224.

Flavio Manenti, Gintaras V. Reklaitis (Eds.), Proceedings of the 34th European Symposium on Computer Aided Process Engineering / 15th International Symposium on Process Systems Engineering (ESCAPE34/PSE24), June 2-6, 2024, Florence, Italy

Robust stability analysis of Koopman based MPC system

Gajanand Verma,[a] William Heath,[b] Constantinos Theodoropoulos[a*]

[a]*School of Chemical Engineering and Analytical Science, The University of Manchester, M13 9PL, UK*
[b]*School of Electrical and Electronic Engineering, University of Manchester, Manchester, M13 9PL, UK*
k.theodoropoulos@manchester.ac.uk

Abstract

Linearization of complex large-scale non-linear systems offers several advantages from the perspective of Model predictive control (MPC). The Koopman operator is an infinite dimensional operator which globally linearizes a non-linear dynamical system, however a finite dimensional approximation of the Koopman operator is required for its employment in MPC. The reduction of dimensionality introduces unstructured uncertainty in the system and hence robust stability analysis is required to ensure the system remains stable. In our work, we have developed a linear MPC for a non-linear tubular reactor system based on a neural network approximated Koopman operator. Subsequently, we investigate the robust stability of the system utilizing the Integral Quadratic Constraint (IQC) methodology.

Keywords: Robust stability, Koopman operator, model predictive control, large-scale systems, integral quadratic constraints

1. Introduction

Model Predictive Control (MPC) is an advanced control strategy that leverages a predictive model of the process to compute optimal control input trajectories. Its widespread adoption in various engineering branches is attributed to its capability of handling system constraints and multi-input multi-output (MIMO) systems. Nevertheless, MPC is challenged by the computational demands associated with real-time optimization.

With the technological advancements, chemical engineering systems have become more diverse and intricate, involving large scale non-linear systems or distributed parameter systems (DPS). Despite the advancements in computing facilities, the real time optimal control of such systems poses a multitude of challenges. The classical approach to handle large scale non-linear systems is based on dimensionality reduction (Theodoropoulos, 2011) (Theodoropoulos 2010) and model linearization. While dimensionality reduction reduces the computational burden of MPC associated with real time optimization, linear model is favoured as there exists several classical techniques to handle linear systems.

The traditional techniques of linearization are based on local-linearization or Carleman linearization (Korda and Mezić 2018). Koopman operator (KO) on the other hand globally linearizes a non-linear dynamical system in the infinite dimensional space of state functions. Since KO is an infinite dimensional operator, a finite dimensional approximation is required for its exploitation in MPC. The approximated linear system is of great significance from the control perspective as it can be utilized directly in MPC formulation of non-linear systems to reduce the complexity and computational efforts of MPC. Recently, KO based techniques have emerged for MPC formulation of non-linear systems (Korda and Mezić 2018).

Dynamic mode decomposition (DMD) based techniques were reported initially for finite approximation of KO (Kutz et al. 2016). Recently (2018), DMD has been extended to exploit KO for linear predictors or MPC (Korda and Mezić 2018). However, such methods usually require manual selection of lifting functions which may limit the prediction accuracy (Wang et al. 2022). Deep learning (DL)-based KO approximation methods inherently resolve this issue. Therefore, several DL based methods have also been reported for KO approximation and subsequent MPC formulation (Wang et al. 2022). Both DMD and Deep learning are equation free approaches and can be suitably applied to the systems where process model is either difficult or impossible to obtain.

While the finite dimensional KO approximation can simplify a complex non-linear dynamical system to a significant extent, such simplification can introduce unstructured uncertainty and destabilize the system (García et al. 2012). It is not trivial to guarantee robustness under such uncertainty (W. P. Heath and Li 2010). Therefore, the stability analysis post simplification becomes necessary to ensure the robust MPC performance (Bemporad and Morari 1999).

Uncertainties are effectively addressed through input-output stability analysis. The Integral quadratic constraints (IQCs) (Megretski and Rantzer 1997) is a unified approach to handle various kinds of uncertainties. The original IQC theorem was introduced in the frequency domain which can be converted to a linear matrix inequality (LMI) through the (Megretski and Rantzer 1997). The guaranteed stability is then subjected to existence of a symme Koopman Operator tric matrix $P = P^T$ satisfying the LMI. In this study, we conduct an IQC analysis (Petsagkourakis et al. 2020) to evaluate the robustness performance of the Koopman-based MPC.

2. Koopman Operator

The Koopman operator allows the linear evolution of state functions (or observables) in an infinite dimensional Hilbert space, along the trajectories of a given non-linear dynamics. Consider a discrete time non-linear dynamical system given by:

$$x_{k+1} = f(x_k) \tag{1}$$

Where x is the state of the system ($x_k \in R^n$)) and k is the integer index. f is a non-linear map ($f : R \to R$). The Koopman operator ($K: H \to H$) acts on the functions of state (ξ) linearly as following:

$$\xi(x_{k+1}) = K\xi(x_k) \tag{2}$$

Since K is an infinite dimensional operator, the Koopman eigenfunctions (ψ) can be obtained to encompass the Koopman invariant subspace for finite dimensional approximation of Koopman operator.

$$\psi(x_{k+1}) = K'\psi(x_k) \tag{3}$$

where K' is the finite approximation of infinite dimensional Koopman operator K. Now consider a non-linear dynamical system with control input u as following

$$x_{k+1} = f(x_k, u_k) \tag{4}$$

From the perspective of MPC we are interested in the linear predictor of the form:

$$\psi_{k+1} = A\psi_k + Bu_k \tag{5}$$

where $(x \in R^n)$, $(u \in R^m)$, $(\psi \in R^N)$ is the lifted state $(N \gg n)$.

We have employed Neural networks to approximate matrices A and B. The obtained linear model was then exploited for model predictive control of exit temperature of a tubular reactor.

3. Integral quadratic constraints (IQC) analysis

The IQC approach introduced by Megretski and Rantzer (1997), is powerful framework for analyzing robust stability and performance of systems in the presence of uncertainties or non-linearities. It unifies all the classical methods for stability analysis and thus can capture important properties of uncertainties or non-linearities. In IQC framework, the system is considered as a interconnection of a LTI system and a uncertain/non-linear perturbation whose input/output behaviour can be described by IQC (Pfifer and Seiler 2015). Two signals p and q satisfy the IQC defined by Π if the following condition holds

$$\left\langle \begin{bmatrix} \hat{p} \\ \hat{q} \end{bmatrix}, \Pi \begin{bmatrix} \hat{p} \\ \hat{q} \end{bmatrix} \right\rangle = \int_{-\infty}^{\infty} \begin{bmatrix} \hat{p} \\ \hat{q} \end{bmatrix}^* \Pi(j\omega) \begin{bmatrix} \hat{p} \\ \hat{q} \end{bmatrix} d\omega \geq 0 \tag{6}$$

Where $\hat{p}$ and $\hat{q}$ represent the Fourier transformations of signals p and q. For further information on IQCs one can refer to (Megretski and Rantzer 1997). The Kalman–Yakubovich–Popov (KYP) lemma converts the frequency domain criteria to a LMI criteria.

The introduction of frequency domain IQCs was followed by the development of time domain IQCs, through the factorization of the multiplier $\Pi(j\omega)$ and the application of dissipation theory (Pfifer and Seiler 2015). The time domain IQC theory is notably applicable to hard IQCs, which remain valid over any finite time period. The factorization for time domain IQCs is given as follows:

$$\Pi = \psi * M\psi \tag{6a}$$

According to (W. Heath et al. 2005) any MPC with input constraints only satisfy the IQC with following multiplier:

$$\Pi = \begin{bmatrix} 0 & I \\ I & -2H \end{bmatrix} \tag{6b}$$

where $-\phi^T H \phi + \phi^T f \geq 0$ is the result of KKT conditions ((W. Heath et al. 2005))

4. Application

We applied the Koopman based MPC framework to a tubular reactor (with recycle ratio r) where an irreversible, exothermic first order chemical reaction ($A \rightarrow B$) takes place. The system exhibits oscillations (Hopf bifurcation) at recycle ratio of 0.5 (Jensen and Ray 1982). The governing dimensionless equations are as follows:

$$\frac{\partial C}{\partial t} = \frac{1}{Pe_m}\frac{\partial^2 C}{\partial x^2} - \frac{\partial C}{\partial x} - Da(1 + C)\exp\left(\frac{\gamma T}{1 + T}\right) \tag{7}$$

$$\frac{\partial T}{\partial t} = \frac{1}{Pe_h}\frac{\partial^2 T}{\partial x^2} - \frac{\partial T}{\partial x} + cDa(1 + C)\exp\left(\frac{\gamma T}{1 + T}\right) + \beta(u_w - T) \tag{8}$$

while the boundary conditions are given as

$$\left.\frac{\partial C}{\partial x}\right|_{x=0} = -Pe_m[(1 - r)C_0 + rC|_{x=1} - rC|_{x=0}] \tag{9}$$

$$\left.\frac{\partial T}{\partial x}\right|_{x=0} = -Pe_h[(1 - r)T_0 + rT|_{x=1} - rT|_{x=0}] \tag{10}$$

$$\frac{\partial T}{\partial x} = \left.\frac{\partial C}{\partial x}\right|_{x=1} = 0 \tag{11}$$

Here C and T are dimensionless concentration and temperature, u_w is the wall temperature which was divided into 3 sectors to control the temperature of the system. $Pe_m = Pe_h = 7.0, Da = 0.1, \gamma = 10, c = 2.5, \beta = 2, x \in [0,1]$.

The discretized system was lifted from 30 state variables to 51 state variables using neural networks and subsequently finite dimensional Koopman operator was obtained to linearize the system. The linearized system was then used in MPC formulation to control the exit temperature of the reactor. Figure 1 depicts the performance of PDE based MPC (NMPC) and Koopman based MPC. As it can be seen, the Koopman-based MPC can successfully achieve performance very close to the NMPC one with significant computational savings.

5. Conclusions and future work

This work successfully demonstrates the efficacy of a Koopman-based MPC system for a non-linear tubular reactor. By employing a neural network to approximate the Koopman operator, we were able to linearize the non-linear dynamics of the reactor effectively. This linearization significantly simplified the control problem, allowing us to use a linear MPC approach. Our findings indicate that despite the dimensionality reduction and associated unstructured uncertainties the controller was able to dampen the oscillations and achieve the set point. Figure 1(a) demonstrates the system's response without MPC, showing significant oscillations with recycle (r=0.5), while Figure 1(b) reveals the stabilizing effect of the Koopman MPC in comparison to the PDE based MPC (NMPC) and open-loop responses, highlighting its efficacy in controlling the exit temperature of the system with linearized model. The control input profiles in Figures 1(c) and 1(d) depicts the control input trejectories for NMPC as well as Koopman MPC. We are currently investigating the robust stability analysis using the IQC methodology described in Section 3. The IQC study will ensure the theoretical guarantee of robustness within certain bounds.

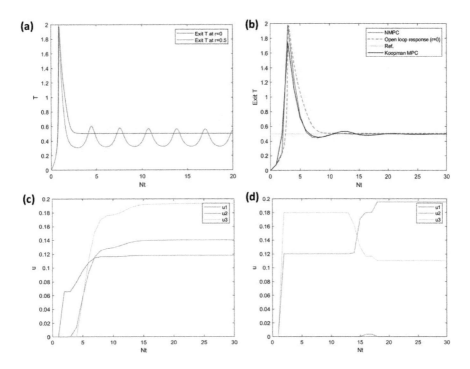

Figure 1: **(a)**: Exit temp. of reactor at r = 0 and r = 0.5 without MPC; **(b)** Exit temp. profile with non-linear MPC and Koopman MPC; **(c)** Control input profile obtained from NMPC; **(d)** Control input profile obtained from Koopman MPC

References

Bemporad, A., and M. Morari. 1999. 'Control of Systems Integrating Logic, Dynamics, and Constraints'. *Automatica* 35 (3): 407–27.

García, M. R., C. Vilas, L. O. Santos, and A. A. Alonso. 2012. 'A Robust Multi-Model Predictive Controller for Distributed Parameter Systems'. *Journal of Process Control* 22 (1): 60–71.

Heath, W. P., and G. Li. 2010. 'Multipliers for Model Predictive Control with Structured Input Constraints'. *Automatica* 46 (3): 562–68.

Heath, WP, G Li, AG Wills, and B Lennox. 2005. 'IQC Analysis of Linear Constrained MPC'. In *IEEE Sponsored Colloquium on Predictive Control, University of Sheffield.*

Jensen, K. F., and W. H. Ray. 1982. 'The Bifurcation Behavior of Tubular Reactors'. *Computers and Chemical Engineering* 37: 199–222.

Korda, M., and I. Mezić. 2018. 'Linear Predictors for Nonlinear Dynamical Systems: Koopman Operator Meets Model Predictive Control'. *Automatica* 93 (July): 149–60.

Kutz, J. N., S. L. Brunton, B. W. Brunton, and J. L. Proctor. 2016. *Dynamic Mode Decomposition: Data-Driven Modeling of Complex Systems.* Society for Industrial and Applied Mathematics.

Megretski, A., and A. Rantzer. 1997. 'System Analysis via Integral Quadratic Constraints'. *IEEE Transactions on Automatic Control* 42 (6): 819–30.

Pfifer, H., and P. Seiler. 2015. 'Robustness Analysis of Linear Parameter Varying Systems Using Integral Quadratic Constraints'. *International Journal of Robust and Nonlinear Control* 25 (15): 2843–64.

Petsagkourakis P., WP Heath, and C Theodoropoulos 2020 ' Stability analysis of piecewise affine systems with multi-model predictive control' *Automatica* 111, 108539.

Theodoropoulos, C. 2010. 'Optimisation and Linear Control of Large Scale Nonlinear Systems: A Review and a Suite of Model Reduction-Based Techniques'. *Coping with Complexity: Model Reduction and Data Analysis*, 37–61.

Wang, M., X. Lou, W. Wu, and B. Cui. 2022. 'Koopman-Based MPC with Learned Dynamics: Hierarchical Neural Network Approach'. *IEEE Transactions on Neural Networks and Learning Systems.*

Flavio Manenti, Gintaras V. Reklaitis (Eds.), Proceedings of the 34th European Symposium on Computer Aided Process Engineering / 15th International Symposium on Process Systems Engineering (ESCAPE34/PSE24), June 2-6, 2024, Florence, Italy

Boosted Ensemble Learning for Model Predictive Control with Reconfiguration of Modular Facilities

Yi Dai[a] and Andrew Allman[a*]

[a]*University of Michigan, 500 S. State Street, Ann Arbor, MI 48109 USA*
Corresponding Author: allmanaa@umich.edu

Abstract

The presence of discrete decisions in mixed-integer model predictive control (MPC) renders the optimization problem more significantly difficult to solve than a traditional continuous MPC problem. A solution is the use of data-driven models which help decouple the integer decisions from optimization and enable solution of control problem online. However, when considering the dynamic reconfiguration problem of modular facilities, there is a trade-off between the prediction accuracy and the magnitude of error in the incorrect predictions. In this work, we present an approach to determine integer control decisions *a priori* to solving the MPC problem using the ensemble method that takes advantages of several member classifiers trained by simulation data. Results demonstrate that the ensemble method achieves a breakthrough in the trade-off between classification accuracy and the magnitude of error in the incorrect predictions. A setpoint tracking case study demonstrates the MPC with ensemble method generally chooses configurations that give quicker set point recovery than the other member classifiers.

Keywords: Ensemble learning, Machine learning, Network reconfiguration, Modular manufacturing, Model predictive control

1. Introduction

In recent years, it has become clear that worldwide issues such as pandemics, climate change, and political conflict highlight the need for sustainable infrastructure to produce critical chemicals such as fuels and fertilizers. A promising approach to further enabling sustainability is to implement modular production units which are small-scale, standardized units that can perform traditional or intensified chemical unit operations (Baldea et al., 2017; Shao and Zavala, 2020). When considering a numbered-up modular facility to achieve desired throughput, the opportunity exists to dynamically transition between modular configurations, i.e. switching from operating modules in parallel to in series, as dictated by intermittent economic conditions. Our recent work (Dai et al., 2023) demonstrates that operational conditions will often affect which configuration of the numbered-up modular system most effectively controls the system, and that switching module configurations can be an effective way of tracking large changes in set points or rejecting large disturbances.

Modern chemical process control of complex systems is often performed using model predictive control (MPC), whereby an optimization problem is repeatedly solved in a moving horizon fashion in order to determine control actions. Introducing the action of reconfiguration to the optimal control problem adds integer variables that correspond to the module connectivity, resulting in a mixed integer nonlinear program (MINLP) which is extremely challenging to solve online in a time scale relevant for control. Our previous work (Dai and Allman, 2023) built a data-driven model embedded MPC which creates mathematical models for classifying the optimal operation configuration, decoupling the integer configuration decision from optimization, and enabling solution of the mixed integer nonlinear control problem online. However, it indicates that there is a trade-off between the classification accuracy and the magnitude of error in the incorrect predictions, the latter of which can lead to severely degraded controller performance.

A promising way to address this issue is the ensemble method which aggregates multiple weighted models to obtain a combined model that captures the best behaviors of its constituent models. The success of ensembles has been explained from statistical, computational, and representational aspects (Dietterich, 2000), bias-variance decomposition (Kohavi and Wolpert, 1996), and strength correlation (Breiman, 2001). Ensembles can be built by dependent frameworks which take advantage of knowledge generated in previous iterations by base classifiers to guide the learning in the next iterations. The most well-known dependent ensemble method, boosting, is a general method for constructing a single composite strong classifier combined by weak classifiers to achieve improvement on the performance of weak learners. One of the most popular boosting algorithms is AdaBoost (Adaptive Boosting) whose main idea is to pay more attention to patterns that are harder to classify (Freund and Schapire, 1996). Researchers have applied AdaBoost in a wide range of applications, such as supervisory building control rules (May-Ostendorp, 2012), identifying key parameters and steps for semiconductor manufacturing (San et al., 2016), life prediction for LEDs (Lu et al., 2017), and recognizing the coupling faults of complex industrial process (Xu et al., 2021), to name a few examples.

This work provides an approach to pre-establish integer control decisions by implementing AdaBoost algorithms in MPC problem solving. The remainder of the paper is structured as follows. The following section presents the optimal model predictive control problem and case studied in this work. Then, we introduce the multi-class AdaBoost algorithms with additional information from the training data. Furthermore, we present the AdaBoost classifiers' performance and analyze a set point tracking case study of the MPC with new classifiers. Finally, we conclude by summarizing this work and suggesting some potential ideas for future development.

2. Problem Statement and Case Study

In this work, we develop an online configuration switching approach according to the dynamic system condition in the MPC of numbered-up modular systems. In this control feedback loop, as the left part of Figure 1 shows, the current operational conditions, such as set point, measured disturbance, and state measurements, are imported into the classifiers trained offline by machine learning algorithms. After dealing with the control condition information, classifiers tell the MPC which configuration the system should use for next time step. Then the MPC takes action on the process system by manipulating process inputs (flow rates and heating rates), switching configurations if necessary, and all of which lead the system to a new state for the next loop.

For the case study analyzed here, we consider a benchmark three module reactor system consisting of three nonisothermal CSTR's with models adapted from Liu et al., 2009. We assume that these modules can operate in any of the configurations specified in Figure 1 right. In particular, a parallel configuration (a), a configuration with mixing (b), a hybrid series-parallel configuration (c), and a series configuration (d) are considered. Additional details on the benchmark modular system are the same as we introduced in our recent work (Dai et al., 2023).

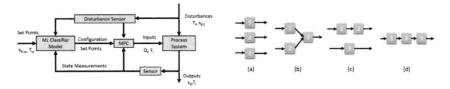

Figure 1. (Left) MPC/ML classifier feedback loop schematic; (Right) All configurations considered for the 3 module system.

3. Multi-class Adaptive Boosting Algorithms

Boosting has been a very successful technique for solving the binary classification problem. However, the ways to extend AdaBoost from two-class to multi-class depend on the interpretation or view of the success of AdaBoost in binary classification, which still remains controversial. Here we choose a widely used multi-class AdaBoost algorithm (Hastie et al., 2009) which directly extends to the multi-class problem without reducing it to multiple two-class problems.

In order to better quantify the performance of a classifier prediction, we propose a the following score metric which is zero when the best configuration is chosen, and gets gradually larger if a configuration is chosen that gives worse performance.

$$Score = \frac{PI_{predicted} - PI_{best}}{PI_{best}} \tag{1}$$

Where $PI_{predicted}$ represents the controller performance index (PI) using MPC based on the configuration chosen by the classifier, and PI_{best} represents the PI using the best performing configuration. When the $PI_{predicted} = PI_{best}$, it indicates that the predicted configuration is the optimal configuration, and the corresponding $Score = 0$. When $PI_{predicted} > PI_{best}$, the classifier is inaccurate in choosing the best configuration and the $Score > 0$. It is apparent that $Score$ can be quite large in magnitude when the degradation in controller performance is large, which could happen if the controller is unable to stabilize the system or reach the desired set point in the given configuration.

To encourage the trained classifier to avoid inaccurate decisions with high $Score$ values we modify the multi-class AdaBoost algorithm with the aforementioned $Score$. We call the resulting algorithm S-AdaBoost, which proceeds as shown in Algorithm 1:

Algorithm 1. *S-AdaBoost*
1. *Initialize the observation weights $w_i = \frac{1}{n}, i = 1,2,\dots,N$.*
2. *For $m = 1$ to M:*
   (a) *Fit a classifier $T^{(m)}(\boldsymbol{x})$ to the training data using weights w_i.*
   (b) *$err^{(m)} = \sum_{i=1}^{N} w_i \cdot s_i \mathbb{1}(c_i \neq T^{(m)}(x_i)) / \sum_{i=1}^{N} w_i$.*
   (c) *$\alpha^{(m)} = \log\frac{1-err^{(m)}}{err^{(m)}} + \log(K-1)$.*
   (d) **if** $\alpha^{(m)} < 0$ **then**
       $m \leftarrow m + 1$
       exit loop
   end if
   (e) *$w_i := w_i \cdot \exp(\alpha^{(m)} \cdot \mathbb{1}(c_i \neq T^{(m)}(x_i)))$, for $i = 1,2,\dots N$*
   (f) *Re-normalize w_i*

3. Output

$$C(\boldsymbol{x}) = \max_k \sum_{m=1}^{M} \alpha^{(m)} \cdot \mathbb{1}(T^{(m)}(\boldsymbol{x}) = k)$$

Where N represents the number of all training data points, M represents the number of member classifiers, K represents the number of all possible classifications, $\boldsymbol{x}$ represents the feature matrix of all training data points, s_i represents the score and c_i represents the target of the ith data point, and $C(\boldsymbol{x})$ represents the classification results of all training data. $\alpha^{(m)}$ is the weight of output of weak classifiers to build *S-AdaBoost*. Note that the only difference between S-AdaBoost and multi-class AdaBoost is the existence of s_i in 2(b), in which s_i increases the weights of misclassified instances in terms of the magnitude of incorrectness from PI. Instead of only focusing on prediction accuracy, this modification helps the classifier avoid configurations that may cause severe degradation in controller performance and increases the tolerance for inaccurate predictions where there is little degradation in PI compared to the best configuration.

4. Results and Discussion

Our previous work (Dai et al., 2023) considered control of numbered-up modular systems with fixed configurations, and which demonstrated that operational conditions could affect selection of the optimal configuration of modules. Using the same benchmark modular three reactor system, in this work we collect data on the control performance of different modular configurations for various initial conditions of states, values of disturbances and set points of process outputs from a space-filling sampling of the parameter space. We run 8641 different control simulations considering 4 configurations to construct the training and test data set. The simulated ranges of all features are listed in Table 1. Following data collection, various classifier models are trained which fall within three major types: support vector machines (SVM), decision trees (DT), and k-nearest neighbors (KNN). Output of these classifiers are used to construct ensemble classifiers using both traditional AdaBoost and the S-AdaBoost algorithm proposed in Section 3. All classifiers are trained using LIBSVM v0.8.0, DecisionTree v0.12.3, and NearestNeighborModels v0.2.3 in the MLJ v0.19.5 package. Other details on packages and computing environments are the same as our recent work (Dai et al., 2023).

The performance of machine learning classifiers has been listed in Table 2. The classifier based on AdaBoost model is limited to KNN classifiers due to its highest prediction accuracy. After applying S-AdaBoost, the magnitude of error in the incorrect prediction significantly decreases without losing too much accuracy on predicting the optimal configuration, with the worst case value of *Score* an order of magnitude less than it is in any of the individual classifiers. This is due to the fact that the S-AdaBoost algorithm specifically takes the *Score* into account when choosing the configuration, thus decreasing the likelihood of severe degradation in performance from an incorrect choice in modular configuration and mitigating the risk of a poor control decision.

Table 1. Range of features that have been used for generating training data.

Features	Range
Feed temperature (K)	300 - 340
Temperature set point in each reactor (K)	$388.7 - 438.7$
Initial mol fraction of B in each reactor	0.11-0.26
Output mol fraction of B set point	0.01-0.25

After implementing MPC with S-AdaBoost classifier, for most cases, it performs as well as the most accurate individual classifier KNN. This is demonstrated in Figure 3, which shows a setpoint tracking case study with different MPCs, in which the classifier embedded MPC takes action of switching configuration from (a) to (b) in Figure 1 (right). The switched strategy gives the lowest number on PI and the quickest change to the new setpoint, demonstrating that MPC with KNN/S-AdaBoost classifier has the best control performance for some setpoint tracking cases. Note that the PI in Figures 3 and 4 are calculated from the real-time control simulations, while the PI used to generate *Score* are calculated by the MPC optimal solution which contains the control performance in a forward horizon at the starting point right after setpoint change.

Figure 4 shows the set point tracking case that is the worst prediction of KNN classifier, where KNN embedded MPC uses the series configuration (d), and S-AdaBoost one

Table 2. Machine learning classifiers performance comparison

Classifier Model	% cases selecting the best configuration	% cases when *Score* > 0.1	Worst case value of *Score*
SVM	81.7	1.48	12.10
DT	85.0	1.03	38.59
KNN	94.4	3.87	39.09
AdaBoost	94.4	2.78	39.09
S-AdaBoost	91.0	1.71	3.86

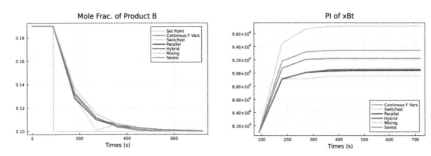

Figure 3. Mole fraction profile (left) and performance index (right) of the desired product B in the final output stream. "Switched" represents the profile generated by MPC with machine learning classifiers, including KNN and S-AdaBoost which have the same performance.

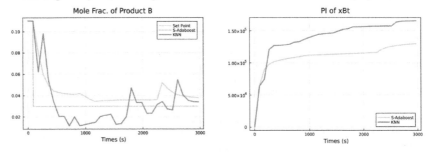

Figure 4. Mole fraction profile (left) and performance index (right) of B in the final output stream for MPCs embedded with KNN and S-AdaBoost respectively.

chooses the parallel configuration (a). Neither of them switches configuration during the simulated control process. Compared to KNN, MPC with S-AdaBoost guides the system to the new setpoint quicker with less oscillations because it is able to identify the best configuration. Although the classifier is trained on single iteration of an MPC optimization solve, the results demonstrate superior performance in a moving horizon, closed loop simulation as well. Overall, our results demonstrate that while S-AdaBoost sacrifices some accuracy, it successfully avoids choosing configurations that severely degrade controller performance.

5. Conclusion

In this work, an approach to determine integer control decisions *a priori* to solving the MPC problem using improved data-driven machine learning classifier algorithms was presented. A metric was proposed to demonstrate how similar the performance of the predicted configuration is to that of the best configuration. Based on that, a new AdaBoost algorithm was proposed to help guide decision-making on optimal configuration away from those that severely degrade performance. Finally, a set point tracking case study was analyzed which demonstrates the MPC with AdaBoost classifier has the best performance on decreasing the magnitude of error in the incorrect prediction and generally chooses configurations that give quicker set point recovery than the other classifiers with fewer cases of severely degraded performance. As future work, we aim to extend this framework to systems with larger numbers of modules, and modules of different functionality.

References

M. Baldea, T. F. Edgar, B. L. Stanley, A. A. Kiss (2017), Modular manufacturing processes: Status, challenges, and opportunities. AIChE Journal 63, 4262–4272.

L. Breiman (2001), Random forests, Mach. Learn., vol. 45, no. 1, pp. 5–32.

Y. Dai and A. Allman (2023), Foundations of process/product analytics and machine learning fopam 2023, university of california, davis ca, july 30-aug 3, 2023 learning the best configuration for controlling modular dynamic systems, Ann Arbor, vol. 1001, p. 48109.

Y. Dai, S. Fay, and A. Allman (2023), Analysis of model predictive control in numbered-up modular facilities, Digital Chemical Engineering, vol. 7, p. 100088.

T. G. Dietterich (2000), Ensemble methods in machine learning, Multiple Classifier Systems. Berlin, Germany: Springer-Verlag, pp. 1–15.

S. K. S. Fan, S. C. Lin, and P. F. Tsai, (2016), Wafer fault detection and key step identification for semiconductor manufacturing using principal component analysis, AdaBoost and decision tree. Journal of Industrial and Production Engineering, 33(3), 151-168.

Yoav Freund and Robert E. Schapire (1996), Experiments with a new boosting algorithm. icml. Vol. 96.

T. Hastie, S. Rosset, J. Zhu, and H. Zou (2009), Multi-class AdaBoost, Statistics and its Interface, vol. 2, no. 3, pp. 349–360.

R. Kohavi and D. H. Wolpert (1996), Bias plus variance decomposition for zero-one loss functions, in Proc. Int. Conf. Machine Learning, pp. 275–283.

J. Liu, D. Munoz de la Pena, P. D. Christofides (2009), Distributed model predictive control of nonlinear process systems. AIChE Journal 55, 1171–1184.

P. T. May-Ostendorp, G. P. Henze, B. Rajagopalan, and C. D. Corbin, (2013). Extraction of supervisory building control rules from model predictive control of windows in a mixed mode building. Journal of Building Performance Simulation, 6(3), 199-219

Y. Shao, V. M. Zavala (2020), Modularity measures: Concepts, computation, and applications to manufacturing systems. AIChE Journal 66, e16965.

Y. Xu, K. Cong, Q. Zhu, and Y. He, (2021), A novel AdaBoost ensemble model based on the reconstruction of local tangent space alignment and its application to multiple faults recognition. Journal of Process Control, 104, 158-167.

Flavio Manenti, Gintaras V. Reklaitis (Eds.), Proceedings of the 34th European Symposium on Computer Aided Process Engineering / 15th International Symposium on Process Systems Engineering (ESCAPE34/PSE24), June 2-6, 2024, Florence, Italy

Simulation-Based Robust Model Predictive Control for n-Dimensional Linear Multi-Agent Systems with Uncertain and Heterogeneous Dynamics in Modular Plants

Helaleh Badrnoebashar [a], Anselm Klose [a,c], Jonathan Mädler [b,c], Leon Urbas[a,b]

[a] *Faculty of Electrical and Computer Engineering, Chair of Process Control Systems, TUD Dresden University of Technology, 01069 Dresden, Germany.*

[b] *Faculty of Mechanical Engineering, Process Systems Engineering Group, TUD Dresden University of Technology, 01069 Dresden, Germany;*

[c] *School of Engineering Sciences, Process-to-Order Lab, TUD Dresden University of Technology, 01069 Dresden, Germany*
helaleh.badrnoebashar@tu-dresden.de

Abstract

The process industry has effectively used model predictive control (MPC), a potent advanced process control approach. Multi-agent systems (MASs), on the other hand, are built with various subsystems that cooperate to accomplish a particular goal. Similarly, modular plants are connections of several modules, each intended to carry out a particular task in the larger system. In this paper, first, we discuss modular plants and MASs to see if they are comparable. Then, we propose a simulation-based robust MPC strategy for n-dimensional linear MASs with uncertain and heterogeneous dynamics. The proposed control strategy consists of state space MPC and robust control. As a result, our work indicates the potential of distributed MPC for n-dimensional linear MASs with uncertain and heterogeneous dynamics in modular plants, which could help enhance the accuracy, effectiveness, and robustness of the control strategy in the process industry. The proposed control strategy can be extended to other applications in the process industry, and ongoing research is focused on using existing MAS control techniques further to improve the performance of the controller in modular plants.

Keywords: modular plants, multi-agent systems, model predictive control, robustness

1. Introduction

This paper focuses on comparing modular plants and MASs, exploring the application of MAS principles for controlling and optimizing modular plants, and examining the potential of distributed MPC for MASs in modular plants. The hypothesis is based on the idea that MAS principles can be utilized to simplify the controller design of modular plants and as a result, enhance their effectiveness and robustness in the process industry. Modular plants are instrumental in process engineering, notably within sectors such as chemicals, pharmaceuticals, and fine chemicals. They excel at rapidly deploying plants for industrial production and efficiently integrating package units and logistics systems into existing or new facilities. At the heart of these modular plants are Process Equipment Assemblies (PEAs). PEAs are self-sufficient, automated units with one or more functional equipment assemblies. These assemblies, known as Functional Equipment Assemblies (FEAs), are composed of adaptable components working together to perform specific process steps. On the other hand, components (COMP) are the smallest unit which is no longer separable in modularization. The COMPs are determined by function, performance, and type (VDI 2776-1, 2020). Modularization significantly expedites the construction of tiny to large-sized production plants. By utilizing industry-specific PEAs as self-contained functional units, this approach reduces engineering efforts, minimizes early-stage errors, and yields substantial cost and time savings (Baldea et al., 2017). Mädler et al. (2022) propose the fundamental idea of using so-called smart PEAs (= models combined with PEAs) to enable online optimization in modular plants. Multi-agent systems (MASs) are composed of multiple subsystems that collaborate towards a common objective, offering numerous advantages when compared to traditional and single-agent systems. Notably, the presence of multiple agents ensures system functionality even in the event of agent failures, showcasing the fault tolerance of such systems. Furthermore, new agents can be added to the system without significant redesign, and control is distributed among agents, leading to more efficient decision-making and less dependency on a central control point (Bloch et al., 2018). The similarity between MASs and modular plants is that each MAS agent can be considered a module in the modular plant. Therefore, the idea of MASs and consensus control can be extended to the modular plant level. Hence, we can apply controller designs specifically designed for MASs to simplify the controller design of modular plants. However, only a few papers have explored modular plants as MASs, leaving a gap in research. Hence, this study aims to fill this gap by comparing these two concepts and examining an example of achieving consensus in linear time-invariant (LTI) heterogeneous Multi-Agent Systems (MASs) in the process industry. Zamfirescu et al. (2003) present an engineering approach to address the increasing demand for managing highly modular plants. It discusses the implementation of an agent-based manufacturing controller, inspired by the social behavior of ants. The objective is to tackle challenges like variations in production resources and planning processes while maintaining optimal plant performance. Moreover, MASs have been highlighted as a useful tool in the process industry by Denkena et al. (2003) and Mönch et al. (2003) in two separate studies. In Komesker et al. (2022), the flexibility of production lines has been increased considering the modular production concept, which is like having building blocks to quickly adapt to changing production needs. However, this approach needs new ways to plan and control production. To achieve this, taking advantage of MASs has been proposed.

2. Comparing MASs and Modular Plants

As modular plants and MASs live on different levels of abstraction, comparing them would be challenging. In other words, MASs are rather an automation architecture while modular plants in their entirety, are a technology. This technology comprises a default automation architecture with Module Type Package (MTP), services, Process Orchestration Layer (POL), and recipes. To compare MASs and modular plants, a common ground for assessment should be created. This common ground can be created by mapping modular automation components into automation architecture categories where MAS also fits. Imagine we have three modules with individual MTPs, each providing different services. Here, the POL defines how these modules collaborate in a process and recipes guide the actions of these modules. To clarify this, imagine we have a toolbox and a set of rules to construct different things. The tools we are using, are our MTP. The rules telling how to use these tools are our recipes and how we organize our tools following the rules is like POL. Besides, the different tasks, our tools can do, are our services. On the other hand, if we compare this concept with a MAS, each agent has its own set of tools or MTPs and can follow the rules or recipes to fulfill its tasks or services. The MAS automation architecture defines how they coordinate and work together and who decides what to do. Now, considering factors like decision-making processes, communication patterns, fault tolerance, and adaptability, this common frame could assess how well MAS principles align with the modular plant's structure. Several aspects of MASs are comparable with modular plants, and this can lead to using the MAS principles to ease the control and optimization of the modular plants. For instance, collaboration is essential in MASs to achieve common goals and efficient operation. The cooperative approach also applies to modular plants, where PEAs, services, and the POL work together to enhance efficiency. One of the most critical aspects of both MASs and modular plants is decision-making based on local information, with modules relying on internal states, inputs, and predefined rules encoded in recipes and control algorithms for decision-making. Also, coordination between these autonomous units becomes vital in certain situations. Considering resiliency aspects, in MASs, adaptation to failures, and integrating new agents are paramount. On the other hand, as in MASs, when one module fails, the other ones reconfigure the system to maintain the overall performance and efficiency and in the case of module removal or addition, modular plants can perform the plug-and-play integration of modules more easily. However, it is noteworthy that modules have very different capabilities which means that the redistribution of workload is heavily constrained. Furthermore, in both MASs and the case, modular plants are associated based on the choreography method, decisions are made in a distributed way and agents or modules are interconnected, exchanging data to reach an agreement or to optimize the performance of the plant, (Stutz et al., 2020). However, it is important to note that the specific control methods and organizational forms used in MASs require adaptation and tailoring to be appropriate for the objectives, constraints, and characteristics of modular plants for different industrial applications. In the context of applying the MAS concept to modular plants, the leader-follower form would be more applicable. In a modular plant, we can consider a 'leader' module that leads the actions of the other 'follower' modules. The leader module would be responsible for managing and orchestrating the actions of the whole plant, by taking decisions and defining control objectives. On the other side, similar to the MASs, the follower modules would execute the control commands of the leader. The choice of the leader module would be important due to the capabilities of different PEAs, both in terms of physical attributes and software functionalities. Also, the consensus form of the MASs and modular plants are comparable and it can be an interesting approach to consider for the control of the modular plants. For instance, both consensus-based MAS and modular plants need communication among different components. In modular plants, PEAs require coordination to achieve specific goals and similarly, in consensus systems, agents agree on a common state or value. The consensus and leader-follower forms are just examples, and another organizational form of MASs may suit better depending on the system's complexity. The dynamics, interactions, and goals of the plants should be carefully analyzed to determine the most suitable MAS approach. In conclusion, the synergy of modules in the plants and MASs can result in higher flexibility and resiliency in the industry. There are several reasons for this claim. For example, in a modular plant, similar to MASs, as mentioned before, each module can act as an autonomous agent that can make local decisions based on the requirements. This form of decentralized decision-making allows modules to adapt to condition changes. Besides, communication and coordination between different modules, similar to MASs, enables adaptiveness against disturbances. For instance, if one module faces changes in production requirements, it can communicate with the neighbor modules to adjust resource allocation.

3. Develop a Consensus Achievement MAS Case for the Modular Plants

Consensus achievement in MASs refers to a collaborative process in which agents aim to reach a common state or decision through communication. Despite having different initial information and preferences, agents coordinate their decisions to agree on a shared objective (Mesbahi et al., 2010). In Badrno et al. (2023), the distributed consensus control of the linear n-order MASs using model predictive control has been investigated. Each agent has different dynamics from the others, but the number of the inputs and outputs of the systems has been considered the same. In this study, two types of model uncertainties are considered: polytopic and multi-model uncertainties. In reality, multi-model uncertainties refer to the cases in which the specific model of the system is not precisely known or when we have different operational modes or different task requirements, user commands, and environmental conditions. The ability of an industrial process to tolerate the expected variability of raw materials, operating conditions, environmental variables, parameter uncertainties, and human factors is referred to as robustness. Even when levels of input variables and noise parameters undergo severe and substantial variations, a robust process maintains its steady performance consistently at the target level and minimizes the impact of disturbances on product quality (Wei et al., 2010). In the mentioned paper, consensus is achieved using linear matrix inequalities and slack variables. The graph representing the communication among different neighbor agents is considered as a directed graph or digraph meaning the collaboration among agents is directional. Also, in this paper, the determined common point for all agents is point zero, but this condition does not restrict the application while we can control the deviations from a setpoint, or in other words, control the error signals. Besides, in safety-critical systems, converging to point zero, can be considered for certain safety-related variables in which returning to point zero in certain circumstances is crucial. Also, while doing module reconfigurations, reaching point zero can be considered as a reset or initial condition.

4. Case Study

To clarify the applicability of the consensus form of MASs in modular plants, consider the following simulation example implemented in MATLAB. There are five PEAs with linearized dynamics, each fulfilling a task in a modular plant. The dynamics of each PEA are different from the others, but they have the same dimensions, or in other words, same number of inputs and outputs, and all systems are stable and controllable. The purpose is to simulate the consensus-based predictive control of these PEAs. As mentioned before, all PEAs would agree on a common point of zero. Different quantities could be considered as the states of the systems. For instance, in one PEA, the state would be the deviation between the desired temperature and the real temperature, in the other PEA, it would be the deviation between the desired level and the real level, and in other PEAs, the states would be safety critical variables of the systems. These PEAs interact with each other based on a predefined communicational fixed digraph as follows.

Figure 1: System digraph

In other words, PEAs would send and get data only from the neighboring PEAs. These communications would be defined based on the purpose of the plant and the requirements of the other PEAs. The dynamics of the PEAs can be considered unknown or different operational modes can be considered for each PEA. Here it is assumed that the exact dynamics of each PEA is unknown and it may be one of the three given linear dynamics in the example in Badrno et al. (2023). Multi-model uncertainty, which is considered in this paper, is one of the prevalent uncertainties in the process industry, and addressing this issue would be an achievement in increasing system resiliency. The initial conditions, constraints, weighting matrices, the eigenvalues of the Laplacian matrix, and dynamics of the PEAs are assumed to be the same as in Badrno et al. (2023). The eigenvalues of the Laplacian matrix are representative of the communication features of our digraph. The digraph of figure 1, fulfills the necessary conditions of consensus achievement, which contains a spanning tree. The states of the system are 3 in 1 vector indicating the physical quantities in different zones. It is important to note that, to do the mathematical calculations, the value of the states should be normalized at first. All mathematical formulations used in the code are derived from the aforementioned reference Badrno et al. (2023). The consensus protocol guarantees the convergence of all defined states as follows in figure 2. The control inputs of all PEAs are depicted in figure 3.

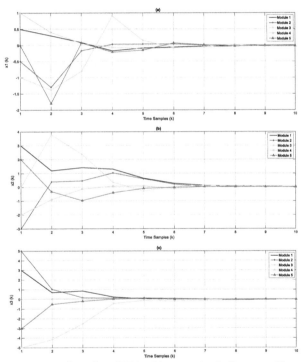

Figure 2: State Trajectories of PEAs, (a) state value in first zone, (b) state value in second zone, (c) state value in third zone

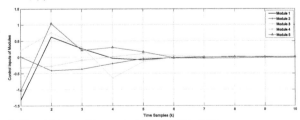

Figure 3: Time history of the control inputs of the PEAs

5. Conclusion

In this study, the research brings together three fields MASs, MPC, and modular plants. Recognizing the common principles in these domains, which are adaptability and modularity, the study proposes a robust model predictive control of n-order LTI MASs interpreting agents of MASs as modules of a modular plant. Therefore, we can apply controller designs specifically designed for MASs to the modular plants. Besides, the application of distributed consensus control in MASs, specifically addressing multi-model uncertainty, is explored in this research, with the help of simulations. However, it is important to note that the specific control methods and organizational forms used in MASs require tailoring to be appropriate for the objectives and characteristics of modular plants and this can be the future work.

References

H. Badrno, M. Baradarannia, P. Bagheri, M. Badamchizadeh, 2023, Distributed Predictive Consensus Control of Uncertain Linear Multi-agent Systems with Heterogeneous Dynamics, Iranian Journal of Science and Technology, Transactions of Electrical Engineering, 47(1), 255–267.

M. Baldea, T. F. Edgar, B. L. Stanley, A. A. Kiss, 2017, Modular manufacturing processes: Status, challenges, and opportunities, AIChE Journal, 63(10), 4262–4272.

H. Bloch, T. Grebner, A. Fay, S. Hensel, A. Menschner, L. Urbas, M. Hoernicke, T. Knohl, J. Bernshausen, B. Ag, 2018, Orchestration of Services in Modular Process Plants, IECON 2018 - 44th Annual Conference of the IEEE Industrial Electronics Society, 2935–2940.

B. Denkena, M. Zwick, P.-O. Woelk, 2003, Multiagent-Based Process Planning and Scheduling in Context of Supply Chains, In V. Mařík, D. McFarlane, & P. Valckenaers (Eds.), Holonic and Multi-Agent Systems for Manufacturing, 2744, 100–109.

S. Komesker, W. Motsch, J. Popper, A. Sidorenko, A. Wagner, M. Ruskowski, 2022, Enabling a Multi-Agent System for Resilient Production Flow in Modular Production Systems, Procedia CIRP, 107, 991–998.

J. Mädler, I. Viedt, J. Lorenz, L. Urbas, 2022, Requirements to a digital twin-centered concept for smart manufacturing in modular plants considering distributed knowledge. In Computer Aided Chemical Engineering, 49, 1507–1512.

M. Mesbahi, M. Egerstedt, 2010, Graph Theoretic Methods in Multiagent Networks: Princeton University Press.

L. Mönch, M. Stehli, J. Zimmermann, 2003, FABMAS: An Agent-Based System for Production Control of Semiconductor Manufacturing Processes. In V. Mařík, D. McFarlane, & P. Valckenaers (Eds.), Holonic and Multi-Agent Systems for Manufacturing, 2744, 258–267.

A. Stutz, A. Fay, M. Barth, M. Maurmaier, 2020, Orchestration vs. Choreography Functional Association for Future Automation Systems, IFAC-PapersOnLine, 53(2), 8268–8275.

VDI 2776-1, 2020, Verfahrenstechnische Anlagen—Modulare Anlagen—Grundlagen und Planung modularer Anlagen (Richtlinie 1). Beuth.

D. Wei, K. Ji, 2010, Resilient industrial control system (RICS): Concepts, formulation, metrics, and insights, 2010 3rd International Symposium on Resilient Control Systems, 15–22.

C. Zamfirescu, P. Valckenaers, H. H. Van Brussel, B. S. Germain, 2003, A Case Study for Modular Plant Control, In V. Mařík, D. McFarlane, & P. Valckenaers (Eds.), Holonic and Multi-Agent Systems for Manufacturing, 2744, 268–279.

Flavio Manenti, Gintaras V. Reklaitis (Eds.), Proceedings of the 34th European Symposium on Computer Aided Process Engineering / 15th International Symposium on Process Systems Engineering (ESCAPE34/PSE24), June 2-6, 2024, Florence, Italy

Causality-driven dynamic scheduling of multipurpose batch plants

Taicheng Zheng[a], Dan Li[a], Jie Li[a*]

a Centre for Process Integration, Department of Chemical Engineering, School of Engineering, The University of Manchester, Oxford Road, Manchester, M13 9PL, United Kingdom

*Corresponding author email: jie.li-2.manchester.ac.uk;

Abstract

Modern multipurpose batch plants often require non-periodic rescheduling in response to random disturbances. The rescheduling strategy, that is, when to reschedule and how to reschedule, is crucial not only for reducing long-term cost, but also for the alleviation of nervousness within production environment. However, such two objectives often conflict in practice. In this study, we propose a causality-driven rescheduling strategy to address this challenge in multipurpose batch plants that widely exist in chemical, pharmaceutical, and food industries. The main idea is to use a directed Probabilistic Graphical Model (PGM) to formalize the temporal and spatial causal relationships between tasks. As the dynamic system evolves, given the evidence of observed disturbances, the PGM serves as a standby knowledge base to help scheduler infer the posterior distribution of impacted level of unobserved tasks. When the combined count of observed highly affected tasks and unobserved but highly likely to be impacted tasks exceeds a threshold, rescheduling is triggered. Also, the strategy alleviates system nervousness by fixing tasks that are less likely to be highly impacted. We compare this strategy with the classic exhaustively-minimize-cost strategy on a standard benchmark problem. Numerical results show that, comparatively, our strategy reduces 91.4% computational time and 91.2% count of task changes, at a sacrifice of 18.7% cumulative cost.

Keywords: dynamic scheduling, causality, directed Probabilistic Graphical Model, multipurpose batch plant.

1. Introduction

Practically, due to the presence of irregularly arriving disturbances, multipurpose batch plants often operate in a dynamic pattern (Ouelhadj and Petrovic, 2009). This pattern often involves a repeating process of scheduling, execution, observation, feedback, and next-round rescheduling. For example, in chemical, pharmaceutical, and food industries, during schedule execution, schedulers may need to frequently reschedule in response to various disruptions such as machine breakdown, task delay, raw material shortage, and demand variation. As indicated by the literature, in such dynamic environments, the rescheduling strategy is crucial for enhancing long-term performance. The rescheduling strategy includes two principal aspects: *when* to reschedule and *how* to reschedule. In the case of multipurpose batch plants, arguably because of the complexity of operational logic, previous studies mostly follow a periodically, completely rescheduling strategy (Gupta and Maravelias, 2019). However, as we will provide evidence later in the case study, such strategy often causes a high-level nervousness within the production environment. In plain terms, schedules before and after rescheduling are often quite different. Such nervousness often causes the plant personnel being strained to adjust to a constantly changing schedule, which has negative impacts on the production process (Pinedo, 2016).

When experienced human schedulers implement dynamic scheduling, they do not mechanically reschedule in a periodic manner. Instead, they often at first evaluate the impact of newly observed disturbances on the schedule by causal reasoning, and then adjust only the targeted part of the schedule. In multipurpose batch plants, spatially, if an upstream task was affected by a disruption, downstream tasks in the production process will be affected as well; temporally, if an earlier task is delayed, subsequent tasks on the shared machine will also be affected. Such causality-based expertise, which is mainly achieved by click-and-drag human-machine interaction in scheduling software, has been proved to be effective in many cases (Harjunkoski et al., 2014). However, to the best of our awareness, no literature has formalized this idea before. In this study, we propose a causality-driven rescheduling strategy for dynamic scheduling of multipurpose batch plants. The main idea is to use this logical causality to factorize the joint probability distribution of impacted level of to-be-executed tasks by a directed Probabilistic Graphical Model (PGM). When a disturbance is observed, the PGM performs inference algorithms to derive a posterior distribution that presents the overall impacted level of remaining unobserved part of the schedule. This posterior distribution is then used to further design the rescheduling strategy. We test the effectiveness of this idea in one of the standard benchmark problems in process scheduling community (Kallrath, 2002). The results show that the strategy can significantly reduce production nervousness in the measure of task change counts and computational time at a cost of 18.7% cumulative objective value.

2. Methodology

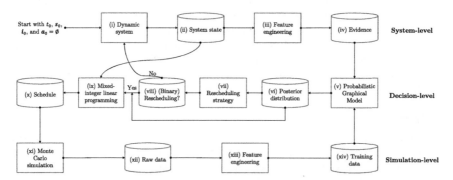

Figure 1. Flowchart of causality-driven dynamic scheduling.
In the flowchart, while squared boxes denote mathematical models or algorithms, cylindrical containers denote datasets.

We first describe the dynamic scheduling problem of multipurpose batch plants and then illustrate our methodology by going through the flowchart in Fig. 1. We consider a discrete-time dynamic system $s_{t+1} = T(s_t, a_t, i_t)$ of a multipurpose plant that can be characterized by an encapsulating parameter λ (include plant layout, recipes, and supply/demand profile). In the system, starts from t_0 and ends at t_f, s_t is vectorized notation for system state; a_t is action set that the system is scheduled to take within horizon $[t, t + H)$; i_t is informational state that has been revealed to the scheduler; and T denotes transition function. For informational state i_t, we assume that (1) we have known information about the distribution of i_t; (2) we have a certain length of *vision* v over i_t. That is, at v-time-periods ahead of the instantiation of disturbance i_t, the information is revealed to the scheduler; (3) after i_t is instantiated, it will not change. The target of the problem is to find a policy π such that $a_{t+1} = \pi(s_t, a_t, i_t)$ to minimize the cumulative cost $c = \sum_{t_0}^{t_f} c_t$ and the cumulative action difference $d = \sum_{t_0}^{t_f-1} \Delta(a_t, a_{t+1})$, where Δ is a difference-measuring function that maps the tuple (a_t, a_{t+1}) to a non-negative integer. At the system-level, the system dynamics starts with t_0, s_{t_0}, i_{t_0}, and $a_{t_0} = \emptyset$. If $a_t = \emptyset$ or binary rescheduling decision (viii) is triggered, the system state (ii) is fed to a Mixed-Integer Linear Programming (MILP) (ix) to generate a to-be-executed schedule (x); otherwise (viii) is not triggered, the system evolves to a new system state s_{t+1} as time advances. The essential part of the causality-driven policy is the active interaction between the rest modules. Specifically, after a schedule (x) is output by (ix), rather than directly advance the system by taking actions from (x), we first perform multiple episodes of Monte Carlo simulation (xi) to sample different realizations of unobserved disturbances in the horizon of (x). Then, for the set of tasks that are in (x) but fall beyond vision v, which is denoted by $\tilde{X} = \{X_1, X_2, ..., X_n\}$, we construct a PGM $\mathcal{G} = (\tilde{X}, \mathcal{A})$, such that each node X_i is a random variable that describes the impacted level of unobserved task X_i and the set of directed arcs $\mathcal{A}$ is the temporal and spatial causal relationship that described in Sec. 1. The PGM factorizes the joint probability distribution of $\tilde{X}$ in the semantics that $P(\tilde{X}) = \prod_{i=1}^{n} P(X_i | u(X_i))$, where $u(X_i)$ denotes the parent nodes of X_i. Then, by feeding the training data (xiv) that was generated from (xi) and processed by feature engineering (xiii), we can estimate a full-fledged PGM as a buffered knowledge base to help the scheduler to infer the posterior distribution $P(X_i | \bar{X}), \forall i \in \tilde{X} \backslash \bar{X}$ from evidence (iv), where $\bar{X}$ is the set of tasks that has been observed being affected by disturbance. In other words, the distribution of impacted level of remain unobserved tasks can be updated by realizations of $\bar{X}$. Finally, the framework iterates between the three different abstraction levels and advance until t_f.

3. Case study

We test the effectiveness of our causality-driven policy on one of the standard benchmark problems in process scheduling community (Kallrath, 2002). The State-Task Network (STN) representation of the problem is shown in Fig. 2. The processing time, minimum and maximum batch size parameter are identical to the supplementary material of (Li et al., 2022). In addition, we assume that there is a \$1 setup cost for each task and proportional cost of batch size is 0. The capacity for raw material k0 is infinity, for k11 and k21 is 25 ton, and for the rest is 15 ton. The price for each material is listed in Table 1. The inventory cost per time-period is 0.15 multiple of price and backlog cost for products is 1.5 multiple of price.

Table 1. Price for each material (unit: \$)

Material	k0	k11	k21	k22	k31	k41	k42	k43	k44	k51
Price	1	5	10	10	10	10	10	15	10	15
Material	k52	k61	k62	k63	p1	p2	p3	p4	p5	
Price	15	15	20	20	50	50	50	50	50	

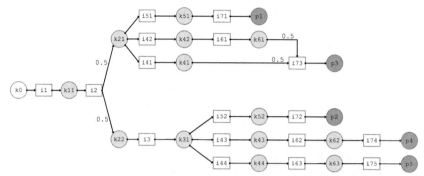

Figure 2. State-Task Network (STN) representation of the benchmark problem (Kallrath, 2002).

For system dynamics, we assume that the horizon of each schedule is 72 h (3 days), and we perform a rolling-horizon dynamic scheduling experiment over 336 h (2 weeks) timespan. For raw material k0, the regular supply is 20 ton every hour. For each product, there is a regular demand of 12 tons per 12h that starts from t_0. We assume five types of possible disturbances (Table 2), and the scheduler has a vision of 36h over each type of disturbance.

Table 2. Assumed disturbances in the dynamic scheduling problem

Disturbance	Raw material supply change	Demand change	Processing time change
Distribution	$\mathcal{N}_{clipped}(1, 0.5^2)$ [a]	$\text{Poisson}_{clipped}(0.02) *$ $\mathcal{U}(0.5, 1.5)$ [b]	$\mathcal{N}_{clipped}(1, 0.5^2)$ [c]
Disturbance	Machine breakdown (occurrence)	Machine breakdown (duration)	Yield change
Distribution	$\text{Bern}(0.02)$ [d]	$\mathcal{U}(2, 5)$ [e]	$\mathcal{U}(0.5, 1)$ [f]

[a]: The raw material supply will be affected by a clipped Gaussian random variable such that the maximum purchasable amount of raw material will be limited to $\mathcal{N}_{clipped}(1, 0.5^2)$-multiple of the regular supply. The random variable is clipped (that is, when the random variable is sampled beyond the boundary, the value will set to its closest boundary value) between $[0.5, 1]$ for the consideration of nonnegativity. [b]: The unexpected arrival of demand will be count of orders (clipped Poisson random variable) multiplies amount for each order (uniform random variable). The Poisson random variable is clipped between $[0, 2]$ to avoid infinity. [c]: The processing time for tasks will be affected by a clipped Gaussian random variable such that the varied processing time will be $\left\lceil \tau \cdot \mathcal{N}_{clipped}(1, 0.5^2) \right\rceil$, where τ is the nominal processing time and $\mathcal{N}_{clipped}(1, 0.5^2)$ is Gaussian random variable that is clipped between $\left[\frac{1}{\tau}, 2\right]$. [d]: Whether there is a breakdown disruption on a machine is a Bernoulli random variable with $p = 0.02$. In other words, for each time-period and each machine, there is 0.02 chance that there will be a machine breakdown disruption. [e]: When a machine breakdown is occurred, the duration of the breakdown is a uniform random variable $\mathcal{U}(2, 5)$. [f]: The yield of each task is $\mathcal{U}(0.5, 1)$-multiple of the original batch size.

4. Results

There are various measures to quantify how effective a rescheduling strategy performs in a dynamic environment. To set up a standard benchmark for the numerical results, we consider the following metrics:

- c^*. The optimal objective cost of the static version of scheduling problem under *nominal* conditions. That is, we regard the dynamic scheduling problem as static by assuming that there is no disturbance through the entire dynamic scheduling timespan. Since the occurrence of a disturbance event will usually deteriorate objective, c^* is served as a reference lower bound for the cumulative objective cost in our case study.

- c^∞. The optimal value of the dynamic scheduling problem with the assumption that the scheduler has infinite vision over uncertain events. In other words, we assume that the scheduler can foresee all realizations of uncertain events at t_0. c^∞ is obtained by solving a MILP that involves all realized uncertainties through the timespan. c^∞ is served for two purposes: (1) when comparing to c^*, c^∞ reflects how unstable a system is due to the existence of disturbance. Specifically, the larger gap between c^* and c^∞ is, the more unstable the system is. (2) c^∞ is the theoretical lower bound for any dynamic scheduling policies because a longer vision will at least not worsen the cumulative objective value.
- c^v. The cumulative objective value of a dynamic scheduling policy with finite vision v. c^v is the measure for the effectiveness of dynamic scheduling policies in practice. In this study, we compare c^v of the *causality-driven* policy with two other classic policies: *exhaustively-minimize-cost* and *periodically-minimize-cost*. To explain:
  a) c^v_{causal}. The cumulative cost of the proposed causality-driven policy. In this policy, we assume that a task is categorized as highly impacted either there is a breakdown on the execution machine, or the task is delayed over 50% of the nominal processing time, or the yield loss exceeds 40% of the original batch size. Rescheduling is triggered when the count of observed highly impacted tasks and unobserved tasks but with over 50% probability being highly impacted exceeds half of the task count in the schedule. When rescheduling is triggered, those not highly impacted tasks are fixed.
  b) $c^v_{exhaust}$. The cumulative cost of exhaustively-minimize-cost policy. That is, the objective cost is minimized through MILP every hour. For the consideration of computational time, the MILP solver is terminated either when the relative MIP gap is below 10% or runtime exceeds 300s. Also, the value of integer variables are hinted from previous solutions.
  c) $c^v_{periodic}$. The cumulative cost of periodically-minimize-cost policy. That is, the objective cost is minimized every 24h and the count of task changes is minimized every hour. When two types of minimization problems overlap, the former takes priority. The parameter for MILP solver is set identical to that in $c^v_{exhaust}$.

In addition to cumulative cost, another metric that is of our interest is the cumulative value of difference-measuring function $d = \sum_{t_0}^{t_f-1} \Delta(a_t, a_{t+1})$. d is the measure for plant nervousness of a dynamic scheduling process in practice. That is, the larger value d takes, more frequent schedule adjustment is required in production. However, it is not straightforward to define Δ since there are some subtleties in the notion of task change in multipurpose batch plant. First, unlike discrete manufacturing where the number of tasks is often predetermined, multipurpose batch plants may have schedules with variable number of tasks. Second, it can be challenging to determine whether a task is shifted from previous time slots or is a completely new addition. To setup a unified metric for comparison, we define $\Delta(a_t, a_{t+1})$ as follows: for the overlapping horizon of a_t and a_{t+1}, $\Delta(a_t, a_{t+1})$ is the sum of (1) number of tasks appear in a_t but not in a_{t+1}, and (2) number of tasks appear in a_{t+1} but not in a_t.

The numerical results are presented in Table 3. In such experimental setup, we observe that c^∞ is 8.94 multiple of c^*. This large gap between c^* and c^∞ indicates that this system is highly unstable due to the existence of disturbance that described in Table 2. Also, we notice that $c^v_{exhaust}$ is even slightly lower than the theoretical lower bound c^∞. This is because the computation of c^∞ is terminated due to 3600s time limit and there is still 1.27% MIP gap for c^∞. Therefore, $c^v_{exhaust}$ is very close to the theoretical lower bound. However, the exhaustive strategy suffers from a high value of d and a very long computational time. As a compromise, if we reduce the rescheduling frequency from every hour to every 24 h, as shown by $c^v_{periodic}$, we can see an 89.2% reduction of computational time and a 72.6% decrease of d. However, $c^v_{periodic}$ is 76.2% higher than $c^v_{exhaust}$, in which is often unacceptable practice. While the trade-off between c and d seems hard to balance, the causality-driven strategy reduces d to 830, which is even significantly lower than that in periodic strategy. Also, c^v_{causal} is only 18.7% higher than exhaustive policy. Finally, notably, the computational time for the causality-driven policy is only 8.57% of the exhaustive one.

Table 3. Numerical results for the case study

Metrics	c^*	c^∞	c^v_{causal}	$c^v_{exhaust}$	$c^v_{periodic}$
c [a] (unit: M$)	0.235[c]	2.102[d]	2.482	2.091	3.684
d [b]	-	-	830	9412	2581
Computational time (unit: CPUs)	3600	3600	657	7666	923

[a]: Cost. For c^* and c^∞, c denotes for the objective value of the static MILP solution. For c^v_{causal}, c^v_{causal}, and $c^v_{periodic}$, c is the cumulative cost. The lower c is, the lower long-term cost of a rescheduling strategy can achieve. [b]: Cumulative value of difference-measuring function $\Delta(a_t, a_{t+1})$. The lower d is, less frequent schedule adjustment is needed in dynamic scheduling. [c]: MILP solver terminates because 3600s time limit is reached with relative MIP gap of 20.68%. [d]: MILP solver terminates because 3600s time limit is reached with relative MIP gap of 1.27%.

5. Conclusions

In this study, we propose a causality-driven rescheduling strategy for dynamic scheduling problems in multipurpose batch plants. The main idea originates from the human expertise that schedule modification in practice is often driven by causal relationships between tasks. To formalize such idea, we use directed Probabilistic Graphical Model (PGM) to serve as a standby knowledge base to help scheduler quickly infer the posterior distribution of impacted level of unobserved tasks when disruption events occur. The causality-driven strategy is tested on the benchmark problem (Kallrath, 2002). The numerical results show that, compared to the exhaustively-minimize-cost strategy, our strategy reduces 91.4% computational time and 91.2% count of task changes, at a sacrifice of 18.7% cumulative cost.

6. Acknowledgements

Taicheng Zheng and Dan Li appreciate financial support from UOM-CSC (202106440020, 201908130170). Jie Li appreciates financial support from Engineering and Physical Sciences Research Council (EP/T03145X/1, EP/V051008/1).

References

Gupta, D., Maravelias, C.T., 2019. On the design of online production scheduling algorithms. Computers & Chemical Engineering 129, 106517.
Harjunkoski, I., Maravelias, C.T., Bongers, P., Castro, P.M., Engell, S., Grossmann, I.E., Hooker, J., Méndez, C., Sand, G., Wassick, J., 2014. Scope for industrial applications of production scheduling models and solution methods. Computers & Chemical Engineering 62, 161–193.
Kallrath, J., 2002. Planning and scheduling in the process industry. OR Spectrum 24, 219–250.
Li, D., Rakovitis, N., Zheng, T., Pan, Y., Li, J., Kopanos, G., 2022. Novel Multiple Time-grid Continuous-time Mathematical Formulation for Short-term Scheduling of Multipurpose Batch Plants. Ind. Eng. Chem. Res. 61, 16093–16111.
Ouelhadj, D., Petrovic, S., 2009. A survey of dynamic scheduling in manufacturing systems. J Sched 12, 417–431.
Pinedo, M.L., 2016. Scheduling. Springer International Publishing, Cham.

Flavio Manenti, Gintaras V. Reklaitis (Eds.), Proceedings of the 34th European Symposium on Computer Aided Process Engineering / 15th International Symposium on Process Systems Engineering (ESCAPE34/PSE24), June 2-6, 2024, Florence, Italy

Assessment of parameter uncertainty in the maintenance scheduling of reverse osmosis networks via a multistage optimal control reformulation

Bogdan Dorneanu,[a] Mina Keykha,[a] Harvey Arellano-Garcia[a]

[a]*LS Prozess- und Anlagentechnik, Brandenburgische Technische Universität Cottbus-Senftenberg Burger Chaussee 2, D-03044 Cottbus, Germany*
arellano@b-tu.de

Abstract

In this work, the influence of uncertain parameters on the maintenance scheduling of Reverse Osmosis Networks (RONs) is explored. Based on a foundation of successful applications in various maintenance optimization domains, this paper extends the methodology to the domain of RON regeneration actions planning, highlighting its adaptability to diverse areas of dynamic processes with planning uncertainty. Traditional approaches in membrane cleaning scheduling have predominantly relied on Mixed-Integer Nonlinear Programming (MINLP), often leading to combinatorial problems that fail to capture the dynamic nature of the system. As part of this study, a novel approach based on the Multistage Integer Nonlinear Optimal Control Problem (MSINOCP) formulation is used to automate and optimize membrane cleaning scheduling without requiring combinatorial optimization. To evaluate the consequences of parameter uncertainty, 26 scenarios are considered in which the cost of the energy unit is considered as variable based on a random distribution, and these results are compared to a scenario where a fixed cost parameter is assumed. The findings show that when the cost of energy is considered as an uncertain parameter, the optimization process requires more frequent cleaning measures.

Keywords: reverse osmosis networks, maintenance scheduling optimization, energy cost uncertainty, multistage optimal control.

1. Introduction

Reverse osmosis (RO) is recognized as a prominent desalination technology, using pressure driven membrane processes (Wenten, 2016). Although RO is currently used in a variety of applications including selective separation, purification, and concentration processes, as well as in the food industry (Wenten, 2016), water scarcity has led to the global adoption of RO for cost-effective water desalination and wastewater treatment (Ahmed et al., 2023).

However, membrane fouling is a significant issue in RO processes, diminishing membrane lifespan, permeability, and increasing operational challenges. This phenomenon negatively impacts the quality and quantity of desalinated water, posing a hurdle to the sustainable use of RO membranes due to compromised efficacy and economic aspects. Fouling results from physicochemical interactions between water pollutants and membrane materials, leading to the accumulation of foulants on membrane surfaces and inside pores (Ahmed et al., 2023).

Therefore, regular membrane cleaning is essential to maintain long-term performance in RO systems, restore system productivity, minimize overuse of instruments, reduce environmental impacts, and reduce the generation of unwanted byproducts (Mappas et al., 2022).

Various approaches, including nonlinear programming, Artificial Intelligence (AI), and Genetic Algorithms (GA), have been explored in the literature to address the long-term cleaning scheduling of RO membrane systems. The predominant focus in existing literature revolves around the Mixed-Integer Nonlinear Programming (MINLP) formulation of the problem (Guzman et al., 2022)

In this paper, the Multistage Mixed-Integer Optimal Control Problem (MSMIOCP) method is used to address the RON scheduling problem (Mappas et al., 2022). This method divides the time horizon into stages, characterizing each stage with process models represented by Differential Algebraic Equations (DAEs) and associated constraints. The decision variables, which determine the process operation, shutdowns, plant operating conditions, and product costs at each stage, are discretized over the time horizon. The "feasible path approach" is employed for the sequential solution of the DAEs using an integrator. The solution benefits from the bang-bang nature of cleaning decisions, allowing relaxation of integer restrictions, transforming the problem into a standard Nonlinear Programming (NLP) problem without the need for combinatorial optimization methods. In the following sections, the implementation of the MSMIOCP approach is extended to enable the inclusion of specific parameters, such as the unit cost of energy, as non-deterministic in order to facilitate improved decision-making for the maintenance of the RONs.

2. Maintenance scheduling of reverse osmosis networks

Reverse osmosis (RO) is a water purification process that uses a partially permeable membrane to remove ions, unwanted molecules, and larger particles from water. The process involves applying pressure to the water on one side of the membrane, forcing it to pass through the membrane while leaving the contaminants behind.

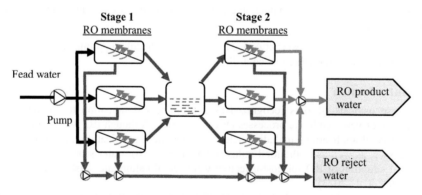

Figure 1: Simplified process flow diagram of a reverse osmosis network

Maintenance scheduling of RO networks refers to the planning and organization of maintenance activities for the components and systems involved in the RO water purification process. RO systems are critical for producing clean and purified water, and like any complex system, require regular maintenance to ensure optimal performance, efficiency, and longevity.

In this following, a case study is conducted to evaluate the influence of parameter uncertainty on the maintenance scheduling of a reverse osmosis network (RON) with 2 stages of 3 separate RO modules in each stage, as shown in Fig. 1.

3. Parameter uncertainty

In the area of maintenance scheduling of RON, especially related to fouling models, it is imperative to regard certain parameters as non-deterministic or uncertain. This consideration is crucial, as the uncertainties associated with operational parameters mirror real-world variations capable of influencing the performance of the system. The influence of the uncertain parameters on the fouling process presents challenges in predicting the system behavior, measurement accuracy, or can lead to variation in fouling over time (Al Ismaili et al., 2019). Failing to incorporate them into the analysis may result in the formulation of suboptimal strategies. Thus, measures to address parameter uncertainty serve to enhance the adaptability of the model to unforeseen changes, thereby augmenting the reliability and effectiveness of the optimization process (Tang et al., 2024).

In the context of co-scheduling for seawater desalination and power generation, the inclusion of electricity prices as uncertain parameters is crucial. The variability of energy costs exerts a direct influence on the optimal operation of combined water and power (CWP) plants. Treating these uncertainties as non-deterministic parameters in the optimization model facilitates the formulation of a robust and resilient strategy that does not rely on specific probability distributions (Jabari et al., 2019).

4. Methodology

The proposed solution approach for addressing this issue consists of two main components. The initial part of this methodology employs a multiple scenario approach to account for parametric uncertainty. This involves generating various scenarios, each assigning specific values to uncertain parameters within predefined ranges. The scenarios created using any random sampling technique.

In the next section, these generated scenarios are used as non-deterministic parameters (energy unit cost) in the calculation of the other parameter (energy cost and income) within the Ordinary Differential Equations (ODEs) of the MSMIOCP formulation. Subsequently, the average influence of these randomly generated scenarios on the objective function is assessed. The operational efficiency of the RO membrane units is simulated through an approximate model, as presented in Mappas et al. (2022).

4.1. Objective Function

$$Min\ Objective = Cost - Income \tag{1}$$

Cost here is the sum of cleaning cost C_C and energy cost C_E, in euros. Based on the membrane cleaning cost per membrane unit per cleaning action C_{ca} and the total number of cleaning actions N, the cleaning cost is calculated through the following:

$$C_C = C_{ca} \cdot N \tag{2}$$

The energy unit cost parameter C_{el} is examined in both deterministic and non-deterministic scenarios. In the deterministic scenario, a value of 0.08 euro/kWh is considered. Thus, the energy cost is determined through two distinct approaches, one of which assumes a constant unit energy cost:

$$C_E = C_{el} \frac{\sum_{i=1}^{6} I_i \cdot \Delta P_i}{\rho} \qquad \text{for } i = 1, 2, ..., 6 \tag{3}$$

where

$I_i =$ inlet flowrate of RO module i (m3/days)

$\Delta P_i =$ pressure across the units (Pa)

while the other considers it as an uncertain parameter.

In the non-deterministic setting, 26 random scenarios are defined with a normal distribution. If Eq. 3 is defined as D, and S denote the total number of energy unit cost scenarios, the energy cost for the uncertainty formulation is given by following equation:

$$C_E = \frac{\sum_{s=1}^{26} C_{el,s} \cdot D}{S} \qquad \text{for } s = 1, 2, ..., 26 \tag{4}$$

For a permeate selling price denoted as *Pr*, in euro/m3, and a permeate flowrate of RO module i denoted as $\mathcal{P}_i$, in kg/s, the income is calculated according to the following equation:

$$Income = Pr \cdot \sum_{i=1}^{6} \mathcal{P}_i \qquad \text{for } i = 1, 2, ..., 6 \tag{5}$$

4.2. Constraints

Simulations are conducted to demonstrate the application of the proposed framework over 26 time periods, with each lasting one week. The model constraints are given as follows:

Subject to

$$P_{c,i} = \frac{K \cdot F_{c,i}}{Y \cdot M_i (\Delta P_i - \Delta \Pi_i)} \tag{6}$$

$$\Delta \Pi_i = T \cdot \bar{R} \cdot F_{c,i} \tag{7}$$

$$\Delta P_i = X_i \left(\frac{\mathcal{P}_i}{Y \cdot A \cdot M_i} + \Delta \Pi_i \right) \tag{8}$$

$$I_i = \frac{1}{3} \cdot X_i \cdot F_T \tag{9}$$

$$I_j = \frac{1}{3} \cdot X_i \cdot E_k \tag{10}$$

$$\mathcal{P}_i = I_i \cdot \delta \cdot X_i \tag{11}$$

$$\text{for } i = 1, 2, ..., 6; \quad j = 1, 2, 3; \quad k = 4, 5, 6 \quad X_i = 0, 1$$

Here, X_i is a binary variable and equal to 1 if the RO unit is in operation and 0 if the unit is undergoing cleaning. F_T denotes the total rate of flow entering the RON, in m3/days, E_k the retentate flowrate, in m3/days, and $P_{c,i}$ the permeate concentration, in ppm, for the RO module i. The parameters utilized in the implementation of this case study are adopted from Mappas et al. (2022) and are summarised in Table 1.

Table 1: RON model parameters

Parameters	Value	Units	Description
ρ	0.6	-	pump energy efficiency coefficient
C_{el}	0.08	euro/kWh	energy unit cost
K	4.0e-6	kg/s m2	solute transport
$F_{c,i}$	34,800	ppm	feed stream concentration for the RO module i
Υ	5.0	days	permeability constant
M_i	3.0e10	kg/day N	membrane permeability across the units
T	298.0	K	operational temperature
$\bar{R}$	8.31	J/K mol	ideal gas constant
A	152.0 * 1.0e0	m2	membrane area
δ	0.65	-	permeate recovery ratio

5. Results and discussion

The optimisation problem is implemented in Python 3.11 and run on a computer with Intel(R) Core(TM) i7-7800X CPU @ 3.50GHz, 16,0 GB RAM. The minimize solver from scipy.optimize is used. The CPU time is 140.14 minutes (64.90 and 75.24 minutes for deterministic and non-deterministic scenario, respectively).

Of the 100 multiple start cycle considered, 61 were successful. Fig. 2 illustrates the outcome of optimizing maintenance scheduling, considering the energy unit cost as a deterministic parameter (Fig. 2a-b) and as an uncertain parameter (Fig. 2c-d), respectively.

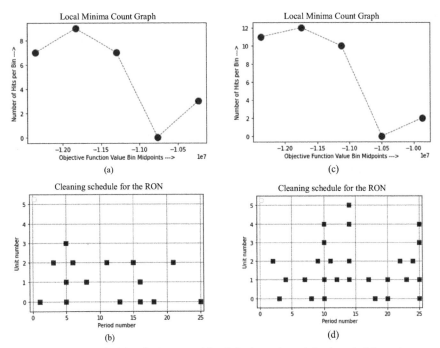

Figure 2: Local minima for the successful optimization cycles and cleaning schedule graphs

As can be seen in Fig. 2b and d, when the energy unit cost parameter is considered as non-deterministic, the number of required maintenance operations increase from 15 cleaning actions to 27 cleaning actions (blue squares indicate the cleaning operations). There is also a small increase in the best value of the objective function, from €12.624 million when the energy unit cost is considered as a deterministic parameter and €12.682 million when the energy unit cost is a non-deterministic parameter. As a consequence, this increase in both the number of required maintenance operations and the value of the objective function highlights to the importance of considering uncertainty in parameters to make models more realistic and relevant to real-life situations.

6. Conclusions and outlook

This research focuses on evaluating the impact of parameter uncertainty on the maintenance schedule of reverse osmosis networks. It emphasizes the critical importance of incorporating non-deterministic parameters into optimization models and provides valuable insights into the complex dynamics of maintenance planning for such systems. The observed increase in the number of required maintenance actions and the value of the objective function shows the importance of considering parameter uncertainty in order to provide models more realistic and relevant to commercial applications. For future research, investigating the interaction of multiple uncertainties simultaneously and their collective impact on maintenance planning can provide valuable insights into system resilience under different real-world scenarios.

References

I.G. Wenten & Khoiruddin, 2016, Reverse osmosis applications: Prospect and challenges, Desalination, vol. 391, pp. 112-125.

R. Al Ismaili et al., 2019, Optimisation of heat exchanger network cleaning schedules: Incorporating uncertainty in fouling and cleaning model parameters, Computers & Chemical Engineering, vol. 121, pp. 409-421.

F. Jabari et al., 2019, Robust optimal self-scheduling of potable water and power producers under uncertain electricity prices, Applied Thermal Engineering, vol.162, 114258.

S.D. Adloor et al., 2020, An optimal control approach to scheduling and production in a process using decaying catalysts, Computers & Chemical Engineering, vol. 135, 106743.

S.D. Adloor & V.S. Vassiliadis, 2021, An optimal control approach to considering uncertainties in kinetic parameters in the maintenance scheduling and production of a process using decaying catalysts, Computers & Chemical Engineering, vol. 149, 107277.

E. Guzman et al., 2022, Models and algorithms for production planning, scheduling and sequencing problems: A holistic framework and a systematic review, Journal of Industrial Information Integration, vol. 27, 100287.

V. Mappas, et al., 2022, Maintenance scheduling optimisation of Reverse Osmosis Networks (RONs) via a multistage Optimal Control reformulation, Desalination, vol. 543, 116105.

M.A. Ahmed et al., 2023, Fouling in reverse osmosis membranes: monitoring, characterization, mitigation strategies and future directions, Heliyon, vol. 9, 4.

J. Tang et al., 2024, A possibility-based solution framework for interval uncertainty-based design optimization, Applied Mathematical Modelling, vol. 125, pp. 649-667.

Flavio Manenti, Gintaras V. Reklaitis (Eds.), Proceedings of the 34th European Symposium on Computer Aided Process Engineering / 15th International Symposium on Process Systems Engineering (ESCAPE34/PSE24), June 2-6, 2024, Florence, Italy

Multistage Optimal Control and Nonlinear Programming Formulation for Automated Control Loop Selection

Vasileios Mappas[a*], Bogdan Dorneanu[a], Vassilios S. Vassiliadis[b], Harvey Arellano-Garcia[a]

[a]*LS Prozess, und Anlagentechnik, Brandenburgische Technische Universität Cottbus-Senftenberg Burger Chaussee 2, D-03044, Cottbus, Germany*
[b]*5 Ammohostou Street, 7550 Kiti, Larnaca, Cyprus*
mappas@b-tu.de

Abstract

Control loop design, as well as controller tuning, constitute the pillars of process control to achieve design specifications and smooth process operation, and to meet predefined performance criteria. Currently, state-of-the-art approaches have focused on methods that yield only the pairings between input and output methods, and are not able to incorporate path and end-point constraints. This work introduces a novel strategy based on the multistage optimal control formulation of the control loop selection problem. This approach overcomes the drawbacks of traditional methods by producing an automated integrated solution for the task of control loop design. Furthermore, it obviates the need for any form of combinatorial optimization and incorporating path and terminal constraints. The results show that the proposed solution framework produces the same control loops as in the case of traditional approaches, however the inclusion of path and end-point constraints improves the performance of the control profiles.

Keywords: Control Loop Selection, Controller Tuning, Multistage Integer Nonlinear Optimal Control Problem, Feasible Path Approach

1. Introduction

Process control plays a pivotal role in process industries, where complex integrated systems, environmental and safety regulations, and as well as economic uncertainty pose challenges to their operation. The most widely used types of controllers are of the Proportional-Integral (PI) and Proportional-Integral-Derivative (PID) types, due to their simplicity, robustness, easy realizability and non-fragility (Khandelwal and Detroja, 2020).

In real-world applications, industrial processes are described by Multi-Input Multi-Output (MIMO) systems, that are difficult to control due to the cross interactions among variables (Novella-Rodríguez et al., 2019). Several strategies, based on heuristics, machine learning techniques and statistics methods, have been proposed to handle the best allocation between the input and the output variables. Nonetheless, the state-of-the-art methods exhibit the following limitations:

1. Important information or interactions between input-output pairings are not taken into consideration, leading to suboptimal results.
2. Path and end-point constraints relating to operational limitations, environmental restrictions and safety specifications are not considered.

3. The approximation of the differential equations using steady-state information prevents the accurate representation of the process dynamics, which affects the coupling decisions between input and output variables.

To address these drawbacks, a novel solution framework, based on Optimal Control theory, is proposed in this work that involves formulating the problems as a multistage optimal control problem for finding the control loop selection problem and controller tuning parameters, simultaneously.

2. Methodology

In this work, the control loop selection and the corresponding controller tuning parameters problems are solved simultaneously and the whole problem is formulated as a Multistage Integer Nonlinear Optimal Control Problem (MSINOCP), where each stage has different values for the parameters of the controller. A stage is determined as a part of the time horizon of the process within which the decision variables have to be decided by the solution algorithm. Each stage is described by a process model given by Differential Algebraic Equations (DAEs) system, process constraints, initial and junction conditions that link any two consecutive stages, as shown in Figure 1.

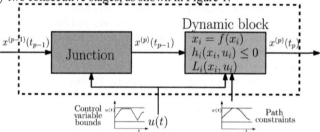

Figure 1: Graphical representation of the model for an individual stage of the control loop selection and tuning problem.

The general formulation of the Optimal Control Problem (OCP) is given by:

$$
\begin{aligned}
\text{minimize} \quad & \sum_{p=1}^{NS} \left\{ \left[E_1\left(x^{(p)}(T), u^{(p)}(T)\right) \right]^T u^{(p)} + E_2\left(x^{(p)}(T), u^{(p)}(T)\right) \right. \\
& \left. + \int_{t_{p-1}}^{t_p} \left[\left[L_1\left(x^{(p)}(t), u^{(p)}(t)\right) \right]^T u^{(p)} + L_2\left(x^{(p)}(t), u^{(p)}(t)\right) \right] dt \right\} \\
\text{subject to} \quad & \dot{x}^{(p)}(t) = f_1\left(x^{(p)}(t), u^{(p)}(t)\right) u^{(p)} + f_2\left(x^{(p)}(t), u^{(p)}(t)\right) \quad p = 1, 2, \dots, NP \quad (1) \\
& \left[h_1\left(x^{(p)}(t), u^{(p)}(t)\right) \right] u^{(p)} + h_2\left(x^{(p)}(t), u^{(p)}(t)\right) \leq 0 \quad p = 1, 2, \dots, NP \\
& \left[r_1\left(x^{(p)}(T), u^{(p)}(T)\right) \right] u^{(p)} + r_2\left(x^{(p)}(T), u^{(p)}(T)\right) \leq 0 \quad p = 1, 2, \dots, NP \\
& x(0) = x_0 \\
& 0 \leq t \leq T
\end{aligned}
$$

where E_1 is the coefficient of the linear control and E_2 is the coefficient independent of the linear controls for the point performance index. The corresponding terms for the continuous performance index, the differential equations, the path and end-point constraints are L_1 and L_2, f_1 and f_2, h_1 and h_2 and r_1 and r_2 for stage p, respectively. Differential state and control variables are denoted by x and u, respectively, while t is the simulation time.

The OCP problem, defined by Eq. (1), is solved obtaining the control actions u (control loop selection and corresponding controller's tuning parameters) and satisfying the constraints for each stage.

The backbone of the proposed methodology is the property that control variables appearing linearly in the OCP tend to take values at either bound in the optimal solution, leading to a "bang-bang" behaviour. Furthermore, the control variables, u, are considered as continuous, rather than discrete variables and are incorporated into the controller's tuning parameters. Therefore, the resulting optimization problem can be solved as a Nonlinear Programming (NLP) optimization problem, using a feasible path approach and without the use of mixed-integer optimization techniques. The proposed OCP formulation constitutes a superstructure that permits various connections between the control and the manipulated variables, with the optimizer allowing more than one coupling to occur between them.

The benefits of the proposed solution scheme are summarised below:
1. The MSINOCP framework has the ability to select the "best" control loop between the manipulated and control variables and find the optimal tuning parameters of the controllers at the same time.
2. The control variables are considered as continuous variables leading to a NLP reformulation of the problem. This reformulation obviates the need of utilising mixed-integer techniques with the challenges associated with their combinatorial nature.
3. The MSINOCP solution framework can handle and use dynamic models of any complexity and nonlinearity that describe the system's behaviour as well as path and terminal constraints imposed on the system.

3. Computational results

In the following section, two commonly used case studies are examined using the methodology proposed above, to introduce the implementation of the MSINOCP approach and formulation to obtain the "best" control loops and the optimal tuning parameters for the corresponding controllers without the need of combinatorial solution frameworks.

The following assumptions are applied for all of them:
1. The type of controller is assumed to be PI.
2. The continuous control variables $u(t)$ are considered to be piecewise constant.
3. The control loop selection problem is regarded as a single stage of a multistage OCP. Therefore, the total number of stages is assumed to be one.

All the simulations are performed in MATLAB R2020a, where the functions *fmincon* and *ode15s* are used for solving the optimization problem and the system of DAEs, respectively. For all case studies investigated, the results obtained from the proposed solution scheme are compared to the Relative Gain Array (RGA) and Ziegler-Nichols methods. RGA is a well-established method for evaluating the controllability of a process with multiple inputs and outputs (Juneja et al., 2023), while the Ziegler-Nichols method is one of the most widely used and cited methodologies for tuning controller's parameters (Huba et al., 2021).

3.1. Case study 1

A liquid tank with two inlet streams and a single outlet stream is considered, as shown in Figure 2. The mass and the energy balance of the liquid tank model are given by:

$$\frac{dh}{dt} = \frac{1}{A}F_c(t) + \frac{1}{A}F_h(t) - \frac{1}{A}c_1\sqrt{h} \qquad (2)$$

$$\frac{dT}{dt} = \frac{1}{A}\frac{F_c}{h}\left(T_c(t) - T(t)\right) + \frac{1}{A}\frac{F_h}{h}\left(T_h(t) - T(t)\right) \tag{3}$$

where h is the height of the liquid tank inside the tank, F_c and F_h are the inlet flowrates of the cold and hot streams, respectively, c_1 is the coefficient of the outlet flowrate, T is the temperature inside the liquid tank, T_c and T_h denote the temperatures of the cold and the hot inlet streams, respectively and A is the cross sectional area of the tank.

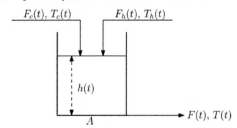

Figure 2: Liquid tank process representation.

The manipulated variables are the inlet flowrate of the cold and hot streams, while the volume and the temperature of the tank are the controlled variables. The pairings between the controlled and the manipulated variables are not known in advance. The possible pairings that can be considered are any combination linking F_c and F_h with outputs T and h.

The objective function for the MSINOCP optimization problem is to minimize the Integral Square Error (ISE) for the height and the temperature. Furthermore, path constraints for the controlled and the manipulated variables, as well as for the controller's tuning parameters are imposed.

3.2. Case study 2

In this case, the system described by the following 3×3 transfer function matrix is examined and is given by

$$G(s) = \begin{bmatrix} \dfrac{-2e^{-s}}{10s+1} & \dfrac{-1.5e^{-s}}{s+1} & \dfrac{e^{-s}}{s+1} \\[2mm] \dfrac{1.5e^{-s}}{s+1} & \dfrac{e^{-s}}{s+1} & \dfrac{-2e^{-s}}{10s+1} \\[2mm] \dfrac{e^{-s}}{s+1} & \dfrac{-2e^{-s}}{10s+1} & \dfrac{-1.5e^{-s}}{10s+1} \end{bmatrix} \tag{4}$$

A Padé approximation is used to overcome the dead time which transforms the matrix into a system of differential equations that can be handled by the proposed MSINOCP solution scheme. To find the best pairings and the optimal tuning parameters for the corresponding controller, two reformulations are considered based on first and second order Padé approximations.

The initial condition of the system is set to zero and the aim is to react to the new set-point which has the value of 1. In the MSINOCP problem formulation, the objective is to minimize the ISE for the state variables $x_1 - x_3$, while path constraints for the controlled and the manipulated variables, and for the tuning parameters of the controllers are taken into consideration.

4. Results and Discussion

4.1. Case study 1

Different scenarios are considered. Table 1 demonstrates the parameter values of an example scenario selected to test the ability of the solution framework to satisfy the path and end-point constraints.

Table 1: Initial and target values for Case study 1

	Values	
	Initial	Target
h (m)	3.0	1.0
T (°C)	35.0	15.0

The proposed methodology and the classical method (RGA) give the same control loops, as shown in Figure 3. The pairings given by the MSINOCP solution scheme confirm the theoretical prediction of bang-bang optimal control behaviour. Furthermore, the proposed methodology reaches the target values, obeying the constraints of the problem.

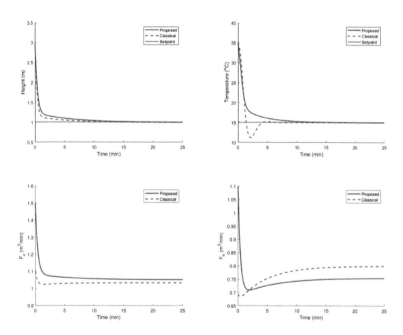

Figure 3: Trajectories for controlled and manipulated variables for Case study 1.

It can be observed that the obtained control tunings and the resulting control profiles do not have the same values, due to the fact that the OCP-based solution scheme considers and solves the control loop selection and controller tuning problem simultaneously compared to the classical method that solves each one separately. Specifically, the temperature trajectory violates the path constraint for the temperature in the case of the classical tuning (Ziegler-Nichols), as shown in Figure 3.

4.2. Case study 2

The MSINOCP methodology produces the same control loops with the RGA methods, as shown in Figure 4. It can be seen that both methods reach the new set-points after approximately 10 min. Specifically, an underdamped response is observed for the state variable x_2 using the Ziegler-Nichols methods compared to the proposed solution scheme, as shown in Figure 4.

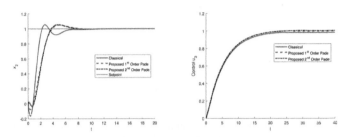

Figure 4: Trajectories for state and control variables for Case Study 2.

This behaviour can be explained by the implementation of the path constraints in the optimization problem, which are not considered by the classical method. Furthermore, the order of the Padé approximation plays a minor role in the system's behaviour, as shown in Figure 4. Therefore, a first order Padé approximation can be used for obtaining the optimal control pairings and their tuned controller parameters leading to the reduction of the computation burden compared to the second order Padé approximation.

5. Conclusions

In this work, a new approach for the automatic control loop selection and simultaneous controller tuning using Optimal Control theory is presented. The proposed solution scheme is based on the property that control variables appearing linearly in the OCP lead to bang-bang control behaviour, which is confirmed for the examined case studies. The numerical results indicate that the MSINOCP methodology is practical and effective to handle set-point switching and is able to satisfy path and end-point constraints. Furthermore, the solution framework yields one-to-one coupling of inputs to outputs variables which are in agreement with the classical methods. This methodology can be extended to larger/industrial case studies or experimental set-ups to determine the "best" control loops and the optimal tuning parameters for the corresponding controllers and the obtained results will be compared with real-time data.

References

A. Rodríguez-Molina et al., 2020, Multi-objective meta-heuristic optimization in intelligent control: A survey in the controller tuning problem, Applied Soft Computing, vol. 93, 106342.

S. Khandelwal & K.P. Detroja, 2020, The optimal detuning approach based centrilized control design ofr MIMO processes, Journal of Process Control, vol. 96, pp. 23-36.

P.K. Junejaet al., 2023, Interaction analysis of a multivariable process in a manyfacturing industry – A review. In: V. Suma, P. Lorenz, Z. Baig (eds) Inventive Systems and Control. Lecture Notes in Networks and Systems, 672, Springer, Singapore.

M. Hubaet al., 2021, Making the PI and PID controller tuning inspired by Ziegler and Nichols precise and reliable, Sensors 2021, vol. 21, 18, 6157.

Z.Y. Nie et al., 2022, A unifying Ziegler-Nichols tuning method based on active disturbance rejection. Int. J. Robust. Nonlinear Control, vol. 32, pp. 9525 – 9541.

Flavio Manenti, Gintaras V. Reklaitis (Eds.), Proceedings of the 34th European Symposium on Computer Aided Process Engineering / 15th International Symposium on Process Systems Engineering (ESCAPE34/PSE24), June 2-6, 2024, Florence, Italy

Deep Neural Networks-Based Fault Diagnosis Model For Process Systems

Mohammad Shahab[a]*, Zoltan Nagy[a], and Gintaras Reklaitis[a]

[a] Davidson School of Chemical Engineering, Purdue University, West Lafayette, IN-47907, USA

* Corresponding Author: moshahab@purdue.edu.

Abstract

The diagnosis of faults is crucial to ensure process safety and increased product quality. Faults can emerge with time across different unit operations due to changes in the process that the process controllers are unable to handle appropriately. This undesirable divergence in the variables of the system is found to adversely affect the product quality in process industries. In this work, a deep neural network (DNN) model driven by feature engineering on the process dataset using genetic programming is developed to classify faults in a process system. Feature extraction and construction using process data is carried out before the transformed features are used for fault diagnosis in a DNN. The DNN model performs fault diagnostics on the process data that contains the normal operating conditions and the abnormal operating conditions which arise due to variations in the characteristic quality of the system. The genetic programming driven DNN methodology is illustrated on a benchmark chemical process, where its effectiveness is evaluated by classifying faults in the Tennessee Eastman Process (TEP) and is compared against existing methodologies.

Keywords: fault diagnosis, deep neural networks, genetic programming, feature engineering, pharmaceutical process

1. Introduction

Fault diagnosis refers to the identification of abnormality present in a system which implies determining the type, location, magnitude and time of the fault (Isermann R., 1995). Therefore, a fault diagnosis methodology is essential for the elimination of faults. Several fault diagnosis methods have been proposed in the past and the approaches can be broadly categorized into three types namely quantitative model methods, qualitative model methods, and data driven methods (Venkatasubramanian et al., 2003b). The first two model methods are integrated with a priori domain knowledge which is derived from a fundamental understanding of the process dynamics. On the other hand, data driven methods require large amounts of process data. However, with the increase in complexity of modern processes, creating a mathematical model that accurately represents the dynamic behavior of the system becomes increasingly difficult. Therefore, data-driven methods, which depend on process data are getting increased attention (Venkatasubramanian et al., 2003a).

The most crucial step in data driven methods is the feature extraction process which allows the transformation and conversion of the process data as priori knowledge to the fault diagnosis system. The transformed data can be used by the data driven model for fault diagnosis of the system by describing itself as a classification problem. Deep neutral networks (DNN) are a prominent data driven tool and has received significant interest in machine learning community as a preferred method for monitoring of process systems. However, instead of using raw process data as an input to DNNs, the efficiency of this data driven method can be increased multifold by filtering out redundant and irrelevant information present in the process data, while reducing computational cost during the classification of faults. This can be carried out by using a suitable feature engineering step which essentially retains useful process variables and also constructs new features from the data.

In this work, we propose a genetic programming (GP)-based methodology for construction/extraction of features from raw process data for classification of faults. The effectiveness of the approach is tested on a benchmark chemical process for fault diagnosis, the Tennessee Eastman process (TEP) as an illustrative example and the performance of the approach is compared with other data driven methods.

2. Proposed methodology

Genetic programming (GP) is an evolutionary computation (EC) technique and a popular feature construction method. GP automatically and adaptably constructs high level features from low level ones using variable length tree-based representation. GP usually generates programs for feature construction using operators (like +, −, and ×) and given initial features (Vouk et al., 2023). The use of GP allows to gain insight into what features are important for construction and why the features that are constructed work well by interpreting the tree-based solutions of GP. These benefits have led to the development of many GP techniques that have shown promise in feature construction across a range of applications and therefore has been deployed in the current study. Figure 1 shows an example of a GP program which represents a mathematical expression $(x1 - (x2 \times x3)) + (x4 / x5)$, where the intermediate nodes (i.e., +, -, /, etc.) belong to the function set and leaf nodes such as arguments $x1$, $x2$, etc. belongs to the terminal set which can be associated with the process dataset in the current study.

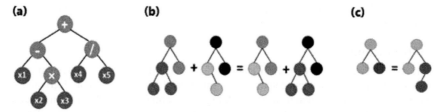

Figure 1: (a) An example of GP individual; (b) Crossover operation; (c) Mutation operation

The GP based feature extractor starts with randomly initializing a population of tree programs in the search space, each evaluated by a fitness function. The evolutionary process generates a new population through Elitism, Crossover, and Mutation operations at each generation. The Elitism operation copies the best individuals from the current generation to the next, while the Selection operation selects individuals with better fitness values for Crossover and Mutation operations (Figure 1). The process is terminated when a termination criterion is met, and the best GP derived tree is returned. For the fitness calculation of individual GP trees, DNNs are employed to evaluate the fault classification/diagnosis performance by the extracted and constructed features. By utilizing DNN, the GP technique may automatically extract and create significant features while avoiding redundant or unnecessary features.

The evaluation process involves standardization of the extracted/constructed features from the process data by the GP individuals. The standardization ensures classification performance without singular values or feature bias. In addition, the five-fold cross-validation method is used to improve the generalization ability of the features. The DNN is fed with the standardized features and is evaluated five times, using one-fold as the test set and the remaining four folds for training. The average test classification results of the five-folds are used as the fitness value of the individual GP tree. Figure 2 shows the schematic of the GP-DNN model for fault diagnosis.

1.2 Fault diagnosis as a classification problem

The fault classification problem can be formulated as a multiclass classification problem where the extracted features by GP can be used as inputs to the DNNs. The performance of the GP-DNN model can be assessed using accuracy and confusion matrix. The diagonal elements of the confusion matrix can be directly used to calculate the accuracy which serves as the fitness value for the GP. The final GP-DNN model is tested on an unseen test data set to calculate the model performance.

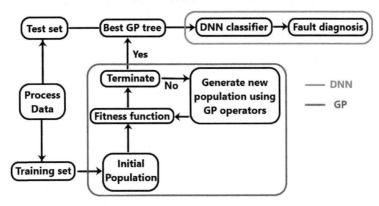

Figure 2: The main principle of GP-DNN model for fault diagnosis

3. Illustrative Example – Tennessee Eastman Process

In this section, we illustrate the effectiveness of the GP-DNN model using the Tennessee Eastman Process (TEP). The widely used TEP first introduced by Downs and Vogel, 1993 is a realistic chemical plant simulation tool that serves as a standard for process control and monitoring research (Lagare et al., 2023). The process consists of five major unit operations, the reactor, separator, condenser, stripper, and compressor and produces two products G and H, a by-product F from four reactants A, C, D, and E along with an inert compound B. The process data has 41 process variables and 11 manipulated variables (52 measurement variables) and a total of 21 different fault types. The process data which is available in Chiang et al. (2001), provides 21 training datasets that logs process measurements for 24 hours. Furthermore, for a 48-hour operating period, 21 test datasets were generated, with the faults appearing after 8 simulation hours.

Table 1: Genetic programming parameters

Function Set	Terminal Set	Pop. Size/ generations	Initial Pop. /Max tree depth	Selection method/size	Crossover/ mutation rate/Elitism
+, -, ×, protected division	Process variables	100/30	Ramp half and half/8	Tournament/ 7	0.8/0.2/1

The GP-DNN model uses the TEP data to extract features using GP and identify the best GP tree which describes the selected features (process variables) in the leaf nodes and the constructed feature(s) in the root node (top node). The selected features and the constructed features are fed as inputs to the DNN after standardization of the combined features. The DNN uses the combined features to classify the process sample into one of the 21 different faults. Therefore, the approach not only allows us to select relevant features but also construct useful new features from the process data. Before using DNN for evaluating the fitness of GP individuals, the hyperparameters of the neural networks such as learning rate, hidden layers, neurons, optimizer, and activation function can be fine-tuned to increase the performance of the GP-DNN model. Therefore, a single GP-DNN model can be used to classify faults for the TEP.

Table 2: Deep neural network parameters

Hidden layers	Learning rate	Neurons	Optimizer	Activation function	Dropout
6	0.124	128	Adagrad	elu	0.06

4. Results and Discussion

Our proposed GP-DNN selects certain features (process variables) from the process dataset using GP and it is noteworthy that in the current work, we have constructed only one feature from the selected features by GP for demonstration purposes. However, even the addition of a single constructed feature was found to be very useful for fault diagnosis. The feature extraction using GP is implemented using DEAP library in python and its parameters like the function set, terminal set, population size, generations, and other parameters are mentioned in Table 1. The DNNs are optimized using Bayesian optimization to identify the optimal learning rate, neurons, hidden layers, and also the optimizer and the activation function using the TEP dataset using *bayes_opt* library in python and is shown in Table 2.

We demonstrate the effectiveness of the proposed approach for fault diagnosis in TEP. In order to carry out a fair comparison between different model performances, we have considered studies like Jing et al., 2014 and Eslamloueyan R., 2011, where a principal component analysis (PCA) model and a multilayer perceptron (MLP) model are used for classification of all 21 faults using a single model only, respectively. The results are reported in Table 3 after averaging the multiclass classification accuracy for 10 simulation runs on the unseen TEP test data set. The accuracy of our GP-DNN model is based on 25 extracted features (averaged across 10 simulations) from the process data along with one constructed feature. The following observations can be made: First, our proposed approach results in a higher average accuracy across all 21 faults using a single model which is 7% and 40% more than the PCA and MLP method, respectively; Secondly, the average fault diagnosis accuracy of incipient faults such as 3, 9, 15 is also relatively higher compared to other techniques which are very difficult to diagnose due to absence of any observable changes in means, variances or peak time. It is to be noted that both these findings occur with lower number of features along with a constructed feature that assisted in increasing the performance by identifying what kind of feature operations in the GP tree would result in a better discrimination of faults. The confusion matrix, which measures performance of classification problems, for one of the simulations using the GP-DNN model is shown in Figure 3.

Table 3: Fault classification accuracy of our proposed approach against single Principal component analysis (PCA) model (Jing et al., 2014), single multilayer perceptron (MLP) model (Eslamloueyan R. 2011).

Fault type	PCA	MLP	GP-DNN
1	88	81	90
2	89	82	89
3	21	0	49
4	81	79	83
5	87	73	85
6	89	84	91
7	88	80	89
8	83	48	86
9	22	0	45
10	76	12	80
11	70	18	81
12	87	25	87
13	69	15	86
14	88	29	86
15	26	0	46
16	73	15	77
17	75	52	86
18	73	75	84
19	85	14	71
20	79	48	73
21	85	0	80
Average (%)	73	40	80

5. Conclusions

In this study, we proposed a GP-DNN model for fault diagnosis in process systems. It was shown that the GP-DNN model is capable of generating useful features and reducing redundant information in process data used to execute fault classification. The tree-based GP approach allows interpretability of which process variables are useful for classifying faults. The optimized DNN boosts performance when appropriate features are plugged in giving a balance of both model interpretation and high learning speed. The GP-DNN model is also compared with existing technologies for fault diagnosis and is found to outperform most methods when all 21 faults are considered. Therefore, feature engineering can be a key step in transforming process data into useful a priori domain knowledge which is one of the major challenges in developing data driven methods for fault detection and diagnosis.

Although, the results indicating that a single GP-DNN model can be used to diagnose all process faults seem to be promising, numerous points need to be addressed in future work to improve the effectiveness. First, the DNN needs to be tuned proportional to which features in process data are deemed useful and optimizing the DNN using the entire dataset might not be efficient. Second, instead of constructing single feature from the selected features by GP, multiple constructed features can be concatenated for improved performance, in which case, the selected features may be not be needed at all. Finally, the DNNs could be replaced with recurrent neural network (RNN) models that are much more relevant to sequential data which occurs in process industries.

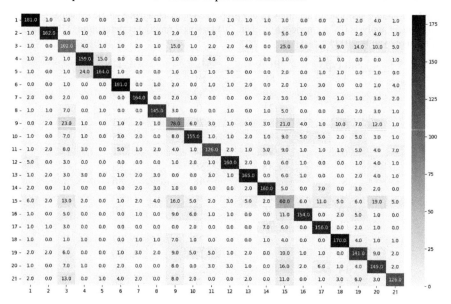

Figure 3: Confusion matrix for test data using the GP-DNN model (the axes denote the fault classes from 1-21)

References

Downs, J.J., Vogel, E.F. (1993). A plant-wide industrial process control problem. *Comput. Chem. Eng.*, 17(3), 245–255.

Eslamloueyan R. (2011) Designing a hierarchical neural network based on fuzzy clustering for fault diagnosis of the Tennessee–Eastman process. *Appl. Soft Comput.*, 11(1), 1407-15.

Isermann, R. (1995). Model base fault detection and diagnosis methods. In Proceedings of 1995-*ACC'95 IEEE*, Vol. 3, 1605-1609.

Jing C, Gao X, Zhu X, Lang S. (2014) Fault classification on Tennessee Eastman process: PCA and SVM. In *ICMC-IEEE*. pp. 2194-2197.

Lagare, R.B., Gonzalez, M., Nagy, Z.K. and Reklaitis, G.V. (2023). Modular Development of Condition Monitoring Systems for the Tennessee Eastman Process. In *Comput. Aided Chem. Eng.* Elsevier. Vol. 52, 1579-1584.

Venkatasubramanian, V., Rengaswamy, R., Yin, K., and Kavuri, S. (2003b). A review of process fault detection and diagnosis: Part I: Quantitative model-based methods. *Comput. Chem. Eng.*, 27(3), 293–311.

Venkatasubramanian, V., Rengaswamy, R., Kavuri, S., and Yin, K. (2003a). A review of process fault detection and diagnosis: Part III: Process history based methods. *Comput. Chem. Eng.*, 27(3), 327–346.

Vouk, B., Guid, M. and Robnik-Šikonja, M., 2023. Feature construction using explanations of individual predictions. *Eng. Appl. Artif. Intell.*, 120, p.105823.

Flavio Manenti, Gintaras V. Reklaitis (Eds.), Proceedings of the 34th European Symposium on Computer Aided Process Engineering / 15th International Symposium on Process Systems Engineering (ESCAPE34/PSE24), June 2-6, 2024, Florence, Italy

Enhancing Human Operators Trust in MPC Controllers Through an Explainable AI Methodology

Anurag Pathak[a] , Babji Srinivasan[b,c] , Rajagopalan Srinivasan[a,c]

[a] Department of Chemical Engineering, Indian Institute of Technology Madras, Chennai, 600036, India

[b] Department of Applied Mechanics and Biomedical Engineering, Indian Institute of Technology Madras, Chennai, 600036, India

[c] American Express Lab for Data Analytics, Risk and Technology, Indian Institute of Technology Madras, Chennai, 600036, India

raj@iitm.ac.in , babji.srinivasan@iitm.ac.in

Abstract

Model predictive control (MPC) utilizes a system model to obtain optimal control sequences and takes action that improves plant efficacy. However, the successful deployment of MPC in industrial plants requires that plant operators trust them. In complex, real-life, tightly integrated processes, the MPC's inherent complexity and the lack of interpretability of its actions, especially for a non-expert, can lead to a loss of trust, even when the MPC operates as intended. We seek to address this gap in this work. Specifically, we introduce the concepts of explainable AI (XAI) to understand MPCs actions in real-time. Specifically, we use the well-known SHapley Additive exPlanations (SHAP) to provide to the operator with the subset of variables that contribute to a particular MPC action. The effectiveness of the proposed method is demonstrated on a nonlinear Continuous Stirred Tank Reactor (CSTR). We show that the results from SHAP align with the operator's understanding of the process causality and thus aid the operator in interpreting MPC's actions.

Keywords: Model Predictive Control, Explainability, SHAP, Machine learning, Attributions

1. Introduction

Process industries are composed of many interconnected processes with multiple interacting units, and it is necessary to maintain control over all these units to optimize production and increase plant efficiency. To achieve this, Model Predictive Control (MPC) is employed to provide superior control for multivariable systems. MPC operates as a control paradigm by utilizing a prediction model of the controlled system. It generates optimized control sequences, taking into account both system constraints and interdependencies among process variables. Consequently, it is widely recognized as the industry standard for managing large-scale processes, as it often takes actions that improve plant performance beyond what a skilled and experienced operator can achieve. However, a key challenge for MPC is the interaction between the operator and the optimization techniques. The evolution of advanced automation has led to a transformation in the role of operators, shifting towards monitoring and supervision, thereby placing them out of the loop with the system and making situation awareness challenging. The complex algorithmic framework of MPC may not synchronize with the familiar, intuitive single-loop control mechanism operators typically use (Lindscheid et al.,2016). This makes MPC a black box model for the operator, which lacks interpretability. Therefore, monitoring, diagnosing, and controlling MPC is a challenging task for the operator, and there are numerous instances where plant operators may deactivate MPC when faced with difficulties in understanding its predictions, resulting in diminished trust in the system's control actions. The significance of human factors is often overlooked or disregarded and plays a pivotal role in the effective functioning of MPC solutions (Forbes et al., 2015). To tackle these trust and comprehension challenges, we propose a methodology that offers explainability of the MPC actions to the operators, thus bridging the gap between human intuition and automated systems.

Explainability refers to insights behind the output of a model. When model explanations are available through that we can establish an intuitive relationship between the input and output. Various studies have been done regarding explainability in the context of process monitoring applications. Bhakte et al. (2022) applied an Integrated Gradient (IG) approach to interpret the fault detection results obtained from a deep neural network. IG is a gradient-based attribution method based on the Shapely value concept from game theory. The effectiveness of any XAI method in a chemical process relies on the ability to establish a meaningful correlation between attributions and the chemical process. If such a correlation can be established, it enhances model interpretability. Bhakte et al. (2023) utilized an XAI method that provides domain-specific explanations by providing important variables with a supervised variable range that causes faults in the system. They also explain why it is preferable to have local explanations (explains the result for each individual sample) than a global explanation (explains the entire AI model) in process monitoring applications. XAI methods can be classified as transparent models and post-hoc techniques. Transparent models are self-interpretable, whereas post-hoc techniques generate explanations by extracting relevant information from a complex, already trained model. Post hoc explainability can be provided in various ways, and among all of those, feature relevance explanations are widely used because sensor data (tabular) is predominant in the chemical industry.

In this paper, we demonstrate how XAI methods can be used to provide insights into MPC and enhance human operator trust in its control action. Section 2 provides a comprehensive explanation of the proposed methodology. Section 3 presents the outcomes of this methodology applied to a basic chemical process. Lastly, the concluding section 4 concisely summarizes the observed outcomes and suggests potential future research directions.

2. Methodology
In this study, we have proposed an approach to understand MPC's actions using the XAI technique. To implement this XAI technique on machine learning-based models, an MPC controller is initially designed and simulated for a series of changes in the input variables. Its output is recorded, and the data accumulated is then used to train various machine learning models like- XGBoost regressor, Random Forest regressor, and Neural Network (NN) Model. Empirical validation on a distinct dataset substantiates the efficacy of these models in approximating the MPC's predictions. Given a trained machine learning model, denoted as f_x, the interpretation of its predictions can be addressed through a cohesive

framework known as SHAP (SHapley Additive exPlanations) (Lundberg ,2017). SHAP provides explanations in the form of feature importance, calculated as the Shapley value from coalition game theory. In this context, features are conceptualized as players in a game, capable of being either present or absent for a specific prediction. This study uses KernelSHAP, a model agnostic approximation technique, to calculate Shapley values for feature attribution.

Firstly, all the possible combinations of coalitions are generated, and these coalitions have entries in the form of 1's and 0's. The length of each coalition is equal to the number of features. These coalitions are then superimposed on the input features, and the features masked with '1' preserve their original values, while those masked with '0' have their values replaced with random values from the corresponding features in the background data, thereby generating hypothetical samples. This process is iterated multiple times to minimize the bias the masking feature introduces, thereby generating numerous hypothetical samples for a particular coalition. These samples are evaluated on the black box model, and its output is averaged to get the coalition's output values. Then, a linear model is fitted to the pairs of coalition-output values, revealing the influence of each feature's presence or absence on the output.

This study focuses on explaining machine learning models trained on MPC data that successfully replicate the actions taken by MPC, assuming single control input u_k where k denotes a particular instance to be explained in the dataset. Next, we describe the procedure for calculating SHAP values for a specific input-output pair (x_k, u_k) as follows:

1) Generating 'm' coalitions with the help of binary masking features $z'_m \in \{0,1\}n_x$, where n_x is the number of input features, to create an entire coalition set M.

2) For each of the coalition z'_m: Calculate the weight $\pi_x(z'_m)$ of every coalition with the help of the SHAP kernel

$$\pi_x(z'_m) = \frac{n_x - 1}{\binom{n_x}{|z'_m|}|z'_m|(n_x - |z'_m|)},$$ (1)

where $|z'_m|$ denotes the number of present features (1's) in z'_m. To get the prediction of these coalition sets using f_x, we pass it through a one-to-one mapping function h_x, such that $h_x(z'_m)|_{z'_m=1} = x_k$, $h_x(z'_m)|_{z'_m=0} = x_{k,q}$ where q is randomly sampled from the background data. The optimal control output of the mapped feature is calculated by passing it through the model f_x: $u_{z'm} = f(h_x(z'_m))$. The above process is repeated l times, and the output is averaged to get the coalition's output values.

$$\bar{u}_{z'_m} = \frac{\sum_{r=1}^{l} u_{z'_m}}{l}$$ (2)

3) Fitting linear model $g(\cdot)$:

$$g(z'_m) = \phi_0 + \phi_j z'_m$$ (3)

by minimizing the sum of squares loss (4) over the coalition set M

$$\text{minimize} \quad \sum_{m \in M} \left[u_{z'_m}^- - g(z'_m) \right]^2 \pi_x(z'_m) \tag{4}$$
$$\text{subject to} \quad g(z'_m) = u_k \forall m \in M \, ||z'_m| = n_x$$

The solution of the above optimization formulation would be:

$$\begin{bmatrix} \phi_1 \\ \phi_2 \\ \vdots \\ \phi_M \end{bmatrix} \approx (X^T W X)^{-1} X^T W y = R y \quad \text{where } X = \begin{bmatrix} z'_1 \\ z'_2 \\ \vdots \\ z'_{2^M} \end{bmatrix}, \, y = \begin{bmatrix} y_1 \\ y_2 \\ \vdots \\ y_{2^M} \end{bmatrix} = \begin{bmatrix} f_x(z'_1) - \phi_0 \\ f_x(z'_2) - \phi_0 \\ \vdots \\ f_x(z'_{2^M}) - \phi_0 \end{bmatrix},$$

$$W = \begin{bmatrix} \pi_x(z'_1) & 0 & \cdots & 0 \\ 0 & \pi_x(z'_2) & \cdots & 0 \\ \vdots & \vdots & \ddots & 0 \\ 0 & 0 & \cdots & \pi_x(z'_{2^M}) \end{bmatrix} \tag{5}$$

Implementing the proposed approach on an MPC-based machine learning model involves using background data as a baseline, which represents the normal operating state of the process to which MPC is applied. This ensures that when binary masking arrays are imposed on the input feature, those masked with '0' have their values substituted from the baseline data, and the generated hypothetical samples would then represent the baseline. The model prediction for these samples aligns with the normal operating state since ϕ_0 represent the expected value of all model predictions. Consequently, from (5), the attribution for that particular input-output pair would be zero.

The SHAP values acquired through the above formulation signify that when the model prediction differs from the background data, the contribution of each variable to this deviation is indicated by their corresponding SHAP values. The higher these values, the higher their impact on the model prediction and vice versa. Applying this methodology to explain MPC's actions would reveal how each input variable to the MPC model affects its output and its level of impact. The results of the implementation of the above methodology are shown in the subsequent section.

3. Case Study – Linear MPC for an Exothermic Chemical Reactor

Table 1: Parameters for the CSTR System

Parameter	Value	Unit
F	1	m3/h
V	1	m3
R	1.985875	kcal/(kmol·K)
ΔH	-5,960	kcal/kmol
E	11,843	kcal/kmol
k_o	34,930,800	1/h
ρCp	500	kcal/(m3·K)
UA	150	kcal/(K·h)

An adiabatic CSTR in which a single first-order exothermic and irreversible reaction A→B takes place in the vessel. The system is assumed to be perfectly mixed. Parameter values for the CSTR is shown in Table 1. As the reaction is highly exothermic, the excess heat generated should be removed from the CSTR to maintain the residual concentration. Therefore, the control objective is to maintain the residual concentration, C_A, at its setpoint by adjusting the jacket coolant temperature, T_c. Changes in the feed concentration, C_f, and feed temperature T_f causes disturbances in the CSTR system. For the above purpose, a linear MPC is designed using the MPC toolbox in

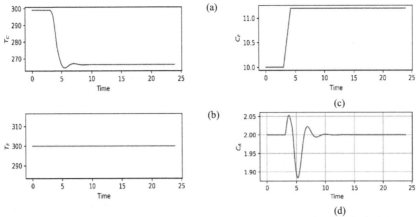

Fig. 1. Plant Input: (a)Jacket Coolant Temperature, (b) Inlet feed Concentration, (c) Inlet feed Temperature, Plant Output: (d) Outlet Concentration

MATLAB by considering T_c as the manipulated variable, C_f, T_f as the measured disturbance, and the residual concentration C_A as the measured output. This MPC is then simulated for numerous changes in the measured disturbance, and the output is recorded. The data collected is then utilized to train machine learning models, and the feature attribution is calculated by following the methodology mentioned in section (2). For the Explainability of the MPC Model, a single ramp change is provided in the C_f variable. This change affects other variables, C_A and T_c, but not T_f, as they are independent of each other. The trends in plant input and output are illustrated in Fig.1, showcasing the impact of this change. Fig 2(a) shows the variation in the MPC model output T_c, and Fig.2(b) shows a feature attribution plot of all the input variables to the MPC model. This feature attribution plot is derived by applying the proposed methodology to an NN-based MPC model. Analyzing the plot shown in Fig.2(b) provides insights into the ongoing process. Firstly, it is evident that from time t=0 to t=3, the attribution of all the input variables is

zero, indicating that variables are at their steady-state values and there is no change in the output Tc. This ensures that operators can easily understand the logic behind the proposed attribution method. After t=3, attributions are observed in the variables C_f and C_A, but T_f remains at zero attribution, implying that it has no impact on the output T_c. This observation aligns with the notion that changing the feed's concentration will have no effect on the temperature of the feed. Also, this would assist the operator in identifying the variables that impact MPC output and which are the most significant ones. In feature attributions, positive SHAP values

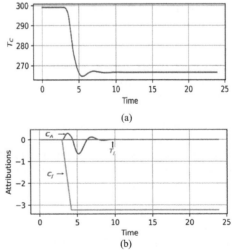

Fig. 2. MPC Output: (a)Jacket Coolant Temperature; (b) Attributions of MPC Input variables

positively impact the model prediction, while those with negative values have a negative impact, and the magnitude measures how strong the impact is. Fig 2(b) shows that variable C_f has the highest negative attribution followed by a smaller attribution, C_A, indicating that C_f has more impact on the output T_c. This interpretation remains valid, considering that C_f was the variable driving the change in the system state. After t=4.2, the attribution of variable C_f becomes constant and consistently negative (see Fig 2(b)), implying that its value has stabilized at a level different from its initial baseline, which can be observed in Fig 1(c). Post t=10, the attribution for variable C_A returns to zero, signifying that the variable has reached its steady state value again. This suggests to the operator that in instances where attributions remain constant or zero, the corresponding variable values stabilize or attain a steady state, thereby indicating a consistent or negligible impact on the model output. Also, after t=4.2, variable C_f maintains a constant negative attribution; this suggests that the negative impact of C_f persists, and it needs to be counterbalanced by another variable, even after the system achieves a steady state. Fig.2(a) shows that the variable T_c does not return to its original position even after the disturbance is rejected, indicating that it is offsetting the effect of C_f. Hence, it would aid the operator in understanding that certain variables may not return to their initial state even after the controlled variable regains a steady state.

4. Conclusions
In this study, we proposed a methodology to explain MPC's actions by utilizing the XAI technique, SHAP. For this purpose, MPC input-output data is used to train different machine-learning models that imitate the strategy of an optimization-based MPC. Then, it is simulated for a ramp change in a measured disturbance signal, and feature attribution is calculated using KernelSHAP. The subsequent attribution analysis, conducted specifically for the test case, revealed that this approach has the potential to enhance operators' understanding of the MPC's actions. This analysis offers valuable insights into the variables influencing the MPC output as well as the role played by different variables and their significance. Additionally, this analysis deepens their understanding of the dynamics of the closed-loop process. For future research endeavors, the emphasis will be on extending the work by implementing SHAP on multivariate systems and the systems involving the application of nonlinear MPC.

5. References
C. Lindscheid, A. Bremer, D. Haßkerl, A. Tatulea-Codrean, S. Engell, 2016, A test environment to evaluate the integration of operators in nonlinear model-predictive control of chemical processes. IFAC Papers OnLine, 49, 32, 129–134

Forbes, M.G., Patwardhan, R.S., Hamadah, H., Gopaluni, R.B., 2015. Model predictive control in industry: challenges and opportunities. IFAC-Papers OnLine, 48, 8, 531-538

Bhakte, A., Pakkiriswamy, V., Srinivasan, R., 2022, An Explainable Artificial Intelligence Based Approach for Interpretation of Fault Classification Results from Deep Neural Networks, Chemical Engineering Science, 250, 117373

Bhakte, A., Chakane, M., Srinivasan, R., 2023, Alarm-based explanations of process monitoring results from deep neural networks, Computers & Chemical Engineering,179, 108442

Lundberg, S. M., Lee, S.I., 2023, A unified approach to interpreting model predictions, Advances in neural information processing systems, Proceedings of the 31st International Conference on Neural Information Processing Systems, (pp. 4768–4777)

Flavio Manenti, Gintaras V. Reklaitis (Eds.), Proceedings of the 34th European Symposium on Computer Aided Process Engineering / 15th International Symposium on Process Systems Engineering (ESCAPE34/PSE24), June 2-6, 2024, Florence, Italy

Coupling Electrodialysis with bipolar membranes with renewable energies through advanced control strategies

Calogero Cassaro[a], Giovanni Virruso[a], Andrea Cipollina[a,b*], Adriano Fagiolini[a], Alessandro Tamburini[a,b], Giorgio Micale[a,b]

aDipartimento di ingegneria, Università degli studi di Palermo, Viale delle scienze Ed. 6, Palermo, 90128, Italy
bResourSEAs srl, Palermo, Italy
corresponding author: andrea.cipollina@unipa.it

Abstract

Recently, EU is directing its priorities to the implementation of innovative strategies for waste valorisation and smart use of energy, pushing towards ecological transition. Powering water treatment technologies with renewable energies, using the process buffering capacity as a way to indirectly store energy, has been recently proposed as an effective strategy for smart energy use. With this respect, electrodialysis with bipolar membranes (EDBM) can be particularly suitable due to the high energy intensity, coupled with an extreme flexibility of its operational modes. EDBM is an electro-membrane process able to convert saline wastewater into valuable products such as acids and bases, simply by supplying electric power. This work was focused on the development of advanced control systems allowing EDBM to operate under transitory regimes following the highly variable trend of renewable energy availability, adapting the operating conditions and the process targets according to the variable power input offered during a normal day. To this aim, a pilot scale EDBM unit (provided by FuMA-Tech GmbH) was operated and tested in Lampedusa island (Italy) in feed and bleed configuration under two different scenarios (summer and winter) at a fixed concentration target of acids and base (0.5 M of NaOH and HCl). In the hours of the day with an available power higher than a minimum threshold value (2.0-6.5 kW), the controller was able to keep the outlet concentration at its target (0.5 M of NaOH and HCl) by letting the outlet flowrate of the product to vary from 0.5 up to 3 l min^{-1}. In these operating conditions, the controller was able to guarantee high product quality, still retaining high specific productivity (in the range of 0.1-0.2 kg h^{-1}m^{-2}) and low consumption (in the range of 1.3- 1.9 kWh kg^{-1} of NaOH and 1.8- 2.4 kWh kg^{-1} of HCl). In all cases, the parallel control logic allowed to tune the applied voltage in order to meet the electric power availability, while manipulating the outlet flowrate to meet the desired product specification. The obtained results demonstrate for the first time at the pilot scale how EDBM can be particularly suitable to valorise, in industrial relevant scenarios, available saline streams and unstable energy sources, thus pushing towards the industrial implementation according to sustainable and circular values approaches.

Keywords: brine mining, renewable energy, electro-membrane, circular economy, advanced control

1. Introduction

Nowadays, researchers are focusing their efforts to find new strategies for a sustainable exploitation of energy sources through the valorization of concentrated brines coming from industrial processes. Currently, the world desalination capacity stands at, approximatively, 100 millions of cubic meters per day (Ihsanullah et al. 2021), being dominated by membrane processes. The most used membrane technology in the world is reverse osmosis (RO) covering the 70% of the global production of desalinated water (Jones et al. 2019). However, this process has two main drawbacks: (i) the production of a desalination waste (which represents the 60% of the treated water) and (ii) the significant energy consumption. In order to make the process more sustainable and reduce its environmental foot-print, different treatment chains based on Minimum/Zero Liquid Discharge approaches have been proposed so far to valorize waste brines by extracting valuable raw materials and energy from them. With this respect, electrodialysis with bipolar membranes (EDBM) (Filingeri et al. 2023) plays a key role allowing the production of chemical reagents which can be reused in-situ in accordance to a circular economy approach. EDBM is an electro-membrane technology, enabling the synthesis of chemicals as acids and bases, from waste saline waters, applying an electrical field. The repeating unit of an EDBM stack is called triplet and consists of a sequence of three ion exchange membranes, namely cationic, bipolar and anionic one, and three channels: basic, acid and salt channel (Figure 1). Through the application of an external electric field, the cations and anions dissolved in the saline solution migrate selectively towards the cathode and towards the anode, respectively, encountering the protons and hydroxide ions generated inside the bipolar membrane in the acid and base channel, respectively (Culcasi et al. 2022). Additional information about the working principle of the EDBM unit can be found in Strathmann's book (Strathmann 2004). The utilization of EDBM technology in MLD/ZLD treatment chain has energetic benefits due to the smart use of renewable energy sources (RESs) to produce valuable product (Virruso et al. 2023). Furthermore, the utilization of RESs could allow an off grid-spreading of this process in remote areas. Herrero-Gonzalez et al. (Herrero-Gonzalez et al. 2018) have proposed a PV-EDBM set-up coupling a lab-scale EDBM stack (A_m=0.01 m^2) with a PV solar array simulator. The system was operated in semi-batch configuration switching on and off the outlet flowrates according to the pH of the acid tank and the conductivity of the salt tank. They have demonstrated that the use of a rudimental control system could already lead to an improvement in the performance indicators, reducing the specific energy consumption (SEC) of the acid from 7.3 kWh kg^{-1} (at fixed current density) to 4.4 kWh kg^{-1} (at variable current density).

The purpose of this work was to pair a pre-industrial scale EDBM plant (Herrero-Gonzalez et al. 2023) with a renewable energy source. To reach this aim, advanced control systems were developed and tested firstly through the Matlab dynamic simulation toolbox (Simulink). Subsequently, the controllers were implemented in LabVIEW software and tested in the real plant mimicking a PV array. The objective of the control system was to allow continuous operation of the equipment in highly transitory regimes, to reach and maintain the set-point concentration for both, acid and base. At the same time, the controller ensured stability over time maximizing the use of the available energy in terms of performance indicators.

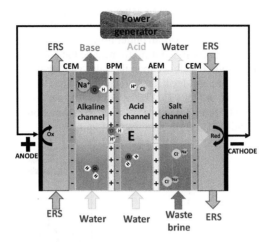

Figure 1. Schematic representation of the repetitive unit (triplet) of an EDBM stack

2. Description of the pilot and its control schemes

2.1. The EDBM pilot plant

The EDBM pilot, built within the framework of the Water Mining project, consists of two fundamental parts: the hydraulic pumping station and the EDBM stack itself. The pumping station housed all the hydraulic lines as well as the monitoring and control instrumentation such as flowmeters, conductivity meters, pressure transducers, pumps and electro-actuated valves. Furthermore, the hydraulic skid included the electrical cabinet where the acquisition and command hardware were located. More precisely, a chassis with analog acquisition and command cards was employed to collect data and provide signals to the actuators. The acquisition and command hardware were provided by National Instrument. LabVIEW was employed as software to develop the Programmable Logic Controller (PLC) and the Human Machine Interface (HMI) of the plant. The EDBM stack was an FT-ED1600-3 unit provided by FuMA-Tech GmbH (Germany). The stack consisted of 40 triplets divided into two modules with 20 triplets each, reaching a total active membrane area of 19.2 m². These two modules were put in communication in series using as internal staging the channels derived in the anode plate. The EDBM was powered using a Rectifier (GIUSSANI Srl) able to release a maximum power of 17.5kW corresponding to 80V and 200A. Additional information were reported in a previous work (Cassaro et al. 2023). The plant was operated in feed and bleed configuration, feeding continuously acid, base and salt solutions, while the electrode rinse solution was always operated in closed-loop mode.

2.2. Advanced control strategies

Several control systems were designed and implemented inside the PLC to make the EDBM plant able to work automatically under dynamic conditions. Particularly, the dynamic behavior of the uncontrolled system was investigated, in order to understand the dynamic features of main variables involved in the process. The dynamic trends collected from the experimental campaign were fitted, using first order transfer function model, to obtain reliable relationships having the outlet variables as a function of the inlet ones. This investigation led to the development of four advanced controllers: (i) the recirculation flowrate-maximum pressure using override logic to prevent from possible clogging phenomena which could damage the stack; (ii) the product quality cascade control, where the slave controller was an outlet flowrate controller with split range logic while the master was a conductivity control, to manage the concentration of the acid and base products; (iii) the ratio control between the salty and alkaline streams to guarantee the desired molar ratio among feed and product;(iv) the DC drive control for PV maximum power point tracker (MPPT). The latter was realized to operate the system with dynamic power set-point, through the use of a gaussian function fitting the real power produced by a solar field (EU 2023) as showed in Figure 2.

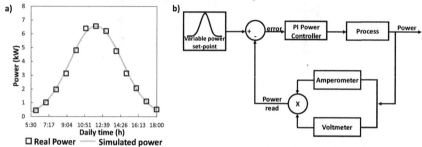

Figure 2. a) Comparison between the real and the simulated power; b) DC drive feedback control.

3. Results

In this section, a summary of the obtained results relevant to the summer and winter scenario was reported. In both cases, the quality of the product, for both acid and base, was controlled via cascade composition controller (i.e. controller (ii)). As a consequence, the flowrates of the outlet streams were varied by the controller according to the power availability in the two investigated cases (Figure 3). The summer scenario, in the month of July, guaranteed the highest peak irradiation in Lampedusa, equal to 980 W m^{-2} at midday. On the other hand, the winter scenario, in the month of December provided the lowest peak irradiation of the year, equal to 600 W m^{-2}. Moreover, the sunny hours decreased significantly from 12h in July down to 8h in December. Furthermore, it was observed a significant drop in the maximum power available, going down from a maximum of 6.5 kWp in July to 3.2 kWp in December. This power reduction dramatically affected the maximum current density reached in the winter scenario, equal to 265 A m^{-2} compared to the summer scenario, equal to 435 A m^{-2}.

Notwithstanding this effect, the control system was found always able to guarantee the conductivity set-point during the working day for both acid and base. However, acid and base in the summer scenario reached values slightly different compared to the set-point. As a matter of fact, in the summer scenario, the power changed rapidly, generating abrupt variations in the current density (disturbance) both, before and after the maximum value (Figure 3). Under these conditions, the control system was unable to delete the off-set completely, since the time required to reach the set-point value was greater than the disturbance variation time. On the other hand, in the winter scenario, even though the power varied as well, the controller kept the concentration fixed to the set-point value, throughout the working day (Figure 3). Table 1 showed an overall comparison of the average parameters obtained in both scenarios, in terms of performance indicators, power, voltage and current density, for the base, which represented the product with higher added value. The average available power was found equal to 3.2 and 2.0 kW for the summer and winter scenarios, respectively. This means that the DC drive control system supplied an 11% higher external voltage in the summer scenario compared to the winter scenario to follow the available power. Consequently, the average value of current density was higher in the summer scenario (250 A m^{-2}) respect to the winter one (180 A m^{-2}). Looking at the performance parameters, concerning the current efficiency (CE), high average values were reached in both scenarios, both higher than 60%. However, CE in the summer scenario was 7% higher since the EDBM stack operated in feed and bleed configuration performed better at higher current densities (Cassaro et al. 2023). As regards the specific energy consumption (SEC), it was found the same value for both, summer and winter, likely due to the lower reduction of the average external voltage than the average current efficiency. Last, but not the least, the average specific productivity (SP) resulted 25% lower in the winter scenario compared to the summer one. This effect is related to the higher values of current density and current efficiency in summer compared to winter.

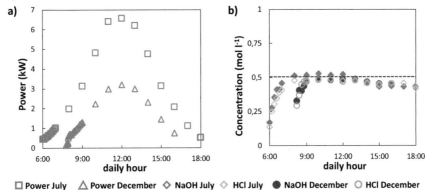

□ Power July   △ Power December   ◇ NaOH July   ◇ HCl July   ● NaOH December   ○ HCl December

Figure 3. Comparison between a) Power and b) concentrations temporal trends, for base and acid, in summer and winter scenarios

Table 1. Summary of the average performance parameters in the summer and winter scenarios for the alkaline stream.

Scenario	Power (kW)	Voltage (V)	Current density (A m^{-2})	CE (%)	SEC (kWh kg^{-1})	SP (kg h^{-1} m^{-2})
Summer	3.2	35.8	250	70	1.6	0.08
Winter	2.0	31.9	180	65	1.6	0.06

4. Conclusions

The aim of this work was the development of advanced control systems allowing to operate the EDBM technology powered by renewable energy. The synergy of these control schemes and the automation logic (PLC) implemented in the LabVIEW environment allowed to test the EDBM pilot plant powered by simulated solar panels in two different scenarios, namely summer and winter. The control system guaranteed, in both scenarios, a concentration equal to the target of 0.5 mol l^{-1} (fixed at set-point value). During the dynamic operation of the unit, valuable information were obtained in terms of performance indicators. Concerning CE, very high values were achieved, exceeding 65% for the base, in both scenarios. Moreover, the control system enabled to obtain very low values of SEC for the base, always lower than 2.0 kWh kg^{-1}. In terms of specific productivity, high values were obtained. In particular, in the summer scenario a value of 0.2 kg h^{-1} m^{-2} was reached for the base. These results confirmed the EDBM technology particularly suitable to operate in highly dynamic regimes such those established in presence of renewable energy availability. Following works will be focused on the potentiality of this coupling, on its viability at a higher scale and on the implementation of further advanced controllers achieving an overall optimization of the process.

Acknowledgments

This project has received funding from the European Union's Horizon 2020 research and innovation program under Grant Agreement no. 869474 (WATER-MINING – Next generation water-smart management systems: large scale demonstrations for a circular economy and society). www.watermining.eu.

References

Cassaro, Calogero, Giovanni Virruso, Andrea Culcasi, Andrea Cipollina, Alessandro Tamburini, and Giorgio Micale. 2023. "Electrodialysis with Bipolar Membranes for the Sustainable Production of Chemicals from Seawater Brines at Pilot Plant Scale." *ACS Sustainable Chemistry and Engineering* 11 (7). https://doi.org/10.1021/acssuschemeng.2c06636.

Culcasi, A., R. Ktori, A. Pellegrino, M. Rodriguez-Pascual, M. C.M. van Loosdrecht, A. Tamburini, A. Cipollina, D. Xevgenos, and G. Micale. 2022. "Towards Sustainable Production of Minerals and Chemicals through Seawater Brine Treatment Using Eutectic Freeze Crystallization and Electrodialysis with Bipolar Membranes." *Journal of Cleaner Production* 368. https://doi.org/10.1016/j.jclepro.2022.133143.

EU. 2023. "PV-GIS." 2023. https://joint-research-centre.ec.europa.eu/photovoltaic-geographical-information-system-pvgis_en.

Filingeri, Antonia, Julio Lopez, Andrea Culcasi, Tamara Leon, Alessandro Tamburini, José Luis Cortina, Giorgio Micale, and Andrea Cipollina. 2023. "In-Depth Insights on Multi-Ionic Transport in Electrodialysis with Bipolar Membrane Systems." *Chemical Engineering Journal* 468 (July): 143673. https://doi.org/10.1016/J.CEJ.2023.143673.

Herrero-Gonzalez, Marta, Pedro Diaz-Guridi, Antonio Dominguez-Ramos, Raquel Ibañez, and Angel Irabien. 2018. "Photovoltaic Solar Electrodialysis with Bipolar Membranes." *Desalination* 433. https://doi.org/10.1016/j.desal.2018.01.015.

Herrero-Gonzalez, Marta, Julio López, Giovanni Virruso, Calogero Cassaro, Alessandro Tamburini, Andrea Cipollina, Jose Luis Cortina, Raquel Ibañez, and Giorgio Micale. 2023. "Analysis of Operational Parameters in Acid and Base Production Using an Electrodialysis with Bipolar Membranes Pilot Plant." *Membranes* 13 (2). https://doi.org/10.3390/membranes13020200.

Ihsanullah, Ihsanullah, Muataz A. Atieh, Muhammad Sajid, and Mazen K. Nazal. 2021. "Desalination and Environment: A Critical Analysis of Impacts, Mitigation Strategies, and Greener Desalination Technologies." *Science of the Total Environment.* https://doi.org/10.1016/j.scitotenv.2021.146585.

Jones, Edward, Manzoor Qadir, Michelle T.H. van Vliet, Vladimir Smakhtin, and Seong mu Kang. 2019. "The State of Desalination and Brine Production: A Global Outlook." *Science of the Total Environment.* https://doi.org/10.1016/j.scitotenv.2018.12.076.

Strathmann, H. 2004. *Ion-Exchange Membrane Separation Processes, First Ed. Elsevier Science.* Vol. 9. Amsterdam: Elsevier. https://doi.org/10.1007/s13398-014-0173-7.2.

Virruso, Giovanni, Calogero Cassaro, Alessandro Tamburini, Andrea Cipollina, and Giorgio D M Micale. 2023. "Performance Evaluation of an Electrodialysis with Bipolar Membranes Pilot Plant Operated in Feed & Bleed Mode" 105 (February): 73–78. https://doi.org/10.3303/CET23105013.

Flavio Manenti, Gintaras V. Reklaitis (Eds.), Proceedings of the 34th European Symposium on Computer Aided Process Engineering / 15th International Symposium on Process Systems Engineering (ESCAPE34/PSE24), June 2-6, 2024, Florence, Italy

Real-time optimization with machine learning models and distributed modifier adaptation applied to the MDI-process

Jens Ehlhardt[a], Inga Wolf[b], Sebastian Engell[a]

[a] *TU Dortmund, Process Dynamics and Operations Group, Emil-Figge-Str. 70, 44227 Dortmund, Germany*
[b] *Covestro Deutschland AG, Process Technology, Kaiser-Wilhelm Allee 60, 51373 Leverkusen, Germany*
jens.ehlhardt@tu-dortmund.de

Abstract

In this work, the allocation of steam in a part of the isocyanate (MDI) production process is optimized with the goal to reduce fouling of the heat exchangers. Real-time optimization (RTO) based upon a rigorous stationary model is applied to optimize the corresponding temperature set-points. The plant-model mismatch is handled by an iterative optimization using Modifier Adaptation with Quadratic Approximation (MAWQA). The rigorous models that are available in a proprietary flowsheet simulator are approximated by surrogate models. In order to reduce the number of input moves in MAWQA for this large-scale plant, concepts of distributed optimization are applied in a tailored fashion. The scheme is tested at the operator training simulator (OTS) of the production plant, and a fast convergence to optimal operating conditions is achieved.

Keywords: Isocyanate Production, Modifier Adaptation with Quadratic Approximation, Distributed Modifier Adaptation, Surrogate Models.

1. Introduction

The transition to a sustainable and green industry is currently the biggest challenge of the chemical industry. Towards this goal, an important factor is the optimal operation of the processes and plants in terms of material and energy efficiency. Real-time optimization (RTO) can be used to identify the optimal stationary operating conditions and set-points by model-based optimization. However, the inevitable mismatch between the optimization model and the plant may lead to suboptimal performance or even infeasible set-points. Iterative RTO with correction of the model gradients (Gao and Engell, 2005) is a powerful approach to resolve this problem. In this approach, later termed Modifier Adaptation (MA) (Marchetti et al. 2016), the cost and constraint functions of the optimization problem are adjusted based on measured data. In practice with noisy measurements, the determination of the "true" gradients of the cost function and of the constraints from measured responses is challenging. Often finite difference methods are used which are inaccurate for large step sizes and vulnerable to noise for small step sizes. Gao et. al (2016) proposed Modifier Adaptation with Quadratic Approximation (MAWQA) in which the cost and constraint functions are first approximated by quadratic functions and subsequently, the gradients are computed from the approximations as a solution to this problem.

An additional issue in this industrial application is that the stationary process model is only available in a proprietary software and the evaluation is too slow for real-time application. As reported by Ehlhardt et al. (2023), this problem can be overcome by computing surrogate models of the responses of the flowsheet simulator. The simulator is then used as a data source for the identification of artificial neural networks (ANNs) that represent the nominal behavior of the plant.

A bottleneck of MAWQA (and of MA in general) is the number of data points, i.e. setpoints for which the plant is probed, that are needed for the estimation of the gradients. In MAWQA the minimum number of experiments grows quadratically with the number of inputs. Distributed modifier adaptation schemes as proposed by Schneider et al. (2017) are a possible solution to this problem.

In this paper, we propose an efficient decomposition of the optimization problem based on the structure of the MDI-process in order to apply MAWQA to the large-scale system at hand. Compared to previous investigations of the straightforward application of the MAWQA scheme as described in Ehlhardt et al. (2023), less iterations are needed to converge to the optimal set-points. In section 2, MAWQA and its proposed decomposition is explained. Section 3 gives an overview about the investigated process and corresponding optimization problem. The results are discussed in section 4 and a conclusion is given in section 5.

2. Real-time optimization via modifier adaptation

2.1. Modifier Adaptation with Quadratic Approximations

The general formulation of modifier adaptation is given in equation (1). In iteration k, the next set-point $u^{(k+1)}$ is determined by the solution of the following optimization problem (Gao and Engell (2005)):

$$\min_{u^{(k+1)}} J_{ad}^{(k)}\left(u^{(k+1)}\right) := J_m\left(u^{(k+1)}\right) + \left(\nabla_u J_p^{(k)} - \nabla_u J_m^{(k)}\right)^T\left(u^{(k+1)} - u^{(k)}\right) \tag{1}$$

$$s.t. \quad G_{ad}^{(k)}\left(u^{(k+1)}\right) := G_m\left(u^{(k+1)}\right) + \left(G_p^{(k)} - G_m^{(k)}\right)^T + \left(\nabla_u G_p^{(k)} - \nabla_u G_m^{(k)}\right)\left(u^{(k+1)} - u^{(k)}\right) \le 0 \tag{2}$$

$$u^{lb} \le u^{(k+1)} \le u^{ub} \tag{3}$$

The adapted cost function J_{ad} and constraint functions G_{ad} consist of the nominal plant functions (J_m and G_m) and affine corrections, the so-called modifiers. Thereby, the subscripts m and p denote the model and plant functions respectively. u^{lb} and u^{ub} are the upper and lower bounds of the set-points. ∇_u depicts the gradients of the model and plant functions with respect to the set-points. The true plant functions however are usually not known but are approximated from observations of the plant. In MAWQA, quadratic approximations (QA) of the objective function J_Φ and the constraint functions G_Φ are identified and used to calculate the necessary plant gradients. For this, a minimum number of $\frac{(n_u+1)(n_u+2)}{2}$ data points are required to determine the parameters of the quadratic models, where n_u is the number of inputs for which the set-points are optimized.

The algorithm is as follows. In the first step, probing inputs are applied to the plant to compute the gradients by finite differences. Then the algorithm from (Gao and Engell, 2005) is applied to compute the next steps until enough information is available for the quadratic approximation. The MAWQA algorithm includes also other elements of derivative-free optimization. The optimization problem may be solved solely based on the fitted quadratic functions J_Φ and $\boldsymbol{G}_\Phi$ instead of the adapted cost and constraint functions if the accuracy of the quadratic approximation was better in the last step. A trust region constraint is added to ensure the validity of the approximations. For details see Gao et al. (2016).

2.2. Distributed MAWQA

For processes and plants in which multiple units are operated in parallel with input-dependent couplings, the number of required data points required to estimate the quadratic functions can be reduced. An illustrative example is the operation of parallel reactors with subsequent downstream processing of the combined output streams. The input to the separation section depends only on the total load and the concentrations are defined by the mixing rule. Therefore, they can be introduced as local coupling variables. After the introduction of the coupling variables $\boldsymbol{v}_i$, the description of the distributed optimization problem for the case of an additive cost function $J_{ov,ad}$ and additive global constraints $\boldsymbol{G}_{ov,ad}$ as well as local constraints $\boldsymbol{G}_{loc,ad,i}$ reads:

$$\min_{\boldsymbol{u}^{(k+1)},\boldsymbol{v}^{(k+1)}} J_{ov,ad}^{(k)} = \sum_{i=1}^{N} J_{ad,i}^{(k)}\left(\boldsymbol{u}_i^{(k+1)}, \boldsymbol{v}_i^{(k+1)}\right) \tag{4}$$

$$s.t. \quad \boldsymbol{G}_{ov,ad}^{(k)} = \sum \boldsymbol{G}_{ov,ad,i}^{(k)}\left(\boldsymbol{u}_i^{(k+1)}, \boldsymbol{v}_i^{(k+1)}\right) \leq 0 \tag{5}$$

$$\boldsymbol{v}_i^{(k+1)} = \boldsymbol{h}_i\left(\boldsymbol{u}_1^{(k+1)}, \dots, \boldsymbol{u}_j^{(k+1)}, \dots, \boldsymbol{u}_N^{(k+1)}\right), \forall i \in N, j \neq i \tag{6}$$

$$\boldsymbol{G}_{loc,ad,i}^{(k)}\left(\boldsymbol{u}_i^{(k+1)}, \boldsymbol{v}_i^{(k+1)}\right) \leq 0, i = 1, \dots, N \tag{7}$$

$$\boldsymbol{u}_i^{lb} \leq \boldsymbol{u}_i^{(k+1)} \leq \boldsymbol{u}_i^{ub}, i = 1, \dots N \tag{8}$$

The global inequality constraints are defined as the sum of the contributions of the N sub-models $\boldsymbol{G}_{ov,ad,i}$. Eq. (6) defines the local coupling variables $\boldsymbol{v}_i$ in terms of the inputs of the other sub-models. $\boldsymbol{h}(\cdot)$ is a known, continuously differentiable function. For each sub-system, the modifiers, quadratic approximations and required gradients can then computed only with respect to the local inputs and coupling variables. Hence, the adapted contributions of the sub-models to the additive cost function read as follows:

$$J_{ad,i}^{(k)} = J_{m,i}\left(\boldsymbol{u}_i^{(k+1)}, \boldsymbol{v}_i^{(k+1)}\right) + \left(\boldsymbol{\nabla}_{\boldsymbol{z}_i} J_{p,i} - \boldsymbol{\nabla}_{\boldsymbol{z}_i} J_{m,i}\right)^T \left(\boldsymbol{z}_i^{(k+1)} - \boldsymbol{z}_i^{(k)}\right) \tag{9}$$

with

$$\boldsymbol{z}_i = [\boldsymbol{u}_i^T, \boldsymbol{v}_i^T]^T \tag{10}$$

The variables $\boldsymbol{z}_i$ consist of the local inputs and the coupling variables and $\boldsymbol{\nabla}_{\boldsymbol{z}_i}$ indicates the gradient with respect to the individual input vector $\boldsymbol{z}_i$. Their dimensions are often smaller than that of the full input vector $\boldsymbol{u}$.

$$\max(\{dim(\boldsymbol{z}_1), \dots, dim(\boldsymbol{z}_N)\}) < dim(\boldsymbol{u}) \tag{11}$$

The $\boldsymbol{z}_i$ with the largest dimension determines the number of initial probing moves required. If (11) holds true, fewer data points are needed for the local quadratic approximations and gradient computations because the quadratic approximations are functions only of the individual input vectors z_i. For more information on distributed optimization, the interested reader is referred to (Boyd 2010).

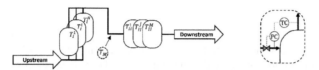

Figure 1: Schematic representation of the considered stage of the isocyanate production process. Multiple reactors are operated in parallel, and their output streams are added up and fed into the train of separation units. T_I and T_{II} are the temperature set-points of the heat exchangers of the reactors and of the separators. T_M is the temperature of the sum of the outgoing streams of the reactors. Each heat exchanger is equipped with a cascaded control structure, with a temperature controller in the outer loop and a pressure controller for the steam flow in the inner loop.

3. Application to the isocyanate production

In this case study, we consider a process stage of the production of diphenylmethane diisocyanate (MDI) as described by Ehlhardt et al. (2023). In this process stage, methylenedianiline (MDA) reacts to MDI in several reactors. The streams from all reactors are then mixed and MDI is separated from other gaseous reaction products. During both the reaction and the separation task, several heat exchangers provide heat to the different units via steam. The layout of the process stage is displayed in Figure 1. The goal is to operate the heat exchangers to reduce fouling. In the test of the algorithm, an operator training simulator (OTS) serves as a plant replacement. Operator training simulators are typically used to train new plant operators, to increase operator awareness for abnormal operating conditions, and to train operators to handle challenging situations. OTS simulation results can also be used to increase the acceptance of advanced process control methods among plant personnel.

3.1. Modelling of the isocyanate production process

The iterative RTO scheme uses multiple artificial neural network models (ANNs) that were trained on simulation data from a first-principle steady-state model. Each heat exchanger is modeled by an individual ANN, and all ANNs are combined to represent the complete model in the optimization. The first-principles model consists about 160,000 equations and is implemented in Covestro's in-house simulator. The manipulated variables were sampled on an equidistant grid and the outputs such as steam pressures p_{VP} and heat duties $\dot{Q}$ were calculated by the simulation program. Equations (12) and (13) show the modelled input-output relationships:

$$\dot{Q}_{I,i} = f(T_{I,i}), \quad \dot{Q}_{II,i} = f(T_{II,i}, T_M) \tag{12}$$

$$p_{VP,I,i} = f(T_{I,i}), \quad p_{VP,II,i} = f(T_{II,i}, T_M). \tag{13}$$

The operation of the heat exchangers of the reactors is determined by the corresponding set-points $T_{I,i}$, and the operation of the heat exchangers of the separators is determined by the associated set-points $T_{II,i}$ and the mixing temperature T_M. The ANNs have one layer each with 8 to 32 neurons per layer. The *tanh*-activation function is used, and all models were trained using the MATLAB deep learning toolbox. The models in the flowsheet simulator and in the OTS are different, so there is a significant plant-model mismatch.

3.2. Optimal steam distribution for the isocyanate process

The goal of the case study is to optimally distribute the total amount of heat required in this process stage among the available heat exchangers in such a way that fouling processes are reduced and cleaning activities have to be performed as seldom as possible. The fouling processes are directly related to the vapour pressures and temperatures of the steam (Engell et al. 2022). It is preferable that the vapour pressures of all heat exchangers remain close to their values for a clean state. This mode of operation extends the time until the next cleaning activities are required. The associated optimization problem is given below:

$$\min_{T_I, T_{II}, T_M} \sum_{i=1}^{N_I} \left(p_{VP,I,i} - p_{VP,I,i}^{clean} \right)^2 + \sum_{i=1}^{N_{II}} \left(p_{VP,II,i} - p_{VP,II,i}^{clean} \right)^2 \tag{14}$$

$$s.t. \quad \dot{Q}_{j,i} \leq 0, i = 1, \ldots, N_j, j = \{I, II\} \tag{15}$$

$$\dot{Q}_{tot}^{lb} \leq \left(\sum_{i=1}^{N_I} \dot{Q}_{I,i} + \sum_{i=1}^{N_{II}} \dot{Q}_{II,i} \right) \leq \dot{Q}_{tot}^{ub} \tag{16}$$

$$p_{VP,j,i} \leq p_{VP,j,i}^{max}, i = 1, \ldots, N_j, j = \{I, II\} \tag{17}$$

$$T_j^{lb} \leq T_j \leq T_j^{ub}, j = \{I, II\} \tag{18}$$

$$T_M = w_I T_I. \tag{19}$$

The objective penalizes the sum of the differences between the actual steam pressures p_{VP} and their clean values p_{VP}^{clean} of the N_I-reactors and the N_{II}-separators. The manipulated variables are the temperature set-points of the heat exchangers of the reactors T_I and of the separators T_{II}. The coupling variable is the mixing temperature T_M, which depends on all reactor set-points T_I and a vector of constant weighting coefficients w_I. The coefficients are calculated from the mass flows and heat capacities. In this case, the mappings $h_i(\cdot)$ are linear or identities. The first constraint (15) ensures that the heat exchangers are used for heating only. The total heat supplied is bounded by (16). The constraints (17) and (18) result from the maximum available steam pressure and the a priori given bounds on the temperature set-points.

4. Results

Distributed MAWQA, as presented in section 2, was applied to the OTS of the MDI-process shown in section 3. The resulting trajectories are shown in Figure 2. The algorithm starts with a predefined sequence of perturbations for iterations 1-3. Due to the reduced number of degrees of freedom of each sub-model, enough data is available to construct the quadratic approximations for all models in the reaction section in step 3. Starting with iteration 4, set-points are calculated by distributed MAWQA but for the separation section quadratic approximations can only be built after iteration 6. After a slight violation of the total heat flow constraint, the algorithm converges to an optimal combination of the temperature references in iteration 7. The value of the objective function is reduced to approximately 50% of the initial value.

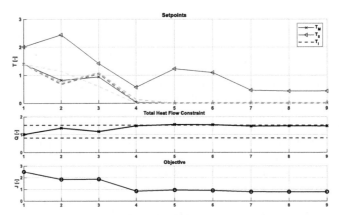

Figure 2: Results of the application of distributed MAWQA to the OTS of the MDI process. The second and third subplot display the trajectories of the total heat flow and the value of the objective function. The dashed lines represent the constraints. In all subplots, the iteration count is shown on the x-axis and the values on the y-axes are scaled.

5. Conclusion

In this work, distributed Modifier Adaptation with Quadratic Approximations was successfully applied to a stage of the isocyanate production process to optimize the distribution of steam between the heat exchangers of the process units. The optimization model consists of individual artificial neural networks for each sub-model that were trained on data provided by a flow-sheet simulator. The number of iterations performed before the quadratic approximations are available is significantly lower than when solving the full problem. Consequently, the time to convergence to optimal operating conditions is reduced by half compared to previous work (Ehlhardt et al. 2023). In future work, different scenarios such as load changes and load sharing will be investigated.

6. Acknowledgements

The German Ministry of Economic Affairs and Climate Action (BMWK) is acknowledged for funding the KEEN project under the grant number 01MK20014S.

References

Boyd, S., 2010, Distributed optimization and statistical learning via alternating direction method of multipliers. Found. Trends® Mach. Learn. 3 (1), 1-122

Ehlhardt, J., Ahmad, A., Wolf, I., Engell, S., 2023. Real-Time Optimization Using Machine Learning Models Applied to the 4,4′-Diphenylmethane Diisocyanate Production Process. Chemie Ing. Tech. 95, 1096–1103.

Engell, S., Ahmad, A., Ehlhardt, J., Wolf, I., Arras J., Hielscher A., 2022. Method for controlling a distributed control system. EP22209645.5.

Gao, W., Engell, S., 2005. Iterative set-point optimization of batch chromatography. Comput. Chem. Eng. 29, 1401–1409.

Gao, W., Wenzel, S., Engell, S., 2016. A reliable modifier-adaptation strategy for real-time optimization. Comput. Chem. Eng. 91, 318–328.

Marchetti, A.G., François, G., Faulwasser, T., Bonvin, D., 2016. Modifier adaptation for real-time optimization - Methods and applications. Processes 4, 1–35.

Schneider, R., Milosavljevic, P., Bonvin, D., 2019. Distributed modifier-adaptation schemes for the real-time optimisation of uncertain interconnected systems. Int. J. Control 92, 1123–1136.

Flavio Manenti, Gintaras V. Reklaitis (Eds.), Proceedings of the 34th European Symposium on Computer Aided Process Engineering / 15th International Symposium on Process Systems Engineering (ESCAPE34/PSE24), June 2-6, 2024, Florence, Italy

Model Predictive Control Strategies for Continuous Manufacturing Processes

Ioana Nascu[a,d,*], Nikolaos A. Diangelakis[b], Mircea Şuşcă[a], Vlad Mihaly[a] and Zoltan Nagy [c]

[a] Department of Automation Technical University of Cluj Napoca, Romania
[b] School of Chemical and Environmental Engineering Technical University of Crete
[c] Davidson School of Chemical Engineering, Purdue University, West Lafayette, USA
[d] Academy of Romanian Scientists, Romania
Ioana.Nascu@aut.utcluj.ro

Abstract

Under the influence of Pharma 4.0, the pharmaceutical manufacturing industry is experiencing a paradigm change from traditional batch manufacturing to continuous manufacturing, a faster and more efficient approach. This work paves the way towards state-of-the-art Quality-by-Control advanced model based predictive control (MPC) strategies for a continuous manufacturing process. Model based predictive control strategies are a great fit for assuring a Quality-by-Control approach and facilitate the transition towards Industry 4.0. An advanced model-based predictive control strategy is designed for the control of a continuous manufacturing process in the pharmaceutical industry, specifically for solid dosage forms. The model employed for the development of the advanced controlled strategies is first validated and calibrated with real data from a pilot plant. The results show enhanced process performance, characterized by increased process efficiency and flexibility, and reduced environmental impact, even in the presence of process uncertainties and measurement noise.

Keywords: pharmaceuticals, process control, rotary tablet press, model based predictive control, Quality by Control.

1. Introduction

The pharmaceutical industry involves complex processes that have to operate close to operational and regulatory constraints with strict quality specifications for its products. It deals with highly integrated and intricate processes, process/model uncertainty, varying production targets, and raw material variability (Su et al, 2019, Chen et al, 2022, Huang et al, 2022). Traditionally, pharmaceutical manufacturing follows a batch processing approach, where the quality control is implemented using quality-by-testing where the drug product quality is assessed in the final processing step of each batch.

Motivated by the need for cost-effectiveness enhanced sustainability, reliability, and the pursuit of targeted solutions for smaller patient populations, coupled with advancements in modern manufacturing technology, continuous manufacturing has started to replace batch manufacturing in the pharmaceutical industry (Naşcu et al, 2023, Destro and Barolo 2022, Nascu et al, 2022). This transition will also result in a shift towards quality-by-control (QbC). QbC involves designing and operating robust manufacturing systems that employs an active process control system, relying on the robustness of process design. This shift represents an important step towards smart manufacturing (Su et al, 2019, Nascu et al, 2023, Diangelakis et al, 2023, Pistikopoulos et al, 2021).

This work establishes the foundation for state-of-the-art Quality-by-Control model based predictive control (MPC) strategies for a tablet manufacturing process. Initially, a process model is developed, validated, and calibrated using actual data obtained from a pilot plant. Subsequently, this model is employed to design advanced MPCs with a focus on robustness, particularly in handling uncertainties, variable time delays, effective disturbance rejection, and explicit incorporation of constraints. This is a great advantage for the pharmaceutical manufacturing industries particularly when dealing with the exigent Food and Drug Administration (FDA) regulations.

2. Theoretical Background

2.1. Process Model

The lubricant/glidant feeder and the rotating tablet press represent key unit operations in pharmaceutical manufacturing. Mechanistic models of the glidant's impact on die filling and compression processes are employed to monitor and control the tensile strength and porosity of the tablets (de Meira et al, 2017). To determine the weight (W) of the convex tablet formed using Natoli D-type tooling with a shallow cup depth, Eq (1) is used.

$$W = \rho_b V_{fill}\left(1 - \xi_1 \frac{n_T}{n_F} + \xi_2 \frac{H_{fill}}{D}\right) \tag{1}$$

The variables ρ_b, V_{fill}, H_{fill}, n_T, n_F, and D denote the powder bulk density, die cavity volume, position of the dose, turret speed, speed of the feed frame, and the diameter of the die, respectively. The model parameters $\xi1$ and $\xi2$ are estimated using experimental data. The tablet's production rate, $\dot{m}_{tablet}$ is calculated using :

$$\dot{m}_{tablet} = W n_T N_{station}, \tag{2}$$

where $N_{station}$ represents the number of available turret stations. The pre-compression force (PCF) can be computed using:

$$F_{pc} = \frac{\pi D^2}{4b}\left[\frac{\rho^{pc} - \rho_c}{\rho^{pc}(a-1) + \rho_c}\right]. \tag{3}$$

a and b represents the Kawakita constants, ρ_c represents the critical density and ρ^{pc}, the relative density of the pre-compression involves the use of the following equations:

$$p^{pc} = \frac{W}{V^{pc}\rho_t} \qquad V^{pc} = \frac{\pi D^2 H^{pc}}{4} + \frac{\pi h\left(\frac{3D^2}{4} + h^2\right)}{3}. \tag{4}$$

H^{pc} denotes the true density of the powder, and ρ_t represents the pre-compression thickness. Therefore, the main compression force, F_{punch}, is determined using:

$$F_{punch} = \frac{\pi D^2}{4b} + \left[\frac{\rho^{in-die} - \rho_c}{\rho^{in-die}(a-1) + \rho_c}\right] \tag{5}$$

The in-die relative density ρ^{in-die} is determined as follows:

$$\rho^{in-die} = \frac{W}{V^{in-die}\rho_t} \text{ and } V^{in-die} = \frac{\pi D^2 H^{in-die}}{4} + \frac{\pi h\left(\frac{3D^2}{4} + h^2\right)}{3}. \tag{6}$$

The main compression thickness is represented by H^{in-die}. The density of the tablet, ρ^{tablet}, is determined using the elastic recovery, ε_ρ:

$$\rho^{tablet} = \left(1 - \varepsilon_\rho\right)\rho^{in-die}. \tag{7}$$

The tensile strength (σ_t) is influenced by glidant conditions and is calculated using the following equation:

$$_t = \sigma_0 \left(1 - \left| \frac{1 - \rho^{tablet}}{1 - \rho_{c,\sigma_t}} \right| e^{\left(\rho^{tablet} - \rho_{c,\sigma_t} \right)} \right). \tag{8}$$

σ_0 represents the tensile strength when porosity is zero, while σ_{c,σ_t} denotes the relative critical density, where tablets do not exhibit any tensile strength.

In this study, a Natoli NP-400 tablet press and SOTAX AT4 tablet tester are used to produce tablets and collect data from experiments at steady-state conditions. The data obtained from experiments is utilized to determine the parameters for the real model. These parameters are then used to fit and calibrate the model used for simulations.

2.2. Extended Prediction Self-Adaptive Control

Fig. 1 presents a schematic representation of the developed hierarchical control system layers. For the implementation of the MPC we have used the Extended Prediction Self-Adaptive Controller (EPSAC) approach, described in detail in De Keyser 2003) with four inputs and four outputs. To obtain the EPSAC control laws the following cost function is minimized:

$$J(U) = \sum_{i=1}^{2} \sum_{k=N_{1i}}^{N_{2i}} [r_i(t + k|t) - y_i(t + k|t)]^2 + \sum_{j=1}^{2} \sum_{k=0}^{N_{uj}-1} \lambda_j [\Delta u_j(t + k|t)]^2. \tag{9}$$

Where r_i are the reference trajectories for the controlled outputs, u_i the process inputs and y_i the measured process outputs.

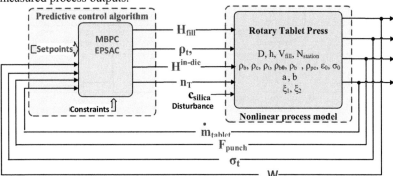

Fig 1. Schematic representation of the rotary tablet press control diagram

2.3. Control Design

To design the controller, the tuning parameters that are determined for this work are: the control horizons for the four inputs we have $N_{ui}=1$ and for the prediction horizons we have $N_1=5$, $N_2= N_3= N_4=10$. The selection of control and prediction horizons considers the characteristics of the process and the desired closed-loop performances. For processes without unstable underdamped or unstable poles, as in the current process, a value of $Nu=1$ is generally sufficient when determining N_u. The sample time is set at Ts=1 s since measured data is available from the plant every 1 second. Constraints will be applied to all the manipulated inputs. Model predictive controllers offer the advantage of seamlessly integrating constraints. The specific constraints on the manipulated inputs are as follows: dosing position between 6mm and 20mm, pre-compression thickness between 0.5mm and 14mm, main compression thickness between 0.5mm and 6mm, and turret speed between 0 rpm and 60 rpm.

3. Results

In this work, based on the process model outlined in Section II.A, a total of 4 inputs and 4 outputs are employed to determine the multiple input multiple output (MIMO) linear model using the System Identification toolbox in MATLAB. This linear model will be subsequently utilized in the controller design. The four controlled variables in this process encompass the tablet weight, pre-compression force, production rate, and tensile strength. The corresponding manipulated variables are: dosing position, pre-compression thickness, main compression thickness, and turret speed. Sensor measurements for tablet tensile strength are available every second. The model parameters employed in this paper are derived from experimental data and include: $\xi_1 = 0.036$, $\xi_2 = 0.03$, ρ_b=0.365 g/cm^3, ρ_c=0.265, $a = 0.8$, $1/b$= 10.26 MPa, $\rho_l = 1.53$ g/cm^3, , ε_0=0.08, $\rho_{c,\varepsilon} = 0.57$, $\sigma_0 = 11.67$ MPa, ρ_0=0.57, ρ_∞=0.61, $b_1 = 0.31$, $b_1 = 0.38$, $b_1 = 8.4$, $\rho_{b,\infty} = 0.45$ g/cm^3, $\rho_{b,0} = 0.33$ g/cm^3, $r_1 = 0.361$, $r_2 = 1.394$, r_3 =23.326.

3.1. Setpoint Changes

To test the performance of the implemented control strategy, setpoint changes are given for the tablet weight, from 225 mg to 255 mg at time t = 60 s, for the pre-compression force, from 0.37 kN to 0.67 kN at time t = 100 s, for the production rate, from 7.4 kg/h to 8.4 kg/h at time t = 20 s, and for the tensile strength, from 5.6 MPa to 6.4 MPa at time t=140 s.

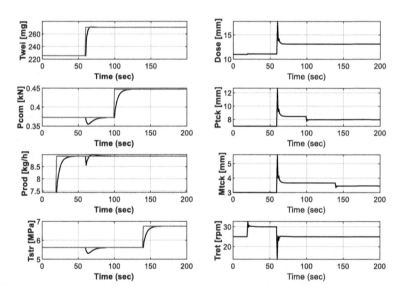

Fig. 2. MPC, setpoint (red line) tracking – output variables (blue line) (left side) (Twei - tablet weight, Pcom - pre-compression force, Prod - production rate, and Tstr tensile strength) and control variables (right side) (Dose - dosing position, Ptck - pre-compression thickness, Mtck - main compression thickness and Tret - turret speed).

Fig. 2 illustrates the closed loop system response for setpoint changes using the EPSAC assuming no noise on the measured outputs. On the left side we have the response for the controlled variables. It can be discerned that the outputs are coupled. This means that a setpoint change in any output affects the others. On the right side we have the close-loop response control action, highlighting that the setpoint change in tablet weight (introduced at time t=60 s) has the most significant impact on all outputs.

The EPSAC controller exhibits good performance characteristics, including rapid settling time, small overshoot and undershoot, and no setpoint offset for consecutive changes in all references. Being multivariable, the control algorithm efficiently manages the interdependencies between inputs and outputs, effectively minimizing deviations of other outputs from reference values when the reference of one output changes. The manipulated variables evolve within saturation limits, and every change illustrated in this study is realistic and feasible under normal operation conditions of the tablet press.

3.2. Noise and Disturbance Rejection

To conduct a more comprehensive assessment of controller performance, sensor measurement noise is incorporated. To simulate this noise, a normally distributed error with zero mean and variance is introduced to the real sensor variability, sourced from historical plant data. The results of the closed-loop response for both controlled variables and control actions are depicted in Fig. 3. The EPSAC controller shows good performers in the presence of sensor measurement noise, with all dynamic and stationary parameters of the response maintained. Through an appropriate selection of design parameters, it becomes feasible to attenuate oscillations arising from measurement noise while maintaining a balance between response time and the propagation of these oscillations in the control loop. Should a damping of these oscillations be desired for all manipulated variables, one can achieve this by reducing the controller's aggressiveness on the respective loops through the selection of appropriate design parameters.

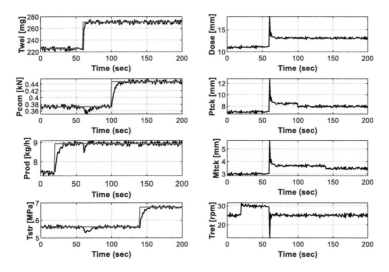

Fig. 2. MPC, setpoint (red line) tracking with sensor measurement noise– output variables (blue line) (left side) (Twei - tablet weight, Pcom - pre-compression force, Prod - production rate, and Tstr tensile strength) and control variables (right side) (Dose - dosing position, Ptck - pre-compression thickness, Mtck - main compression thickness and Tret - turret speed).

4. Conclusions

For the pharmaceutical manufacturing industry to advance into smart manufacturing and align with the Industry 4.0 revolution, a transition towards Quality-by-Control is imperative. The principal objective of this study is to develop advanced model-based predictive control techniques for a continuous pharmaceutical manufacturing process involving a rotary tablet press, following the Quality-by-Control paradigm. To assess the performances of the developed model predictive controller, it is implemented on a simulation platform utilizing the developed high fidelity model, validated and calibrated with real data obtained from a pilot plant. The controller performances are tested for: (i) tracking of reference changes, involving step changes in dosing position, pre-compression thickness, main compression thickness, and turret speed inputs; (ii) rejection of measurement noise

The developed control strategies exhibit promising performances, characterized by fast settling times, absence of offset errors, and negligible undershoot or overshoot, even in the presence of sensor measurement noise. These outcomes imply enhanced process efficiency, heightened process flexibility, and decreased environmental impact, even in the presence of process model uncertainties and measurement noise.

Acknowledgments

Financial support from Ministry of Research, Innovation and Digitization, CCCDI - UEFISCDI, project number PN-III-P2-2.1-PED-2021-1147, within PNCDI III

References

Chen, Y., Bhalode, P., Ou, Y. and Ierapetritou, M. (2022) 'PSE Tools and Challenges in the Development of Advanced Pharmaceutical Manufacturing' in *Computer Aided Chemical Engineering*, 21-24.

De Keyser, R. (2003) *Model Based Predictive Control, Invited Chapter, in UNESCO Encyclopedia of Life Support Systems (EoLSS),* Eolss Publishers Co Ltd, Oxford, 2003,.

de Meira, R. Z. C., Maciel, A. B., Murakami, F. S., de Oliveira, P. R. and Bernardi, L. S. (2017) 'In Vitro Dissolution Profile of Dapagliflozin: Development, Method Validation, and Analysis of Commercial Tablets', *International Journal of Analytical Chemistry,* 2017, 2951529.

Destro, F. and Barolo, M. (2022) 'A review on the modernization of pharmaceutical development and manufacturing – Trends, perspectives, and the role of mathematical modeling', *International Journal of Pharmaceutics,* 620, 121715.

Diangelakis, N. A., Pappas, I. and Pistikopoulos, E. N. (2023) 'Robust (explicit) optimization and control via Mixed Integer Programming' in *Computer Aided Chemical Engineering*, 1711-1716.

Huang, Y. S., Sheriff, M. Z., Bachawala, S., Gonzalez, M., Nagy, Z. K. and Reklaitis, G. V. (2022) 'Application of MHE-based NMPC on a Rotary Tablet Press under Plant-Model Mismatch' in *Computer Aided Chemical Engineering*, 2149-2154.

Nascu, I., Diangelakis, N. A., Huang, Y.-S., Nagy, Z. K., Birs, I. and Nascu, I. (2023) 'Multi-parametric Model Predictive Control Strategies for a Rotary Tablet Press in Pharmaceutical Industry', *IEEE INTERNATIONAL CONFERENCE ON SYSTEMS, MAN, AND CYBERNETICS*

Naşcu, I., Diangelakis, N. A., Muñoz, S. G. and Pistikopoulos, E. N. (2023) 'Advanced model predictive control strategies for evaporation processes in the pharmaceutical industries', *Computers & Chemical Engineering,* 173, 108212.

Nascu, I., Diangelakis, N. A. and Pistikopoulos, E. (2022) 'Multiparametric Model Predictive Control Strategies for Evaporation Processes in Pharmaceutical Industries', *32nd European Symposium on Computer Aided Process Engineering; Elsevier, 2016;, Computer Aided Chemical Engineering.*

Pistikopoulos, E. N., Barbosa-Povoa, A., Lee, J. H., Misener, R., Mitsos, A., Reklaitis, G. V., Venkatasubramanian, V., You, F. Q. and Gani, R. (2021) 'Process systems engineering - The generation next?', *Computers & Chemical Engineering,* 147.

Su, Q., Ganesh, S., Moreno, M., Bommireddy, Y., Gonzalez, M., Reklaitis, G. V. and Nagy, Z. K. (2019) 'A perspective on Quality-by-Control (QbC) in pharmaceutical continuous manufacturing', *Computers and Chemical Engineering,* 125, 216-231.

Flavio Manenti, Gintaras V. Reklaitis (Eds.), Proceedings of the 34th European Symposium on Computer Aided Process Engineering / 15th International Symposium on Process Systems Engineering (ESCAPE34/PSE24), June 2-6, 2024, Florence, Italy

Integration of real-time optimization and model-predictive control: Application to refinery diesel pool

Pelin Dologlu,[a,*] A. Eren Vedin,[a] Rıdvan Memiş,[a] Sadık Ödemiş,[b] Kemal Burçak Kaplan,[a] Shaig Goyushov,[c] Mehran Isgandarli,[c]

aSOCAR Turkey, Digital Transformation Department, Istanbul 34485, Turkey
bSOCAR STAR Oil Refinery, Advanced Process Control Department, Aliaga, Izmir 35800, Turkey
cSOCAR STAR Oil Refinery, Planning Department, Aliaga, Izmir 35800, Turkey
pelin.dologlu@socar.com.tr

Abstract

The manual adjustment of the refinery's diesel pool flash point to meet planning department quality specifications is challenging due to multiple input flows from units like HCU, KHT, and DHT. Operational changes, tank operations, and blending scenarios further complicate flash point management. Additionally, conditions like tank change operations in the diesel pool while the process is ongoing make it difficult to adjust flash points solely by intermittently taking samples to determine the tank's flash point. For this reason, maintaining the flash point close to the low specification limit reduces giveaway and maximizes profits. However, if the flash point value falls below the low limit, the product cannot be sold as it will be out of specification. Since managing such a sensitive operation with open-loop control is not feasible, integration of RTO and MPC for refinery diesel pool is studied in this paper. The RTO minimizes the giveaway coming from the deviation of the target flash points in the diesel pool tanks, where blends of HCU, KHT and DHT units' middle products are stored. The optimizer determines the flash points at all blending and individual product flow points, which are then sent to the diesel pool. The optimizer sends the found flash point values as set points for the current operation directly to the MPC that controls the HCU naphtha product flow rate. Through the integration of RTO and MPC in the refinery diesel pool, significant financial improvements have been realized.

Keywords: real-time optimization, model-predictive control, hydrocracker unit, diesel pool, flash point

1. Introduction

Stringent environmental regulations, with the goal of reducing sulfur oxide emissions from land and sea vehicles, compel refineries to generate low sulfur fuels. The demand for ultra-low-sulfur (ULSD) diesel, ULSD gasoline, and low-sulfur marine grade fuels has surged in compliance with the latest Emission Control Area regulations (Iplik et al., 2021). To meet these evolving standards, refineries employ various processes, such as kerosene hydrotreatment (KHT), diesel hydrotreatment (DHT), and the hydrocracker unit (HCU). KHT focuses on improving the quality of kerosene, DHT targets enhancements in diesel properties, and HCU involves the conversion of heavy hydrocarbons into lighter, more valuable products. These processes collectively contribute to the production of low sulfur fuels, aligning with the imperative to minimize environmental impact. However, the manual adjustment of flash points in the diesel pool, where the outputs of KHT, DHT, and HCU are stored, poses a significant challenge. EN-590 ULSD fuel specifications (E. C. for Standardization, 2009) necessitate the ULSD flash point to be above 55°C. Diesel produced from various units are being pooled into final product tanks. Traditionally, each unit adheres to planning instructions to ensure the final tank content meets the required specification. The flash point, fundamentally, is the lowest temperature at which a liquid can form an ignitable mixture in air. Contrary to conventional arithmetic blending, the flash points of components in a mixture don't linearly combine (Riazi, 2005). This non-linearity poses challenges. Operating safely often means maintaining a flash point significantly above the 55°C benchmark, which can lead to financial losses referred to as 'giveaway'. The financial implications are twofold: blending off-spec can be costly, and maintaining a flash point much higher than necessary results in the inclusion of excess high-value components, leading to giveaway. One primary factor influencing the flash point is the presence of light components in the mixture, particularly wild naphtha in the stripper column. Therefore, the challenge lies in optimizing the blend to include a greater proportion of naphtha – a lower value component – in the high-value diesel product, while simultaneously adhering to the flash point specifications.

In addition to these challenges, refineries produce a product known as heavy naphtha. This heavy naphtha can also be blended into the diesel pool. However, the inclusion of heavy naphtha necessitates meticulous formulation and a robust system for close monitoring of pool values. Using naphtha can effectively counteract the giveaway, further optimizing the value derived from the diesel pool. Compounding the challenge is the fact that the flash point of naphtha cannot be measured within the refinery's laboratory. To address these challenges, integration of real-time optimization (RTO) and model predictive control (MPC) for heavy naphtha addition to diesel pool is proposed minimizing giveaway coming from the deviation of the target flash points in the diesel pool tanks.

2. Materials and Methods

2.1. Flash Point Prediction of ULSD Fuel Blends

The non-additive nature of the flash point, as previously mentioned, precludes its calculation through simple arithmetic averages. This has led to numerous attempts to establish an index for the flash point of a given component, as documented in various studies. These indices help to linearize the problem of blending. Several noteworthy formulations from the literature include; flash point prediction proposed by Wickey and Chittenden shown in Eq. (1), and another method introduced by Hu and Burns shown in Eq. (2) (Riazi, 2005).

$$\log(I_{FP}) = -6.1188 + \frac{2414}{T_{FP}+503.71} \quad (1) \qquad I_{FP} = (T_{FP})^{\frac{1}{-0.06}} \quad (2) \qquad F_m = [\textstyle\sum_i^n I_{FP} * v_i]^{-0.06} \quad (3)$$

where I_{FP}, T_{FP}, F_m and v_i are the flash point index, the flash point of component, the flash point of mixture in (K) and the volume fraction of component i.

Among these, the formula developed by Hu and Burns demonstrates the most accurate alignment with our historical data. Moreover, the default power factor of -1/0.06 is consistently adjusted and fed back into the calculation based on the flash point measurements reported by the laboratory. This power factor parameter (r) is adaptively optimized based on residuals from the last 8 samples. After determining the index, the flash point of mixture is calculated using Eq. (3) (Riazi, 2005).

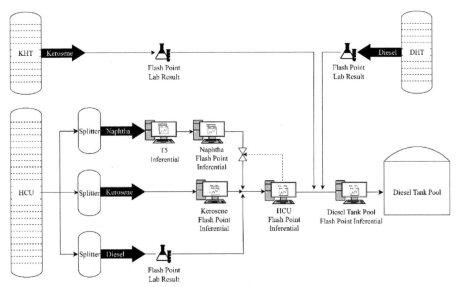

Figure 1. Diesel pool flow schema for proposed methodology

Diesel, kerosene and naphtha output flows from KHT, DHT, and HCU are blend and stored in diesel tank pool (see Figure 1). In order to adjust the flash point of diesel tank pool, it is important to know flash point of product flows simultaneously as a first step. Afterwards, blend flash points can be predicted. Flash point inferentials for naphtha and kerosene flows of HCU, HCU blended flow and diesel tank pool flow are created for closely monitoring. HCU diesel, KHT kerosene and DHT diesel laboratory samples are taken often enough, and not change too much, thus final lab results can be used for blends flash point. HCU kerosene flash point inferential is a soft sensor and its inputs are splitter bottom temperature, splitter top pressure and reboiler duty. HCU naphtha flash point inferential calculated via experimental equation calculated from %5 temperature (T5), since they are highly correlated. T5 inferential model is linear regression model which are inputs are naphtha splitter tray temperature and overhead pressure. HCU kerosene and naphtha flash point inferential models are developed via linear regression method, and then blending point flash points are calculated based on these models. Two blending point inferentials, which are HCU and diesel tank pool, are calculated via Eq. (3). All these individual product inferentials provide the most accurate and up-to-date result for the next blending point inferentials. Thus, the flash points of HCU and diesel tank pool are calculated to minimize giveaway in real-time according to the current product flow.

In addition to real-time flash point prediction for blending points, it is important to know the flash point of critical tank levels for the future. This enables the business unit to make decisions in advance regarding plant flows, especially in the HCU. Flash points of tank critical levels and tank closure for the future are forecasted in this work. This forecasting is done by assuming that if each plant flow and flash point of each plant is stable, then the flash point of the blended product will be calculated for each critical level and tank closure.

2.2. Integration of Real-Time Optimization and Model-Predictive Control

MPC is a control strategy that optimizes the control inputs of a system over a certain prediction horizon by solving an optimization problem at each time step. It involves manipulating variables (MV) and controlled variables (CV) to achieve desired performance while satisfying constraints.

RTO is a layer within the process automation hierarchy that provides set-points to a regulatory control layer determined through economic optimization (Darby et al., 2011). In this work, RTO-MPC integration is proposed, in which a prediction of the closed-loop response of the HCU naphtha flow MPC regulation is utilized within the RTO optimization formulation. "Implied" naphtha flashpoint is calculated based on adaptive optimization techniques that minimizes residuals from the blend prediction within given bounds. This provides the HCU diesel flash point as a set point to the underlying MPC level. In the developed MPC application, the CV is the flash point of the diesel coming out of the HCU, while the MV variable is the amount of naphtha added to the diesel (see Figure 1 and Eq. (7)). The RTO's objective function for a diesel production process is designed to minimizing giveaway, which is directly related to flash point minimization of diesel tank flash point. Displayed below are the objective function (Eq. (4)) and constraints (Eqs. (5-11)) utilized for solving the Nonlinear Programming (NLP) problem.

$$\text{Min } F_{Diesel\ Tank} = \left[\sum_i^n F_i * v_i\right]^{-r} \quad i \in [\text{DHT, KHT, HCU}] \tag{4}$$

$$s.t. \ F_{Diesel\ Tank} \geq F_{min,\ Diesel\ Tank} \tag{5}$$

$$F_{HCU} = \left[\sum_j^n F_j * v_j\right]^{-r} \quad j \in [\text{ HCU Naphtha, HCU Kerosene, HCU Diesel]} \tag{6}$$

$$F_{HCU\ Naphtha} = f(v_{HCU\ Naphtha}) \quad \text{(MPC Layer)} \tag{7}$$

$$F_{HCU\ Naphtha} = f(T5_{HCU\ Naphtha}) \tag{8}$$

$$F_{min,k} \leq F_k \leq F_{max,k} \quad k \in [\text{ DHT, KHT, HCU, HCU Naphtha, HCU Kerosene, HCU Diesel]} \tag{9}$$

$$v_{min,k} \leq v_k \leq v_{max,k} \quad k \in [\text{ DHT, KHT, HCU Naphtha, HCU Kerosene, HCU Diesel]} \tag{10}$$

$$0.04 \leq r \leq 0.08 \tag{11}$$

where F is flash point, v is flow rate ratio, and r is hyperparameter that should be also regularized mentioned in Eq. (3). Gradient descent algorithm is used for solving that NLP problem. Our algorithm employs a heuristic approach that iteratively searches for the optimal solution within a predefined search space. While this approach does not guarantee global optimality, it is effective in reaching near-optimal solutions efficiently in practical refinery scenarios. When a sufficiently good result, often identified as a local minimum, is attained, the iterative process is brought to a halt.

3. Results and Discussion

This study delves into the optimization of diesel blending processes in refineries to meet the demand for ULSD fuels. The focus lies on addressing the complex issue of flash point adjustment in the diesel pool. Our investigation incorporates RTO and MPC, proposing a systematic approach to minimize financial losses associated with both blending off-spec and excessive use of high-value components. The primary objective is to strike a balance, ensuring the flash point remains above the mandated 56.5°C benchmark while maximizing the inclusion of lower-value components, such as wild naphtha.

The first aspect of this study involves the development and application of flash point prediction models for ULSD fuel blends. Figure 1 illustrates the proposed methodology, emphasizing the integration of diesel, kerosene, and naphtha flows from various refinery units into the diesel tank pool. Real-time flash point predictions are crucial in this process, considering the scarcity of laboratory samples and the need for constant monitoring. This approach involves the use of inferentials for naphtha and kerosene flows, creating a dynamic system that adapts to changing conditions and minimizes giveaway in real-time.

Furthermore, this study extends beyond immediate operational concerns to forecast future flash points of critical tank levels. A comparison of before and after the commissioning of this forecasting study can be seen in Figure 2a and 2b. Instead there are multiple tanks in diesel pool, one of the busiest tank closure flash point lab is selected and prediction model results is compared for selected tank. Tank closure flash point results are plotted as one year duration for each before and after the commissioning of this forecasting study. The average tank closure flash point before this study was 57.3 °C, flash point of tank closure is 56.75 °C with the help of this project. Since the target flash point is 56.5 °C because of buffer of lower flash point limit for this RTO, giveaway is minimized successfully. Additionally, the flash point for the diesel pool can be easily forecasted with this project, closely matching the actual tank closure lab results. While flash point prediction average is 56.77 °C, actual tank closure flash point lab result average is 56.75 °C for the same dates (Figure 2b). Since margin of error for the laboratory flash point experiment is 0.5 °C, 0.25 °C bias is quite acceptable improvement. With the help of this successful forecasting results, this proactive approach allows refineries to make informed decisions in advance, particularly in the context of the HCU.

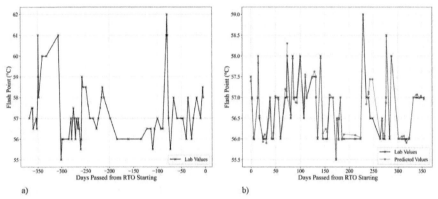

a)   b)

Figure 2. Selected tank closure flash point result from diesel tank pool, a) before this project, b) after this project

The integration of RTO and MPC emerges as a key strategy in our proposed methodology. By utilizing the dynamic model of the system and considering constraints, we optimize control inputs over short prediction horizons. In the developed MPC application, the flash point of HCU blend serves as the controlled variable, with the manipulated variable being the amount of naphtha added to the diesel pool. The provided trend in Figure 3 represents a 5-days representative section where MPC is active on HCU. During this time interval, the planning instruction was given within the range of 50-52 °C, and the average of 15 HCU diesel and kerosene blending point (before naphtha is added) samples taken in total was realized as 50.3 °C, approaching the minimum target by as close as 0.3 °C on average (Figure 3a). Thanks to MPC applications, it is possible to provide external set points for CVs. As a result, it becomes much more frequent to reach the set point, within operational limits, and most importantly, in an automatic manner, thus significantly reducing giveaways compared to manual operations. This integrated approach not only ensures compliance with flash point specifications but also enhances the overall efficiency of the blending process (Figure 3b).

As delving into the specific results and observations, the proposed methodology holds promise in addressing the intricate challenges posed by environmental regulations while optimizing the economic value derived from the diesel pool.

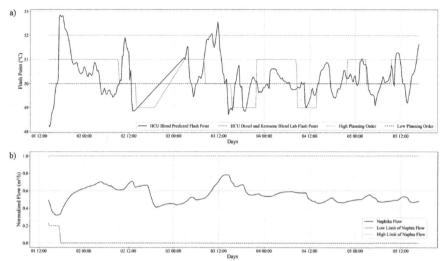

Figure 3. 5-days representative section where MPC is active on HCU a) HCU blending points flash point changes, b) adaptive naphtha flow to adjust flash point of HCU blend

4. Conclusions

In summary, this study navigates the optimization of diesel blending processes, with a primary focus on the intricate task of adjusting the flash point within the diesel pool. By leveraging real-time predictions and inferentials for naphtha and kerosene flows, the minimization of giveaway has been effectively achieved. Beyond immediate operational concerns, this study has successfully forecasted future flash points, resulting in a substantial reduction of average tank closure flash points from 57.3 °C to 56.75 °C.

The integrated approach extends to easy forecasting of the diesel pool flash point, aligning closely with actual lab results. The use of RTO and MPC has proven pivotal, as demonstrated in Figure 3, ensuring not only compliance with flash point specifications but also a significant enhancement in overall blending efficiency.

This proactive methodology does not just meet regulatory requirements; it strategically optimizes the economic value derived from the diesel pool. The success of the forecasting results and the automatic nature of the approach empower refineries to make informed decisions in advance, particularly in the dynamic context of the HCU. In essence, this study showcases the potential for addressing environmental challenges while simultaneously maximizing the economic efficiency of the diesel blending process.

References

Darby, M. L., Nikolaou, M., Jones, J., & Nicholson, D. (2011). RTO: An overview and assessment of current practice. *Journal of Process Control*, *21*(6), 874–884. https://doi.org/10.1016/J.JPROCONT.2011.03.009

E. C. for Standardization (2009). *EN-590: Automotive Fuels-Diesel-Requirements and test methods*. European Committee for Standardization Brussels.

Iplik, E., Tsirikoglou, P., Aslanidou, I., & Kyprianidis, K. (2021). Parameter estimation and sensitivity analysis for a diesel hydro-processing model. *Computer Aided Chemical Engineering*, *50*, 573–578. https://doi.org/10.1016/B978-0-323-88506-5.50091-7

Riazi, M. R. (2005). *Characterization and properties of petroleum fractions* (Vol. 50). ASTM international.

Flavio Manenti, Gintaras V. Reklaitis (Eds.), Proceedings of the 34th European Symposium on Computer Aided Process Engineering / 15th International Symposium on Process Systems Engineering (ESCAPE34/PSE24), June 2-6, 2024, Florence, Italy

An MILP based-approach to logistics of air separation supply chains with a heterogeneous fleet of trucks

Sergio G. Bonino, [a] Luis J. Zeballos, [a] Akash Moolya, [c] Jose Lainez, [c] Jose M. Pinto, [c] Ignacio E. Grossmann, [b] Carlos A. Méndez [a,*]

[a] Instituto de Desarrollo Tecnológico para la Industria Química (INTEC), UNL-CONICET, Güemes 3450, Santa Fe 3000, Argentina
[b] Carnegie Mellon University, 5000 Forbes, Pittsburgh 15213, United States
[c] Linde Digital Americas, Linde PLC, United States
cmendez@intec.unl.edu.ar

Abstract

This article addresses the production and distribution scheduling of industrial-sized gas problems when a heterogeneous fleet of trucks is considered. In the work, an MILP-based approach is proposed to deal with the characteristics of the problem. In the distribution part, for each size of truck considered, a set of feasible routes is previously generated and selected. Then, the model is solved by considering the routes selected, choosing the ones that satisfy all the conditions imposed while optimizing production and distribution activities. It is worth remarking that the approach takes into account the lead time on production and distribution decisions. Finally, an illustrative example is presented and solved to show the impact of multi-size trucks. The results obtained demonstrate the effectiveness of the proposed approach in reasonable CPU times.

Keywords: Supply chain management, Production routing problem, Mathematical modelling.

1. Introduction

When examining the operation and management of industries specializing in industrial gas production, a critical aspect is identified in the design and management of the supply chain (SC). In the SC, decisions regarding production and distribution of products to customers are critical. Ramaswamy et al., (2020) provide a comprehensive analysis about the design and management of industrial gas supply chains. Additionally, Barbosa-Povoa and Pinto, (2020) conduct an exhaustive study of the most significant problems and challenges within SC, offering proposals for their resolution.

2. Problem statement

This work deals with the production and distribution problem of an industrial gas supply chain that operates under a vendor-managed inventory (VMI) policy. The aim is to optimize the operation of the SC, seeking to minimize the resulting total cost. One particularity of this problem, is the consideration of a heterogeneous fleet of trucks. Due to the characteristics of customers (i.e., location, demands, tank sizes), the adoption of multi-size trucks is necessary. In some cases, customers who are located inside a city or that have low-capacity tanks, cannot receive a delivery from big-sized trucks and smaller trucks are needed. By taking this issue into account a more efficient utilization of the truck's capacities is expected. As mentioned above, the company must generate optimal production and distribution strategies that allow it to visit customers on time to meet their demands. For this reason, knowing the monthly demands of customers and their maximum and minimum inventory capacities, the company has to decide the plant's production rate and the sizes of trucks to use, in terms of supplying the requested product. An important aspect of the problem under consideration is that trucks can either make multiple short trips per day or a single trip of several days. The duration of the trip is determined by factors such as the distance to the clients involved, the sequence in which customers are visited, and the loading and unloading times of the products. Given that trips can extend over several days, this problem explicitly takes into account the impact of lead time on: a) the date when the product is released from the plant and reaches the customer, and b) the time during which the trucks are unavailable for other trips.

3. Solution strategy and main assumptions

To address the problem, the MILP model and the route generator algorithm introduced in Bonino et al., (2023) are the basis for the current paper. Thus, the route generator algorithm is still employed for the creation of all potential trips between customers and plants. Regarding the mathematical formulation, the previous equation blocks and decision variables introduced in Bonino et al., (2023) are used to face the new problem. Also, to include the sizes of trucks in the previous developed model, a new set indicating the different available sizes is added. The truck sizes taken into account are: "Small", "Medium" and "Big". This new index impacts in the variables that consider: a) amount of product i delivered by plant p using a specific route s at day t: "$\overline{DL}_{i,p,s,\text{size},t}$", b) amount of product i delivered to customer c from plant p using a specific route s at day t: "$\widehat{DL}_{i,p,s,c,\text{size},t}$", c) trucks in the plant p for the product i available on a given day t: "$TU_{i,p,\text{size},t}$", d) the activation or deactivation of the route s associated with plant p and product i at day t: "$A_{i,p,s,\text{size},t}$". It is worth noting that the resulting increase in the model size is related to the new set added and not to the number of trucks available.

The following assumptions underlie the proposed solution strategy: a) Trucks can only be used a given number of hours per day. More time implies a multiday trip, b) Routes of more than one day are considered, c) Routes of several customers are considered, d) Lead time is taken into account when scheduling a customer visit, e) Trucks making trips longer than the limit of hours per day are not available for use until their return to the plants, f) The total ending inventory must be greater than or equal to the total beginning inventory, g) A truck can have multiple trips in one day only if the total time of all trips is less than or equal to the limit of hours per day, h) A customer can be visited at most twice on the same day, i) All the parameters and variables representing quantity of product are standardized to medium-sized truck units,

3.1. Model formulation

The extended MILP model is designed to minimize the costs associated with production and distribution operations when considering a heterogeneous fleet of trucks. The introduction of a new index indicating the size of the trucks has an impact on the variables mentioned earlier and, consequently, on all equations related to them. Unfortunately, due to space limitations, the complete model cannot be included. Nevertheless, to illustrate the impact of the changes in constraints, Equations (1) and (2) are given as example. Both constraints are performed for trucks that are engaged in trips with durations longer than the maximum number of working hours per day (hd). Constraint (1) calculates the number of trucks for each size that are available to perform multi-day trips. $LC_{i,p,\text{size}}$ is a parameter that indicates the total number of trucks of a given size available in plant p to transport product i. SP_p, SI_i, SAS_t are the sets of routes departing from plant p, transporting product

i, and available routes on day t, respectively. IP_i are the set of plants producing product i. Constraint (2) calculates the number of unavailable trucks for transporting the product i since the plant p in the period t ($TU_{i,p,size,t}$). To calculate the trucks not available in period t, equation (2) takes into account the parameter $Duration_s$ in order to consider the trucks that are in use in period t because they are yet performing a given route s.

$$\sum_{s \in (SP_p \wedge SI_i \wedge SAS_t),(\tau_s > hd))} A_{i,p,s,size,t} \leq (LC_{i,p,size} - TU_{i,p,size,t}) ,$$

$$\forall i \in I, \forall p \in IP_i, \forall t, \forall size \in Size \tag{1}$$

$$TU_{i,p,size,t} = \sum_{\substack{s \in \left(SP_p \wedge SI_i \wedge SAS_t \wedge (Duration_s > 1)\right), \\ tt:((tt \geq t - Duration_s + 1) \wedge (tt \leq t - 1))}} A_{i,p,s,size,tt}$$

$$\forall i \in I, \forall p \in IP_i, \forall t: t > 1, \forall size \in Size \tag{2}$$

3.2. Strategy for matching routes with trucks considering their sizes

In this section, the proposed strategy is presented in order to establish an efficient relationship between the generated routes and the available truck sizes. In this work the truck capacities ($Capacity_{size}$) considered are 0.5, 1, and 1.4 for small, medium, and large trucks, respectively. To match routes and truck sizes, the characteristics of the clients involved in the trips are considered. Customer location is a key aspect because not all trucks can deliver product to customers due to accessibility issues. On the other hand, tank capacity and daily customer demand substantially affect the minimum and maximum delivery connected to the routes. For the generated routes that do not have limitations (for example, due to the location of customers), Algorithm 1 establishes the set of routes that can be used by the trucks of the different sizes. It is important to note that for each route generated the minimum and maximum amount of product ($DeliveryMin_s$, $DeliveryMax_s$) that the route can deliver is determined. These parameters are computed considering the daily customer demands and the difference between the tank capacity and the reserve levels of the customers included on the routes, respectively.

Algorithm 1. Truck-size / route matching
---
input: S {*route list*}, $DeliveryMin_s$, $DeliveryMax_s$, $Capacity_{size}$
output: SS {*Small − Size list*} , MS {*Medium − Size list*}, BS {*Big − Size list*}
begin
   $SS \leftarrow [\ ]$, $MS \leftarrow [\ ]$, $BS \leftarrow [\ ]$ {*empty list*}
   for $s \in S$ **do**
      if $DeliveryMin_s \leq Capacity_{small}$
         if $DeliveryMax_s \geq 0.8 * Capacity_{medium}$
            Add *route s to list MS*
         else
            Add *route s to list SS*
      if $Capacity_{small} < DeliveryMin_s \leq Capacity_{medium}$
         if $DeliveryMax_s \geq 0.8 * Capacity_{big}$
            Add *route s to list BS*
         else
            Add *route s to list MS*
      if $DeliveryMin_s \geq Capacity_{medium}$
         Add *route s to list BS*
end

The procedure is initiated by generating empty lists for the different truck sizes, where the assigned routes will be stored. For each route, a comparison is made between the minimum delivery and the capacities of different trucks to determine if, in any case, the lowest quantity to be shipped exceeds the available capacity for a given truck size. If the minimum shipment for a route is less than the capacity of the truck size under analysis, the maximum shipment is then compared with the available capacity of the next size of truck. If the highest delivery of the route is greater than the 80% of the capacity of the next truck, the route is assigned to that truck size; otherwise, the route is assigned to the initial size.

The algorithm presented outlines the assignment of a single truck size per route. Nevertheless, with slight adjustments, it can also be extended to consider two truck sizes per route. In this case, the sizes are determined by those ensuring the minimum delivery of the route, along with the inclusion of the next larger truck size.

4. Illustrative example and computational results

To demonstrate the advantage of considering a heterogeneous fleet of trucks, an illustrative example is presented. Figure 1, illustrates the logistic decisions expected with a heterogeneous truck fleet. The case addressed involves one production plant, one product, 14 customers with different demands and storage tank sizes, three vehicles of different sizes, and a time horizon of 28 days. The geographical locations of the plant and customers are depicted in Figure 2. As observed in the image, customers have different daily demand and tank sizes. All the customers are located to less than 24 hours of the plant. The maximum number of working hours per day (*hd*) considered is 12.

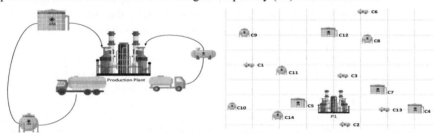

Figure 1. Trips with heterogeneous fleet   **Figure 2**. Plant and customer location

To assess the performance of the mathematical formulation, nine different scenarios were tested. In each scenario, the number of trucks considered varies, as well as the number of possible truck sizes per route. Table 1 provides a detailed description of the conditions in each scenario. The model was implemented in GAMS 32.0 and all scenarios were solved with GUROBI 10.0.0 on a desktop computer with 2.80GHz Intel(R) Core(TM) i9-10900F processor and 16 GB RAM on Windows 10. The maximum run time for each scenario was set to 900 seconds.

Table 1. Scenarios tested

Scenario	Number of trucks per capacity			Truck sizes per route		
	Small	Medium	Big	All posible (*)	1 size	Up to 2 sizes
S1	3	-	-	●	-	-
S2	-	3	-	●	-	-
S3	-	-	3	●	-	-
S4	1	1	1	●	-	-
S5	-	2	1	●	-	-
S6	-	1	2	●	-	-
S7	1	1	1	-	●	-
S8	1	1	1	-	-	●
S9	-	1	2	-	-	●

(*)In S1, S2, and S3, the allowed truck sizes per route are small, medium, and large, respectively.

The results obtained for the scenarios are presented below in Tables 2 and 3. For the addressed example, the goal is to satisfy all customer demands through the company's production. If it is not possible, and external purchases are needed to meet the total demand, the result is considered to be infeasible. The scenarios S1 and S7 were found to be infeasible, and therefore, no results will be displayed in the tables. The infeasibility is attributed to the fact that both scenarios only consider a single truck size per route, and the assigned trucks cannot fulfill the entire demand.

The performance of the model for the scenarios tested is shown in Table 2. It includes the size of the resulting MILP model, the processing time, and the value of the objective function with the associated optimality GAP. Table 3 provides a detailed analysis of the solution in terms of distribution.

Table 2. Model performance

	S2	S3	S4	S5	S6	S8	S9
Equations	27,372	28,632	74,606	51,619	51,619	43,974	43,974
Continuous var.	12,293	12,853	35,813	24,333	24,333	20,497	20,497
Binary var.	3,332	3,472	10,416	6,944	6,944	5,768	5,768
Cost [$]	89,551.7	83,600.4	85,183.5	84,356.7	82,817.7	85,977.8	82,812.7
CPU Time [s]	900	900	900	900	900	900	900
GAP [%]	1.79	1.06	1.79	1.44	0.75	2.31	0.98

Table 2 shows that the variation in model sizes between scenarios is predominantly due to the number of enabled routes to solve the problem. In terms of solution quality, it can be observed that within 900 seconds, results close to the optimum were obtained, where the optimality GAPs range from 0.75% to 2.31%. Regarding costs, the best solution was obtained for scenario S9, which considered a medium-sized truck and two big-sized trucks. In this scenario, each route is allowed to have up to two truck sizes assigned, when it is possible. The results obtained for S9, compared with the ones achieved for S2 and S3, show the advantages of considering heterogeneous fleets. S2 and S3 assume all medium and big trucks, respectively. While S3 outperforms S2 by considering larger trucks for the trips, both scenarios are surpassed by S9 given that the flexibility to choose the appropriate truck size for each trip.

For each scenario, Table 3 displays the number of trips, customer visits, and average truck utilization for each considered size. When contrasting S2 with S9, it is noticeable that in S2, there were 62 trips with 82 customer visits. In S9, with the inclusion of larger truck sizes, the number of trips decreased to 48, and the visits reduced to 67. This reduction is attributed to the capability of transporting a larger quantity of product in each trip, if needed.

Table 3. Solutions obtained for transportation decisions

		S2	S3	S4	S5	S6	S8	S9
Trips		62	45	58	52	48	59	48
Visits		82	70	75	73	66	74	67
Truck utilization [%]	**Small**	-	-	88.46	-	-	89.29	-
	Medium	96.19	-	98.19	92.80	80.75	98.59	85.92
	Big	-	94.66	99.32	99.80	99.10	98.45	98.91
Possible number of routes		119	124	292	243	243	206	206

Figures 3 and 4 illustrate the inventory profile for customer 12. This customer demands 0.5 units daily of product and can receive a maximum product delivery of 2.5 units. Figure 3 shows the inventory evolution obtained for S2, where only medium trucks with a capacity of 1 are considered. The graph indicates that to meet the customer's demand, 14 visits with full trucks are scheduled. In Figure 4, the evolution of C12 in scenario S9 is presented. In this case, with the inclusion of big trucks with a capacity of 1.4, only 10 visits (using big-sized trucks) are performed, resulting in a number of visits less than in S2. This highlights that the use of heterogeneous trucks enables a more efficient allocation of trucks to trips, optimizing the available capacities.

The perceived reduction in trips for C12 in the S9 scenario also results in reduced distribution costs. In the case presented in the figures, the scheduling of visits for C12 in S2 incurs a total cost of $13,013, while for S9, the cost is $11,154. This trend in distribution costs explains the difference in total cost between S2 and S9. While the production cost for both scenarios is $33,043.5, the distribution costs are $56,508.2 and $49,769.2 for S2 and S9, respectively. A lower transportation cost is observed in S9 due to the consideration of heterogeneous trucks.

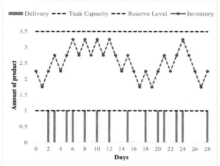 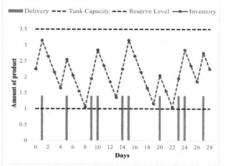

Figure 3. C12 inventory in S2   **Figure 4**. C12 inventory in S9

5. Conclusions

In this work, an MILP-based model was presented to optimize daily production and delivery decisions when considering multiple truck sizes and multiday trips. Considering the distribution decisions, it is important to remark that the way in which the types of trucks are represented in the formulation and the use of strategies for linking routes with the different truck sizes allow obtaining very good quality solutions in short CPU times. From a practical point of view, the analysis of various scenarios addressed shows the advantage of incorporating trucks of different sizes in order to improve transport efficiency and reduce distribution costs.

References

Barbosa-Povoa, A.P., Pinto, J.M., 2020. Process supply chains: Perspectives from academia and industry. Comput Chem Eng 132, 106606.
    https://doi.org/10.1016/J.COMPCHEMENG.2019.106606

Bonino, S.G., Zeballos, L.J., Moolya, A., Lainez, J., Pinto, J.M., Grossmann, I.E., Méndez, C.A., 2023. A MILP-based approach to manage logistics in large industrial gas supply chains. Computer Aided Chemical Engineering 52, 3319–3324. https://doi.org/10.1016/B978-0-443-15274-0.50529-1

Ramaswamy, S., Madan, T., Thyagarajan, K., Pinto, J.M., Laínez-Aguirre, J.M., 2020. Advanced decision-support technologies for the design and management of industrial gas supply chains. Smart Manufacturing: Applications and Case Studies 387–421. https://doi.org/10.1016/B978-0-12-820028-5.00011-4

Flavio Manenti, Gintaras V. Reklaitis (Eds.), Proceedings of the 34th European Symposium on Computer Aided Process Engineering / 15th International Symposium on Process Systems Engineering (ESCAPE34/PSE24), June 2-6, 2024, Florence, Italy

Market-oriented Decision Making in Power Generation Investment

Maria Kanta, [a] Evangelos G. Tsimopoulos, [a] Christos N. Dimitriadis, [a] Michael C. Georgiadis [a,*]

[a]Department of Chemical Engineering, Aristotle University of Thessaloniki, University Campus, Thessaloniki, 54124, Greece
mgeorg@auth.gr

Abstract

In recent times, owning a Gas-Fired Power Plant (GFPP) is considered an appealing choice for investors in the power sector. GFPPs offer flexibility, to compensate for the stochastic nature of renewable energy sources, and high production efficiency. This work considers a bi-level model for optimizing investment decisions of a producer participating in both electricity and natural gas markets. The investor endeavors to maximize his profit and acts as a strategic player in the electricity market and as a non-strategic player in the gas market. That implies that he can exercise market power in the electricity market. However, he cannot manipulate gas prices. A Carbon Emission Trading Scheme (CETS) is incorporated towards a low-carbon economy. The bi-level algorithm is initially recast into a Mathematical Program with Equilibrium Constraints (MPEC) and is further transformed into a Mixed Integer Linear Program (MILP) by utilizing the Karush-Kuhn-Tucker (KKT) optimality conditions, a binary expansion method and the strong duality theory. The model's application to a modified Pennsylvania-New Jersey- Maryland (PJM) 5-bus power system and a single-node gas system captures the contrasting impact of emission allowance trading and gas prices on investments in GFPPs. The results indicate that CETS implementation moderates profit loss, resulting from rising gas prices, while increasing carbon prices elevate the importance of GFPPs over high-emission non-GFPP units.

Keywords: bi-level optimization, strategic offering, electricity market, natural gas market, carbon emission trading

1. Introduction

To mitigate climate change, high-emissive power units are replaced with environmentally cautious ones. Thus, GFPPs constitute an economically attractive investment option. Approaches for the optimal coordination of natural gas and power markets have been presented in the open literature (Dimitriadis et al., 2021). Dimitriadis et al. (2023) focused on optimizing the scheduling of different storage technologies within an integrated natural gas and electricity market framework. Moreover, deriving optimal offering strategies in the electricity sector have been thoroughly investigated. This problem was studied by Tsimopoulos and Georgiadis (2020) for a producer with a mixed-generation portfolio and later by Dimitriadis et al. (2022) for an energy storage agent. Strategic investment in an imperfect integrated electricity and gas market has been modelled by Chen et al. (2020). The incorporation of emission reduction policies in generation expansion problems has been assessed by several studies within the context of carbon neutrality. Boffino et al. (2019) studied the generation investment problem, implementing a cap-and-trade policy and a carbon tax policy. However, there is a lack of comprehensive research on how CETS can affect the investment and production strategies in integrated electricity and gas market. This work aims to bridge the above gap by proposing an integrated framework for deriving optimal investment decisions for a producer owing GFPPs and participating in a decoupled gas and emission-embedded electricity market.

2. Problem statement

The formulation of the proposed bi-level model is presented below. Uncertainty is introduced in the model through a set of possible scenarios ω. Furthermore, a cap-and-trade system is adopted in the carbon market. As indicated in Eq. (1), the total carbon emission allowance, Q_t, is contingent upon the emission allowance factor η (tCO$_2$/MW) and the difference between electricity demand $L_{t,d}^E$ and wind power generation w_j. Each conventional unit h is granted emission allowances Q_h^H, as outlined in Eq. (2). The allocated factor regarding carbon emission permits α_h, required to determine Q_h^H, is calculated in Eq. (3) using the emission factor of each conventional unit ζ_h.

$$Q_t = \eta \cdot \left(\sum_{d^E} L_{t,d}^E - \sum_j w_j \right) \tag{1}$$

$$Q_h^H = \alpha_h \cdot Q_t \tag{2}$$

$$\alpha_h = \frac{\zeta_h}{\sum_h \zeta_h} \tag{3}$$

2.1. Upper-level problem
This section presents the upper-level problem.

$$\begin{aligned}
\textbf{\textit{maximize}}\ \sum_\omega \pi_\omega \cdot \sum_t \sigma_t \\
\cdot \left[\sum_{g \in \text{GaN}, g \in \text{GE}} v_{t,g,\omega}^e \cdot \lambda_{t,n,\omega}^E - \sum_{g \in \text{GaR}, g \in \text{GE}} \varphi_g^e \cdot \lambda_{t,r,\omega}^{NG} \cdot v_{t,g,\omega}^e \right. \\
- cp \cdot \left(\zeta_g \cdot v_{t,g,\omega}^e - Q_{t,g,\omega}^H \right) \\
+ \sum_{g \in \text{GaN}, g \in \text{GC}} v_{t,g,\omega}^c \cdot \lambda_{t,n,\omega}^E - \sum_{g \in \text{GaR}, g \in \text{GC}} \varphi_g^c \cdot \lambda_{t,r,\omega}^{NG} \cdot v_{t,g,\omega}^c \\
\left. - cp \cdot \left(\zeta_g \cdot v_{t,g,\omega}^c - Q_{t,g,\omega}^H \right) \right] - \sum_{g \in \text{GC}} K_g^c \cdot X_g^c
\end{aligned} \tag{4}$$

$$\textbf{\textit{s.t.}}\ \ X_g^c = \sum_l X_{l,g} \cdot u_{l,g} \ :\ \forall g \in \text{GC} \tag{5}$$

$$\sum_l u_{l,g} = 1 \ :\ \forall g \in \text{GC} \tag{6}$$

$$u_{l,g} \in \{0,1\} \quad : \quad \forall g \in GC \tag{7}$$

$$\zeta_g = \sum_l \zeta_{l,g} \cdot u_{l,g} \quad : \quad \forall g \in GC \tag{8}$$

$$\alpha_h = \sum_l \alpha_{l,h} \cdot u_{l,g} \quad : \quad \forall g \in GC, h \tag{9}$$

The upper-level problem aims at the profit maximization of the strategic producer. In the objective function (4) the term $v_{t,g}^e \cdot \lambda_{t,n}^E$ corresponds to the revenue from the existing GFPP from producing $v_{t,g}^e$ of power at a price of $\lambda_{t,n}^E$. The term $\varphi_g^e \cdot \lambda_{t,r}^{NG} \cdot v_{t,g}^e$ represent the gas purchase cost at a gas price $\lambda_{t,r}^{NG}$, while considering a φ_g^e electricity-gas conversion factor. The actual emission ($\zeta_g \cdot v_{t,g}^e$) and the permitted allowances $Q_{t,g}^H$, allocated to the existing GFPP, are used to determine the final cost of carbon trading for a carbon price of cp. cp is treated as a parameter. The related terms are also applied for the candidate GFPP, as shown in the fourth and fifth line in (4). The hourly operations profit for the strategic producer is multiplied by the probability π_ω of the scenario ω and by the weight σ_t of the corresponding operating condition t. Hence, the operations profit matches the annualized investment cost for a new unit with X_g^c maximum capacity. K_g^c denotes the annualized investment cost. Constraints (5)-(7) allow the selection of a single MW-investment option. Constraints (8)-(9) ensure that if no investment is realised, the candidate GFPP cannot contribute to the emission trading.

2.2. Lower-level problem: Electricity market clearing
This section represents the electricity market clearing problem.

$$\boldsymbol{minimize} \ \sum_{g \in GE} o_{t,g,\omega}^e \cdot v_{t,g,\omega}^e + \sum_{g \in GC} o_{t,g,\omega}^c \cdot v_{t,g,\omega}^c$$

$$+ \sum_{g,r:g \in GaR, g \in GNS} \lambda_{t,r,\omega}^{NG} \cdot \varphi_g^{ns} \cdot v_{t,g,\omega}^{ns} + \sum_i C_{t,i} \cdot p_{t,i,\omega}$$

$$+ \sum_{g \in GE} cp \cdot (\zeta_g \cdot v_{t,g,\omega}^e - Q_{t,g,\omega}^H) + \sum_{g \in GC} cp \cdot (\zeta_g \cdot v_{t,g,\omega}^c \tag{10}$$

$$- Q_{t,g,\omega}^H) + \sum_{g \in GNS} cp \cdot (\zeta_g \cdot v_{t,g,\omega}^{ns} - Q_{t,g,\omega}^H) + \sum_i cp \cdot (\zeta_i$$

$$\cdot p_{t,i,\omega} - Q_{t,i,\omega}^H) \quad \forall t, \forall \omega$$

$$\textbf{s.t.} \ - \sum_{g \in GaN, g \in GE} v_{t,g,\omega}^e - \sum_{g \in GaN, g \in GC} v_{t,g,\omega}^c - \sum_{g \in GaN, g \in GNS} v_{t,g,\omega}^{ns} - \sum_{i \in IaN} p_{t,i,\omega}$$

$$- \sum_{j \in JaN} w_j + \sum_{d^E \in DaN} L_{t,d,\omega}^E + \sum_{m \in NaM} B_{nm} \cdot (\delta_{t,n,\omega} - \delta_{t,m,\omega}) \tag{11}$$

$$= 0 \ : \left[\lambda_{t,n,\omega}^E\right] \forall n, \forall t, \forall \omega$$

$$-Q^H_{t,h,\omega} + \alpha_h \cdot \eta \cdot \left(\sum_{d^E} L^E_{t,d,\omega} - \sum_j w_j \right) = 0 : \left[\rho_{t,h,\omega} \right] \quad \forall h, \forall t, \forall \omega \tag{12}$$

$$0 \le v^c_{t,g,\omega} \le X^c_g : \left[\underline{\beta^c_{t,g,\omega}}, \overline{\beta^c_{t,g,\omega}} \right] \quad \forall g \in GC, \forall t, \forall \omega \tag{13}$$

The negative social welfare is derived from the objective function (10). $o^e_{t,g,\omega}$, $o^c_{t,g,\omega}$ and $C_{t,i}$ correspond to the strategic offers for existing/candidate GFPPs g and the cost offers of non-GFPPs *i*. The offers of the non-strategic GFPP depend on the natural gas price. $v^{ns}_{t,g,\omega}$, $v^c_{t,g,\omega}$ and $p_{t,i,\omega}$ denotes the hourly power production for non-strategic/candidate GFPPs and non-GFPP units. Constraints (11) ensure that the generation-demand balance is satisfied at each electric bus n, considering power demand $L^E_{t,d,\omega}$ and the susceptance $B_{n,m}$ for the transmission line connecting buses *n, m*. Constraints (12) allocate the emission allowances for each conventional power unit *h*. Constraints (13) enforce capacity limits for the candidate GFPP. Constraints imposing transmission capacity limits and capacity limits on the other generating units are also implemented in the model. Moreover, voltage angle $\delta_{t,n,\omega}$, used to formulate power flow in (11) is bound in each bus *n* and bus 1 is imposed as the slack bus, setting its voltage angle to zero.

2.3. Lower-level problem: Natural gas market clearing
This section represents the gas market clearing problem.

$$\textbf{\textit{minimize}} \quad \sum_k C_{t,k} \cdot f_{t,k,\omega} \quad \forall t, \forall \omega \tag{14}$$

$$\begin{aligned} \textbf{\textit{s.t.}} \quad &- \sum_{k \in KaR} f_{t,k,\omega} + \sum_{d^{NG} \in DaR} L^{NG}_{t,d,\omega} + \sum_{g \in GaR, g \in GE} \varphi^e_g \cdot v^e_{t,g,\omega} \\ &+ \sum_{g \in GaR, g \in GNS} \varphi^{ns}_g \cdot v^{ns}_{t,g,\omega} + \sum_{g \in GaR, g \in GC} \varphi^c_g \cdot v^c_{t,g,\omega} = 0 \\ &: \left[\lambda^{NG}_{t,r,\omega} \right] \forall r, \forall t, \forall \omega \end{aligned} \tag{15}$$

$$0 \le f_{t,k,\omega} \le \bar{F}_k : \left[\underline{\varepsilon_{t,k,\omega}}, \overline{\varepsilon_{t,k,\omega}} \right] \quad \forall k, \forall t, \forall \omega \tag{16}$$

Objective function (14) aims at minimizing the operating cost of the natural gas market. The cost offers of each gas suppliers *k* are indicated as $C_{t,k}$. Constraints (15) guarantee the energy balance at each gas node *r* considering gas demand $L^{NG}_{t,d,\omega}$. Constraint (16) enforce capacity limits on the natural gas production $f_{t,k,\omega}$ of each gas supplier.

2.4. Solution strategy
The lower-level problems are convex and therefore they can be replaced by their KKT optimality conditions, reducing the bi-level model to an MPEC. Using disjunctive constraints, the strong duality theory, and a binary expansion method the model is further recast into a MILP.

3. Illustrative example

The proposed model for strategic investment decisions is applied on a modified PJM 5-bus power and a single-node natural gas system, as illustrated in Fig. 1(a). The coupling between these two systems includes an existing and non-strategic GFPP, a strategic existing GFPP and a strategic candidate GFPP. Three non-GFPPs and a wind farm are also located at the power network. Additionally, two gas suppliers and three gas loads exist at the gas network. GFPPs are considered as additional gas loads with capacities equal to the power that GFPPs provide to the electricity market. The capital cost of the candidate unit is 22,900 €/MW (Cong et al., 2019) and carbon price is set to be 35.5 €/tCO$_2$ (Bank, 2023). It should be mentioned that the wind power plant is considered cost-free and emission-free, hence the wind farm cannot participate in emission trading.

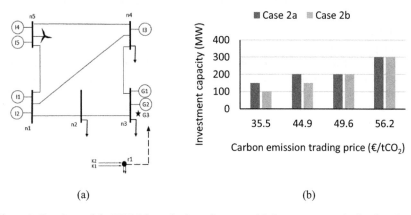

(a)   (b)

Figure 1: Topology of the PJM 5-bus, single-node system (a). Investment results for Case 2a and Case 2b (b).

Table 1: Data and results for Case 1a, Case 1b and Case 1c.

	Case 1a	Case 1b	Case 1c
Gas price increase	0%	10%	20%
Capacity investment (M W)	150	100	50
Emission cost (M €)	4.4	0.4	-1.8
Profit (€)	30.1	26.2	22.9

4. Results and discussion

4.1. Case 1

The proposed model is solved using GAMS/CPLEX. Regarding the investment decisions, a static approach is adopted, and decisions are made at a single time point considering a single future target year. This case contemplates the impact of gas prices on the expansion planning decisions. Different gas prices are considered in Case 1a, Case 1b and Case 1c. Table 1 summarizes the results indicating that the strategic producer opts for a less capacitated GFPP as the fuel cost increases. Furthermore, carbon emission trading acts as a coping mechanism in Case 1c to navigate profit loss. Negative values in emission costs indicate that the strategic producer profits from trading the unused allowances.

4.2. Case 2

In this case an increased carbon price and uncertainty regarding gas and electric demands are implemented. Two cases (Case 2a and Case 2b) are used to demonstrate the results. In Case 2b the probability for the scenarios with high gas demand increases compared to Case 2a. CETS and gas demand-load act in an opposite manner. Increasing carbon prices promote investments in GFPPs. The producers increase their bids according to their emission factor to account for the additional carbon cost. Consequently, the system relies on GFPPs to replace high-emission non-GFPPs to moderate electricity prices and emissions. Higher gas demand enables expensive gas producers to enter the market, increasing the fuel cost of GFPPs and discouraging new investments. However, for higher carbon prices the economic benefits derived from carbon trading outweigh the economic drawbacks of increased gas prices. Consequently, as shown in Fig. 1(b) the strategic producer does not alter his investment decisions, even though his marginal costs differ.

5. Conclusions

This work presents an integrated market framework for strategic investment in decoupled emission-embedded electricity and natural gas markets. The results demonstrate that an increase in gas prices signifies profit loss and lower investment for the strategic producer, while higher carbon prices lead the GFPPs to increase their market share. Implementing high uncertainty on gas demand discourages new investments for low carbon prices. Nevertheless, there is not such impact for higher carbon prices.

Acknowledgements

This research is co-financed by the European Union and Greek National Funds through the Region of Central Macedonia, under the operational program "Region of Central Macedonia 2014-2020" and the specific action/call "Investment Plans on Innovation". (Project code: KMP6-0077560). Project title: Development of a software tool for the optimization of production scheduling in the manufacturing industries.

References

Bank, W., 2023. State and Trends of Carbon Pricing 2023. https://doi.org/10.1596/39796

Boffino, L., Conejo, A.J., Sioshansi, R., Oggioni, G., 2019. A two-stage stochastic optimization planning framework to decarbonize deeply electric power systems. Energy Economics 84, 104457. https://doi.org/10.1016/j.eneco.2019.07.017

Chen S., Conejo A.J., Sioshansi R., Wei Z., 2020, Investment Equilibria Involving Gas-Fired Power Units in Electricity and Gas Markets, IEEE Transactions on Power Systems, 35, 2736–2747.

Cong, H., Wang, X., Jiang, C., 2019. Two-stage nested bilevel model for generation expansion planning in combined electricity and gas markets. IET Generation, Transmission & Distribution 13, 3443–3454. https://doi.org/10.1049/iet-gtd.2019.0293

Dimitriadis C.N., Tsimopoulos E.G., Georgiadis M.C., 2023, Optimization-based economic analysis of energy storage technologies in a coupled electricity and natural gas market. Journal of Energy Storage, 58, 106332.

Dimitriadis C.N., Tsimopoulos E.G., Georgiadis M.C., 2022, Strategic bidding of an energy storage agent in a joint energy and reserve market under stochastic generation. Energy, 242, 123026.

Dimitriadis C.N., Tsimopoulos E.G., Georgiadis M.C., 2021, A Review on the Complementarity Modelling in Competitive Electricity Markets. Energies, 14, 7133.

Tsimopoulos E.G., Georgiadis M.C., 2020, Withholding strategies for a conventional and wind generation portfolio in a joint energy and reserve pool market: A gaming-based approach. Computers & Chemical Engineering, 134, 106692.

Flavio Manenti, Gintaras V. Reklaitis (Eds.), Proceedings of the 34th European Symposium on Computer Aided Process Engineering / 15th International Symposium on Process Systems Engineering (ESCAPE34/PSE24), June 2-6, 2024, Florence, Italy

An Optimization Model for the Maximization of Crop Productivity, Biodiversity, and Ecosystem Services

Caleb H. Geissler[a,b], Christos T. Maravelias[a,b,c*]

[a]*Department of Chemical and Biological Engineering, Princeton University, Princeton, NJ 08540, USA*
[b]*DOE Great Lakes Bioenergy Research Center, USA*
[c]*Andlinger Center for Energy and the Environment, Princeton University, Princeton, NJ 08540, USA*
maravelias@princeton.edu

Abstract

Agricultural expansion has led to significant losses in biodiversity and ecosystem services. Empirical studies have shown that integrating strips of native prairie into croplands can improve biodiversity and ecosystem services, and that these improvements increase with the amount of prairie and the length of edges between the prairie and crop. Researchers have developed models to balance profit and biodiversity or ecosystem services at large landscape scales. However, at such large scales, these models are often limited to coarse resolutions and cannot consider edge effects. Furthermore, they must be solved with local-search techniques or other heuristics that do not guarantee an optimal solution. We present a multi-objective mixed-integer optimization model for cropland design consider crop production, biodiversity, and ecosystem services. To illustrate the model, we apply it to a case study of a field in central Michigan, USA.

Keywords: Conservation planning, biodiversity, ecosystem services, mixed-integer optimization

1. Introduction

Increasing industrial agriculture has provided the high crop yields needed to feed a growing population but has come with significant degradation to the natural environment. One element of this degradation is a loss of native wildlife. In an effort to counteract this, many studies have developed models for conservation planning, which select planning units in a landscape to protect or revert to natural cover. These models often seek to minimize the area or cost of establishing a reserve that adequately protects either a specific species or a group of endangered species (Billionnet, 2013). To correlate habitat area with species survival, models of species persistence have been developed, which may include the size of individual habitats, distances between them, and the dispersal of each species. One such model developed by Polasky includes a penalty for habitat fragmentation but does not support any potential benefit from habitat fragmentations that some species may have (Polasky et al., 2008).

Another aspect of the natural environment impacted by agriculture is the delivery of ecosystem services, such as greenhouse gas (GHG) sequestration. Detailed models have been developed to predict some ecosystem services based on crop data, soil type, weather, and terrain. However, these models are computationally demanding to run and typically can only simulate results when the land cover type is specified, making them difficult to incorporate into models for the design of the cropland (Basso and Ritchie, 2015).

Some researchers have examined the design of large landscapes considering economic, biodiversity, or ecosystem services objectives. For example, Williams et al. (2020) used a simple allocation model with static agriculture production, biodiversity, and ecosystem services values for planning units in Colombia. Another study built on the biodiversity model developed by Polasky et al. and used it to study agricultural profit, biodiversity, and water quality in Brazil (Kennedy et al., 2016). However, these and other studies in the literature have a few key limitations. Because they involve binary decisions variables and highly nonlinear interactions, they are solved using local search techniques which cannot guarantee optimal, or even near-optimal, solutions. These studies also typically ignore field management decisions such as fertilization. Furthermore, even the models with a fine spatial resolution do not include edge effects for any objectives, which have been shown to impact biodiversity and ecosystem services (Robinson et al., 2009).

In this paper, we present a mixed-integer linear multi-objective optimization model to design a cropland while simultaneously considering crop production, biodiversity, and GHG emissions. We include field management decisions and the impact that edges between different plants can have on these objectives, which previous studies have ignored. To highlight the capabilities of the model, we examine a case study on a real field in central Michigan, USA for which we have experimental data.

2. Cropland Model

2.1. Model Overview

A summary of the key elements in the model is given in Fig. 1.

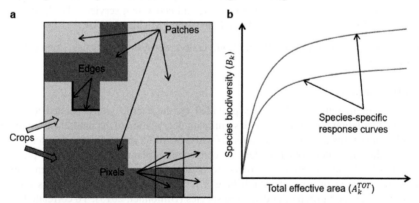

Figure 1. a) summary of the key elements in the model b) example of the species response curves used for calculating biodiversity.

The cropland is split up into a grid of pixels $i \in \mathbf{I}$. Given that real data for yield is available as square pixels, we assume square pixels in the model. In each pixel, one crop $j \in \mathbf{J}$ can be established, controlled by the binary variable $X_{i,j}$,

$$\sum_j X_{i,j} = 1 \quad \forall i \in \mathbf{I} \tag{1}$$

The model we present includes constraints for biomass production, biodiversity, and GHG emissions. Each of these aspects is briefly discussed in the following sections.

2.2. Biomass Production

It is assumed that it is known how much of each crop would be produced if it is established in a given pixel ($\psi_{i,j}$), and how much the production would increase if that pixel is fertilized ($\psi_{i,j}^F$). The additional yield from fertilization is assumed to have a linear response. Therefore, the amount of crop production in a pixel, $P_{i,j}$, can be calculated,

$$P_{i,j} = \psi_{i,j} X_{i,j} + \psi_{i,j}^F N_{i,j} \quad \forall i \in \mathbf{I}, \forall j \in \mathbf{J} \tag{2}$$

where $N_{i,j}$ is the amount of fertilizer applied to a crop in a pixel. The total amount of fertilizer applied to a pixel is also bounded,

$$N_{i,j} \leq \beta_{i,j}^N X_{i,j} \quad \forall i \in \mathbf{I}, \forall j \in \mathbf{J} \tag{3}$$

where $\beta_{i,j}^N$ is the upper bound of fertilizer application to a crop in a pixel. The total profit of the cropland, R, can be calculated,

$$R = \sum_{i,j} \pi_j^S P_{i,j} - \sum_{i,j} \pi_{i,j}^C X_{i,j} - \sum_{i,j} \pi^N N_{i,j} \tag{4}$$

where π_j^S is the sale price or a crop, $\pi_{i,j}^C$ is the total cost of planting and harvesting a crop, and π^N is the price of purchasing and applying fertilizer.

2.3. Biodiversity

Biodiversity can be difficult to quantify, and therefore we must make some simplifying assumptions. We use flow-based constraints to group contiguous pixels with the same crop established into patches. Flows go between pixels within the same patch and go towards a sink. Different crops provide varying qualities of habitat for different species $k \in \mathbf{K}$. The area of a patch of crop j with its sink at pixel i, $A_{i,j}^P$, is multiplied by a species-specific habitat compatibility score ($\eta_{j,k} \in [0,1]$) and the area of a pixel to determine the adjusted area of a patch for a given species, $A_{i,k}^{ADJ}$,

$$A_{i,k}^{ADJ} = \alpha \sum_j \eta_{j,k} A_{i,j}^P \quad \forall i \in \mathbf{I}, k \in \mathbf{K} \tag{5}$$

The adjusted areas of each patch are added together, with an adjustment for each type of edge, to find the total effective area for a given species, A_k^{TOT},

$$A_k^{TOT} = \sum_i A_{i,k}^{ADJ} + \sum_{j,j'<j} \eta_{j,j',k}^E E_{j,j'} \quad \forall k \in \mathbf{K} \tag{6}$$

where $\eta_{j,j',k}^E$ is the parameter for the impact of an edge between two crops on the biodiversity of a species and $E_{j,j'}$ is the number of edges between two crops in the cropland. We note that $\eta^E_{j,j',k}$ can be positive, negative, or zero for each combination of species and edge between two different plants. From the total effective area, species-specific saturating response curves are used to generate a biodiversity score for each species, B_k.

2.4. Ecosystem Services

GHG emissions are generated from planting, maintenance, and harvesting of each plant, and some crops sequester emissions in the form of soil organic carbon. The balance of these emissions for each crop in each pixel, $\phi_{i,j}$, is assumed to be known. Additional emissions are generated if fertilizer is added, both from producing and applying the fertilizer. Further, in some cases edges between crops can affect emissions. Therefore, the balance of GHG emissions in the cropland, G, can be calculated,

$$G = \sum_{i,j} \left[\phi_{i,j} X_{i,j} + \phi^F_{i,j} N_{i,j} \right] + \sum_{j,j'<j} \phi^E_{j,j'} E_{j,j'} \tag{7}$$

where $\phi^F_{i,j}$ is the additional emissions from the application of fertilizer and $\phi^E_{j,j'}$ is the change in emissions from an edge between two plants.

2.5. Overall objective

From these three different objectives, we evaluate the total objective (OBJ),

$$OBJ = \xi^P R + \frac{\xi^B}{|\mathbf{K}|} \sum_k B_k + \xi^G G \tag{8}$$

where ξ^P, ξ^B, and ξ^G are weights for profit, biodiversity, and GHG emissions, respectively.

3. Case Study

3.1. Input Parameters

We use experimental data for crop yield from the long-term scale-up experiment by the Great Lakes Bioenergy Research Center (GLBRC) at Marshall farms, with each pixel having a 20x20 meter resolution. Habitat compatibility scores for ants and butterflies in corn and prairie grass and the species-specific saturating response curves are generated from experimental data from the Biofuel Cropping System Experiment, also performed by the GLBRC. Additional data are taken from the literature. In all instances, the model is implemented in GAMS 45.2 and solved with Gurobi 10.0 to a 0.1% optimality gap on 2.6 GHz Linux cluster machines. For the following sections, the epsilon-constraint method was used to generate results, for which equal weights are applied to all objectives.

3.2. No Edge Impacts

First, we present results for designing the cropland without considering edges. In this case, the model consists of 11,461 continuous and 2,964 binary variables. Using the model, a pareto frontier of profit and biodiversity was generated. For a given minimum value of profit and biodiversity, the optimal GHG balance was determined similarly. These results are shown in Fig. 2a.

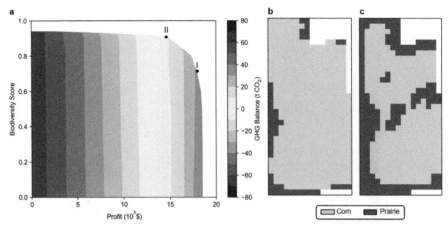

Figure 2. a) Plot showing the pareto frontier of profit, biodiversity, and GHG balance. Note that a positive GHG balance indicates net emissions. Resulting cropland designs for two example points (I and II) on the pareto curve are shown in panels b and c, respectively.

When only profit is maximized, the biodiversity score of the cropland is at most 0.36. However, with minor decreases in profit, biodiversity can be greatly increased, reaching a score of 0.8 for only a 10% reduction in profit. This occurs because there are pixels, often on the perimeter of the field, where corn yield is very low, allowing them to be replaced with prairie at only a small financial cost. Further, the biodiversity benefit of prairie is assumed to depend on area instead of yield, so even low-yielding areas contribute to biodiversity. Figs. 1b-c show how with increasing prioritization of biodiversity, more prairie is planted in pixels around the perimeter of the cropland and other low-yielding pixels. Fig. 1a also shows that GHG emissions largely scale linearly with the amount of land dedicated to corn. When profit is maximized, there are net emissions of 32 tCO_2e/y. This can be improved to net sequestration of 67 tCO_2e/y if there is no constraint on profit. Generally, the GHG balance is not strongly influenced by a minimum biodiversity score. The exception is that when maximizing biodiversity with a constraint on a minimum profit, it becomes optimal to fertilize pixels with prairie to meet the profit requirement. Fertilization increases emissions, leading to a minor increase in the GHG balance at the upper limit of biodiversity score for a given minimum profit.

3.3. Edge impacts

With the additional consideration of edges, the model can include the impact of patch shape on biodiversity, as well as the impact of edges on the GHG balance. The impact of edges can affect species in different ways. In this section, we highlight different croplands designs that would be obtained based on the inclusion of edge effects for butterflies and ants when maximizing biodiversity subject to no more than a 10% reduction in maximum profit. Here, the model consists of 10,937 continuous and 6,105 binary variables. The results are shown in Fig. 3. As seen when comparing Fig. 3b to 3a, penalizing the presence of edges results in a decrease from 6 patches of prairie to 4, reducing the number of edges between prairie and corn. The patch of prairie along the outside of the cropland does not become more compact (thus reducing the number of edges) because to do so would require planting prairie in pixels that have high corn yield. Comparing Fig. 3b to 3c shows that when there is a biodiversity benefit of edges, a marked change in the optimal cropland design can appear, with many more small patches of prairie being planted.

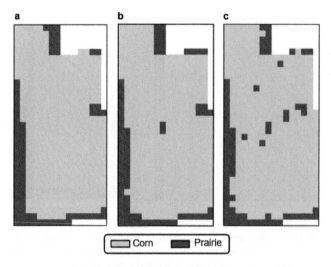

Figure 3. Example cropland designs for when the edges between corn and prairie a) decreases biodiversity b) has no effect on biodiversity c) increases biodiversity.

4. Conclusions

We present a multi-objective optimization model that considers crop production, biodiversity, and ecosystem services. Unlike other models in the literature, our model 1) considers edge effects 2) includes fertilization as a decision variable and 3) can be solved to global optimality. To highlight the capabilities of the model, we apply it to the design of a field for which experimental yield data is known. We show that dramatic increases in biodiversity can be obtained for relatively minor decreases in profit and demonstrate how species response to the presence of edges can affect the optimal cropland design.

References

B. Basso, J.T. Ritchie, 2015, Simulating crop growth and biogeochemical fluxes in response to land management using the SALUS model, The Ecology of Agriculutral Landscapes: Long-Term Research on the Path to Sustainability, Oxford University Press, New York, USA, 252-274.

A. Billionnet, 2013, Mathematical optimization ideas for biodiversity conservation, Eur. J. Oper. Res., 231, 3, 514-534.

C.M. Kennedy, P.L. Hawthorne, D.A. Miteva, L. Baumgarten, K. Sochi, M. Matsumoto, J.S. Evans, S. Polasky, P. Hamel, E.M. Vieira, P.F. Develey, C.H. Sekercioglu, A.D. Davidson, E.M. Uhlhorn, J. Kiesecker, 2016, Optimizing land use decision-making to sustain Brazilian agricultural profits, biodiversity, and ecosystem services, Biol. Conserv., 204, 221-230.

S. Polasky, E. Nelson, J. Camm, B. Csuti, P. Fackler, E. Lonsdorf, C. Montgomery, D. White, J. Arthur, B. Garber-Yonts, R. Haight, J. Kagan, A. Starfield, C. Tobalske, 2008, Where to put things? Spatial land management to sustain biodiversity and economic returns, Biol. Conserv., 141, 6, 1505-1524.

D.T. Robinson, D.G. Brown, W.S. Currie, 2009, Modelling carbon storage in highly fragmented and human-dominated landscapes: Linking land-cover patterns and ecosystem models, Ecol. Model., 220, 9-10, 1325-1338.

B.A. Williams, H.S. Grantham, J.E.M. Watson, S.J. Alvarez, J.S. Simmonds, C.A. Rogéliz, M. Da Silva, G. Forero-Medina, A. Etter, J. Nogales, T. Walschburger, G. Hyman, H. Beyer, 2020, Minimizing the loss of biodiversity and ecosystem services in an intact landscape under risk of rapid agricultural development, Environ. Res. Lett., 15, 1, 014001.

Flavio Manenti, Gintaras V. Reklaitis (Eds.), Proceedings of the 34th European Symposium on Computer Aided Process Engineering / 15th International Symposium on Process Systems Engineering (ESCAPE34/PSE24), June 2-6, 2024, Florence, Italy

Solar-driven Calcium Looping Cycle for Time-flexible Carbon-free Power Generation with Thermochemical Energy Storage Capability

Calin-Cristian Cormos [*], Letitia Petrescu, Ana-Maria Cormos, Simion Dragan

Babes-Bolyai University, Faculty of Chemistry and Chemical Engineering, Arany Janos 11, Cluj-Napoca, Postal code: RO-400028, Romania
calin.cormos@ubbcluj.ro

Abstract

Renewable energy sources represent an important aspect of the solution in deploying low carbon economy. In addition, the Carbon Capture, Utilization and Storage (CCUS) systems are also relevant technological options to be used for overall decarbonization of industrial sectors. In this respect, the integration of renewables and CCUS systems shows promising results for developing energy- and cost-efficient decarbonized applications. The Calcium Looping (CaL) technology is particular promising system showing a high overall energy efficiency as well as thermochemical energy storage capability. In this work, a detailed techno-economic and environmental evaluation was done for the flexible solar-based calcium looping cycle to produce 100 MW net carbon-free power. The thermochemical CaL cycle was evaluated in time-flexible conditions for energy storage using solid sorbent storage (in both calcinated and regenerated conditions) to facilitate the integration of renewable energy sources. As shown, the investigated renewable-based calcium looping system shows promising performances in terms of high overall energy efficiency (around 43 %) and carbon capture rate (90 %) as well as attractive cost elements (e.g., specific capital investments below 3,500 €/kW net, levelized cost of electricity around 75 €/MWh). The flexibility of the investigated system (by exploiting the sorbent and CO_2 storage facilities) is a very attractive feature for an energy- and cost-efficient utilization of time-variable renewable sources (such as solar and wind).

Keywords: Calcium looping cycle, Solar energy, Power generation, Energy storage.

1. Introduction

The energy-intensive industrial sectors (e.g., heat and power generation, iron, steel, cement and chemicals production etc.) are facing significant challenges in short to medium terms in respect to their mandatory decarbonization for achieving the global climate neutrality. For significant reduction of greenhouse gas emissions several options are available: increasing the renewable energy production, improving the overall energy efficiencies of conversion, utilization and storage steps, deployment of CCUS technologies and decarbonized energy carriers (e.g., electricity, hydrogen) etc. This work is evaluating the Calcium Looping (CaL) cycle as an innovative energy-and cost-efficient system having also the thermochemical energy storage capability (Tregambi et al., 2023). This advanced thermochemical cycle involves two separate gas-solid reactors operated in a Circulated Fluidized Bed (CFB) conditions: one carbonator reactor where the CO_2 is captured from the gas phase using a calcium-based sorbent followed by a calciner where carbonated sorbent is thermally regenerated using a heat source (in this analysis, a renewable heat source from a concentrated solar power plant was assessed as shown by Khosravi et al., 2022). The overall chemical reaction of CaL cycle is the following:

$$CaO \quad + \quad CO_2 \quad \leftrightarrow \quad CaCO_3 \qquad \Delta H = -178 \, kJ/mole \tag{1}$$

Based on this highly exothermic reaction and utilizes both the solid sorbent (both CaO and CaCO₃) and the CO_2 storage facilities, this thermochemical cycle can be used for energy storage. A detailed techno-economic and environmental evaluation was done for the flexible solar-based calcium looping cycle to produce 100 MW net carbon-free power. In addition, potential utilization of CaL reactive gas-solid system for decarbonization of other energy-intensive applications (e.g., cement and metallurgy) as well as a promising Direct CO_2 Air Capture (DAC) option were also presented in the analysis to show its great potential in developing energy- and cost-efficient low-carbon applications.

2. Plant configuration, design assumptions and thermal integration

The conceptual layout of CaL cycle used in conjunction with a Concentrated Solar Plant (CSP) for time-flexible carbon-free power generation is presented in Figure 1. As noticed, the storage facilities for both solid forms (as carbonated and calcinated sorbent) and gaseous (CO_2) reactants are used for flexible operation. The power block consists of a CO_2 Brayton cycle and a steam (Rankine) cycle to maximize the power generation.

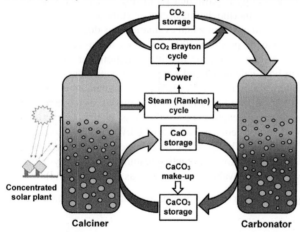

Figure 1. Calcium looping (CaL) cycle integrated with concentrated solar plant (CSP)

The evaluated CSP - CaL power plant has an installed 100 MW net power output. Table 1 presents the main design assumptions of the investigated concept (Carro et al., 2023). The calciner operates 8 h/day but the carbonator works 24 h/day based on reaction heat.

Table 1. Key design assumptions of integrated CSP - CaL power plant

Unit	Design parameters
Solar-based calciner	Operating temperature & pressure: 950 °C & 1.25 bar
	Conversion: 99 %
	Operating time (per day): 8 h
Carbonation reactor	Operating temperature & pressure: 650 °C & 3.5 bar
	CO_2 capture rate: 90 %
	Operating time: (per day): 24 h

CO₂ storage unit	Pressure: 75 bar
	Temperature: 25 °C
Solid storage units	Pressure: 1 bar
	Temperature: 25 °C
CO₂-based Brayton cycle	Inlet CO₂ pressure: 75 bar
	Final CO₂ pressure: 1.25 bar
	Compressor efficiency: 88 %
	Turbine efficiency: 92 %
Steam (Rankine) cycle	Steam temperature & pressure: 565 °C & 120 bar
	Steam turbine efficiency: 90 %
	Final steam expansion pressure: 40 mbar
Heat exchangers	Temperature difference: 10 °C
	Pressure drops: 2 - 3 % from inlet pressure
Thermodynamic package	Predictive Soave-Redlich-Kwong (PSRK)

To optimize the overall energy efficiency, a detailed thermal integration analysis using pinch methodology was performed (Smith, 2016). The correspondent composite curves (HCC - Hot Composite Curve; CCC - Cold Composite Curve) are presented in Figure 2 showing a significant heat recovery (186 MW$_{th}$ HP steam) from available heat sources.

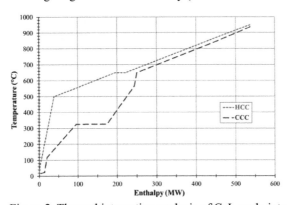

Figure 2. Thermal integration analysis of CaL cycle integrated with CSP

3. Results and discussions

After simulation, the CSP - CaL power plant was validated by comparing key performance indicators to experimental / industrial data. The main simulated indicators of CaL cycle (e.g., calcination and carbonator conversion rates, operating parameters) were fully in line with experimental data (Hornberger et al., 2021; Rodrigues et al., 2023). Following validation, the main technical performance indicators are shown in Table 2.

Table 2. Main performance indicators of CSP-CaL power plant

Parameter	Unit	Value
Solar (thermal) heat to the calciner (A)	MW$_{th}$	232.23
Gross power output (B)	MW$_e$	113.02
Ancillary power consumption (C)	MW$_e$	13.02
Net power output (D = B - C)	MW$_e$	100.00
Net power efficiency (D/A * 100)	%	43.06

As can be observed from Table 2, the overall solar heat to power efficiency is very high (about 43 %). Considering a 11 % heat loss in CSP, the heliostat has to supplies about 261 MW$_{th}$ which corresponds to an area of about 0.28 km^2 (Khosravi et al., 2022). For the economic evaluation of CSP - CaL power plant, the main economic assumptions used are presented in Table 3. The capital costs of various plant sub-systems (except the heliostat reported in Table 3) e.g., CaL cycle, sorbent / CO$_2$ storage and power block units were calculated with cost correlation method using the following equation (Smith, 2016):

$$C_E = C_B * (\frac{Q}{Q_B})^M \tag{2}$$

where: C_E - capital cost of specific plant sub-system / equipment with capacity Q, C_B - base cost of plant sub-system / equipment with base capacity Q_B, M - constant which depends on equipment type. The main assumptions (base cost, capacity and exponent) used for capital cost being presented in a different work (Cormos, 2022).

Table 3. Main economic assumptions

Parameter	Value
Heliostat capital cost	150 €/m^2
Limestone price	20 €/t
Make-up rate of solid sorbent	5 %
Boiler feed water (BFW) price	0.10 €/t
Cooling water (CW) price	0.02 €/t
Chemical treatment of cooling water	0.0025 €/m^3
Chemical treatment of BFW	45.00 k€/month
Direct working plant personal	80 persons
Yearly salary for direct operational personnel	50.00 k€/person/y
Administrative costs, share of direct personnel cost	30 %
Maintenance costs, share of capital cost	4 %
Operational time per year	7,884 h
Construction time & plant location	2 years & Southern Europe
Operational life	25 years

Power production cost was then calculated using annualized investment (capital) cost and operational & maintenance (O&M) costs as well as the installed plant capacity output (100 MW net power) following the Net Present Value (NPV) methodology (Smith, 2016). The calculated power production cost was about 74.80 €/MWh which is competitive for today market. The sensitivity analysis of electricity cost vs. main economic parameters (e.g., capital cost, interest rate, plant capacity factor) are presented in Figure 3.

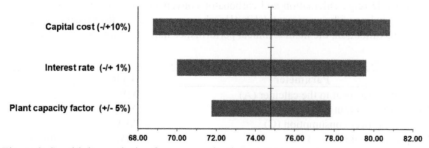

Figure 3. Sensitivity analysis of power production cost

Solar-driven calcium looping cycle for time-flexible carbon-free power generation with thermochemical energy storage capability

2021

As can be noticed the most important influence on the electricity production cost was recorder for the capital cost (which accounts for about 62 % of electricity cost with a specific capital investment cost of about 3464 €/kW net) followed by the interest rate and the plant capacity factor. The overall conclusion is that the investigated flexible design is able to generate 100 MW carbon-free power 24 h/day based on exothermic carbonation reaction heat exploiting the energy storage of regenerated sorbent during day time (8 h).

4. Other potential applications and development issues

The CaL cycle can be successfully used for decarbonization of other energy-intensive industrial applications (e.g., power generation, cement and steel production etc.) or for direct air capture (DAC). A conceptual layout of the CaL cycle for these applications using renewable energy either solar-based heat (solar operation) or a renewable fuel (thermal operation) is presented in Figure 4 in a Circulated Fluidized Bed (CFB) arrangement of the carbonation and calcination reactors (Ferrario et al., 2023).

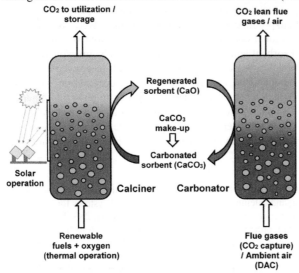

Figure 4. Renewable-based calcium looping cycle for CO_2 capture

As an illustrative example, Table 4 presents the main performance indicators of a decarbonized cement plant using a thermal-based CaL technology with a 90 % carbon capture rate (Case 2) in comparison to the conventional case without carbon capture (Case 1). Both cement plant concepts produce 1 Mt/y cement (IEAGHG, 2008).

Table 4. Integration of CaL technology for cement plant decarbonization

Plant performance indicator	Case 1	Case 2
Cement production capacity (Mt/y)	1.00	1.00
Coal demand for ancillaries (t/h)	0.00	22.03
Net power production (MW_e)	0.00	15.80
Cement plant decarbonization rate (%)	0.00	90.00
Specific CO_2 emissions (kg/t)	770.44	58.37
Cement production cost (€/t)	80.20	124.18
CO_2 avoided cost (€/t)	-	83.23

As can be observed, the utilization of CaL technology for decarbonization of cement production implies a significant reduction of CO_2 emissions (from 770 to 58 kg/t) coupled with additional decarbonized power generation which can be sent to the grid. From economic point of view, the decarbonization implies an important increase of cement production cost (by about 55 %). The CO_2 avoided cost is comparable to current CO_2 emission tax, a fact which suggests a positive economic potential for implementation.

The CaL decarbonization technology still requires significant development and scale-up activities from the current state of the art (demonstrated up to 10 MW) to full industrial capacities. However, the CFB technology, which is already demonstrated up to 300 - 400 MW sizes (Lockwood, 2013) can help the deployment of CaL technology since there are significant similarities among them. In addition, relevant aspects such as sorbent cyclic capacity and make-ups must be optimized for best techno-economic performances.

5. Conclusions

The present work evaluated the techno-economic and environmental performances of a flexible solar-based CaL cycle to produce 100 MW carbon-free net power. The CaL cycle was evaluated in flexible operational conditions due to time behaviour of solar energy. The flexible design uses solid sorbent and CO_2 storage facilities. The investigated solar-based CaL system shows promising performances in comparison to conventional CSP plant: high energy efficiency (about 43 %), competitive electricity cost (about 75 €/MWh) etc. The flexibility of the investigated solar-based design to generate power 24 h per day based on reaction heat as well as other potential decarbonization applications makes this technology very promising. It worth mentioning that CaL technology still requires significant scale-up from current proven level (up to 10 MW) to industrial relevant sizes.

References

A. Carro, R. Chacartegui, C. Ortiz, J. Arcenegui-Troya, L.A. Pérez-Maqueda, J.A. Becerra, 2023, Integration of calcium looping and calcium hydroxide thermochemical systems for energy storage and power production in concentrating solar power plants, Energy, 283, 128388

C.C. Cormos, 2022, Decarbonization options for cement production process: A techno-economic and environmental evaluation, Fuel, 320, 123907

D. Ferrario, S. Stendardo, V. Verda, A. Lanzini, 2023, Solar-driven calcium looping system for carbon capture in cement plants: Process modelling and energy analysis, Journal of Cleaner Production, 394, 136367

M. Hornberger, J. Moreno, M. Schmid, G. Scheffknecht, 2021, Experimental investigation of the calcination reactor in a tail-end calcium looping configuration for CO_2 capture from cement plants, Fuel, 284, 118927

International Energy Agency - Greenhouse Gas R&D Programme (IEAGHG), 2008, CO_2 capture in the cement industry, Report2008/3, Cheltenham, UK

S. Khosravi, S. Hossainpour, H. Farajollahi, N. Abolzadeh, 2022, Integration of a coal fired power plant with calcium looping CO_2 capture and concentrated solar power generation: Energy, exergy and economic analysis, Energy, 240, 122466

T. Lockwood, 2013, Techno-economic analysis of PC versus CFB combustion technology, IEA Clean Coal Centre, Report CCC/226, London, UK

D. Rodrigues, C.I.C. Pinheiro, R.M. Filipe, L.F. Mendes, H.A. Matos, 2023, Optimization of an improved calcium-looping process for thermochemical energy storage in concentrating solar power plants, Journal of Energy Storage, 72, 108199

R. Smith, 2016, Chemical process design and integration, second edition, Wiley, Hoboken, USA

C. Tregambi, F. di Lauro, S. Pascual, P. Lisbona, L.M. Romeo, R. Solimene, P. Salatino, F. Montagnaro, 2023, Solar-driven calcium looping in fluidized beds for thermochemical energy storage, Chemical Engineering Journal, 466, 142708

Flavio Manenti, Gintaras V. Reklaitis (Eds.), Proceedings of the 34th European Symposium on Computer Aided Process Engineering / 15th International Symposium on Process Systems Engineering (ESCAPE34/PSE24), June 2-6, 2024, Florence, Italy

Model-based techno-economic analysis for integrated synthetic natural gas production system using atmospheric CO_2 captured by metal organic framework adsorbent

Hideki Harada,[a] Anshuman Sinha,[b] Tomoyuki Yajima,[a] and Yoshiaki Kawajiri[a,c*]

[a]Department of Materials Process Engineering, Nagoya University, Furo-cho 1, Chikusa, Nagoya, Aichi 464-8603, Japan
[b]School of Chemical and Biomolecular Engineering, Georgia Institute of Technology, 311 Ferst Drive, Atlanta, Georgia 30332, United States
[c]School of Engineering Science, LUT University, Mukkulankatu 19, 15210 Lahti, Finland
kawajiri@nagoya-u.jp

Abstract

This study proposes an integrated system of carbon capture and utilization (CCU) to produce synthetic natural gas (SNG), and performs a techno-economic analysis. The proposed system employs a direct air capture (DAC) process using a metal organic framework adsorbent and converts the captured CO_2 into CH_4 product using H_2 produced by water electrolysis. Mass and energy balances in the main components of the system are described by rigorous mathematical models, enabling us to evaluate the capital and operating costs and energy consumption. In addition, a sensitivity analysis is carried out to find model parameters that influences the SNG cost.

Keywords: carbon capture and utilization, direct air capture, methanation, metal-organic framework, process simulation

1. Introduction

Direct air capture (DAC) is a CO_2 removal technology that physically or chemically captures CO_2 from the atmosphere. Various schemes have been proposed for DAC operation, among which the system using solid adsorbents for CO_2 capture is considered promising due to the possibility of utilizing waste heat to regenerate the adsorbent (Fasihi et al., 2019). In particular, the DAC process using a metal organic framework (MOF) as a CO_2 adsorbent has attracted much attention recently.

Carbon dioxide capture and utilization (CCU) is considered a promising mitigation measure for climate change. Using CO_2 captured by DAC as a feedstock, a CCU system synthesizes materials or fuels. As a measure for CO_2 utilization, methanation has recently gained attention, which converts CO_2 into CH_4 using H_2. The CH_4 produced here is referred to as synthetic natural gas (SNG).

To assess the performance and feasibility of CCU systems, rigorous mathematical models are required. Although model-based analytical studies of CCU systems that integrate DAC and methanation processes have increased in recent years, no study has conducted a model-based techno-economic analysis for the CCU system where the DAC process using a MOF adsorbent and the methanation process are integrated.

In this study, we perform a techno-economic analysis of a system that integrates three processes: DAC, methanation, and water electrolysis processes. This study carries out a dynamic simulation of the DAC process using MOF adsorbent for the techno-economic analysis, and detailed cost estimation for the water electrolysis process. Dynamic simulation allows detailed sizing of equipment and determining operating conditions for each unit, which enables more accurate economic analysis than steady-state simulation. The dynamic simulation of the DAC process performed in this study is based on Sinha et al. (2017). The solid adsorbent used is mmen-Mg$_2$(dobpdc) (McDonald et al., 2012), which is one of the promising MOFs for DAC. The reactor used in the methanation process is assumed to be a tube-bundle type. For the catalyst in the reactor, a Ni-based catalyst is employed. The water electrolysis process splits the H$_2$O into O$_2$ and H$_2$ using electricity. The produced H$_2$ is used as a feedstock in the methanation reactor, and the O$_2$ is discarded. The power requirement for the water electrolysis process is also estimated. Using these models, capital and operating costs are obtained to estimate the SNG production cost.

2. Methodology

2.1. Process description

Figure 1 shows a block flow diagram of the proposed integrated CCU system. There are three processes in the integrated system: DAC, methanation, and water electrolysis. The DAC process captures CO$_2$ from the atmosphere and produces a highly concentrated CO$_2$ stream. The MOF adsorbent used in the DAC process is mmen-Mg$_2$(dobpdc) (McDonald et al., 2012). The MOF adsorbents are coated on a monolithic contactor (Darunte et al., 2017). The water electrolysis process decomposes H$_2$O into H$_2$ and O$_2$. The produced H$_2$ is sent to the downstream processes, and the O$_2$ is discarded into the atmosphere. The methanation process produces SNG, whose main component is CH$_4$, through a chemical reaction using CO$_2$ from the DAC process and H$_2$ from the water electrolysis process. The byproduct, H$_2$O, is cooled and removed from the system. Some unreacted H$_2$ from the methanation process is recycled. The methanation process is assumed to produce SNG at a rate of 10,000 Nm^3/h. More detailed information on the design of the system is provided in Harada et al. (2023).

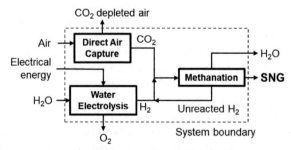

Figure 1. Schematic diagram of the integrated system of carbon capture and utilization.

2.2. Model description

2.2.1. DAC process model

For the DAC process model using a MOF adsorbent, temperature vacuum swing adsorption (TVSA) operation is modeled in this study. Figure 2(a) shows the strategy of

TVSA operation. The operation has three steps: adsorption, desorption, and cooling. During the adsorption step, air passes through the monolithic contactor by blowers to capture CO_2. During the desorption step, saturated steam passes through the contactor to raise the temperature of the adsorbent, resulting in the desorption of the adsorbed CO_2. For a certain time after the start of this step, the gas obtained from the contactor outlet, which contains inert species (O_2 and N_2), is discarded to improve the product CO_2 purity. To purify CO_2 mixed with steam from the contactor outlet, it is cooled down to 298 K in heat exchangers to remove the steam. During the final cooling step, vacuum pumps depressurize the contactor and evaporate the condensed water, leading to a temperature decrease in the contactor. This step is necessary to avoid a high-temperature condition in the contactor at the beginning of the adsorption step, which is considered to oxidize the amine groups in the adsorbent. These three steps are repeated to capture CO_2 continuously. The details of the model including the mass and heat balance equations are introduced in Sinha et al. (2017).

Modeling is performed on a single monolithic channel described in Figure 2(b). We assume the channel to be cylindrical. The simulation results obtained from that modeling are used to determine the scale of the DAC process that can produce the required amount of CO_2.

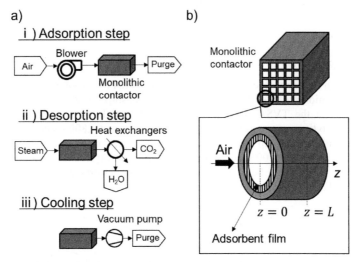

Figure 2. (a) Schematic diagram of the operation for temperature vacuum swing adsorption, and (b) monolithic contactor with multiple channels and schematic diagram of its single channel.

2.2.2. Methanation process model

The methanation process produces CH_4 through the Sabatier reaction given by:

$$CO_2 + 4H_2 \leftrightarrow CH_4 + 2H_2O, \ \Delta_r H_{298K} = -165 \text{ kJ/mol} \tag{1}$$

The process model is based on Tsuboi et al. (2022). We assume a chemical reaction using a tube-bundle reactor in which 45,000 tubes are packed with the methanation catalysts. The reaction heat is removed using molten salt flowing outside the tube and utilized in the DAC process described in Section 3.2.1. Modeling is performed on a single tube. We use the Sabatier reaction rate equation given by Koschany et al. (2016).

2.2.3. Water electrolysis process model

In the water electrolysis process, alkaline water electrolysis is used. To calculate the power required for water electrolysis, the electrolytic cell voltage is estimated using the electrochemical model developed by Sakas et al. (2022).

2.3. Energy requirements and cost estimation

Using the results obtained from the model of each process in the integrated system, we calculate the thermal and electrical energy required to operate the integrated system. We carry out heat integration to design a heat exchanger network of maximum energy recovery (MER) to reuse the heat from the Sabatier reaction and reduce the thermal energy requirement in the integrated system. Electrical energy is required to run process equipment such as pumps and compressors and is used for water electrolysis.

The costs for each process in the integrated system are also estimated. We classify the costs into capital and operating costs. For the capital cost, the annualized cost is calculated considering the lifetime of each process equipment in the system based on cost correlation equations. The operating cost includes the cost of utilities such as electricity and cooling water.

3. Results

3.1. TVSA operation in DAC process

Figure 3(a) and (b) show the simulation results of TVSA operation in the DAC process: CO_2 concentration profiles in adsorbent during the adsorption step and desorption step, respectively. In the TVSA operation, the channel length, adsorption step time, and desorption step time are set to be 0.3 m, 1,500 seconds, and 1,800 seconds, respectively. During the adsorption step (Figure 3(a)), it can be seen that the adsorbent is almost saturated with CO_2 at 1,500 seconds after the start of adsorption. During the desorption step (Figure 3(b)), it can be seen that the CO_2 in the adsorbent is almost completely desorbed and discharged from the channel.

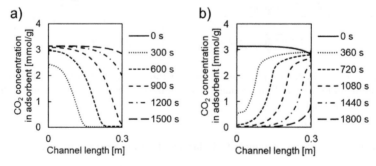

Figure 3. TVSA simulation: CO_2 concentration profiles in adsorbent during (a) adsorption step and (b) desorption step, respectively.

3.2. Overall integrated system

Table 1 shows the results obtained from each process model in the integrated system. In the DAC process, the CO_2 purity is defined on a steam-free basis. In the methanation process, SNG with a high CH_4 fraction is obtained by removing the byproduct H_2O. In the water electrolysis process, 173 MW of electric power is required to split water into H_2 and O_2.

Table 1. Results obtained from each process model in the integrated system.

Process	Item	Value
DAC	Productivity [mmol-CO_2/channel/h]	0.0478
	CO_2 purity [%]	99.9
Methanation	CO_2 molar fraction in product SNG [%]	0.477
	H_2 molar fraction in product SNG [%]	3.88
	CH_4 molar fraction in product SNG [%]	95.6
	CO_2 conversion rate [%]	99.5
Water electrolysis	Cell voltage [V]	1.62
	Electric power [MW]	173

3.3. Energy and cost analysis

3.3.1. Energy analysis

Table 2 shows the net energy required for each process in the integrated system. For comparison, the amount of energy is given per unit volume of SNG. The heat energy required in the DAC process can be reduced to zero by heat integration described in Section 2.3, which recovers and utilizes the reaction heat from the Sabatier reaction in the methanation process. Only the methanation process requires heat energy from an external heat source. Regarding electrical energy, it can be seen that the water electrolysis process is the most energy-intensive in the integrated system.

Table 2. Net energy requirement for each process in the integrated system.

Process	Heat [MJ/Nm³-SNG]	Electricity [kWh/Nm³-SNG]
DAC	0	0.98
Methanation	0.41	1.24
Water electrolysis	0	17.3

3.3.2. Cost analysis

Figure 4 shows the cost breakdown of the integrated system. The methanation process accounts for the largest portion of the capital cost, while the water electrolysis process accounts for the largest portion of the operating cost. The majority of the capital cost is the gas holder in the methanation process, while the majority of the operating cost is the electricity in the water electrolysis process. These results indicate that the costs of gas holder and electricity have a significant impact on the overall costs of the integrated system.

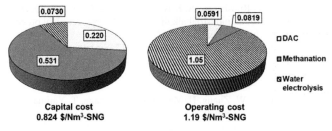

Figure 4. Results of cost estimation for each process in the integrated system.

3.3.3. Sensitivity analysis

We perform a sensitivity analysis on the parameters regarding SNG production cost. The parameters to be analyzed are chosen considering their uncertainty and impact on the cost. The values of the parameters chosen are considered for optimistic and pessimistic cases. From the results of the sensitivity analysis, we confirm that electricity cost has the largest impact on SNG production cost. Table 3 shows the result of the sensitivity analysis in which electricity cost varies. When electricity cost changes in the range of 30-90 \$/MWh, SNG production cost changes in the range of 1.43-2.60 \$/Nm^3-SNG.

Table 3. Sensitivity analysis for electricity cost.

Process	Optimistic case	Reference case	Pessimistic case
Electricity cost [\$/MWh]	30	60	90
SNG cost [\$/Nm^3-SNG]	1.43	2.01	2.60

4. Conclusions

In this study, we proposed an integrated system consisting of DAC, methanation, and water electrolysis processes to produce SNG, and performed a techno-economic analysis. We also performed an energy analysis to estimate the amount of thermal and electrical energy required in each process. Finally, we performed economic and sensitivity analyses. It was found that electricity cost dominates the total SNG production cost; the use of cheaper electricity is critical to reduce the cost.

Acknowledgment

This work was supported by the Japan Gas Association.

References

L. Darunte, Y. Terada, 2017, C. Murdock, K. Walton, D. Sholl, C. Jones, Monolith-supported amine-functionalized Mg$_2$(dobpdc) adsorbents for CO$_2$ capture, ACS Applied Materials and Interfaces, 9, 17042-17050

M. Fasihi, O, Efimova, C. Breyer, 2019, Techno-economic assessment of CO$_2$ direct air capture plants, Journal of Cleaner Production, 224, 957-980

H. Harada, A. Sinha, T. Yajima, Y. Kawajiri, 2023, Model-based techno-economic analysis for integrated synthetic natural gas production system with direct air capture and water electrolysis, submitted

F. Koschany, D. Schlereth, O. Hinrichsen, 2016, On the kinetics of the methanation of carbon dioxide on coprecipitated NiAl(O)x, Applied Catalysis B: Environmental, 181, 504-516

T. McDonald, W. Ram Lee, J. Mason, B. Wiers, C. Seop Hong, J. Long, 2012, Capture of carbon dioxide from air and flue gas in the alkylamine-appended metal−organic framework mmen-Mg$_2$(dobpdc), Journal of the American Chemical Society, 134, 7056-7065

G. Sakas, A. Ibáñez-Rioja, V. Ruuskanen, A. Kosonen, J. Ahola, O. Bergmann, Dynamic energy and mass balance model for an industrial alkaline water electrolyzer plant process, International Journal of Hydrogen Energy, 47, 4328-4345

A. Sinha, L. Darunte, C. Jones, M. Realff, Y. Kawajiri, 2017, Systems design and economic analysis of direct air capture of CO$_2$ through temperature vacuum swing adsorption using MIL-101(Cr)-PEI-800 and mmen-Mg$_2$(dobpdc) MOF adsorbents, Industrial and Engineering Chemistry Research, 56, 750–764

T. Tsuboi, S. Yasuda, C. Choi, W. Zhang, H. Machida, K. Norinaga, T. Yajima, Y. Kawajiri, 2022, Modeling and estimating kinetic parameters for CO$_2$ methanation from fixed bed reactor experiments, Journal of Advanced Manufacturing and Processing, e10145

Flavio Manenti, Gintaras V. Reklaitis (Eds.), Proceedings of the 34th European Symposium on Computer Aided Process Engineering / 15th International Symposium on Process Systems Engineering (ESCAPE34/PSE24), June 2-6, 2024, Florence, Italy

TDES:Transformation of the Dutch Energy System

Jan van Schijndel,[a] Rutger de Mare,[a] Nort Thijssen,[a] Jim van der Valk Bouman,[a]

[a]QuoMare, Kampenringweg 45A, Gouda 2803PE, The Netherlands
janvanschijndel@quomare.com

Abstract

In 2018, the Dutch Energy System used 93 mln ton of fossil resources (natural gas, crude oil, coal). Power-generation units and refineries converted 70 mln ton of these resources into heat, power, transportation fuels and cracker feeds to meet demand set by Residential, Mobility, Agriculture and Industry Sectors. Some 23 mln ton crude was refined for export. In 2018, the Dutch CO_2 emissions amounted to 200 megaton CO_2-equivalent.

Transformation of the Dutch Energy System entails both decarbonisation and recarbonisation of these fossil resources. Decarbonisation can be achieved by electrification, carbon capture & storage and use of waste heat and H_2. Recarbonisation needs carbon from biomass, waste streams and/or CO_2. It is estimated that in 2050 the domestic need for sustainable transportation fuels and chemicals will require the equivalent of 19 megatons renewable carbon. This calls for significant imports of biomass and waste streams as the Dutch production potential for biomass and waste is limited. Furthermore, annually some 4 to 8 megatons of H_2 is expected to be needed. A portfolio of renewable-carbon-based technologies complementing, partly replacing the current set of refineries needs to be build and commissioned for this recarbonisation challenge. These technologies are electrolysis, pyrolysis, gasification, oxy-firing, fermentation, Fischer-Tropsch synthesis, methanol synthesis, and auto-thermal reforming with carbon capture.

TDES is a decision support framework developed by QuoMare that supports this transformation challenge. Based on mathematical programming, TDES guides the development of an 'optimal transition pathway' towards a fully de-/re-carbonised system with zero CO_2 emissions by 2050 at lowest costs.

This paper describes TDES and how it supports the development of pathways towards an effective and efficient transformation of the Dutch Energy System towards 2050. Two transformation scenarios are presented: the Net-Zero CO_2 Case and the Fossil Free Case.

Keywords: Mixed-Integer Multi-Period Linear Programming, Decision Support System, Optimal Transition Pathways, Policy Making.

1. Problem Statement and Methodology

The transformation of the Dutch Energy System, today largely based on fossil energy resources, towards a system that fully relies on renewable energy resources, requires the systemic analysis of a large set of decarbonisation and recarbonisation investment options. Decarbonisation options include electrification, carbon capture & storage and use of waste heat and H_2. Recarbonisation options cover process technologies that convert renewable carbon from biomass, waste streams as well as CO_2 into transportation fuels and chemicals. The challenge is to deliver a credible, affordable, competitive and robust transformation pathway from today towards 2050. To this end, a large set of decarbonization, recarbonisation and transport infrastructure investment options (integer variables) need to be evaluated on a year-to-year basis simultaneously with unit capacities and interconnecting flows (continuous variables) subject to various constraints (like CO_2 targets, infrastructure capacities, availability of resources, demand requirements etc.). The objective is to find that combination of options that minimizes the net present value of the accumulated costs over the 2020-2050 time-horizon. TDES is the vehicle that has been designed to support this analysis and decision process. TDES is based on the QuoMare proprietary, generic TEACOS framework.

TEACOS stands for Techno-Economic Analysis of Complex Option Spaces. TEACOS is an optimization framework based on Multi-Period Mixed-Integer Linear Programming (van Schijndel, 2019). TEACOS contains four general building blocks, as shown below.

TEACOS: Techno-Economic Analysis of Complex Option Spaces

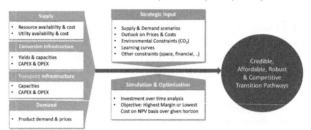

Investments are analysed **over time** and **at specific locations**

These building blocks together represent a classical supply or value chain with temporal and spatial granularity: both location and timing aspects are included. TEACOS can either maximize the Net Present Value (NPV) of the supply chain margin or minimize the NPV of supply chain costs, both over the time horizon imposed with due respect for boundary conditions and environmental constraints. Sensitivity analyses through Monte Carlo optimization demonstrate the robustness of transition pathways and detect tipping points to understand the relative attractiveness of the investments over time. The mathematics (MP-MILP) behind TEACOS and its deployment have been described in a decarbonisation study for the industrial cluster of the Port of Rotterdam (Davelaar, 2023).

2. Reference Case Transformation

In 2018, the Dutch energy system used 29 mln ton natural gas (NG), 11 mln ton coal and 53 mln ton crude. The latter includes 23 mln ton crude that is refined and exported as naphtha, kerosene and gasoil. Together with domestically generated nuclear and renewable power, the corresponding energy input is 4005 PJ, including 920 PJ for export. Resources for domestic use (3085 PJ) provide power and heat for the residential sector (670 PJ), power & heat for the agricultural sector (145 PJ), transportation fuels (505 PJ) and feedstocks for the production of steel, NH_3 & derivatives and a portfolio of high value chemicals (1190 PJ). Conversion losses amount to 575 PJ. Apart from 33 mln crude (23 mln ton export and 10 mln ton crude turned into chemicals), the remaining 60 mln ton intake ends up as CO_2 to air: some 180 mln ton of CO_2. Some 20 mln ton of CO_2 equivalent emissions to be added for CH_4 and N_2O emissions by the agricultural sector.

3. Definition Transformation Scope

A significant part of the 200 mln ton CO_2-equivalent emissions (2018) will be eliminated over time by the replacement of NG and coal as the main sources of power and heat by renewable power (solar & wind) and residual heat (as well as geo-thermal and aqua-thermal heat). The key vehicles to accomplish this are a combination of investments. The replacement of power generation units by wind and solar park investments will take place through tendering of multi-bln€ projects. On the demand side, the transformation towards consumption of low-level heat will be accomplished by development of district heating networks and installation of heat pumps. Investments in renewable power and renewable heat are expected to eliminate 85 mln ton of CO_2 emissions in the next 25 years, predominantly in the residential, agriculture and power sector.

The Light Duty Vehicle part of the mobility sector is expected to be electrified over time and fully transitioned by 2050. The Heavy Duty Vehicle part will in 2050 be driven by a combination of H_2 (1 mln ton) and batteries. These transformations are projected to lower CO_2 emissions by some 23 mln ton.

The industrial CO_2 emissions of some 57 mln ton need to be reduced by a series of measures. A significant part of this CO_2 comes from the provision of high temperature heat, currently delivered by natural gas. Depending on actual temperature levels, some part will be electrified. The remaining need for high temperature (HT) heat will be provided by H_2 (2 mln ton). Over time, electrification and H_2 supplies for HT Heating (HTH) may eliminate some 23 mln ton of CO_2 emissions per year. The remainder of industrial CO_2 emissions is caused by the production of steel by TATA (some 6 mln ton of CO_2 per year), the production of ammonia and derivatives by Yara and OCI (some 6 mln ton of CO_2 per year) and the production of transportation fuels and chemicals by refineries and naphtha crackers (some 22 mln ton of CO_2 per year). TATA is planning to decarbonize its steel manufacturing by replacing its coal driven blast furnace operation by a DRI-EAF combination powered by H_2. This calls for at least 0,5 mln ton H_2 per year. It is assumed that H_2 from reforming natural gas to meet current H_2 needs by Yara and OCI will have been replaced by H_2 from electrolysis (some 0,5 mln ton H_2). Hence, the steel and fertilizer sections of the Dutch industry sector may eliminate some 12 mln ton of CO_2 emissions the next decades.

What remains are 22 megaton CO_2 emissions by refineries and naphtha crackers, plus the Dutch Scope-3 kerosene and gasoil emissions of some 15 mln ton CO_2 assigned to the aviation and marine sectors, plus the remaining 20 mln ton CO_2 equivalent emissions by the agri-sector. Together 57 mln CO_2 per year.

This provides the basis for the TDES challenge. Due to the transition to electricity driven mobility (either directly through battery storage or indirectly through H_2 driven fuel cells), crude intake is expected to come down from 53 mln ton per year to 37 mln ton in 2050: 22 mln ton naphtha (of which 10 designated export) and 11 mln ton middle distillates (7 mln for domestic use and 4 mln ton to be exported). Some 4 mln ton of crude intake is needed for refinery operations. The 12 mln ton domestic naphtha yields 10 mln ton High Value Chemicals per year whilst 2 mln ton naphtha is used to fuel the crackers.

The optimization challenge is to deliver the 31 mln ton of nett hydrocarbon output without any CO_2 emissions by 2050. Furthermore, at least 4 mln ton of H_2 has to be produced or imported to meet H_2 demand requirements by the HDV part of the mobility sector to drive Fuel Cell Electric Vehicles (1 mln ton H_2), by YARA, OCI and TATA to decarbonize their feeds (1 mln ton H_2) and by the Chemicals sector to provide High Temperature Heat (2 mln ton H_2). These demands are all to be met without any CO_2 emissions.

TDES shows how this 31 mln ton of nett hydrocarbon output can be delivered within sustainability constraints at lowest costs. Regarding carbon intake, TDES may still select fossil sources (crude intake to refineries and LPG/condensate imports for crackers as well final products) or renewable carbon sources, both with CCS as decarbonization option.

TDES considers 3 sources of renewable carbon: (1) bio-based carbon, including bio-CH_4 (green gas) from manure fermentation and/or wet oxidation, lignocelluloses from wood pellets and agricultural residues, lipids from Used Cooking Oil and waste from meat factories (fatty esters); (2) recycled carbon as Refuse Derived Fuel extracted from Municipal Solid Waste and Plastic Waste; (3) atmospheric carbon, like biogenic CO_2 from processing lipids and lignocelluloses, CO_2 from green gas powered electricity generation, and CO_2 from Direct Air Capture.

TDES includes yields & expense statements for a portfolio of renewable carbon processing units, including Biomass to Liquids (BTL), Waste to Liquids (WTL), Power to Liquids (PTL, both Fisher-Tropsch and methanol synthesis based), Hydrotreated Vegetable Oil (HVO) and Plastic Waste to Oil (Pyrolysis).

Maximum expected availabilities of lipids (5 mln ton), lignocelluloses (22 mln ton), Refuse Derived Fuel (3 mln ton) and plastic waste (5 mln ton) to feed these units are specified as boundary conditions in TDES. In total, 35 mln ton biomass & recycled material is assumed to be available yearly by 2050.

H_2 production has been modelled in TDES in four ways: by electrolysis, by Steam Methane Reforming, by Auto Thermal Reforming of Natural Gas and by biomass gasification followed by water-gas shift. CO_2 produced in the latter two cases is to be stored (CCS). Biomass gasification with CCS delivers a "negative CO_2 emission bonus" as BECCS.

Maximum CO_2 storage capacity is set at 27,5 mln ton CO_2 in the model, in line with the envisaged scope of the Porthos & Aramis CCS projects (two Dutch CCS projects).

For this paper, two scenarios have been explored regarding the optimal combination of fossil and renewable carbon feedstocks to deliver a new Dutch Energy System without any direct CO_2 emissions to air: the Net-Zero Case and the Fossil Free Case. In the Net-Zero Case, fossil feeds are allowed to be used as long as any CO_2 emissions to air are avoided. In the Fossil Free Case only renewable carbon and renewable power are allowed to be used to meet the 31 mln ton nett hydrocarbon output: 17 mln ton for domestic use and 14 mln ton for export). Both cases also need to deliver 4 mln ton of green or blue H_2. Also, the 20 mln ton CO_2-equivalent emissions due CH_4 and N_2O emissions by the agricultural sector need to be compensated. Hence, negative emissions of 20 mln ton CO_2 are to be identified as part of the optimization challenge for both scenarios.

4. Towards CO_2 Neutral Dutch Energy System in 2050: Net-Zero Case

In the Net-Zero Case the optimal transition path shows investments over time for: (1) the production of 4 mln ton pyrolysis oil as cracker feed from 5 mln ton plastic waste; (2) the production of 3 mln ton jet fuel from 15 mln ton lignocelluloses; and (3) the production of 4 mln ton gasoil from 5 mln ton lipids (kero and gasoil thereby declared as Scope-3 neutral). The remaining 10 mln ton biomass (7 mln ton lignocelluloses and 3 mln ton RDF) is used for electricity generation (17 TWh). Its CO_2 emissions (20 mln ton) are captured and stored. This qualifies as BECCS negative emissions and compensate the 20 mln ton CO_2 equivalent emissions by the agricultural sector. TDES imports 8 mln ton condensate as cracker feed to complement the 4 mln ton pyrolysis oil.

The 4 mln ton H_2 for HDV and for TATA, Yara, OCI and Chemicals (HTH) may come from domestic electrolysis or H_2 import. The electrolysis case calls for an investment in 24 GW electrolyser capacity with a 95% green electricity availability and utilization through PPA's. In the Net-Zero Case, fossil-based production of 4 mln ton H_2 would be allowed and is cheaper, but requires an intake of 16 mln ton NG and 32 mln ton O_2 to feed an ATR system that apart from the 4 mln ton H_2 also yields 44 mln ton CO_2 to be captured and stored (CCS). This brings the total CCS requirement at 64 mln ton of CO_2 storage per year from 2050 onwards. This is beyond the Porthos and Aramis design capacities for CO_2 storage (27,5 mln ton CO_2): TDES does not select the ATR option.

Due to availability limitations on renewable carbon resources, TDES decides to import the hydrocarbons needed for the export of 14 mln ton kero, marine gasoil and naphtha. As a result, refinery operations are scaled down over time and closed by 2050.

Investments over time, adding up to some 30 bln€ in 2050, are listed below.

	2025	2030	2035	2040	2045	2050	Cumulative
Electrolysis units	0,0	4,5	4,5	4,5	0	4,5	18,0
Power on Biomass feed	0,0	0,3	0,5	0,4	0,3	0,1	1,6
PO & ATJ & HVO	2,4	3,8	2,8	1,2	0,4	0,4	11,0
Total	2,4	8,6	7,8	6,1	0,7	5,0	30,6

The resulting optimal renewable carbon conversion superstructure is given below.

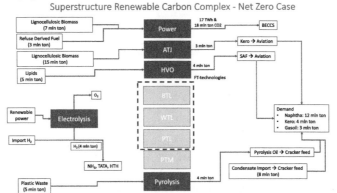

Superstructure Renewable Carbon Complex - Net Zero Case

5. Towards a Fossil Free Dutch Energy System by 2050

The fossil free requirement is essentially a full recarbonisation challenge: 37 mln ton of crude oil needs to be replaced by renewable carbon sources to yield 10 mln ton Chemicals, 7 mln ton of kerosene and gasoil for the aviation and marine sectors and 14 mln ton hydrocarbons for export. The remaining 6 mln ton of the 37 mln ton intake are needed to fuel the refineries (4 mln ton) and the crackers (2 mln ton).

With availabilities of lipids, lignocelluloses, RDF, waste plastic and CO_2 as given above, TDES shows that replacement of the domestic demand of fossil hydrocarbons (19 mln ton) calls for 5 mln ton lipids, 8 mln ton lignocelluloses, 3 mln ton RDF, 5 mln ton Waste Plastic and 28 mln ton CO_2. The latter volume is delivered by 14 mln ton lignocelluloses into an oxy-fired power generation unit. Some 4 mln ton of green H_2 is needed as co-feed to the PTL process, turning this 28 mln ton of CO_2 into synthetic hydrocarbons (naphtha, kerosene and gasoil). Additionally, 3 mln ton O_2 and chemicals are needed as additional input to this "renewable carbon" based system, e.g. for the gasification of biomass & waste into synthesis gas as first step of the BTL and WTL processes.

Apart from the 19 mln tons of hydrocarbons, the system also delivers 25 mln ton waste water, 2 mln tons CO_2 and 11 mln ton biogenic residuals. The latter can be used for power generation (30 TWh) resulting in an additional 17 mln of biogenic CO_2. Together with the 2 mln ton biogenic CO_2 rest stream, the resulting 19 mln ton of CO_2 qualify to be stored as negative emissions (BECCS) or can alternatively be used as CO_2 feed for the PTL unit.

TDES also decides not to produce the 14 mln ton hydrocarbons for export due to the lack of renewable carbon and power. To understand this result, the following analysis is made. To produce 14 mln ton by PTL, assuming an unrealistically high carbon efficiency of 100%, an amount of 6 mln ton green H_2 will be needed plus 44 mln ton bio-based CO_2. To generate 6 mln ton of H_2 per year assuming an utilization rate of 4500 hours per year, an electrolyser capacity of some 70 GW needs to be installed. Its corresponding power demand would entirely absorb the projected 2050 Dutch off-shore wind-power capacity of 70 GW. And, the 100 GW solar power capacity expected to be installed in the Netherlands by 2050 and operating at 1500 hours per year would significantly fall short to deliver the projected 2050 renewable power demand of some 300 TWh. Alternatively, the production of 14 mln ton hydrocarbons by BTL, WTL, pyrolysis and HVO at an average thermal efficiency of 75% would call for an additional amount of biomass and recycled carbon of 30 mln ton (assuming an average LHV of 25 GJ/ton for these feeds). This is beyond the biomass / recyclate availability constraints imposed on TDES.

The resulting superstructure for the Fossil Free Case is given below.

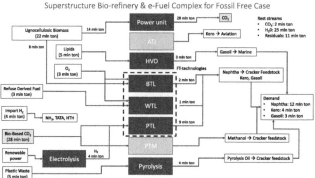

Corresponding investments for the Fossil Free Case amount to some 70 bln €.

	2025	2030	2035	2040	2045	2050	Cumulatief
Electrolysers	0,0	9,0	4,5	4,5	9,0	9,0	36,0
Power block	0,0	0,3	0,6	0,6	0,6	0,0	2,2
FT Complex (WTL, BTL, PTL)	0,0	2,2	2,2	0,2	0,0	18,9	23,4
HVO & PO units	1,8	2,2	1,0	1,2	0,4	0,4	7,0
Total Investment	1,8	13,7	8,3	6,5	10,0	28,3	68,6

6. Conclusions

The investment in the Fossil Free Case exceeds the Net-Zero Case by almost 40 bln€. This is not a surprise as the Fossil Free Case calls for investments in capital intensive systems like the Reverse Water Gas Shift system and Fisher-Tropsch (FT) based process technologies (BTL, WTL and PTL). Furthermore, the marginal hydrocarbon tranche of 9 mln ton has to come from expensive bio-based CO_2 and H_2 volumes.

This analysis shows the important role of CCS in the transition. A CCS storage capacity of 40 – 45 mln ton CO_2 would significantly widen the operating window for both cases.

Both scenarios show the significant impact that recarbonisation will have on the Dutch export position of hydrocarbons. Currently, some 40% of crude intake is processed for export. The transition to the use of renewable carbon as key feedstock for the Dutch energy system will significantly erode this export and is projected to disappear by 2050. Alternatively, TDES shows that the scale of wind and solar power investments (70 GW North-Sea wind and 100 GW solar) provide an attractive new export position based on green electricity and/or green H_2 in combination with import and transit of H_2 carriers like NH_3, Methanol and LOHC's.

TDES also allows to analyse "make or buy" decisions for the H_2, NH_3, Methanol options as part of the transformation of the Dutch energy system. TDES evaluates the value of methanol production against the value of methanol import with methanol as feedstock for lower olefins as well as hydrogen carrier and energy carrier (e.g. for marine services).

TDES is a powerful model that supports industry and policy makers to develop robust and transparent strategies and road maps towards a low carbon future for the Netherlands.

References

J. van Schijndel, 2019, Energy System Modelling in support of the Energy Transition, 29th European Symposium on Computer Aided Process Engineering, Elsevier, p. 1621-1626;

J. Davelaar, 2023, Accelerating the Energy Transition: Determining No-Regret Transition Pathways in the Port of Rotterdam, Proceedings International Conference on Operations Research (OR 2023), Springer.

Flavio Manenti, Gintaras V. Reklaitis (Eds.), Proceedings of the 34th European Symposium on Computer Aided Process Engineering / 15th International Symposium on Process Systems Engineering (ESCAPE34/PSE24), June 2-6, 2024, Florence, Italy

Integrated design and location of a green hydrogen production chain from waste biomass. A case study in western Andalusia.

Silvia Moreno*, Laura R. Piñeiro, Alicia Ronda, Bernabé A. Fariñas, Pedro Haro.

Department of Chemical and Environmental Engineering.
Escuela Técnica Superior de Ingniería. Universidad de Sevilla.
Camino de los Descubrimientos. Seville, Spain.
spuerta@us.es

Abstract

Green hydrogen is a promising energy vector for decarbonising the industrial, transport, and heating sectors. The foremost renewable technology used to produce it is nowadays electrolysis. Nevertheless, there are some problems related to this technology. Among them, the use of pure water, the need of large solar and wind power plants, and the seasonality of this kind of resources. Within this context, the use of residual biomass to produce green hydrogen can be essential to face these problems. However, when using residual biomass as a feedstock, one of the main challenges is the definition of a supply chain at the local level ensuring the economic and environmental viability of this resource. Against this background, the application of holistic models that analyse the availability and composition of raw materials and their relationship to process design is crucial. Therefore, the objective of this study is to apply a holistic systematic model to determine the value chain of biomass as a green hydrogen feedstock. Hence, different alternatives have been studied for the valorisation of waste biomass in western Andalusia. Waste biomass from olive groves without assigned use, burnt, or deposited in landfills has been selected as raw material. The results show that using the proposed methodology, the emissions when using hubs for coprocessing do not lead to a significant increase in emissions. Figure 1 shows the system boundaries of the analysed base case proposed in this work.

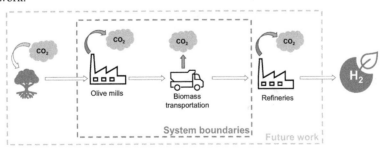

Figure 1. System boundaries of present and future work.

Keywords: Value chain model, location-allocation problem, waste biomass, hydrogen.

1. Introduction

Life cycle analysis (LCA) represents one of the best methods used to study the sustainability of projects. However, in these analyses, the calculation of emissions due to transport is usually carried out in a generalised way to allow it to be applied to a wider number of geographical areas (Freer, 2022). In the case of biomass, emissions, and costs due to transport have a strong influence, so the LCA for a specific project involving the use of biomass in a specific location needs another kind of analysis. Furthermore, the location of raw material hubs not only affect the cost of production, but also has an environmental impact associated with the production of the final product (Taifouris et al., 2020). For this reason, an in-depth analysis in addition to LCA is needed when biomass is involved to study the environmental, social, and economic impact in a specific area.

According to the Andalucian government, this community has a great potential for biomass, especially olive grove biomass. Due to the large amount of olive pruning waste, for example, its management consists of burning it on site or chipping it. In both cases, the CO_2 stored in the tree during its growth is returned to the atmosphere (Galán-Martín et al., 2022). Valorisation of this type of residues producing green hydrogen can have a great impact to decarbonise the energy system and also to reduce issues associated to its current management, but alternatives should be studied in-depth in order to guarantee its environmental, economic and social benefits.

2. Methodology

2.1. Waste biomass

Biomass selection was based on a previous work in which an analysis of potential biomass (to produce green hydrogen through thermochemical process) and availability in western Andalusia was carried out. Of a total list of 43 possible residual biomasses generated in the area, only three have been selected. The filters used for that were based on the total amount generated, the hydrogen yield of each biomass, and the consideration of other current uses of this biomass. Once the filters have been applied, the available biomasses are olive-tree pruning, olive stone, and olive pomace. After selecting the biomasses to be used in the process, different paths for the supply chain have been proposed, as shown in Figure 2. The path in bold shows one of the possible supply chain routes. The proposed scheme to define the value chain implies that hydrogen will be produce directly in the refinery, so in this work, only biomass transport will be evaluated. This is owing to the risk associated to hydrogen transport (Li et al., 2022).

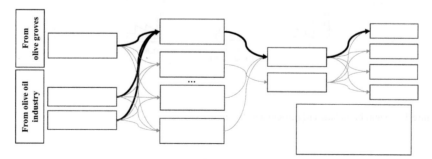

Figure 2. Possible pathways for the supply chain

Integrated design and location of a green hydrogen production chain from
waste biomass. A case study in western Andalusia.
2037

Considering that the selected biomass is generated in oil mills, the location of the hubs will be based on the existing sites of the oil mills in the study area. For this purpose, a manual compilation was made of the active mills in the region, as well as their geographical coordinates. As the data concerning the amount of biomass generated is allocated to the municipalities, a GIS approximation has been made to assign each amount of biomass to its nearest olive mill. A total of 116 oil mills have been considered in the work.

Regarding the energy efficiency of the selected biomasses, it has been estimated using the yield of hydrogen production by gasification and the low heating value (LHV) of hydrogen and biomass on a dry basis.

2.2. Biomass transportation

Biomass transport will be approached in two possible ways: i) a base case in which biomass will be transported from each olive mill to the nearest refinery and ii) considering that some olive mill will be used as hubs in which a pretreatment of biomass will be applied before it is transported to the refineries. It has also been considered that each olive mill should produce at least 11.4 tonnes of biomass. This amount is based on the useful load capacity of a commercial dump truck. The volume that can be transported with the selected truck is 19.32 m^3. According to the literature, most of the biomass supply chains are small and have radii between 50 and 386 km. Rail and maritime transport is often used for more distributed supply chains, where distances range from 100 to 1 500 km (Freer et al., 2021).

A polygon restriction shape has been included to verify whether the areas where biomass facilities will be installed are available for this purpose. This shape contains data about airports, watercourses, mining extraction areas, wetlands and marshes, sand flats, livestock trails, or railway, among others.

2.3. Environmental impact

To calculate the environmental impact, the carbon footprint has been used to measure the direct effect on the atmosphere of the greenhouse gases (GHG) of each of the raw materials considered. To evaluate this, the distances between the suppliers and the chemical poles considered must be considered. Emissions in the mass of CO_2, CH_4 and N_2O per kilometre travelled for road transport by lorries were obtained from the Ministry of Ecological Transition and Demographic Challenge (Ministerio para la transición ecológica y el reto demográfico, 2023). To compare the three emissions, GWP 100 (Global Warming Potential) has been used (IPCC, 2023).

Emissions associated with the transport of biomass to the pretreatment hubs and from the hubs to the industrial hydrogen production plants have been calculated from Eq. (1)

$$Emission_{hub} = distance_{hub} \cdot kgCO_{2\,eq}/km \quad (\forall hub) \tag{1}$$

Where:

$CO_{2\,eq}$ is the sum of CO_2, CH_4 and N_2O emissions using the GWP 100

However, the emission calculated with the above equation does not consider the number of travels necessaries according to the amount of biomass and its density and the load capacity of the selected truck. Regarding the unit emission associated with transport (considering the unit emission as the emission generated in one single path, that is, the way from the olive mill to the refinery), it is calculated according to equations Eq. (2) and Eq. (3).

$$EmissionU_{hub} = \frac{Emission_{hub}}{Loading\ capacity} \quad (\forall hub) \tag{2}$$

$$EmissionT_{ye,hub} = EmissionU_{hub} \cdot \sum_i av_{ye,i,hub} \quad (\forall hub) \tag{3}$$

Where:

$av_{ye,i,hub}$ is the available volume of the dry residual biomass i from the hub *hub* in the year ye (m_i^3/year)

3. Results

3.1. Waste biomass

Given the biomasses used in the study and their location, the distances from the different points of origin to the possible destinations were calculated. For this purpose, a road transport by dump truck has been used. The results obtained for one of the clusters are presented in Table 1. Each olive mill has been represented with a number to anonymise the study.

Table 1. Distances for analysis in a cluster in Case 2

Olive mill	Hub	Distance (km)
18	47	101
32	47	40
33	47	12
37	47	32
41	47	25
47	47	121[1]

[1]*Distance between the hub and the refinery considered in this work.*

Energy efficiency is shows in Figure 3 using a Sankey diagram.

Figure 3. Energy efficiency of hydrogen production (MWh, LHV basis)

3.2. Biomass transportation

Based on the literature consulted, the type of transport selected is the road. This decision is reinforced by a study carried out in Andalusia in which it was found that there is an absolute predominance of road over rail for distances of less than 200 km (Caceres-Sanchez & Ruiz De Alarcón-Quintero, 2014). According to the area proposed for this study (which includes the provinces of Cadiz, Seville, and Huelva), the maximum distance by road between the biomass generation point and the hydrogen production hubs is 169 km. Furthermore, there are logistical and accessibility reasons, as the areas where biomass is generated are easily accessible by road.

To study the effects of creating pretreatment hubs, three cases have been proposed:

1. Base case. Biomass is transported from each olive mill to the refinery without pretreatment.
2. Case 1. The biomass is pelletised in each olive mill and then transported to the refinery.
3. Case 2. The mills are grouped into clusters, and the one with the largest amount of biomass is selected as the hub for pretreatment before being transported to the refinery.

Figure 4 shows the study area with the location of the refineries and olive mills considered in this study. Each cluster is indicated with a different symbol and the hub where the biomass will be pelletised in the case 2 is indicated with a circle surrounding the selected points.

Clusters were calculated using the restricted Delaunay triangulation in ArcGIS Pro with a cluster size restriction that guarantees the minimum availability of biomass in each cluster so that the selected truck can be fully loaded.

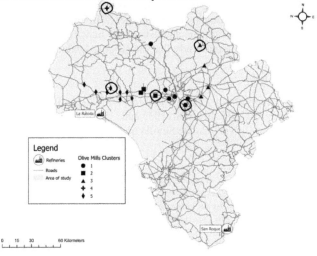

Figure 4. Olive mill cluster and f ' location

3.3. Environmental impact

The selected value for the greenhouse gases emitted per kilometre travelled corresponds to the estimated value for N2 (good vehicle with maximum mass exceeding 3.2 t but not exceeding 12 t) and N3 (good vehicle with a maximum mass exceeding 12 t) diesel trucks. Table 2 shows the emission factor values per gas for the year in question.

Table 2. Greenhouse gas emission factors for road transport and GWP 100

2022	CO_2 (kg/km)	CH_4 (g/km)	N_2O (g/km)
Diesel trucks	0.586	0.012	0.029
Gas trucks	0.673	0.140	0.006
GWP 100	1	27.9	273

The load capacity has been established at 19.32 m^3. This factor has been selected in terms of volume because the main problem in biomass is its low density. Moreover, when calculating the final emissions of each hub in one year, the available volume of biomass is used instead of the mass amount. Consequently, in this study it will be compare the transport of raw biomass and its transport after a pretreatment.

The CO_2 equivalent obtained in the three proposed cases is shown in Table 3.

Table 3. Greenhouse gases emissions in one year depending on the case of study.

Case Study	t CO_2 eq/year
Base Case	210
Case 1	196
Case 2	199

4. Conclusions

The results show that pretreatment on site of biomass is crucial to reduce GHG emissions when transporting biomass. However, the selection of hubs for the coprocessing of biomass does not imply a significant increase in emissions if the methodology used in the study is followed. The establishment of hubs can, nevertheless, facilitate the technical and economic reduction when proposing the biomass value chain for its subsequent transformation into green hydrogen at the refinery. In order to continue with this approach, future work will include the analysis of the hubs for the other refinery in the study area, as well as the economic study that the proposed value chain would entail.

5. Acknowledgements

This study has been supported by grant PID2020-114725RA-I00 of the project GH2T funded by MCIN/AEI/10.13039/501100011033 and   h "E   U   ". h h.D. grant of S. Moreno from Universidad de Sevilla under VII PPIT-US is acknowledged.

References

Caceres-Sanchez, N., & Ruiz De Alarcón-Quintero, C. (2014). *Nueva Metodología para la Evaluación de la Demanda de Transporte de Mercancías Peligrosas Por Vía Férrea en la Comunidad Autónoma de Andalucía*. Universidad de Sevilla.

Forster, P., Storelvmo, T., Armour, K., Collins, W., Dufresne, J.-L., Frame, D., Lunt, D. J., Mauritsen, T., Palmer, M. D., W   , M., W   , M., & Zh   , .   . h E h' E Budget, Climate Feedbacks and Climate Sensitivity. *Climate Change 2021 – The Physical Science Basis*, 923–1054. https://doi.org/10.1017/9781009157896.009

Freer, M. (2022). *Carbon-Efficient Transportation via Spatially Explicit Modelling of Large-Scale Bioenergy with Carbon Capture and Storage Supply Chains*. Tyndall Centre for Climate Change Research.

Freer, M., Gough, C., Welfle, A., & Lea-Langton, A. (2021). Carbon optimal bioenergy with carbon capture and storage supply chain modelling: How far is too far? *Sustainable Energy Technologies and Assessments*, *47*. https://doi.org/10.1016/j.seta.2021.101406

Galán-Martín, Á., Contreras, M. del M., Romero, I., Ruiz, E., Bueno-Rodríguez, S., Eliche-Quesada, D., & Castro-Galiano, E. (2022). The potential role of olive groves to deliver carbon dioxide removal in a carbon-neutral Europe: Opportunities and challenges. *Renewable and Sustainable Energy Reviews*, *165*, 112609. https://doi.org/10.1016/j.rser.2022.112609

Li, H., Cao, X., Liu, Y., Shao, Y., Nan, Z., Teng, L., Peng, W., & Bian, J. (2022). Safety of hydrogen storage and transportation: An overview on mechanisms, techniques, and challenges. *Energy Reports*, *8*, 6258–6269. https://doi.org/https://doi.org/10.1016/j.egyr.2022.04.067

Ministerio para la transición ecológica y el reto demográfico. (2023). *Factores de emisión. Registro de huella de carbono, compensación y proyectos de absorción de dióxido de carbono*.

Taifouris, M., Martín, M., Martínez, A., & Esquejo, N. (2020). On the effect of the selection of suppliers on the design of formulated products. *Computers and Chemical Engineering*, *141*. https://doi.org/10.1016/j.compchemeng.2020.106980

Flavio Manenti, Gintaras V. Reklaitis (Eds.), Proceedings of the 34th European Symposium on Computer Aided Process Engineering / 15th International Symposium on Process Systems Engineering (ESCAPE34/PSE24), June 2-6, 2024, Florence, Italy

Switching from fossil fuel-based to concentrated solar power driven tri-generation systems: an optimization model

Rachid Klaimi,[a] Sabla Y. Alnouri,[b] Mirko Stijepovic [c]

[a]*Chemical Engineering Program, Notre Dame University-Louaize, Zouk Mosbeh, Lebanon*
[b]*Gas Processing Center, College of Engineering, Qatar University, Doha, Qatar*
[c]*Faculty of Technology and Metallurgy, University of Belgrade, Karnegijeva 4, 11000 Belgrade, Serbia*
sabla@qu.edu.qa

Abstract

In light of the increase in the consumption of fossil fuels in tri-generation systems integrated with desalination plants and the associated environmental damage, switching into renewable energy sources became a necessity. Various technologies have been identified as potential energy sources for tri-generation systems, among which concentrated solar power (CSP) was found an appealing and viable option for driving large-scale desalination plants. However, CSP is well known for its high investment cost, which makes the switching process very expansive. In order to address this challenge, different types of fuel with lower carbon emission than conventional energy sources could be utilized in a transient phase allowing for a gradual reduction in carbon emissions. This work presents a Mixed Integer Nonlinear mathematical model that can be used for planning the shift from fossil fuels to CSP. The model is capable of identifying the optimal combination of fuels to be utilized besides CSP in the transient phase for a tri-generation system integrated with a reverse osmosis (RO) unit. Hence, the aim is to determine the best fuel options to be integrated with CSP, in addition to their corresponding energy contributions using a series of different net carbon reduction targets (NCRT) ranging from 0 to 100%. The fuel options incorporated into the model include natural gas, biomass and municipal solid waste (MSW). Moreover, two different technologies for MSW incineration are involved: grate fired and fluidized bed boilers. The model has been implemented on a tri-generation system integrated with Carlsbad desalination plant in California for illustration purposes. The optimal fuel source(s) and technologies during the transition from fossil fuels to a concentrated solar power-based desalination system have then been identified. It was found that when the NCRT levels are below 40%, biomass emerges as the most suitable fuel option, whereas for higher NCRT values, solid waste incineration is the preferred choice.

Keywords: Tri-generation systems, desalination, concentrated solar power, biomass, municipal solid waste

1. Introduction

Thermal and electrical energy generation from conventional fossil fuels is becoming expansive, and it is associated with many detrimental effects on health and environment. In 2018, a significant rise in power consumption produced from fossil fuel sources of energy was reported, while carbon dioxide emissions reached a critical level of 33.5 Gt. Although a decline in power sector emissions in developing countries was observed in the following year, global CO_2 emissions showed a very small reduction of less than 1% (Ma'aji et al., 2022). On the other hand, desalination processes are well known for their high thermal and electrical energy demand and fossil fuels consumption. Therefore, the past half-century witnessed the integration of various concentrated solar power (CSP) technologies with desalination units coupled with tri-generation systems. For instance, Klaimi et al. (2021) have presented a Mixed Integer Non-linear mathematical model for designing a standalone CSP-desalination tri-generation system producing three pressure levels of steam, power and freshwater simultaneously, while Ma'aji et al. (2022) have proposed a design of a tri-generation plant for electricity, freshwater production and district heating in Lagos, Nigeria. One of the main challenges associated with CSP is the high investment cost. Therefore, the integration of other energy sources with CSP was found a great strategy to overcome this challenge. For instance, an energy and economic analysis of a novel biomass-solar hybrid system presented by Khosravi et al. (2021) showed a minimum attainable levelized cost of energy of 7.865 cents/kWh. Klaimi et al. (2022a) have presented a multi-period model for designing a CSP-desalination tri-generation system integrated with a natural gas boiler, while Najjar et al. (2021) have studied the energy generation from the anaerobic digestion of municipal solid waste (MSW) to drive a reverse osmosis unit. Moreover, Klaimi et al. (2022b) have investigated seasonal variations and multiple fuel options (natural gas, biomass and MSW) in a novel tri-generation CSP integarted hybrid energy process. Although the backup energy sources of CSP could significantly reduce the cost of the system, their existence is associated with carbon dioxide emissions. Therefore, these sources could not be utilized when the target is to design a carbon neutral system. However, it is recommended to incorporate such sources in a transient phase while switching from fossil fuels to CSP allowing a gradual reduction in CO_2 emissions. This paper assess different types of fuel and technologies to be utilized in a tri-generation system during the transient phase subject to a specific net carbon reduction target. The novelty of this work lies in the incorporation of a wide number of fuels and technologies which helps policy makers in selecting the appropriate energy sources based on the specifications of the system.

2. Methodology

The proposed CSP-desalination hybrid tri-generation system is depicted in Figure 1. This system is divided into three stages: 1) Very high pressure (VHP) steam generation section, 2) Low pressure (LP) steam, very low pressure (VLP) steam, shaft and electric power generation section, and 3) Freshwater generation section. The first section includes a natural gas boiler, a solar steam generator and an additional boiler specific to the fuel to be utilized in the transient phase. The fuels that will be considered in this work are biomass and municipal solid waste. Moreover, two different boilers will be investigated for the incineration of solid waste: a fluidized bed (FB) boiler and a grate-fired (GF) boiler. The main difference between the two boilers lies in the type of solid waste incinerated and the amount of carbon emissions which allows a more controlled incineration when the process takes place in a fluidized bed boiler. VHP steam at 41 bars and 450 °C is produced in this section and fed to the next stage of the system. The second stage includes a throttling valve (TV), a back-pressure driver (DRBP) and turbo-generator (TGBP) for the production of LP steam at 2 bars, in addition to a condensing driver (DRCD) and turbo-generator (TGCD) for the production of VLP steam at 0.4 bar. The VLP steam produced is condensed, pumped and deaerated before being relocated as boiling feed water (BFW) to the first section, while the shaft and electric power produced are distributed to the desalination technologies in the following section. Two different desalination technologies are incorporated in this system: thermal desalination using multi-stage flashing (MSF) and membrane desalination using reverse osmosis (RO). A portion of freshwater stream generated is recycled back as makeup water to the deaerator in order to compensate for any loss of steam during VHP steam expansion and deaeration.

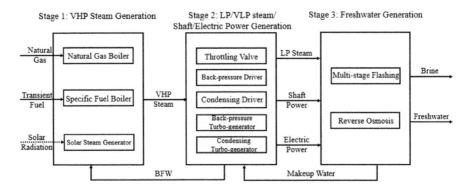

Figure 1: Proposed tri-generation system structure

3. Mathematical Model

The proposed tri-generation system has been converted into a Mixed Integer Non-linear Problem (MINLP) that aims at minimizing the total cost of the system. The objective function is described in Eq. (1) below, where $Cost^{sec1}$ is the VHP steam generation cost from the different energy sources and technologies embedded in section 1 of the system, $Cost^{sec2}$ is the cost of utilities (LP and VLP steam, electric and shaft work) generated in section 2 of the system for desalination purposes, and $Cost^{sec3}$ is the cost of desalination process which takes place in the third section of the system.

$$Minimize \quad Cost^{sec1} + Cost^{sec2} + Cost^{sec3} \tag{1}$$

Equality and inequality constraints have been added to the model. The equality constraints cover the material and energy balances around all technologies and headers in the system. For instance, Eq. (2-5) represents the mass balances on natural gas boiler, solar steam generator, back-pressure turbo-generator and reverse osmosis unit, respectively, while the energy balances of the same technologies are represented in Eq. (6-9), respectively. In these equations, the variables G, H, Q and W denote the mass flowrate, specific enthalpy, thermal energy and electric power, respectively, while the subscripts B, S, SG, TB, RO, DSW and NG refer to boiler, steam, steam generator, turbo-generator, reverse osmosis, desalinated water and natural gas, respectively. Moreover, HV, η and λ are the parameters corresponding to the calorific value of natural gas, technology efficiency and electric power requirement per unit of water, respectively.

$$G_{BFW-B} = G_{S-B} + G_{blowdown} \tag{2}$$

$$G_{BFW-SG} = G_{S-SG} \tag{3}$$

$$G_{TB-in} = G_{TB-out} \tag{4}$$

$$G_{RO-in} = G_{RO-brine} + G_{RO-DSW} \tag{5}$$

$$(G_{BFW-b}H_{BFW-b} + G_{NG}HV_{NG})\,\eta_B = G_{S-B}H_{S-B} + G_{blowdown}H_{blowdown} \tag{6}$$

$$Q_{absorbed} = \eta_{SG}\,Q_{released} \tag{7}$$

$$W_{TB} = \eta_{power}\,\eta_{TB}\,\Delta H_{TB} \tag{8}$$

$$W_{RO} = \lambda_{RO}\,G_{RO-DSW} \tag{9}$$

On the other hand, the inequality constraints, described in Eq. (10-13) below, address the limitations on certain aspects of the system, such as the capacities of technologies, solar availability, minimum freshwater production and maximum allowable CO_2 emissions subject to a net carbon reduction target (NCRT) imposed on the system. In these equations, b represents a binary variable, A_{SF} is the required solar field area, *DNI* is the average direct normal irradiance, while G_{NG}^{CO2}, G_{TF}^{CO2}, and $G^{CO2,BC}$ are the carbon dioxide emissions from natural gas boiler, transient fuel boiler and total CO_2 emissions of a base case scenario, respectively.

$$b\,G_{min} \leq G \leq b\,G_{max} \tag{10}$$

$$G_{S-SG}(H_{S-SG} - H_{BFW-SG}) \leq A_{SF}\,DNI \tag{11}$$

$$G_{DSW,min} \leq G_{DSW} \tag{12}$$

$$G_{NG}^{CO2} + G_{TF}^{CO2} \leq (1 - NCRT)\,G^{CO2,BC} \tag{13}$$

4. Case Study

The proposed model was implemented on a trigeneration system integrated with Carlsbad desalination plant in California, USA. This plant operates using reverse osmosis (RO) membranes with a total capacity of 160,000 m³/d and inlet seawater salinity of 33.5 g/L. Moreover, the energy consumption of RO was estimated at 3.5 kWh/m³. The main energy supplier of Carlsbad plant is San Diego Gas and Electric (SDG&E) plant which currently generates 55% of its energy from natural gas and 45% from solar panels and wind (Klaimi et al., 2022c). Since the aim of this study is to assess the utilization of various fuel options and technologies in a transient phase towards a carbon neutral system, two base case scenarios will be considered. In the first scenario, the net carbon reduction target will be based on the amount of CO_2 emitted from a system that is operating on natural gas only, whereas the second base case scenario is similar to the current situation. As previously mentioned, biomass and municipal solid waste are the transient fuels to be investigated in this work, while the technologies that will be incorporated are biomass boiler, grate-fired boiler and fluidized bed boiler. Moreover, the option of making some revenues through the selection of grate-fired boiler was added to the model, since this policy is adopted in many countries to reduce the total volume of generated solid waste. On the other hand, in order to determine the maximum amount of energy that could be generated from CSP, an average monthly DNI value of 168 kWh/m² was considered. The MINLP optimization problem has been implemented using "Whats'Best 17.0" LINDO Global

Solver for MS-Excel 2016. Figure 2 below shows the variation of total water production cost (WPC) using different transient fuels and technologies at a series of NCRT values ranging from 0 to 100% based on the first scenario.

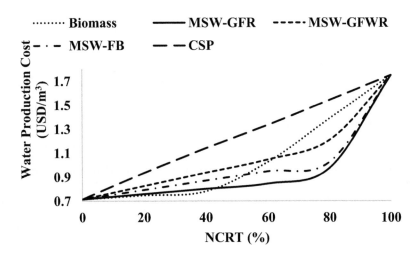

Figure 2: Water production cost vs NCRT for different fuel options

The obtained results showed that water production cost of a tri-generation system operating using natural gas only (0% NCRT) is 0.715 USD/m³, while the amount of CO_2 emissions associated with the utilization of natural gas is estimated at 299 tons/day. This WPC varies differently with increasing NCRT values depending on the type of transient fuel and technology. Figure 2 shows that biomass is the most appropriate fuel to be selected in the transient phase for NCRT values below 40%. At low NCRT values, energy generation from biomass was found the cheapest among the available options, followed by MSW incineration using grate fired boiler with revenues (MSW-GFR). However, when the revenues from the utilization of grate fired boiler are ignored (MSW-GFWR), the fluidized bed boiler (MSW-FB) becomes the most suitable technology for the incineration of MSW. This is mainly due to the high amount of CO_2 emissions resulted from the incorporation of a grate fired boiler which necessitates a significant contribution of CSP in this case in order to meet the carbon reduction target. Thus, a higher WPC was observed due to the high investment cost of CSP. Similarly, when NCRT exceeds 40%, the high emissions from biomass combustion require a higher contribution of CSP. This resulted in a drastic increase in WPC when biomass is selected as a transient fuel. In addition, MSW incineration option using grate fired boiler with revenue was preferred over biomass for a NCRT beyond 40%, while the fluidized bed and grate fired boiler without revenues become more desirable at NCRT values of 50% and 60%, respectively. On the other hand, when a 100% carbon reduction is required, the WPC of a system operating using CSP only was found 1.75 USD/m³.

The capital and investment costs of the investigated technologies were not the only reason behind the results observed in Figure 2. The amount of carbon emissions associated with the combustion of transient fuels could also affect the water production cost of the system.

Higher CO_2 emissions result in the selection of CSP as a secondary energy source for desalination which increase the WPC. Since the transient fuels have different carbon emission factors, it should be noted that CSP technology appeared for the first time in the optimal configurations at different NCRT values depending on the type of transient fuel involved. Table 1 below summarizes the NCRT values at which CSP was selected for the first time, the contribution of this energy source and WPC for the studied fuels.

Table 1: Summary of CSP related results

Transient Fuel	NCRT (%)	CSP Contribution (%)	WPC (USD/m^3)
Biomass	60	24	1.39
MSW-GFR	80	11	0.98
MSW-GFWR	80	11	1.21
MSW-FB	100	100	1.75

All NCRT values were based on a carbon emission flowrate of 162 tons/day. Surprisingly, the results showed the same trend of WPC variation with NCRT for the different fuels and technologies. The only difference was found in the values of WPC which were higher in the second case due to the higher contribution of CSP as a result of the stringent allowable carbon emissions. Thus, it can be concluded that fuel optimality does not depend on the base case scenario, whereas the water production cost does.

5. Conclusion

This study has presented an assessment strategy for detrmining the most appropriate fuel and technology to be adopted in a transient phase while switching from fossil fuel to concentrated solar power based desalination system. The results showed that biomass is the best fuel to be utilized for this purposes at NCRT values below 40%, whereas solid waste incineration is preferred at higher NCRT values.

References

Khosravi, A., Santasalo-Aarnio, A., & Syri, S. (2021). Optimal technology for a hybrid biomass/solar system for electricity generation and desalination in Brazil. *Energy, 234*, 121309.

Klaimi, R., Alnouri, S. Y., & Stijepović, M. (2021). Design and thermo-economic evaluation of an integrated concentrated solar power–Desalination tri-generation system. *Energy Conversion and Management, 249*, 114865.

Klaimi, R., Alnouri, S. Y., & Stijepovic, M. (2022a). Design and Evaluation Strategies for a Novel Hybrid Trigeneration System. In *Computer Aided Chemical Engineering* (Vol. 51, pp. 673-678). Elsevier.

Klaimi, R., Alnouri, S. Y., & Stijepović, M. (2022b). Investigation of seasonal variations and multiple fuel options in a novel tri-generation CSP integrated hybrid energy process. *Energy, 261*, 125338.

Klaimi, R., Alnouri, S. Y., Zeaiter, J., & Stijepović, M. (2022c). Optimization of multiple fuel utilization options in Tri-generation systems. *Energy Reports*.

Ma'aji, N. S., Adun, H., Shefik, A., Adedeji, M., & Dagbasi, M. (2022). Design of trigeneration plant for electricity freshwater production, and district heating: A case study Periwinkle Lifestyle Estate, Lagos Nigeria. *Case Studies in Thermal Engineering, 35*, 102041.

Najjar, E., Al-Hindi, M., Massoud, M., & Saad, W. (2021). Life Cycle Assessment of a seawater reverse osmosis plant powered by a hybrid energy system (fossil fuel and waste to energy). *Energy Reports, 7*, 448-465.

Flavio Manenti, Gintaras V. Reklaitis (Eds.), Proceedings of the 34th European Symposium on Computer Aided Process Engineering / 15th International Symposium on Process Systems Engineering (ESCAPE34/PSE24), June 2-6, 2024, Florence, Italy

Energetic Comparison of Electrochemical versus Mechanical Compression of Hydrogen

Georgia Ioanna Prokopou,[a] Matthias Leon Mödden,[a] Alexander Mitsos, [c,a,b] Dominik Bongartz [d,*]

[a]*RWTH Aachen University, Process Systems Engineering (AVT.SVT), Aachen, Germany*
[b]*Forschungszentrum Jülich GmbH, Institute for Energy and Climate Research IEK-10: Energy Systems Engineering, Jülich, Germany*
[c]*JARA-ENERGY, Aachen, Germany*
[d]*Department of Chemical Engineering, KU Leuven, Leuven, Belgium*
[*]*dominikbongartz@alum.mit.edu*

Abstract

Compression is a necessary step for the efficient storage and transportation of hydrogen. Mechanical compressors are a mature technology widely used for this purpose. Electrochemical hydrogen compression is also considered a promising alternative, however, as a novel technology, there are still open questions regarding to what extent it can be competitive with mechanical compressors. In the present work, we compare the energetic performance of these two compression technologies. We first build a model of a multi-stage mechanical compressor. Then we use the model together with our existing electrochemical compressor model to analyze and compare their energetic performance at different pressure levels. The results show that improvements in the membranes and the catalysts need to be made to make the electrochemical compressor energetically competitive with the mechanical compressor.

Keywords: Electrochemical compression, mechanical compression, energetic performance, hydrogen, modeling.

1. Introduction

Hydrogen exhibits low volumetric energy density at atmospheric conditions, presenting challenges for hydrogen storage for extended periods and long-distance transportation, particularly when large quantities of hydrogen are needed. Several methods exist to address this issue and increase the hydrogen energy density. Among them, the most widely used is compression (Sdanghi et al., 2019). Besides storage and transportation, compression is also crucial since high-pressure hydrogen is required in several industrial applications. Hydrogen compression is therefore an essential step of the hydrogen value chain.

Mechanical compressors are a mature technology that is widely used (Tahan, 2022), especially when significant hydrogen flow rates are required. However, they suffer from high capital and maintenance costs (Sdanghi et al., 2020). Lately, innovative emerging compression technologies have thus been proposed as alternatives to mechanical compressors, including the electrochemical hydrogen compressor (EHC) (Zou et al., 2020). To enable a wider penetration of EHC in the market (Toghyani et al., 2021), it is necessary to analyze their energetic performance. More specifically, it is unclear under which conditions they can compete with mechanical compressors.

To answer this question, we implement a standard model of a multi-stage mechanical compressor in the modeling language Modelica (Modelica Association, 2023). We use this model and a model of the EHC (Prokopou et al., 2023) to analyze hydrogen compression from 0.2 to 70 MPa. The objective is to evaluate the energy consumption of the two compressors and to identify the improvements that need to be made so that the EHC exhibits comparable energetic performance with the mechanical compressor.

2. Modeling

2.1 Electrochemical Compressor

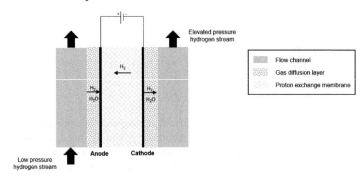

Figure 1: Schematic representation of an electrochemical hydrogen compressor

Figure 1 shows a schematic representation of the EHC. A potential difference is applied to an electrochemical cell in which low-pressure humidified hydrogen is fed at the anode. Hydrogen is oxidized at the anode and then the produced electrons are transferred through the external circuit to the cathode. The protons migrate from the anode to the cathode through the membrane and at the cathode, protons are recombined with electrons to form hydrogen at higher pressure. Due to the pressure difference between the cathode and the anode, hydrogen also permeates back into the membrane, a phenomenon known as back-diffusion, which is particularly relevant for high target pressures. The total cell voltage is equal to the sum of the Nernst potential, derived by the Nernst equation, the activation losses at the anode and cathode as well as the ohmic losses in the membrane.

In our recent work (Prokopou et al., 2023), we proposed a dynamic and spatially distributed (1D) model of the EHC in Modelica, accounting for the different overpotentials, namely Ohmic, activation, mass transport losses, and the back-diffusion effect. In the model, state-of-the-art catalysts (Stühmeier et al., 2021) and membranes (Nafion Association, 2023) are assumed. The model is fitted to literature experimental data (Nguyen et al., 2011), and the electrochemical parameters are determined via parameter estimation, enabling its use in a wide range of operating conditions.

2.2 Mechanical Compressor

For this work, a standard model of a multi-stage mechanical compressor is also implemented in Modelica. The compressor compresses hydrogen in multiple stages to a target pressure level. After each compression stage, hydrogen is cooled to the inlet temperature to minimize the compression work. In this way, the behavior of the process approaches the isothermal one. The number of stages of a multi-stage compressor is selected so that the temperature after each stage does not exceed 200 ºC. The compressor ratio r_p per stage is given by

$$r_{\mathrm{p}} = \left(\frac{p_{\mathrm{out}}}{p_{\mathrm{in}}}\right)^{1/N_{\mathrm{stages}}},$$

where p_{out} is the target pressure level, p_{in} is the inlet pressure, and N_{stages} is the number of stages. The power of each stage, assuming an adiabatic process, can be calculated from the following equation:

$$P_i = \dot{m} \cdot \left(h_i - h_{i-1,\mathrm{cool}}\right),$$

where $\dot{m}$ is the compressor mass flowrate, h_i is the enthalpy of hydrogen leaving stage *i*, and $h_{i-1,\mathrm{cool}}$ is the enthalpy of hydrogen leaving the intercooler of stage *i-1* and entering compressor stage *i*. A correlation for the isentropic efficiency η_{is} (Rothuizen et al., 2014) is used, which is valid for $1.1 < r_{\mathrm{p}} < 5$ and results in isentropic efficiencies in the range of 60-80%, which increase with the pressure ratio. The total compression power P_{tot} is

$$P_{\mathrm{tot}} = \sum_{i=1}^{N_{\mathrm{stages}}} P_i.$$

Polynomial fittings for the specific enthalpy and the specific entropy of hydrogen as functions of pressure and temperature were done in MATLAB using the National Institute of Standards and Technology database (NIST, 2023) to describe the thermodynamic properties of hydrogen, for a pressure range of 0.1-100 MPa, and a temperature range of 0-250 °C.

3. Case studies

The case of hydrogen compression via an electrochemical and a mechanical compressor is studied from an inlet pressure of 0.1 MPa to target pressures ranging from 0.2 to 70MPa.

The operating temperature of the electrochemical compressor is assumed to be 70 °C, at which the electrochemical compressor demonstrates good performance (Prokopou et al., 2023). The performance of the EHC is evaluated at different current densities since the operating current density influences both the energy consumption and the economics of the compression system (Prokopou et al., 2023).

The energy consumption of the electrochemical compressor is compared with a 3-stage mechanical compressor for pressure levels up to 10 MPa, and a 7-stage mechanical compressor for pressure levels up to 70 MPa. For the mechanical compressor, we consider intercooling down to 20 °C, as it performs better at low operating temperatures. The energy consumption of the mechanical compressor with intercooling down to 70 °C is also presented for comparison reasons to understand better the performance differences.

4. Results and discussion

Figure 2 shows the specific energy consumption of a 3-stage and a 7-stage mechanical compressor compared to the energy consumption of an electrochemical compressor at different current densities. The operating temperature of the EHC is 70 °C, while for the mechanical compressor intercooling down to 20 °C is assumed. The energy consumption of the EHC is significantly higher than that of the mechanical compressor. At low pressure and current densities, the energy consumption of the EHC approaches the one of the mechanical compressor. As the target pressure increases, the energy consumptions of the

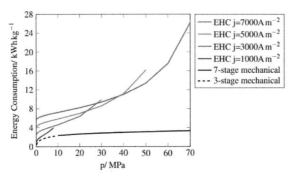

Figure 2: Energy consumption of a three-stage and seven-stage mechanical compressor, and an electrochemical compressor (EHC) for a target pressure range of 0.2-70 MPa and an inlet pressure of 0.1 MPa.

two compressors deviate more, mainly due to the back-diffusion loss of the EHC. In particular, the steep rise of the energy demand towards the ends of the solid lines shows the effect of the back-diffusion. At higher current densities, the energy consumption increases as well due to increased Ohmic and activation losses. Thus, operating at higher current densities increases the operating cost, while decreasing the capital cost.

To better understand the differences in the performance of the two compressors, in Figure 3 the energy consumption distributions of the electrochemical compressor at a temperature of 70 °C and a current density of 100 A m^{-2}, and 2000 A m^{-2}, together with the energy consumption of a 3-stage mechanical compressor with intercooling down to 20 °C and 70 °C are represented. A very low current density (100 A m^{-2}), to identify the range at which the energy consumption of the EHC is comparable to the mechanical, as well as a higher current density (2000 A m^{-2}) near the optimal operating point (Prokopou et al., 2023) are chosen for the EHC.

At a very low current density (100 A m^{-2}, see Fig. 3a) and low-pressure levels, the energy consumption of the electrochemical compressor is lower than that of the mechanical compressor. This can be explained by the fact that at such low current density, the cell potential is close to the Nernst potential, which corresponds to the exergy increase of the isothermal compression. The Ohmic and activation losses have lower contributions, which are not significantly influenced by the pressure. When the pressure level is kept low, the contribution of back-diffusion losses is minor. As the pressure level increases and the back-diffusion effect becomes more prominent, the electrochemical compressor becomes less efficient than the mechanical. The results suggest that the electrochemical compressor can be competitive with the mechanical compressor in terms of energy demand when low-pressure levels and low flow rates are required so that the compressor can operate at low current densities. However, operating the compressor at low current densities increases the capital cost, and the effect of these two factors needs to be analyzed. Moreover, at higher target pressures, membranes with a lower back-diffusion effect would be also needed.

Regarding the effect of the operating temperature on energy consumption, 70 °C was found to be a good compromise between conductivity, kinetics, and back-diffusion for the EHC (Prokopou et al., 2023). High operating temperatures are beneficial in terms of energy demand, as they reduce the activation and ohmic losses, except for very high-pressure levels and very low current densities, where the back-diffusion effect dominates (Prokopou et al., 2023). An intercooling temperature of 20 °C is chosen for the mechanical compressor, as cooling down to low temperatures improves its energetic performance. Since lowering the temperature also reduces the minimum energy demand for compression, we compared the energy consumption of the mechanical compressor with cooling to 70 °C with the one of EHC, to check whether this difference in operating temperature is a major factor in the observed performance differences. However, the results suggest that even with cooling down only to 70 °C, the mechanical compressor is more efficient than the EHC for most target pressures.

At higher current density (2000 A m^{-2}, see Fig. 3b), the energy consumption of the electrochemical compressor is significantly higher than that of the mechanical compressor even at low target pressures. The higher the current density, the higher the Ohmic loss in the membrane and the activation loss. The back-diffusion effect is less prominent than in Figure 3a, as higher amounts of hydrogen are compressed and the Faradaic efficiency increases (Prokopou et al., 2023). The results suggest that there is a need to improve the membrane characteristics (thickness, conductivity), as well as the used catalysts to achieve energy consumption comparable to the mechanical ones.

It should be noted that the present analysis focuses only on the energetic aspect of the compression alternatives. Factors like the investment and maintenance cost of the two compressors must also be considered for a comprehensive assessment of the different options for specific applications.

a)

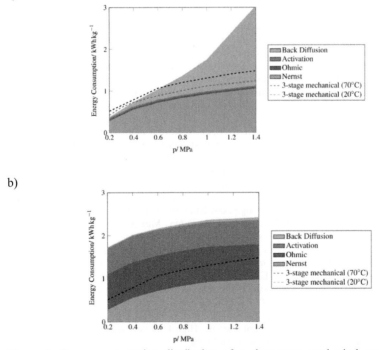

Figure 3: Energy consumption distribution of a three-stage mechanical compressor with intercooling down to 20 °C and 70 °C, and an electrochemical compressor at a current density of a) 100 A m^{-2}, and b) 2000 A m^{-2}, for a pressure range of 0.2-1.4 MPa at an operating temperature of 70 °C.

5. Conclusion

The energetic performance of an electrochemical and a mechanical compressor for hydrogen compression from 0.1 MPa to different pressure levels was studied. The analysis shows that the energy demand of the electrochemical compressor is higher than that of the mechanical compressor, except for very low current densities and low-pressure levels. This suggests that EHC is mostly suitable for low-pressure applications where low hydrogen flow rates are required. Moreover, the results reveal the need to improve the membrane and the catalyst characteristics of the EHC to be competitive with the mechanical compressors at higher pressure levels. Finally, for a more comprehensive evaluation, it is important to consider both the energy and the investment cost when designing a compression system for specific applications, which will follow in future work.

Acknowledgments

The authors gratefully acknowledge the financial support by the German Federal Ministry for Education and Research (BMBF) within the project HyInnoSep of Zukunftcluster Wasserstoff.

References

Modelica Association, 2023, https://modelica.org/, Accessed on 24/11/2023.

Nafion Association, 2023, https://www.nafion.com/en, Accessed on 30/11/2023.

Nguyen M. T., Grigoriev S. A., Kalinnikov A. A., Filippov A. A., Millet P., & Fateev V. N., 2011, Characterization of an electrochemical hydrogen pump using electrochemical impedance spectroscopy, Journal of Applied Electrochemistry, 41(9), 1033–1042.

NIST (National Institute of Standards and Technology Standard Reference Data, 2023, https://webbook.nist.gov/chemistry/fluid/, Accessed on 13/11/2023

Prokopou G. I., Mödden M. L., Mitsos A., Bongartz D., 2023, Optimal Design and Operation of Electrochemical Hydrogen Compression. Submitted.

Rothuizen E., & Rokni M., 2014, Optimization of the overall energy consumption in cascade fueling stations for hydrogen vehicles, International Journal of Hydrogen Energy, 39(1), 582–592.

Sdanghi G., Maranzana G., Celzard A., & Fierro V., 2019, Review of the current technologies and performances of hydrogen compression for stationary and automotive applications. Renewable and Sustainable Energy Reviews, 102, 150–170.

Sdanghi G., Maranzana G., Celzard A., & Fierro V., 2020, Towards non-mechanical hybrid hydrogen compression for decentralized hydrogen facilities, Energies, 13(12).

Stühmeier B. M., Pietsch M. R., Schwämmlein J. N., & Gasteiger H. A., 2021, Pressure and Temperature Dependence of the Hydrogen Oxidation and Evolution Reaction Kinetics on Pt Electrocatalysts via PEMFC-based Hydrogen-Pump Measurements, Journal of The Electrochemical Society, 168(6), 064516.

Tahan M. R., 2022, Recent advances in hydrogen compressors for use in large-scale renewable energy integration, International Journal of Hydrogen Energy, 47(83), 35275–35292.

Toghyani S., Baniasadi E., & Afshari E., 2021, Performance assessment of an electrochemical hydrogen production and storage system for solar hydrogen refueling station. International Journal of Hydrogen Energy, 46(47), 24271–24285.

Zou J., Han N., Yan J., Feng Q., Wang Y., Zhao Z., Fan J., Zeng L., Li H., & Wang H.,2020, Electrochemical Compression Technologies for High-Pressure Hydrogen: Current Status, Challenges and Perspective, Electrochemical Energy Reviews, 3(4), 690–729.

Flavio Manenti, Gintaras V. Reklaitis (Eds.), Proceedings of the 34th European Symposium on Computer Aided Process Engineering / 15th International Symposium on Process Systems Engineering (ESCAPE34/PSE24), June 2-6, 2024, Florence, Italy

A simulation-based approach for energy-flexible scheduling of integrated energy process systems

R. Michael Kalpagé [a*], Wei Yu[a], Martin Atkins[b], Brent Young[a]

[a]Department of Chemical and Materials Engineering, The University of Auckland, 22 Symonds Street, Auckland 1010, New Zealand
[b] Energy Systems Integration Group, School of Engineering, University of Waikato, Hamilton 3216, New Zealand
rkal282@aucklanduni.ac.nz

Abstract

The shift towards green process engineering poses the challenge of adopting sustainable practices, notably in the context of intermittent renewable energy sources, while still meeting operational needs. To meet this challenge, hybrid utility systems are potential solutions that are expected to be more effective together than their individual components, ensuring reliability while advantageously engaging in demand response. This paper proposes a simulation-based scheduling approach, with intent for further development into a digital twin, with application to different asset lifecycle stages. Non-uniform configurations were found to be more appropriate for design and retrofit purposes, with optimal sizing determined. Demand response regimes that aligned with the energy cost ratio demonstrated superior performance. The proposed approach can be further extended to explore more energy flexible components such as energy storage and on-site generation.

Keywords: digital simulation, demand response, energy flexibility, integrated energy systems, renewable energy

1. Background

To address climate change and achieve decarbonization, transitioning the industrial sector toward integration with renewable energy sources is essential, especially for process heat generation. New Zealand's (NZ's) grid is already significantly integrated with renewable energy sources, incentivising electrification as a sustainable approach. However, renewable energy sources suffer from intermittency, thus increasing variability of grid supply. Industrial processes require continuous heat and secure energy supply, especially in sectors like dairy processing. Hybrid utility systems present a promising solution, combining energy sources like electric and biomass boilers in smart plants. Biomass boilers provide stability to the overall energy system and electric boilers allow sites to participate in demand response. Greater energy flexibility can also be achieved through storage integration and production shifting (Pierri *et al.*, 2021).

Given the investment required and potential changes to operational strategy, digital methods such as simulation and digital twins are an appropriate approach to exploring potential solutions. These methods allow for virtual testing of hypothetical scenarios to de-risk changes at low cost. The majority of research in demand response has focused on mathematical programming methods, which have been noted to be challenging for industry adoption (Bank *et al.*, 2019; Howard *et al.*, 2021). Simulation and digital twin approaches provide alternatives focused on operability, thought to be more conducive to practical application.

This paper presents a novel simulation-based approach for energy flexible scheduling of multi-energy process systems, with a focus on biomass-electricity hybrid utility systems. Research on biomass-electric energy systems is also lacking. A model of the system is developed with scenario-based evaluation conducted for applications to design, retrofit and operations. Case studies considered are dairy processing plants in NZ of various magnitudes of energy demand.

2. Approach

2.1. Hybrid utility system

The chosen system consists of an electric boiler (EB) and a biomass boiler (BB), working in tandem to produce steam to meet the site's required demand. A uniform steam demand is considered throughout this work, but non-uniform steam demands can be managed. The key boiler parameters are outlined in Table 1. The boilers are not allowed to turn off, to avoid concerns associated with start-up (e.g., cold starts). It has also been noted that in practice, biomass boilers should not operate below 40% of their maximum duty (Salman *et al.*, 2021), hence the minimum operating limit specified. The scheduler is responsible for determining the set points for the boilers' duties, based on the system's state and various demand response regimes. In this paper, historical data of wholesale electricity prices is provided to the scheduler to aid in decision making, as opposed to inclusion of a forecasting model. The price of biomass is assumed to be a fixed value due to stability.

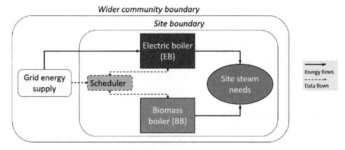

Figure 1 – Hybrid utility system diagram

A multiple steady state approach is taken, meaning that the system variables, such as duty, change instantly at each time step, thus not being a 'true' dynamic model. This was chosen to align with process scheduling, where set points of process variables are determined for the system to be driven towards by process control (Baader *et al.*, 2022). The exclusion of boiler start-up also satisfies this approach. A temporal fidelity of 30-minute time steps was chosen as it is thought to be more practical, ruling out rapid changes in duty, and be more conducive to implementation in industrial practice.

Table 1 – Key boiler parameters for simulation

	Biomass boiler (BB)	Electric boiler (EB)
Thermal efficiency (EECA, 2019)	90%	98%
Allowable duty operating range	40% to 100%	10% to 100%

Two types of system configurations were considered. The first is where the BB and EB are equivalent in size, which shall be referred to as uniform configurations. The second, termed non-uniform configurations, are where the BB is sized so that it can meet the full site demand by itself (accounting for efficiency), and the size of the EB is a free variable. The non-uniform configuration is thought to be more practical for industry, providing a greater level of certainty on energy supply given the volatility of grid supply.

This system is digitally modelled in Python, with the CoolProp package used for thermodynamics. The model is further verified using an Aspen HYSYS simulation of the system.

2.2. Simulation framework

A modular structure was adopted with the simulation model and the algorithm constructed as independent entities. Firstly, the unit operations and material stream conditions were defined using object-oriented programming. The look-ahead window and time period of the simulation were then specified, with values of 30 minutes and the historical data of 2022 being used for the main results of this paper. The steam demand and the system configuration specifications (i.e., unit operations, materials streams) are passed to the simulation as parameters.

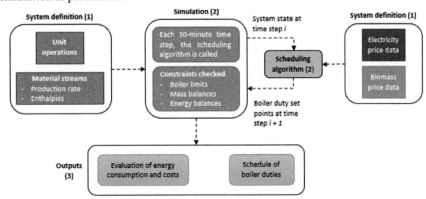

Figure 2 – Modular simulation framework with sequence indicated in brackets

The algorithm was called at every time step, to emulate application in live operation, as opposed to determining a longer-term schedule all at once. The scheduling algorithm takes into consideration the system state at the current time step, and the price data for the time step dictated by the look-ahead window. The future duties of the EB and BB for the next time step were determined by the following demand response regime specified:

$$EB\ duty_{t+1} = EB\ duty_t\ \pm \alpha EB\ duty_{max} \qquad (1)$$

$$EB\ duty_{t+1} = (1 - \beta \frac{Future\ electricity\ price}{Biomass\ price} + \beta)EB\ duty_t \qquad (2)$$

$$EB\ duty_{t+1} = (\frac{Biomass\ price}{Future\ electric\ price})^\gamma EB\ duty_t \qquad (3)$$

Eq. (1) represents a regime where the duty changes by a fixed percentage of the maximum duty of the specified EB, $EB\ duty_{max}$, with an increase in duty corresponding to the electricity price being lower than the biomass price and vice versa. Eq. (2) and (3) represent regimes where the magnitude of the duty change depends on the ratio of the biomass price and electricity price. The regimes of Eq. (1) to (3) are referred to as Fixed, Varying A and Varying B. The parameters α, β and γ denote tuning factors to adjust the sensitivity of the duty changes to future price changes, with different ranges for each regime's parameter ($0.1 \leq \alpha \leq 0.4$, $0.25 \leq \beta \leq 2$, $0.1 \leq \gamma \leq 2$). A price tolerance was also implemented, with a default value of $\pm$ \$1/MWh.

The duties were passed to the simulation, where the constraints were checked before implementing the changes to the system. The evaluation criteria were then calculated, with these being returned at the end of each simulation run. The average run time for a simulation period of one year was of the order of 2 seconds on a desktop PC. Simulations were run individually for each permutation/various combinations of size and configuration of hybrid system. A baseline system of approximately 15 MW of steam demand was chosen based on a real-life dairy plant, with other systems also considered based on industrial cases.

3. Results and discussion

3.1. Application to design and retrofit

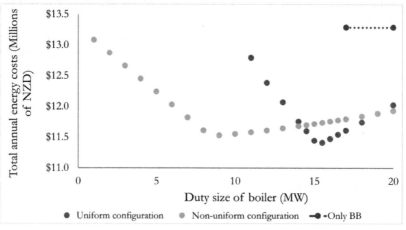

Figure 3 - Energy consumption costs of different system configurations and sizing for a 15 MW steam demand site using a 'Fixed $\alpha = 0.1$' demand response scheme

As shown by Figure 1, both configuration series appear convex over the range considered. The decline towards the minima is due to the increased size of the EB, allowing for greater energy flexibility and more steam produced from the EB. The subsequent increase in costs with increasing boiler size is due to the increasing minimum boiler duties, since the lower limit is a percentage of the maximum duty. The gradient is less steep for non-uniform configurations, since the BB size remains constant and thus only the increase in EB size has an effect.

The costs of a system with only a BB act as a reference, indicating the savings from the hybrid system configurations. The minimal/optimal uniform configuration achieves a greater reduction in energy consumption costs compared to that of the non-uniform configuration (14.13% and 13.27% respectively relative to the BB-only system). However, the optimal uniform configuration for the 7 MW and 40 MW sites performed worse than their non-uniform counterparts (Figure 4).

With sites that are currently retrofitting existing boilers to run on biomass, the non-uniform configuration displays the value in adding on a smaller EB. In a complete greenfield design, the non-uniform configuration should be more practical. This is because the BB can provide a secure base load, while the EB advantageously performs demand response. Implementation of energy storage could also reduce the size of the boilers, aiding with exploitation of low electricity costs.

Two other sites were selected with different demand magnitudes to the base case site: 7 MW and 40 MW. The shape of the curves was found to be roughly the same across different site demands. Energy savings were found to increase with site demand, as shown in Figure 4. The non-uniform configuration was found to perform better at the largest demand considered, with negligible differences in performance at the smallest demand.

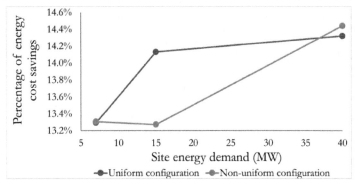

Figure 4 - The energy savings of optimal configurations, compared with an only BB system, across different site demands

3.2. Application to operations

Due to the points above, demand response regimes were examined with respect to non-uniform configurations only. Table 2 shows a selection of schemes considered. Overall, the best performing regime was the 'Varying B' regime, with performance being similar across γ values. Taking the 'Fixed $\alpha = 0.1$' scheme as a benchmark, the optimal configuration for the 'Varying B' regime reduced annual costs by approximately 0.75% ($88,500). The 'Fixed $\alpha = 0.3$' scheme also performed well (reducing costs by 0.71%), with greater divergence from the 'Varying B' schemes with larger EB sizes. The 'Varying A' schemes were found to perform worse than the benchmark scheme. The 'Varying B' regime was found to perform best across all sizes, likely due to the magnitude of demand response adjusting for future price, as opposed to being constant. However, this is dependent on the accuracy of the future price value and price volatility, thus more extensive investigation should be undertaken.

With respect to tuning factors, non-linear relationships were found between their values and performance. The value of γ appeared to have a negligible effect on the performance of the 'Varying B' regime, as opposed to the value of α and the 'Fixed' regime. This is likely due to the influence of the price ratio dwarfing the tuning factor effects and/or the simulation constraints bounding the effects of 'Varying B' more than the 'Fixed' regime. More extreme γ values should be examined to further improve the performance of 'Varying B' schemes.

Table 2 - Comparison of demand response regimes and tuning factor values

Demand response regime	Tuning factor value	Total annual energy costs of optimal non-uniform system configuration
Fixed	$\alpha = 0.1$	$11,526,656
	$\alpha = 0.3$	$11,444.895
Varying A	$\beta = 0.5$	$11,585,552
	$\beta = 1$	$11.541,162
Varying B	$\gamma = 0.5$	$11,450,747
	$\gamma = 1$	$11,438,154

4. Conclusions

Hybrid utility systems show great potential for the transition towards decarbonisation, especially when engaging in demand response. A simulation-based approach is proposed to evaluate applications of these systems for design, retrofit and operations. Non-uniform system configurations were found to be more appropriate for application. Demand response schemes with magnitudes proportional to the energy cost ratio were found to perform best. The proposed approach is thought to be conducive for industry adoption, with further development into a digital twin.

Work is currently underway to examine the integration of energy storage (both electrical and thermal) and on-site renewable generation. which would increase the energy flexibility of the overall system. Techno-economic assessment, as well as environmental assessment and operability considerations should be incorporated into the methodology for a more holistic evaluation.

Acknowledgment

This research has been supported by the programme "Ahuora: Delivering sustainable industry through smart process heat decarbonisation", an Advanced Energy Technology Platform, funded by the New Zealand Ministry of Business, Innovation and Employment.

References

Baader, F. J., Bardow, A., & Dahmen, M. (2022). *Simultaneous mixed-integer dynamic scheduling of processes and their energy systems.* https://doi.org/10.1002/aic.17741

Bank, L., Rösch, M., Unterberger, E., Roth, S., Rohrer, A., Köberlein, J., Braunreuther, S., & Schilp, J. (2019). *Comparison of simulation-based and optimization-based energy flexible production planning.* https://doi.org/10.1016/j.procir.2019.03.051

EECA. (2019). *Electrode and Electric Resistance Steam Generators and Hot Water Heaters for low carbon process heating.*

Howard, D. A., Ma, Z., & Jorgensen, B. N. (2021). *Evaluation of Industrial Energy Flexibility Potential: A Scoping Review.* https://doi.org/10.1109/ICIT46573.2021.9453652

Pierri, E., Hellkamp, D., Thiede, S., & Herrmann, C. (2021). *Enhancing Energy Flexibility through the Integration of Variable Renewable Energy in the Process Industry.* https://doi.org/10.1016/j.procir.2020.12.001

Salman, C. A., Li, H., Li, P., & Yan, J. (2021). *Improve the flexibility provided by combined heat and power plants (CHPs) – a review of potential technologies.* https://doi.org/10.1016/j.prime.2021.100023

Flavio Manenti, Gintaras V. Reklaitis (Eds.), Proceedings of the 34th European Symposium on Computer Aided Process Engineering / 15th International Symposium on Process Systems Engineering (ESCAPE34/PSE24), June 2-6, 2024, Florence, Italy

Towards Environmentally Sustainable Production of Diphenyl Carbonate: Comparative Analysis of Alternative Pathways

Tsai-Wei Wu,[a*] Alexander Guzman-Urbina,[a,b] Hajime Ohno,[a] Yasuhiro Fukushima,[a,c] Hsin-Hao Liang,[d] Shiang-Tai Lin[d]

[a]*Department of Frontier Science for Advanced Environment, Graduate School of Environmental Studies, Tohoku University, 6-6-07 Aramaki-Aza Aoba, Sendai, Japan*
[b]*Department of Materials, Chemistry, and Life Sciences, Graduate School of Engineering, Osaka Metropolitan University, 3-3-138 Sugimoto Sumiyoshi-ku, Osaka, Japan*
[c]*Department of Chemical Engineering, Graduate School of Engineering, Tohoku University, 6-6-07 Aramaki-Aza Aoba, Sendai, Japan*
[d]*Department of Chemical Engineering, National Taiwan University, Taipei 10617, Taiwan*
tsai-wei.wu.b5@tohoku.ac.jp

Abstract

Diphenyl carbonate (DPC) plays a key role as a feedstock in the synthesis of polycarbonate (PC), a widely used plastic material. However, conventional DPC production routes are burdened by environmental concerns stemming from the use of toxic reagents, such as phosgene. Considering the urge to foster sustainability, this study undertakes a comprehensive evaluation of cradle-to-gate greenhouse gas (GHG) emissions associated with diverse industrial pathways for DPC synthesis, including:

1. Direct phosgenation of phenol (PhOH) as the base case.

2. Transesterification of CO_2-based dimethyl carbonate (DMC) to yield DPC.

3. Transesterification of CO_2-based diethyl carbonate (DEC) to yield DPC.

4. Transesterification of CO_2-based dipropyl carbonate (DPrC) to yield DPC.

While the emission inventory data of the first two pathways were extracted from comprehensive commercial reports, the latter two were simulated in Aspen Plus according to patented approaches due to limited process data availability. The simulations serve as a foundation for comparative analysis among these routes. Notably, the alternative pathways leverage CO_2-derived carbonates as feedstock, offering greener alternatives to the conventional approach. Through cradle-to-gate GHG emissions assessment, this research aids in identifying the potentially most environmentally benign alternative route for DPC production. An analysis of alternative feedstocks contributes to the assessment of current developments and potential pathways towards emission-free DPC production. The central aim of this study is to leverage industry insights to propose optimal pathways for future development, guiding towards a carbon-neutral paradigm in PC manufacturing.

Keywords: Diphenyl carbonate production, Cradle-to-gate emissions, CO_2 conversion, Sustainable manufacturing

1. Introduction

Diphenyl carbonate (DPC) is a key precursor for the production of polycarbonate (PC), a widely used plastic. However, current manufacturing uses the highly toxic phosgene (Bell, 2017), which can be fatal even in small doses (Diller, 1985). Alternative feedstocks are crucial for more sustainable DPC production. Routes like phosgenation, oxidative carbonylation, and transesterification of phenol with dialkyl carbonates (DRCs) have been reported (Cao et al., 2005). Transesterification is promising since DRCs can be converted from CO_2, potentially reducing greenhouse gases. Among DRCs, dimethyl carbonate (DMC) is widely studied, while diethyl carbonate (DEC) and dipropyl carbonate (DPrC) are promising candidates which can be produced from CO_2 (Lee et al., 2021). Japanese government aims to cut emissions 46% by 2030, so understanding of the CO_2 emission in chemical industry is necessary. This study employs a Cradle-to-gate life cycle CO_2 assessment, which covers feedstock and process emissions (Kleinekorte et al., 2020). In this way, this study compares three CO_2-to-DRC-to-DPC processes against conventional toxic phosgene route, analysing if they meet emission reduction targets. The scope in Figure 1 shows the DPC production routes compared in this study.

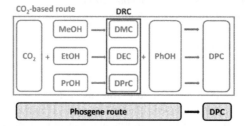

Figure 1 Cradle-to-gate research scope of DPC production

2. Method

2.1. Process Information

Process information of the conventional phosgene process was extracted from PEP commercial report (Bell, 2007) to calculate CO_2 emission amount and represent current manufacturing process.

The DMC-to-DPC process has two main licensors, Asahi Kasei and Versalis/Lummus. Detailed information of both processes can be extracted from PEP commercial report (Bell & Pavlechko, 2020) and used in comparison with other processes. The two main reactions included are as Eq. (1) and Eq. (2), representing (1) the transesterification of DMC and phenol to produce methyl phenyl carbonate (MPC) and methanol (MeOH), and (2) the disproportionation of MPC to DPC and DMC. Both licensors use reactive distillation to deal with the involved reactions.

$$DMC + PhOH \leftrightarrow MPC + MeOH \qquad (1)$$

$$2MPC \leftrightarrow DPC + DMC \qquad (2)$$

The DEC-to-DPC process lacks specifics but a patent (Yong Ryu, 2012) provides a basis to model it in Aspen Plus for accurate CO_2 emission estimates. Like DMC process, main reactions are transesterification to ethyl phenyl carbonate (EPC) and EPC disproportionation in reactive distillation, shown in Eq. (3) and (4). A byproduct phenetole (EPE) also forms, shown in Eq. (5). Using patent data, a temperature conversion correlation was developed for Eq. (3), shown in Eq. (6). No data existed for other reactions, so average conversions were assumed according to the reported experimental data: 28.7% for Eq. (4) and 3% for Eq. (5).

$$DEC + PhOH \leftrightarrow EPC + EtOH \tag{3}$$

$$2EPC \leftrightarrow DPC + DEC \tag{4}$$

$$DEC + PhOH \leftrightarrow EPE + EtOH + CO_2 \tag{5}$$

$$Conv. = -88966.8 + 3274664.8/T + 14564\ln(T) - 16.2T \tag{6}$$

Flowsheet and the result of DEC-to-DPC process in the simulation can be seen in Figure 2, which includes 3 reactive distillation columns and 3 conventional distillation columns. The configuration was set corresponding to the process flowsheet in the patent (Yong Ryu, 2012), with Eq. (3) and Eq. (5) occurring in C1 and C2, Eq. (4) occurring in C5. C3 serves as the light components' separator, while C4 serves as EPE purge column. C6 is the product separation column where DPC comes out from the bottom and EPC can be recovered from the top.

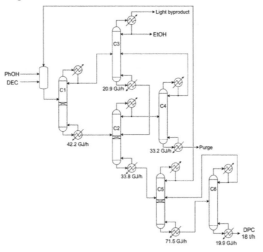

Figure 2 DEC-to-DPC Process Flowsheet

For DPrC-to-DPC process, the two main reactions are Eq. (7) and Eq. (8), representing the generation of the intermediate propyl phenyl carbonate (PrPC) and its disproportionation. No literature reported process can be found for DPrC-to-DPC process, but there's reported equilibrium constant for the transesterification reaction of diisopropyl carbonate and phenol (Van Der Heide et al., 2010). The value was thus taken as the approximate value of K_{eq} for Eq. (7) reaction in the Aspen Plus simulation. Given that there is no information available for Eq. (8) reaction, it was assumed to have a conversion the same (28.7 %) as the disproportionation reaction of DEC to DPC route tentatively.

$$DPrC + PhOH \leftrightarrow PrPC + PrOH \tag{7}$$

$$2PrPC \leftrightarrow DPC + DPrC \tag{8}$$

PrPC, the intermediate of DPrC-to-DPC process, plays a key role in the reaction, and it is necessary to review the thermodynamic parameters before further developing the process model. However, as an uncommon component, neither built-in PrPC-related thermodynamic parameters, nor thermodynamic experimental data can be found in the Aspen Plus databank and literature. For pure component parameters, group-contribution method was used for estimation; for binary interaction parameters, the conventional UNIFAC group-contribution method does not support estimation of PrPC-related parameters due to its special chemical structure. To fill this gap, an alternative estimation method using COSMO-SAC model was chosen. This estimation method has the advantage of being more flexible in dealing with a wider variety of chemical functionality (Lin & Sandler, 2002). After using COSMO-SAC model to provide a priori estimate of the thermodynamic properties for previously unmeasured components and phase equilibria for new mixtures, missing binary parameters were derived by using the estimated data.

The process configuration of DPrC to DPC was developed according to the process description in a patent regarding producing diaryl carbonate (Harada et al., 2021). Flowsheet and the result of DPrC-to-DPC process in the simulation can be seen in Figure 3, which includes 3 reactive distillation columns and 3 normal distillation columns. Eq. (7) occurs in C1, while Eq. (8) occurs in C2 and C3. A purge stream is designed here at the top of C2 distillate stream to prevent the accumulation of potential impurities. C4 serves as the product separator, whereas C5 serves as the recovery column of PrPC, with the bottom stream recycling back to C3 for disproportionation reaction. C6 is an assumptive catalyst recovery column, which simulates the separation of DPC and the homogeneous catalyst.

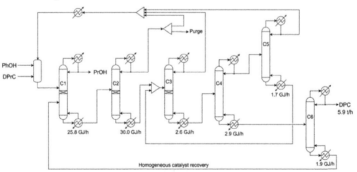

Figure 3 DPrC-to-DPC Process Flowsheet

2.2. Calculation Basis for CO₂ Emission

A cradle-to-gate scope was adopted for the life cycle analysis of CO_2 emission. For phosgene route, it should include the CO_2 emissions from raw materials production (Liao et al., 2020) (Ecoinvent v3.6 Database) and the phosgenation process (Bell, 2007). Analysis for CO_2-to-DRC-to-DPC processes, on the other hand, should include the CO_2 emissions from raw materials production (Ecoinvent v3.6 Database), CO_2 capture process (Guandalini et al., 2019), CO_2-to-DRC process (Lee et al., 2021), dehydrating agent (used in CO_2-to-DRC process) regeneration process (Harada et al., 2023), and DRC-to-DPC processes (detailed process information as discussed in Section 2.1).

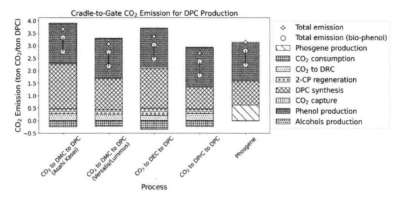

Figure 4 Cradle-to-gate CO_2 emissions for different processes

3. Results and Discussion

Cradle-to-gate CO_2 emissions of different processes can be seen in Figure 4. The hollow star points present total emission amount for each process, and apparently the process with the lowest emission is CO_2 to DPrC to DPC. While CO_2 consumption in the CO_2-to-DRC process only helped little in CO_2 emission reduction, emissions from phenol production, assumed to be conventional Hock process, account for a significant amount of percentage in every processes. Since phenol is the main carbon source in DPC production, alternative greener phenol production process is necessary to reduce the CO_2 emissions in DPC manufacturing. Therefore, CO_2 emission amount from biomass-based phenol production was alternatively used (Liao et al., 2020) and the corresponding values of CO_2 emissions are presented in the figure by the hollow circle points. The values have a range since the non-renewable hydrogen used in the bio-phenol production process has a CO_2 emission amount range of $1.354 - 0.736$ kg CO_2/kg H_2, as reported in Liao et al. (2020). CO_2 emission amount due to alcohols production can be barely seen because alcohols are almost recycled to be used in the CO_2-to-DRC processes and thus leading to negligible results. It is worth noting that if we expand the research scope to PC production, as shown in Figure 5, in which can be seen that the byproduct of PC production is phenol, and it can be mostly recycled to the DPC production process as well. Under this circumstance, the burden of CO_2 emission reduction would lie in the DPC synthesis processes which require mostly steam as energy source.

Comparing the current, phosgene-based manufacturing process to the most optimistic scenario which uses bio-phenol in the CO_2-to-DPrC-to-DPC process, around 42 % of CO_2 emission can be saved, showing potential to meet the Japan's emission reduction target (46%) by 2030.

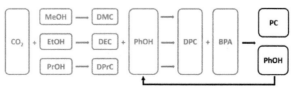

Figure 5 Cradle-to-gate research scope of PC production

4. Conclusion

This research investigates cleaner and more diverse methods for diphenyl carbonate (DPC) production, seeking alternatives to the toxic phosgene-based process while assessing their feasibility and environmental impact, including newer and less-known options. The evaluation of cradle-to-gate CO_2 emission in this study highlighted both eco-friendly feedstock utilization and the importance of selecting route in guiding early-stage technology development in the chemical industry. CO_2 emission because of DPC production can be reduced to at most 42 % if the CO_2-to-DPrC-to-DPC route is chosen and bio-phenol is used as one of the feedstocks. Research scope will have huge influence on the assessment results, and it is recommended that the scope covers as wide as to the end-product. Also, it is essential to keep developing more efficient DPC synthesis processes and greener source for steam usage in the processes to deal with the real cause of CO_2 emission in DPC production.

References

Bell, S., 2007, PEP Report 50E POLYCARBONATE, SRI Consulting.

Bell, S., 2017, Diphenyl Carbonate by Asahi Kasei Process, Process Economics Program Review, IHS Chemical.

Bell, S., & P. D. Pavlechko, 2020, PEP Report 50F Polycarbonate Update, IHS Markit.

Cao, M., Y. Meng, & Y. Lu, 2005, Synthesis of diphenyl carbonate from dimethyl carbonate and phenol using O2-promoted PbO/MgO catalysts, Catalysis Communications, *6*(12), 802–807.

Diller, W. F., 1985, Early Diagnosis of Phosgene Overexposure, Toxicology and Industrial Health, *1*(2), 73–80.

ecoinvent v3.6 database (cutoff): direct impact contributions GWP 100a.

Guandalini, G., M. C. Romano, M. Ho, D. Wiley, E. S. Rubin, & J. C. Abanades, 2019, A sequential approach for the economic evaluation of new CO2 capture technologies for power plants, International Journal of Greenhouse Gas Control, *84*, 219–231.

Harada, H., T. Isobe, H. Liu, Y. Shinkai, & R. Umezu, 2023, *Method for regenerating catalyst and method for producing carbonate ester* (Patent US 11,596,936 B2).

Harada, H., J. Taguchi, & Y. Isahaya, 2021, *DIARYL CARBONATE AND METHOD FOR PRODUCING THE SAME, AND METHOD FOR PRODUCING AN AROMATIC POLYCARBONATE RESIN* (Patent US 11,142,506 B2).

Kleinekorte, J., L. Fleitmann, M. Bachmann, A. Kätelhön, A. Barbosa-Póvoa, N. Von Der Assen, & A. Bardow, 2020, Life Cycle Assessment for the Design of Chemical Processes, Products, and Supply Chains, Annu. Rev. Chem. Biomol. Eng. 2020, *11*, 2020.

Lee, C. T., C. C. Tsai, P. J. Wu, B. Y. Yu, & S. T. Lin, 2021, Screening of CO2 utilization routes from process simulation: Design, optimization, environmental and techno-economic analysis, Journal of CO2 Utilization, *53*, 101722.

Liao, Y., S. F. Koelewijn, G. van den Bossche, J. van Aelst, S. van den Bosch, T. Renders, K. Navare, T. Nicolaï, K. van Aelst, M. Maesen, H. Matsushima, J. M. Thevelein, K. van Acker, B. Lagrain, D. Verboekend, & B. F. Sels, 2020, A sustainable wood biorefinery for low-carbon footprint chemicals production, Science, *367*(6484), 1385–1390.

Lin, S. T., & S. I. Sandler, 2002, A Priori Phase Equilibrium Prediction from a Segment Contribution Solvation Model, Industrial & Engineering Chemistry Research, *41*(5), 899-913.

Van Der Heide, E., T. M. Nisbet, C. G. Vaporciyan, & C. L. M. Vrouwenvelder, 2010, *PROCESS FOR THE PREPARATION OF DIARYL CARBONATE* (Patent US 7,732,629 B2).

Yong Ryu, J., 2012, *PROCESS FOR PRODUCING DIPHENYL CARBONATE* (Patent US 2012/0190878 A1).

Flavio Manenti, Gintaras V. Reklaitis (Eds.), Proceedings of the 34th European Symposium on Computer Aided Process Engineering / 15th International Symposium on Process Systems Engineering (ESCAPE34/PSE24), June 2-6, 2024, Florence, Italy

A Simulation-based Integration of Carbon Capture and Utilization in a Urea Production Process

Christopher Varela,[a,*] Fernando Zea,[a] Oris Correa,[b] Kyle V. Camarda[b]

[a]*Escuela Superior Politécnica del Litoral, ESPOL, Facultad de Ciencias Naturales y Matemáticas, Centro de Energías Renovables y Alternativas, Campus Gustavo Galindo km. 30 Via Perimetral, Guayaquil, P.O. Box 09-01-5863, Ecuador*
[b]*Department of Chemical and Petroleum Engineering, University of Kansas, 1530 West 15th Street, Lawrence, KS 66045, USA*
covarela@espol.edu.ec

Abstract

In this work, we address a novel method to produce urea from CO_2 and ammonia. This proposal allows for a high level of integration of energy and materials, reducing the costs of carbon capture and utilization. In this process, ammonia is produced via green hydrogen, nitrogen is removed from the air, and CO_2 is captured from flue gases using aqueous ammonia. Thus, ammonia is used both as a reactant and sorbent. We evaluate through simulation the direct use of the rich solvent in the urea synthesis loop, compared with conventional urea production which uses pure CO_2 and ammonia. A techno-economic analysis demonstrates that the capital and operational expenditures decrease with our proposed process by 49.2 % and 38.8 %, respectively. This substantial decrease occurs as there is no need for solvent regeneration and compression of CO_2, allowing the removal of the stripping column and multistage compression. Instead, a significant amount of water that enters the urea synthesis loop is removed via vacuum evaporation before the urea granulation. While the conventional process demands 134 GJ/h at the stripper, the evaporation units only require 75 GJ/h. The fact that renewable energy sources and renewable-based chemicals can be used for all units within the process means that the novel system provides a urea production solution that is cheaper and has a smaller environmental footprint.

Keywords: Carbon capture and utilization, green urea production, green ammonia, process integration, techno-economic assessment.

1. Introduction

Carbon capture and utilization (CCU) is a key technology within the energy transition framework. IEA (2020) stated that CCU will contribute to reducing around 4% of global emissions by 2030, mainly through newly introduced capture plants in the power and industry sectors. While there are commercial sorbents to capture CO_2 from flue gases, namely MEA and MDEA, there is currently an increased focus on aqueous ammonia solutions as a renewable replacement for fossil amines. Bak et al. (2015) conducted an experimental study on carbon capture with an ammonia sorbent at low temperature, while Zea et al. (2023) introduced different process configurations to enhance the operational performance of a simulated capture facility, including rich-solvent flashing, lean-vapor compression, and a novel crystallization unit. In addition to its role as a sorbent, ammonia plays a crucial part in producing nitrogen-based fertilizers. Urea, a highly utilized fertilizer globally, forms when CO_2 and ammonia combine, via the intermediate ammonium carbamate. This highlights a potential for integrating the carbon capture and utilization processes, offering a promising alternative to decrease overall costs.

Alfian et al. (2019) investigated various technologies to reduce the cost of producing green urea, utilizing syngas derived from biomass gasification as a raw material. In a related study, Antonetti et al. (2016) examined the utilization of municipal solid waste as an input for the urea production process. In this contribution, we present an innovative approach that utilizes the rich solvent of carbon capture (post-combustion absorption) as feed for a urea reactor. This novel method eliminates the requirement for the energy-intensive stripper column, leading to a substantial reduction in capture costs. In addition, this approach yields a valuable product, urea, from the combination of green ammonia and CO_2 sequestrated from flue gases. This results in a process with negative emissions, showing a high potential to greatly improve the fertilizers industry while capturing the emissions within a hard-to-abate sector of the chemical industry.

2. Methodology

The integration of carbon capture and urea production is assessed using the process simulators ASPEN PLUS ® and PRO/II ®. The key component is green ammonia, as it is utilized as a sorbent in post-combustion carbon capture and as a feed to a urea reactor. Ammonia is obtained via a traditional Haber-Bosch process, with the hydrogen created efficiently and at high purity from an electrolysis unit and the nitrogen recovered from air via pressure-swing absorption. Thus, the simulation includes several processes, namely alkaline water electrolysis, air separation, ammonia synthesis, post-combustion carbon capture, urea synthesis, and urea granulation. The process flowsheets and supplementary material can be found on the project website: https://co2tourea.github.io/index.html.

The evaluation is based on a comparison of capital expenditure (CAPEX) and operating expenditure (OPEX) for the base case process, denoted as *conventional* process, and for our proposed process, denoted as *integrated* process, for a fixed production capacity of 300 kilotons of urea per year. The differences between these processes are depicted in Figure 1. On the one hand, the process on the left side of Figure 1 presents a conventional urea synthesis, which uses CO_2 from flue gases captured with aqueous ammonia. This is the base case for carbon capture and utilization, where CO_2 is absorbed from flue gases, stripped out of the solvent, and compressed at high purity to feed the urea reactor. On the other hand, the process on the right side of Figure 1 presents our proposal for integration, where the rich solvent stream is directed to the urea reactor, bypassing the energy-intensive stripping section. There is a higher content of water in the urea reactor compared to the conventional process, requiring additional evaporators to be installed before the granulation section. This major modification requires adapting the operating conditions of the absorption column and urea synthesis loop. However, we expect a significant reduction in operating costs as the stripping column and the multistage compression are no longer required.

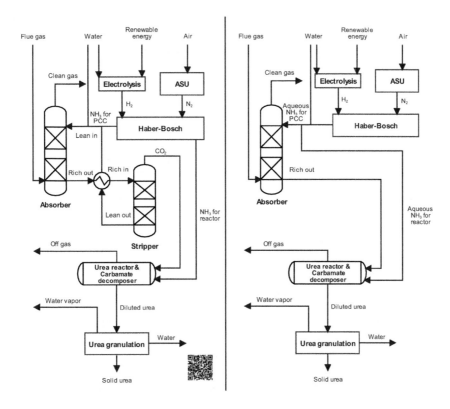

Figure 1: Base case for CCU in urea synthesis (left) and integrated process (right). The QR code directs to the project website, where detailed process flow diagrams and supplementary information can be found.

3. Results

The conventional and integrated processes enable the production of 300 kilotons per year of granular urea, by utilizing CO_2 captured from flue gases and green ammonia as main raw materials. To comprehensively assess the performance of both processes, we propose the key performance indicators (KPIs) with corresponding values provided in Table 1.

The reboiler at the stripper demands 134.1 GJ/h of heat for the conventional process, whereas the integrated process eliminates this requirement but instead demands 74.98 GJ/h of heat to concentrate the urea solution. This strategic shift in the energy demand for solvent regeneration from the capture section to the solution concentration units at the urea synthesis results in a substantial reduction in overall heat requirements. CO_2 separation from water and ammonia at the stripper takes place at around 135 °C, while water separation from urea (comprising combined CO_2 and ammonia) at the evaporators occurs at less than 100 °C using a vacuum system. Despite challenges due to the thermodynamics that govern the chemical systems of water-ammonia-CO_2 and urea-water, we find that the selection of a thermal separation that removes water from a non-reacting system yields a more effective outcome than the conventional CO_2 stripping. Thus, for this case of carbon capture and utilization in the urea synthesis, evaporating water from the urea solution is more efficient compared to stripping the CO_2 out of the ammonia sorbent.

Table 1: Comparison between the conventional and integrated CCU for urea synthesis.

KPI	Conventional process	Integrated process
Carbon capture rate in the absorber (%)	81.1	78.5
Regeneration energy (MJ/kg$_{CO2}$)	3.64	-
Reboiler duty (GJ/h)	134	-
Evaporation energy (MJ/kg$_{H2O}$)	-	2.41
Evaporators total duty (GJ/h)	-	75.0
CAPEX* (MUSD)	63.75	32.34
OPEX* (MUSD/year)	35.97	22.39

*These calculations consider the post-combustion carbon capture, CO2 compression, urea synthesis, and urea granulation solely.

The processes present significant differences in both CAPEX and OPEX. The cost shares of the individual processes are depicted in Figures 3 and 4. While extensive discussions have centered around the stripper in the conventional process, it is crucial also to highlight the compression of CO_2 from nearly atmospheric pressure to a supercritical state at 40 bar in that process. This requires the addition of several compressors and interstage coolers. Also, a large volume of gases (mainly NH_3) must be liquified at around -25 °C to be recycled back to the reactor after the decomposition of carbamate. Therefore, conditioning the streams for the urea reactor requires a large CAPEX and OPEX. In contrast, the process integration we propose keeps the CO_2 in the liquid phase, combined with ammonia, after the absorption stage. This approach allows the process to feed the urea reactor at the required pressure with a reduced cost, as it requires pumps instead of compressors. This proposal yields a potential decrease in CAPEX by 49.2 % and OPEX by 38.8 %.

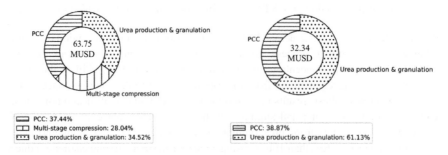

Figure 2: CAPEX of the conventional process (left) and integrated process (right).

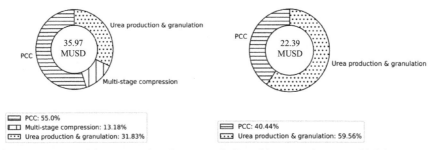

Figure 3: OPEX of the conventional process (left) and integrated process (right).

The stripping column accounted for approximately 35% of the CAPEX in the post-combustion capture (PCC) system. The primary CAPEX reduction, amounting to 14.4 million USD, was achieved by eliminating the multistage compression. Notably, the most significant impact on OPEX was observed in the PCC process, where process integration led to a 50% reduction due to the elimination of regeneration energy requirements. Moreover, the conditioning of CO_2 and ammonia, constituting 24% of the OPEX in the conventional process, was shifted to the evaporation section in the proposed process integration. This adjustment resulted in an almost 50% increase in the OPEX of urea synthesis. However, it still represented a notable reduction compared to the conventional case.

4. Conclusions and outlook

This study introduces an integrated process for carbon capture and utilization in urea synthesis to lower the OPEX and CAPEX. Our focus is on eliminating the stripping column, which demands a significant energy input for solvent regeneration in the traditional process. Instead, the novel process benefits from the composition of the rich solvent (CO_2-ammonia-water) to directly supply the urea reactor. This approach also allows for the avoidance of the compression of CO_2 to supercritical conditions. The strategic shift allows for the elimination of costly components in the process, such as the stripping section, multistage compressors, and ammonia liquefaction equipment. However, it is to be noted that this approach yields urea with a lower concentration when it leaves the reactor due to the high content of water. This leads to additional energy demand in the implemented evaporation stage before granulation. The outcome of this study is that there is a potential decrease in CAPEX by 49.2 % and OPEX by 38.8 %.

In future work, we intend to develop advanced models for the urea reactor that consider the modified feed composition involving dissolved CO_2 in aqueous ammonia solutions. This will allow us to understand the behavior of the chemical system and optimize the operating conditions, aiming to increase the conversion. Furthermore, it is required to validate our proposal through experiments, given that the current study relies on simulations.

Acknowledgments

The authors would like to thank James Sturgill for assistance with the economic calculations, and the Department of Chemical and Petroleum Engineering at the University of Kansas and the Faculty of Natural Sciences and Mathematics at Escuela Superior Politécnica del Litoral for access to computing resources.

References

IEA, 2020, Energy Technology Perspectives 2020 - Special Report on Carbon Capture Utilisation and Storage, OECD.

C. u. Bak, M. Asif, W. S. Kim, 2015, Experimental study on CO2 capture by chilled ammonia process, Chemical Engineering Journal, vol. 265, pp. 1–8

F. Zea, D. Tinoco, C. Varela, 2023, A techno-economic evaluation of post-combustion carbon capture using renewable ammonia with different process configurations, Case Studies in Chemical and Environmental Engineering, vol. 8, p. 100502

M. Alfian, W. W. Purwanto, 2019, Multiobjective optimization of green urea production, Energy Science and Engineering, 7(2), 292-304

E. Antonetti, G. Iaquaniello, A. Salladini, L. Spadaccini, S. Perathoner, G. & Centi, 2017, Waster-to-Chemicals for a Circular Economy: The Case of Urea Production (Waste-to-Urea), ChemSusChem, 10(5), 912-920

Flavio Manenti, Gintaras V. Reklaitis (Eds.), Proceedings of the 34th European Symposium on Computer Aided Process Engineering / 15th International Symposium on Process Systems Engineering (ESCAPE34/PSE24), June 2-6, 2024, Florence, Italy

Innovative Structure of a Liquefied Natural Gas (LNG) Process by Mixed Fluid Cascade Using Solar Renewable Energy, Photovoltaic Panels (PV), and Absorption Refrigeration System

Masoud Taghavi[a,b], Ha-Jun Yoon[a], Jung-Ung Choi[a], Chul-Jin Lee[a,b,*]

[a] *School of Chemical Engineering and Materials Science, Chung-Ang University, 84 Heukseok-ro, Dongjak-gu, Seoul 06974, Republic of Korea*
[b] *Department of Intelligent Energy and Industry, Chung-Ang University, 84 Heukseok-ro, Dongjak-gu, Seoul 06974, Republic of Korea*
Corresponding author: cjlee@cau.ac.kr

Abstract

Among the principal industrial approaches for conveying natural gas, aside from pipeline transportation, is the liquefaction of natural gas (LNG). In recent years, a significant portion of natural gas imports has been done through the transportation of LNG. The economic viability of an LNG venture is substantially influenced by the pivotal role of the liquefaction procedure in determining its financial returns. Conversely, a paramount concern within LNG plants revolves around enhancing the energy efficiency of the liquefaction procedures. In this research, an Innovative structure of a liquefied natural gas process by mixed fluid cascade using solar renewable energy, photovoltaic panels (PV), and absorption refrigeration system is presented and evaluated. This structure relies on substituting the vapor compression refrigeration cycle with the absorption refrigeration system. The required power of the cycle is 19.37 MW and is provided by renewable solar energy and PV, and the absorption refrigeration system derives its necessary heat load from the existing surplus heat within the facility. Aspen HYSYS V12.1 software, a conventional chemical process simulator, performs process simulation. Also, the design and simulation of PV were performed using the PVsyst 7.3.1 software, with the weather conditions in Rafsanjan City, Kerman Province, in Iran. To supply the part of cycle power, out of 3 modules of AXITEC AC-550MBT and 157 inverters Canadian Solar CS-125KTL have been used. The highest and lowest of performance ratio (PR) were 89.6 % in January and 78.9 % in July, respectively. Also, the highest and lowest of available energy were 3,726.8 in September and 3,304.6 MWh in February, respectively. Additionally, the maximum and minimum losses due to mismatch were recorded in September and February in the amount of 83.79 and 72.77 MWh, respectively. The ammonia-water cycle has a coefficient of performance (COP) at a value of 0.48. As well as the presented innovative structure displays a specific energy consumption (SEC) of 0.172 kWh/kgLNG, illustrating a 30 % decrease in energy usage. Also, the presented novel system offers the potential to achieve a reduction of up to 31 % in the necessary heat transfer area.

Keywords: Process integration, liquefied natural gas, solar energy, photovoltaic panels (PV), absorption refrigeration system.

1. Introduction

The exponential surge in energy and environmental challenges over recent decades can be attributed to the swift expansion of commercial domains and the global economy (Ebrahimi et al., 2021). Environmentalists have expressed profound concern for decades regarding the substantial threats posed to global ecosystem sustainability by climate change and ozone layer degradation (Ghorbani et al., 2021 and Taghavi and Lee, 2024). LNG transportation, comprising 32 % of natural gas imports in 2012, stands as a pivotal industrial approach for natural gas conveyance, distinct from the predominant pipeline mode (Mehrpooya et al., 2016). The economic viability of an LNG project hinges significantly on the efficacy of the liquefaction process. Enhancing energy efficiency is paramount within LNG plants, given the substantial energy consumption inherent in liquefying and sub-cooling natural gas to temperatures below -160 °C. The predominant contributor to this energy demand lies in the compression refrigeration cycles (CRCs). The utilization of the Mixed Fluid Cascade (MFC) process is prevalent in high-capacity LNG plants. The Linde and Statoil MFC methodology incorporates three refrigeration cycles employing a blend of methane, ethane, propane, or nitrogen as refrigerants. These cycles facilitate pre-cooling (around -25 °C), liquefaction (approximately -86 °C), and sub-cooling (about -160 °C) stages in the natural gas processing (Ghorbani et al., 2018). In this paper, a novel structure of a LNG process is presented, employing a mixed fluid cascade using solar renewable energy, PV, and an absorption refrigeration system. The process is simulated using Aspen HYSYS V12.1 software and Peng Robinson thermodynamic equation of states, while photovoltaic panels are simulated using PVsyst 7.3.1 software.

2. Process description

Ammonia-water emerges as an efficient working fluid, reaching -60 °C in the Absorption Refrigeration Cycle (ARC). In the ARC, a pump elevates solution pressure, aiding the refrigerant's separation (Chen et al., 2021). Essential cooling in the condenser utilizes ambient air or cooling water (Hunt et al., 2023). Waste heat from turbines and boilers, including gas discharge, drives the energy-intensive separation process. This waste heat is used to generate low-pressure steam (T=180 °C and P=4.5 bar), fueling the separation of ammonia from water in the generator. Effectively utilizing waste heat in an ARC proves practical and feasible for low to medium temperature heat sources (Táboas et al., 2014). Table 1 presents the molar composition data for the input streams used in simulating the developed structure. Also, the process flow diagram (PFD) of the mixed fluid cascade cycle illustrated in Fig. 1.

Table 1. Molar composition for the integrated structure.

Str.	N_2	CH_4	C_2H_6	C_3H_8	n-Butane	i-Butane	i-Pentane	H_2O	NH_3
A1	0.040	0.875	0.055	0.021	0.005	0.003	0.001	0	0
A6	0.370	0.629	0	0	0	0	0	0	0
A7	0.015	0.893	0.059	0.022	0.005	0.003	0.001	0	0
A9	0	0	0	0	0	0	0	0.750	0.250
A11	0	0	0	0	0	0	0	0.933	0.066
A14	0	0	0	0	0	0	0	0.001	0.999
A16	0	0	0	0	0	0	0	0.233	0.766
A17	0	0	0	0	0	0	0	0.001	0.999
A22	0	0	0	0	0	0	0	0.739	0.260
A24	0	0.126	0.329	0.277	0.266	0	0	0	0

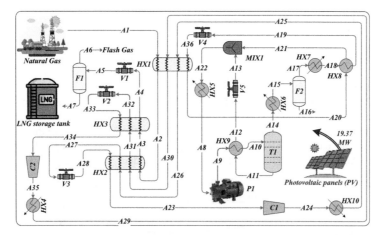

Fig. 1. The process flow diagram (PFD) of the mixed fluid cascade cycle. Modified from reference (Mehrpooya et al., 2016).

The thermodynamic details of compressors (C) and pump (P) utilized in the mixed fluid cascade cycle is detailed in Table 2.

Table 2. Operational specifications the thermodynamic details of compressors (C) and pump (P) in the mixed fluid cascade cycle.

Equipment	Adiabatic Efficiency (%)	Power (kW)	ΔP (kPa)	Pressure Ratio (−)
C1	80.00	7,149.75	3,037	9.603
C2	80.00	11,977.6	2,481	9.015
P1	90.00	243.3	1,180	10.83

3. Simulation and design of photovoltaic panels (PV)

Amidst rising global energy needs, solar power, especially photovoltaic cells, emerges as a crucial player in harnessing renewable energy through the photovoltaic effect (Soonmin & Taghavi, 2022). The International Energy Agency (IEA) prescribes key performance parameters, crucial for on-grid PV system assessment (Ebrahimi et al., 2022). A vital metric, the final system yield (YF), gauges on-grid energy production over a specified period, computed by dividing the AC energy by the PV unit's maximum power under standard test conditions (STC) and presented in Eq. 1 (Afrouzy & Taghavi, 2021). The PV system's performance is gauged by crucial metrics: YF (final yield) in kWh/kWp, E_{AC} (energy yield) in kWh/kWp, P_{PV} (peak power output) under STC, and YR (reference yield) by Eq. 2 (Taghavi et al., 2023). YA represents DC energy per kWh of nominal power per kWp under STC. PR gauges final yield against reference yield. Total energy loss is calculated using Eq. 5. Array absorber loss, obtained by Eq. 6, is the deviation between reference and array yield. Inverter efficiency (Eq. 7) is AC power produced divided by PV array's DC power output. PV system efficiency (Eq. 8) is the product of PV module and inverter efficiency (Taghavi et al., 2021).

$$Y_F = E_{AC}/P_{PV} \tag{1}$$
$$Y_R = H_t(kWh\ m^{-2})/G_o(kW\ m^{-2}) \tag{2}$$
$$Y_A = E_{DC}/P_O \tag{3}$$
$$PR = Y_F/Y_R \tag{4}$$

$$L = Y_R - Y_F \tag{5}$$
$$L_C = Y_R - Y_F \tag{6}$$
$$\eta_{inv} = P_{AC}/P_{DC} \tag{7}$$
$$\eta_{system} = \eta_{PV} \times \eta_{inv} \tag{8}$$

4. Result and discussion

PVsyst 7.3.1 software modelled photovoltaic panels for Rafsanjan City, Iran (latitude 30.4015, longitude 55.9945, altitude 1,519 m), considering local weather conditions. It shares borders with Bafgh to the north, Shahrebabak to the west, Sirjan to the south, and Kerman to the east. Fig. 2 contrasts monthly yield and energy output between the reference (Afrouzy & Taghavi, 2021) and proposed models.

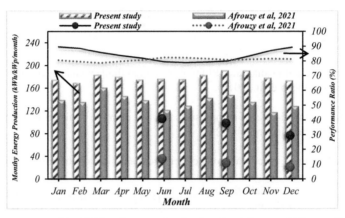

Fig. 2. Presents monthly yield and energy production for reference (Afrouzy & Taghavi, 2021) and proposed models.

Analyse location specifics and meteorological data for precise modelling. The study used fixed-tilt panels with a 32° slope angle in the PV system. According to the photovoltaic simulations, Rafsanjan's monthly average global radiation spans 117.5 kWh/m² (December) to 253.4 kWh/m² (June). In July, the hottest month, the temperature averages 41.77 °C, while January, the coldest, sees 2.566 °C. Rafsanjan's annual average environmental temperature is 29.43 °C. Table 3 outlines the details of the examined PV system. Fig. 3 illustrates the performance ratio (PR), array energy output, and grid-injected energy.

Table 3. Characteristics of investigated PV system.

PV module characteristics	
Length × Width × Thickness (mm) ; Weight (kg)	2,278 × 1,134 × 35 ; 28.5
Number of Module	3
Manufacturer	Axitec Energy
Description and details	AXITEC AC-550MBT/144
PV inverter characteristics	
Length × Width × Thickness (mm) ; Weight (kg)	714 × 1,176 × 315 ; 84
Number of Inverter	157
Manufacturer	Canadian Solar Inc.
Description and details	CS-125KTL-GI-E

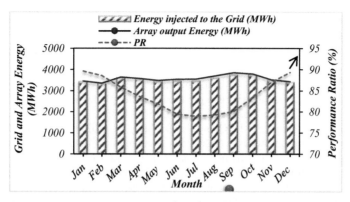

Fig. 3. Monthly array energy production and energy injected into the grid and PR.

Fig. 3 showcases monthly solar energy injection for various systems throughout the year. The highest PR was 89.6 % in January, while July recorded the lowest at 78.9 %. Fig. 4 shows losses of PV system during the year based on simulations.

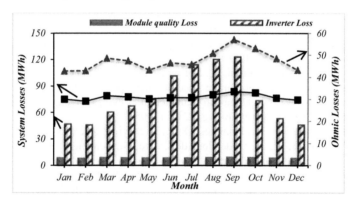

Fig. 4. Schematic illustrates system losses throughout the entire year in Rafsanjan.

In September, the mismatch loss peaked at 83.79 MWh, while it reached its lowest point in February at 72.77 MWh.

5. Conclusions

Incorporating absorption refrigeration cycles in the mixed fluid cascade LNG process aims to reduce electrical power consumption by utilizing plant waste heat. In this research, the ARC replaced the pre-cooling compression refrigeration cycle. Also, renewable solar energy was used to supply the electricity required for the cycle the amount of 19.37 MW using PV. The main results of the developed process analysis are presented as follows:

- Specific energy consumption was 0.172 kWh/kgLNG, signaling a 30 % consumption reduction; modified process reduces heat transfer area by up to 31 %.
- Coefficient of performance (COP) of NH_3-H_2O was 0.48, revealing cycle efficiency.
- Achieving a peak PR of 89.6 % in January and minimizing losses to 72.78 MWh in February, the system demonstrates robust efficiency.

- The highest available energy was in September (3,726.8 MWh) and the lowest was (3,304.6 MWh) in February, which showed that the power generation is sufficient for the cycle.

References

Afrouzy, Z. A., & Taghavi, M. (2021). Thermo-economic analysis of a novel integrated structure for liquefied natural gas production using photovoltaic panels. *Journal of Thermal Analysis and Calorimetry, 145*(3), 1509–1536.

Chen, J., Li, D., Klemeš, J. J., Qian, Y., & Yang, S. (2021). A sustainable syngas cryogenic separation process combined with ammonia absorption refrigeration pre-cooling cycle. *Journal of Cleaner Production, 313*, 127612.

Ebrahimi, A., Ghorbani, B., & Taghavi, M. (2021). Pinch and exergy evaluation of a liquid nitrogen cryogenic energy storage structure using air separation unit, liquefaction hybrid process, and Kalina power cycle. *Journal of Cleaner Production, 305*, 127226.

Ebrahimi, A., Ghorbani, B., & Taghavi, M. (2022). Novel integrated structure consisting of CO_2 capture cycle, heat pump unit, Kalina power, and ejector refrigeration systems for liquid CO_2 storage using renewable energies. *Energy Science & Engineering, 10*(8), 3167–3188.

Ghorbani, B., Mehrpooya, M., Shirmohammadi, R., & Hamedi, M.-H. (2018). A comprehensive approach toward utilizing mixed refrigerant and absorption refrigeration systems in an integrated cryogenic refrigeration process. *Journal of Cleaner Production, 179*, 495–514.

Ghorbani, B., Salehi, G., Ebrahimi, A., & Taghavi, M. (2021). Energy, exergy and pinch analyses of a novel energy storage structure using post-combustion CO_2 separation unit, dual pressure Linde-Hampson liquefaction system, two-stage organic Rankine cycle and geothermal energy. *Energy, 233*, 121051.

Hunt, J. D., Montanari, P. M., Hummes, D. N., Taghavi, M., Zakeri, B., Romero, O. J., Zhou, W., Freitas, M. A. V. de, José de Castro, N., Schneider, P. S., & Wada, Y. (2023). Solid air hydrogen liquefaction, the missing link of the hydrogen economy. *International Journal of Hydrogen Energy, 48(75),* 29198–29208.

Mehrpooya, M., Omidi, M., & Vatani, A. (2016). Novel mixed fluid cascade natural gas liquefaction process configuration using absorption refrigeration system. *Applied Thermal Engineering, 98*, 591–604.

Soonmin, H., & Taghavi, M. (2022). Solar Energy Development: Study Cases in Iran and Malaysia. *International Journal of Engineering Trends and Technology, 70*(8), 408–422.

Táboas, F., Bourouis, M., & Vallès, M. (2014). Analysis of ammonia/water and ammonia/salt mixture absorption cycles for refrigeration purposes in fishing ships. *Applied Thermal Engineering, 66*(1–2), 603–611.

Taghavi, M., & Lee, C. J. (2024). Development of novel hydrogen liquefaction structures based on waste heat recovery in diffusion-absorption refrigeration and power generation units. *Energy Conversion and Management*, Accepted 30 Dec 2023.

Taghavi, M., Salarian, H., & Ghorbani, B. (2021). Thermodynamic and exergy evaluation of a novel integrated hydrogen liquefaction structure using liquid air cold energy recovery, solid oxide fuel cell and photovoltaic panels. *Journal of Cleaner Production, 320*, 128821.

Taghavi, M., Salarian, H., & Ghorbani, B. (2023). Economic Evaluation of a Hybrid Hydrogen Liquefaction System Utilizing Liquid Air Cold Recovery and Renewable Energies. *Renewable Energy Research and Applications (RERA), 4*(1), 125–143.

Flavio Manenti, Gintaras V. Reklaitis (Eds.), Proceedings of the 34th European Symposium on Computer Aided Process Engineering / 15th International Symposium on Process Systems Engineering (ESCAPE34/PSE24), June 2-6, 2024, Florence, Italy

Techno-economical evaluation and comparison of various CO_2 transportation pathways

Mustafa Cakartas[a], Jianzhao Zhou[b], Jingzheng Ren[b], Anders Andreasen[c], Haoshui Yu[a]*

[a]*Department of Chemistry and Bioscience, Aalborg University, Niels Bohrs Vej 8, 6700 Esbjerg, Denmark*
[b]*Department of Industrial and Systems Engineering, The Hong Kong Polytechnic University,*
Hong Kong Special Administrative Region, China
[c]*Rambøll Danmark A/S Esbjerg, Bavnehøjvej 5, 6700 Esbjerg, Denmark*
hayu@bio.aau.dk

Abstract

Carbon Capture and Storage (CCS) is regarded as one of the most promising solutions for reducing emissions of greenhouse gases. Following capture, the CO_2 must be transported to the designated storage site. This transportation process can be achieved via various means, such as trucks/trains, or ships. Considerable research has focused on optimizing CO_2 transportation, particularly on converting CO_2 from a gas to a liquid to reduce volume and transportation costs. After thorough evaluation, it has been determined that acquiring CO_2 at 7 bar and -49 °C, as well as at 15 bar and -28 °C, represents the most efficient and cost-effective options for truck/train and ship transportation. To transport CO_2 in liquid state, liquefaction is a critical step in the pathway. In this paper, three different liquefaction systems including internal refrigeration (open liquefaction), external refrigeration (closed liquefaction) and precooled Linde Hampson process (open liquefaction) were studied. Each process was simulated in Aspen HYSYS, and optimized with a particle swarm optimization (PSO) algorithm in MATLAB to minimize the energy consumption. Afterwards, cost analysis was conducted to compare the liquefaction processes in terms of levelized cost. This study found that precooled Linde Hampson liquefaction process is the most cost-effective for the 7 bar scenario, with a cost of 19.18 \$/tCO$_2$ liquified. On the other hand, it was found that the lowest levelized cost is given by external liquefaction with the use of ammonia as refrigerant for 15 bar case, with a levelized cost of 17.54 \$/tCO$_2$ liquified.

Keywords: Carbon capture and storage, Internal refrigeration, External refrigeration, Precooled Linde Hampson process, Transportation of CO_2.

1. Introduction

Renewable energy or carbon capture and storage (CCS) technology are playing a pivotal role in reducing the carbon dioxide (CO_2) emissions. CCS can be defined as a technology which aims to prevent or reduce the effects of climate change by capturing CO_2 from source points or the atmosphere and then storing it at safe conditions. The main goal of CCS is to reduce carbon emissions from energy production, industrial processes and other sources. CCS comprised three critical stages: capture, transport and storage. There are different carbon capture technologies including but not limited to post-combustion, pre-combustion, and oxyfuel combustion carbon capture. Later, transportation takes place and the captured CO_2 is transported to designated sites for storage or utilization. Transportation is usually provided by truck/tanker, ship or pipeline (Metz et al., 2005). However, conditioning of CO_2 is very important for the transportation because CO_2 is captured in the gas form, but it is usually more efficient and cost-effective to transport in the liquid form (Seo et al., 2015). Therefore, liquefaction becomes a vital procedure to facilitate the transportation. The final phase of CCS involves storage, where the transported CO_2 is injected into the geological formations such as underground and ocean floor (Metz et al., 2005). While CCS is a prominent technology to reduce carbon emissions in the energy industry, its techno-economic viability and environmental impacts are still being actively researched.

There are various liquefaction methods available for CO_2 liquefaction, which can be categorized into open and closed liquefaction processes. The primary difference lies in the use of a refrigerant is required in the closed system (Seo et al., 2015). In the open liquefaction, there is no need for the refrigerant as the CO_2 is compressed before it is sent to a valve where Joule-Thomson effect applies and CO_2 is converted from gas to liquid-gas mixture. Moreover, the liquefaction process which uses refrigerant can be named as external refrigeration whereas the process without a refrigerant is known as internal refrigeration (Øi et al., 2016). There are different studies for liquefaction of CO_2 at different conditions. When the pressure varied between 7 and 70 bar, it was found that the highest cost belongs to the liquefaction at 7 bar whereas the lowest cost was obtained for 40-50 bar (Deng et al., 2019). Decarre et al. (2010) stated that when the liquefaction of CO_2 was compared for 7 and 15 bar options, 15 bar was found as more economically favorable for transportation of CO_2 by ship. On the other hand, Roussanaly et al. (2021) conducted a study for 7 and 15 barg shipping, and 7 barg shipping of CO_2 was found as cheaper. Rather than varying pressure, studies were also conducted for different processes at chosen pressures. Since the cost of liquefaction was determined as lower at the liquefaction pressure of 15 bar when it is compared with 6 bar for ship transportation (Seo et al., 2016), four different processes were evaluated and it was determined that closed system has lowest life cycle cost compared with Linde Hampson system, Linde dual-pressure and precooled Linde Hampson system. Moreover, precooled Linde Hampson system had the lowest life cycle cost among open liquefaction systems (Seo et al., 2015). When internal and external refrigeration were compared for 7 bar option, external refrigeration with ammonia was deemed more cost effective compared to internal refrigeration (Øi et al., 2016). Furthermore, Seo et al. (2015) mentioned that among the refrigerants that can be used in the external refrigeration, ammonia has the lowest work requirement. In summary, the liquefaction pressure is mostly compared between 7 and 15 bar and there are different processes that can be used, but there is no consistent conclusion. This paper focuses on the internal refrigeration (IR), external refrigeration (ER) and precooled Linde Hampson liquefaction (PLHL) processes for 7 and 15 bar liquefaction pressure conditions.

2. Methodology

In this section, assumptions that are used to create the process flowsheet are presented as well as the optimization process. Moreover, methods that are used in economic analysis were also presented.

2.1. Process simulation modelling and optimization

For performing process flow-sheeting and simulation Aspen HYSYS v9 is applied. For the simulations the Peng-Robinson equation of state was chosen as a comprise between calculation speed and accuracy for pure CO_2. An automated process of running the defined process simulation flowsheet models was made by combining the process simulator with MATLAB via COM (Microsoft Component Object Model). A black-box wrapper was made in MATLAB, exposing the process simulation as a simple callable object/function taking the independent variables as input, and returning the desired output when the simulation has converged. This approach is similar to the implementation in Olsen et al. (2021). Furthermore, particle swarm optimization (PSO) is used to optimize the built flowsheets in Aspen HYSYS v9 based on the approach by Yu et al. (2019). After defining the variables, lower and upper bounds were set for each variable. Later, constraints and objective function were defined to obtain the lowest duty in each process. In the optimization spreadsheet that was used in Aspen HYSYS, duty was defined as the sum of shaft power of compressors. The inlet conditions were determined as 1.5 bar and 40 °C. Also, 50 t/h pure CO_2 was assumed at the inlet. Ammonia was chosen as a refrigerant due to its low energy requirement.

Table 1. Assumptions used in simulations.

Parameters	Value	Unit
Adiabatic efficiency of compressors	80	%
Maximum compression ratio	4	-
Temperature of hot streams at the outlet of air coolers	38	°C
Pressure drops in the coolers and heat exchangers	0	bar
Minimum approach temperature in heat exchangers	5	°C
Minimum approach temperature in multi-stream heat exchangers	3	°C

Internal refrigeration, external refrigeration and precooled Linde Hampson liquefaction processes were simulated for 7 and 15 bar cases in Aspen HYSYS v9. Figure 1 illustrates the process flow diagram of internal refrigeration. As previously mentioned, compressed CO_2 is liquified through valve due to the Joule-Thomson effect. The compression stages of internal refrigeration were determined as 5 and 4 for 7 bar and 15 bar cases, respectively. Moreover, compression stages of external refrigeration were determined as 5 for both 7 and 15 bar cases. While 2 stages were used to compress the CO_2, 3 stages were used to compress the ammonia. Lastly, the compression stage number was determined as 5 for 7 and 15 bar cases in precooled Linde Hampson process. Whereas 3 stages were used to compress the CO_2, 2 stages were used to compress the ammonia. Process flow diagram of external refrigeration and precooled Linde Hampson processes were not presented in this paper due to space limitation.

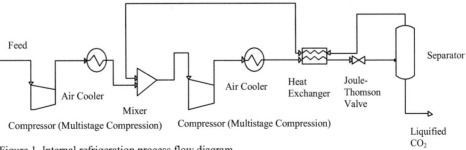

Figure 1. Internal refrigeration process flow diagram.

2.2. Techno-economic analysis

CAPEX estimation is performed by combining the elaborate equipment cost database published by Woods (2007) with the Enhanced Detailed Factor (EDF) (Aromada et al., 2021) method for total Inside Battery Limit (ISBL) plant cost estimation in a similar fashion as previously applied to CO_2 liquefaction (Øi et al., 2016). The methods are programmed in an internal tool (Jensen et al., 2024) and extensive testing and benchmarking against vendor quotes as well as total plant costs have been conducted. The main equipment considered in the present study includes compressors, separators and heat exchangers. For coolers in gas service or condensing service (refrigerant), air cooled heat exchangers (ACHE) have been assumed and heat exchangers for heat recovery or CO_2 condensing service have been assumed as Shell and Tube heat exchangers (SHE). As input to the EDF method the material factor is set as stainless steel for all equipment handling CO_2 and as carbon steel for all equipment handling refrigerant only. Furthermore, additional construction specific factors have been adjusted to reflect cold insulation, establishment of external power supply, as compressor building.

In this study we use the following simplified definition of levelized cost in analogy with NREL's Levelized Cost of Energy (LCOE) (Short et al., 1995) which assumes overnight capital cost and O&M costs being invariant over the years. The Levelized Cost of CO_2 Liquefaction (LCOCL) is given as:

$$LCOCL = \frac{CRF \cdot TPC + O\&M_{fixed} + O\&M_{variable}}{\int_{t=0}^{1\ year} \dot{m}} \tag{1}$$

In Eq. (1), CRF is the capital recovery factor, TPC is the overnight capital cost as calculated via the EDF method. $O\&M_{fixed}$ is the yearly fixed Operations and Maintenance cost invariant of the plant load/capacity and $O\&M_{variable}$ is the yearly Operations and Maintenance cost that scales with plant load. The denominator in the equation is the yearly amount of liquefied CO_2, which we set as the nominal mass flow (kg/s) integrated over the year where we assume 8000 hours at the design rate. The variable O&M costs will for simplicity be set at the cost of electricity to power compressor and air cooler fans. The capital recovery factor, which can be seen in Eq. (2), is defined as:

$$CRF = \frac{i(1+i)^n}{(1+i)^n - 1} \tag{2}$$

where i is the interest rate and n is the number of annuities over project lifetime. In this study, i is set to 10 % and the project lifetime is set to 20 years (namely $n = 20$). The fixed O&M cost is set to 5 % of the CAPEX in this study.

3. Results and discussion

After simulating the process flowsheets and optimizing them through MATLAB, cost calculations were completed and following results are obtained.

Table 2. Operating Expenses (OPEX) of liquefaction processes.

Liquefactions Processes	Fixed OPEX (MM \$/y)	Power (MW)	Variable OPEX (MM \$/y)
IR, 7 bar	1.46	7.20	4.03
IR, 15 bar	1.25	6.33	3.55
ER, 7 bar	1.29	6.10	3.42
ER, 15 bar	1.24	5.12	2.87
PLHL, 7 bar	1.39	5.39	3.02
PLHL, 15 bar	1.35	4.87	2.73

In Table 2, fixed operating expenses (OPEX) values are obtained by assuming maintenance cost as 5 % of capital expenses (CAPEX). They were obtained as higher for 7 bar cases in all of these liquefaction processes. Variable OPEX values are directly related to power values, so higher power and variable OPEX values were obtained for 7 bar cases. Power is the sum of electricity consumed by compressors and air coolers. For air coolers, it is assumed that 10 kW of electricity is required to cool 1 MW of hot stream. Upon comparing the results of this study with those presented by Deng et al. (2019), it was observed that the power values are higher than the ones reported in our study. Nonetheless, the consistent pattern prevails, with power values being lower for the 15 bar cases compared to the 7 bar cases, regardless of the chosen liquefaction method. Notably, the primary contributor to power consumption is the electricity utilized by compressors.

Table 3. Levelized Costs of Liquefaction Processes.

Liquefactions Processes	CAPEX (MM \$)	OPEX (MM \$/y)	Annualized CAPEX (MM \$/y)	LCOCL (\$/tCO$_2$ liquified)
IR, 7 bar	29.15	5.49	3.42	22.29
IR, 15 bar	25.00	4.80	2.94	19.33
ER, 7 bar	25.75	4.70	3.02	19.32
ER, 15 bar	24.79	4.11	2.91	17.54
PLHL, 7 bar	27.78	4.41	3.26	19.18
PLHL, 15 bar	26.97	4.08	3.17	18.11

In Table 3, annualized CAPEX values were calculated by multiplying corresponding values with Capital Recovery Factor (CRF) which was found as 0.12 as a result of using Eq. (2). Later, they were summed up with OPEX values and divided to multiplication of operating hours and tons of CO_2 treated in an hour to obtain the levelized costs. It is clear that CAPEX and OPEX values are higher for liquefaction at 7 bar option. Also, levelized cost follows the same trend as it is directly related to them. By comparing levelized costs, 15 bar case seems economically favourable compared to 7 bar. Moreover, external refrigeration with ammonia seems the cheapest liquefaction option for 15 bar case. Deng et al. (2019) presented the LCOCL values as 15.2 and 14.1 €/tCO$_2$ liquified for 7 and 15 bar, respectively. In comparing the LCOCL values obtained in this study with those reported in Deng et al. (2019), it is evident that slight variations exist due to differing assumptions made during flowsheet completion and cost calculations. Despite these discrepancies, the overall trend remains consistent, with the cost for the 15 bar case being lower than that for the 7 bar case, irrespective of the liquefaction method employed.

4. Conclusion

This study investigated several liquefaction techniques to facilitate the transportation of CO_2. At 7 bar, precooled Linde Hampson is the most cost-effective option in terms of the levelized cost. Although external refrigeration is an economically good option, using it to liquify the CO_2 at 7 bar is technically challenging because ammonia has low vapor pressure at the target temperature (-49 °C). At 15 bar, external refrigeration is the most cost-effective option since it has the lowest levelized cost. In both scenarios, internal refrigeration is the most expensive liquefaction option. Also, the study reveals that 15 bar is more cost-effective option than 7 bar for the liquefaction of CO_2 before transportation.

References

S.A. Aromada, N.H. Eldrup, and L. Erik Øi, 2021, Capital cost estimation of CO2 capture plant using Enhanced Detailed Factor (EDF) method: Installation factors and plant construction characteristic factors, International Journal of Greenhouse Gas Control, 110, p. 103394. Available at: https://doi.org/10.1016/j.ijggc.2021.103394.

S. Decarre, J. Berthiaud, N. Butin, and J.-L. Guillaume-Combecave, 2010, CO2 maritime transportation, International Journal of Greenhouse Gas Control, 4(5), pp. 857–864. Available at: https://doi.org/10.1016/j.ijggc.2010.05.005.

H. Deng, S. Roussanaly, and G. Skaugen, 2019, Techno-economic analyses of CO2 liquefaction: Impact of product pressure and impurities, International Journal of Refrigeration, 103, pp. 301–315. Available at: https://doi.org/10.1016/j.ijrefrig.2019.04.011.

E.H. Jensen, A. Andreasen, J. K. Jørsboe, M. P. Andersen, M. Hostrup, B. Elmegaard, C. Riber, and P. L. Fosbøl, 2024, Electrification of amine-based CO2 capture utilizing heat pumps, Carbon Capture Science & Technology, 10, p. 100154. Available at: https://doi.org/10.1016/j.ccst.2023.100154.

B. Metz, O. Davidson, H. de Coninck, M. Loos, and L. Meyer (eds), 2005, IPCC Special Report on Carbon Dioxide Capture and Storage. 1st edn. New York: Cambridge University Press.

L.E. Øi, N. Eldrup, U. Adhikari, M. H. Bentsen, J. L. Badalge, and S. Yang, 2016, Simulation and Cost Comparison of CO2 Liquefaction, Energy Procedia, 86, pp. 500–510. Available at: https://doi.org/10.1016/j.egypro.2016.01.051.

E.R. Olsen, J.-O. Hooghoudt, M. Maschietti, and A. Andreasen, 2021, Optimization of an Oil and Gas Separation Plant for Different Reservoir Fluids Using an Evolutionary Algorithm, Energy & Fuels, 35(6), pp. 5392–5406. Available at: https://doi.org/10.1021/acs.energyfuels.0c04284.

S. Roussanaly, H. Deng, G. Skaugen, and T. Gundersen, 2021, At what Pressure Shall CO2 Be Transported by Ship? An in-Depth Cost Comparison of 7 and 15 Barg Shipping, Energies, 14(18), p. 5635. Available at: https://doi.org/10.3390/en14185635.

Y. Seo, H. You, S. Lee, C. Huh, and D. Chang, 2015, Evaluation of CO2 liquefaction processes for ship-based carbon capture and storage (CCS) in terms of life cycle cost (LCC) considering availability, International Journal of Greenhouse Gas Control, 35, pp. 1–12. Available at: https://doi.org/10.1016/j.ijggc.2015.01.006.

Y. Seo, C. Huh, S. Lee, and D. Chang, 2016, Comparison of CO2 liquefaction pressures for ship-based carbon capture and storage (CCS) chain, International Journal of Greenhouse Gas Control, 52, pp. 1–12. Available at: https://doi.org/10.1016/j.ijggc.2016.06.011.

W. Short, D.J. Packey, and T. Holt, 1995, A manual for the economic evaluation of energy efficiency and renewable energy technologies. NREL/TP--462-5173, 35391. Available at: https://doi.org/10.2172/35391.

D.R. Woods, 2007, Rules of Thumb in Engineering Practice. 1st edn. Wiley. Available at: https://doi.org/10.1002/9783527611119.

H. Yu, D. Kim, and T. Gundersen, 2019, A study of working fluids for Organic Rankine Cycles (ORCs) operating across and below ambient temperature to utilize Liquefied Natural Gas (LNG) cold energy, Energy, 167, pp. 730–739. Available at: https://doi.org/10.1016/j.energy.2018.11.021.

Flavio Manenti, Gintaras V. Reklaitis (Eds.), Proceedings of the 34th European Symposium on Computer Aided Process Engineering / 15th International Symposium on Process Systems Engineering (ESCAPE34/PSE24), June 2-6, 2024, Florence, Italy

Integrated modelling of Concentrated Solar Power plants networks: Electricity production, storage, conversion and distribution in Spain

José A. Luceño Sánchez,[a*] Mariano Martín,[b] Sandro Macchietto[a]

[a]*Department of Chemical Engineering, Imperial College London, South Kensington Campus, London SW7 2AZ, United Kingdom*
[b]*Departamento de Ingeniería Química y Textil, Universidad de Salamanca, Pza. Caídos 1-5, 37008 Salamanca, Spain*
j.luceno-sanchez@imperial.ac.uk

Abstract

A multiperiod MILP model is proposed for the optimal location, sizing and operation of a sustainable energy production network based on Concentrated Solar Power (CSP) plants, energy storage and transmission, and use of H_2 as an energy vector. The model takes into account time and region-dependent variables (e.g., direct normal irradiance, land, regional electricity demand), technical and economic variables of the facilities (e.g., production capacity, investment), energy storage (CAES or H_2), the potential social impact (e.g., economic development, population ratios, and unemployment). A case study is presented where 5 potential Spanish locations are evaluated over a year of operation. Results highlight the importance of locating CSP plants considering technical, economic and social aspects. The impact of prices on policies related to energy self-sufficiency indicates that incentives are required for the development of cheaper storage solutions.

Keywords: Concentrated Solar Plant, optimal location, social impact, energy distribution and storage, energy network.

1. Introduction

Green energy transition is one of the most ambitious key tasks for countries to achieve the Net-zero policies goals. Concentrated Solar Power (CSP) plants employ solar radiation to produce electricity in a renewable, sustainable way, and have a leading role in the selection of national energy mixes (Shi, 2016; Ainou et al., 2023). The construction of these plants is influenced by the location, as the achievable production capacities is affected by factors such as distribution of solar radiation, and water and land availability, energy distribution infrastructure, and the social impact of the facility, in terms of economic development or jobs creation (Heras and Martín, 2020). Previous work (Luceño Sánchez et al., 2023) optimized the location and capacity of CSP plants at national scale based on techno-economic and socio-environmental models, but did not consider the distribution of electricity, the possibility of storing energy surplus or converting it to other energy vectors, which could also be transported to other regions. In this work, a new mathematical model is proposed to address simultaneously the location of CSP facilities, the distribution of energy to satisfy the regional demand, the possible strategies that should be followed for energy storing in case of electricity surplus, and the techno-socio-economic evaluation related to these aspects. Potential locations and distribution strategies are evaluated, together with the possibility to use compressed air storage as energy storage system (ESS) and the production of green H_2 for fuel-cell applications.

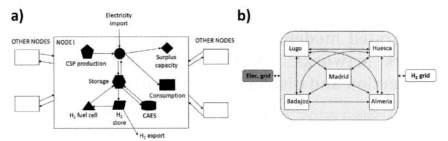

Figure 1: a) Node representation; b) Five nodes network.

2. Problem formulation

A territory is subdivided in regions, each represented by a node as depicted in Figure 1a, which is connected to all other nodes in a network superstructure (see Figure 1b for the 5-node case study used later). Each node (region) is characterized by a CSP plant for electricity production and the electricity demand (consumption). Energy may be stored in the form of compressed air (CAES) and H_2 and returned back to the node as electricity. Excess unused electricity, labelled "surplus", may be transmitted to other nodes or otherwise must be disposed of. Additional electricity requirements may be met by transmission from other nodes or import from external sources. Demands and factors such as irradiation and water availability vary both over time and location. We wish to calculate the location and capacity of CSP plants, as well as the type and size of storage at each node and the energy transmitted between nodes in the form of either electricity or H_2, that optimize overall economic, social and environmental impacts. The existence of each facility is represented by binary variables, and their capacity or utilization by continuous variables. The model is divided into four sections:

-Node energy balances: each region is presented as a node of a network, with the energy balance for node l given in eq. 1. Each node includes the electricity production ($EnPr_{t,l}$ [GWh]), the charge ($EnSto_{t,l}$ [GWh]) and discharge from storage ($EnDch_{t,l}$ [GWh]), the electricity imported or exported from node l to other nodes n in the network ($EnDis_{t,n,l}$ [GWh]), consumed ($EnCon_{t,l}$ [GWh]), unused ($EnSurplus_{t,l}$ [GWh]), and that which must be bought from other sources ($EnImport_{t,l}$ [GWh]). This formulation enables to calculate all energy transmission between nodes at each time-step, and the energy to be stored and to be discharged in each node.

$$EnPr_{t,l} + EnDch_{t,l} + \sum_{n=1}^{Nod} EnDis_{t,n,l} + EnImport_{t,l} = \tag{1}$$
$$= EnCon_{t,l} + \sum_{n=1}^{Nod} EnDis_{t,l,n} + EnSto_{t,l} + EnSurplus_{t,l}$$

-Energy storage and energy vectors: Using the values of $EnSto_{t,l}$ and $EnDch_{t,l}$, the storage requirements are evaluated, including their size and costs. Two types of storage were considered: compressed air energy storage (CAES), and hydrogen. Thus, both $EnSto_{t,l}$ and $EnDch_{t,l}$ present two terms related to each technology ($CAESSto_{t,l}$ and $HydroSto_{t,l}$), which are involved in a node balance to determine the available energy stored; for example, the CAES energy stored ($CAESAva_{t,l}$ [GWh]) is given by eq. 2.

$$CAESAva_{t,l} = CAESAva_{(t-1),l} - CAESDch_{t,l} + CAESSto_{t,l} \tag{2}$$

In addition, hydrogen generation and distribution between nodes is also considered, together with the use of hydrogen fuel cells in each node for electricity generation, and the scenario where hydrogen could be sold externally (in a similar way than node energy balances).

-**Economic and social evaluation**: The cost of the facilities in each region (production, storage, and hydrogen conversion) is modelled, as well as the cost of hydrogen distribution if applicable. The social impact related to the investment in each region is evaluated based on creation of new jobs, following the methodology proposed by Heras and Martin (2020) and previous work (Luceño Sánchez et al., 2023).

-**Objective function**: A multi-period MILP optimization problem is formulated whereby several aspects of network structure are chosen simultaneously: production variables (e.g., location, number and size of CSP plants), storage solutions (e.g., CAES or hydrogen technologies), energy transportation solutions (as electricity and H_2 vectors within the network and their external import-export), and social impact of new facilities. Inputs include location-dependent parameters (e.g., direct normal irradiance and available land) and costs and bounds on various quantities. The objective (eq. 3) is to minimize the annualized capital cost of all facilities (z_{cost} [M€/y]), the annual net cost of total external import and export of electricity (z_{ener} [M€/y]), the annual cost of hydrogen (distribution and/or sale) (z_{H2} [M€/y]), and the related economic effect of social impact (SI) (z_{SI} [M€/y]):

$$\min(z_{cost} + z_{ener} + z_{H2} - z_{SI}) \tag{3}$$

3. Solution procedure and Case Studies

Five regions across Spain (Almería [south-east], Badajoz [south-west], Madrid [middle], Huesca [north-east], and Lugo [north-west]) are chosen as potential production locations (CSP plants) and/or storage locations (Figure 1b). The timeframe selected for this study is 1 year of operation with 12 monthly intervals. The monthly direct normal irradiance (DNI) for each region is obtained from EU PVGIS database (PVGIS, 2023). The regional energy demand was calculated using monthly average national demand data and population/social statistics from Spanish governmental databases (INE, 2023). Table 1 shows electricity demand for two locations: Madrid and Lugo. The model is applied for two case studies: 1) a scenario where all the electricity needed is to be produced from renewable CSP sources alone, with no imports at any time ($EnExtra_{t,l}=0$, $\forall t, l$); and 2) a scenario where it is possible to buy electricity from the outside grid to meet the demand. The following assumptions are made: 1) 20 years of operation (for annualizing costs); 2) electricity and H_2 are distributed using existing networks; 3) electricity transmission losses are neglected; 4) the external electricity export is calculated at network level; 5) the maximum plant area for a CSP plant is 0.5% of a region area; 6) the hydrogen sale price is 3€/kg, same as grey hydrogen (IRENA 2022); 7) the penalty for exporting electricity is 150€/MWh, and the cost of external purchase is 500€/MWh (higher than market prices to impose an economic penalty); 8) CAES and fuel cells have an efficiency of 70%; 9) CSP plants use dry-cooling systems.

Table 1. Monthly average electricity demand for two regions [GWh] over 1 year.

Month	1	2	3	4	5	6	7	8	9	10	11	12
Madrid	2,226	1,956	1,880	1,627	1,660	2,132	2,492	2,391	2,248	2,038	1,730	1,837
Lugo	106	93	89	77	79	101	118	114	107	97	82	87

4. Results

4.1. Case Study 1: Optimal CSP green energy production to meet the full demand

The results shown in Table 2 indicate that the optimal solution is to build CSP plants in the south of Spain: Almeria and Badajoz present the maximum capacity allowed, while Huesca has a lower design capacity. Electricity is distributed to the other regions such as Madrid, which receives around 50% of electricity from Almeria and 50% from Huesca in August (see Figure 2). This result is because southern regions i) have larger DNI values, which means larger production, and ii) new plants there result in a more significant impact on social development (e.g. salaries, unemployment reduction).

Regarding the energy storage, no energy storage system is selected in any region and the electricity surplus was exported, as seen in Figure 3 – Case Study 1. The reason is related to the price of storage technologies and the assumed selling price of H_2. The green H_2 from CSP would have a larger cost and cannot compete against grey H_2 production cost (3€/kg). Furthermore, energy surplus during summer results from the need to over-design the network so as to meet the peak demand during winter.

Table 2. Production capacity, storage, SI, and investment for both Case studies.

Region	Capacity (MW)	CAES (GWh)	H_2 (GWh)	SI (M€)	Investment (M€)
			Case Study 1		
Almeria	2,844	0	0	209.12	6,537.41
Badajoz	7,454	0	0	523.06	13,636.42
Madrid	0	0	0	0	0
Huesca	2,261	0	0	95.10	5,639.38
Lugo	0	0	0	0	0
			Case Study 2		
Almeria	2,844	0	0	209.07	6,537.41
Badajoz	5,696	0	0	412.94	10,928.86
Madrid	0	0	0	0	0
Huesca	0	0	0	0	0
Lugo	0	0	0	0	0

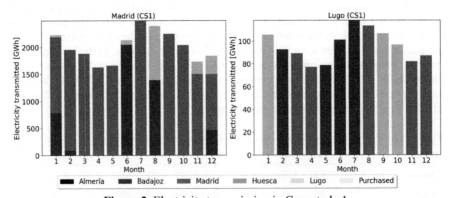

Figure 2. Electricity transmission in Case study 1.

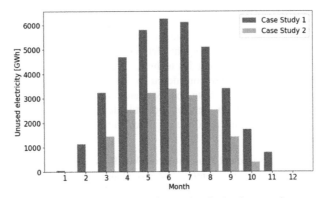

Figure 3. Surplus unused capacity for both scenarios.

4.2. Case Study 2: Optimal energy production and distribution with external supply

When it is allowed to buy energy from outside the grid to meet demand, again, no storage is selected, but two main differences are noted (Table 2) relative to Case Study 1:

1) A notable reduction of investment is shown (8,347 M€, -32%). In spite of the high penalties, it is still cheaper to build smaller facilities and pay to acquire electricity from the grid than having an unused electricity generation capacity surplus, as can be inferred comparing the value of Figure 3 for Case Study 1 (more than 6,000 GWh) and Case Study 2 (less than 3,500 GWh). That means that additional policies and incentives are required to promote the green transition using CSP plants coupled with hydrogen technologies.

2) The reduction of social impact (SI) values in Case 2 is lower (25%) than the investment reduction but impact is still important. The Huesca CSP plant is no longer built and the one in Badajoz has a lower capacity, but the Almeria plant remains the same. Even though Almeria and Badajoz present similar irradiation, Almeria is the most affected region in terms of social impact, thus it is the region that the model selects as a priority to build a CSP plant.

The comparison of Figure 2 and Figure 4 shows that the volume of electricity transmitted through the grid is lower than in Case Study 1, particularly during winter because it is better to fully meet the energy demand with electricity from the grid in Huesca and Lugo. In addition, the reduction of energy transmission during winter matches the lack of energy surplus from October to February (see Figure 3 – Case Study 2). This shows that there is a trade-off between grid dependency and energy production.

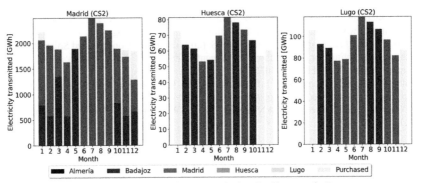

Figure 4. Electricity transmission in Case study 2.

5. Conclusions

A mathematical model is proposed for the integrated modelling of a sustainable energy network based on CSP plants, following the Net-zero policies and the goal of decarbonize the energy network. The model includes technical, economic, social, and geographical aspects, which are simultaneously considered to optimize the production, storage and distribution of electricity and H_2 as an energy vector. The social impact model captures the importance and benefits of developing underdeveloped areas with large solar irradiation, and allows analysing the trade-off between investment, production and social impact.

The model formulation is a scalable multi-period MILP, in which the timeframe of 1 year of operation is divided into 12 months. The model was applied to evaluate 5 regions selected through Spain, considering two case studies. The results show that the southern regions (Almeria and Badajoz) are more suitable for production and for meeting the total energy demand using the distribution network, because of larger DNI values and higher social impact of the new facilities. To fully meet demand with no external import, 3 CSP plants are required, over-designed to meet the demand during winter, resulting in an energy surplus and unused electricity during the rest of the year. If external electricity import is allowed, 2 smaller CSP are optimal, because the benefits of producing green energy are not as competitive as purchasing some electricity from the grid during certain months. Both case studies highlight the need for policies and incentives to encourage the use of green hydrogen as an energy vector, if its prices are to compete with grey hydrogen.

References

The authors acknowledge Imperial College London and University of Salamanca for access to scientific sources and databases. The authors acknowledge the Margarita Salas grant, co-funded by the European NextGenerationEU Fund, Spanish "Plan de Recuperación, Transformación y Resiliencia" Fund, Spanish Ministry of Universities, and University of Salamanca ("Ayudas para la recualificación del Sistema Universitario español 2021-2022"), to JA Luceño Sánchez.

References

Ainou, F.Z.; Ali, M.; Sadiq, M. (2023). Green energy security assessment in Morocco: green finance as a step toward sustainable energy transition. Environ. Sci. Pollut. Res., 30, 61411-61429.

Heras, J.; Martín, M. (2020). Social Issues in the Energy Transition: Effect on the Design of the New Power System. Appl. Energy, 278, 115654.

INE, Instituto Nacional de Estadística (Spanish National Institute of Statistics). Last accessed Sep 2023. https://www.ine.es/

IRENA, International Renewable Energy Agency. Hydrogen Overview. 2022 (Last accessed Sep 2023). https://www.irena.org/Energy-Transition/Technology/Hydrogen

Luceño Sánchez, J.A.; Martín, M.; Macchietto, S. (2023). Optimal Concentrated Solar Plant (CSP) location accounting for social and environmental impact: A three location study in Spain. Comput. Aided Chem. Eng. 52, 3031-3036.

PVGIS, Photovoltaic Geographical Information System. Interactive tools. Last accessed Sep 2023. https://re.jrc.ec.europa.eu/pvg_tools/en/

Shi, X. (2016). The future of ASEAN energy mix: A SWOT analysis. Renew. Sust. Energ. Rev., 53, 672-680.

Flavio Manenti, Gintaras V. Reklaitis (Eds.), Proceedings of the 34th European Symposium on Computer Aided Process Engineering / 15th International Symposium on Process Systems Engineering (ESCAPE34/PSE24), June 2-6, 2024, Florence, Italy

A Novel Optimisation Framework to Design Market-Based Policy Interventions for the Uptake of Alternative Fuels in the UK Chemical Industry

Gbemi Oluleye,[a,b] Devan Patel,[c] Pauline Matalon,[a] Elisabeth Maya Rosa[a]

[a]Centre for Environmental Policy, Imperial College London
[b]Sargent Centre for Process Systems Engineering, Imperial College London
[c]Department of Chemical Engineering, Imperial College London
o.oluleye@imperial.ac.uk

Abstract

Shifting to clean alternatives like biomethane, green hydrogen, and blue hydrogen for industrial heating offers emission reductions, yet their high costs hinder adoption. There is no systematic way to design policy interventions that enable cost reduction at minimum cost to government and industry. This study aims to formulate and apply a novel multi-period Mixed-Integer Market Penetration Optimization Model to fill this gap and inform decisions about transitioning to alternative fuels for heating in the UK Chemical Industry. The model cost-effectively designs a policy pathway whilst accounting for the fuel cost reduction due to demand-pull induced learning effects in the policy design. The model is applied to 490 boilers in the UK chemical industry, the model designs effective policy mixes to reduce the cost of green hydrogen by 60%, blue hydrogen by 36%, and green gas biomethane by 17%, with revenue from taxes supporting subsidies for cost neutrality.

Keywords: market penetration optimisation, clean innovation diffusion, fuel switching, industrial heat decarbonisation, market-based policy.

1. Background

In 2020, the chemical industry accounted for 2.3 Gt of GHG making up 6% of global emissions (IEA, 2021). Of this 86% emissions are from the combustion of fossil fuels to generate heat and power. The UK Chemical industry, consuming 26.3 TWh annually, heavily relies on natural gas for process heating. Shifting to clean alternatives like biomethane, green hydrogen, and blue hydrogen offers emission reductions, yet their high costs hinder adoption. Reducing emissions in the chemical industry is crucial because it is closely interconnected with other societal and technical systems. High mitigation cost associated with alternative fuels has become the biggest challenge for transition (Chung et al., 2023). Implementation of market-based policies can stimulate enough demand pull for the alternative fuel to bring about significant cost reduction. Previous studies focus on the technical feasibility of switching to alternative fuels (Griffin et al., 2018), investigating the emissions and performance of combusting alternative fuels (Cellek and Pinarbasi, 2018) and the possibility of repurposing natural gas infrastructure for alternative fuels (Efthymiadou et al., 2023 and Mertins et al., 2023). Techno-economic assessments (TEAs) have been applied to evaluate the economic impact of fuel switching in the chemical industry with majority of them concluding with the need for policies to make it cost-effective (Hong et al., 2023 and Luh et al., 2018). There is a pressing need to further design market-based policy interventions (consisting of taxes and subsidies). Policies for net-zero in industry have been explored (Chung et al., 2023). However, existing literature on policy primarily focuses on the qualitative aspects and overlook using the quantitative impact on cost reductions from demand pull created to design policy support. No existing study has shown how policy induced cost parity between the heat produced from the alternative fuel and the incumbent can translate into fuel cost reduction for the rest of the economy. This study builds on the Market Potential Assessment concept in Oluleye et al., 2021 and integrates the complexities of time and the interplay of different policies. The novel temporal market penetration optimisation model is a systematic approach to design and assess interventions for fuel switching to biomethane, blue hydrogen and green hydrogen in the UK chemical industry by harnessing the power of learning and leveraging diffusion theory.

2. Methodology

A novel market penetration optimisation framework is developed based on the hypothesis that policy interventions are required to reduce cost and generate sufficient demand pull to achieve cost parity with end use of alternative fuels, and this can lead to reduction in primary fuel price for the entire economy. The problem is formulated as a multi-period mixed integer non-linear problem to determine the policy offering and associated timeline to achieve 100% switch for the three fuels given the end-use technologies and economic factors. The objective function minimises the cost difference between the alternative fuel (j) and the incumbent fuel (natural gas) – Eq.1. A binary variable x is introduced to determine boilers that form part of the market (demand pull) subject to achieving the constraint in Eq. 6. Two policy typologies are explored, a feed-in tariff (FiT) for every MWh of fuel consumed and a carbon tax on every tonne of CO_2 produced (Eq.6 – Eq.9). Eq.2 – Eq.5 estimates the various costs, Eq.10 estimates the new fuel price, and the cost to government and industry is determined using Eq.10 and Eq. 11. The description of all terms is provided in the nomenclature below.

$$MC_t = \sum_{i=1}^{495} x_i * (ACOH_{i,j,t} - ACOH_{i,natural\ gas,t}) \tag{1}$$

$$ACOH_{i,j,t} = FC_{i,j,t} + VC_{i,j,t} + \ell_{i,j,t} * \alpha CAPEX_{i,j,t}) \tag{2}$$

$$\ell_{i,j,t} = 1\ for\ i = natural\ gas\ and\ 2030 \leq t \leq 2040$$

$$\ell_{i,j,t} = 0\ for\ all\ other\ cases$$

$$CAPEX_{i,j,t} = CAPEX * \frac{r_j * (1+r_j)^{n_j}}{(1+r_j)^{n_j-1}}\ \forall i, \forall j \tag{3}$$

$$VC_{i,j,t} = c_{i,j,t} \times FP_{i,j,t} \tag{4}$$

$$FC_{i,j,t} = 0.02 * \alpha CAPEX_{i,j,t} \tag{5}$$

$$ACOH_{i,j,t} \leq ACOH_{i,natural\ gas,t} \tag{6}$$

$$\varepsilon_{i,j,t} = c_{i,j,t} * f_{j,t} \tag{7}$$

$$ACOH_{i,j,t} = FC_{i,j,t} + VC_{i,j,t} + \ell_{i,j,t} * \alpha CAPEX_{i,j,t} + \varepsilon_{i,j,t} * \gamma_t \qquad (8)$$

$$ACOH_{i,j,t} = FC_{i,j,t} + c_{i,j,t} \; x \; (FP_{i,j,t} - \tau_{j,t}) + \ell_{i,j,t} * \alpha CAPEX_{i,j,t} \qquad (9)$$

$$FP_{i,j,t+1} = FP_{i,j,t} * \left(\frac{O_t}{O_{t+1}}\right)^{LP} \qquad (10)$$

$$G_t = \sum_{i=1}^{497} x_i * (\tau_t) - (1 - x_i) * (Y_t) \qquad (11)$$

$$I_t = MC_t - G_t \qquad (12)$$

The model was implemented in Python 3.11, Pyomo 6.5.0 and a third party extension Mindtpy MINLP problem solved with CPLEX 22.1.1.0 and IPOPT 3.14.9.

Nomenclature

i, boiler	ε_i, Emission
j, alternative fuel	f_i, Emission Factor
t, year	E_i, Energy
v, Availability	FC_i, Fixed Cost
γ_t, Carbon Tax	τ_t, Feed-In Tariff
c_i, Consumption	FP_i, Fuel Price
C_i, Capacity	G_t, Government Cost
M_j, Energy Permit Trading	I_t, Industry Cost
O_t, Capacity of Alternative Fuel in Year t	ℓ_i, Status of boiler
	VC_i, Variable Cost
O_{t+1}, Capacity of Alternative Fuel in Year t+1	ACOH, Annualised Cost of Heat
	CAPEX, Capital Expenditure
η_i, Efficiency	LP, Learning Parameter
	MC, Mitigation Cost

3. Case Study: Fuel Switching to Green Hydrogen, Blue Hydrogen, and Biomethane for Heat Decarbonisation

The market considered is the existing gas boiler population of the UK chemical industry totalling to 490 natural gas boilers consuming 9.6 TWh per year (Table 1).

Table 1. Number of equivalent boilers per cluster

Clusters (Boiler size)	1MW	5MW	9MW	15MW	30MW	60MW
Number of boilers	117	270	44	21	12	26

Policies explored are the carbon tax and an incentive per MWh fuel consumed (feed-in tariff). Assumption on all fuels is provided in Table 2. The fuel prices in Table 2 is without government support.

Table 2. Clean Fuel Assumptions

Item	Natural gas	Green Hydrogen	Blue Hydrogen	Biomethane
Discount rate (%)	3.5	3.5	3.5	3.5
Lifetime	30	25	25	30
Efficiency (%)	90	95	95	90
Capital cost (£/MW)	166,000	199,000	199,000	166,000
Fuel price (£/MWh)	31.96	110-187.5	68.8-84	57.44-90
Emission factor (tCO$_2$/MWh)	0.184	0.02	0.06	0.0138
Learning rate (%)	-	19%	7%	5%

4. Main Findings

The output of the model is represented in Fig. 1 to Fig. 4. Without policy support end-use heating cost parity between natural gas and the alternative fuels is not achievable. With the optimally designed carbon tax and FiT 100% uptake of alternative fuels for heating is possible in 10 years. The highest mitigation cost is from the sole use of the carbon tax, and industry bears the burden (Fig.1 a – c). The tax would need to be as high as 615 £/t to achieve a 1% green hydrogen uptake in 2024 reducing to 55 $/t with 100% uptake (Fig. 1a). The value of the carbon tax for blue hydrogen and biomethane is lower due to lower fuel costs (Table 1), however green hydrogen requires the lowest tax at 100% uptake due to the having the highest reduction in cost due to demand pull (evidence with the highest learning rate in Table 2). Implementing an incentive like the FiT means government alone bears the burden (Fig. 2). Incentivizing blue hydrogen has the lowest mitigation cost (Fig.2 b), and biomethane has the highest mitigation cost (Fig. 2c).

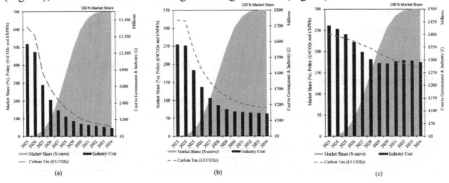

Figure 1 Designed carbon tax and associated mitigation cost to achieve fuel switching to (a) green hydrogen, (b) blue hydrogen and (c) biomethane

The minimum mitigation cost overall (94% reduction compared to single use of a carbon tax) is for a case where a mix of the FiT and carbon tax is applied to achieve end-use heating cost parity; in this case revenue from taxes is used to fund the FiT ensuring cost neutrality for government (Fig. 3). In this case, the maximum carbon tax required is 15 $/t for green hydrogen (Fig. 3a), 9 $/t for blue hydrogen (Fig. 3b) and 19 $/t for biomethane (Fig. 2c).

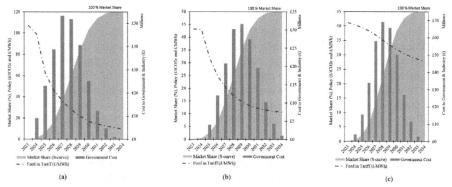

Figure 2 Designed feed in tariff and associated mitigation cost to achieve fuel switching to (a) green hydrogen, (b) blue hydrogen and (c) biomethane

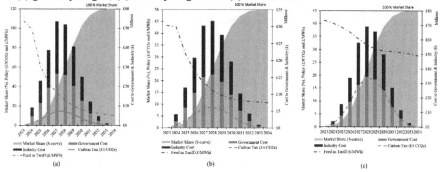

Figure 3 Optimal policy mix and associated mitigation cost to achieve fuel switching to (a) green hydrogen, (b) blue hydrogen and (c) biomethane

The impact of designing policies to achieve end-use heating cost parity for all fuels (subject to Eq. 6) is a positive spillover effect on primary fuel cost reduction for the rest of the economy (Fig. 4).

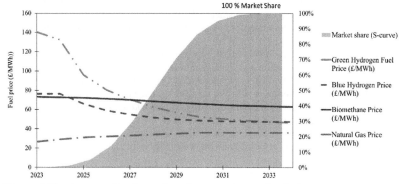

Figure 4 The impact of end-use 'heat' cost parity on the fuel cost

5. Conclusions and Future Work

As the shift towards alternative fuels for heating gains momentum, the importance of optimisation-based market penetration models in shaping their policy induced adoption becomes increasingly pivotal. This study has provided valuable insights into the design and effectiveness of policy interventions in promoting the uptake of alternative fuels in the UK's chemical sector. Results confirm that a mix of market-based policies (incentives and taxes) is required to achieve end-use heating cost parity at minimum mitigation cost spilling over to reducing the prices of the alternative fuels. Cost reduction is strongly related to learning effects which differ for the three alternative fuels studied. Blue hydrogen and biomethane offer minor cost reduction compared to green hydrogen. Subsequently, other economy sectors can benefit from cost reduction of the fuels to efficiently transition towards carbon neutral by 2050. These findings provide optimal policies and timelines to drive fuel switching, forming a basis for crucial discussions among academia, the chemical industry, and the government. For further work, the model's robustness could be enhanced by incorporating uncertainties across all parameters, resulting in designing policy packages immune to uncertainty.

References

M. S. Cellek, and A. Pınarbaşı, 2018, Investigations on performance and emission characteristics of an industrial low swirl burner while burning natural gas, methane, hydrogen-enriched natural gas and hydrogen as fuels, *International Journal of Hydrogen Energy,*. 43 (2), 1194-1207.

C. Chung, J. Kim, B. K. Sovacool, S. Griffiths, M. Bazilian, and M. Yang, 2023, Decarbonizing the chemical industry: A systematic review of sociotechnical systems, technological innovations, and policy options. *Energy Research & Social Science.* 96 102955. 10.1016/j.erss.2023.102955.

E. M. Efthymiadou, V. M. Charitopoulos, L. G. Papageorgiou, 2023, Hydrogen infrastructure planning for heat decarbonisation in Great Britain, Editor(s): Antonios C. Kokossis, Michael C. Georgiadis, Efstratios Pistikopoulos, Computer Aided Chemical Engineering, 52, 3025-3030

P. W. Griffin, G. P. Hammond, and J. B. Norman, 2018, Industrial energy use and carbon emissions reduction in the chemical sector: A UK perspective. *Applied Energy.* 227 587-602. 10.1016/j.apenergy.2017.08.010.

X. Hong, Z. Liao, Y. Yang, J. Wang, Y. Yang, 2023, Techno-enviro-economic analysis of H2 economy in China from H2 production to utilization, Editor(s): Antonios C. Kokossis, Michael C. Georgiadis, Efstratios Pistikopoulos, Computer Aided Chemical Engineering, 52, 2959-2964

International Energy Agency (IEA), 2021, Net Zero by 2050 - A Roadmap for the Global Energy Sector. https://iea.blob.core.windows.net/assets/deebef5d-0c34-4539-9d0c-10b13d840027/NetZeroby2050-ARoadmapfortheGlobalEnergySector_CORR.pdf accessed 06/09/2023

S. Luh, S. Budinis, T. J. Schmidt, A. Hawkes, 2018, Decarbonisation of the Industrial Sector by means of Fuel Switching, Electrification and CCS, Editor(s): Anton Friedl, Jiří J. Klemeš, Stefan Radl, Petar S. Varbanov, Thomas Wallek, Computer Aided Chemical Engineering, 43, 1311-1316

A. Mertins, M. Heiker, S. Rosenberger, and T. Wawer, 2023, Competition in the conversion of the gas grid: Is the future of biogas biomethane or hydrogen? *International Journal of Hydrogen Energy.* 10.1016/j.ijhydene.2023.04.270.

G. Oluleye, M. Gandiglio, M. Santarelli, A. Hawkes 2021, Pathways to commercialisation of biogas fuelled solid oxide fuel cells in European wastewater treatment plants, Applied Energy, 282, 116127

Flavio Manenti, Gintaras V. Reklaitis (Eds.), Proceedings of the 34th European Symposium on Computer Aided Process Engineering / 15th International Symposium on Process Systems Engineering (ESCAPE34/PSE24), June 2-6, 2024, Florence, Italy

Integration of process and working-fluid design for Combined Heating and Power (CHP) systems

Andres Pina-Martinez*, Romain Privat, Jean-François Portha, Jean-Marc Commenge

Université de Lorraine, CNRS, LRGP, F-54000 Nancy, France
andres david.pina martinez@univ lorraine.fr

Abstract

In this work, a product- and process-design approach for the selection of suitable working fluids and flowsheet configuration for novel Combined Heating and Power applications is presented. First, molecules that meet the requirements imposed by the process, and thus, could be used as working fluid are screened from a set of about 2500 compounds. After the screening, an optimisation procedure based on a superstructure approach is implemented to identify simultaneously the optimal process flowsheets and the corresponding working fluid. The design problem is expressed as a multi-objective MINLP problem and solved using MIDACO, an extended evolutionary Ant Colony Optimization (ACO) solver. The analysis of the set of Pareto points reveals that, in terms of process, regeneration and two bleedings should be included in the flowsheet. Moreover, turbine bleeding should be used to provide heating power to the end-user. In terms of working-fluid design, HFC-152 and HFCO-1233zd (E) seem to be promising candidates for CHP applications.

Keywords: process synthesis, superstructure optimisation, combined heat and power.

1. Introduction

The promotion of DES has opened the way to different technologies such as combined heat and power (CHP) or combined cooling, heating and power (CCHP) systems. Recently, Briola (2017) presented a novel CCHP cycle that enables the development of an all-in-one device capable of producing electric, heating and cooling power with a single working fluid. Among the design challenges of this novel CCHP system, the working fluid selection appears as a key stage of its development.

In this way, a first study (Piña-Martinez et al., 2021) devoted to the working fluid selection was carried out by implementing a database search to screen about 60 000 structures included in the Dortmund Data Bank (DDB), the Design Institute for Physical Properties (DIPPR) database and the NIST ThermoData Engine 103b (NIST TDE 103b). The screening considered thermodynamic, process-related, constructional, safety and environmental constraints. In such study, the process flowsheet was not considered as a degree of freedom of the design problem. However, the choice of a working fluid is inherently coupled to the choice of the appropriate process flowsheet.

In order to have a first overview of the trade-off between design variables, the CHP configuration of the original CCHP cycle is considered in this study. The objective of this work is to design a complete CHP cycle – including the selection of the working fluid - by implementing simultaneously product and process design approaches: first, molecules that could be used as working fluid are searched for from a set of about 2500 compounds. Then, an optimisation procedure based on a superstructure approach is implemented to identify simultaneously the optimal process flowsheet and the corresponding working fluid. The paper describes of the original CHP cycle, the methodology for the integrated process and working-fluid design implemented in this work. It also introduces the case study for the design of a CHP cycle and presents the results of the integrated design.

2. Brief description of the original CHP cycle

The basic CHP process comprises five main steps: the fluid in a liquid state is compressed by a pump (1-2), preheated, evaporated at constant pressure (2-3), expanded in a first turbine (3-4), cooled at constant pressure in a condenser in order to provide the required end-user heating power (Q_m) at T_M. Then, it is expanded in a second turbine (5-6) and condensed at constant pressure (6-1) to the initial state.

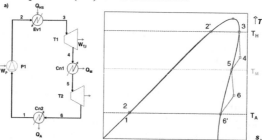

Figure 1: a) Schematic view of a CHP cycle. b) Corresponding temperature-entropy diagram.

3. Design methodology and implementation

The methodology implemented in this work is inspired from the main stages described by Piña-Martinez et al. (2021): 1) needs and goals; 2) generation of the initial set of molecule candidates, and 3) flowsheet and working fluid optimisation.

3.1. Needs and goals

Even if the considered operation is CHP, the original needs for CCHP are maintained. This is to ensure that the working fluid is still able to operate in CCHP mode. The needs are: 1) subcritical operation; 2) no freezing at T_C; 3) low mechanical stress 4) no air infiltration, 5) compact units; 6) toxicity and flammability risks, and steel compatibility equivalent to n-pentane since it is already used in commercial ORC applications, 7) low environmental impact (Global Warming Potential and Ozone Depletion Potential).

3.2. Generation of the initial set of molecule candidates and screening procedure

In this study, the experimental or estimated data available in the DDB, the DIPPR and the NIST databases are used to generate the initial set of 2540 molecule candidates. The screening order is: (1) critical temperature, (2) triple-point temperature, (3) vapor pressure at T_C, (4) density at T_C, (5) vapor pressure at T_H, (6) toxicity, (7) GWP, (8) ODP, (9) autoignition temperature (AIT), (10) compatibility and (11) stability.

3.3. Flowsheet and working fluid optimisation

Superstructure modelling. To consider the flowsheet structure as a degree of freedom in the design problem, a superstructure including several process alternatives simultaneously is defined. To do so, additional units are added to the flowsheet to act as switches that divert the overall incoming mass flow towards a specific downstream section of the process, as described by Quintero-Masselski et al. (2022). The path selection is represented by binary structural decision variables:

$$y_i = \begin{cases} 1 & \textit{if path i is selected,} \\ 0 & \textit{otherwise} \end{cases} \qquad (1)$$

Working-fluid selection. After the screening, the selection of the working fluid is considered in the design problem by means of a non-negative discrete variable w corresponding to the total number of candidate molecules. The working fluid stream is defined as a multicomponent stream and molar fractions are defined as follows:

$$z_w = 1.0; z_{j \neq w} = 0.0 \tag{2}$$

3.4. Implementation and optimization algorithm

The superstructure simulation is performed with the steady-state software simulation ProSimPlus. The *translated-consistent* Peng-Robinson (*tc*-PR) model (Le Guennec et al., 2016) is used to estimate saturation and caloric properties. As presented in section 4.3, the design problem corresponds to a mixed-integer nonlinear programming (MINLP) problem. For this work, MIDACO, an extended ant colony optimization algorithm for non-convex MINLP, is used. As all metaheuristic algorithms, it does not guarantee global optimality, however the exploration limits for the algorithm are considered sufficiently large to achieve a good trade-off between the performance indicators.

4. CHP integrated design

4.1. Superstructure description and process considerations

The superstructure embeds four flowsheet options and their combinations. Three of them are classically related to power applications: a) reheating, b) turbine bleeding (open), and c) regeneration. The fourth option is related to the end-user heat supply: in the case of turbine bleeding, the extracted stream may be used for end-user heating.

For the description of the CHP superstructure (Figure 2), consider the stream entering switch **S1**. If the total reheat option is active, turbine **T1** and reheater **Rh1** are active. On the contrary, a high-pressure (HP) bleeding can be selected. If it is the case, turbine **T2** and splitter **Sp1** are active. If the end-user heat supply by bleeding is active, condenser **Cn1** is active. The remaining stream exiting splitter **Sp1** may be reheated. In that case, turbine **T6** and reheater **Rh2** are active. Analogously, a low-pressure (LP) bleeding with reheat and/or EU heat supply options can be represented by switches **S4**, **S5** and **S7**. The working fluid exiting closing switch **Cs4** enters turbine **T4**. After this point, if end-user heating power has not been supplied by condensers **Cn1** or **Cn2**, then condenser **Cn3** and turbine **T5** are active. Then, if the regeneration option is active, regenerator **Rg1** is active. After that, the working fluid is condensed (**Cn4**), compressed (**P1**), and regenerated (**Rg1**) if $y_{reg} = 1$. Finally, if bleeding options are active, the feedwater stream is mixed (mixers **Mx1** and **Mx2**) with bleeding stream 1, or 2, or both depending on the number of active bleeding streams.

The assumptions used in this work have been adopted from those outlined by Pina-Martinez et al. (2021). The required power and heating needs are 3 and 4 MW respectively. The heat transfer fluid with an unknown mass flow rate enters evaporator **Ev1** at $T_{HS} = 220°C$, the maximum temperature reached by the working fluid during the operation is set to 150 °C. Cooling water is assumed as cooling medium in condenser **Cn4** with an inlet temperature of $T_{cool} = 15°C$ and an outlet temperature of 30°C. The end-user heating power is used for hot water generation. Depending on the configuration, water stream enters either condensers **1**, **2** or **3** at 15°C and leaves at 80°C.

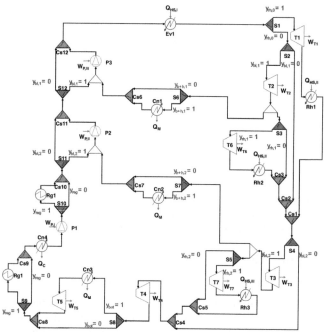

Figure 2: Flowsheet of the CHP cycle superstructure. Abbreviations: Cn: condenser; Ev: evaporator; Mx: mixer; P: pump; Rg: regenerator; S: switch, Sp: splitter; T: turbine.

This condition imposes that the working fluid should be condensed at $P^{sat}(90°C)$, in order to avoid a temperature cross. In consequence, if the bleeding option and end-user heat supply by bleeding are both active, bleeding pressure must be equal to $P^{sat}(90°C)$. Otherwise, it is a degree of freedom of the problem. In addition, the stream exits condenser **Cn4** as saturated liquid at 40°C. For all heat exchangers, the minimum temperature approach is equal to 10 K.

4.3. Problem statement

Given Combined Heating and Power cycle specifications, constraints and a thermo-economic pair of objective functions, an optimisation problem is formulated to determine an optimal process flowsheet and the corresponding working fluid:

$$\min_{x,y,w} f(x, y, w)$$

$$s.t. \quad h(x, y, w) = 0; \quad g(x, y, w) \leq 0 \tag{3}$$

where $x \in \mathbb{R}^c$ represents a vector of c continuous process variables; $y \in \{0,1\}^b$ represents a vector of b binary structural decision variables; and $w \in \mathbb{N}$ represents a non-negative discrete variable and enables the selection of a given working fluid. The set of equations h corresponds to a vector of e equality constraints including mass and energy balances, thermodynamic relations, and sizing equations. The set of equations g corresponds to a vector of m inequality constraints that enforce bounds on the operating conditions and binary variables in order to satisfy design specifications. The presented structural options represented by 7 binary variables correspond to a maximum number of $2^7 = 128$ potential integer combinations. However, many combinations are infeasible due to logic constraints, e.g., if the total reheat option is active, HP bleeding cannot be active.

4.3.1. Objective functions

Levelized cost of electricity (LCOE). According to the International Energy Agency (IEA) report: Projected Costs of Generating Electricity, (IEA, 2020), LCOE (Eq. 4) is the principal tool for comparing the plant-level unit costs of different baseload technologies over their operating lifetimes.

$$LCOE = \left(CAPEX \cdot \frac{i(1+i)^n}{(1+i)^n - 1} + OPEX - HC \right) / PROD_{elec} \tag{4}$$

where i represents the discount rate, and n the project lifetime. CAPEX and OPEX accounts for the capital and operational expenditures respectively. For CHP, the heat credit (HC) consists of the total cash flow related to the heat supply in a yearly basis. For this case study, the project lifetime is equal to 25 years, with a discount rate of 7%, and 7446h of annual operation. Maintenance cost of each equipment is fixed at 3% of the purchased cost. Heat price is equal to 34.87 €/MWh. Biomass price is 16.4 €/MWh. Cooling water price is 1.12 €/MWh (Schilling et al., 2020). The exchange rate is 1 USD/€. The economic evaluation is based on the Manual of Process Economic Evaluation (Chauvel et al., 2003), and more specifically, the Pré-Estime method.

Primary energy savings ratio (PESR). This parameter provides information on how much primary energy is saved by using a multigeneration system instead of separated ones to supply the required duties. PESR is defined as:

$$PESR = 1 - \dot{Q}_{HS,CHP} / \dot{Q}_{HS,SS} \tag{5}$$

where $\dot{Q}_{HS,CHP}$ and $\dot{Q}_{HS,SS}$ are the amount of energy per unit of time from the heat source required by the CHP system and separated systems (SS) to provide electric and heating powers respectively. Detailed calculations are provided by Piña-Martinez et al., 2021.

5. Results of the integrated design of the CHP cycle

The results of the integrated working-fluid and CHP cycle design are presented in detail. Three parallel MIDACO instances took 56 h and evaluated 156 840 points. Optimization procedure was stopped when the Pareto front was not improved after 50 000 consecutive evaluations. Out of the 128 structural alternatives, 36 are found feasible. This optimization contains 52 505 feasible points, 104 335 unfeasible points and 24 Pareto points were obtained. It is worth recalling that the structural options present in the superstructure were represented by 7 binary variables. In order to have a better insight of the results, it was decided to create 2 meta-variables (y_I and y_{II}). Variable y_I groups binary variables (y_{rh0}, y_{bl1} and y_{bl2}) and their feasible combinations (Table 1), while variable y_{II} groups binary variables (y_{rh1} and y_{rh2}) (Table 2).

From Figure 3, it is possible to observe that all the configurations lying on the Pareto front consist of two turbine bleedings, end-user heat supply with the LP bleeding and regeneration. Hereafter, such features are called *general features*. In terms of y_{II}, it is possible to distinguish three configurations on the Pareto front. The first zone corresponds to $y_{II} = 3$, it corresponds to a configuration with the general features and the reheating of the remaining streams exiting splitters **Sp1** and **Sp2**. This configuration cluster results in an average PESR and LCOE of 19.5% and 171.8 USD/MWh respectively. Points lying on the second zone ($y_{II} = 2$) represent a flowsheet with the general features and the reheating of the remaining stream exiting splitter **Sp1**. This cluster exhibits a lower average PESR (18.6%) and LCOE (168.2 USD/MWh) than cluster 1. Finally, the third zone of the Pareto front ($y_{II} = 0$) corresponds to a configuration with the general features and no reheat at all. Such a cluster exhibits the lowest average PESR (16.9%) and LCOE

(164.6 USD/MWh). In terms of working fluids (Figure 3.e), only three molecules passed all the filters: 1) 1,2-difluoroethane (HFC-152), 2) neopentane and 3) (E)-1-chloro-3,3,3-trifluoro-1-propene (HCFO-1233zd(E)). Figure 3.e shows that HFC-152 is used with configuration 1, while HCFO-1233zd(E) is the best match for configurations 2 and 3.

Table 1. Definition of variable y_I.

y_I	$y_{rh,0}$	$y_{bl,1}$	$y_{bl,2}$
0	0	0	0
1	0	1	0
2	0	1	1
3	1	0	0
4	1	0	1

Table 2. Definition of variable y_{II}.

y_{II}	$y_{rh,1}$	$y_{rh,2}$
0	0	0
1	0	1
2	1	0
3	1	1

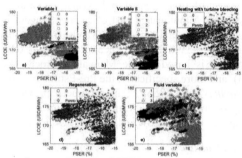

Figure 3. Trade-off figures between LCOE and PESR as a function of meta-variables y_I, y_{II}, binary variables y_{b+h} and y_{reg}, and the working fluid integer variable (w).

6. Conclusions

In the present work, a product-and process-design approach for the selection of suitable working fluids and flowsheet configuration for novel Combined Heating and Power applications has been presented. Integrated design of the CHP system enabled to identify two promising working fluids (HFC-152 and HCFO-1233zd(E)), and three process structures highlighting that optimal configurations consist of turbine bleedings with heating supply, and regeneration.

References

S. Briola, 2017, Plant and method for the supply of electric power and/or mechanical power, heating power and/or cooling power (World Intellectual Property Organization WO2017158511A1).

A. Chauvel, G. Fournier, C. Raimbault, 2003. Manual of Process Economic Evaluation. Editions TECHNIP.

International Energy Agency (IEA), 2020, Projected Costs of Generating Electricity 2020.

Y. Le Guennec, R. Privat, J.N. Jaubert, 2016, Development of the translated-consistent *tc*-PR and *tc*-RK cubic equations of state for a safe and accurate prediction of volumetric, energetic and saturation properties of pure compounds in the sub- and super-critical domains. Fluid Phase Equilibria, 429, 301–312.

A. Piña-Martinez, S. Lasala, R. Privat, V. Falk, J.N. Jaubert, 2021, Design of Promising Working Fluids for Emergent Combined Cooling, Heating, and Power (CCHP) Systems. ACS Sustainable Chemistry & Engineering, 9(35), 11807–11824.

C. Quintero-Masselski, J.F. Portha, L. Falk, 2022, Conception and optimization of an ammonia synthesis superstructure for energy storage. Chemical Engineering Research and Design, 177, 826–842.

J. Schilling, C. Horend, A. Bardow, 2020, Integrating superstructure-based design of molecules, processes, and flowsheets. AIChE Journal, 66(5), e16903.

Flavio Manenti, Gintaras V. Reklaitis (Eds.), Proceedings of the 34th European Symposium on Computer Aided Process Engineering / 15th International Symposium on Process Systems Engineering (ESCAPE34/PSE24), June 2-6, 2024, Florence, Italy

Multi-period stochastic optimization of integrating carbon capture and storage/utilization (CCS/CCU) for cement industry

Pingping Wang [a, *], Stavros Papadokonstantakis [a]

[a]Institute of Chemical, Environmental and Bioscience Engineering, TU Wien, Getreidemarkt 9, 1060 Vienna, Austria

*pingping.wang@tuwien.ac.at

Abstract

This work introduces a comprehensive network to model various CCS/CCU supply chains for the Austrian cement industry. Our framework considers carbon capture, various transportation options, and multiple storage and utilization possibilities, including depleted oil and gas reservoir in Austria and offshore storage sites in the North Sea, as well as utilization in synthetic fuels. An optimization framework is employed to strategically design CCS/CCU systems, accounting for both inherent and external uncertainties including production costs, carbon pricing, storage capabilities, and product pricing within a dynamic temporal framework. The future projections of energy supply from REMIND model are integrated into the prospective life cycle assessment for the overall systems. The optimal design problem is formulated as a multi-period stochastic programming model that finds the trade-off between environmental impacts evaluated by prospective life cycle assessment and total annual profit of the superstructure paths for different emissions reduction pathways over a deployment time horizon of 30 years. The results suggest that the Levelized Cost of Avoided Carbon can be lower than €150 per ton CO_2 stored for Austrian emissions at a baseline scenario. Furthermore, while the adoption of CO2 utilization could potentially enhance system profitability that depends on the competitiveness of synthetic fuel production costs, it also results in diminished CO_2 reduction efficiency due to the increased carbon footprint of the utilization processes.

Keywords: Carbon capture and storage, Carbon capture and utilization, Prospective LCA, Stochastic optimization, Multi-period optimization.

1. Introduction

The cement industry accounts for approximately 7% of global and 4% of European CO_2 emissions, predominantly due to the calcination process of limestone. Austrian cements production, in a global context, reaches the lowest CO_2 emissions, recording 549kg per ton of cement. This notable achievement is attributed to the adoption of cutting-edge kiln technologies, and optimization of clinker content in the cement and a continuously increased use of alternative fuels. However, further reductions in CO_2 emissions are imperative to attain carbon neutrality by 2050. Carbon Capture Storage and Utilization (CCS/CCU) can significantly reduce both the process related and fuel related emissions. It is identified as the single measure that has the largest potential for further overall emission reductions in the cement industry.

Nonetheless, the integration of CCS/CCU technologies into the cement industry faces numerous challenges. This include varying technological readiness levels (TRLs) for carbon capture and utilization technologies, the absence of extensive CO_2 pipeline infrastructures in the EU, and the limited policy support for underground storage. There are doubts about the durability of underground storage for permanent sequestration. Economic barriers also exist, such as high production costs for CO_2-based products compared with fossil-based products, uncertainties regarding future energy prices, and the necessity for future system optimization in tandem with dynamic transition of social-economic systems. Moreover, inconsistences and lack of transparency in input data for techno-economic analysis and life cycle assessment, along with insufficient consideration of time-dependent scenarios and capacities of on-going real-world projects, present significant hurdles for further development in this field.

Process system engineering (PSE) methods and tools are instrumental in bridging the gap and overcome some of the challenges in developing current CCS/CCU systems. Specifically, mathematical programming provides flexible and comprehensive frameworks for designing and optimizing systems. By optimizing supply chain networks and designing integrated processes, the overall system efficiency can be significantly enhanced. Hasan et al. (2014) employed a mixed-integer linear programming (MILP) mathematical model to optimize the supply chain network of CCS in US, assuming revenue generation solely from enhanced oil recovery (EOR), with most CO_2 stored underground. Han et al. (2012) introduced a multi-period stochastic optimization model for CCS/CCU systems accounting for the uncertainties in CO_2 emissions, product prices and operating cost, although they overestimated the available storage capacities in North Sea for South Korea. Tina et al. (2021) proposed a conceptual MINLP approach for developing a CO_2 supply chain in Slovenia, considering the revenue from the avoided tax and selling of products. Viola et al. (2022) devised a novel optimization framework to minimize the total costs while complying with multi reduction pathways over 25 years, capturing emissions from Swiss waste-to-energy sector for storage in the North Sea and a hypothetical Swiss site. Most existing studies have concentrated on the static design of cost-optimal single CO_2 supply chains that achieve specific reduction goals. However, the failure to account for changes in energy systems and technologies improvement over different time periods renders these results insufficiently adaptable to complex and dynamic environments. In this work, we propose a multi-period stochastic optimization model that considers the variation of CO_2 reduction target, production cost of CO_2 capture and utilization technologies, underground storage and transportation capacities, carbon tax prices, and CO_2-based product values in multi-scenario frameworks. This mathematical model is formulated as a MILP problem, which helps in determining the optimal strategies for capturing, transporting, storage, or utilizing CO_2 maximize total net profit while meeting CO2 emissions reduction targets.

2. System Description

The CCS/CCU supply chains developed aim at decarbonizing the Austrian cement production industry. The nine cement plants emit a total 3.22 $MtCO_2$/year. The reference cement plant is a Best Available Technique (BAT) defined by the European Cement Research Academy. We consider the most mature MEA absorption capture technology derived from the CEMCAP project. Five CO_2 storage sites are considered, which are located at Vienna Basin (SINK 1), Porthos of NL (SINK 2), East UK (SINK 3), Greenland of DK (SINK 4) and Norwegian North Sea (SINK 5). The annual capacities in North Sea is assumed to not exceed 5 $MtCO_2$/year and storage in Vienna Basin is not larger than 2 Mt/year. The estimation of the capacity of each storage site is based on the maximum theoretical capacity and duration, as well as the relative share of Austrian emissions in the EU. Additionally, we incorporate two transit terminals located in the ports of Rotterdam and Linz. Each site is equipped for CO_2 conditioning to meet the requirements for transportation or storage. Post-capture, CO_2 undergoes one of two pre-treatment processes, resulting in either a pressurized state at 110 bar and approximately 30°C for pipeline transport, or a liquefied form at 6.5 bar and around -52°C for other transportation methods. Our system considers five transportation modes: trucks, trains, barges, ships, and pipelines. Based on the information of the 'Carbon2ProductAustria' (C2PAT) project, our chosen utilization technology involves CO_2 refinery concepts coupled with green hydrogen to produce synthetic kerosene fuels by Fischer-Tropsch process.

A unique aspect of our approach is the dynamic integration of CCS/CCU. We consider evolving CO_2 reduction targets over three distinct periods, aiming for 30%, 60%, and 90% reductions, respectively. This phased strategy enables a progressive and feasible shift towards lower emissions. Additionally, we account for expected decreases in CO_2 capture technology costs, based on a learning curve reflecting the anticipated expansion in installation capacities. Regarding the synthetic kerosene, its revenue projection is highly uncertain due to unknown production costs and fluctuating policy incentives. To address this, we employ Monte Carlo sampling to generate stochastic values for production costs and incentives, determining the revenue potential of CO_2-based kerosene. Another critical element of our study is the prospective life cycle assessment (pLCA), which evaluates the environmental impacts of the overall system. The pLCA considers changes in both background and foreground systems. We utilize a tool named 'premise' (Sacchi et al., 2022) to integrate the prospective inventory database from the REMIND SSP2-Base scenario. Under this scenario, we generate pLCA results for our CCS/CCU systems across multiple periods.

3. Mathematical Model

The mathematical model is formulated as MILP with two objective functions: maximize profit and minimize global warming potential impact of CCS/CCU systems.

$$max\ TAP_{p,s}(y,Y,Z)\ =\ Total\ Anual\ Profit(TAP) \tag{1}$$

$$min\ GWP_{p,s}(y,Y,Z)\ =\ Global\ Warming\ Potenial(GWP) \tag{2}$$

$$s.t.\ \begin{matrix} h(y,Y,Z) = 0 \\ g(y,Y,Z) \geq 0 \end{matrix} \begin{cases} Mass\ balance \\ Facility\ and\ Transporation\ capacity\ constraints \\ Reduction\ target\ constraints \end{cases} \tag{3}$$

where y, Y, Z represent the vectors of continuous, binary, and integer variables respectively, while P and S are the sets of time periods and scenarios.

The total annual profit is calculated by the difference between total net benefit (TNB) and total annual cost (TAC).

$$TNB_{p,s} = \sum_{st}\sum_{ut} Carbon_{p,s,st,ut} CA_{p,s,st,ut} + \sum_{ut} UC_{p,s,ut} PF_{p,s,ut} \tag{4}$$

where ST and UT represent the sets for CO2 storage and utilization sites, Carbon is the carbon price, CA is the amount of CO2 emissions avoided of the systems, UC is the production capacity of CO2-based product, PF is the price of selling of fuels. TAC is the of total cost of CO2 capture and conditioning, transport (1 stands for in Austria, 2 stands from Linz port to aboard storage sites, see also in Figure 1), storage and utilization costs. To formulate the multiperiod stochastic model under uncertain production costs and policy incentives, we employ a multi-scenario stochastic programming approach that aims to use a finite set of scenarios to maximize the expected value of the profit.

$$max\ E[TAP] = \sum_r prob_r TAP_r \tag{5}$$

where r is a subscript that represents a particular stochastic scenario and $prob_r$ is the probability of occurrence of this stochastic scenario.

In our research, we also employ several economic and environmental indicators to evaluate the performance of the overall CCS/CCU systems. The first indicator, the Levelized Cost of Stored Carbon (LCSC), is calculated by dividing the total annual cost by the amount of CO_2 stored at a given time. The second indicator, the Levelized Cost of Avoided Carbon (LCAC), is determined by dividing the Total Annual Cost (TAC) by the amount of CO_2 avoided. Another key metric is the CCS/CCU Efficiency, defined as the ratio of CO_2 avoided to CO_2 stored or utilized. Additionally, we measure CO_2 Reduction, which is calculated by dividing the CO_2 avoided by the total CO_2 emissions emitted.

4. Case Study

In the case study, we explore different scenarios for CCS and CCS/CCU systems in Austria in three time periods (now-2030,2030-2040 and 2040-2050), considering varying policy environments.

(1) CCS Scenarios:

1. **Scenario 0 (Pessimistic):** Assumes no underground storage or pipeline transportation in Austria across all periods.
2. **Scenario 1 (Conservative):** No underground storage projects in Austria, but pipeline transportation is allowed in periods 2 and 3.
3. **Scenario 2 (Baseline):** Underground storage and pipeline transportation start from period 2 in Austria with a conservative capacity of 1 million tons per year.
4. **Scenario 3 (Optimistic):** CCS projects begin from period 2 with sufficient storage capacity for the cement industry's CO_2 emissions in Austria.

(2) CCS/CCU Scenario:

Building on Scenario 2 from the CCS-only system, we examine the introduction of CCU projects in Austria. This scenario involves a hypothetical synthetic fuel facility producing kerosene for the European market, priced at typical petroleum kerosene rates. We base our market price projections on the Energy Information Administration's (EIA) jet fuel forecasts. The carbon price is consistent with the baseline scenario in the CCS-only system. For e-kerosene production costs in the EU, we refer to The International Council on Clean Transportation (ICCT) estimates, averaging the lowest and highest cost projections as shown in the Table 1. These values are used in a Monte Carlo simulation for stochastic sampling, assuming a normal distribution with a standard deviation of $\pm 3\%$.

Table 1. Parameters for Estimating Uncertain Revenue of Synthetic Kerosene

€/liter	Production_min	Production_max	Kerosene Price	Carbon Price (€/tonCO2 avoided)
Period 1	1.538	3.178	0.54	150
Period 2	1.224	2.807	0.80	175
Period 3	0.951	2.304	1.00	200

5. Results and Discussion

5.1. CCS-only in the system

From Figure 1 (a), we observe that the LCAC consistently surpasses the LCSC, indicating nonignorable emissions associated with CCS systems. In Scenario 2, the capture costs demonstrate a decrease from Period 1 to Period 3. Starting in Period 2, transportation costs in Austria become predominant due to the expensive pipeline installation, which, nonetheless, contributes to improved CCS Efficiency. The most cost-effective transport options to the North Sea involve barges and ships, which are assumed for the transit from Linz to the storage sites. As the capacity for capture and storage in Austria increases in Period 3, there is a potential for cost reduction and further enhancement of CCS

Efficiency. The pipeline transportation cost declines closely tied to capacity expansion. If the system only keeps the truck and trains options in Austria for transporting (Scenario 0 and 3), the LCSC is gradually decreased from period 1 to 3 (not shows in the Figure). But the trend of LCAC decay comes weaker as more CO_2 emissions comes from mobilities. Transporting all CO_2 emissions to the North Sea in Period 3 of Scenario 1 is slightly costlier than storing 1 million tons of CO_2 in Austria as outlined in Scenario 2. In the pessimistic Scenario 0 for Period 3, the absence of pipelines and underground storage in Austria allows for keeping LCAC under €100, albeit with the lowest CCS efficiency, but still achieving CO_2 reduction exceeding 70%. Conversely, the optimistic Scenario 3 for Period 3 showcases the highest CCS efficiency and CO_2 reduction, predicated on the availability of at least two storage sites in Austria. This case study underscores that the viability of CCS is a balance between LCAC and the price of carbon emission credits. With robust carbon pricing place (at least €150/ton), the CCS systems could be profitable even without storage or under conservative estimations for underground storage in Austria (S0, S1 and S2). The findings advocate that, despite uncertain policies and the absence of infrastructures (i.e., pipeline), proactive measures are preferable to inaction.

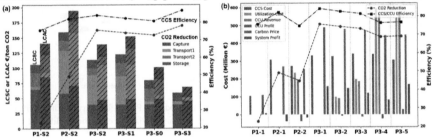

Figure 1. Economic and Environmental Performance Indicators for (a) CCS Systems, (b)CCS/CCU Systems Across Different Scenarios and Periods (S0 to S3 in (a) represents multi scenarios, 1 to 5 in (b) represents r, scenarios with stochastic value of utilization costs)

5.2. CCS/CCU in the system

Figure 1(b) delineates the cost, revenue, and efficiency metrics of the CCS/CCU systems. In the baseline scenario for the CCS-only framework, system profitability depends upon the value attributed to CO_2 avoided. In the second period (P2-1), the high costs of implementing CCS make it difficult to achieve profit, especially with a carbon price set at €150. However, the anticipated financial gains in the third period (P3-1) with higher carbon pricing are projected to offset the preceding losses. The integration of CCU into the system introduces a dual dependency for profitability: not only the carbon tax avoided from CO_2 reduction is considered, but the economic viability of the utilization system itself is also crucial, hinging on both the reduction of production costs and the policy incentives. During P2-2, the stochastic estimate for synthetic kerosene production costs €0.96/liter emerges as significantly high, though with a minimal likelihood of occurrence, it remains noncompetitive with fossil-based alternatives. By the third period, if the cost of synthetic kerosene falls below that of traditional fossil kerosene (P3-5), the system stands to gain extra profits from the utilization process. However, the integration of CO_2 utilization into the system notably diminishes CCS/CCU efficiency relative to the CCS-only model. As depicted in Figure 2(a), under the assumption that synthetic hydrogen is exclusively derived from wind energy and accounting for the energy transition within the national electrical grid, the prospective LCA reveals a downward trajectory for the GWP impact of kerosene synthesis. Yet, the GWP impact per ton of CO_2 utilized remains significantly higher in period 3 (235 kg eq-CO_2/ton CO_2 saved) compared to only CCS-systems that has a peak in scenario P3-S0 (192 kg eq-CO_2/ton CO_2 stored). Consequently, the supplementary revenue generated, combined with the marginal decline in profits due to augmented emissions from the utilization process, together influence the net benefits of the systems. In scenario P3-5, which boasts the highest system profitability, further multi-objective analysis utilizing the ε-constrained method clarifies the trade-off between GWP and profit, as visualized in Figure 2(b). When profitability in the CCU system materializes in period 3, the decision-making process should navigate the balance between environmental impact and financial return. The Pareto curve illustrates that reducing the CCU share from 47.7% to 29.6% correlates with a decrease in profit, yet concurrently yields benefits from a reduction in CO_2 emissions for the system.

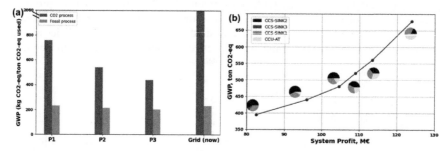

Figure 2. (a) GWP of kerosene production process in multi-periods; (b) Pareto-font curve of the profit and GWP of CCS/CCU systems (the pie charts show the share of storage/utilization capacities at different sites)

6. Conclusions

In summary, this study assesses the economic and environmental impact of integrating CCS/CCU in Austrian cement industry. We find that the feasibility of systems heavily depends on policy and carbon pricing. Even without new infrastructure for underground storage and pipeline transport in Austria, CCS could still achieve over 70% CO_2 reduction efficiency for the cement industry. Allowing underground storage in Austria would significantly boost profitability and reduction efficiency. CCU can additionally enhance profits, conditional on lower production costs and supportive policies. The study underlines the efficiency and profit trade-offs with CCS/CCU adoption and addresses the need for policymakers to adapt to changing environmental and economic landscapes.

References

M. M. Faruque Hasan et al., 2014, Nationwide, Regional, and Statewide CO2 Capture, Utilization, and Sequestration Supply Chain Network Optimization. Ind. & Eng. Chem. Res.53 (18), 7489-7506

J.-H. Han et al., 2012, Multiperiod Stochastic Optimization Model for Carbon Capture and Storage Infrastructure under Uncertainty in CO2 Emissions, Product Prices, and Operating Costs. Ind. & Eng. Chem. Res. 51 (35), 11445-11457.

T. Kegl et al., 2021, Conceptual MINLP approach to the development of a CO2 supply chain network – Simultaneous consideration of capture and utilization process flowsheets. J. Clea. Prod. 314: 128008.

V. Becattini et al., 2022, Carbon dioxide capture, transport and storage supply chains: Optimal economic and environmental performance of infrastructure rollout. Inter. J. Gre. Gas Cont. 117: 103635.

R. Sacchi et al., (2022). PRospective EnvironMental Impact asSEment (premise): A streamlined approach to producing databases for prospective life cycle assessment using integrated assessment models. Renew. Sustain. Energy Rev. 160: 112311.

Flavio Manenti, Gintaras V. Reklaitis (Eds.), Proceedings of the 34th European Symposium on Computer Aided Process Engineering / 15th International Symposium on Process Systems Engineering (ESCAPE34/PSE24), June 2-6, 2024, Florence, Italy

MMC Rectifier as an Interface for Sustainable Energies Sources on MTDC Grids

Guillermo Adolfo Anaya-Ruiz[a*], Pascual Eduardo Murillo-Alvarado[a], Alejandra Guadalupe Andrade-Partida[a], Gabriela Guadalupe Esquivel-Barajas[a], Rogelio Gudiño-Valdez[a] and Daniel Miranda-Carrasco[a].

a Department of Energy Engineering, Universidad de La Ciénega del Estado de Michoacán de Ocampo. Av. Universidad Sur 3000, Lomas de Universidad, 59103 Sahuayo de Morelos, Michoacán México.

Corresponding author: gaanaya@ucemich.edu.mx

Abstract

Modular multilevel converters (MMC) had been proposed for several applications on middle and high voltage direct current (DC) grids due to its flexibility, modular characteristic and its fault tolerance, This work presents an MMC rectifier composed by half bridge submodules (SMs), voltage equations on each state of communication are presented, the voltage of MMC rectifier is presented with a technique of capacitor balance called carrier rotation algorithm, and in order to ensure the advantages of this technique, a comparison between traditional phase disposition (PD) technique is presented, the use of capacitor balance shows an CD output voltage whit high gain advantages in comparison with PD technique.

Keywords: MMC rectifier, smart grids, power electronics.

1. Introduction

At end of the 80's The World Commission on Environment and Development declared than humanity have the ability to realize sustainable development, which satisfy present needs without compromise the capacity of satisfy they own future needs (UN. Secretary-General World Commission on Environment and Development, 1987).

In the same way, increase of energy demand and reduction of fossil fuel reserves have triggered the research of alternative solutions (Burhanudin et al., 2022), one of those alternatives are the renewables energies sources (RES) which have the next characteristics, clean sustainable and obtained from inexhaustible resources. Nevertheless, RES are intermittent since there is not a continual production of electrical energies due to natural inherent behavior of RES which can affect the transmission and distribution grid (A. Alneami el al. 2022).

High voltage direct current (HVDC) and multiterminal direct current (MTDC) grids are both, possible solutions of intermittent behavior presented by RES, these technologies use power electronics such as inverters (DC-AC converters), DC-DC converters and rectifiers (AC-DC converters) in order to bring energy since generation grids trough transmission and distribution across the electrical grid. At the same time, in order to decrease the carbon footprint.

Figure 1 presents an example of implementation of converters on HVDC electric grids, the possible connection of several energies sources as conventional as noun conventional is observed. At the same time a series of converter, inverters and rectifiers are required which ensure an output signal on a HVDC CD bus which is connected to the transmission HVDC line.

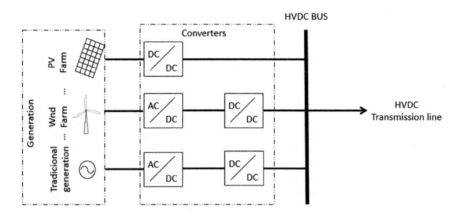

Figure 1. Example of connection of several energy sources to a HVDC transmission line.

One of the key converters on the last decades for such application had been the modular multilevel converter (MMC), as inversion and rectification applications, this converter is formed by an upper and a lower arm, such as legs by every phase, each arm is built by submodules (SMs) composed by half or full bridges of IGBTs o MOSFETs interrupters with antiparallel diodes on each interrupter, and a capacitor in parallel of each bridge, finally the converter has diodes connected on parallel at the output,(Liu et al., 2022). Figure 2 presents an example of this converter as rectifier.

Due to their flexibility and fault tolerance, MMC rectifiers have been proposed for several HVDC systems, producing cost-efficient systems(Hai Nguyen & Thinh Quach, 2021). However, in order to reach HVDC levels an extra DC-DC converter is required increasing those cost-efficient systems.

This work presents a comparison of an MMC rectifier using a traditional phase disposition (PD) modulation technique and a rectifier based on MMC structure, with high voltage gain, which uses a technique of capacitor balance called carrier rotation algorithm (K. Shen et al, 2013). This technique routes the carries signals on each cycle of the modular signal, reducing the switch modulation time of the MMC converter submodules, distribution output voltage in each of submodules, this converter will reduce the number of converters uses for implement Figure 1, grouping together converter AC-DC and DC-DC in just one converter AC-DC, reducing production costs.

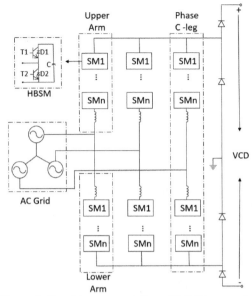

Figure 2. Graphic representation of MMC converter.

2. Operation principal

In order to present the operation principal of device, a single phase is presented on Figure 3, the rest phases will be supposed to work in the same way with a modulation phase shift, *VU* and *VL* represents the upper and lower arm's voltages. Formed by the addition of SMs' voltages, at the same time, V_{mp} represents the middle point of converter, while i_{dc_u} and i_{dc_l} represents DC currents at output, at the same time, $i_{\_u}$ and $i_{\_l}$ represents the upper and lower currents on arms.

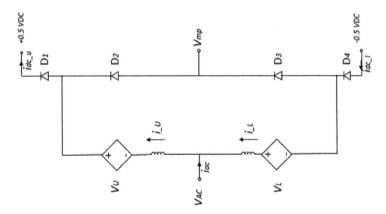

Figure 3 Single phase representation for converter voltage and current obtention.

The four voltage, product of the commutation of SMs in each arm are presents by Eq. (1) to Eq. (4).

$$Vp = 0.5Vdc - VAC, \quad VL = 0.5Vdc + VAC \tag{1}$$

$$Vp = 0.5Vdc - VAC, \quad VL = VAC - Vmid \tag{2}$$

$$Vp = Vmid - VAC, \quad VL = VAC - Vmid \tag{3}$$

$$Vp = Vmid - VAC, \quad VL = 0.5VDC + VAC \tag{4}$$

At the same time, the currents flow for the four commutations of SMs in each arm are presented on Table 1.

Table 1 currents at upper and lower arm on each state

Currents at upper and lower arm on each state	
$iu > 0, il > 0$	Currents at first state
$iu > 0, il < 0$	Currents at second state
$iu < 0, il < 0$	Currents at third state
$iu < 0, il > 0$	Currents at fourth state

3. Modulation technique

The presented configuration implements a traditional PD modulation technique, nevertheless this work proposes the implementation of capacitor balance called carrier rotation algorithm, which routs the carrier signal at the end of every cycle of modular signal, the modular signal is always fixed.

Figure 4 presents an example of the rotation algorithm for upper arm, the commutation for lower arm is complementary with upper arm, in which is observed there are four carrier signals and one modular, at the same time, when modulation period is finished, the carrier signal four pass to first position while carrier one pass to second position and successively, in order to finish a rotation cycle of carriers signal four cycles of modular signal must pass.

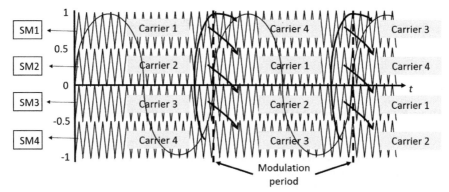

Figure 4. Carrier rotation example.

This technique ensures that voltage across each capacitor on each SMs is stable and equal, reducing the voltage stress product of switching components and increasing the voltage output at the same time, due to the addition of voltage of several capacitors of every SMs, without the addition of sensors on each SMs.

4. Simulation

The rectifier based on MMC on its five-level configuration and a single phase which uses four SMs for upper arm and four SMs for lower arm had been simulated using a regular PD commutation technique, at the same way, the rectifier was simulated using a technique of capacitor balance called carrier rotation algorithm proposed and presented on previous section, using a sinusoidal 100 V, 60 Hz source and 1.8 kHz carrier signals or 30 times the frequency of modulation signal.

Figure 5 presents the output voltage signal of the rectifier, using a traditional PD modulation technique, it is observer than voltage output is approximately twice the voltage peak of input sinusoidal signal.

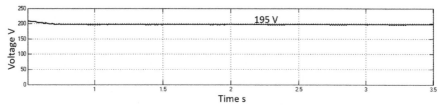

Figure 5 Simulation output voltage of MMC rectifier with PD modulation without capacitor balance.

In the other hand, Figure 6 presents output voltage of MMC rectifier using the capacitor balance technique carrier rotation algorithm, it is observer than voltage gain is around six times the voltage peak of sinusoidal input signal, working as a rectifier with gain.

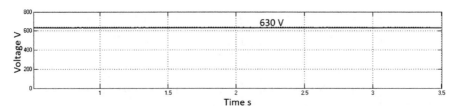

Figure 6. Output voltage of MMC rectifier using the capacitor balance technique carrier rotation algorithm.

Form the comparison of those simulations is important to emphasize than form the implementation of technique carrier rotation algorithm results in an increase of the output voltage of the rectifier without the need to implement other control systems or sensors that would increase the cost of building this device.

5. Conclusions

The uses of converter, as inverters as rectifiers of power electronics for MVDC and HVDC applications have been increased on last years, making them an important research topic for upcoming technologies.

The comparison of MMC rectifiers using a conventional PD technique and with a capacitor balance carrier rotation algorithm simulations was presented, it is observer than the rectifier with capacitor balance has the advantage of obtaining higher levels of gain compared to its counterpart, achieving to reduce the costs that would be necessary for the construction of two converters, one which rectifier and other which increases the voltage to the necessaries transmission and distribution levels.

References

UN. Secretary-General World Commission on Environment and Development (1987). Report of the World Commission on Environment and Development : "Our common future". [New York] UN, 4 Aug. 1987.

A. Alneami, A. Vahidnia and L. Meegahapola, (2022). "Enhancing the Stability of Integrated Power System With Renewable Energy Through Advanced Controls," 2022 32nd Australasian Universities Power Engineering Conference (AUPEC), Adelaide, Australia, 2022, pp. 1-6, doi: 10.1109/AUPEC58309.2022.10215685.

Liu, J., Member, S., Zhang, D., Member, S., & Dong, D. (2022). *Analysis of Hybrid Modular Multilevel Rectifier Operated at Non-Unity Power Factor for HVDC Applications*.

Hai Nguyen, T., & Thinh Quach, N. (2021). A hybrid HVDC converter based on M2C and diode rectifiers without DC capacitors for offshore wind farm integration. *International Journal of Electrical Power and Energy Systems*, *133*.

J. Burhanudin, A. S. A. Hasim, A. M. Ishak, J. Burhanudin, and S. M. F. B. S. M. Dardin, (2022). "*A Review of Power Electronics for Nearshore Wave Energy Converter Applications*," *IEEE Access*, vol. 10. Institute of Electrical and Electronics Engineers Inc., pp. 16670–16680, 2022. doi: 10.1109/ACCESS.2022.3148319.

K. Shen, Bailu Xiao, Jun Mei, Leon M. Tolbert, Jianze Wang, Xingguo Cai, Yanchao Ji., *(2013).* "*A modulation reconfiguration based fault-tolerant control scheme for modular multilevel converters,*" *2013 Twenty-Eighth Annual IEEE Applied Power Electronics Conference and Exposition (APEC), Long Beach, CA, USA, 2013, pp. 3251-3255.*

Flavio Manenti, Gintaras V. Reklaitis (Eds.), Proceedings of the 34th European Symposium on Computer Aided Process Engineering / 15th International Symposium on Process Systems Engineering (ESCAPE34/PSE24), June 2-6, 2024, Florence, Italy

Multi-objective Optimization Applied to the Thermal Hydrolysis and Anaerobic Digestion system for Biosludge from the Pulp Kraft Industry

Nicolás Goycoechea[a*], Liliana Borzacconi[a], Jimena Ferreira[b,c], Martin Pedemonte[c], Iván López[a]

[a] *Biotechnological Processes for the Environment Group, Universidad de la República, 11300 Montevideo, Uruguay.*

[b] *Heterogenous Computing Laboratory, Universidad de la República, 11300 Montevideo, Uruguay.*

[c] *Chemical & Process Systems Engineering Group, Universidad de la República, 11300 Montevideo, Uruguay.*

*: ngoycoechea@fing.edu.uy

Abstract

Anaerobic digestion (AD) is a method for generating energy from renewable sources and mitigating greenhouse gas emissions by replacing fossil resources. Pretreatments are employed to enhance biosludge biodegradability, improving biogas production and waste-to-energy conversion in AD. Although thermal hydrolysis (TH) is a widely used technology with high energy recovery, it can generate recalcitrant compounds, presenting operational and environmental challenges. After TH and AD detectable recalcitrant nitrogen compounds, such as Dissolved Organic Nitrogen (DON), may be present. Usually, TH and AD systems are optimized based on methane production, energy, or economic balances. However, incorporating a multi-objective approach that considers conflicting objectives, including recalcitrant reduction, is beneficial. This study performed a multi-objective optimization, determining the Pareto front for the system energy profit (EP) and the recalcitrant generation quantified as DON in a thermally hydrolyzed cellulose industry biosludge. Results showed a 43 % reduction in recalcitrant generation using multi-objective optimization compared to a single-objective optimization of EP, with only an 8 % reduction in EP compared to the maximum achievable EP.

Keywords: Anaerobic Digestion; Thermal Hydrolysis; Multi-objective Optimization; Recalcitrant; Methane.

1. Introduction

Anaerobic digestion (AD) is a technology used to generate energy from waste, replace fossil resources, and avoid greenhouse gas emissions, but waste used in this process may contain challenging-to-digest fractions (Castro-Amoedo et al., 2021). Therefore, pretreatments can enhance the biodegradability of biosludge, leading to higher biogas production in AD, thus improving waste-to-energy conversion. The cellulose industry sludge has not been studied much, and previous works have shown that degradation can be a challenge. In addition, there is evidence of improvements obtained in biogas production by AD when thermal hydrolysis (TH) is applied, achieving increases of 100 % to 220 % of Biomethane Potential (BMP) (Goycoechea et al., 2023). On the other hand, achieving energy self-sufficiency of the TH and AD process to reduce costs is essential. TH is the most widely used technology for the pretreatment of solid waste and increases energy recovery from waste treated with anaerobic digestion. However, the use of TH can generate recalcitrant compounds, leading to potential operational and environmental problems (Toutian et al., 2020). After TH and AD, detectable recalcitrant nitrogen compounds may be present, such as dissolved organic nitrogen (DON), which affect wastewater disinfection due to the UV absorbance of these compounds.

Therefore, it is crucial to investigate the impact of temperature and time conditions of the TH process on the generation of recalcitrant and take them into account to reduce their production as an objective function to optimize. Typically, TH and AD systems are optimized based on methane production, energy balances, and/or economic balances, which are correlated. However, when the objective is also to reduce the generation of recalcitrant compounds, it is beneficial to follow a multi-objective optimization approach that considers two or more objective functions in conflict. Multi-objective optimization is not limited to finding a single solution but searches for a set of solutions, known as non-dominated solutions. Each solution in this set is considered a Pareto optimum (Deb, 2001), which reflects different trade-offs between the conflicting objectives. Previous studies have presented a multi-objective approach for the revalorization of sludge to obtain energy by incineration, but at the cost of discharges with higher nitrogen contents (Hreiz et al., 2015). In this work, we performed a multi-objective optimization by determining the Pareto front of the energy profit of the TH and AD system and the recalcitrant generation of the TH, which achieves considerable increases in energy profit.

2. Material and Methods

2.1. Substrate Characterization and Testing

The substrate used was biological sludge from the wastewater treatment of a cellulose industry in Uruguay. The sludge was treated with TH and AD, and biogas and recalcitrant compounds were quantified. Goycoechea et al. (2023) presented the response surface of biogas based on laboratory experiences.

2.2. Energy Profit

2.2.1. Parameters used in the Energy Balance

Table 1 presents the parameters used in the energy balances (EB). These parameters are used to evaluate different TH conditions.

2.2.2. Thermal Energy Demand and Recovery for TH

The energy required to increase the sludge temperature to that of the TH reactor is presented in **Eq. (1)**. The **Eq. (2)** presents the energy recovery of the outlet stream of TH. The energy recovery stage is necessary to not compromise the biological process. Finally, **Eq. (3)** presents the total energy. Biological sludge contains total solids (TS) and water. This is modeled as a binary mixture with its corresponding heat capacity of sludge (Cp_{sludge}) and water (Cp_{H_2O}). The calculation and model were performed as it was presented by Barber (2020).

$$E_{THdemand} = \left(\frac{TS\, Cp_{sludge} + (1-TS)Cp_{H_2O}}{TS} \right) (T_{amb} - T_{TH})\, \eta \qquad [1]$$

$$E_{THrecovery} = \left(\frac{TS\, Cp_{sludge} + (1-TS)Cp_{H_2O}}{TS} \right) (T_{TH} - T_{AD})\, \xi \qquad [2]$$

$$E_{TH} = E_{THdemand} + E_{THrecovery} \qquad [3]$$

Table 1: Summary of parameters used for the developed EB.

Parameters	Symbol	Value	Units	References
Ambient temperature	T_{amb}	20	°C	Assumed
Temperature AD	T_{AD}	37	°C	Assumed
Wet sludge density	ρ	1000	kg m^{-3}	Xiao et al. 2018
Time of residence AD	τ	30	days	Xiao et al. 2018
Energy requirement associated with pumping	θ	0.5	kWh m^{-3}	Lu et al. 2008
Energy requirement associated with AD agitation.	ω	0.083	kWh m^{-3} d^{-1}	Lu et al. 2008
Lower calorific value biogas	LHV	9.94	kWh Nm^{-3}CH4	Metcalf & Eddy, 2003
Energy recovery efficiency	η_{BMP}	80	%	Lu et al. 2008
Heat capacity of sludge	Cp_{sludge}	4.2×10^{-4}	kWh kgTS^{-1} K^{-1}	Barber, 2020
Heat capacity of water	Cp_{H_2O}	1.2×10^{-3}	kWh kgH$_2$O^{-1} K^{-1}	Barber, 2020
Total solids concentration	TS	10.0	%	This study
Volatile solids concentration	VS	5.1	%	This study
Heat exchanger efficiency upstream of TH	η	90	%	Lu et al. 2008
Heat exchanger efficiency after TH	ξ	80	%	Lu et al. 2008

2.2.3. Heat Losses in the AD

Heat losses are calculated in the AD, operating at 37 °C. Heat losses through the digester walls, floor, and roof were considered using the heat transfer coefficient values recommended by MetCalf and Eddy (2003), resulting in the heat loss $E_{loss\,AD}\left(\frac{kWh}{tonST}\right)$.

2.2.4. Energy Benefits of Biogas

The corresponding calculation of the energy generated by the biogas is seen in **Eq. (5)**. Based on a previous work (Goycoechea et al., 2023), the BMP was obtained as a function of pretreatment temperature and time conditions.

$$E_{Benefit} = \frac{LHV\,BPM\,VS}{TS}\eta_{BMP} \qquad [5]$$

2.2.5. Energy Profit Calculation

Based on the energy flows presented, we proceed to calculate the variable corresponding to the energy profit (EP) in **Eq. (6)**. The EP variable can be positive in the case of having a net generation or negative in the case of having an energy deficit.

$$E_{EP} = E_{TH} - E_{loss\,AD} - E_{Electricity} + E_{Benefit} \qquad [6]$$

2.3. DON

The objective function associated with DON was based on a Doehlert experimental plan performed for a study domain of TH conditions in a temperature range from 125 °C to 205 °C and times from 15 to 45 min. The resulting function is presented in **Eq. (7)**, where T is the temperature (°C) and t is residence time (min). The methodology was presented in previous work (Goycoechea et al., 2023), where response surfaces based on TH temperature and time conditions were developed for the cellulosic sludge substrate.

$$DON(ppm) = 176 + 0.045\,t - 2.4\,T + 0.0043\,T\,t - 0.0073\,t^2 + 0.0082\,T^2 \quad [7]$$

2.4. Multi-Objective Optimization

For multi-objective optimization, the functions generated by the response surfaces of EP and DON were normalized using $Y_{normalized} = \frac{Y - Y_{min}}{Y_{max} - Y_{min}}$, where Y is the vector of values for the corresponding variable. The objective function related to DON concentration is considered as costs in the optimization problem. Therefore, EP was also analyzed as a cost and was defined as $(1-EP_{normalized})$. Finally, feasible solutions belonging to the Pareto set were evaluated by simulating different TH conditions within the study domain. The study domain was defined based on the validation range of the BMP and DON functions used in previous works. This range is from 125 °C to 205 °C and from 15 min to 45 min. The study domain was subdivided into 1 °C and 1 min to evaluate the different solutions and generate the possible combinations of candidate solutions. We developed algorithms using Matlab to identify the non-dominated solutions of the Pareto front. The solution of the Pareto front whose distance is minimum to a reference point, was identified using the compromise programming method (Deb, 2001). The chosen reference point corresponds to the one that generates the minimum value of both costs, which does not belong to the Pareto front, and corresponds to (0,0) in the normalized ranges. The Euclidean distance was used for the calculation. **Eq. (8)** shows the multi-objective optimization problem formulation.

$$\min_{\{T,t\} \in \Omega} \begin{cases} (1 - EP_{normalized}) \\ DON_{normalized} \end{cases} \qquad [8]$$

$$s.t.:\ Eq.\,(6), Eq.\,(7), \Omega = \{T \in [125\,°C, 205\,°C]; t \in [15\,min, 45\,min]\}$$

3. Results and discussion

3.1. Mono-objective Optimization Approach

3.1.1. Energy Profit Optimization

Figure 1 shows the obtained values for the different TH conditions within the study domain. The obtained function presents a maximum of 306 kWh tonST^{-1} at TH conditions of 172 °C and 30 min. The energy balance results are greater than zero for most of the TH conditions, thus denoting an energy self-sufficiency of the AD process when using TH.

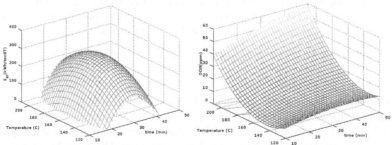

Figure 1: E_{GE} (left) and response surface for DON concentration (right) at different TH conditions.

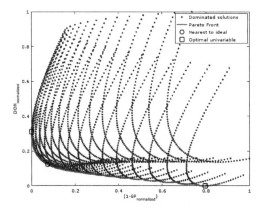

Figure 2: Result of the objective functions within the study domain (blue dots), Pareto front (red solid line), closest point to the ideal (O) and extremes of the front (□).

3.1.2. DON Optimization

Figure 1 presents DON concentration obtained at the end of the AD. The recalcitrant compound has a general increase with increasing temperature. The DON concentration has a local minimum at the boundary of the study domain of 15 min at 143 °C.

3.2. Multi-Objective Optimization Approach

Figure 2 presents the set of values obtained for the objective functions when evaluating the solutions considering the discretized domain (blue dots). Also, **Figure 2** shows the Pareto front in red dots. The extremes of the Pareto front are marked as □, these points are solutions that minimize one of the objective functions within the study domain, being the optimal values previously presented as the maximum indicated for the GE (E_{GE}) and the minimum DON (DON_{opt}). A solution was selected as the one that belongs to the Pareto front and minimizes the Euclidean distance to the reference point. This solution is marked with O in **Figure 2** and represents the nearest point to the ideal solution (0,0). The nearest point translated to TH conditions results in 150 °C and 29 min, corresponding to a value of 280 kWh tonST^{-1} for the objective function corresponding to E_{GE} and 11.1 ppm DON. **Table 2** presents a summary of the values obtained from the single-objective and multi-objective approaches. When comparing the solution selected using the multi-objective formulation with DON_{opt}, it is found that it is possible to obtain a much higher value of energy recovery (x70) at the cost of doubling the recalcitrant. On the other hand, a 43 % reduction in recalcitrant generation is obtained using multi-objective optimization compared to a single-objective optimization of EP, with only an 8 % reduction in EP compared to the maximum achievable EP.

Table 2: E_{GE} and DON values obtained from the optimizations.

Optimization	TH Conditions		E_{GE}	DON
	Temperature (°C)	Time (min)	kWh/tonST	ppm
Multi-Objective	150	29	280	11.1
$E_{GE\ opt}$	172	31	305	19.6
DON_{opt}	143	15	4	5.6

4. Conclusions

This study performed a multi-objective optimization, determining the Pareto front for the system energy profit (EP) and the recalcitrant generation quantified as DON in a thermally hydrolyzed cellulose industry biosludge. When only energy optimization is considered, the energy profit generates a positive energy balance, therefore, an economic benefit from the sale or use of energy. However, this mono-objective optimization implies a recalcitrant generation of 19.6 ppm DON leading to possible environmental problems. On the other hand, including a multi-objective optimization based on considering recalcitrant such as DON as a second objective function allows to produce a 43 % reduction in recalcitrant compounds. Consequently, when recalcitrant generation is considered as another objective function, the multi-objective optimization leads to lower temperature optima than $E_{GE\ opt}$. This allows for the reduction of impacts on UV disinfection of such waters and potential emerging pollutants with nitrogen content, with a scarce reduction of 8 % in energy balance profits.

Also, the multi-objective approach allows to select from the Pareto front solutions with different balances of the objective functions. For instance, if the environmental aspect is more relevant, a different solution can be selected, obtaining a better energy profit than the minimum DON situation, without producing a substantial increment in the recalcitrant concentration.

As a future work, it can be considered the inclusion of other objective functions related to environmental indicators. Also, from the set of Pareto front solutions found in this work, different trade-offs between environmental issues and energy profit can be analyzed.

5. References

Barber, W. (2020). Sludge Thermal Hydrolysis: Application and Potential. In Sludge Thermal Hydrolysis: Application and Potential. IWA Publishing.

Castro-Amoedo, R., Morisod, N., Granacher, J., & Maréchal, F. (2021). The Role of Biowaste: A Multi-Objective Optimization Platform for Combined Heat, Power and Fuel. Frontiers in Energy Research, 9, 718310.

Deb K. Multi-objective optimization using evolutionary algorithms. New York (NY, USA): John Wiley & Sons, Inc.; 2001.

Goycoechea, N., López, I., & Borzacconi, L. (2023). Optimization of anaerobic digestion and solubilization of biosludges from the kraft cellulose industry using thermal hydrolysis as pretreatment. Journal of Environmental Management, 344, 118504.

Hreiz, R., Roche, N., Benyahia, B., & Latifi, M. A. (2015). Multi-objective Optimization of Small-size Wastewater Treatment Plants Operation. Computer Aided Chemical Engineering, 37, 2495–2500.

Lu, J., Gavala, H. N., Skiadas, I. V., Mladenovska, Z., & Ahring, B. K. (2008). Improving anaerobic sewage sludge digestion by implementation of a hyper-thermophilic prehydrolysis step. Journal of Environmental Management, 88(4), 881–889.

Metcalf & Eddy, Inc. (2003). Wastewater engineering : treatment and reuse. Boston :McGraw-Hill.

Toutian, V., Barjenbruch, M., Unger, T., Loderer, C., & Remy, C. (2020). Effect of temperature on biogas yield increase and formation of refractory COD during thermal hydrolysis of waste activated sludge. Water Research, 171.

Xiao, B., Qin, Y., Wu, J., Chen, H., Yu, P., Liu, J., & Li, Y. Y. (2018). Comparison of single-stage and two-stage thermophilic anaerobic digestion of food waste: Performance, energy balance and reaction process. Energy Conversion and Management, 156(August 2017), 215–223.

Flavio Manenti, Gintaras V. Reklaitis (Eds.), Proceedings of the 34th European Symposium on Computer Aided Process Engineering / 15th International Symposium on Process Systems Engineering (ESCAPE34/PSE24), June 2-6, 2024, Florence, Italy

Evaluation of energy requirements for chemicals and fuels manufactured via electrochemical reduction of carbon dioxide

Riccardo Dal Mas,[a] Ana Somoza-Tornos,[a] Anton A. Kiss [a,*]

[a] *Department of Chemical Engineering, Delft University of Technology, Van der Maasweg 9, 2629 HZ Delft, Netherlands*

A.A.Kiss@tudelft.nl

Abstract

As the urgency of reducing greenhouse gas emissions increases, the chemical industry is moving towards more sustainable applications, such as substituting fossil feedstock with renewable ones. The development and implementation of novel technologies will entail momentous, system-wide changes to allow for the production of chemicals and fuels. This work aims at providing an overview of the energy requirements for the production of several chemicals by means of electrochemical reduction of CO_2 (ECO2R), in order to aid the decision-making process to select the products on which further research and development efforts should focus.

The results demonstrate that the production of C_1 oxygenated molecules, such as carbon monoxide and methanol, via ECO2R would have significantly lower requirements in terms of renewable energy generation when compared to fully reduced hydrocarbons (methane, ethylene) and ethanol. This would lead to a less demanding implementation of electrochemical CO_2 utilisation technologies, allowing for a more streamlined deployment of ECO2R within existing supply chains.

Keywords: CO_2 electroreduction; CO_2 utilisation; green processing; electrification

1. Introduction

The electrochemical reduction of CO_2 (ECO2R) has emerged in recent years as an interesting path for the production of sustainable chemicals and fuels within the wider scope of de-fossilisation of the chemical industry (i.e. substitution of fossil resources with renewable ones). It also holds the promise of valorising CO_2, thus incentivising its capture, and potentially helping in mitigating greenhouse gas emissions.

Many factors will play a role in determining the development of ECO2R as part of the chemical industry of the future, alongside biomass-based productions, green hydrogen and overall electrification. Parallel to the experimental efforts dedicated to improving the performance of the electrochemical conversion step, high-level (Verma et al. 2016) and detailed techno-economic assessments (Somoza-Tornos et al. 2021) have studied the economic viability of the production of several chemicals through ECO2R. However, the scale of renewable electricity generation required by these processes, once deployed at the industrial level, appears to be a factor often overlooked.

The many products which synthesis has been demonstrated via low temperature electrolysis of CO_2 (in scope for this work, while the high temperature process is not as it only allows for the production of carbon monoxide) will place different requirements in terms of electricity generation. The integration of chemical and electricity productions will have effects on the economics and environmental performance of the processes, assessed at a high level studying two different scenarios based on carbon intensity of the grid electricity and electricity price. Emphasis is placed on comparing the scale of the renewable power plants that would fulfil the demand for the production of selected chemicals and fuels, comparing the currently demonstrated performance with the forecasted one, before assessing the primary energy input required for the production of the latter and comparing it to their specific energy.

2. Problem statement

In the perspective of a future process industry, in which a number of possible sustainable routes will be available and will go alongside one another, decisions will be made on what the best technologies to substitute current supply chains are, taking into account the scale at which these currently operate. The production of the chemicals and fuels will place requirements of different magnitude on the overall production system, once scaled up to industrial level.

To aid these decisions, a fundamental analysis of the different products has been carried out, evaluating the energy requirement for their production via ECO2R and checking how much CO_2 can be converted and considering the different scales at which each product is typically manufactured.

3. Methodology

The analyses have been based on fundamental calculations for each product, assumed to be manufactured in a plant of 100 kt/y capacity. The stoichiometry of the cathodic semi-reaction (Zhang et al. 2018) is used to calculate the electric current i. For the example of methanol, assuming alkaline environment, the reaction can be written as:

$$CO_2 + 5H_2O + 6e^- \rightarrow CH_3OH + 6OH^- \tag{1}$$

and based on the desired production rate of methanol the current is calculated as:

$$i = \dot{n}_e \cdot F, \tag{2}$$

where $\dot{n}_e$ is the rate at which electrons are transferred and F is Faraday constant.

Combining this with the voltage V applied to the electrochemical cell, the total power requirement P has been calculated as:

$$P = i \cdot V \tag{3}$$

The products analysed, with their respective market price, are carbon monoxide (600 $/t), formic acid (740 $/t), methanol (600 $/t), methane (180 $/t), ethanol (1000 $/t) and ethylene (1300 $/t). These products are the ones to which the greatest attention has been dedicated in the ECO2R literature. The electrolytic cell performance data can be found in Huang et al. 2021, while the carbon footprint of electricity data are obtained from Gabrielli et al. 2023. As the goal of the analysis is the comparison of products and the evaluation of the energy requirements for the electrolysis process, Faradaic efficiencies have been considered 100% for each product and separation processes have not been included in the scope.

The energy consumption of separation processes derives from literature (Strojny et al. 2023 for CO_2 capture; Muñoz et al. 2015 for methane/CO_2; Shahandeh et al. 2015 for methanol/water; Kunnakorn et al. 2013 for ethanol/water).

4. Results and discussion

Figure 1 and Figure 2 display the effect of carbon emissions intensity and electricity price on a gross margin model for different products and on a gross CO_2 emissions mitigation through ECO2R potential. It appears clearly that the current conditions (carbon footprint of the grid of 0.45 kg CO_2/kWh and electricity price of 0.18 \$/kWh) and cell performance would not allow for a profitable nor environmentally friendly production of any chemical by means of these technologies, while for the conditions considered in the 2050 scenario (0.01 kg CO_2/kWh, 0.03 \$/kWh) all products would allow for CO_2 emissions mitigation, albeit at different gross margin levels. Methanol, ethanol and methane do not appear to be profitable even taking into account future, forecasted cell performance and low electricity price. On one hand, this analysis demonstrates the importance of a low-carbon energy system to power ECO2R, as the CO_2 emissions from the electricity generation alone would vastly offset the carbon fixed in the products. On the other hand, it is evident that the profitability at industrial scale could only be achieved under very favourable conditions and not for all the chemicals and fuels considered.

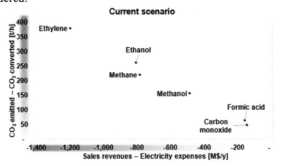

Figure 1: Gross margin and gross CO_2 emissions reduction for different products in the current scenario (0.45 kg CO_2/kWh, 0.18 \$/kWh).

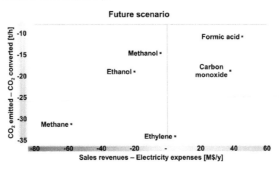

Figure 2: Gross margin and gross CO_2 emissions reduction for different products in the 2050 scenario (0.01 kg CO_2/kWh, 0.03 \$/kWh).

Figure 3 shows the overview of the requirements in terms of number of electrolysers and renewable power generation installation (either offshore wind turbines, assuming a capacity factor of 50%, or PV farm area) for the production of different chemicals, evaluated on the same production basis of 100 kt/y. As these products have different market sizes and supply chains, the additional context of the conventional plant capacity is added, together with an indication of how much CO_2 is converted to each product.

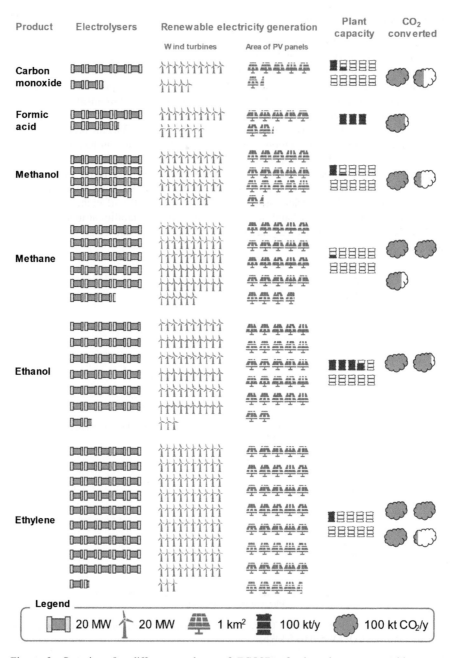

Figure 3: Overview for different products of ECO2R of: electrolysers; renewable power generation given by either number of offshore wind turbines or area of PV panels in the Netherlands; comparison of plant capacity with representative conventional plant size; CO_2 converted. The common production basis for each product is 100 kt/y. Biomethane and bioethanol plants are used for the plant capacity comparison for methane and ethanol, respectively.

Table 1: Summary of results for most relevant products of ECO2R for different scenarios (C: current performance; F: future performance). Electrolyser size: 20 MW; Wind turbine size 20 MW (currently at the prototype level for offshore installations), 50% capacity factor; PV performance in the Netherlands; conventional plants for methane and ethanol are taken for biomethane and bioethanol productions, respectively.

| Product | Electrolysers | | Renewable power generation | | | | Capacity | CO_2 converted [kt/y] |
| | | | Wind turbines | | Area of PV [km²] | | | |
	C	F	C	F	C	F		
CO	7.4	4.6	15	9	6.3	3.9	14%	157.1
HCOOH	8.4	6.0	17	12	7.1	5.1	287%	95.7
CH_3OH	19.2	12.9	38	26	16.3	11.0	12%	137.5
CH_4	28.1	15.9	56	32	23.9	13.5	3%	275.0
CH_3CH_2OH	31.7	25.0	63	50	27.0	21.2	37%	191.3
C_2H_4	46.4	26.1	93	52	39.4	22.2	10%	314.3

A distinction can be draw between the first three products (carbon monoxide, formic acid and methanol) and the last three, as a product such as ethylene requires extremely large amounts of energy even for small capacity as compared to classic steam crackers, whereas formic acid can be produced at scale with relatively contained installations.

These results are further corroborated by the data in Table 1, which includes a comparison of the current (C) and future (F) performance. The forecast improvement in the performance is likely to be significant for some products, such as methane and ethylene, while for ethanol the development is going to be lower. In all cases, the energy usages are very significant, as can be seen by the tens of wind turbines necessary for the production of ethylene, even at relatively small scale. C_1 oxygenated molecules, on the other hand, appear to be more scalable, even though when extrapolating at the actual industrial scale the energy demand is still extremely high (a methanol plant of 2500 t/d would require ~220 wind turbines of 20 MW with 50% capacity factor).

Special attention can be given to ECO2R fuels, which might play a role in the de-fossilisation of hard to abate sectors such as aviation and transportation. Figure 4 shows how the energy input to produce fuels – considering the capture of CO_2, the electrolysis (current performance) and the separation – is about 3-7 times higher than the specific energy content of the fuel itself.

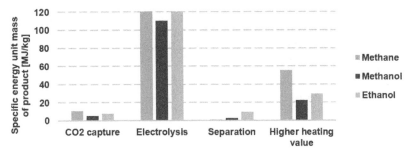

Figure 4: Comparison of energy input for the production of e-fuels via ECO2R and specific energy of the fuel (higher heating value).

Such a holistic view taking into account primary energy consumption is believed to be an important factor in the decision-making process for the selection of the technologies for the production of the fuels of the future.

5. Conclusions

The green electricity demand for the products of low temperature electrolysis has been successfully analysed, highlighting the importance of widely available and cheap renewable power to ensure not only the basic economic viability of the products, but also the possibility of mitigating CO_2 emissions.

Relevant ECO2R products have been compared on a common production basis to demonstrate the vast demand for renewable energy to allow for industrial deployment of these technologies: based on this, it can be concluded that C_1 oxygenated products, namely CO, HCOOH and CH_3OH would offer a better potential for implementation, compared to C_2, such as ethanol and ethylene.

Moreover, e-fuels produced by means of ECO2R, have a specific energy content which is only a fraction of the actual energy required for their production and appear not to be profitable, even when the costs of separation is neglected.

References

Gabrielli, P., Rosa, L., Gazzani, M., Meys, R., Bardow, A., Mazzotti, M., Sansavini, G., 2023, Net-Zero Emissions Chemical Industry in a World of Limited Resources, One Earth 6 (6): 682–704.

Huang, Z., Grim, R.G., Schaidle, J.A., Tao, L., 2021, The Economic Outlook for Converting CO_2 and Electrons to Molecules, Energy & Environmental Science 14 (7): 3664–78.

Kunnakorn, D., Rirksomboon, T., Siemanond, K., Aungkavattana, P., Kuanchertchoo, N., Chuntanalerg, P., Hemra, K., Kulprathipanja, S., James, R.B., Wongkasemjit, S., 2013, Techno-Economic Comparison of Energy Usage between Azeotropic Distillation and Hybrid System for Water–Ethanol Separation, Renewable Energy 51 (March): 310–16.

Muñoz, R., Meier, L., Diaz, I., Jeison, D., 2015, A Review on the State-of-the-Art of Physical/Chemical and Biological Technologies for Biogas Upgrading, Reviews in Environmental Science and Bio/Technology 14 (4): 727–59.

Shahandeh, H., Jafari, M., Kasiri, N., Ivakpour, J., 2015, Economic Optimization of Heat Pump-Assisted Distillation Columns in Methanol-Water Separation, Energy 80 (February): 496–508.

Somoza-Tornos, A., Guerra, O.J., Crow, A.M., Smith, W.A., Hodge, B.M., 2021, Process Modeling, Techno-Economic Assessment, and Life Cycle Assessment of the Electrochemical Reduction of CO2: A Review, iScience 24 (7): 102813.

Strojny, M., Gładysz, P., Hanak, D.P., Nowak, W., 2023, Comparative Analysis of CO2 Capture Technologies Using Amine Absorption and Calcium Looping Integrated with Natural Gas Combined Cycle Power Plant, Energy 284 (December): 128599.

Verma, S., Kim, B., Jhong, H.R., Ma, S., Kenis, P.J.A., 2016, A Gross-Margin Model for Defining Technoeconomic Benchmarks in the Electroreduction of CO_2, ChemSusChem 9 (15): 1972–79.

Zhang, W., Hu, Y., Ma, L., Zhu, G., Wang, Y., Xue, X., Chen, R., Yang, S., Jin, Z., 2018, Progress and Perspective of Electrocatalytic CO_2 Reduction for Renewable Carbonaceous Fuels and Chemicals, Advanced Science 5 (1): 1700275.

Flavio Manenti, Gintaras V. Reklaitis (Eds.), Proceedings of the 34th European Symposium on Computer Aided Process Engineering / 15th International Symposium on Process Systems Engineering (ESCAPE34/PSE24), June 2-6, 2024, Florence, Italy

Process simulation of BECCS-to-X: Investigating the potential of Hydrogen and Sustainable Aviation Fuel Production

Mathew Dennis Wilkes [a], Solomon Brown [a]*.

[a] *Department of Chemical and Biological Engineering, University of Sheffield, Mappin Street, Sheffield, S1 4LZ, United Kingdom,*
s.f.brown@sheffield.ac.uk

Abstract

Bioenergy with Carbon Capture and Storage (BECCS) combined with Biomass-to-X (BtX), BECCS-to-X, is a potential technology for generating power and syngas, which can be further processed into useful chemicals and fuels. Herein, the authors discuss and develop process models for converting biomass into hydrogen and sustainable aviation fuel (SAF) – BECCS-to-H_2 and BECCS-to-SAF, respectively. Both processes use the same biomass input and produce the same amount of power. Results show the higher energy efficiency for producing H_2 (50%) compared to SAF (34%) and total Fischer-Tropsch fuels (47%).

Keywords: BECCS, BECCS-to-X, H_2, SAF

1. Introduction

Negative Emissions Technologies (NET), such as Bioenergy with Carbon Capture and Storage (BECCS), are essential for achieving Net Zero (DESNZ, 2023). Most scenarios/ pathways to limit global temperature rise to less than 1.5°C require carbon dioxide removal (CDR) technologies such as BECCS in order to remove CO_2 from the atmosphere (Almena, et al., 2022). The generation of useful products from biomass is referred to as Biomass-to-X or BtX (Poluzzi, et al., 2021). BECCS typically refers to thermo-chemical conversion routes with carbon capture and storage (CCS) (Shahbaz, et al., 2021). Thermo-chemical conversion of biomass via gasification produces heat and syngas, downstream processing coupled with power generation can convert biomass resources into both power and useful products, i.e., **BECCS-to-X**.

Depending on the processing route, biomass can be converted into ammonia, bio-char, dimethyl ethers, hydrogen, methane, methanol, and Fischer-Tropsch fuels (Poluzzi, et al., 2021; Hanel, et al., 2022). Hydrogen is an energy carrier and chemical building block, it has the potential to decarbonize industry, power, heating, and transportation (Osman, et al., 2021). Fischer-Tropsch synthesis can produce Sustainable Aviation Fuel (SAF), which is an important mitigation strategy for one of the most difficult to abate industrial sectors - aviation (Doliente, et al., 2020). Hanel et al. (2022) performed an energetic and technical evaluation on gasification based BtX processes. Interestingly, no single optimal BtX was presented, the authors showed the key process indicators (KPIs) are subjective to that processing route. Hence, further investigation for specific scenarios is required.

1.1. Aims & Objectives

This study is a technical evaluation and comparison of BECCS-to-H_2 and BECCS-to-SAF using Aspen Plus. The analysis highlights key operating parameters (KOPs) and KPIs for each process. Our previous study focused on the production of H_2, whereby hydrogen is separated and purified from bio-syngas alongside CO_2 (CCS) with heat-recovery steam generation to provide power (Wilkes, et al., 2023).

The purpose of this paper is to investigate and showcase:

- Process model development and description for BECCS-to-H_2 and BECCS-to-SAF.
- Process analysis and identification of KOPs and KPIs.
- Technical comparison between the two BECCS-to-X systems.

2. Process description and modelling

The process models are developed in Aspen Plus® v11.1, the model topology for the BECCS-to-H_2 and BECCS-to-SAF processes are shown in Figure 1 and Figure 2, respectively. Wet biomass enters and **DRYER** unit and the output moisture content is set to 10.05 wt.%. Within Aspen, biomass is a non-conventional solid and needs to be decomposed (**DECOMP**) into its constituent elements before gasification (**GASI**). An RGibbs reactor is chosen for the gasification unit, which calculates chemical equilibrium based on Gibbs free energy minimization (Tauqir, et al., 2019). The syngas produced in the gasification unit needs upgrading to improve the H_2/CO ratio. The syngas upgrading using the water-gas shift (WGS) reaction unit is based on Marcantonio et al. (Marcantonio, et al., 2019) and Moneti et al. (Moneti, et al., 2016), both of which simulated the experiments conducted within the UNIfHY project (UNIfHY, 2016). The WGS reaction (Equation 1) favors the production of CO and H_2O at high temperatures, thus the UNIfHY project looked at high temperature shift (HTS) at 400°C and low temperature shift (LTS) at 200°C. Both **HT-WGS** and **LT-WGS** reactors are operated at 27 bar (Cohce, et al., 2011), and are modelled as REquil reactors representing the WGS reaction (Marcantonio, et al., 2019):

$$CO + H_2O \leftrightarrows CO_2 + H_2 \qquad\qquad 1$$

Sulphur within the biomass is converted into H_2S and COS in the gasification unit, and all of the COS is converted in H_2S in the WGS units. Therefore, prior to H_2/CO_2 separation H_2S is removed using Selexol, which also co-captures CO_2. The separation efficiency for H_2S is 100% and for CO_2 it is 95% (Chiesa, et al., 2005). H_2S is removed in the **SELEXOL1** unit and CO_2 is removed in the **SELEXOL2** unit, both are modelled as separation units. The CO_2 conditioning unit ensures the CO_2 stream is ready for pipeline transportation, it uses sub-critical liquefaction at 66 bar (**CO2-COMP**) and liquid pumping to 111 bar (**CO2-PUMP**) which reduces the energy consumption for the conditioning train (Wilkes, et al., 2021). The energy demand for the Selexol process is 0.6 GJe/tCO2 and 0.63 GJth/tCO$_2$ (Kuramochi, et al., 2012). For the BECCS-to-H_2 process, H2 is separated in a pressure swing adsorption (**PSA**) unit (85% capture rate and 99.99% purity (Chiesa, et al., 2005). Heat is recovered in the **HRSG** unit, and the high-pressure steam produces power in the **HP-ST**, **IP-ST**, and **LP-ST** turbines.

BECCS-to-SAF requires additional processing units to convert the syngas into useful Fischer-Tropsch (FT) fuels. The FT reactor model is based on the conversion-based reactor model presented in (Dahl, 2020), using an RStoic reactor in Aspen Plus with conversion data from (Shafer, et al., 2019). The **FT-C** unit is operated at 220°C and 27.6 bar (Shafer, et al., 2019). Only Paraffins (alkanes) are considered in this study, the overall reaction is shown in Equation 2 (Hillestad, 2015).

$$CO + U_1H_2 \rightarrow v_{1,1}C_1^P + v_{1,2}C_2^P \ldots + v_{1,[21,\infty]}C_{21+}^P + H_2O \qquad\qquad 2$$

Where U is the hydrogen stoichiometric coefficient, v is the hydrocarbon stoichiometric coefficient, and the superscript P denotes the paraffin component. The heavy hydrocarbons are lumped into C_{21+}^P. The ASF distribution underestimates the CH_4 production, thus Equation 3 is added to the RStoic unit.

$$CO + 3H_2 \rightarrow CH_4 + H_2O \qquad\qquad 3$$

The stoichiometric coefficients (Equation 4 and 5) follow the ASF distribution (Hillestad, 2015), where the chain growth factor (α_1) is set to 0.9 (Swanson, et al., 2010; Campanario & Ortiz, 2017). The subscript i denotes the carbon number. The fractional conversion for the paraffin and methanation reactions is set to 0.394 and 0.077 (Dahl, 2020).

$$v_{1,i} = (1 - \alpha_1)^2 \alpha_1^{i-1} \qquad\qquad 4$$

$$v_{1,[21,\infty]} = (1 - \alpha_1)^2 \alpha_1^{21-1} \qquad\qquad 5$$

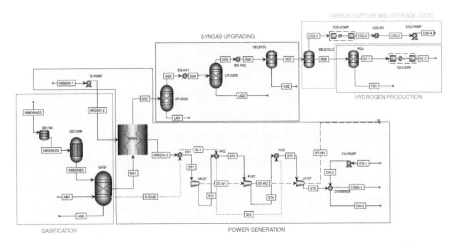

Figure 1: Biomass gasification for H_2 and power production, model topology using Aspen Plus

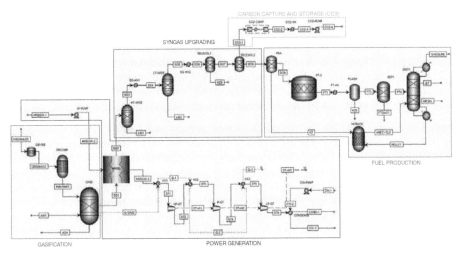

Figure 2: Biomass gasification for SAF and power production, model topology using Aspen Plus

The products from the FT unit are sent to a separation unit (**SEP1**) to separate gaseous hydrocarbons (C_{1-4}), liquid hydrocarbons (C_{5-21+}), and water. Unreacted syngas and gaseous hydrocarbons are recycled. The liquid hydrocarbons are fractionally distillation (**DIST1**) at atmospheric pressure, modelled as a distillation column, to produce commercial hydrocarbon products: gasoline fraction (C_{5-7}), jet fuel fraction (C_{8-16}), diesel fraction (C_{17-20}), and heavy hydrocarbons/waxes (C_{21+}). The heavy hydrocarbons are sent to the hydrocracking unit (**HCRACK**), modelled using an RStoic reactor, which converts the waxes into 50% jet fuel, 30% diesel, 15% gasoline, and 5% light gases. The hydrocracker is operated at 50 bar and 277°C. The process also uses 1.5% H_2 sent from the **PSA** unit stationed after the syngas cleaning section and prior to the FT-C. The additional H_2 specification ensures the production of middle distillates (mild hydrocracking) (Michaga, et al., 2022).

As the purpose of these processes is to produce H_2 and SAF, the hydrogen energy efficiency (η_{H_2}) and jet fuel energy (η_{SAF}) efficiency are defined as:

$$\eta_{H_2} = \frac{\dot{m}_{H_2} \times LHV_{H_2}}{\dot{m}_{dry\ biomass} \times LHV_{biomass}} \qquad 6$$

$$\eta_{SAF} = \frac{\dot{m}_{SAF} \times LHV_{SAF}}{\dot{m}_{dry\ biomass} \times LHV_{biomass}} \qquad 7$$

Where $\dot{m}$ is the mass flowrate in kg/s and the lower heating value (LHV) is in MJ/kg. For the BECCS-to-SAF process there are several useful products that also need to be considered, thus the overall fuel energy (η_{fuel}) efficiency is defined as (Michaga, et al., 2022):

$$\eta_{fuel} = \frac{\left(\dot{m}_{gasoline} \times LHV_{gasoline}\right) + \left(\dot{m}_{SAF} \times LHV_{SAF}\right) + \left(\dot{m}_{diesel} \times LHV_{diesel}\right)}{\left(\dot{m}_{dry\ biomass} \times LHV_{biomass}\right)} \qquad 8$$

The net efficiency in both cases is the electrical efficiency combined with the thermal energy efficiency of the specified fuel type. In the case of BECCS-to-SAF there are two net efficiencies, one for the overall fuel production and one purely for the SAF production.

3. Results and discussion

Both models have the same biomass feedstock - hardwood chips proximate and ultimate analysis from (Tauqir, et al., 2019). Both systems process 3,600 kg/hr of biomass with an input energy of 18,850 kW. The air flowrate for the gasification chamber is 6,934 kg/hr (0.214 equivalence ratio). The HRSG unit uses 10,487 kg/hr of steam at a 1:1 syngas/HRSG steam ratio. Validation is carried out against operating conditions for the gasification unit for run #14 from Wei et al. (2009), shown in our previous study (Wilkes, et al., 2021).

Table 1 highlights the KPIs for the BECCS-to-H_2 process and Table 2 shows the KPIs for the BECCS-to-SAF process. The BECCS-to-H_2 process has higher thermal energy output, as H_2 is more energy dense than hydrocarbon fuels (on a mass basis). In both cases the energy demand for the CO_2 separation process (1050 kW) is 6% of the total biomass energy input. Figure 3 highlights the fuel/H_2 efficiency and product flowrates for the two processing routes. Focusing only on fuel efficiencies, the production of hydrogen from biomass is 36% efficient compared to 19% for Jet Fuel production, which increases to 32% with the inclusion of gasoline and diesel fractions. In both cases the additional power generated from the HRSG improves the energy efficiency, to almost 50% in BECCS-to-H_2 and 47% in BECCS-to-SAF if all FT fuels are considered (see Table 1 and Table 2). The results highlight the improved efficiency when incorporating BECCS into BtX processes.

Table 1: BECCS-to-H2 KPIs

KPI	BECCS-to-H2
Power demand (kW)	1,475
Power generated (kW)	3,846
Net power output (kW)	2,371
Hydrogen output (kg/hr)	185.3
Hydrogen output (kW)	6,176
Electrical efficiency (%)	13.80
η_{H_2} (%)	35.94
Net efficiency (%)	49.74

Table 2: BECCS-to-SAF KPIs

KPI	BECCS-to-SAF
Power demand (kW)	1,274
Power generated (kW)	3,846
Net power output (kW)	2,572
Gasoline output (kg/hr)	88.50
Jet fuel output (kg/hr)	275.6
Diesel output (kg/hr)	99.40
Total fuel output (kg/hr)	463.4
Total fuel output (kW)	5,510
Electrical efficiency (%)	14.97
η_{SAF} (%)	19.06
η_{fuel} (%)	32.06
Net SAF efficiency (%)	34.03
Net Fuel efficiency (%)	47.03

Overall, the net efficiency is higher in the BECCS-to-H_2 process; however, the BECCS-to-SAF process produces 150% more product (on a mass basis). Despite the lower efficiency, higher profits could be achieved depending on the cost associated with the FT equipment. Hence, a full techno-economic assessment is required to compare these two biomass utilization pathways.

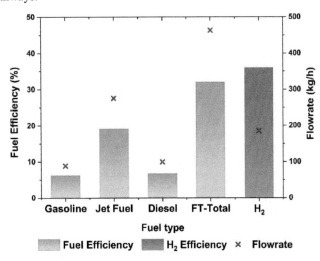

Figure 3: Fuel efficiency and production flowrate for BECCS-to-H_2 and BECCS-to-SAF

4. Conclusion

Bioenergy with Carbon Capture and Storage (BECCS) and biomass-to-X (BtX) can be combined into BECCS-to-X, a pathway to convert biomass resources into both power and useful products. This paper focuses on the production of hydrogen (H_2) and sustainable aviation fuel (SAF). Herein, BECCS-to-H_2 and BECCS-to-SAF processes are evaluated and compared using process model developed in Aspen Plus. The study highlighted key operating parameters and performance indicators. Interestingly, producing H_2 results in a higher energy conversion, 15.71% points higher than SAF and 2.71% points higher than all FT fuels combined. However, on a mass basis more product is produced in BECCS-to-SAF, hence an economic study is required to ascertain the most cost-effective pathway.

5. References

A. Almena, P. Thornley, K. Chong, M. Röder, 2022, Carbon dioxide removal potential from decentralised bioenergy with carbon capture and storage (BECCS) and the relevance of operational choices, Biomass and Bioenergy, 159, 106406.

F. J. Campanario, F. J. Ortiz, 2017, Fischer-Tropsch biofuels production from syngas obtained by supercritical water reforming of the bio-oil aqueous phase, Energy Conversion and Management, 150, 599-613.

P. Chiesa, S. Consonni, T. Kreutz, R. Williams, 2005, Co-production of hydrogen, electricity and CO_2 from coal with commercially ready technology. Part A: Performance and emissions, International Journal of Hydrogen Energy, 30, 747-767.

M. K. Cohce, M. A. Rosen, I. Dincer, 2011, Efficiency evaluation of a biomass gasification-based hydrogen production, International Journal of Hydrogen Energy, 36(17), 11388-11398.

R. Dahl, 2020, Evaluation of the new Power & Biomass to Liquid (PBtL) concept for production of biofuels from woody biomass. Norwegian University of Science and Technology, Faculty of Natural Sciences, Department of Chemical Engineering. Stockholm, Sweden: Norwegian University of Science and Technology.

DESNZ, 2023, Biomass Strategy, Department for Energy Security and Net Zero, Crown copyright.

S. S. Doliente, A. Narayan, J. F. Tapia, N. J. Samsatli, Y. Zhao, S. Samsatli, 2020, Bio-aviation Fuel: A Comprehensive Review and Analysis of the Supply Chain Components, Frontiers in Energy Research, 8(1), 10.

A. Hanel, V. Dieterich, S. Bastek, H. Spliethoff, S. Fendt, 2022, Entrained flow gasification-based biomass-to-X processes: An energetic and technical evaluation, Energy Conversion and Management, 274, 116424.

M. Hillestad, 2015, Modeling the Fischer-Tropsch Product Distribution and Model Implementation, Chemical Product and Process Modeling, 10(3), 147-159.

T. Kuramochi, A. Ramírez, W. Turkenburg, A. Faaij, 2012, Comparative assessment of CO_2 capture technologies for carbon-intensive industrial processes. Progress in Energy and Combustion Science, 38(1), 87-112.

V. Marcantonio, M. D. Falco, M. Capocelli, E. Bocci, A. Colantoni, M. Villarini, 2019, Process analysis of hydrogen production from biomass gasification in fluidized bed reactor with different separation systems, International Journal of Hydrogen Energy , 44, 10350-10360.

M. F. Michaga, S. Michailos, M. Akram, E. Cardozo, K. J. Hughes, D. Ingham, M. Pourkashanian, 2022, Bioenergy with carbon capture and storage (BECCS) potential in jet fuel production from forestry residues: A combined Techno-Economic and Life cycle Assessment approach, Energy Conversion and Management, 255, 115346.

M. Moneti, A. D. Carlo, E. Bocci, P. U. Foscolo, M. Villarini, M. Carlini, 2016, Influence of the main gasifier parameters on a real system for hydrogen production from biomass, International Journal of Hydrogen Energy, 41(28), 11965-11973.

A. I. Osman, N. Mehta, A. M. Elgarahy, M. Hefny, A. Al-Hinai, A. H. Al-Muhtaseb, D. W. Rooney, 2021, Hydrogen production, storage, utilisation and environmental impacts: a review, Environmental Chemistry Letters , 20, 153-188.

A. Poluzzi, G. Guandalini, F. d'Amore, M. C. Romano, 2021, The Potential of Power and Biomass-to-X Systems in the Decarbonization Challenge: a Critical Review, Current Sustainable/Renewable Energy Reports, 8, 242-252.

W. D. Shafer, M. K. Gnanamani, U. M. Graham, J. Yang, C. M. Masuku, G. Jacobs, B. H. Davis, 2019, Fischer–Tropsch: Product Selectivity–The Fingerprint of Synthetic Fuels, Catalysts, 9, 259.

M. Shahbaz, A. AlNouss, I. Ghiat, G. Mckay, H. Mackey, S. Elkhalifa, T. Al-Ansari, 2021, A comprehensive review of biomass based thermochemical conversion technologies integrated with CO_2 capture and utilisation within BECCS networks, Resources, Conservation and Recycling, 173, 105734.

R. M. Swanson, J. A. Satrio, R. C. Brown, A. Platon, D. D. Hsu, 2010, Techno-Economic Analysis of Biofuels Production Based on Gasification, Colorado, United States: National Renewable Energy Laboratory.

W. Tauqir, M. Zubair, H. Nazir, 2019, Parametric analysis of a steady state equilibrium-based biomass gasification model for syngas and biochar production and heat generation, Energy Conversion and Management, 199, 111954.

UNIfHY, 2016, Final Report Summary - UNIFHY (UNIQUE gasifier for hydrogen Production).

M. D. Wilkes, O. Asuni, S. Brown, 2023, Bioenergy with carbon capture and storage (BECCS) – power generation coupled with hydrogen production, Computer Aided Chemical Engineering, 52, 2897-2902

M. D. Wilkes, S. Mukherjee, S. Brown, 2021, Linking CO_2 capture and pipeline transportation: sensitivity analysis and dynamic study of the compression train, International Journal of Greenhouse Gas Control, 111, 103449.

Flavio Manenti, Gintaras V. Reklaitis (Eds.), Proceedings of the 34th European Symposium on Computer Aided Process Engineering / 15th International Symposium on Process Systems Engineering (ESCAPE34/PSE24), June 2-6, 2024, Florence, Italy

Exergo-Techno-Economic Comparison of Power&Biomass-to-Kerosene Pathways

Simone Mucci[a], Dominik P. Goldstein[a], Dominik Bongartz[b], Alexander Mitsos[c,a,d,*]

a Process Systems Engineering (AVT.SVT), RWTH Aachen University, Aachen, Germany
b Department of Chemical Engineering, KU Leuven, Leuven, Belgium
c JARA-ENERGY, Aachen, Germany
d Energy Systems Engineering (IEK-10), Forschungszentrum Jülich, Jülich, Germany
* Corresponding author: amitsos@alum.mit.edu

Abstract

Sustainable kerosene-like fuel can be synthesized from green hydrogen and biomass in so-called Power&Biomass-to-Kerosene plants. Although several kerosene production pathways have been proposed, it is still unclear what plant configuration is most efficient and has the lowest production cost. To answer these questions, a model of kerosene production processes based on either biomass combustion or gasification is built in Aspen Plus. For each of these, two kerosene production pathways are investigated, i.e., via Fischer-Tropsch and methanol-to-olefins processes. An exergy analysis shows that gasification-based processes are more efficient than combustion-based ones due to the lower exergy losses of the gasification unit and the water electrolyzer for hydrogen production. Finally, a techno-economic comparison shows that the gasification-based kerosene production via the methanol-to-olefins pathway results in the lowest specific production cost.

Keywords: Power&Biomass-to-Kerosene, Sustainable aviation fuels (SAF), Exergy analysis, Techno-economic comparison.

1. Introduction

Hydrogen-fueled or electric aircrafts are often proposed as a possible solution to defossilize the aviation sector. However, in the short-to-medium term, they are more suitable for short-haul flights due to the relatively low volumetric or gravimetric energy density of hydrogen and batteries. Instead, sustainable aviation fuels could play a relevant role also in long-haul flights since they are energy-dense kerosene-like fuels and would not require the substitution of the existing aviation fleet.

Such sustainable kerosene can be synthesized from green hydrogen and a carbon source, e.g., carbon dioxide, in Power-to-Kerosene processes (Schmidt et al., 2018). An interesting alternative to carbon dioxide is biomass since it can also provide a valuable energy input to the Power-to-Kerosene process, thus being called Power&Biomass-to-Kerosene (P&B2K) process.

Biomass can be converted via combustion or gasification to supply either CO_2 or syngas (a mixture of mainly CO and H_2) to the kerosene synthesis unit after supplying additional green hydrogen to adjust the H:C ratio. Under idealized assumptions, gasification-based P&B2X processes show clear thermodynamic advantages over combustion-based ones due to the lower demand of additional hydrogen (Mucci et al., 2023). In contrast, combustion-based P&B2X processes have practical advantages due to the lower energy demand and cost of the flue gas cleaning. Therefore, it is not clear whether realistic gasification-based P&B2K processes outperform the combustion-based ones in all the considered key performance indicators, i.e., energy and exergy efficiencies and specific production cost of kerosene.

To answer this question, we model combustion-based and gasification-based kerosene production processes in Aspen Plus by considering two production pathways each, i.e., via Fischer-Tropsch (FT) and methanol-to-olefins (MTO) processes (Schmidt et al., 2018). While the FT pathway is often considered in P&B2K processes (Hillestad et al., 2018; Habermeyer et al., 2021; Nielsen et al., 2022), we are not aware of works focusing on the MTO pathway for kerosene production in the context of P&B2K. The considered processes are then compared via exergy and techno-economic analysis.

2. Process description

In the considered kerosene production processes from biomass and green hydrogen, three key sections can be identified, i.e., biomass conversion (via combustion or gasification), hydrogen production via water electrolysis, and kerosene synthesis sections.

In the combustion-based P&B2K process (Fig. 1, top), biomass is oxidized using oxygen, a side-product of water electrolysis. This choice leads to high concentration of CO_2 in the flue gas. Nevertheless, a carbon capture unit is needed to obtain a pure CO_2 stream since the residual oxygen in the flue gas can be poisonous for the catalyst of the downstream conversion units. The CO_2 stream is mixed with the H_2 produced via low-temperature electrolysis, the most mature electrolysis technology, to adjust the CO_2:H_2 ratio according to the following kerosene production pathway.

In the FT pathway, the CO_2-H_2 stream is first converted to syngas in a reverse water gas shift (RWGS) unit and then supplied to the low-temperature FT unit. The produced hydrocarbon mixture is separated according to the carbon chain length. In particular, C_{5-7} (gasoline range), C_{8-16} (kerosene range), and C_{17-19} (diesel range) hydrocarbons are recovered. Lighter and heavier hydrocarbons are reformed and hydrocracked, respectively, to increase the selectivity of the process to the hydrocarbon range of interest.

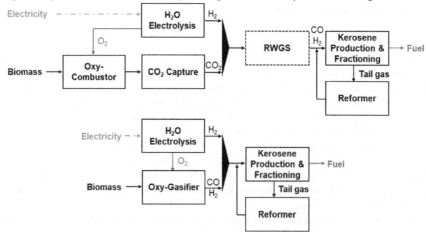

Figure 1. Sketch of the combustion-based (top) and gasification-based (bottom) P&B2K processes for both the FT and MTO pathways. Note: In the combustion-based P&B2K process via the MTO pathway, the RWGS unit (dashed) is not present since direct hydrogenation of CO_2 to methanol is considered.

In the MTO pathway, the CO_2 stream is converted to methanol via direct hydrogenation. The produced crude methanol is converted to short-chain olefins, which are then oligomerized. Finally, the long-chain olefins are converted into alkanes via hydrogenation before fractioning the produced hydrocarbons according to their carbon chain length.

In the gasification-based P&B2K process (Fig. 1, bottom), the main difference stands in the biomass conversion unit: biomass is partially oxidized to produce syngas instead of CO_2. Therefore, the carbon capture and RWGS units are not included.

3. Methodology

3.1. Process model

A detailed model of the above-described P&B2K processes was built in Aspen Plus.

3.1.1 Biomass conversion

For the biomass combustion unit, an operating temperature of 1000 °C and a biomass conversion factor of 100 % are assumed. Moreover, a partial recycle of flue gases is considered to dilute the reactants and reduce the adiabatic temperature of flame since pure oxygen is the oxidizer. A pure CO_2 stream is then separated from the flue gases via amine washing (Lee et al., 2016). A carbon capture rate of 90% is assumed.

For the biomass gasification unit, an operating temperature of 900 °C and a biomass conversion factor of 95 % are assumed. As CO_2, a side-product of gasification processes, is generally inert in FT processes, a pressure swing adsorption unit (Santos et al., 2023) is included, and the separated CO_2 is recycled into the gasifier to increase the carbon efficiency of the P&B2K process. This additional unit is instead not included in the MTO pathway since CO_2 participates in methanol production.

For both biomass conversion units, no flue gas or syngas cleaning treatment is modeled.

3.1.2 Water electrolysis

For the low-temperature water electrolysis unit, we consider a polymer electrolyte membrane (PEM) technology and we assume an efficiency equal to 60% and 59% (based on the LHV) when H_2 is produced at atmospheric or high pressure (25 bar), respectively, according to the pathway. The size of the unit depends on the considered pathway.

3.1.3 Kerosene synthesis

In the combustion-based kerosene production via the FT pathway, the CO_2 stream is reduced to CO via hydrogenation in a catalytic RWGS unit modeled with Vázquez et al.´s kinetic model (Vázquez et al., 2017). Moderate pressure and nearly stoichiometric H_2:CO_2 ratio are considered to inhibit methanation. Hydrogen is then added to adjust the H_2:CO ratio before supplying syngas to the slurry bubble FT reactor. Long-chain hydrocarbons are synthesized in the FT reactor according to the modified Anderson-Schulz-Flory distribution (Habermeyer et al., 2021) at a relatively low operating temperature and a substoichiometric H_2:CO ratio, as these operating conditions enable high selectivity to the hydrocarbons of interest. The hydrocarbon mixture is then separated via distillation. The light hydrocarbons (less than 5 carbon atoms) are converted into syngas in a steam reformer, modeled as a RGibbs reactor; the produced syngas is then fed into the FT reactor to increase kerosene production. Heavy hydrocarbons are hydrocracked.

In the combustion-based kerosene production via the MTO pathway, CO_2 is converted into methanol via direct hydrogenation (Van-Dal and Bouallou, 2013). Crude methanol is converted into short-chain olefins (Nesterenko et al., 2016), which are then oligomerized. In the absence of a suitable kinetic model, the oligomerization process is modeled by considering experimental data of the oligomerization of pure olefins (ethene, propene, butene, pentene, and hexene) over an acidic zeolite catalyst (Moon et al., 2018; Monama et al., 2020; Díaz et al., 2020; Cowley, 2002), and assuming that these reactions occur in parallel. The long-chain olefins are then hydrogenated (Brooks et al., 2016), before being separated. Similarly to the modeled FT pathway, light hydrocarbons are reformed, and the produced syngas is supplied to the methanol plant.

In the gasification-based processes via FT and MTO pathways, the produced syngas is fed directly into the FT and methanol reactors, respectively.

3.2. Heat integration

To reduce the hot utility demand to zero thus improving the overall process efficiency, matches between hot and cold streams are identified and heat integration is performed. For instance, the biomass combustion unit supplies heat to the endothermic units, e.g., the RWGS unit. Also, heat integration between the reactant and product streams of the gasification unit allows reducing the injected oxidizer, thus increasing the syngas quality. Further, the residual process heat is supplied to a steam power cycle (or organic Rankine cycle in the gasification-based processes) to reduce the process net electricity demand.

3.3. Exergetic and techno-economic analysis

The considered P&B2K processes are modeled assuming a woody biomass flow rate of 10 t/y (around 50 MW based on LHV). The size of the other components, e.g., the electrolyzer, is defined according to the modeling assumptions and considered pathway.

The P&B2K pathways are compared concerning their efficiency and the production cost of kerosene. Furthermore, an exergy analysis is carried out to identify the main bottlenecks of the processes.

For the economic analysis, the capital cost (CAPEX) of the main equipment modules is estimated with the cost models proposed by Biegler et al. (1997). The cost of the biomass conversion units, the carbon capture unit, PEM water electrolyzer, and the FT reactor is instead estimated with the correlations from Bridgwater et al. (2002), Lee et al. (2016), Reksten et al. (2022), and Habermeyer et al. (2021), respectively. The correlations were updated to 2021 as the reference year. A replacement for the electrolysis unit in the 10th year is also considered. Further assumptions are collected in Table 1.

Table 1. Main assumptions for the economic analysis.

Plant lifetime	20 y
Yearly operating hours	8000 h
Yearly O&M costs	5 % of initial investment cost (CAPEX)
Interest rate	5 %
Electricity cost	60 €/MWh
Biomass cost	70 €/t

4. Results and discussion

Figure 2 (left) shows the energy efficiency of the modeled P&B2K processes when considering both kerosene and the whole produced liquid fuel (i.e., including the gasoline and diesel side products) as target products. Gasification-based P&B2K processes are significantly more efficient than combustion-based ones. The same holds for the exergy efficiency (not shown in Fig. 2). This result can be explained by analyzing the exergy flows of the processes (Fig. 3). The combustion and electrolysis units contribute significantly to exergy destruction; therefore, the substitution of the combustion unit with the gasification unit as well as the corresponding reduced size of the electrolysis unit of the gasification-based processes lead to higher energy (and exergy) efficiency. Moreover, the electricity production in the steam power cycle of the combustion-based P&B2K processes is not able to offset the higher electricity demand of the electrolysis unit.

In terms of the whole liquid fuel production, the two kerosene production pathways, i.e., FT and MTO, have similar efficiencies (Fig. 2). However, in terms of kerosene production only, the MTO pathway is more efficient than the FT pathway due to the higher selectivity to the C_{8-16} hydrocarbon range. This observation differs from that of Atsonios et al. (2023), who however considered a different design and model of a P2K process.

The P&B2K processes via the MTO pathway also have a lower kerosene production cost than those via the FT pathway (Fig. 2, right). In particular, gasification-based P&B2K processes via the MTO pathway have the lowest production cost (ca. 2 €/kg) thanks to the reduced investment and operating costs for the electrolysis unit, which is the main economic driver. Nevertheless, this pathway has a lower technological maturity and is still missing the certification for producing drop-in fuels suitable for aviation purposes.

The calculated kerosene production costs are in line with other literature works (ca. 3 €/kg of e-kerosene in Schmidt et al., 2018; ca. 1.1 €/L and 1.7 $/L of liquid e-bio-fuels in Habermeyer et al., 2021 and Hillestad et al., 2018, respectively), but, as expected, they are not competitive with the current price of fossil-based kerosene for the considered boundaries. However, considering the sale of side products, e.g., gasoline and diesel, carbon certificates, or subsidies could reduce the price gap.

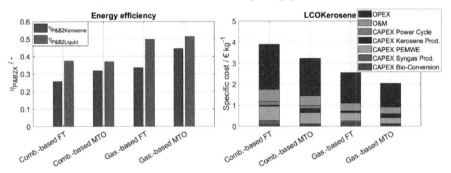

Figure 2. The energy efficiency (left) and the specific production cost of kerosene (right) for the considered P&B2K processes are shown.

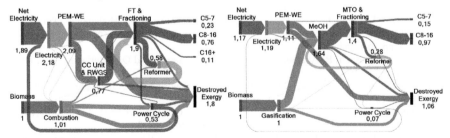

Figure 3. Exergy flows for the least efficient (combustion-based P&B2K process via FT) and the most efficient (gasification-based P&B2K process via MTO) P&B2K processes are shown on the left and right of the figure, respectively. Note: the exergy flows are scaled with respect to the biomass exergy input, which is the same for the considered case studies.

5. Conclusions

Four processes for sustainable kerosene production from biomass and green hydrogen were modeled and compared concerning efficiency and economic indicators: combustion-based versus gasification-based routes and Fischer-Tropsch versus methanol-to-olefins pathways. The exergy analysis shows that gasification-based processes are more efficient than combustion-based ones since the electrolysis and combustion units are the main contributors to exergy destruction. Finally, the techno-economic comparison shows that gasification-based kerosene production via the methanol-to-olefins pathway has not only the highest efficiency but also the lowest specific production cost due to its high selectivity to kerosene.

Acknowledgments

The authors gratefully acknowledge the financial support by the German Federal Ministry of Education and Research (BMBF) within the H2Giga project DERIEL (grant number 03HY122D).

References

K. Atsonios, J. Li, V.J. Inglezakis, 2023, Energy, vol. 278, p. 127868

L.T. Biegler, I.E. Grossmann, and A.W. Westerberg, 1997, "Systematic Methods of Chemical Process Design", Prentice Hall PTR, Upper Saddle River, New Jersey, Chpt. 4-5, pp. 110–174

A.V. Bridgwater, A.J. Toft, J.G. Brammer, 2002, Renewable & Sustainable Energy Reviews, vol.6, pp. 181-248

K.P. Brooks, et int., J. Plaza, R. Handler, and D. Shonnard, 2016, "Low-Carbon Aviation Fuel Through the Alcohol to Jet Pathway", in Biofuels for Aviation, Chpt. 6, pp. 109-150

M. Cowley, 2002, "Conversion of n-pentenes over H-ZSM-5", MSc thesis, Cape Town University

M. Díaz, E. Epelde, Z. Tabernilla, A. Ateka, A.T. Aguayo, and J. Bilbao, 2020, Energy, vol. 207, p. 118317

F. Habermeyer, E. Kurkela, S. Maier, and R.-U. Dietrich, 2021, Frontiers in Energy Research, vol. 9, pp. 1–15

M. Hillestad, M. Ostadi, G.d. Alamo Serrano, E. Rytter, B. Austbø, J.G. Pharoah, and O.B. Burheim, 2018, Fuel, vol. 234, pp. 1431–1451

U. Lee, J. Burre, A. Caspari, J. Kleinekorte, A.M. Schweidtmann, and A. Mitsos, 2016, Industrial and Engineering Chemistry Research, vol. 55, no. 46, pp.12014–12026

W. Monama, E. Mohiuddin, B. Thangaraj, M.M. Mdleleni, and D. Key, 2020, Catalysis Today, vol. 342, pp. 167–177

S. Moon, H.-J. Chae, and M.B. Park, 2018, Applied Catalysis A: General, vol. 553, pp.15–23

S. Mucci, A. Mitsos, and D. Bongartz, 2023, Combustion vs Gasification in Power&Biomass-to-X: An Exergetic Analysis, *in preparation*

N. Nesterenko, J. Aguilhon, P. Bodart, D. Minoux, and J.P. Dath, 2016, "Methanol to Olefins: An Insight Into Reaction Pathways and Products Formation", in Zeolites and Zeolite-like Materials, Chpt. 5, pp. 189–263

A.S. Nielsen, M. Ostadi, B. Austbø, M. Hillestad, G. del Alamo, and O.S. Burheim, 2022, Fuel, vol. 321, p. 123987

A.H. Reksten, M.S. Thomassen, S. Møller-Holst, and K. Sundseth, 2022, International Journal of Hydrogen Energy, vol. 47, no. 90, pp. 38106–38113

M.F. Santos, S.F. Interlenghi, A.E. Bresciani, N.L. Ferreira, G.S. Bassani, and R.M. de Brito Alves, 2023, Computer Aided Chemical Engineering, vol. 52, pp. 2069–2074

P. Schmidt, V. Batteiger, A. Roth, W. Weindorf, and T. Raksha, 2018, Chemie-Ingenieur-Technik, vol. 90, no. 1, pp. 127–140

E.S. Van-Dal and C. Bouallou, 2013, Journal of Cleaner Production, vol. 57, pp. 38–45

F.V. Vázquez, P. Pfeifer, J. Lehtonen, P. Piermartini, P. Simell, and V. Alopaeus, 2017, Industrial and Engineering Chemistry Research, vol. 56, no. 45, pp. 13262–13272

Flavio Manenti, Gintaras V. Reklaitis (Eds.), Proceedings of the 34th European Symposium on Computer Aided Process Engineering / 15th International Symposium on Process Systems Engineering (ESCAPE34/PSE24), June 2-6, 2024, Florence, Italy

Design of carbon neutral methanol production via integration of renewable hydrogen and dry reforming process

Mahmoud Abdalla,[a] Mohammed G. Mohammed,[a,b] Umer Zahid[a,c] *

[a]*Department of Chemical Engineering, King Fahd University of Petrolume & Monerals, Dhahran 31261, Saudi Arabia*
[b]*Interdisciplinar Research Center for Hydrogen & Energy Storage, King Fahd University of Petrolume & Monerals, Dhahran 31261, Saudi Arabia*
[c]*Interdisciplinar Research Center for Membranes & Water Security, King Fahd University of Petrolume & Monerals, Dhahran 31261, Saudi Arabia*
uzahid@kfupm.edu.sa

Abstract

Carbon emission poses a huge threat to the environment. Despite recent advancements in carbon capture technology, the economic viability of utilizing captured CO_2 is considered a challenge to further progress. This work aims to study the technical feasibility of an environmentally friendly process for producing methanol as a liquid hydrogen carrier while utilizing captured CO_2. In this study, methane and CO_2 are used as a feedstock to produce synthesis gas (syngas), while green hydrogen produced via water electrolysis adjust the composition of the syngas to enhance the methanol synthesis reaction. The process is simulated using Aspen Plus assuming annual production capacity of 100,000 t of methanol with a purity of 99.5 mol.%. The study also includes an evaluation of energy requirements in each section of the process.

Keywords: Methanol, Green Hydrogen, Sustainable Process, Dry Methane Reforming.

1. Introduction

One of the major growing global concerns is CO_2 emissions and its impact on global warming. CO_2 emissions have increased over recent years causing a rise in global temperature leading to an unprecedented series of climatic events, underscoring the urgency and gravity of addressing this environmental challenge. Among the proposed solutions, carbon capture and utilization (CCU) hold great promise. CCU involves capturing CO_2 emissions from industrial processes and power plants and preventing them from entering the atmosphere. In addition, CCU approach includes developing methods for utilizing the captured CO_2 in various ways, such as production of fuels, chemicals, and building materials, contributing to a circular carbon economy.

Methanol is a clean fuel that is produced employing carbon dioxide as feedstock with diverse industrial applications such as the production of acetic acid, formaldehyde, and plastics. The design of a carbon-neutral methanol production process is a complex and multifaceted challenge, requiring the integration of various technologies. (Ugwu et al., 2022) proposed a gas switching dry reforming (GSDR) process, which efficiently converts CO_2 and CH_4 into syngas suitable for methanol production. This is complemented by (Roh et al., 2015), who explored sustainable CO_2 conversion processes, including combined reforming and CO_2 hydrogenation, to reduce CO_2 emissions and production costs. (Kar et al., 2018) further enhanced the sustainability of the process by developing a system for CO_2 capture and hydrogenation to methanol, with a focus on catalyst and amine reuse. Finally, (Yang et al., 2018) introduced a parallel-series system combining steam and dry methane reforming to achieve high-efficiency CO_2 utilization in methanol production. Although, some of the previous studies discussed the production of methanol by dry reforming, none of these studies proposed the integration of green hydrogen as a way of adjusting the composition of the syngas. This study investigates the feasibility of methanol production through the integration of green hydrogen with dry reforming, demonstrating a case wherein methanol serves as a carrier for hydrogen while concurrently mitigating CO_2 emissions.

2. Process Details

In this study, Aspen Plus and Aspen Custom Modeler were employed as simulation tools. The whole process simulation, excluding the electrolyzer, was conducted utilizing Aspen Plus. Peng-Robinson (PR) thermodynamic property package was selected due to its widespread applicability and reasonably high accuracy across a broad spectrum of pressures and temperatures.

2.1. Dry Reforming Unit

The feedstock composition, consisting of pure CO_2 and CH_4, is introduced into a Dry Reformer (DR), the simulation of which is performed using RPlug kinetic reactor model. The kinetic model of Eq.(1)&(2), with power law kinetics, developed by (Luyben, 2014) is used.

$$CH_4 + CO_2 \leftrightarrow 2H_2 + 2CO \tag{1}$$

$$H_2 + CO_2 \rightarrow CO + H2O \tag{2}$$

The DR consists of 800 tubes, each with a diameter of 0.1 m and 4 m in length. The tubes are filled with a catalyst whose density is 2000 kg/m³ and a voidage of 0.6. To prevent coke formation, the operating temperature of the DR is 1000 °C. Subsequently, the effluent undergoes a heat exchange process to harness the thermal energy from the very high temperature effluent stream for elevating the temperature of the feedstock.

2.2. Reactor Feed Preparation and Conditioning Unit

The product of the dry reforming process, syngas, then goes through a series of compressions and cooling stages to attain the required temperature and pressure conditions (200 °C and 80 bar) required for the methanol synthesis reaction. The stoichiometric number which represents the ratio of hydrogen to carbon in the syngas mixture should be above 2 for an optimal methanol synthesis reactor performance Eq. (3). The syngas produced from the dry reformer is deficient in hydrogen, therefore a solar-assisted electrolyzer for green hydrogen production by a proton exchange membrane (PEM) is integrated with the dry reformer as shown in Figure 1.

$$SN = \frac{y_{H2} - y_{CO_2}}{y_{CO} + y_{CO_2}} \tag{3}$$

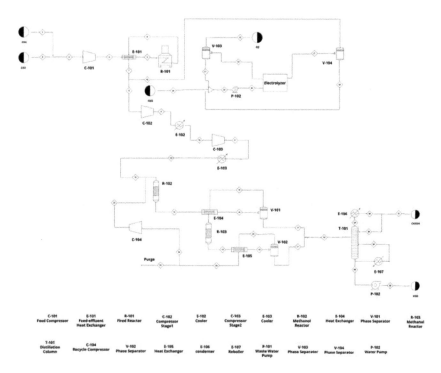

Figure 1: Process Flow Diagram of Methanol Production via Dry Reforming and Water Electrolysis as a Source of Green Hydrogen

1.1. Methanol Reactor unit

The syngas with adjusted stoichiometric number then enters the first methanol reactor modeled using an adiabatic kinetic RPlug model. The reaction kinetics used are (Langmuir-Hinshelwood - Hougen-Watson) (LHHW) with three reactions of Eq. (4) - (6) taking place simultaneously (Al-Qadri et al., 2023).

$$CO + 2H_2 \leftrightarrow CH_3OH \tag{4}$$

$$CO_2 + 3H_2 \leftrightarrow CH_3OH + H_2O \tag{5}$$

$$CO_2 + H_2 \leftrightarrow CO + H_2O \tag{6}$$

The methanol reactor consists of 2000 tubes with a tube diameter of 0.0375 m and length of 4 m, filled with a catalyst with a density of 2000 kg/m^3 and a voidage of 0.5. According to Le Chatelier's principle, any removal of products will shift the reaction towards the forward direction. Therefore, methanol and water are separated from the unreacted non-condensable syngas using a flash drum. The syngas is then sent to the second methanol synthesis reactor with an identical configuration to the first one. To prevent the accumulation of inert substances, 10% of the recycled stream is purged while the remaining unreacted syngas from the second reactor is recycled back to be mixed with the feed to the first reactor.

2.3. Electrolyzer Unit

Electrolysis is a chemical process where a chemical reaction takes places induced by an electric current. The chemical reaction in this case is considered a redox reaction where one molecule gains an electron and the other loses it. The reaction of water splitting takes place in a special electrolytic cell called "electrolyzer". In this work, Aspen Custom Modeler is used to model a Proton Exchange Membrane electrolyzer (PEM) in order to calculate the size and electrical power required to supply enough hydrogen for methanol production.

2.3.1. Voltage

Electrolyzer is an assembly of electrochemical cells connected in series, therefore the same current passes through all the cells while the voltage depends on the number of cells. The operating voltage Eq. (7) is the sum of the ideal voltage V_{id} and the losses that are commonly named "overvoltage".

$$V = V_{id} + V_{act} + V_{ohm} + V_{diff} \tag{7}$$

The ideal voltage V_{id} is the thermodynamic energy required for the water splitting and can be calculated by Gibbs free energy. The activation overvoltage V_{act} represents the energy required to initiate the chemical reaction. This voltage depends on the catalyst, current density, and the reaction. The ohmic overvoltage V_{ohm}, delineates the energy dissipation attributable to membrane and electrode resistivity. The diffusion overvoltage V_{diff} characterizes the energy losses resulting from mass transport limitations. However, based on many experimental evidences, the diffusion overvoltage can be neglected since the contribution of this term is very small as stated in the work of (Carmo et al., 2013).

2.3.2. Mass Balance and Hydrogen Production rate

The rate of hydrogen production and water consumption inside the electrolyzer cell is directly dependent on the rate of the current flow as Eq. (8) implies.

$$\dot{N}_{H_2} = \frac{i\,A}{n\,F} \tag{8}$$

Where $\dot{N}_{H_2}$ is the mole flow rate of hydrogen, i is the exchange current density, A is the cross-sectional area for electrolyzer cell, n is the number of electrons involved in the reaction and F is the Faraday constant with a value of 96485 C/mol.

The mass balance inside a cell, mainly the flow of hydrogen proton and water due to the effect of electro-osmotic drag, diffusivity and pressure difference are calculated as shown in a study conducted by (Colbertaldo et al., 2017).

Table 1 summarizes the input specifications for the major units of the process, the reactors and electrolyzer.

Table 1: Input specifications for simulation models

Unit/ system	Aspen Model	Parameters
Dry Reformer	Reactor model: RPlug	Temperature = 1000 °C Pressure = 4 bar CO_2/ CH_4 (mol./mol.) = 1
Methanol Synthesis	Reactor model: RPlug	Temperature = 200 °C Pressure = 80 bar Syngas SN = 2 Cu-based catalyst
Electolyzer	Custom Modeler	Temperature = 55 °C Pressure: Anode = 2.5 bar Cathode = 30 bar Cell Area = 1 m^2 Current density = 0.6 A/cm^2 Number of Cells = 4362

3. Result and Discussion

3.1. Electrolyzer performance
The polarization curve as shown in Figure 2(a) intercepts with the y-axis at the ideal voltage, which is about 1.23 V. The curve then steadily increases until it reaches a plateau where the voltage remains relatively constant. This plateau represents a required voltage to overcome all the three overpotentials activation, diffusion, and ohmic. Also, it corresponds to the region where the electrolysis reaction is efficiently taking place.

3.2. Energy consumption
The energy consumption analysis for the process is shown in Figure 2(b) illustrates the energy consumption in different process sections. Electricity usage dominates energy consumption with ~ 50 % of the total required energy. The largest portion of energy is consumed by the electrolyzer in comparison with other process sections. The required electricity for green hydrogen production will be supplied from renewable sources such as solar, wind, or hydropower which is out of focus in this study and would be worthy of investigation in a future study.

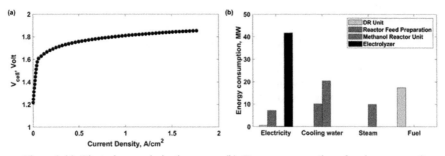

Figure 2 (a): Electorlyzer polarization curve, (b): Energy consumption of each process unit

Cooling water represents the only cooling utility for this process since the lowest temperature in this process is ~ 20 ˚C. DR required heating utility out of usual hot steam in form of a fuel, in this case natural gas to be able to reach the operating temperature of 1000 ˚C.

4. Conclusions

A complete simulation of a methanol production process via green hydrogen and dry methane reforming has been developed. A PEM electrolyzer is utilized to provide pure hydrogen in order to raise the stoichiometric number of syngas to meet the required composition for methanol synthesis. The results show a significant consumption of electricity, mainly in electrolyzer to drive the water splitting reaction. They also show that approximately 90,000 t/y of CO_2 is utilized to produce 100,000 t/y of methanol, which demonstrates a significant positive environmental impact. Further work is needed to address the economic viability of the process, highlighting the CO_2 subsidy amount or renewable electricity price required to reach a breakeven point.

Acknowledgement

The author(s) would like to acknowledge the support provided by the Deanship of Scientific Research at King Fahd University of Petroleum & Minerals (KFUPM).

References

Abdin, Z., Webb, C.J., Gray, E.MacA., 2015. Modelling and simulation of a proton exchange membrane (PEM) electrolyser cell. Int. J. Hydrog. Energy 40, 13243–13257.

Al-Qadri, A.A., Ahmed, U., Jameel, A.G.A., Ahmad, N., Zahid, U., Zein, S.H., Naqvi, S.R., 2023. Process design and techno-economic analysis of dual hydrogen and methanol production from plastics using energy integrated system. Int. J. Hydrog. Energy 48, 10797–10811.

Carmo, M., Fritz, D.L., Mergel, J., Stolten, D., 2013. A comprehensive review on PEM water electrolysis. Int. J. Hydrog. Energy 38, 4901–4934.

Colbertaldo, P., Gómez Aláez, S.L., Campanari, S., 2017. Zero-dimensional dynamic modeling of PEM electrolyzers. Energy Procedia, Proceedings of the 9th International Conference on Applied Energy 142, 1468–1473.

Kar, S., Sen, R., Goeppert, A., Prakash, G.K.S., 2018. Integrative CO2 Capture and Hydrogenation to Methanol with Reusable Catalyst and Amine: Toward a Carbon Neutral Methanol Economy. J. Am. Chem. Soc. 140, 1580–1583.

Luyben, W.L., 2014. Design and Control of the Dry Methane Reforming Process. Ind. Eng. Chem. Res. 53, 14423–14439.

Roh, K., Nguyen, T.B.H., Suriyapraphadilok, U., Lee, J.H., Gani, R., 2015. Development of sustainable CO2 conversion processes for the methanol production 37, 1145–1150.

Ugwu, A., Osman, M., Zaabout, A., Amini, S., 2022. Carbon Capture Utilization and Storage in Methanol Production Using a Dry Reforming-Based Chemical Looping Technology. Energy Fuels 36, 9719–9735.

Yang, Y., Liu, J., Shen, W., Li, J., Chien, I.-L., 2018. High-efficiency utilization of CO2 in the methanol production by a novel parallel-series system combining steam and dry methane reforming. Energy 158, 820–829.

Flavio Manenti, Gintaras V. Reklaitis (Eds.), Proceedings of the 34th European Symposium on Computer Aided Process Engineering / 15th International Symposium on Process Systems Engineering (ESCAPE34/PSE24), June 2-6, 2024, Florence, Italy

Conceptual Design of a Large Ship Propulsion System Fueled by an Ammonia-Hydrogen Blend: Toward a Decarbonized Shipping Transport

Antonio Sánchez[a*], M.A. Martín Rengel[b], Mariano Martín[a]

[a]Department of Chemical Engineering. University of Salamanca. Plz. Caídos 1-5, Salamanca, 37008, Spain
[b]Departament of Materials Science, Universidad Politecnica de Madrid. Avd. de la Memoria 4, Madrid, 28040, Spain
antoniosg@usal.es

Abstract

In the pursuit of decarbonizing maritime transport and achieving net-zero greenhouse gas emissions, ammonia is gaining prominence as a green fuel. In this work, an integrated ship propulsion system based on ammonia is proposed consisting of ammonia decomposition, internal combustion engine, and NO_x removal which collectively address the inherent challenges associated with ammonia combustion. The optimal system configuration demonstrates an energy and exergy efficiency of 42.4% and 48.1% respectively, with NO_x emissions (one of the critical issues in ammonia combustion) below 0.5 g/kWh. The economic evaluation shows that the initial investment is reasonable at 784 €/kW, but operating costs are high at 210 €/MWh. The success of green ammonia as a marine fuel relies on achieving competitive production costs, namely below 0.4 €/kg.

Keywords: Ammonia, Decarbonization, Hydrogen, Maritime transport, Ship.

1. Introduction

A considerable portion of current greenhouse gas emissions is attributed to passenger and cargo transportation, primarily through shipping, which plays a pivotal role in global trade. Maritime transport accounts for approximately 3% of global greenhouse gas emissions. To address this issue, the International Maritime Organization (IMO) has set ambitious targets to achieve net-zero greenhouse gas emissions from international shipping by 2050. This is a great challenge, considering that over 95% of existing ships rely on internal combustion engines powered by fossil fuels. To decarbonize the shipping sector, various alternatives have been proposed. Direct electrification is an efficient method to introduce renewables into ships. However, it may be limited to shorter distances due to the challenges associated with the size of the batteries.
Hydrogen and its derivatives, such as methanol and ammonia, are also promising energy vectors for maritime transport (Korberg et al., 2021). The main limitation in the use of hydrogen onboard is related to its storage. Hydrogen is a gas at ambient conditions with a low volumetric energy density. In addition, due to its small molecular size, hydrogen is prompt to leak. Compressed or liquefied hydrogen can enhance energy density but at a remarkable cost, making it suitable for specific applications with limited operating hours. To face these challenges, there is a growing focus on producing green fuels from renewable hydrogen (McKinlay et al., 2021). These options offer substantial improvements in energy density, thereby enhancing storage conditions and reducing

associated costs. Notably, two green fuels have emerged as particularly promising alternatives: methanol and ammonia. Methanol is liquid at ambient conditions, resulting in a reduced storage cost of approximately 0.13 €/kWh. However, a significant concern is addressing the entire CO_2 cycle. When methanol is burned, it releases CO_2 and water. While the idea of reusing this CO_2 to synthesize more methanol for maritime purposes is promising, implementing an onboard capture system is fraught with technical and economic limitations. An alternative involves direct air capture onshore, but with substantially higher removal costs. In contrast, ammonia presents a more straightforward solution, as it is a carbon-free fuel synthetized through the combination of hydrogen and nitrogen. The maritime industry is increasingly drawn to ammonia as a sustainable option (Wang et al., 2023). Ammonia can be stored as a liquid at 240 K and atmospheric pressure or at 10 bar and ambient temperature, with a storage cost of approximately 0.25 €/kWh. Due to its carbon-free nature and the extensive experience in ammonia production and storage, this alternative is the selected choice in this study.

Nonetheless, there are two primary challenges that must be addressed when using ammonia as a fuel in maritime internal combustion engines. Firstly, ammonia is considered a relatively unreactive fuel due to its low flame speed and high autoignition temperature. To overcome this limitation, a common approach is to use a co-fuel in conjunction with ammonia. Hydrogen is the alternative of choice, primarily because it is a carbon-free chemical, ensuring that the blend has no associated CO_2 emissions. Moreover, hydrogen can be produced from ammonia through its decomposition. Secondly, during the combustion of ammonia, a non-negligible amount of nitrogen oxides can be produced, which is a significant pollutant. As a result, it becomes imperative to implement emission control measures when using ammonia in combustion engines to mitigate the environmental impact and ensure compliance with emission standards.

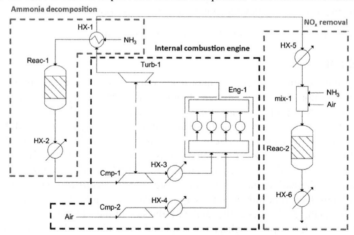

Figure 1: Process diagram of the proposed propulsion system

Currently, most research efforts are primarily concentrated on the isolated analysis of ammonia engines, analyzing them from both experimental and theoretical perspectives. However, achieving a comprehensive understanding of the entire propulsion system is essential. This necessitates considering not just the engine but also the processes associated with raw material preparation and exhaust gas cleanup. In this study, a more holistic approach is taken by conducting an integrated analysis of an ammonia-based propulsion system using a process perspective. This assessment includes all the stages required to convert ammonia into usable energy, including the production of hydrogen as a co-fuel and the treatment of exhaust gases from the engine. This comprehensive analysis represents a significant step to introduce ammonia as a viable and environmentally friendly fuel in the maritime transport sector, allowing for the decarbonization of this critical activity.

2. Propulsion system description and modelling

The proposed propulsion system is based on three main sections: ammonia decomposition, internal combustion engine (ICE), and NO_x removal. The complete design of this propulsion system is illustrated in Figure 1. In the initial stage of the proposed system, ammonia decomposition takes place. The objective of this step is to generate a blend of ammonia/hydrogen for utilization as fuel in the internal combustion engine. Specifically, a mixture comprising 70% ammonia and 30% hydrogen is chosen, as this ratio is commonly recommended in the literature to enhance the flammability properties of ammonia. The reaction carried out in this reactor is as follows:

$$2NH_3 \leftrightarrows N_2 + 3H_2 \tag{1}$$

The ammonia decomposition reaction occurs within an adiabatic fixed-bed reactor and is highly endothermic. To address the energy requirements of this process, a heat exchanger is introduced prior to the reactor unit. For heat integration within the system, the exhaust gases from the internal combustion engine serve as the heating agent in this unit. The design of this reactor involves the formulation of a set of differential equations that combine mass, heat, and momentum transfer. In this configuration, Ni/Al_2O_3 catalyst is selected with the following kinetic expression for the ammonia decomposition:

$$r = 3k_{reac}\left[K_p^2 a_{N_2}\left(\frac{a_{H_2}^3}{a_{NH_3}^2}\right)^{\alpha} - \left(\frac{a_{NH_3}^2}{a_{H_2}^3}\right)^{1-\alpha}\right]\Phi\Omega \tag{2}$$

The second stage of the proposed propulsion system is the internal combustion engine (ICE). Specifically, a two-stroke compression ignition (CI) internal combustion engine equipped with a turbocharger is selected for this study. The selection of the CI alternative is motivated by the considerable ignition energy required for marine systems. A thermodynamic modeling technique is used that employs an ideal Miller-Sabathe cycle, comprising the following steps: adiabatic compression, constant volume heat addition, constant pressure heat addition, adiabatic expansion, and heat removal. Several parameters are required to model this unit collected from real maritime ICEs and for experimental ammonia-based engines. These are presented for the four different engine loads analyzed in this work in Table 1.

Table 1: Parameters fixed in the modeling of the engine performance

	100%	75%	50%	25%
Inlet pressure into the cylinder (bar)	4.0	3.2	2.2	1.3
Maximum pressure (bar)	180	165	145	110
Compression ratio (CR)	14	14	14	14

Moreover, to control the maximum temperature within the engine, an equivalence ratio (ER) of 0.85 has been established. The combustion of the ammonia/hydrogen blend primarily results in the generation of nitrogen and water. However, it is essential to note that a non-negligible quantity of nitrogen oxides (NO_x) is produced within the combustion chamber. Determining the exact concentration of NO_x is challenging due to limited research in real maritime engine conditions. In this study, the NO_x concentration in the exhaust gases is set at 2000 ppm based on the findings presented by Liu et al. (2022). These results are derived from a combustion engine utilizing a mixture of ammonia and hydrogen with the 70/30 ratio.

The final stage in the propulsion system involves the selected catalytic reduction (SCR). Its primary purpose is to reduce the concentrations of NO_x to levels below the stringent limits set forth by the International Maritime Organization (IMO). This reduction process is based on the following chemical reaction:

$$4NO + 4NH_3 + O_2 \rightarrow 4N_2 + 6H_2O \tag{3}$$

For this reduction reaction, a fixed-bed monolithic reactor is employed, featuring a commercial Cu-zeolite catalyst. The operational temperature range of this unit falls between 550 K and 750 K. In this setup, both ammonia (the fuel of the proposed system) and oxygen (from the air) are introduced as reagents. The entire system is subject to optimization to determine the most favorable operating conditions, assess the energy performance, and evaluate the economic aspects associated with this novel propulsion system centered around ammonia.

3. Results and discussion

The baseline of the propulsion system proposed corresponds to a production capacity of 11MW. Furthermore, it has undergone an assessment under four engine load conditions: 100%, 75%, 50%, and 25%. These changes in engine load have a significant impact on the operating conditions of the decomposition reactor. To address the most challenging scenario, which is the maximum load, the decomposition reactor has been designed with a maximum inlet temperature set at 750K. This limitation is imposed due to the limited temperature gradient between the incoming ammonia and the exhaust gases from the engine. This aspect is crucial, primarily because of the substantial endothermicy of the decomposition reaction. As the engine load decreases, it becomes necessary to reduce the inlet temperature of the decomposition reactor to maintain the same ammonia/hydrogen ratio while processing a smaller ammonia flow rate. For instance, at a 25% load, the inlet temperature of the decomposition reactor is reduced to approximately 730 K. There exists a close relationship between the operation of the decomposition reactor and the SCR unit. Both units are arranged in series, and the exhaust gases came from the ammonia decomposition (as heating agent) to the SCR section. Consequently, if the conditions in the decomposition are more restrictive in terms of temperature, the inlet temperature of the SCR reactor is reduced because a higher fraction of the energy of the gases is released in the decomposition section. As a result, at 100% engine load, the inlet temperature in the SCR reactor is around 670 K. This value can be increased to 750 K when the engine load is decreased. These differences in inlet temperature have a direct impact on the NO_x removal yield. Specifically, higher operating temperatures and lower loads result in higher removal efficiency, with the removal rate ranging from approximately 90% at full load to nearly 100% for an engine load of 25%.

The performance of the internal combustion engine is predominantly regulated by the combustion temperature, which is controlled by varying the excess of air (equivalence ratio). This temperature is usually around 2500 K. Thermodynamic calculations indicate that the thermal efficiency of the proposed cycle falls within the range of 60-70%. However, taking a conservative approach and accounting for irreversibilities and energy losses, this value is reduced up to 50%. In the combustion chamber, the concentration of nitrogen oxides in the exhaust gases measures around 3.5-4 g/kWh. This exceeds the current target set by the International Maritime Organization (IMO) in TIER III, 2 g/kWh.

Consequently, the introduction of the SCR section is required to meet the strictest emissions legislation. Following the SCR treatment, which reported removal efficiencies ranging from 90-100%, the NO_x concentration is effectively reduced to below 0.5 g/kWh. As a result, the proposed ammonia-based propulsion system enables maritime transportation with zero direct CO_2 emissions and significantly reduced NO_x emissions, aligning with stringent environmental standards.

To analyze the energy performance, Figure 2 shows the main energy flows of the entire propulsion system (for the 100% of the engine load).

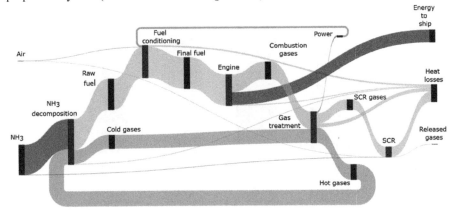

Figure 2: Sankey diagram with the main energy flows of the propulsion system

In the system proposed, ammonia serves as the primary energy input, introduced into the decomposition section. While exhaust gases from the engine are recycled, only approximately 10% of the energy can be transferred to the inlet ammonia due to limitations imposed by temperature gradients. The resulting blend of ammonia/hydrogen is then sent to the engine. Notably, the power generated by the combustion gases is looped back to the fuel conditioning section as part of the turbocharger scheme. The engine's thermal efficiency stands at 50%, as previously mentioned. A considerable amount of energy from the combustion gases is dissipated as heat in various sections of the system. Further integration, for instance, with some of the ship's utilities, has the potential to enhance the overall system's energy efficiency. In its current configuration, the global energy efficiency is 42.4%. Additionally, an exergy analysis is conducted for this configuration. The global exergy efficiency is determined to be 48.1% with the internal combustion engine (35.5%) and the SCR unit (53.2%) as the stages with lowest exergy performance This is primarily attributed to the chemical reactions involved.

An economic analysis of the system is also performed. For the baseline capacity of 11MW, the capital cost (CAPEX) of the system adds up to 8.7 M€ (784 €/kW). The internal combustion engine based on ammonia accounts for the largest share of this investment, representing around 65% of the total CAPEX. This investment cost is slightly higher than current alternatives based on fossil fuels. For instance, marine gas oil is reported to have a capital cost of 530 €/kW. However, it is comparable to other alternative fuels like hydrogen (700-800 €/kW) or methanol (550-600 €/kW). When analyzing the operating cost (OPEX) of the propulsion system, three primary components should be considered: the cost of the fuel (NH_3), the amortization cost, and the maintenance cost. The results for different engine loads assessed in this study are presented in Figure 3.

The current operating cost varies from 210 €/MWh for full load to 243 €/MWh for 25% of the engine load. This propulsion cost is notably higher compared to existing technologies, which typically range from 120 to 160 €/MWh, similar to other alternative green fuels, falling within the 200-300 €/MWh range. As depicted in the figure, the primary contributor to these costs is the fuel cost, accounting for over 90% of the total when operating at full capacity. Therefore, a critical factor for the adoption of ammonia as a fuel in shipping transport is the reduction of the cost of green ammonia.

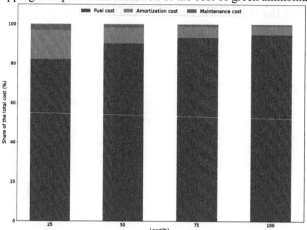

Figure 3: Breakdown of the operating cost for the different engine loads

4. Conclusions

A conceptual design for a ship propulsion system using ammonia is presented, aiming the full decarbonization of the shipping sector. The system proposed involves three core sections (ammonia decomposition, engine, and NO_x removal) to tackle the challenges associated with ammonia combustion. The integrated system shows an energy efficiency of 42.4% and maintains NO_x emissions below 5 g/kWh, aligning with the IMO targets. From an economic standpoint, the capital and operating costs remain relatively high, standing at 784 €/kW and 210 €/MWh, respectively. However, there is potential for cost reduction, mainly if green ammonia can be priced more competitively in the market.

Acknowledgments

The authors acknowledge H2MetAmo project by the financial support.

References

A.D. Korberg, S. Brynolf, M. Grahn, I.R. Skov, 2021, Techno-economic assessment of advanced fuels and propulsion systems in future fossil-free ships. Renew. Sust. Energ. Rev., 142, 110861.

H.Wang, P. Daoutidis, Q. Zhang, 2023, Ammonia-based green corridors for sustainable maritime transportation. Digital Chemical Engineering, 6, 100082.

L. Liu, F. Tan, Z. Wu, Y. Wang, H. Liu, 2022, Comparison of the combustion and emission characteristics of NH_3/NH_4NO_2 and NH_3/H_2 in a two-stroke low speed marine engine, Int. J. Hydrog. Energy, 47, 40, 17778-17787.

C.J. McKinlay, S.R. Turnock, D.A. Hudson, 2021, Route to zero emission shipping: Hydrogen, ammonia or methanol? Int. J. Hydrog. Energy, 46, 55, 28282-28297.

Flavio Manenti, Gintaras V. Reklaitis (Eds.), Proceedings of the 34th European Symposium on Computer Aided Process Engineering / 15th International Symposium on Process Systems Engineering (ESCAPE34/PSE24), June 2-6, 2024, Florence, Italy

Alternative pathways to sustainable aviation fuel from CO_2 and H_2: an enviro-economic assessment

Andrea Bernardi[a, *], David Danaci[a,b], Andrew Symes[c], Benoit Chachuat[a]

[a]*The Sargent Centre for Process Systems Engineering, Imperial College London, UK*
[b]*I-X Centre for AI In Science, Imperial College London, London, UK*
[c]*OXCCU Tech Ltd, Oxford, UK*
*a.bernardi13@imperial.ac.uk

Abstract

With air transportation responsible for 2% of the total GHG emissions and 10% of the fuel consumption worldwide, sustainable aviation fuel (SAF) is considered a key enabler to reach net-zero aviation by 2050. In this work, we carry out an enviro-economic comparison between a one-step Fischer-Tropsch process (1sFT) and a methanol-to-jet process (MTJ). 1sFT is based on a novel Mn-Fe-K catalyst promoting direct conversion of CO_2 and H_2 to liquid hydrocarbons. In MTJ, methanol is produced first, followed by methanol-to-olefin conversion, oligomerization, and hydro-processing. Our analysis considers 1 MJ of liquid fuel as functional unit and the following key performance indicators: levelized cost of production, global warming potential, and monetized end-point environmental impacts. Our results suggest that 1sFT outperforms MTJ by 23-36%, depending on H_2 and CO_2 costs. 1sFT is also found to be superior to MTJ from an environmental point of view, with up to 33% reduction in GWP and 28% reduction in monetized environmental externalities on a well-to-wake basis.

Keywords: SAF, technoeconomic analysis, LCA, Fischer-Tropsch, Methanol-to-Jet

1. Introduction

The aviation industry is heavily reliant on fossil resources, and, unlike other transportation modes, it cannot be decarbonised through electrification due to the high energy density required for long distance travel (Becattini et al. 2021). Sustainable aviation fuel (SAF) is defined as a drop-in alternative that can be used in existing aircrafts while meeting certain sustainability criteria, and it is considered a key step towards net-zero aviation. From a regulatory perspective, alternative fuels need to achieve a minimum of 50 % GWP reduction on a life-cycle basis to be classified as SAF in the UK.

Two routes under investigation for producing SAF from CO_2 and H_2 are Fischer-Tropsch (FT) synthesis and alcohol-to-jet routes with either methanol or ethanol as intermediates. In particular, the methanol-to-jet (MTJ) pathway is attracting significant attention, with major companies such as Honeywell, Topsoe and ExxonMobil announcing the development of proprietary technologies. Recently, Bernardi et al. (2022) compared two FT routes, a one-step FT process (1sFT) based on a novel Mn-Fe-K catalyst (Yao et al., 2020) and a two-step process (2sFT) using a reverse water gas shift reactor to convert CO_2 and H_2 to syngas first, followed by a conventional FT reactor (Zang et al., 2021). 1sFT was found to outperform 2sFT both from an economic and environmental standpoint, but significant reductions in CO_2 and H_2 prices as well as policy interventions such as carbon taxation were deemed necessary for the synthetic fuel to be economically competitive with its fossil counterpart. Schmidt et al. (2018) compared MTJ with a two-step FT process in terms of their economics, GHG emissions, water consumption and land use, and concluded that they were performing similarly.

The main objective of this paper is a comparison of the 1sFT process analyzed in Bernardi et al. (2022) with an MTJ process. These two processes are also compared to a fossil-based alternative in terms of economic and environmental performance. The methodology is described in Section 2, followed by results and discussions in Section 3, before concluding the paper in Section 4.

2. Methodology

Block flow diagrams of the two processes are shown in Figure 1. Aspen HYSYS v11 is used to simulate the processes at scale, considering a feed of 100 t/h of CO_2 either from direct air capture (DAC) or biogenic, and H_2 from water electrolysis. Both CO_2 and H_2 gases are fed at 25 °C and 30 bar, with no significant impurities, and the produced fuel blends are sent to an existing refinery. The NTRL-RK fluid package is used in the methanol synthesis section and the Peng Robinson fluid package everywhere else. Heat integration is performed in Aspen Energy Analyzer.

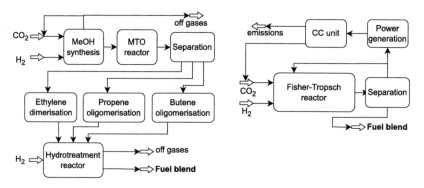

Figure 1: block flow diagrams of the MTJ (left) and 1sFT (right) processes. The power generation and carbon capture units are used for the off-gases of both processes but only represented in 1sFT.

2.1. Process simulation and economic analysis

Feed streams. We considered two options for CO2 procurement: DAC, and carbon capture from a pulp and paper mill (PPCC). In our baseline scenario, we considered a solid sorbent DAC process, with heat requirements fulfilled by a natural gas steam boiler or coming from a low-grade heat source (considered available free of charge), which result in a cost of 430 $/t$_{CO2}$ and 281 $/t$_{CO2}$, respectively (Sabatino et al 2021). The CO_2 captured from the pulp and paper mill is 95% biogenic and has a cost of 75 $/t$_{CO2}$ in the baseline scenario (Onarheim et al. 2017). The H_2 cost is estimated at 4.3 $/kg$_{H2}$, considering an offshore wind electricity price of 67 $/MWh$_{el}$, an energy efficiency of 67.5 %$_{LHV}$, 20 % cost increase to account for electricity intermittency, and 26% added to the total cost to account for capital and operating expenditures other than electricity. An optimistic scenario is also briefly discussed, which considers prices of 1.5 $/kg$_{H2}$ (Brändle et al., 2021), 150 $/t$_{CO2, DAC}$, and 50 $/t$_{CO2,biog}$. All costs throughout the paper are expressed in US$$_{2023}$ for consistency.

One-step FT synthesis (1sFT). The FT reactor operates at 260 °C and 10 bar with conversion and selectivities obtained from Yao et al. (2020). H_2 is fed to the process in a H_2:CO_2 molar ratio of 3:1. The outlet stream enters a sequence of two 3-phase separators operating at 70 °C and 40 °C both under 10 bar. A small (2%) fraction of the gaseous stream coming out of the second separator is burned to produce heat and electricity in a gas and steam cycle, while the rest is recycled to the FT reactor. The other two streams from the 3-phase separators are wastewater and liquid hydrocarbons. The liquid hydrocarbons are mixed, expanded to 1 bar and cooled down to 35 °C. The vapor phase from a flash separator (CO_2 and C1–C4 hydrocarbons) is burned to produce additional electricity, while the liquid phase containing the fuel blend product is sent to the refinery. A carbon capture (CC) unit is installed to capture 95%$_{wt}$ of the CO_2 in the flue gas, which is recycled back to the FT reactor. The fuel blend contains 16.4%$_{wt}$ gasoline (C5-C7), 76%$_{wt}$ SAF (C8-C16), 4.6%$_{wt}$ diesel (C17-C20), 2.8%$_{wt}$ light hydrocarbons (C1-C4), and traces (<1%$_{wt}$) amount of wax (C20+).

Methanol-to-jet process (MTJ). Methanol is produced from direct CO_2 hydrogenation in an isothermal reactor operating at 260 °C and 65 bar, described by the model by Vanden Bussche and Froment (1996). Methanol and water are recovered in two flash separators operating at 50 °C and under 65 bar and 1 bar. The unreacted syngas is recycled back to the methanol reactor except for a 1% purge stream that is burned to produce electricity. A distillation column is used to separate water from the methanol product that is sent to the upgrading section. Methanol is first converted to olefins in a methanol-to-olefins (MTO) reactor, operating at 450 °C and 2 bar. The outlet stream is cooled to 50 °C to remove the water then sent to an adsorption column to remove the CO_2 and a distillation train to separate the ethylene, propene and butene co-products. The olefins stream is compressed to 30 bar before entering the first column, where 99%$_{wt}$ pure ethylene is recovered at the top with a condenser temperature of -13 °C. The bottom stream is sent to a second column operating at 20 bar where propylene and butene are separated. Ethylene reacts at 25 °C and 50 bar to produce n-butane, i-butane and hexene. Propene and butene are further upgraded in oligomerization reactors operating at 270 °C and 40 bar, and 350 °C and 10 bar, respectively. Lastly, a hydrotreatment reactor operating at 300 °C and 30 bar and fed with a stochiometric amount of H_2 is used to convert the olefins into alkanes. The final liquid fuel blend is obtained in a flash separator operating at 40 °C and 1 bar. As in 1sFT the off gases are used to produce electricity and sent to a CC unit to capture and recycle 95% of the CO_2. The liquid fuel blend produced contains 4.5%$_{wt}$ gasoline, 86.2%$_{wt}$ SAF, 2.3%$_{wt}$ diesel, 6.9%$_{wt}$ light hydrocarbons, and no wax.

Economic analysis. In 1sFT, the FT reactor yields and selectivities are obtained from Zao et al. (2020), with correlations from Zang et al. (2021) used to estimate the cost. In the methanol upgrading section of MTJ, conversion and selectivities are obtained from Atsonios et al. (2023). The levelized cost of production (LCP) is calculated assuming a 15% interest rate and 20-year plant lifetime. LCP is compared with the fossil fuel cost, which is assumed to be 14 \$/GJ$_{fuel}$ in the base case, and 23 \$/GJ$_{fuel}$ in the optimistic best-case scenario considering a carbon tax of 150 \$/t$_{CO2}$ (IEA 2020).

2.2. Life cycle analysis

The functional unit (FU) for the LCA analysis is chosen as "*1 MJ of liquid fuel blend*" and the assessment is done considering a Well-to-Wake (WtW) perspective, assuming that all the carbon in the fuel blend is released as CO_2 during the use phase. System expansion via substitution is adopted to deal with multi-functionality.

Data collection and life-cycle inventories. The life-cycle inventories (LCIs) of 1sFT and MTJ are computed from the two process flowsheets (Section 2.1), as summarized in Table 1. The LCIs for DAC, biogenic CO_2, and H_2 are adapted from Sabatino et al. (2023), Onarheim et al. (2017), and Brändle et al. (2021), respectively. Offshore wind electricity is assumed for H_2 production, and credits given for selling any excess electricity are based on the UK production mix.

Table 1: life-cycle inventories of 1sFT and MTJ processes. HPS = high pressure steam, FH = Fired Heater, CW = Cooling water, WW = Wastewater. The FU is 1 MJ of liquid fuel blend.

	1sFT	MTJ			1sFT	MTJ	
Inputs	**Quantity**		**Units**	**Outputs**	**Quantity**		**Units**
CO_2	$7.03 \cdot 10^{-2}$	$7.15 \cdot 10^{-2}$	kg	FU	$1.00 \cdot 10^{0}$	$1.00 \cdot 10^{0}$	MJ
H_2	$1.12 \cdot 10^{-2}$	$1.29 \cdot 10^{-2}$	kg	Electricity	$1.08 \cdot 10^{-2}$	$7.50 \cdot 10^{-4}$	kWh
HPS	$3.90 \cdot 10^{-2}$	$8.63 \cdot 10^{-2}$	MJ	CO_2	$5.55 \cdot 10^{-4}$	$1.16 \cdot 10^{-3}$	kg
FH	-	$2.69 \cdot 10^{-3}$	MJ	CO	$3.71 \cdot 10^{-4}$	$5.69 \cdot 10^{-4}$	kg
CW	$2.19 \cdot 10^{-4}$	$2.88 \cdot 10^{-4}$	m^3	WW	$6.29 \cdot 10^{-5}$	$7.60 \cdot 10^{-5}$	m^3

Environmental impact assessment. The environmental assessment is conducted in SimaPro 9.3, using Ecoinvent 3.9 Cut-Off database for the background process inventories. The business-as-usual (BAU) fossil-based liquid fuel alternative is assumed to be "Petroleum {Europe without Switzerland} | market for petroleum | Cut-off, U", a liquid fuel with a LHV of 43.4 MJ/kg. The environmental KPIs are GWP100 alongside the monetized endpoint impacts to human health, ecosystem quality and resource scarcity, all computed with the ReCiPe2016 impact assessment methodology (Huijbregts *et al.* 2017) and using the monetization factors from Dong *et al.* (2019) converted to $\$_{2023}$.

3. Results and discussion

3.1. Midpoint environmental impacts – global warming potential
The left plot of Figure 2 compares the GWP_{WTW} of 1sFT and MTJ for the different carbon sources against BAU, with the error bars representing the uncertainty of the ecoinvent background data. Both alternatives achieve a significant reduction in GWP_{WtW}, with 1sFT outperforming MTJ by 27-33% depending on the CO_2 source. Overall, 1sFT and MTJ reduce GWP_{WtW} by over 70% and 60% compared to BAU, respectively. With DAC, the process credits for using CO_2 correspond to the amount of CO_2 removed from the atmosphere minus the indirect emissions related to DAC energy requirements; while with PPCC, CO_2 procurement is responsible for 25-32% of the total GWP_{WtW}, but the use phase emissions are 95% lower due to the biogenic CO_2 content. Overall, the best performance is achieved when DAC_{LGH} is used followed by PPCC and DAC_{LT}. H_2 production contributes $9.4 \cdot 10^{-3}$ $kg_{CO2\text{-}eq}/MJ_{fuel, 1sFT}$ and $1.0 \cdot 10^{-2}$ $kg_{CO2\text{-}eq}/MJ_{fuel, MtJ}$ of GWP_{WtW}, while indirect emissions related to hot utilities are ~55% lower in 1sFT compared to MTJ. Finally, the direct emissions from both processes are negligible with PPCC and account only for ~2% of GWP_{WtW} with DAC.

3.2. Endpoint analysis and total cost
The right plot of Figure 2 compares the total cost (TC) of 1sFT and MTJ against BAU. From an economic point of view all the options come significantly more expensive than using fossil fuel. H_2 procurement is always the dominant cost, representing 82% and 77%

of the LCP in 1sFT and MTJ, respectively, when the cheapest CO_2 alternative (PPCC) is used. With DAC, the cost of CO_2 makes up 23-36% of the LCP depending on the heat source. It is worth noting that the CapEx of 1sFT is 40% lower compared to MTJ, but since the LCP is mainly determined by the operating costs the LCP_{1sFT} is only 14-20% lower than LCP_{MTJ} depending on the H_2 and CO_2 prices.

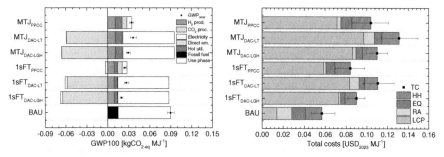

Figure 2: Enviro-economic results for the 1sFT, MTJ and BAU routes, using green H_2 and CO_2 from carbon capture in a pulp and paper mill (PPCC), low temperature direct air capture (DAC-LT) and DAC using low grade heat (DAC-LGH). Left: Well-to-Wake GWP, square symbols indicate net GWP100; Right: total cost (TC) including environmental externalities.

The monetized externalities cost is always lower than BAU, but burden shifting is occurring between GWP (where SAF is performing better than BAU as previously discussed) and other midpoint environmental impacts including particulate matter formation, human toxicity, land use, and water consumption (where SAF is performing worse). This results in overall damage to human health spanning between $1.10 \cdot 10^{-2}$ \$/MJ and $1.18 \cdot 10^{-2}$ \$/MJ, compared to $1.16 \cdot 10^{-2}$ for BAU. Burden shifting also affects damage to ecosystem quality, but all the SAF options have a lower overall impact compared to BAU. Looking at the damage to resource availability, DAC_{LT} is the least sustainable option with a reduction of only 30-35% compared to BAU. Despite the lower externalities costs all the SAF options have a higher TC than BAU, with the best alternative ($1sFT_{PPCC}$) having a 48% higher TC, and the worst alternative (MTJ_{DAC-LT}) a ~2.3 times higher TC than BAU.

In the optimistic scenario, the LCP of 1sFT decreases to 25.8 \$/GJ if $CO_{2,PPCC}$ is used, only slightly higher than the cost of fossil fuels with a CO_2 tax of 150 \$/t (23 \$/GJ), while all the other options remain 42-78% more expensive than BAU. In terms of total cost including externalities, TC_{BAU} is 24-27% higher than TC_{1sFT} and 2-5% higher than TC_{MTJ}.

In terms of fuel blend composition, MTJ produces a higher percentage of SAF and light hydrocarbons, while 1sFT produces a higher percentage of gasoline. A detailed analysis of the effect of fuel composition is beyond the scope of the work, but alternatives to flaring such as a reforming reactor to convert the light hydrocarbons back into syngas to maximize the liquid fuel output could lead to more significant benefits in MTJ, while the fuel blend from 1sFT might require larger intervention at the refinery.

4. Conclusions

This paper presented an enviro-economic assessment of two processes for producing liquid hydrocarbons in the jet fuel range from CO_2 and H_2, an FT-based process and a methanol-mediated process. Green H_2 from water electrolysis was considered along with two carbon sources: low temperature DAC, with heat provided by a natural gas boiler or a low-grade burden-free heat source, and biogenic CO_2 captured from a pulp and paper mill. A one-step FT process using a novel catalyst was compared tothe MTJ process, assuming that the product blend is sent to an existing refinery. One key finding is that the FT process is superior both in economic and environmental terms to the MTJ process, due to a lower capital cost, lower heating requirements, and higher energy efficiency. Importantly, all the alternatives considered can qualify as SAF in the UK since they achieve 60-80% GWP reduction on a life-cycle basis, with the largest reduction obtained when DAC with low-grade heat is combined with the FT process. Our environmental assessment also quantified endpoint impacts, confirming a better overall environmental performance of the synthetic fuels compared to fossil fuels, with 60% reduction for the FT process in an optimistic scenario. Nevertheless, the proposed low-carbon synthetic fuels are significantly more expensive than fossil fuels, and even if the prices of H_2 and CO_2 were to decrease, policy interventions such as carbon taxation would likely remain necessary to make SAF competitive. Future work will focus on adding more options for H_2 and CO_2, including blue hydrogen, alternative DAC processes, biomass gasification and other biogenic carbon sources. Moreover, reforming of the light hydrocarbons and unreacted syngas will be evaluated in order to minimize the CO_2 and H_2 requirements.

Acknowledgements: AB and BC are grateful to EPSRC for financial support under Grant EP/V011863/1. DD is supported by the Eric and Wendy Schmidt AI in Science Postdoctoral Fellowship, a Schmidt Futures program.

References

K. Atsonios *et al.* 2023. Process analysis and comparative assessment of advanced thermochemical pathways for e-kerosene production. Energy, 278, 127868

V. Becattini *et al.* 2021. Role of carbon capture, storage, and utilization to enable a net-zero CO_2-emissions aviation sector. Ind Eng Chem Res, 60, 6848−6862

A. Bernardi *et al.* 2022. Enviro-economic assessment of sustainable aviation fuel production from direct CO_2 hydrogenation. Comput Aided Chem Eng, 52, 2345-2350G.

Brändle *et al.* 2021. Estimating long-term global supply costs for low-carbon hydrogen. Appl Energy, 302, 117481

Y. Dong *et al.* 2019. Evaluating the monetary values of greenhouse gases emissions in life cycle impact assessment. J Clean Prod, 209, 538-549.

M.A. Huijbregts *et al.* 2017. ReCiPe2016: a harmonised life cycle impact assessment method at midpoint and endpoint level. Int J Life Cycle Assess, 22(2), 138-147.

IEA 2020, CCUS in Clean Energy Transitions, IEA, Paris https://www.iea.org/reports/ccus-in-clean-energy-transitionsK.

Onarheim *et al.* 2017. Performance and costs of CCS in the pulp and paper industry part 1: performance of amine-based postcombustion CO_2 capture. Int J Greenh Gas Control, 59, 58-73.

F. Sabatino *et al.* 2021. A comparative energy and costs assessment and optimization for direct air capture technologies. Joule, 5, 2047–2076.

P. Schmidt *et al.* 2018. Power-to-Liquids as Renewable Fuel Option for Aviation: A Review. Chem Ing Tech, 90, 1–2, 127–140

B. Yao *et al.* 2020. Transforming carbon dioxide into jet fuel using an organic combustion-synthesized Fe-Mn-K catalyst. Nat Comms, 11(1).

K.M. Vanden Bussche and G.F. Froment 1996. A steady-state kinetic model for methanol synthesis and the water gas shift reaction on a commercial Cu/ZnO/Al$_2$O$_3$ catalyst. J Catal, 161 (1), 1-10.

G. Zang *et al.* 2021. Performance and cost analysis of liquid fuel production from H_2 and CO_2 based on the Fischer-Tropsch process. J CO_2 Util, 46.

Flavio Manenti, Gintaras V. Reklaitis (Eds.), Proceedings of the 34th European Symposium on Computer Aided Process Engineering / 15th International Symposium on Process Systems Engineering (ESCAPE34/PSE24), June 2-6, 2024, Florence, Italy

Multi-Objective Optimization of the Renewable Methanol for a Defossilized Production

Javier Fernández-González[a], Marta Rumayor[a,*], Jara Laso-Cortabitarte[a], Antonio Domínguez-Ramos[a], Angel Irabien[a], Ignacio E. Grossmann[b]

[a]*Departamento de Ingenierías Química y Biomolecular, Universidad de Cantabria, Santander, Spain*
[b]*Department of Chemical Engineering, Carnegie Mellon University, Pittsburgh, USA*
marta.rumayor@unican.es

Abstract

This work focuses on a technology implementation problem for decarbonizing hard-to-abate CO_2 emissions by carbon storage and carbon utilization approaches. The technological pathway to achieve net-zero emissions within an industry by 2050 is proposed, dealing with the implications of sequestrating the industrial CO_2 or recycling it to produce low-carbon methanol. A multi-objective mixed integer nonlinear programming model is formulated to minimize the net cost, greenhouse gas emissions, and abiotic resource consumption under a life cycle perspective. The outcome provided by Pareto's solution represents the compromises of manufacturing CO_2-based products: a deep decarbonized and defossilised product entails a large production cost, suggesting the need for subsidies to reach the global markets. The results show that investment strategies for achieving decarbonization targets may differ when integrating the defossilization perspective.

Keywords: carbon dioxide, electrochemical reduction, decarbonization, defossilization

1. Introduction

The transition towards a carbon-neutral economy entails a complex and multi-scale technological implementation pathway to reduce greenhouse gas (GHG) emissions across the entire economy. To meet the global climate goals and achieve deep decarbonization, carbon storage (CS) and carbon utilization (CU) alternatives appear as potential technological options for the hard-to-abate emissions of carbon dioxide (CO_2) from certain industrial sectors. While the maturity of the CS approach makes it appealing for its implementation in the short term, the CU strategy is receiving increasing interest in recycling CO_2 as a non-fossil carbon source to produce chemicals and fuels. The question then is whether to store permanently the carbon from fossil sources in a stable form; or try to recycle it as a secondary raw material, simultaneously avoiding the production of those very chemicals or fuels from fossil sources and leading to a progressive reduction in the pressure over limited resources. This latter option represents the transition towards a circular carbon economy: lower emissions and lower consumption.

Among possible products, methanol (MeOH) is a commodity usable not only as a chemical but also as a low-carbon fuel for ship transportation and ultra-long duration energy storage (Olah, 2005). While its current production process is fully commercial and uses natural gas as a carbon source, the CU pathway could make use of the recycled CO_2 to produce MeOH through electrochemical reduction (ER). Recent European directive 2018/2001 regulates the production of renewable fuels of non-biological origin

(RFNBO), establishing a common methodological framework for defining CO_2-based fuels.

The comparison of the CS and CU approaches exhibits several pitfalls when evaluating its implications under a life cycle perspective (von der Assen et al., 2013), and hence, proper decision-making tools need to be developed to disclose the trade-offs and benefits from both alternatives. While some works have explored the prospects of the electrochemical MeOH (Adnan & Kibria, 2020; Guzmán et al., 2021), still its potential benefits for the economy decarbonization are not clear when considering other competing alternatives.

This work's objective is to assess the potential trade-offs between the cost of dealing with a certain amount of CO_2 and the net life cycle emissions of the potential options: direct release of CO_2, capture and sequestration (CS), and/or capture and recycling of CO_2 into MeOH via ER (CU). Additional trade-offs include the life cycle use of fossil resources. The optimization problem is formulated as a Mixed Integer Non-Linear Programming (MINLP) problem, providing a set of Pareto's solutions representing the trade-offs of implementing CU and CS strategies to decarbonize and defossilize the proposed superstructure.

2. Case study definition

The problem to address is the decarbonization during the period 2030-2050 of a facility in Europe, which generates 24 kton of CO_2 per year and must be dealt with by: i) its release into the atmosphere; ii) CS into a saline aquifer at 500 km; or iii) CU by ER route to produce MeOH. To meet RFBNO carbon intensity legislation, the CU route can implement renewable energy alternatives to supply the heat and electricity needs. As temporal restrictions, at least 55% and 100% of direct CO_2 emissions must be managed by CU or CS by 2030 and 2050, respectively. The goal of the study is to determine the optimal technological transition towards a net-zero system by implementing CU and CS alternatives, simultaneously minimizing the net present cost of treating the direct CO_2 emissions and the net life cycle CO_{2e} emissions along the considered period.

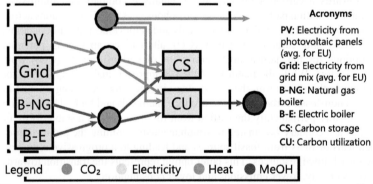

Figure 1. Super-structure of alternatives for managing the CO_2 in the system. Both CU and CS include the capture stage. Additional intermediate flow and elementary output flow are not represented (except the flow of CO_2 released to the atmosphere).

3. Model formulation

A Mixed Integer Non-Linear Programming (MINLP) problem is posed, formulated in GAMS 42.5.0 and solved using BARON 20.10.16. The objective function to be minimized is the net present cost (NPC). In canonical terms, the model is defined as:

$$\min \quad NPC(x,y)$$

$$\text{st} \quad NE(x,y) \leq \varepsilon_{NE}$$

$$NFD(x,y) \leq \varepsilon_{NAR}$$

Where the continuous variables x are related to operation (e.g., installed capacities, mass flowrates) while binary variables y decide investment decisions on CS or CU equipment take place e.g., a certain route to be implemented on a certain year. The two environmental restrictions lead to a Pareto's solution using the ε-constraint method, solving the economic objective while considering the environmental constraints as restrictions, ε_{NE} and ε_{NFD}. The mass and energy needs for the CU route are calculated using a mathematical model adapted from previous works (Fernández-González et al., 2022; Rumayor et al., 2019). The CS pathway is modelled according to the literature works (Rubin et al., 2015).

3.1 Economic assessment

The NPC of treating CO_2 is calculated following a time-variable cash flow estimation. It is formulated including the investment and operation cost of the CS and CU pathways as expressed in eq. 1:

$$NPC = \sum_{i \in I} \sum_{k \in K} \left[F_{i,k}^{in} \sum_{j \in J} I_{i,j} \cdot C_{j,k}^{A} \right] + \sum_{i \in I} \sum_{k \in K} \left[Y_{i,k} \sum_{j \in J} I_{i,j} \cdot C_{j,k}^{B} \right] \tag{1}$$

Where set $i \in I$ denotes the possible routes for managing the CO_2 (release, sequestration, utilization), set $j \in J$ states the energy and material fluxes, and set $k \in K$ stands for the time periods. The variable cost (C^A) and fixed cost (C^B) for each route are accounted for. Revenues from selling the MeOH are considered. CO_2 not captured is released into the atmosphere paying a carbon tax, assumed constant during the timeframe.

3.2 Environmental assessment

The environmental performance of the system is measured according to the Life Cycle Assessment international standards ISO 14040:2006 and ISO 14044:2006. The characterization method ReCiPe 2016 midpoint (H) in the categories of climate change and fossil depletion is used. The net environmental impact for the categories considered can be stated as Eq. (2):

$$NEI_c = \sum_{i \in I} \sum_{k \in K} \left[F_{i,k}^{in} \sum_{j \in J} I_{i,j} \cdot CF_{c,j} \right] \qquad c \in \{NE, NFD\} \tag{2}$$

Set $c \in C$ indicates the environmental impact category considered (climate change: NE, fossil depletion: NFD). The parameters to obtain the value of each environmental metric for each energy and material resource and emissions (CF) are retrieved from the Ecoinvent database v3.9 respectively. The software employed is GaBi v9.5. The produced

MeOH from the CU pathway must have a specific carbon intensity restriction to be considered as an RFBNO, which is calculated using the methodology from the European legislation for producing RFNBO's.

4. Results and discussion

The results provided by Pareto's solution represent the trade-offs of decarbonizing the facility by CS or CU (producing MeOH by ER). Figure 2 corresponds to Pareto's solution when minimizing the NPC and the NE and the NFD. Values are given as a percentage of increase/reduction from a scenario with no CO_2 mitigation (100% release to the atmosphere), as depicted on the right side of the figure. The colormap represents the NFD, normalized per kilogram of CO_2 available from the industry. On the figure's left-hand side, there are the solutions with the minimal emissions, which correspond to the maximum cost. As can be seen, the most cost-efficient reduction of NE means increasing the capacity of the CCS system, as well as moving forward the installation year. However, this approach comes at the expense of increasing the NFD of the system. At NE of around 30%, the only way to improve the reductions is by means of the CU pathway, so a certain range of solutions for reducing NE combines both CCS and ER. Higher CU implementation brings net reductions in the NFD. Deeper decarbonizations and defossilizations mean the exclusive use of CU. At the only use of CU, a severe reduction of 94% of emissions CO_2 would come at a net cost of the system of 339%.

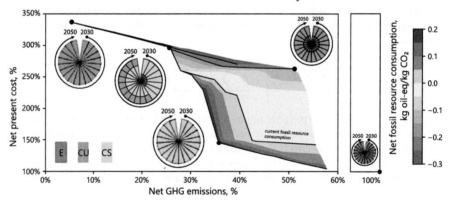

Figure 2. Pareto set of solutions for the NPC and NE (NFD in the colormap). Values of 100% represent a total release of CO_2 into the atmosphere (no decarbonization). The color map depicts the fossil resource use intensity of the system. Each radial segment represents a time slice of one year and the radius share represents the CO_2 share of each option: Emission (E), utilization (CU) and Storage (CS). For example, the minimum cost option (right-hand side) is totally red color, so 100% of the CO_2 is released.

However, significant uncertainty exists regarding the political framework of decarbonization. For example, the prices of low-carbon RFNBO could be potentially bonified by the public administration because of their reductions in CO_2 emissions and consumption of fossil resources. In Figure 3, we represent a bundle of Pareto's solution when minimizing the NPC and the NE under a changing selling price of the low-carbon MeOH. In this case, average selling prices of around 1.1-1.2 €/kg MeOH could make preferable over all the Pareto curve the CU route over the CS, meaning that carbon recycling would become a more cost-effective solution for reducing CO_2 emissions. It should be noted that these minimum MeOH selling prices to become economically competitive could be significantly lower if ER performance exceeds our base set of hypotheses. If ER could achieve optimistic benchmarks (current densities higher than 500 mA/cm^2, net energy efficiencies around 80%) the needed MeOH selling price would drop to 0.87 €/kg MeOH. By-product valorization in the anode or use of curtailed cheap renewable energy could lead to even lower minimum selling prices for low-carbon MeOH production.

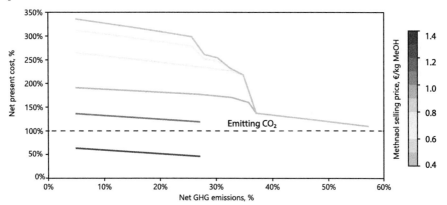

Figure 3. Bundle of Pareto's solutions when the average methanol selling price (€R/kg MeOH) is different. The upper line indicates the base case at 0.5 €/kg MeOH.

5. Conclusions

In this work, two carbon mitigation strategies involving sequestration or recycling have been proposed to decarbonize a hard-to-abate industry in the period 2030-2050. A multi-objective MINLP model has been used to address the problem to account for the most efficient solution considering cost, GHG emissions, and use of fossil resources. Results show that cost-effective decarbonization could be performed by CS. A combined deep decarbonization and defossilization of the economy would need the deployment of CU technologies, whose cost could be partly reduced by economic incentives for producing low-carbon products compiled with RFNBO's restrictions at the level of 1.10-1.20 €/kg MeOH under our hypothesis. Increasing the CU energy efficiency, and surface and aging of the electrode in the ER technology would be critical to reduce the needed incentives to be achieved. It is concluded that suitable decision-making tools may be needed to fully account for the trade-offs that the transition towards a net-zero economy may involve.

Acknowledgments

Financial support from the project PID2020-112845RB-I00 funded by MCIN/AEI/10.13039/501100011033 is gratefully acknowledged. J.F.-G. would like to thank the financial support of the Spanish Ministry of Science, Innovation (MICIN) for the concession of the FPU grant (19/05483).

References

M.A. Adnan & M.G. Kibria. 2020. Comparative techno-economic and life-cycle assessment of power-to-methanol synthesis pathways. Applied Energy, 27, 115614.

J. Fernández-González, M. Rumayor, A. Domínguez-Ramos & A. Irabien. 2022. Hydrogen Utilization in the Sustainable Manufacture of CO_2-Based Methanol. Industrial & Engineering Chemistry Research, 61, 18, 6163-6172.

H. Guzmán, F. Salomone, E. Batuecas, T. Tommasi, N. Russo, S. Bensaid & S. Hernández. 2021. How to make sustainable CO_2 conversion to Methanol: Thermocatalytic versus electrocatalytic technology. Chemical Engineering Journal, 417, 127973.

G.A. Olah. 2005. Beyond oil and gas: The methanol economy. Angewandte Chemie - International Edition, 44, 18, 2636–2639.

E.S. Rubin, J.E. Davison & H.J. Herzog. 2015. The cost of CO_2 capture and storage. International Journal of Greenhouse Gas Control, 40, 378-400.

M. Rumayor, A. Domínguez-Ramos, & A. Irabien. 2019. Innovative alternatives to methanol manufacture: Carbon footprint assessment. Journal of Cleaner Production, 225, 426-434.

N. Von der Assen, J. Jung & A. Bardow. 2013. Life-cycle assessment of carbon dioxide capture and utilization: Avoiding the pitfalls. Energy & Environmental Science, 6, 9, 2721.

Flavio Manenti, Gintaras V. Reklaitis (Eds.), Proceedings of the 34th European Symposium on Computer Aided Process Engineering / 15th International Symposium on Process Systems Engineering (ESCAPE34/PSE24), June 2-6, 2024, Florence, Italy

Global Optimization via Quadratic Disjunctive Programming for Water Networks Design with Energy Recovery

Carolina Tristán,[a] Marcos Fallanza,[b] Raquel Ibáñez,[b] Ignacio E. Grossmann,[c] David E. Bernal Neira[a,d,e,*]

[a]Davidson School of Chemical Engineering, Purdue University, West Lafayette, IN, USA

[b]Department of Chemical and Biomolecular Engineering, University of Cantabria, Santander, Spain

[c]Department of Chemical Engineering, Carnegie Mellon University, Pittsburgh, PA, USA

[d]Research Institute of Advanced Computer Science, Universities Space Research Association, Mountain View, CA, USA

[e]Quantum Artificial Intelligence Laboratory, NASA Ames Research Center, Moffett Field, CA, USA

dbernaln@purdue.edu

Abstract

Generalized disjunctive programming (GDP) models with bilinear and concave constraints, often seen in water network design, are challenging optimization problems. This work proposes quadratic and piecewise linear approximations for nonlinear terms to reformulate GDP models into quadratic GDP (QGDP) models that suitable solvers may solve more efficiently. We illustrate the benefits of the quadratic reformulation with a water treatment network design problem in which nonconvexities arise from bilinear terms in the mixers' mass balances and concave investment cost functions of treatment units. Given the similarities with water network design problems, we suggest quadratic approximation for the GDP model for the optimal design of a large-scale reverse electrodialysis (RED) process. This power technology can recover energy from salinity differences between by-product streams of the water sector, such as desalination brine mixed with regenerated wastewater effluents. The solver Gurobi excels in handling QGDP problems, but weighing the problem's precision and tractability balance is crucial. The piecewise linear approximation yields more accurate yet larger QGDP models that may require longer optimization times in large-scale process synthesis problems.

Keywords: water networks, salinity gradient, renewable energy, bilinear programming, piecewise linear approximation, quadratic approximation, superstructure optimization.

1. Introduction

Water network design often involves bilinear mass balances and nonlinear investment cost functions that lead to nonconvex generalized disjunctive programming (GDP) with bilinear and concave constraints (Ruiz and Grossmann, 2016). This work proposes replacing the nonlinear equations with piecewise or quadratic approximations to define a quadratic generalized disjunctive program (QGDP) for GDP problems. These problems feature bilinearities that commercial solvers, such as Gurobi, can efficiently solve to global optimality (Achkar et al., 2023).

The general form of a process superstructure GDP optimization model reads as follows:

$$
\begin{aligned}
\min_{x,Y} z = \quad & f(x) \\
s.t. \quad & g(x) \leq 0 \\
& \begin{bmatrix} Y_u \\ h_u(x) \leq 0 \end{bmatrix} \underline{\vee} \begin{bmatrix} \neg Y_u \\ B^u x = 0 \end{bmatrix} \quad \forall\, u \in U, \\
& \Omega(Y_1, \dots Y_{|U|}) = True \\
& x \in X \subseteq \mathbb{R}^n \\
& Y_u = \{True,\ False\} \quad \forall\, u \in U
\end{aligned}
\tag{1}
$$

where continuous bounded variables x optimize an objective function $f(x)$ subject to global constraints, $g(x) \leq 0$, and a set of disjunctions that determines whether unit u is selected or not. Boolean variables, Y_u, in each disjunct activate constraints $h_u(x) \leq 0$ relative to that unit when it is selected ($Y_u = True$); otherwise, ($\neg Y_u$) ignore equations in the inactive disjunct and fix some variables to zero $B^u x = 0$, involved in the inactive unit. The logic constraints ($\Omega(Y) = True$) set conditions for selecting specific units.

Water networks involve water-using process and treatment units, offering several water integration alternatives that reduce freshwater consumption and wastewater generation while minimizing the total network cost subject to a specified discharge limit (Ahmetović et al., 2017). Reverse electrodialysis (RED) can recover the salinity gradient energy (SGE) embedded in the mixing of the water network's streams of different salinities, providing a sustainable supply of clean, base-load electricity to regeneration or water-supply processes (Rani et al., 2022). In previous work (Tristán et al., 2023), we developed a GDP model of the RED process that incorporates a detailed model of the RED unit. This GDP resembles the water network design model. Bilinear mass balances in the mixers and nonlinearities in the RED unit model give rise to a nonlinear GDP model. To solve to global optimality, we apply the Global Logic-based Outer Approximation (GLOA) algorithm (Chen et al., 2022), which decomposes the solution to the GDP into a sequence of mixed-integer linear programming (MILP) master problems and reduced nonlinear-programming (NLP) subproblems that need to be solved global optimality to guarantee a global optimum convergence. We explore how the GDP reformulation into a QGDP approach affects the tractability and fidelity of the optimization model, assessing the computational time and accuracy of the optimal solutions for two case studies: water treatment network design and a large-scale RED process synthesis problem.

2. Case Study 1. Water Treatment Network Design

2.1. Problem Statement

Given is a set of water streams with known concentrations of contaminants and flow rate. The objective is to find the set of treatment units and interconnections that minimize the cost of the WTN while satisfying maximum concentrations of contaminants in the reclaimed outlet stream. The WTN superstructure consists of a set of treatment units $t \in TU$, contaminated feed streams $f \in FU$ carrying a set of contaminants $j \in J$, and a discharge unit $disch$. The fouled feed waters can be allocated to one or more treatment units or disposed of in the sink unit. Upon treatment, the reclaimed streams can be recycled, forwarded to other treatment units, or discharged into the sink unit.

2.2. Model formulation

The WTN design GDP problem reads as (1). The mass balances are defined in terms of total flows, F_s, and contaminants concentration, $C_{j,s}$ (Karuppiah and Grossmann, 2006; Quesada and Grossmann, 1995). Together with the treatment unit cost CTU_t, these determine the continuous variables of the problem, i.e., $x = [F_s, C_{j,s}, CTU_t]$. The treatment units have fixed recoveries, $\alpha_{j,t}$ is the recovery of contaminant j in treatment unit t; $C_{j,\text{mt},t}$ and $C_{j,\text{st},t}$ are contaminant concentration at the inlet and the outlet of t. The treatment unit cost CTU_t consists of a linear operating cost term and a concave capital cost term. Nonconvexities arise from bilinear terms "flows times concentration" in the mixers' mass balances and concave investment cost functions of treatment units.

Following Eq. (1), the objective is to minimize the total treatment unit costs $f(x) = \sum_{t \in TU} CTU_t$, the equations set for inexisting units become $B^t x = [\sum_{i \in S_{mt}} F_i, CTU_t] = 0 \quad \forall\, t \in TU$ and the model constraints become

$$g(x) \leq 0 \rightarrow \begin{cases} \sum_{t \in TU} CTU_t \\ F_k\, C_{j,k} = \sum_{i \in S_i \subseteq S} F_i\, C_{j,i} & \forall\, j \in J,\, k \in S_k \subseteq S \\ F_k = \sum_{i \in S_i \subseteq S} F_i & \forall\, k \in S_k \subseteq S \\ C_{j,k} = C_{j,i} & \forall\, j \in J,\, k \in S_k \subseteq S,\, i \in S_i \subseteq S \\ F_i = \sum_{k \in S_k \subseteq S} F_k & \forall\, i \in S_i \subseteq S \\ \sum_{i \in S_{dm} \subseteq S_i} F_i\, C_{j,i} \leq T_j & \forall\, j \in J \end{cases} \quad (2)$$

$$h_t(x) \leq 0 \rightarrow \begin{cases} C_{j,st,t} = (1 - \alpha_{j,t})\, C_{j,mt,t} \\ F_{mt,t}\, C_{mt,t,k} = \sum_{i \in S_i \subseteq S} F_i\, C_{j,i} \\ F_{mt,t} = \sum_{i \in S_{mt} \subseteq S_i} F_i \\ C_{j,t,st} = C_{j,i} \\ F_{t,st} = \sum_{k \in S_{st} \subseteq S_k} F_k & \forall\, t \in TU \\ F_{mt,t} = F_{t,st} \\ F_{mt,t} \geq L_t \\ CTU_t = \beta_t\, F_{mt,t,j} + \gamma_t + \theta_t\, F_{mt,t,j}^{0.7} \end{cases} \quad (3)$$

3. Case Study 2. RED Process Design

3.1. Problem Statement

Given is a set of candidate RED units and the high- and low-salinity feeds' concentration, flow rate, and temperature. The objective is to determine the hydraulic topology and operational conditions of the RED units that maximize the net present value (NPV) of the process. The superstructure definition and notation are outlined in (Tristán et al., 2023).

3.2. Model Formulation

From Eq. (1), $f(x)$ maximizes the NPV of the RED process. The variables x are the molar concentration and flow rate of the streams and the internal variables of the active RED units. The decision variables are the active RED stacks' operating conditions. The global constraints, $g(x) \leq 0$, specify mass balances that must hold for any selection of alternatives. The set of disjunctions determines whether the RED unit r is active, enforcing $h_r(x) \leq 0$, the RED unit model equations. These factor in the capital and operating costs and set bounds on the RED unit's internal variables and the inlet and outlet streams' concentration and flow rate. Nonconvexities arise from bilinear mass balances in the mixers and the RED unit model, the concave investment cost of pumps, and the Nernst electric potential and gross power equations in the RED unit model.

4. Results and Discussion

We implement the GDP models using the algebraic modeling language Pyomo (Hart et al., 2017) and the Pyomo.GDP extension (Chen et al., 2022) for logic-based modeling and optimization. We solve the problems on a Windows 10 (x64) machine with 6 cores processor (Intel® Core™ i7-8700 CPU @3.2 GHz) and 16 GB of RAM using the solver versions from GAMS 34.1.0, and setting a 0.01% optimality gap and 3600 s time limit. We use two proposed reformulation strategies for the nonlinear terms in Eqs. (1). (a) Problem (QGDP-q): fitting a quadratic function, i.e., $f(x) \approx x'Qx$ with Q potentially nonconvex, using the curve_fit() function from the SciPy. (b) Problem (QGDP-pwl): using a piecewise linear approximation using the Piecewiselinear Pyomo functionality. We opted for the incremental model for the piecewise function (Vielma et al., 2010) and split the domain into 101 segments which adds binary variables to the GDP problem.

4.1. Water Treatment Network Design

The WTN comprises five inlet streams with four contaminants and four treatment units. The contaminant concentration and flow rate of the feed streams, contaminant recovery rates ($\alpha_{j,t}$), minimum flow rate (L_t) and cost coefficients ($\beta_t, \gamma_t, \theta_t$) of the treatment units, and the upper limit on the molar flow of contaminant j in the purified stream (T_j), are reported in (Ruiz and Grossmann, 2009). To solve the WTN problem, we convert the GDP models into MINLPs using the Big-M reformulation (Chen et al., 2022). The MINLP model with the concave investment cost is solved with BARON and the MINLPs with the quadratic and piecewise linear approximations with Gurobi and BARON.

Table 2. Model size of the GDP with the concave cost term (original) and the quadratic and piecewise linear (pwl) QGDPs, and MINLP solvers' computational time, minimum WTN cost, and relative error between QGDP and GDP optimal cost.

	Original GDP	Quadratic QGDP-q		pwl QGDP-pwl	
# cont. vars	239	239		749	
# binary vars	10	10		510	
# const (nl)	329 (33)	329 (33)		1339 (28)	
Solver	BARON	BARON	Gurobi	BARON	Gurobi
CPU time [s]	16.12	16.86	6.44	2543	10.06
Objective	$348,337	$349,556	$349,562	$348,337	$348,337
Relative error [%]	n.a.	0.3499 %	0.3516 %	0.0001 %	0.0001 %

The QGDP models and the GDP with the concave capital cost term yield the same optimal WTN design, in which all the polluted streams but one are treated in units one and four (Ruiz and Grossmann, 2009). Table 2 compares the size, computational time, and optimal solution of the WTN design problem for each modeling approach and solution strategy. With a relative error of 0.35 %, Gurobi yields an optimal QGDP-q solution in just half the time it takes BARON to solve the original GDP model with the same number of variables and constraints. BARON requires more time than Gurobi to find the optimal solution of the QGDP-q model. Under the pwl approximation's better fit to the concave capital cost term, Gurobi and BARON obtain the same global optimum to the QGDP-pwl model as BARON does for the GDP. While the pwl approximation offers more accurate models, the increase in size may also render them intractable. For instance, BARON requires almost an hour to find the optimal WTN design. By contrast, Gurobi solves the instance in about the same time as for the QGDP-q.

4.2. RED Process Design

The process consists of a set of candidate RED units, which draw energy from the effluent of a real desalination plant that rejects 733 m³/h of brine (1.67 M NaCl, 20 °C) (Tristán et al., 2020). A wastewater treatment plant provides an equal volume of low-salinity feedwater (20 mM NaCl) (Pérez Talavera and Quesada Ruiz, 2001) for SGE conversion.

Table 3. Model size of the RED unit's NLP without reformulations (original), quadratic and piecewise linear (pwl) QPs, and solver's computational time, maximum net power, and relative error between QPs and NLP optimal solution.

	Original NLP	Quadratic QP-q		pwl QP-pwl	
# cont. vars	179	180		1608	
# binary vars	n.a.	n.a.		1400	
# const (nl)	182 (101)	183 (103)		3011 (89)	
Solver	BARON	BARON	Gurobi	BARON	Gurobi
CPU time [s]	3600⁺	306	115	3600⁺	1986
Objective [kW]	1.013	1.043	1.043	1.008	1.016
Relative error [%]	n.a.	2.9615 %	2.9615 %	0.4936 %	0.2961 %

Prior work (Tristán et al., 2023) showed that the most time-consuming steps in the GLOA algorithm involve the discretized RED unit model, i.e., the initial linearization of the GDP and resolution of the NLP subproblems. As the number of candidate RED units in the process grows, which is expected in large-scale systems, these steps become even more expensive. Therefore, approximating it as a QP model could accelerate the GDP solution without sacrificing fidelity. We compare the solution that maximize the net power from the QP-q and QP-pwl models with the NLP model (with Nernst potential and gross power nonlinear equations) to appraise the QP models' fidelity and tractability in Table 3.

The quadratic approximation's inaccurate fitting of natural logarithms within the Nernst potential leads to errors in the optimal solution for the NLP (Table 3). Despite this, the computational time is decreased with Gurobi and BARON, with Gurobi outperforming, while keeping almost the same number of variables and constraints. The piecewise linear approximation provides a better fit but significantly increases the size. After an hour, BARON could only reach a suboptimal solution to the QP-pwl with an 27 % optimality gap. Despite the increase in the size of the QP-pwl, Gurobi even outperforms BARON solving the rigorous NLP model (original NLP), which finds the optimal net power with a 24 % optimality gap within an hour. The outcomes of this study provide the drive to transform the RED process GDP model into a quadratic one, a subject of future work.

5. Conclusions

Water network design problems generally involve bilinearities and concave functions that may lead to multiple local optima. Solving global optimality thereby requires computationally expensive global optimization approaches. This work presents quadratic and piecewise linear approximations for nonlinearities in GDP models involving bilinearities to derive a quadratic GDP model that solvers like Gurobi can efficiently solve. The implications are far-reaching for problems where bilinear constraints are presents with constraints that fit well with quadratic functions or piecewise linear (or even piecewise quadratic) approximations. For handling this type of problem, Gurobi is a powerful solver, though carefully considering the trade-off between fidelity and tractability is paramount. Using piecewise linear approximations grants higher accuracy, but also introduces additional variables and constraints to the original problem, making it challenging to find the global optimum within an acceptable timeframe, especially for larger-scale problems that may require advanced decomposition strategies.

Acknowledgments

Financial support from projects TED2021-129874B-I00, PDC2021-120786-I00, and PID2020-115409RB-I00 through EU NextGenerationEU/PRTR and MCIN/AEI/ 10.13039/501100011033. C.T. acknowledges the research fellowship PRE2018-086454 funded by the MCIN/AEI/ 10.13039/501100011033 and "ESF Investing in your future".

References

Achkar, V.G., Brunaud, B.B., Pérez, H.D., Musa, R., Méndez, C.A., Grossmann, I.E., 2023. Extensions to the guaranteed service model for industrial applications of multi-echelon inventory optimization. Eur. J. Oper. Res. 21, 47.

Ahmetović, E., Grossmann, I.E., Kravanja, Z., Ibrić, N., 2017. Water Optimization in Process Industries, in: Mondal, P., Dalai, A.K. (Eds.), Sustainable Utilization of Natural Resources. CRC Press, Boca Raton, pp. 487–512.

Chen, Q., Johnson, E.S., Bernal, D.E., Valentin, R., Kale, S., Bates, J., Siirola, J.D., Grossmann, I.E., 2022. Pyomo.GDP: an ecosystem for logic based modeling and optimization development. Optim. Eng. 23, 607–642.

Hart, W.E., Laird, C.D., Watson, J.-P., Woodruff, D.L., Hackebeil, G.A., Nicholson, B.L., Siirola, J.D., 2017. Pyomo — Optimization Modeling in Python, Second Edi. ed, Springer Optimization and Its Applications. Springer International Publishing, Cham.

Karuppiah, R., Grossmann, I.E., 2006. Global optimization for the synthesis of integrated water systems in chemical processes. Comput. Chem. Eng. 30, 650–673.

Pérez Talavera, J., Quesada Ruiz, J., 2001. Identification of the mixing processes in brine discharges carried out in Barranco del Toro Beach, south of Gran Canaria (Canary Islands). Desalination 139, 277–286.

Quesada, I., Grossmann, I.E., 1995. Global optimization of bilinear process networks with multicomponent flows. Comput. Chem. Eng. 19, 1219–1242.

Rani, A., Snyder, S.W., Kim, H., Lei, Z., Pan, S.Y., 2022. Pathways to a net-zero-carbon water sector through energy-extracting wastewater technologies. npj Clean Water 2022 51 5, 1–17.

Ruiz, J., Grossmann, I.E., 2009. Water Treatment Network Design, in: Available from Cyber Infrastructure for MINLP a Collaboration of Carnegie Mellon University and IBM Research at: Www.Minlp.Org/Library/Problem/Index.Php?I=24.

Ruiz, J.P., Grossmann, I.E., 2016. Global optimization of non-convex generalized disjunctive programs: a review on reformulations and relaxation techniques. J. Glob. Optim. 67, 43–58.

Tristán, C., Fallanza, M., Ibáñez, R., Ortiz, I., 2020. Reverse Electrodialysis: Potential Reduction in Energy and Emissions of Desalination. Appl. Sci. 10, 7317.

Tristán, C., Fallanza, M., Ibáñez, R., Ortiz, I., Grossmann, I.E., 2023. A generalized disjunctive programming model for the optimal design of reverse electrodialysis process for salinity gradient-based power generation. Comput. Chem. Eng. 174, 108196.

Vielma, J.P., Ahmed, S., Nemhauser, G., 2010. Mixed-Integer Models for Nonseparable Piecewise-Linear Optimization: Unifying Framework and Extensions. Oper. Res. 58, 303–315.

Flavio Manenti, Gintaras V. Reklaitis (Eds.), Proceedings of the 34th European Symposium on Computer Aided Process Engineering / 15th International Symposium on Process Systems Engineering (ESCAPE34/PSE24), June 2-6, 2024, Florence, Italy

A Model Development and Sensitivity Analysis of a Multitubular Thermochemical Recovery for Internal Combustion Engine Exhaust Heat

Victor E. Morales-Olmedo, Ricardo Morales-Rodriguez, Jesus I. Minchaca-Mojica, Ignacio R. Galindo-Esquivel*

Departamento de Ingeniería Química, Universidad de Guanajuato, Noria Alta S/N, Noria Alta, Guanajuato, Guanajuato, 36050, México.
igalindo@ugto.mx

Abstract

A mathematical model is proposed for the recovery of the internal combustion engines exhaust heat to produce hydrogen using methanol reforming, which was constructed coupling mass and energy conservation principles, chemical reaction, and the heat transfer phenomena to represent an integrated tube and shell reactive heat exchanger. The results showed that it is feasible to design a multitubular reactor for hydrogen production with a good level of conversion; however, both performance criteria depend on several design variables, and it is difficult to identify which are the most relevant. Thereby, a sensitivity analysis (SA) was performed to find the most critical variables, where the diameter of the tubes, feed temperature of methanol, catalyst thickness and number of tubes result as the key design variables for the selected performance criteria. SA was done using the standardized regression coefficient using the results previously obtained using a Monte Carlo simulation, the last allowed to find designs that could provide a 99 % of methanol conversion with feasible dimension to be implemented in a vehicle.

Keywords: Methanol steam reforming, hydrogen production, Monte Carlo Method.

1. Introduction

A large portion of the energy demanded in modern society is used by the transport sector, where private vehicles play a predominant role. Internal Combustion Engines (ICE) have been the main devices used as vehicle's propulsion systems. However, the thermodynamic efficiency of the ICE is generally from 20 % to 40 %, this low efficiency may be identified in the exhaust gases produced from combustion that leave the engine at high temperatures (over 673 K), and the thermal energy that remains in them that is dissipated to the atmosphere without further use. In recent years, thermochemical recovery (TCR) of this residual thermal energy has attracted renewed interest, as a possibility to use the residual heat of the exhaust gases to sustain an energy demanding endothermic reaction, such as alcohols or light hydrocarbons reforming.

Fomin and Makunin (2009) performed a thermodynamic assessment of the effectiveness of a thermal power-producing cycle of an ICE with and without TCR implementation, demonstrating the potential of this technology. Afterwards, Chakravarthy et al. (2010) made a thermodynamic study about the theoretical potential of using TCR applying different fuels: methanol, ethanol, and iso-octane, determining an increase of thermodynamic efficiency of 5 %, 9 %, and 11 %, respectively.

Kirillov et al. (2013) evaluated the production of syngas from methanol and ethanol dry reforming over different catalysts, using a configuration that resembles monolithic reactors. The results showed that the implementation of TCR and the addition of the syngas produced to the feed of the ICE decreased fuel consumption by 11 to 22 %, and furthermore, induced a reduction in the concentration of hazardous emissions (8-12 times for CO, 2-3.5 times for CH_4, and 18-25 times for NO_x). With a different reactor design, Chen et al. (2017) evaluated an onboard methanol steam reformer for hydrogen production on an ICE vehicle, observing a decrease in fuel consumption between 15 % and 25 %, a reduction of pollutant concentration in exhaust gases between 40 % and 50 %, and a 70 % reduction of exhaust smoke.

The previous results have shown that coupling an ICE with TCR represents a real available low-cost option, with the possibility to increase the thermodynamic efficiency of an ICE, simultaneously decreasing fuel consumption and pollutant emissions. On the other hand, all reactor designs have been developed empirically, and a chemical equilibrium is frequently considered in the reactor. Thereby, this research proposes a theoretical model for a multitubular TCR reaction system that considers the catalytic kinetics and heat transport phenomena fundamentals. To the best of our knowledge, this is the first fundamentally based design of this kind of configuration. The proposed system is based on a shell and tube heat exchanger, where the reaction proceeds in the shell side, and the catalyst is deposited in the external wall of the tubes. After model development, a sensitivity analysis is performed to identify the most determinant variables for the system design and construction.

2. Methodology

A mathematical model was developed coupling the fundamental principles of mass and energy conservation, as well as the heat transport phenomena and reaction kinetics, to reach the necessary temperature conditions.

The system is based on the configuration of a shell and tube heat exchanger, considering one pass on the tube side and a thin layer of catalyst applied to the external surface of the tubes. Therefore, the reaction takes place in the shell side of the system, while the exhaust gases flow through the interior of the tubes. The system considers a cocurrent flow system. The endothermic reaction chosen for the TCR system is steam reforming of methanol [Eq. (1)].

$$CH_3OH + H_2O \rightarrow CO_2 + 3H_2 \tag{1}$$

The reaction kinetics for methanol steam reforming catalyzed by Cu-ZnO/Al$_2$O$_3$, was previously reported by Santacesaria and Carrá (1983) [Eq. (2)].

$$R_{CH_3OH} = \rho_b \left(\frac{K_c b_M P_M}{1 + b_M P_M + b_W P_W} \right) \tag{2}$$

Methanol is considered as the limiting reactant and its mass balance is developed for the shell side assuming plug flow in a steady state [Eq. (3)]. The equation is expressed in terms of the conversion reached at each point along the length of the system. The effect of catalyst layer thickness is analyzed, keeping values equal or lower than 0.0005 m to avoid significance of the internal mass transfer phenomena.

$$\frac{dX_{CH_3OH}}{dz} = \frac{R_{CH_3OH}\pi(r_4^2 - N_t r_2^2)}{F_{CH_3OH_o}} \tag{3}$$

The overall heat transfer coefficient is calculated considering the tubes and the catalyst conductivity, and convection in the exhaust gases, while the convection in the reactor stream does not affect the surface temperature. Also, a homogeneous distribution of the tubes is considered so that all tubes have the same contribution to the total heat transfer. As a result, the energy balance for each tube will result in [Eq. (4)].

$$\frac{dT_a}{dz} = -\frac{2\pi r_3 U_z (T_a - T)}{\sum \left(\frac{F_{it}}{N_t}\right) Cp_i} \tag{4}$$

In the shell side, the temperature of the reactants and products stream is the same as the surface catalyst temperature along the system. The resultant energy balance is expressed by [Eq. (5)].

$$\frac{dT}{dz} = \frac{2\pi r_3 N_t U_z (T_a - T) - \pi(r_4^2 - N_t r_2^2) H_{rxn} R_{CH_3OH}}{\sum F_i Cp_i} \tag{5}$$

This model considers that the heat transferred from the exhaust gases causes a decrease in their temperature (T_a), and allows the determination of the temperature profiles along the reactor. Since all fluids in the system are in a gaseous state, their thermophysical properties will experiment significant changes due to temperature variation along the reactor. Hence, the thermophysical properties of exhaust gases are recalculated in every step of the numerical method to determine the heat transfer coefficient. The model is solved with an in-house built code developed in Matlab® applying a first order Runge-Kutta method. Independence test was carried out monitoring the error variation at a fixed point and it was found that the appropriate step size is of 1×10^{-3} m with an error of 7.68E^{-5} for the temperature.

The proposed mathematical model includes diverse design variables that might generate some complexity to find an optimal design. In a previous work, the implementation of a sensitivity analysis before performing the optimization tasks, allowed the identification of the most critical variables (Villarreal-de-Aquino et al., 2023). To this end, in this work 6,000 samples were generated using the Latin hypercube method (LHM) followed by a Monte Carlo simulation to generate enough data and perform a global sensitivity analysis using the standardized regression coefficient method (SRC), which permits to identify the importance of the input variables on the selected performance criteria output variables.

3. Base case

The base case considers the inlet temperature of exhaust gases as 673 K, an estimate of this stream temperature after it passes through the catalytic converter. The reactant feed stream is considered as an equimolar vapor mixture of water and methanol, both in a gaseous state at about 453 K. The shell inside diameter is initially set as 5 cm and a reactor length of 1 m. The methanol molar flow rate (FM), tube external diameter (DT), pipe schedule (PS), tube array configuration (TP), number of tubes (NT) and thickness of catalyst layer (ThCat) considered initially are illustrated in Table 1. The tube arrays considered a fixed pitch of 1.25 of the external tube diameters. No heat loss to the environment was considered (insulated shell).

Table 1. Nominal values for design variables and the variation used in the LHM.

	DT	**PS**	**TR**	**ThCat**	**FM**	**TP**	**NT**
Nominal value	1/8", ¼" and 3/8"	10, 40 and 80	453 K	0.0002 m	75 mol/h	Square/ triangular	1, 2, 3 and 4
Percentage of variation	50 % for each diameter	50 % for each schedule	25 %	50 %	35 %		50 % for each NT

DT: Tube diameter for exhaust gases; PS: Pipe schedule; TR: Feed temperature of methanol and water; ThCat: thickness of catalyst; FM: Methanol feed flowrate; TP: Tube pattern; NT: Number of tubes.

4. Results

The modelling of the limit base case scenarios corresponding to the shortest and largest dimensions for the diameter of the tube and the schedule: (i) 1/8" of diameter using a schedule of 10 and, (ii) 3/8" of diameter using a schedule of 80 was performed initially. For scenario (i) a conversion of 52.88 % for methanol was obtained producing 118.98 mol/h of hydrogen; in case of scenario (ii) the hydrogen production was 73.09 mol/h with a methanol conversion of 32.49 %. These results evidenced the opportunity for further analysis to find the best design of the reactive system. Hence, a global sensitivity analysis was performed to examine the effect of the design variables (input variables) in the selected performance variables, such as, methanol conversion, rate of hydrogen production, number of tubes, temperature of the reactants, temperature for the exhaust gas and shell diameter. The first evaluated scenario considers a fixed shell inside diameter of 5 cm, while in the second scenario the shell diameter is calculated for a fixed number of tubes. The design variables variations of the nominal values for both assessed scenarios are shown in Table 1.

Figure 1 illustrates the ranking of the significant output variables for a) methanol conversion; b) temperature for the exhaust gas; c) temperature of the reactants and products; d) hydrogen production. The diameter of the tubes and the feed temperature for the reactants are identified as significant variables in all the analyzed output variables. The third design variable with more significance in the output variables was the catalyst thickness. The methanol feed flowrate has the highest impact in the methanol conversion; however, it is important to highlight that the feed temperature of the reactants has the highest impact in hydrogen production, which means that higher temperatures induce more total hydrogen production even if methanol is not completely consumed.

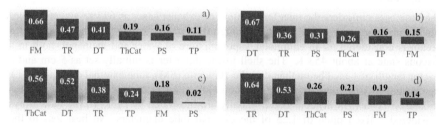

Figure 1. Variable significance ranking for output variables criteria: a) methanol conversion; b) temperature for the exhaust gas; c) temperature of the reactants and products; d) hydrogen production. DT: Tube diameter for exhaust gases; PS: Pipe schedule; TR: Feed temperature of methanol and water; ThCat: catalyst thickness; FM: Methanol feed flowrate; TP: Tube pattern.

Although an optimization task is not the main objective of the present research, the results showed that it is possible to find a better design variables combination when compared with the base case scenario (see Table 2). The results show that a higher temperature of the reactants and products improves the hydrogen production and conversion when compared to the base case. Sensitivity analysis also illustrates that reducing the diameter of the tube promotes conversion and hydrogen production, while the reduction of methanol feed flowrate only improves methanol conversion. In both cases the number of tubes for the exhaust gas flow was 6. It is suspected that the reduction in tube diameter increases the heat transfer efficiency of the system, which improves hydrogen production.

Table 2. Improved design variables for the reactive system maintaining the internal shell diameter of 5 cm and the reactor length of 1 m.

DT	PS	TR, K	ThCat, m	FM, mol/ h	TP	Methanol conversion, %	Hydrogen production, mol/h
1/8"	80	531	$2.94E^{-4}$	89.54	Square	66.06	177.46
1/8"	40	541	$2.99E^{-4}$	50.49	Square	98.09	148.56

DT: Tube diameter for exhaust gases; PS: Pipe schedule; TR: Feed temperature of methanol and water; ThCat: catalyst thickness; FM: Methanol feed flowrate; TP: Tube pattern.

Based on the results from the first scenario, the sampling for the tubes number was varied from 1 to 4 considering the frequency of number of tubes in the first designs. Figure 2 depicts the ranking of the significant input variables on the temperature of the exhaust gas and feed temperature of the reactants and products (Figure 2.a), which are highly influenced by the methanol flowrate and its intake temperature. Regarding the Reynolds number, the number of tubes (where the flowrate is divided) and tube diameter are naturally significant variables that affect it; moreover, it is important to highlight that monitoring the Reynolds number is critical in this model since correlations and properties were determined by correlations applicable for Re > 3000. Finally, the internal shell diameter is highly dependent on the number and diameter of the tubes, since spatial (geometrical) limitations require more space for more tubes or larger diameters.

  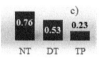

Figure 2. Variable significance ranking for output variables criteria: a) temperature of the exhaust gas and feed temperature of the reactants and products; b) Reynolds number; and c) Internal shell diameter. DT: Tube diameter for exhaust gases; PS: Pipe schedule; TR: Feed temperature of methanol and water; FM: Methanol feed flowrate; TP: Tube pattern

The results of the Monte Carlo simulation provided better design configurations.

Table 3 shows two design configurations with better conversion and hydrogen production when compared with the base case scenarios. The results illustrate that it was possible to obtain the 99 % of methanol conversion with suitable dimensions, just above 1 m and a diameter with one extra cm. The results showed that it is possible to have feasible TCR device designs to render higher conversions of methanol. The necessary number of tubes for both improved designs was 4.

Table 3. Improved design variables for the reactive system calculating the internal shell diameter and reactor length to achieve 99 % methanol conversion.

DT	PS	TR, K	ThCat, m	FM, mol/ h	Hydrogen production, mol/h	Length of the reactor, m	Internal shell diameter, m
1/4"	80	553	$2.65E^{-4}$	49.34	146.53	1.13	0.061
1/4"	10	563	$2.78E^{-4}$	51.67	153.46	1.45	0.061

DT: Tube diameter for exhaust gases; PS: Pipe schedule; TR: Feed temperature of methanol and water; ThCat: catalyst thickness; FM: Methanol feed flowrate.

5. Conclusions

A mathematical model for the design of a shell and tube TCR reactor was developed based on fundamental heat transport and reaction engineering principles. The model enables the possibility to design systems for different reactions, catalysts, reactant feeds and determines the amount of energy that may be transferred from a hot exhaust gas to revalorize thermal energy to produce hydrogen using methanol reforming. The sensitivity analysis demonstrated that it is possible to improve the TCR system design. To this end, the tube diameter and reactor inlet temperature were determined to be of particular importance. The results showed that is possible to make further analyses to obtain an optimal design from the techno-economic perspective, moreover, the mathematical model has the flexibility to evaluate and combine diverse materials for the unit, tailor-made catalysts, internal configuration, etc.

References

V.K. Chakravarthy, C.S. Daw, J.A. Pihl, J.C. Conklin, 2010, Study of the theoretical potential of thermochemical exhaust heat recuperation for internal combustion engines. Energy and Fuels, 24(3), 1529–1537.

S.C. Chen, Y.L. Kao, G.T. Yeh, M.H. Rei, 2017, An onboard hydrogen generator for hydrogen enhanced combustion with internal combustion engine. International Journal of Hydrogen Energy, 42(33), 21334–21342.

V.M. Fomin, A.V. Makunin, 2009, Thermochemical recovery of heat contained in exhaust gases of internal combustion engines (A general approach to the problem of recovery of heat contained in exhaust gases). Theoretical Foundations of Chemical Engineering, 43(5), 834–841.

V.A. Kirillov, A.B. Shigarov, N.A. Kuzin, V.V. Kireenkov, Yu.I. Amosov, A.V. Samoilov, V.A. Burtsev, 2013, Thermochemical conversion of fuels into hydrogen-containing gas using recuperative heat of internal combustion engines. Theoretical Foundations of Chemical Engineering, 47(5), 524–537.

E. Santacesaria, S. Carrá, 1983, Kinetics of catalytic steam reforming of methanol in a cstr reactor. Applied Catalysis, 5(3), 345–358.

M. de los A. Villarreal-de-Aquino, J.D. Ponce-Rocha, E.S. Perez-Cisneros, V. Rodríguez-López, E.I. Murillo-Andrade, D. Rodriguez-Gomez, R. Morales-Rodriguez, 2023, Optimization framework based on a sensitivity analysis for the identification of the critical design variables. Computer Aided Chemical Engineering, 52, 1095–1100.

Flavio Manenti, Gintaras V. Reklaitis (Eds.), Proceedings of the 34th European Symposium on Computer Aided Process Engineering / 15th International Symposium on Process Systems Engineering (ESCAPE34/PSE24), June 2-6, 2024, Florence, Italy

Optimization-based framework for techno-economic and environmental assessment of CO_2 capture, utilization, and storage strategies

Chanhee You,[a] Chanmok Kim,[a] Hyeon Yang,[a] and Jiyong Kim [a,*]

[a]*School of Chemical Engineering, Sungkyungkwan University, 16419, Republic of Korea*
Corresponding Author's E-mail: jiyongkim@skku.edu

Abstract

Carbon capture, utilization, and storage (CCUS) is one of the promising and effective solutions addressing climate change and energy security in the near-term. Since the CCUS technologies have different technological constraints for CO_2 sequestration, it is essential to apply a unified evaluation framework to assess and analyze various CCUS technologies in perspective of CO_2 disposal. In this study, we aim to assess and analyze the CCUS technologies in specific problems of maximizing net present value (NPV) and $CO_{2\text{-eq}}$ reduction considering various constraints. This study developed an optimization-based framework to analyze and assess the CCUS technologies regarding technical, economic, and environmental performance. To achieve this goal, we developed a superstructure involving a series of technologies (e.g., CO_2 capture, transportation, CO_2 conversion, and separation) to storage and utilize captured CO_2. We then estimated the technical and economic parameters (i.e., mass flow, energy flow, sizing data and costing data) based on the literature and the process model by developed Aspen Plus. The optimization models were developed to identify the optimal CCUS strategies with different criteria: NPV, and $CO_{2\text{-eq}}$ reduction. With scenario-based analysis, this study also determined that the priority of various CCUS technologies considering critical constraints such as the cost and $CO_{2\text{-eq}}$ inventory of H_2 according to the resource of H_2 and utility. This paper offers actionable policy guidance with NPV and $CO_{2\text{-eq}}$ reduction for high carbon-footprint nations considering the CCUS strategy.

Keywords: CO_2 utilization and storage, optimization-based assessment, techno–economic analysis, life cycle assessment.

1. Introduction

The increasing challenge of climate change has amplified the significance of carbon capture, utilization, and storage (CCUS) technology (Naims & Eppinger, 2022). Given the increasing global temperatures and the growing urgency of environmental issues, CCUS has become an essential technology in combating these challenges (Abanades et al., 2017). The importance of this technology is emphasized by global efforts aimed at reducing CO_2 emissions and shifting towards environmentally sustainable energy alternatives. Despite the recognized importance of CCUS, its global implementation remains limited, with less than 1% of the projected CO_2 captured (Mac Dowell et al., 2017). This is primarily attributed to the slow pace of CCUS implementation, compounded by issues such as high costs, regulatory obstacles, and technological limitations. The significant disparity between the projected CO_2 captured and actual CCUS implementation highlights the need for more efforts and strategic planning in the field of CCUS. Carbon capture utilization for energy (CCU4E) technologies have demonstrated significant promise among the several CCUS technologies, particularly in the generation of energy products (Hepburn et al., 2019). In our previous study, we conducted a techno-economic assessment of CCU4E technologies comparing their viability and competitiveness with conventional energy sources (Do et al., 2022). However, for successful implementation of CCU4E technologies, it is essential to not only assess their techno-economic viability but also to clearly identify and understand the actual constraints and potential of CCU4E technologies. This involves a detailed understanding of market information (e.g., market size, market price) and global information (e.g., renewable energy potential and hydrogen availability). In this study, we developed an optimization-based assessment framework for planning CCU4E technologies from technical and environmental perspectives. This framework aims to offer a strategic approach to planning CCU4E implementation, considering a practical constraint that impact its feasibility and effectiveness. By integrating technical, economic, and environmental analyses, we identified optimal pathways for CO_2 utilization in energy production, balancing the goals of sustainability, economic viability, and environmental protection.

2. Methodology

Figure 1 presents our methodological approach for assessing CCU4E. We developed a CCU4E superstructure which includes a variety of technologies for converting captured CO_2 into valuable energy products as shown in Figure 2. We developed process models for 20 CCU4E pathways. The mass and energy balance were obtained from developed process model. Sizing and costing data were also estimated. We obtained chemical market information (i.e., product prices and market sizes) and global information (i.e., renewable energy potential and hydrogen availability (Hepburn et al., 2019). We developed an optimization model considering various constraints such as technical, market, and global information. To analyze the capability of optimization model, we developed different scenarios considering different resource type. By analyzing different scenarios, we could provide practical insights for CCU4E implementation, contributing to efforts in combating global climate change. Our methodology also encompasses a long-term perspective, extending our planning and analysis horizon up to the year 2050. This extended timeframe allows for a more comprehensive assessment of the evolving landscape of CO_2 utilization and the changing dynamics of energy production.

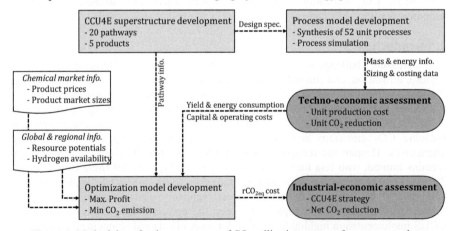

Figure 1. Methodology for the assessment of CO_2 utilization strategy for energy products

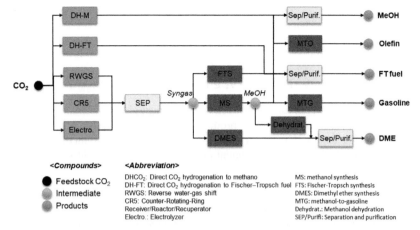

Figure 2. Superstructure of CO₂ utilization for energy products

3. Optimization model

In this study, we developed an optimization model using mixed integer linear programming (MILP) to identify the optimal CO₂ utilization strategies. This model is composed of a comprehensive set of data, including technology-specific, market, and global information. Our strategy for CO₂ utilization encompasses various pathways for producing multiple energy products. Each pathway begins with feedstocks like CO₂ and hydrogen and involves a sequence of conversion and separation technologies to produce one or more target fuels. In this study, we developed two objective functions. The first, defined in Eq. (1), aims at maximizing NPV. The NPV is calculated by considering the total revenue (TRE) and the total costs (TCO) associated with the CO₂ utilization processes, along with depreciation (dp), the discount rate (d), and tax considerations (TAX). The total revenue is derived from the combined profits of selling energy products and by-products and includes the salvage value of facilities at the end of their life cycle. On the other hand, total costs encompass the investment required for facility establishment, operational expenditures, and variable costs like feedstock and utility expenses. In the optimization model, our second objective function is focused on maximizing CO₂-eq reduction, which is crucial for assessing the environmental impact of the CO₂ utilization strategies. This evaluation is conducted through two key parameters: the CO₂ inventory of products (CP) and net CO₂ equivalent emissions (NCE). The CP is a measure of the total CO₂ emissions associated with each produced fuel or by-product. It reflects the environmental footprint of producing these energy products considering all emissions from the point of CO₂ capture to the final product output. On the other hand, the NCE refer to the balance of CO₂ emissions and reductions throughout the entire process of CO₂ utilization.

$$MaxNPV = \sum_t \frac{(TRE_t - TCO_t)(1 - TAX) + dp}{(1 + d)^t} \tag{1}$$

$$MaxCR = \sum_{lt} (CP_{lt} - NCE_{lt}) \tag{2}$$

The optimization model was constrained by the demand satisfaction and feed availability as expressed in Eqs. (3) – (5).

$$S_{ilt} \leq M_{ilt} \quad \forall i \in I^P, \forall l \in L, t \in T \tag{3}$$

$$F_{ilt} = \rho_{lt} \quad \forall i \in I^{F'}, \forall l \in L, t \in T \tag{4}$$

$$F_{ilt} \leq \zeta_{lt} \quad \forall i \in I^{F''}, l \in L, t \in T \tag{5}$$

where S_{ilt} is the production of product I^P and by-product I^B in country l during time t, M_{ilt} is the potential market size of product I^P in country l during time t, F_{ilt} the consumption of feedstock I^F in country l during time t, ρ_{lt} is the amount of CO_2 captured in country l during time t, ζ_{lt} is the amount of hydrogen in country l during time t.

4. Case study

In this study, we consider CO_2 captured from the flue gas of a 500 MW coal-powered electric utility, amounting to approximately 3.1 million tons of CO_2 annually. The detailed process modeling was conducted using Aspen Plus V.11, and the comprehensive specifics of each process can be found in Do et al. (2022). This reference elaborates on mass and energy flow, as well as sizing and costing data for all processes, which were crucial inputs for our model's analysis and development. Several organizations have projected the availability of CO_2 captured in the future. Based on these predictions, there will be a reduction of 20 Gt of CO_2 emissions in the announced pledges scenario (APS) in 2050, compared to stated policies scenario (STEPS). This reduction can be attributed to advancements in CO_2 capture technologies, improved energy efficiency in industries, and a significant shift towards renewable energy sources. By 2020, under the APS, it's anticipated that there will be a cumulative capture of 42 Mt of CO_2. Driven by technological advancements and policy implementations, this amount is expected to see a substantial rise, reaching an estimated 4300 Mt/y by 2050. The economics of CO_2 utilization, particularly for liquid fuel production, are intricately tied to the costs of CO_2 capture. It's noteworthy that almost half (47%) of the expenses of a CO_2-EOR project are attributed to CO_2 capture. For example, costs in the power and heat sector can range from 62 to 163 $/ton. Such fluctuations in costs highlight the uncertainties in gauging the availability of low-cost CO_2 for future capture. Given the range of CO_2 prices and the inherent uncertainties in predicting low-cost CO_2 availability, we assumed that only about 30% of the total CO_2 captured by 2050 in the APS scenario will be available at a cost-effective rate of 35 $/ton. To estimate hydrogen availability, we utilized forecasts for low-carbon hydrogen production up to 2050, as provided by Wood Mackenzie. Based on these projections, we assumed that the availability of green hydrogen to be equivalent to the hydrogen production from electrolysis, while black hydrogen availability was assumed to correspond with the production from fossil with CCS.

5. Results and discussion

Our study primarily aimed to identify optimal CCU4E strategies that maximized NPV and $CO_{2\text{-eq}}$ reduction. To achieve this goal, we developed two different scenarios considering different combinations of utility and hydrogen types. Note that black utility refers to conventional utility sources from the grid, while green utility denotes renewable electricity and heat sources. For considering hydrogen types, black hydrogen refers to natural gas-based hydrogen with a CO_2 capture process, which is one of the most widely used. Green hydrogen refers to the hydrogen from electrolysis which is one of the most ecofriendly hydrogens. By analyzing the most widely used and ecofriendly hydrogen through cost and environmental optimization, we could identify the optimal strategy in terms of financial viability and $CO_{2\text{-eq}}$ reduction for CCUS technologies. In P1 and C1 scenarios, the CCUS technologies only utilizes black hydrogen and black utility. On the other hand, in P2 and C2 scenarios, the CCUS technologies only utilizes green hydrogen and green utility. It is identified that the P1 scenario, utilizing black hydrogen and utility, was found to be the most financially viable option among the scenarios, with the lowest financial loss at -174 MM$/y. On the other hand, the P1 scenario also resulted in the least $CO_{2\text{-eq}}$ reduction among all scenarios, achieving only 472 Mt/y. This is because the P1 scenario relies on black utility and hydrogen which are more cost-effective but result in comparatively lower $CO_{2\text{-eq}}$ reductions. Within the P1 scenario, the optimal strategy included producing a range of fuels through specific processes. The optimal strategy in the P1 scenario involved the production of MeOH via direct hydrogenation, the synthesis of DME from MeOH, the creation of olefin through the MTO process, and the conversion of MTG

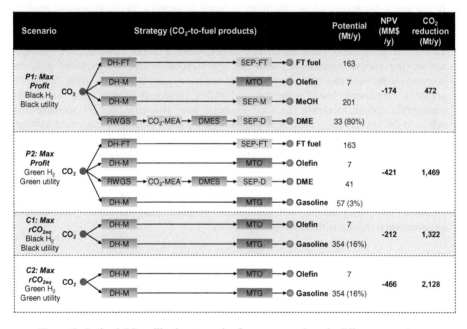

Figure 2. Optimal CO₂ utilization strategies for energy products in different scenarios.

In the P2 scenario, where green hydrogen and utility were implemented, a significant shift in fuel production strategy was observed compared to the P1 scenario. For example, while the P1 scenario involved the production of FT fuel, Olefin, MeOH, and DME, the P2 scenario shifted to producing FT fuel, Olefin, DME, and Gasoline. This is because the adoption of green hydrogen and utility in the P2 scenario led to higher costs, influencing the shift in fuel production strategy. In the P2 scenario, we observed significant shifts in both NPV and $CO_{2\text{-eq}}$ reduction compared to the P1 scenario. For instance, the NPV in the P2 scenario decreased to -421 MM$/y, compared to -174 MM$/y in the P1 scenario, representing a relative decrease of about 142%. On the other hand, the $CO_{2\text{-eq}}$ reduction markedly increased to 1469 Mt/y, up from 472 Mt/y in the P1 scenario, representing a substantial increment of approximately 211%. With these results, we have identified a clear trade-off between economic costs and environmental benefits in CO_2 utilization strategies. In the C1 and C2 scenarios, which prioritized maximizing $CO_{2\text{-eq}}$ reduction, the optimal strategy only consists of the production of olefin and gasoline, due to the $CO_{2\text{-eq}}$ inventory of olefin and gasoline. With these results, we identified that focusing on fuels with a high $CO_{2\text{-eq}}$ inventory can lead to significant environmental improvements. When focusing solely on the $CO_{2\text{-eq}}$ inventory of products, there is an inherent trade-off in terms of economic implications. For example, while the P1 scenario resulted in a financial loss of -174 MM\$/y, the C1 scenario results at higher financial loss of -212 MM\$/y. From our analysis, we identify that CCU4E strategies present a complex interplay between economic costs and environmental benefits. These findings highlight the necessity of carefully considering both economic and environmental factors in CO_2 utilization strategies.

6. Conclusions

In this study, we developed an optimization-based framework for the systematic analysis and evaluation of CO_2 utilization strategies considering economics and environmental impacts. This framework integrates a range of conversion and separation technologies for various fuel production. Then, we developed optimization model with objective functions considering various constraints. With the optimization model, we explored different scenarios with black and green hydrogen and utility sources. It was identified that the P1 scenario, employing black hydrogen and utility, emerged as the most financially sustainable option, incurring the least financial loss. However, the P1 scenario also achieved the lowest $CO_{2\text{-eq}}$ reduction, indicating a trade-off between economic feasibility and environmental impact. The P2 scenario, with green hydrogen and utility, demonstrated a notable shift towards increased $CO_{2\text{-eq}}$ reduction but at a higher economic cost. The results highlight the significance of resource selection and objective function in the planning of CCU4E strategy for the financial viability and $CO_{2\text{-eq}}$ reduction potential. Our study contributes to the understanding of sustainable CO_2 utilization, offering guidance for policymakers and companies in developing strategies that balance environmental impact with economic feasibility.

References

Abanades, J. C., Rubin, E. S., Mazzotti, M., & Herzog, H. J. (2017). On the climate change mitigation potential of CO 2 conversion to fuels. *Energy Environ. Sci*, *10*, 2491. https://doi.org/10.1039/c7ee02819a

Do, T. N., You, C., & Kim, J. (2022). A CO 2 utilization framework for liquid fuels and chemical production: techno-economic and environmental analysis. *Energy & Environmental Science*, *15*(1), 169–184. https://doi.org/10.1039/D1EE01444G

Hepburn, C., Adlen, E., Beddington, J., Carter, E. A., Fuss, S., Mac Dowell, N., Minx, J. C., Smith, P., & Williams, C. K. (2019). The technological and economic prospects for CO2 utilization and removal. *Nature 2019 575:7781*, *575*(7781), 87–97. https://doi.org/10.1038/s41586-019-1681-6

Mac Dowell, N., Fennell, P. S., Shah, N., & Maitland, G. C. (2017). The role of CO2 capture and utilization in mitigating climate change. *Nature Climate Change 2017 7:4*, *7*(4), 243–249. https://doi.org/10.1038/nclimate3231

Flavio Manenti, Gintaras V. Reklaitis (Eds.), Proceedings of the 34th European Symposium on Computer Aided Process Engineering / 15th International Symposium on Process Systems Engineering (ESCAPE34/PSE24), June 2-6, 2024, Florence, Italy

Systematic Analysis of Energy Transition Pathways for Emission Reduction in the Flat Glass Industry Using MILP Formulation

Muhammad Salman[a]*, Daniel Flórez-Orrego[b], Juan Correa-Laguna[c], François Maréchal[b], Grégoire Léonard[a]

[a]*Chemical Engineering, University of Liège, Liège Sart Tilman, 4000, Belgium.*
[b]*Federal Polytechnic School of Lausanne, IPESE group, Sion, Switzerland.*
[c]*EnergyVille, Thor Park 8310-8320, 3600 Genk, Belgium.*
*m.salman@uliege.be / Tel:+32465671822

Abstract

A systemic methodology was developed, employing key performance indicators (KPIs): specific total annual cost (TAC) ($€/t_{glass}$), specific emissions (t_{CO2}/t_{glass}) and specific energy consumption (MWh/t_{glass}) to analyse various energy transition routes for flat glass production, such as NG oxy-combustion, H_2 and hybrid furnaces, and full electrification, along with glass recycle and carbon capture (CC). A Blueprint (BP) model, including steady-state values for mass and energy balance, as well as investment and operating costs, is developed. To determine the optimal route, the OSMOSE Lua optimization framework was employed, which solves the mixed integer linear programming (MILP) problem using the TAC as the objective function. Additionally, three scenarios, namely Central, Electrification and Clean Molecules were implemented, influencing costs of natural gas (NG), H_2, electricity, and CO_2 emission, for years 2030, 2040 and 2050. For 2030, the hybrid furnace becomes the most cost-effective route across all scenarios. However, considering a balance between emissions and cost, pathways such as the H_2 furnace, all-electric furnace, or NG furnace with CC suit moderate emissions target. For higher targets, hybrid with CC is the optimal choice, effectively combining cost efficiency with significant emissions reduction. In 2040, electrification with CC dominates in electrification scenario, achieving significant emissions and TAC reductions, while the hybrid with CC prevails in other scenarios, with 93% emission and 15-16% TAC reductions. By 2050, lower commodity costs and higher CO_2 favour CC-equipped routes of all-electric, H_2, and hybrid, reducing TAC by 34-39% and emissions by 93-95%. In conclusion, for the energy transition in glass sector, an excellent trade-off between all KPIs is required, based on future energy perspectives, to make the right investment decisions.

Keywords: Energy transition, Process integration, Mixed-Integer Linear Programming (MILP), Industrial decarbonisation, Glass Industry

1. Introduction

The glass sector stands out as one of the high-energy-intensity industries, primarily utilizing energy for high-temperature process heat (ranging from 1400 to 1650°C) to melt raw materials (Joint Research Centre, 2013). According to the EU Emissions Trading Scheme (ETS) database, the glass sector contributes 8.5% (0.696 Mt/year) to the total Belgian industrial emissions and 67% of it alone comes from flat glass production. While CO_2 emissions in industrialized nations have consistently decreased (Lindig, 2009), the glass industry has experienced a staggering 165% increase (Hertwich, 2021). Hence, it is imperative to have a comprehensive analysis of energy transition in this sector. Although essential process parameters, such as energy consumption, cullet utilization, or energy sources, vary considerably across different countries, all types of glass products share significant similarities in crucial aspects like furnace type, capacity, and forming processes (Schmitz et al., 2011). Hence, this study is centred around flat glass to develop a generalized methodology to study the energy transition pathways of other glass products as well. Numerous studies have explored technical strategies to decarbonize the glass industry, with a focus on improving energy efficiency and fuel switching. Frassine et al., 2016 developed a predictive model estimating energy requirements for European glass melting furnaces from 2015 to 2030, considering factors like aging, cullet recycling, and energy efficiency measures. (Springer & Hasanbeigi, 2017) examined 16 technologies enhancing energy efficiency in glass production, covering batch preparation, preheating, process control, burner technologies, and combustion. (Galitsky et al., 2008) provided a comprehensive set of technical options for energy efficiency in the glass industry at various levels, including components, processes, systems, and organizations, quantifying the impact of energy management systems. (Papadogeorgos & Schure, 2019) focused on decarbonization pathways for Dutch container glass and tableware, addressing feedstock substitution, fuel switching, process design, recycling, and product design, and briefly exploring carbon capture (CC), storage, and utilization options. Despite extensive studies, research lacks exploration of how energy transition pathways impact CO_2 emissions amid evolving climate policies, particularly in Belgium and globally. The capital-intensive, competitive glass industry faces unique challenges due to its energy intensity and quality emphasis. Moreover, long-term investments significantly shape future CO_2 footprints. A crucial need thus exists for a comprehensive study on energy transition economics, emissions reduction, and energy intensity in the glass production sector. This study systematically analyses innovative pathways—oxy-combustion, H_2, hybrid, and all-electric furnaces with CC—assessing key performance indicators (KPIs) like total annual cost, emissions reduction, and energy consumption. Moreover, it will lay the foundation for the development of a generalized methodology to study the decarbonisation routes in the industries, which is one of the objectives of the TRILATE project.

2. Model Description and Methodology

2.1. Model Description

To analyze the different production routes, a Blueprint (BP) model of flat glass production is developed, which includes various production routes, as depicted in Figure 1. Energy and mass consumption data from open literature (Joint Research Centre, 2013) have been adopted and validated together with industrial plants. Modelling and simulations of other relevant utility systems are also performed in Aspen HYSYS software, using Peng-Robinson and NRTL fluid packages. The main process steps are i) raw materials and cullet batch preparation and preheating at around 25 – 200°C. ii) Melting by introducing batch in the furnace, heated by combustion flames. The main chemical reactions occur here. The fining process removes the impurities and flue gases aided by agents like Na_2SO_4 at high temperatures. iii) Forming, where the molten glass is guided onto a molten tin bath. Temperatures range from 1200 – 600°C further along the process. iv) Lastly, in the post-forming stage, finishing and cooling of flat glass product is done at around 600 – 100°C, which involves annealing and gradual cooling to relieve stress. In the base case, the furnace operates on natural gas (NG) (with 37% efficiency), releasing fossil emissions into the environment due to fossil fuel use as well as decarbonation of glass raw materials. However, to align with recommendations from literature on glass decarbonization (Correa Laguna et al., 2022; Elia, 2022), several additional routes are incorporated into the superstructure: 1) An all-electric furnace with 50% efficiency 2) Partial electrification using a mix of NG oxy-combustion and electric boosting, denominated as "hybrid" route 3) NG oxy-combustion furnace, aiming to decrease fuel consumption by 20%, and 4) H_2 furnace, with same efficiency as base case, but leveraging carbon-neutral fuel to reduce emissions. Each route offers the option of utilizing MEA chemical absorption for CC, capable of a 90% capture rate with a capture cost of 76 €/t_{CO2}. An auxiliary heating system is used to supply energy to the CC unit, however, its own emissions are not captured, when using NG as energy source. Moreover, in all routes, 26% of the total raw material batch is comprised of cullet. For the given scenarios, detailed mass and energy balances of each route are formulated in OSMOSE Lua, a mixed integer linear programming (MILP) optimization framework for industrial process integration and analysis. A detailed superstructure including all routes is depicted in Figure 1.

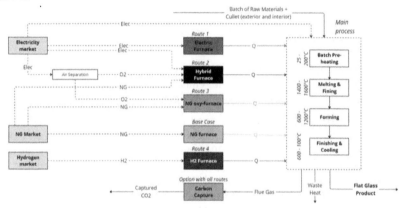

Figure 1. Superstructure of different routes for flat glass production

2.2. Scenarios Description

To evaluate proposed pathways, three scenarios—electrification, clean molecules, and central—are implemented for 2030, 2040, and 2050. These scenarios are named after the favored energy vector and they include electricity, H_2, NG, as well as emission costs assumptions, serving as decision variables to minimize the objective function. These costs are merely assumptions and being used as weights, whose main purpose is to map the decision space. Each scenario operates on specific assumptions influencing these costs. Using the TIMES-BE model which offers adaptable spatial and temporal resolutions, marginal production costs for electricity and H_2 are calculated for Belgium for 10 typical days, totaling 8760 hours, reflecting supply and demand variations over specific yearly periods. Table 1 displays the average costs of electricity and H_2 for all days. Additionally, NG cost is arbitrarily set at 0.37 €/kWh overall. CO_2 emission costs stand at 150, 250, and 350 €/t_{CO2} for 2030, 2040, and 2050, respectively. For a comprehensive understanding of the TIMES model, scenario assumptions, and detail cost assumptions, please refer to (Correa Laguna et al., 2022).

Table 1. Costs of electricity and H_2 (lower heating value) based on an average of 10 representative days for different years and scenarios

€/ kWh	2030						2040						2050					
	Elec.		Central		Molecules		Elec.		Central		Molecules		Elec.		Central		Molecules	
	H_2	EL.	H_2	EL.	H_2	EL.	H_2	EL.	H_2	EL.	H_2	EL.	H_2	EL.	H_2	EL.	H_2	EL.
Avg.	0.1	0.086	0.1	0.101	0.076	0.100	0.064	0.068	0.079	0.079	0.064	0.076	0.043	0.049	0.064	0.079	0.057	0.073

2.3. Optimization Problem Definition and Performance Indicators

To evaluate the performance of each route depicted in Figure 1, a systemic approach is established, leveraging the OSMOSE Lua optimization framework. The goal is to identify the route with the lowest total specific cost (TAC) (€/ton of product) in each scenario, by resolving a MILP problem outlined in equations (1-3). In equation 1, (u) stands for unit, (S) for size of unit, (ref) for the reference unit in CAPEX calculations, and C_{BM} for the bare module cost factor encompassing direct and indirect expenses. For CAPEX annualization, a 40-year lifetime (n) and a 3% discount rate (i) are considered. In equation (2) (C) is for specific cost, ($\dot{Q}$) and ($\dot{m}$) for energy and mass flow rates, respectively, (em) for emissions, TD for typical days and (W) for total power.

$$CAPEX(u_s)_{n,i} = \left(CAPEX(u_{ref}) \cdot \left(\frac{S_0}{S_{ref}} \right)^{0.6} \cdot C_{BM} \cdot \frac{CEPCI_{2022}}{CEPCI_{ref}} \right) \cdot i \cdot \frac{(i+1)^n}{(i+1)^{n-1}} \tag{1}$$

$$OPEX = \sum_{D \in TD} [\sum_{u \in units} (\sum_{e \in energy} (C_{e_u} \cdot \dot{Q}_{e_u}) + (C_{em_u} \cdot \dot{m}_{em_u}) + \sum_{m \in material} (C_{m_u} \cdot \dot{m}_{m_u})) \cdot hrs_D] \tag{2}$$

$$\min TAC \left(\frac{€}{t \text{ of glass}} \right) = \frac{OPEX + CAPEX}{\text{ton of product}} \tag{3}$$

The TAC acts as one of the three KPIs for the evaluation of the production routes. The other two KPIs are the total specific emissions (t_{CO2}/t_{glass}) and specific energy consumption (MWh/t_{glass}), associated with each route.

3. Results and Discussions

The energy transition routes for flat glass production, as depicted in Figure 1, are assessed across the different scenarios for 2030, 2040, and 2050. For 2030 (Figure 2), the hybrid furnace is cheapest, with 30% less energy consumption compared to the base case (1.33 MWh/t_{glass}), reducing TAC by 6%, 4%, and 4% compared to the NG base case (TAC of 195, 198, and 198 €/t_{glass} for the base case in scenarios electrification, clean molecules and central, respectively. The hybrid system uses NG oxy-combustion, cutting fuel usage by 20%. However, emissions are only 32% lower than the base case (0.40 t_{CO2}/t_{glass}). Adding CC to the hybrid case reduces emissions by 93% with 1.7%, 5.3%, and 5.3% higher TAC than the base case. NG with CC reduces emissions by 70% but increases TAC by 6% and energy consumption by 32%. This makes it suboptimal. Instead, NG oxy-combustion reduces emissions by 12% but increases TAC by 6% due to additional costs (such as CAPEX for a large air separation unit). The H_2 furnace becomes viable only under the clean molecules scenario with low H_2 costs and it offers a 55% emissions reduction with a slight TAC increase. All-electric route results in a slight TAC increase of 0.5%, 6%, and 6% for each scenarios respectively, achieving a 55% decrease in emissions compared to the base case with similar energy consumption. However, the implementation of CC to reach 95% emissions reduction is economically feasible only for the electrification scenario where electricity cost is cheaper. For 2030, choices depend on balancing factors. Moderate emissions reduction could favour H_2, all-electric or NG-with-CC furnaces, offering 55-70% emissions reduction with slight TAC increases. For higher targets, the hybrid with CC remains optimal, while H_2 and electric furnaces with CC suit scenarios clean molecules and electrification, respectively. For 2040 (Figure 3), lower electricity and H_2 costs, combined with higher CO_2 emissions costs, significantly raise base case TAC to 228, 231, and 232 €/t_{glass} for the three scenarios respectively. Introducing CC cuts TAC by 7% across scenarios, achieving a 70% emissions reduction. These changes in commodities costs trigger a change in each route. In Electrification scenario, all-electric with CC yields a 19.5% lower TAC and a 95% emissions reduction. Similarly, a hybrid furnace with CC reduces emissions by 93% and TAC by 18%. NG oxy-combustion remains viable only when paired with CC. For the clean molecules scenario, the H_2 furnace with CC cuts TAC by 15%, but the hybrid with CC becomes optimal, offering a 16% lower TAC and a substantial 93% emissions reduction. This trend persists in scenario 3, where the hybrid with CC delivers a 15% TAC reduction.

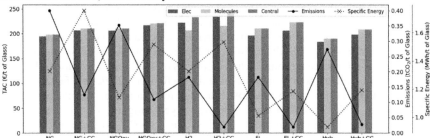

Figure 2. Comparison of all production routes based on given scenarios for the year 2030

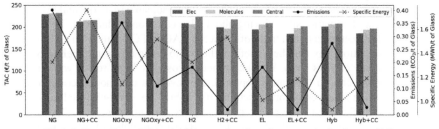

Figure 3. Comparison of all production routes based on given scenarios for the year 2040

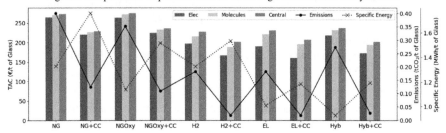

Figure 4. Comparison of all production routes based on given scenarios for the year 2050

For 2050 (Figure 4), reduced commodity costs and higher CO_2 expenses favor the hybrid, H_2, and all-electric furnace routes with CC. Base case TAC increases to 264, 270, and 272 €/t_{glass} for the three scenarios respectively. For electrification scenario, the all-electric with CC remains optimal, offering a substantial 39% lower TAC than the base case. Following closely are the H_2 furnace and hybrid furnace with CC routes, presenting 37% and 34% lower TAC and 95% and 93% emissions reductions compared to the base case, respectively. In the clean molecules scenario, low H_2 cost makes the H_2 furnace with CC the most optimal, delivering a 30% lower TAC compared to the base case. Finally, in the central scenario, the hybrid furnace with CC emerges as the most suitable option, presenting a 26% lower TAC. With lower electricity costs, improved fuel efficiency, and capturing 93% of emissions, it becomes the optimal choice for this scenario. Regarding the specific energy consumption, two main observations can be made. First, the technology using the least energy are not those with the lowest TAC, evidencing the role of the CAPEX in the TAC KPI. Second, it appears that the hybrid and then the electrical routes show the lowest specific energy consumption in all cases.

4. Conclusions

This study conducts a comprehensive analysis of energy transition routes for flat glass production, exploring NG oxy-combustion, hybrid, all-electric, and H_2 furnace pathways, each potentially integrated with CC. An optimization framework uses TAC as the primary objective function and evaluates specific emissions and energy consumption (depicting the important role of CAPEX in TAC) as additional KPIs, under three scenarios which dictate the costs of the commodities. The latter are selected as decision variables in the optimization process. As a result, for 2030, the higher assumed costs of electricity and H_2 makes the hybrid furnace an optimal choice in terms of TAC for all scenarios. However, for a trade-off with emissions, pathways like the H_2 furnace, all-electric furnace, or NG furnace (with CC) cater well to moderate emissions reduction target and the hybrid with CC emerges as the feasible route for higher targets, aligning cost efficiency with substantial emissions reduction. In 2040, all-electric with CC excels in electrification, while hybrid with CC prevails in others. By 2050, lower commodity and higher CO_2 costs support CC-equipped routes. The cheapest technologies vary from all-electric with CC in electrification scenario to H_2 furnace with CC in clean molecule scenario, and hybrid with CC in the central scenario, all achieving about 93% emissions reductions. To conclude, optimal route selection entails a trade-off between TAC and CO_2 emissions. The specific energy consumption may also be a useful indicator to make up for the high uncertainty regarding energy carriers costs. When commodity costs are high, routes with moderate emission targets and no CC can be optimal. However, as commodity costs decrease, routes emphasizing high emission reductions, like hybrid, H_2, or all-electric furnaces with CC, become preferable. Future research will explore directions such as effect of cullet flow and options for inter- and intra-plant heat recovery to enhance efficiencies in the glass sector. Additionally, in the TRILATE project, systemic studies for similar enhancements in other industrial sectors will be performed.

5. Acknowledgment

This research is supported via the Energy Transition Fund project 'TRILATE' organized by the FPS economy.

References

Correa Laguna, J., Moglianesi, A., Vingerhoets, P., & Lodewijks, P. (2022). *Perspective 2050*. https://perspective2050.energyville.be/

Elia. (2022). *Powering Industry Towards Net Zero*. https://www.elia.be/-/media/project/elia/shared/documents/elia-group/publications/studies-and-reports/2022/20221118_visionpaper_en.pdf

Frassine, C., Rohde, C., & Hirzel, S. (2016). Energy saving options for industrial furnaces–the example of the glass industry. *ECEEE Industrial Summer Study Proceedings*.

Galitsky, C., Worrell, E., Masanet, E., & Graus, W. (2008). *Energy Efficiency Improvement and Cost Saving Opportunities for the Glass Industry. an Energy Star Guide for Energy and Plant Managers*. Lawrence Berkeley National Lab.(LBNL), Berkeley, CA (United States).

Hertwich, E. G. (2021). Increased carbon footprint of materials production driven by rise in investments. *Nature Geoscience, 14*(3), 151–155. https://doi.org/10.1038/s41561-021-00690-8

Joint Research Centre. (2013). *Best available techniques (BAT) reference document for the manufacture of glass – Industrial emissions Directive 2010/75/EU: integrated pollution prevention and control*. Publications Office. https://doi.org/doi/10.2791/70161

Lindig, M. (2009). An Improved Solution for Oxy-Fuel Fired Glass Melting Furnaces. *69th Conference on Glass Problems: Ceramic Engineering and Science Proceedings, Volume 30, Issue 1*, 121–131.

Papadogeorgos, I., & Schure, K. . M. (2019). *Decarbonisation options for the dutch container and tableware glass industry*. PBL Netherlands Environmental Assessment Agency.

Schmitz, A., Kamiński, J., Maria Scalet, B., & Soria, A. (2011). Energy consumption and CO2 emissions of the European glass industry. *Energy Policy, 39*(1), 142–155. https://doi.org/https://doi.org/10.1016/j.enpol.2010.09.022

Springer, C., & Hasanbeigi, A. (2017). Emerging energy efficiency and carbon dioxide emissions-reduction technologies for the glass industry. *Energy Analysis an d Environmental Impacts Division, Lawrence Berkeley National Laboratory [LBNL], University of California, Berkeley, CA, USA*.

Flavio Manenti, Gintaras V. Reklaitis (Eds.), Proceedings of the 34th European Symposium on Computer Aided Process Engineering / 15th International Symposium on Process Systems Engineering (ESCAPE34/PSE24), June 2-6, 2024, Florence, Italy

Harvesting the Wind - Assessment of Offshore Electricity Storage Systems

Jan F. Wiegner,[a] Inge M. Ossentjuk,[a] Robbert M. Nienhuis,[b] Antonis I. Vakis,[b] Madeleine Gibescu,[a] and Matteo Gazzani[a*]

[a] *Utrecht University, Princetonlaan 8a, 3584 CB Utrecht, The Netherlands.*

[b] *University of Groningen, Nijenborgh 4, 9747 AG Groningen, The Netherlands*

[*] *m.gazzani@uu.nl*

Abstract

Offshore wind energy will comprise a significant share of the future European electricity supply. This, however, comes with the challenge of intermittency of the wind resource, and the threat of energy droughts. Energy Storage Systems (ESSs) are needed to tackle this challenge; integrating storage within offshore wind farms instead of onshore can provide additional benefits to the power system and enable large-scale integration of wind energy. To this end, we investigate a subsea pumped-hydro storage system utilizing the pressure difference between the seabed and the atmosphere to store electricity in the form of potential energy of a working fluid in two reservoirs. To optimize the design of the storage system in terms of energy and power capacity installed, we introduce a mixed-integer linear program (MILP). The system's design and operation is optimized to maximize profits over a period of one month accounting for both investment and operational cashflows. Results show that the system can have high round-trip efficiencies (~70%) comparable to conventional pumped-hydro storage (70-80%) with a storage size of up to 32 MWh for a sea depth of 50 m. In our case study, the system runs up to 4 full cycles per day. When participating in the day-ahead market exclusively, the system becomes profitable for electricity price fluctuations with standard deviations of at least double the 2019 values (in the Netherlands), which are likely to materialize in the future.

Keywords: energy storage, subsea pumped-hydro, offshore wind, mixed integer linear program, mathematical optimization

Variables					
V	Volume [m³]	p	Price [€/MWh]	$i \in I$	Timestep i in set of timesteps I
$\dot{Q}$	Flow rate [m³/h]	c	Cost Factor [€/unit of size]	$w \in W$	Segment w in set of segments for design fitting W
P	Power [MW]	ϵ	Dead volume as fraction of reservoir size		
x	Binary variable for design formulation.	$\underline{Q}$	Lower bound of piecewise defined function on Q [m³/h]	$v \in V$	Segment v in set of segments for part-load fitting V
y	Binary variable for (part-load) performance formulation.	$\overline{Q}$	Upper bound of piecewise defined function on Q [m³/h]	**Subscripts**	
Π	Profit [€]			r	Reservoir
Parameters				des	Design
α	Parameters of P-Q design fitting	**Indices**		out	Output/outflow
		$u \in U$	Pump u in set of pumps U	in	Input/inflow
β	Parameters of P-Q part-load fitting	$t \in T$	Turbine t in set of turbines T		

1. Introduction

Offshore wind energy is expected to play a crucial role in the future low-carbon power system. In Europe alone, targets are set to install 60 GW of offshore wind capacity by 2030, and 300 GW by 2050 (European Commission, 2020). The intermittent nature of wind energy, however, poses challenges for system integration and supply-demand balancing (Laugs et al., 2020). Energy storage systems (ESSs) are presented as key solutions to overcome these challenges, thereby reducing curtailment and improve reliability. Additional benefits are realized when energy is stored offshore at the production site (Li & DeCarolis, 2015): It can increase the utilization of offshore transmission cables; reduce stress on the grid (both offshore and onshore at the landing points); provide additional revenues for wind park operators; and reduce onshore spatial requirements for storage systems.

This study investigates a novel offshore pumped-hydro storage system as described by Lazdanaite et al. (2022). The technology can store electricity taking advantage of the pressure difference between a reservoir at atmospheric pressure and a second reservoir under hydrostatic pressure. The two reservoirs are connected with pumps and turbines powered by this pressure difference. Designing such a system entails choosing the number and size of pumps and turbines, i.e., the power capacity, as well as the reservoir volume, i.e., the energy capacity. To this end, we introduce a mixed-integer linear program (MILP) approach including the proposed pumped-hydro storage system and subsequently optimize its configuration for different electricity price profiles and cost assumptions to maximize economic profit over a period of one month.

2. Modelling Framework

Figure 1 illustrates the working principles of the offshore pumped-hydro storage system and its representation in the process model. The *lower reservoir* is connected to the sea surface thereby storing the working fluid at atmospheric pressure. The *upper reservoir* stores the pumped working fluid at a constant hydrostatic pressure that scales linearly with the depth of deployment. For each turbo-machinery type, up to six units of equal design can be installed. However, the operation for each individual machine can vary.

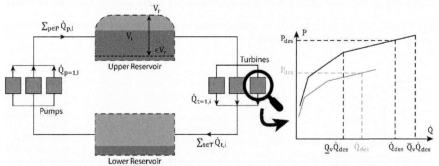

Figure 1. Illustration of the offshore pumped-hydro storage system. The left side shows the overall system with variables used in the model. The right side shows an exemplary turbine performance for two different turbine designs (gray and black). A similar function holds for the pump performance.

2.1. Detailed Model of the Offshore Pumped-hydro Storage System

The state of charge of the upper reservoir is given by the fill-volume in the previous timestep V_{i-1} with respective inflows and outflows (Eq. 1). Additionally, the volume is limited by an upper bound, i.e. the reservoir size V_r, and a lower bound, being the dead-volume as a fraction of total reservoir size:

$$V_i = V_{i-1} + \sum_{u \in U} \dot{Q}_{u,i} \Delta i - \sum_{t \in T} \dot{Q}_{t,i} \Delta i \tag{1}$$

$$\epsilon V_r \leq V_i \leq V_r \tag{2}$$

For the pumps and turbines, we assume that the performance in each timestep is a function of nominal head, design flow and actual flow. As such, we also take into account part-load behaviors of pumps and turbines. The head is assumed to be constant during operation, neglecting changes in head due to tidal or wave effects, as well as due to different states of charge and pressure losses, as these effects are expected to be very small.

The relationship between design flow rate and design power of both pumps and turbines is modelled with a piecewise affine function with a set of segments W (Eq. 3). The available head provides an upper and lower bound to the design flow rate. For readability, we refrain from indexing the variables and parameters for pumps and turbines. The equations hold for both turbomachinery types.

$$P_{\text{des}} = \sum_{w \in W} \left[x_w \left(\alpha_{w,1} \dot{Q}_{\text{des}} + \alpha_{w,2} \right) \right] \tag{3}$$

$$\sum_{w \in W} \left[x_w \underline{Q}_{\text{des},w} \right] \leq \dot{Q}_{\text{des}} \leq \sum_{w \in W} \left[x_w \overline{Q}_{\text{des},w} \right] \tag{4}$$

$$\sum_{w \in W} x_w = 1 \tag{5}$$

$$x_w \in \{0,1\} \tag{6}$$

The part-load performance of the pumps and the turbines are modelled with another piecewise affine function. The relationship of different design flow rates $\dot{Q}_{\text{des}}$, actual flow rates $\dot{Q}_i$ and power P_i is also illustrated in Figure 1.

$$P_i = \sum_{v \in V} \left[y_{v,i} \left(\beta_{v,1} \dot{Q}_i + \beta_{v,2} \dot{Q}_{\text{des}} \right) \right] \tag{7}$$

$$\sum_{v \in V} \left[y_{v,i} \underline{Q}_v \dot{Q}_{\text{des}} \right] \leq \dot{Q}_i \leq \sum_{v \in V} \left[y_{v,i} \overline{Q}_v \dot{Q}_{\text{des}} \right] \tag{8}$$

$$\beta_{v,2} = \left(\underline{P}_v - \beta_{v,1} \underline{Q}_v \right) \, for \, v \neq 1 \tag{9}$$

$$\beta_{v,2}, \beta_{v,1}, \underline{Q}_v, \overline{Q}_v = 0 \, for \, v = 1 \tag{10}$$

$$\sum_{v \in V} y_{v,i} = 1 \tag{11}$$

$$y_{v,i} \in \{0,1\} \tag{12}$$

It is possible for (part) of the equipment to be switched off (see Eq. 10). Eq. 3, 7 and 8 contain bilinearities that were transformed to a MILP formulation using the hull reformulation of the python library Pyomo. The parameters $\alpha_{w,1}$, $\alpha_{w,2}$, $\underline{Q}_{\text{des},w}$, $\overline{Q}_{\text{des},w}$, $\beta_{v,1}$, $\underline{P}_v$, $\underline{Q}_v$, and $\overline{Q}_v$ are fitted to respective pump and turbine performances for a given nominal head determined by the sea depth. The total electricity in- and output in each timestep is given by the sum of pump and turbine energy of all slots respectively:

$$P_{in,i} = \sum_{u \in U} P_{u,i} \tag{13}$$

$$P_{out,i} = \sum_{t \in T} P_{t,i} \tag{14}$$

To prevent symmetry in the resulting MILP we deploy constraints giving priority to pumps/turbines with lower indices (for design and operation):

$$P_{u,i} \leq P_{u-1,i}, P_{t,i} \leq P_{t-1,i} \tag{15}$$

$$P_{\text{des},u} \leq P_{\text{des},u-1}, P_{\text{des},t} \leq P_{\text{des},t-1} \tag{16}$$

We optimize the design and operation of the offshore pumped-hydro storage to maximize profits over one month of operation with an hourly resolution, i.e., $\Delta i = 1h$. As such, the objective function is the sum of electricity revenues over the time horizon minus total system cost. Cost factors for the equipment (c_u, c_t and c_r) are recalculated to a monthly cost:

$$\max \Pi = \sum_{i \in I} \Delta i P_{\text{out},i} p_i - \sum_{i \in I} \Delta i P_{\text{in},i} p_i -$$
$$\sum_{u \in U} c_u \dot{Q}_{u,\text{des}} - \sum_{t \in T} c_t \dot{Q}_{t,\text{des}} - c_r V_r \tag{17}$$

Note that it is also possible to not install the storage system. In this case, reservoir, pump and turbine sizes are zero. The optimization model is formulated with the Python library Pyomo and solved with Gurobi 10.0.3.

2.2. Input data

To obtain the design performance parameters of the hydraulic machines, we used Balje (D_s, ω_s) and efficiency (η, ω_s) diagrams from Cornetti & Millo (1989) for centrifugal pumps and Francis turbines. Part-load operation curves were taken from Kumar et al. (2011) for the turbines, and for the centrifugal pump it was retrieved from an open-source Simscape Block (Centrifugal Pump (IL), 2023).

The cost of electro-machinery can be estimated by a function of the following form: $C = aP^b H^c$. After comparison to the cost values of other studies (Aggidis et al., 2010; Ogayar & Vidal, 2009) we used the values from Alzohbi (2018) to determine the costs for a 1 MW pump/turbine. We then used the work by Aggidis et al. (2010) for size-scaling, which showed a trend highly similar to those of the other relevant literature. The resulting data was fitted with a linear function and is reported in Table 1.

Day-ahead market prices for the Dutch bidding zone in 2019, retrieved from ENTSO-E (2023), were used as price profiles for the optimization scenario. This price profile has a mean price of 58.33 EUR/MWh and a standard deviation (SD) of 13.83 EUR/MWh.

Table 1. Value assumptions used in the model. Pump and turbine values are for a nominal head of 47.5m.

Parameter	Unit	Value
CAPEX turbines	€	CAPEX = 324000 · P [MW] + 189300
CAPEX pumps	€	CAPEX = 322100 · P [MW] + 110900
CAPEX reservoir	€/m³	4.2 – 84

3. Results

We optimized the pumped-hydro design and operation over a one-month period with hourly resolution considering different combinations of reservoir costs and electricity price profiles. The electricity prices for May 2019 were therefore scaled to have different standard deviations. The optimal size for the reservoir and total installed capacities for pump and turbine of 204 optimization runs are shown in Figure 2. Detailed results for the three points indicated in the Figures are shown in Table 2.

Design. For high reservoir costs and low electricity price volatility (low SD), the storage system is unprofitable, leading to zero sizes for both pump, turbine, and reservoir (upper-left region). Conversely, an increase in electricity price volatility (high SD) coupled with lower reservoir costs makes the storage system profitable, with the optimal configurations featuring the largest possible reservoir size of 250,000 m³ resulting in a capacity of 32 MWh and a pump power rating of around 4.5 MW. Only for high reservoir costs and high SDs (upper right corner), it is optimal to reduce the reservoir size and thus pumps and turbines are relatively large compared to the reservoir size. One reason to select large pumps for the system, especially for high SDs, is the occurrence of negative electricity prices: During periods of negative prices, the storage operator is paid for using electricity, and as such, it is profitable to pump water to the upper reservoir and use a bypass of the turbines in case the upper reservoir is full. As a result, the pumps generally have a higher load factor than the turbines, especially for high price volatility scenarios.

Operation. As the flow rate varies in each timestep, also the efficiency of turbomachinery varies over time. In Table 2 we reported the average efficiencies alongside the minimum and maximum efficiencies that occurred over the time horizon for three electricity-price-capex combinations. The round trip efficiency aligns well with conventional pumped-hydro systems and is consistent with findings from previous reports on offshore pumped-hydro systems (Nienhuis et al., 2023). Notably, adding the load factors for pumps and turbines indicates that the system is almost in continuous operation. This also suggests that the system, at least from a purely economic perspective, is suitable for short-term storage. The storage system is thus constantly charged and discharged, reaching up to 4 full cycles per day. The system capitalizes on the modularity of pumps and turbines: Rather than operating all available machines at part-load it is optimal to switch some machines off and operate the remaining ones at a higher flow rate to achieve improved overall efficiency.

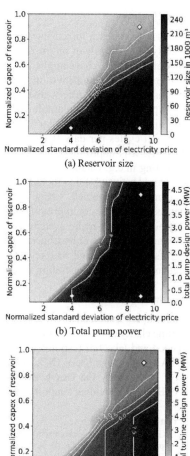

(a) Reservoir size

(b) Total pump power

(c) Total turbine power

Figure 2. Equipment size for different electricity price profiles and reservoir cost assumptions. Reservoir capex was normalized to 84 EUR/m³, SD of electricity prices to the SD of the electricity prices in May 2019.

Table 2. Performance and cost results of three highlighted scenarios.

Scenario			Performance			Economics			Load Factor	
Reservoir CAPEX	SD	Pump efficiency (mean)	Turbine efficiency (mean)	Average roundtrip efficiency	Monthly costs [k€]	Monthly revenues [k€]	Upfront costs [k€/MWh]	Pumps	Turbines
0.05	4	0.80 – 0.92 (0.92)	0.75 – 0.78 (0.78)	0.71	47	71	155	0.40	0.26
0.05	9	0.44 – 0.92 (0.91)	0.51 – 0.83 (0.77)	0.70	63	225	209	0.52	0.19
0.9	9	0.20 – 0.92 (0.89)	0.72 – 0.83 (0.78)	0.69	56	92	1,552	0.42	0.10

4. Conclusion

This paper proposes a mixed-integer linear formulation of an offshore pumped-hydro storage system, capable of optimizing the sizes of pumps, turbines and reservoir as well as their operation. We have applied the model in a case study with a number of scenarios for electricity prices and investment costs. As with any other storage system, higher variations in electricity prices make the system more profitable. The system has high round-trip efficiencies comparable to conventional pumped-hydro storage (~70%) with a storage size of up to 32 MWh for a sea depth of 50 m. In our case study, the system runs up to 4 full cycles per day. If the storage system participates in the day-ahead market exclusively, it is unprofitable for 2019 electricity prices in the Netherlands. However, participating in e.g. balancing or capacity markets, could change this finding. To study this, it would be insightful to include the participation in additional markets. Additionally, optimizing the combined sizing and operation of a wind farm with storage and transmission to shore could provide insights into other system benefits. In future works, the offshore pumped-hydro system will be compared to other storage technologies, such as lithium-ion batteries or hydrogen storage in its potential for emission and cost reduction in an offshore context and with regards to aging. Additionally, its environmental impact during construction and operation as well as spatial requirements will be investigated.

Acknowledgements

During the preparation of this work the authors used ChatGPT 3.5 to enhance readability and refine clarity of the first draft. After using, the authors reviewed and edited the content as needed and take full responsibility for the publication. This work was supported by DOSTA (project number WIND.2019.002) of the NWO research program PhD@Sea, (partly) financed by the Dutch Research Council (NWO). We are grateful to Ocean Grazer B.V. for providing support and the opportunity for collaboration.

References

Aggidis, G. A., Luchinskaya, E., Rothschild, R., & Howard, D. C. (2010). The costs of small-scale hydro power production: Impact on the development of existing potential. *Renewable Energy*, *35*(12), 2632–2638.

Alzohbi, G. (2018). The cost of electromechanical equipment in a small hydropower storage plant. *Journal of Energy Systems*, *2*(4), 238–259.

Centrifugal Pump (IL) (R2023a). (2023). The Mathworks, Inc. https://nl.mathworks.com/help/hydro/ref/centrifugalpumpil.html#responsive_offcanvas

Cornetti, G., & Millo, F. (1989). *Macchine idrauliche*. Il Capitello.

ENTSO-E. (2023). *ENTSO-E Transparency Platform*. https://transparency.entsoe.eu/

European Commission. (2020). An EU Strategy to harness the potential of offshore renewable energy for a climate neutral future. In *Communication from the commission to the European parliament, the council, the European economic and social committee and the committee of the regions*.

Kumar, A., Schei, T., Ahenkorah, A., Caceres Rodriguez, R., Devernay, J.-M., Freitas, M., Hall, D., Killingtveit, A., & Liu, Z. (2011). Hydropower. In *IPCC Special Report on Renewable Energy Sources and Climate Change Mitigation*. Cambridge University Press.

Laugs, G. A. H., Benders, R. M. J., & Moll, H. C. (2020). Balancing responsibilities: Effects of growth of variable renewable energy, storage, and undue grid interaction. *Energy Policy*, *139*.

Lazdanaite, E., Nguyen, P., Tran, M.-Q., Bliek, F., & van Rooij, M. (2022). Integration of Pump-Storage Batteries in Offshore Wind Farms: Evaluation of Effects on Power Exchange. *2022 IEEE PES Innovative Smart Grid Technologies - Asia (ISGT Asia)*, 210–214.

Li, B., & DeCarolis, J. F. (2015). A techno-economic assessment of offshore wind coupled to offshore compressed air energy storage. *Applied Energy*, *155*, 315–322.

Nienhuis, R. M., Van Rooij, M., Prins, W. A., Jayawardhana, B., & Vakis, A. I. (2023). Investigating the efficiency of a novel offshore pumped hydro energy storage system: Experimental study on a scale prototype *Journal of Energy Storage*, *74*, 2352–152.

Ogayar, B., & Vidal, P. G. (2009). Cost determination of the electro-mechanical equipment of a small hydro-power plant. *Renewable Energy*, *34*(1), 6–13.

Flavio Manenti, Gintaras V. Reklaitis (Eds.), Proceedings of the 34th European Symposium on Computer Aided Process Engineering / 15th International Symposium on Process Systems Engineering (ESCAPE34/PSE24), June 2-6, 2024, Florence, Italy

Power system planning integrating hydrogen and ammonia pathways under uncertainty

Georgios L. Bounitsis,[a] Vassilis M. Charitopoulos [a,*]

[a] *The Sargent Centre for Process Systems Engineering, Department of Chemical Engineering, University College London, Torrington Place, London WC1E 7JE, UK*
v.charitopoulos@ucl.ac.uk

Abstract

High penetration of renewable technologies, heat electrification and integration of dense energy carriers on power systems is promising towards decarbonisation. However, a lot of uncertainty sources render the efficient solution of such planning problems challenging. This work aims to investigate a nationwide power system planning problem with integration of hydrogen and ammonia under uncertain wind availability. The proposed snapshot model aims to determine optimal capacity mix in a future year under uncertainty. A risk-neutral two-stage stochastic programming approach is adopted along with a novel data-driven scenario generation technique to efficiently capture the uncertain set and alleviate the computational complexity. The proposed framework is examined on a case study concerning strategic planning of deep decarbonised coupled power and heat systems in Great Britain (GB) and the quality of stochastic solutions is highlighted.

Keywords: Power System Planning, Net Zero, Ammonia, Stochastic Programming, Scenario Generation.

1. Motivation & literature review

UK leads the race towards Net Zero to vitally reduce carbon emissions. Towards the decarbonised power system planning high penetration of renewable technologies is imperative (Dangoumas & Koltsaklis, 2019). However, as renewable generation increases, intermittency of renewable sources impose volatility to the power system. The exploitation of excessive renewable energy is feasible via battery energy storage systems (BESS) or storage via dense energy carriers (DECs) such as hydrogen (H_2) or ammonia (NH_3). Pellow et al. (2015) indicated the benefits of H_2 compared to BESS for cost-efficient energy storage on grid. Moreover, Wu et al. (2022) proposed that NH_3 can complement H_2 for long-term energy storage towards decarbonisation, as NH_3 is more inexpensive for long-term storage and transportation.

DECs are recently included in studies regarding optimal power system planning. For instance, He et al. (2021) showcased the role of H_2 as an energy carrier in power system planning towards decarbonisation in a case study in Noertheast US. Beyond H_2 utilisation, Ganzer et al. (2022) integrated a power-to-methane pathway for grid-scale storage in the capacity expansion planning of GB indicating the role of DEC for inter-seasonal storage. Bounitsis and Charitopoulos (2023) studied the optimal power system planning and operation in GB integrating H_2 and NH_3 pathways towards coupled power and heat systems decarbonisation and NH_3 role for long-term storage was highlighted. Even though capacity expansion planning under uncertainty is a topical field of study (Roald, 2023), the investigation of complex energy planning problems integrating DECs and considering uncertainty is a quite unexplored topic. In this work, we extend the snapshot LP model by Bounitsis and Charitopoulos (2023) to a two-stage stochastic programming (TSSP) problem. Uncertainty is considered on wind availability as it is critical for power systems operation and its quantification has been heavily studied in the literature (Li et al., 2020). Here we capture uncertainty by employing the novel scenario generation framework by Bounitsis et al. (2022) and exploiting wind historical data. Finally, a case study of GB power system planning towards decarbonisation in 2040 is considered to evaluate the value of DECs pathways for the system. The remainder of the article is organised as follows: in Section 2 the problem is outlined, and mathematical modelling is presented. In Section 3, scenario generation and results regarding GB's case study are presented. Finally, conclusions are drawn in Section 4.

2. Optimal power system planning integrating DECs under uncertainty

2.1. Problem description

Power system planning and operation under uncertainty is investigated. Along with conventional technologies, pathways of H_2 and NH_3 are integrated in the problem. Moreover, residential and commercial heat sectors are coupled to power sector due to their high energy consumption and carbon intensity (Charitopoulos et al., 2023). Beyond natural gas, heat can also be satisfied by electricity and H_2. Thus, heat demand mix is determined offering flexibility and electricity peak demand is optimised. The goal of proposed TSSP is to determine power system's capacity planning in a future year (first-stage decisions) before the realization of uncertain wind availability. Then, second-stage scenario-dependent system's operation is optimised on the first-stage capacity decisions. This work focuses on GB's future decarbonised power system and capacity expansion decisions are taken considering GB as a node (whole system). On the operational level, full year hourly ($h \in H, |H| = 8760 \ hours$) data profiles for demands and renewable availability are exploited to define a reduced fine-grained time resolution (H') via Chronological Time-Period Clustering (CTPC) (Pineda and Morales, 2018). This time aggregation method maintains the chronological order of the data capturing the short- and long-term dynamics. We formulate a new version of the Priority CTPC by García-Cerezo et al. (2022) (NPCTPC) which respects the attribute specific extreme events. In Fig. 1 is shown that proposed NPCTPC better captures the extreme events for total power demand.

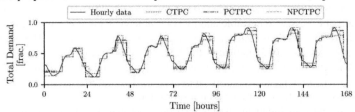

Figure 1: *Chronological clustering methods comparison from 8,760 hours to 2,190 clusters.*

Regarding the superstructure of the problem (visualised in Fig. 2), energy carriers ($a \in A = \{elec, H_2, NH_3\}$) are generated by technologies ($j \in J$) to fulfill system's demands. Storage options are also available for them and especially for electricity bidirectional interconnections to third countries ($i \in I$) are considered. Regarding electricity generation, well-established renewable and conventional technologies are included. DECs introduce alternative generation and storage options via gas turbines (GT) and liquid storage. H_2 can be produced via biomass gasification (BG), natural gas reforming (SMR) or water electrolysis (WE). Developing technologies are considered coupled with Carbon Capture and Storage systems (CCS) to reduce their carbon footprint. Then, NH_3

is produced using H_2 and electricity through Haber-Bosch (HB) process. HB process assumptions include the accompanied air separation units for nitrogen (N_2) production.

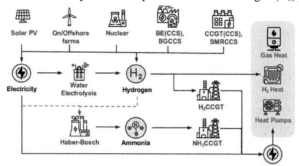

Figure 2: *Superstructure of power and heat systems.*

2.2. Mathematical modelling via Stochastic Programming

An LP TSSP total cost minimisation model is formulated based on the model by Bounitsis and Charitopoulos (2023). Wind availability uncertainty is realised through scenario set $s \in S$. TSSP determines capacity planning via here-and-now decisions Cap_j, while rest operational decisions are wait-and-see (scenario-dependent). System's power and heat demands (DEM_h^{heat}, DEM_h^{elec}) are satisfied. Heat demand can be supplied by all available heating options (Q_{hs}^*), and so electricity demand (D_{hs}) is optimised over the time horizon:

$$DEM_{hs}^{heat} = \frac{Q_{hs}^{elec}}{COP_h} + \frac{Q_{hs}^{H2}}{\eta^{H2,boiler}} + \frac{Q_{hs}^{NG}}{\eta^{gas,boiler}} \quad \forall h \in H, s \in S \tag{1}$$

$$D_{hs} = (1 + DL) \cdot (DEM_{hs}^{elec} + Q_{hs}^{elec}) \quad \forall \, h \in H, s \in S \tag{2}$$

In particular, DL accounts for the distribution losses on the electricity grid and is set equal to 6.5% according to historical data (DUKES, 2023). Then, resources balances in Eq. (3) account for generation or consumption of resources (P_{jhs}), storage charging (CH_{ajhs}) and discharging (DC_{ajhs}). Additionally, only for electricity, interconnections (PIM_{ihs}), renewable curtailment (LC_{hs}) and penalisation of unmet demand (LS_{hs}) is considered.

$$\sum_{j \in PR_{aj}} P_{jhs} \cdot (1 - PL_j) + \sum_{j \in ST_{aj}} DC_{ajhs} + \sum_{i \in I} PIM_{ihs} \cdot (1 - L_i^{int})\Bigg|_{a=\{elec\}}$$
$$= D_{hs}|_{a=\{elec\}} + Q_{hs}^{H2}|_{a=\{H2\}} + \sum_{j \in ST_{aj}} CH_{ajhs} + \sum_{j \in CON_{aj}} \frac{P_{jhs}}{\eta_j^c} + (LC_{hs} - LS_{hs})|_{a=\{el.\}} \tag{3}$$
$$\forall a \in A, h \in H, s \in S$$

Previous operational decisions are scenario-dependent as uncertainty is revealed via the availability profiles of renewable sources (AV_{jhs}), particularly for on/offshore wind:

$$P_{jhs} = AV_{jhs} \cdot Cap_j \quad \forall j \in J^{res}, h \in H, s \in S \tag{4}$$

Towards the adequacy of the system, the de-rated capacity (by factors DF_j) must suffice the peak demand (D^{peak}, equal to maximum value of D_{hs}) increased by a reserve margin factor (assuming $RM = 7\%$) as shown in Eq. (5) (National Grid ESO, 2023a):

$$\sum_{j \in (ST_{elec,j} \cup PR_{elec,j})} DF_j \cdot Cap_{gj} \geq D^{peak} \cdot (1 + RM) \tag{5}$$

In the proposed model, constraints regarding capacity build rates, land availability for renewables, technologies' operation, fuel consumption and storage operation are further included. Finally, an ultimate carbon emission goal towards Net Zero must be met. Ultimately, the total system cost (TSC) includes capital costs ($CAPEX$), O&M costs and the expected value regarding the scenario-dependent operational costs ($OPEX_s$):

$$\text{minimise} \quad TSC = CAPEX + O\&M + \sum_{s \in S} prob_s \cdot OPEX_s \tag{6}$$

3. Case study: Power and heat decarbonisation in the UK under uncertainty

3.1. Preliminaries

Proposed TSSP is tested for GB's power system planning in 2040. Infrastructure as by 2020 (DUKES, 2023) and data on climate year 2015 are used as input. While electricity demand is derived from historical data by National Grid ESO, heat demand profiles are obtained from the UK gas distribution companies. Both demand profiles are projected to the target year 2040 based on predicted demand values of Future Energy Scenarios (FES) by National Grid ESO (2023b). Renewables availability profiles by Renewables.Ninja platform and interconnection prices data by ENTSO-E are calibrated to the real historical data of climate year 2015 (Staffel & Pfenninger, 2016, ENTSO-E, 2023). Finally, carbon budget goals for year 2040 are set cumulatively in line with the UK's Sixth Carbon Budget report (CCC, 2020). Techno-economic parameters predictions for technologies in 2040 can be retrieved from recent governmental reports (BEIS, 2023).

3.2. Scenario Generation for uncertainty quantification

In this work, uncertainty is considered for the total availability of the renewable sources in the target year of 2040. Renewable sources hourly availability data for GB from 1980 to 2019 are obtained by Renewables.Ninja platform and annual load factors are estimated. Wind load factors display variability while solar are more stable and thus neglected from the uncertain set. Scenarios of annual wind load factors are generated using the methodology by Bounitsis et al. (2022). As data are scarce, synthetic data are simulated exploiting the statistics and copula sampling (density plot depicted in Fig. 3). Then, the MILP model for Distribution and Moment Matching Problem (DMP) generates scenarios by selecting from 1,000 copula samples. 20 final

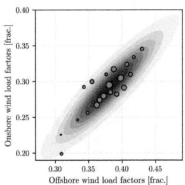

***Figure 3:** 20 generated scenarios for wind load factors.*

scenarios for wind load factors are generated (visualised in Fig. 3) that are forced to match in the statistical sense the original distribution. Finally, original availability profiles are calibrated in order uncertain parameters AV_{jhs} to include the load factors uncertainty.

3.3. Results and discussion

Two instances of the power system are investigated: (i) with conventional technologies only ('PS') and (ii) with integration of H_2 and NH_3 pathways ('PS+NH_3'). The Certainty Equivalent Problem (CEP, deterministic using the mean values of the uncertain parameters) and the proposed TSSP using 20 scenarios are solved for each instance. The here-and-now decisions are obtained and their induced expected results on the problem over the reference set of 1,000 copula-based scenarios are estimated. Optimisation models are solved using solver GUROBI 9.5 in optimisation suite GAMS 45.1. Results from Fig. 4 indicate that the integration of DECs pathways to PS lead to a £1.1b reduction on the total cost. Moreover, the stochastic solutions by TSSP can drive a reduction to expected cost of approximately £800m for both instances compared to the solutions of CEP.

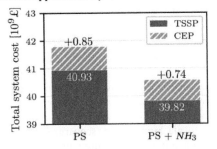
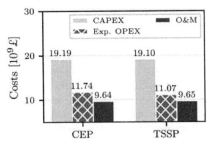

Figure 4: *Expected total system cost.* **Figure 5:** *Cost breakdown for 'PS+NH₃'.*

Then, from Fig. 5 is indicated that for 'PS+NH₃' system this reduction is mainly imposed by the expected value of OPEX, which is dependent on scenarios. Using CEP solutions, OPEX may increase owed to penalisation of unmet demand. This result indicates the system's adequacy issues when using CEP deterministic solutions for planning. In particular, the expected value of Expected Energy Unserved (EEU) is equal to 48 MWh and 43 MWh for 'PS' and 'PS+ NH₃' systems, respectively. However, EEU equal to 0 MWh and so a lower expected OPEX is achieved using the TSSP stochastic solutions.

Regarding capacity mix for electricity generation, TSSP for 'PS+NH₃' system optimally determines high heat electrification of around 84.4% and so higher investments are necessary. Results from Fig. 6 show that TSSP results to increased Nuclear capacity and decreased intermittent Wind Onshore and Solar capacities compared to CEP.

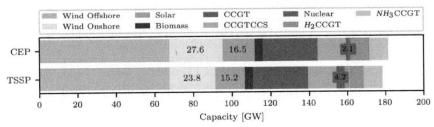

Figure 6: *Capacity mix for electricity generation in 2040 according to CEP and TSSP solutions.*

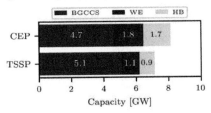

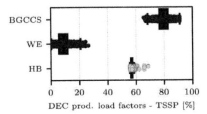

Figure 7: *DEC capacity mix.* **Figure 8:** *DEC production load factors using TSSP solutions over uncertainty.*

Furthermore, DEC capacity mix changes significantly using TSSP. H₂ production merely depends on BGCCS, while WE contributes smaller amounts particularly for scenarios of high wind availability, when electricity is cheaper. Regarding NH₃ production, installed HB capacity is reduced when using TSSP. The same stands for the Liquid NH₃ storage capacity, from 2.43 TWh to 1.99 TWh. However, HB production load factor ranges constantly from 55 to 65% and it slightly increases for high wind availability. Finally, electricity imports up to 50 TWh for scenarios of low wind availability play a vital role for demand satisfaction. Ultimately, the CCC's Net Zero goal for 7.87 $MtCO_2$ is met.

4. Conclusions

The proposed TSSP approach integrating scenario generation method offers safer and cost-efficient optimal power system planning revealing the unsuitability of deterministic approaches to serve system's adequacy over extreme scenarios of wind uncertainty. Moreover, TSSP seems to avoid the overestimation of needs for renewable technologies capacity or energy storage and further indicate the importance of conventional technologies and interconnections for system's security. Future work within our group aims to account for more sources of uncertainty via high fidelity scenario generation towards the solution of stochastic power system planning and scheduling problems.

Acknowledgements: Financial support from the EPSRC (under projects EP/T022930/1 & EP/V051008/1) is gratefully acknowledged.

References

BEIS, 2023. Electricity generation costs, Department of Business, Energy & Industrial Strategy.

G.L. Bounitsis, L.G. Papageorgiou, V.M. Charitopoulos, 2022. Data-driven scenario generation for two-stage stochastic programming. Chem. Eng. Res. Des. 187, 206–224.

G.L. Bounitsis, V.M. Charitopoulos, 2023. Optimal capacity planning integrating ammonia storage for power and heat decarbonisation. Comput. Aided Chem. Eng. 52, 3049–3054.

CCC, 2020. The Sixth Carbon Budget. The UK's path to Net Zero, Climate Change Committee.

V.M. Charitopoulos, M. Fajardy, C.K. Chyong, D.M. Reiner, 2023. The impact of 100% electrification of domestic heat in Great Britain. iScience 26, 108239.

A.S. Dagoumas, N.E. Koltsaklis, 2019. Review of models for integrating renewable energy in the generation expansion planning. Appl. Energy 242, 1573–1587.

DUKES, 2023. Digest of UK Energy Statistics (DUKES) 2023 – National Statistics.

ENTSO-E, 2023. European Network of Transmission System Operators for Electricity.

C. Ganzer, Y.W. Pratama, N. Mac Dowell, 2022. The role and value of inter-seasonal grid-scale energy storage in net zero electricity systems. Int. J. Greenh. Gas Control 120, 103740.

G. He, D.S. Mallapragada, A. Bose, C.F. Heuberger-Austin, E. Gençer, 2021. Sector coupling via hydrogen to lower the cost of energy system decarbonization. Energy Environ. Sci. 14, 4635–4646.

A. García-Cerezo, R. García-Bertrand, L. Baringo, 2022. Priority Chronological Time-Period Clustering for Generation and Transmission Expansion Planning Problems with Long-Term Dynamics. IEEE Trans. Power Syst. 37, 4325–4339.

J. Li, J., Zhou, B. Chen, 2020. Review of wind power scenario generation methods for optimal operation of renewable energy systems. Appl. Energy 280, 115992.

National Grid ESO, 2023a. Electricity Market Reform. Capacity Market.

National Grid ESO, 2023b. Historical data & Future Energy Scenarios.

M.A. Pellow, C.J.M. Emmott, C.J. Barnhart, S.M. Benson, 2015. Hydrogen or batteries for grid storage? A net energy analysis. Energy Environ. Sci. 8, 1938–1952.

S. Pineda, J.M. Morales, 2018. Chronological time-period clustering for optimal capacity expansion planning with storage. IEEE Trans. Power Syst. 33, 7162–7170.

L.A. Roald, D. Pozo, A. Papavasiliou, D.K. Molzahn, J. Kazempour, A. Conejo, 2023. Power systems optimization under uncertainty: A review of methods and applications. Electr. Power Syst. Res. 214.

I. Staffell, S. Pfenninger, 2016. Using bias-corrected reanalysis to simulate current and future wind power output. Energy 114, 1224–1239.

S. Wu, N. Salmon, M.M.J. Li, R. Bañares-Alcántara, S.C.E. Tsang, 2022. Energy Decarbonization via Green H2 or NH3? ACS Energy Lett. 7, 1021–1033.

Flavio Manenti, Gintaras V. Reklaitis (Eds.), Proceedings of the 34th European Symposium on Computer Aided Process Engineering / 15th International Symposium on Process Systems Engineering (ESCAPE34/PSE24), June 2-6, 2024, Florence, Italy

Prospective lifecycle design through process modeling of energy recovery from waste plastics

Shoma Fujii,[a,c] Yuichiro Kanematsu,[b] Yasunori Kikuchi[a,b,c]

[a]Institute for Future Initiatives, The University of Tokyo, 7-3-1 Hongo, Bunkyo-ku, Tokyo, 113-8654, Japan
[b]Presidential Endowed Chair for "Platinum Society", The University of Tokyo, 7-3-1 Hongo, Bunkyo-ku, Tokyo, 113-8656, Japan
[c]Department of Chemical System Engineering, The University of Tokyo, 7-3-1 Hongo, Bunkyo-ku, Tokyo, 113-8656, Japan
shoma.fujii@ifi.u-tokyo.ac.jp

Abstract

A novel energy recovery process for waste plastics has been proposed that combines measures to increase operating rates by thermal spraying on the surface of boiler tubes at waste incineration plants to reduce ash adhesion and deteriorated heat transfer coefficient, and to recover waste heat to generate cold heat. A prospective lifecycle assessment is needed to propose the optimal combination of technologies and provide feedback for technology development. A computer-aided process flow was used to evaluate the size and operating load of the equipment required for the process, and the environmental load of manufacturing and operation was evaluated. The results of the sensitivity analysis show that the thermal spray treatment has a significant effect on annual power generation amount. As for the generation of cold heat, it was found that the waste heat from waste plastics can be supplied as cold heat at off-site locations with reduced environmental impact by improving the performance of the ice maker, absorption chiller, and mobile thermal energy storage system.

Keywords: Circular economy, Waste incineration, Waste heat recovery

1. Introduction

Plastics recycling should be implemented in a cascade of advanced sorting, material recycling, chemical recycling, and energy recovery, and its optimization is important. From the perspective of resource circulation, energy recovery should be avoided as much as possible, but this may result in inefficient energy recovery as plastics with high heating value are reduced from existing waste incineration plants. Therefore, this study focused on a novel energy recovery process (NEDO, 2022) that combines 1) prevention of boiler tube fouling (Naganuma et al.,2022) and 2) waste heat recovery with cold heat generation (Kimura et al., 2022) to maintain energy recovery rates. For the process of waste heat recovery, steam is generated from the exhaust gas and used as a heat source for an absorption chiller, and ice slurry is generated in conjunction with an ice maker.

The purpose of this study is to simulate a process that can recover unused energy, and to conduct a lifecycle assessment (LCA) to identify hot spots and provide feedback for further technology development. In order to clarify the effectiveness of fouling prevention of boiler tubes and waste heat recovery in a computer aided process model simulating the material and energy balance of a waste incineration plant developed in a previous study

(Fujii et al., 2023), a sensitivity analysis was conducted using heat transfer coefficient in the boiler, performance of absorption chiller, ice maker and mobile thermal energy storage system.

2. Materials and Method

2.1. Process modeling

Figure 1 shows the combined process of waste incineration and energy recovery. To improve the efficiency of energy recovery from waste incineration plants, two measures are being considered: one is a high-temperature measure to prevent fouling by thermal spray treatment of the surface of boiler tubes to reduce ash adhesion and to improve power generation and operating rates (Naganuma *et al.*, 2022), and the other is a low-temperature measure to recover waste heat and generate cold heat by combining a two-stage absorption chiller and an ice maker (Kimura *et al.*, 2022). Two types of waste heat recovery are considered: on-site cold heat recovery and off-site cold heat recovery via mobile thermal energy storage systems using adsorbent.

A process flow model has already been developed (Fujii et al., 2023) to simulate the material and energy balance of a waste incineration plant with a 200 t/year class waste input as shown in Figure 1. As a base case, the heat transfer coefficient of the waste boiler was assumed to deteriorate 50% linearly after 8 months of operation. Since the UA value (Overall heat transfer coefficient) of the boiler changes with heat transfer degradation, the UA value after renewal was set as the target value, and the steam flow rate was adjusted until the calculated UA value reaches the target UA value. The calculations were performed for each month, and the total value was used as the annual result. By thermal spray treatment of the boiler tubes surface, the operation period is assumed to be extended by 1 month.

2.2. Setting for lifecycle assessment

The objective of the LCA in this study was to verify whether the novel energy recovery process can replace the conventional power generation recovery process at waste incineration plants with less environmental impact, and to provide feedback for further technology development for each component by conducting sensitivity analysis of system variation parameters. Manufacturing and operating environmental loads of equipment required for the novel process were considered as lifecycle environmental impacts as shown in Figure 2. The waste incineration plant was assumed to operate 24 hours per day, 300 days per year. The functional unit was defined as the operation of a waste incineration plant with a 200 t/year of municipal solid waste applying around 2,300 kW power generation. Material and energy balance results of waste incineration plant from the developed process flow model (Fujii et al., 2023) were used to identify foreground data such as heat exchanger size and required auxiliary power of various equipment, and background data were obtained from an existing database (AIST, 2019, ecoinvent v3.8, 2021). LCA using LIME2 (Itsubo and Inaba, 2012) considered climate change as an intermediate impact item. For the high-temperature side of the process, heat transfer area was calculated from the UA value of the boiler calculated in the developed process flow model, assuming 35 W/(m²·K) of heat transfer coefficient, and the required amount was calculated assuming the thermal spraying is done at a density of 8.0 kg/m², and the manufacturing environmental load was calculated assuming the thermal spraying is done every 2 years. For the waste heat recovery process, a heat exchanger for waste heat recovery, a two-stage absorption chiller, an ice maker, a heat charging and discharging units for off-site mobile thermal energy storage system and adsorbent as heat storage material are required. For the heat exchanger for waste heat recovery, UA value was calculated in the process flow model, and the heat transfer area was calculated assuming 35 W/(m²·K) of heat transfer coefficient, and the manufacturing environmental load was calculated. For the absorption chiller, background data was used (ecoinvent v3.8, 2021). For the ice maker, a combination of heat exchangers, pumps, and tanks was assumed, and the capacity and heat transfer area of each were calculated from the process flow model, and the manufacturing environmental load was calculated. Reported inventory data were used for the heat charging and discharging devices (Fujii et al., 2022). The adsorbent was assumed to be zeolite 4A and manufacturing environmental load was calculated from the existing database (AIST, 2019). Each device was assumed to have a durability of 15 years. The operating load was calculated assuming the COP (Coefficient of performance) of the absorption chiller to be 0.23 (Kimura et al., 2022) and the auxiliary power of the ice maker to be 20%. For the mobile thermal energy storage system, the heat storage density was calculated by equilibrium adsorption water uptake before (4%) and after adsorption (23%) calculated using adsorption isotherms (Miyahara et al., 2020) and the amount of air introduced into the heat charging and discharging devices was calculated, and the blower power was calculated. The number of transports was calculated assuming a truck capacity of 10 t, and fuel consumption was calculated.

For the sensitivity analysis, the heat transfer coefficient of the boiler for the high temperature side, and the COP of the absorption chiller, the auxiliary power of the ice maker, and the heat storage density for the low temperature side were targeted.

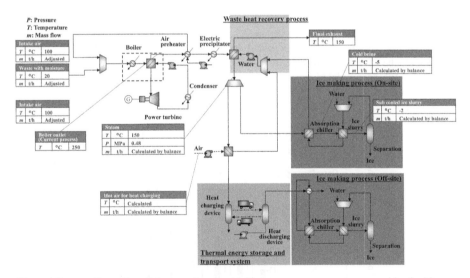

Figure 1 Process flow of waste incineration plant with energy recovery process combined with high-temp. measure and low-temp. measure

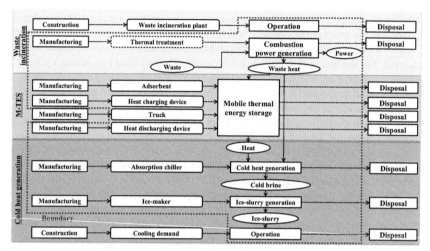

Figure 2 Lifecycle boundary of energy recovery process

3. Result and discussion

The results of the heat transfer sensitivity analysis of monthly and accumulated power generation are shown in Figure 3. Cases in which the heat transfer deterioration can be suppressed by 100% (100% case in Figure 3) and 50% (50% case in Figure 3) due to the thermal spraying treatment after 9 months compared to the heat transfer coefficient in the 8th month of the base case were estimated.

When the operation period is extended by one month due to the thermal spraying treatment, the monthly power generation decreases with the decrease in hourly waste input, but the accumulated power generation increases over the base case due to the extended operation hours.

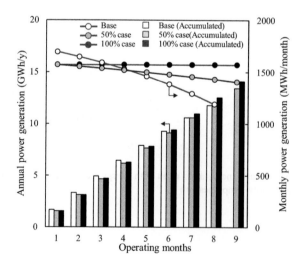

Figure 3 Annual and monthly power generation of base case, case of 50% and 100% heat transfer deterioration prevention (50% case/100% case)

Figure 4 shows the breakdown of lifecycle GHG (Greenhouse gas) emissions both on- and off-site cases, including cold heat generation, when heat transfer degradation is completely suppressed by thermal spray treatment. The deduction for electricity generation is large, indicating that the suppression of heat transfer deterioration is highly effective.

Figure 5 shows the results of the sensitivity analysis of lifecycle GHG emissions on the cold side. In both cases, absorption chillers, ice makers, and heat storage density all had almost similar sensitivity, indicating that improving the performance of either has a significant impact on lifecycle GHGs. Since off-site transportation is not expected to significantly reduce GHGs due to the large airflow and blower power requirements of the heat charging and discharging device and the large environmental impact of adsorbent manufacturing, performance improvement is mandatory.

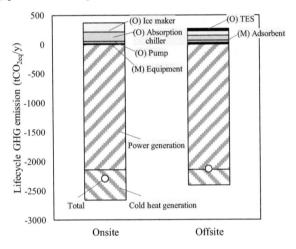

Figure 4 Breakdown of lifecycle GHG emissions both on- and off-site cold energy recovery ((M) and (O) mean Manufacturing and Operating, respectively)

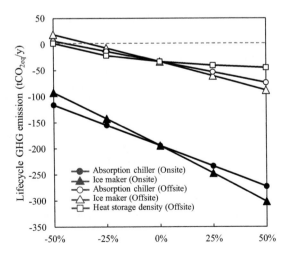

Figure 5 Results of sensitivity analysis for waste heat recovery side

4. Conclusions

The lifecycle assessment was conducted using a process flow that combines the power generation and operation rate improvement by thermal spraying with waste heat recovery and cold heat generation, which is being considered as the novel energy recovery process for the incineration of waste plastics. If the thermal spraying process can prevent the deterioration of heat transfer, it can be expected to improve annual power generation and reduce GHG emissions. It was found that cold heat generation is highly effective onsite, but when implemented offsite, the efficiency of the component equipment needs to be improved. In particular, since small-scale incineration plants and cold heat demand are often separated by distance, the energy recovery of waste plastics through improved performance of ice makers, absorption chillers, and mobile thermal energy storage systems is expected to be highly effective.

Acknowledgement

This work was supported by New Energy and Industrial Technology Development Organization (NEDO, Grant number JPNP20012), JSPS KAKENHI Grant-in-Aid for Early-Career Scientists (Grant Number JP22K18061), JST COI-NEXT (Grant Number JPMJPF2003), JST PRESTO (Grant Number JPMJPR2278) and the Environment Research and Technology Development Fund (Grant Number JPMEERF20213R01) of the Environmental Restoration and Conservation Agency of Japan. The activities of the Presidential Endowed Chair for "Platinum Society" at the University of Tokyo are supported by Mitsui Fudosan Corporation, Sekisui House, Ltd., East Japan Railway Company, and Toyota Tsusho Corporation.

References

AIST National Institute of Advanced Industrial Science, Technology, 2019, LCI database IDEA version 2.3.

ecoinvent v3.8, 2021. https://www.ecoinvent.org/

S. Fujii, T. Nakagaki, Y. Kanematsu, Y. Kikuchi, 2022, Prospective life cycle assessment for designing mobile thermal energy storage system utilizing zeolite, Journal of Cleaner Production, 365, 132592

S. Fujii, Y. Kanematsu and Y. Kikuchi, 2023, Inventory data generation for prospective lifecycle design through process modeling of energy recovery from waste plastics, Computer Aided Chemical Engineering, 52, 3037-3042

N. Itsubo, A. Inaba, 2012, LIME2 Life-cycle Impact assessment Method based on Endpoint modeling. Life Cycle Assessment Society of Japan, Tokyo.

T. Kimura, H. Hatano, H. Noda, T. Inada, M. Tanino, H. Naganuma, M. Hotta, I. Naruse, 2022, High-efficient energy recovery of waste plastics Part 2- Effective utilization of low temperature waste heat (in Japanese), Kagaku-sochi, 64, 1, 48-54

H. Miyahara, M. Suzuki, S. Matsuda, K. Morimoto, K. Mampuku, Y. Kawakami, H. Nawa, K. Yamauchi, K. Matsunaga, M. Tanino, 2020, Development of Open-type Adsorption Thermal Storage Heat Pump System Applying HAS-Clay Part 2 Hydration Heat Caused by Water Vapor Adsorption on Low-Temperature Regenerative Heat Storage Material (in Japanese), Transactions of the Society of Heating, Air-conditioning and Sanitary Engineers of Japan, 285, 1-8

H. Naganuma, I. Naruse, M. Hotta, H. Hatano, H. Noda, T. Inada, M. Tanino, 2022, High-efficient energy recovery of waste plastics Part 1- Effective utilization of high temperature waste heat (in Japanese), Kagaku-sochi, 64, 1, 43-47

NEDO New Energy and Indsutrial Technology Development Organization, 2022, Innovative Plastic Resource Circulation Process Technology Development, https://www.nedo.go.jp/english/activities/activities_ZZJP_100179.html (Access Sep-27, 2022)

Flavio Manenti, Gintaras V. Reklaitis (Eds.), Proceedings of the 34th European Symposium on Computer Aided Process Engineering / 15th International Symposium on Process Systems Engineering (ESCAPE34/PSE24), June 2-6, 2024, Florence, Italy

Techno-Economic and Environmental Sustainability Assessment of Rice Straw-Based Bioenergy with Carbon Capture and Utilization

Ryan Macalino,[a]* Jhud Mikhail Aberilla[a]

[a]*University of the Philippines Diliman, Quezon City 1101, Philippines*
rtmacalino@up.edu.ph

Abstract

Climate-susceptible nations are severely impacted by frequent storms, effects of sea level rise, and seasons with temperatures that already limit worker output. Though agriculture is a vulnerable industry, it can potentially reduce energy-related carbon dioxide emissions through bioenergy production. Bioenergy with carbon capture and utilization (BECCU) could be an emissions-neutral or -negative and a market-driven approach that captures CO_2 and promotes sustainable agricultural waste management. This study investigates rice straw-based BECCU as an agricultural waste management. Using Aspen Plus®, bioenergy conversion of rice straw through power generation and ethanol production followed by methanol or urea production as CO_2 utilization are simulated. Results from the process simulations show that 574 kW of power and 131 kg of ethanol are produced per ton of rice straw. Methanol and urea production per ton of rice straw are 717.57 kg and 1,601.84 kg in the power generation route, and 565.23 kg and 1,265.43 kg in the ethanol route, respectively. Defining the functional unit as managing rice straw as an agricultural waste, producing electricity, steam, ethanol, methanol, and urea provides environmental credits as alternative sources of these products. Still, the carbon capture process outweighs the credits resulting in a net impact in global warming and resource depletion mainly due to utility requirements. Carbon capture and utilization, however, show a benefit in land use impacts. The estimated urea production cost per kilogram is USD 0.20-0.21 and methanol is USD 0.59-0.61.

Keywords: Bioenergy with carbon capture and utilization (BECCU), carbon dioxide, agricultural waste, process simulation, life cycle assessment (LCA)

1. Introduction

Rice is a staple food for most Filipino people, with a production of 19.32 million metric tons, which means that rice farming contributes to 62% of agricultural GHG emissions in the Philippines (Climate Transparency, 2020; Philippine Statistics Authority, 2021). Rice straw is an abundant byproduct of rice farming, accounting for 50-60% of the paddy (Logeswaran et al., 2020). However, rice straw utilization is limited due to labor intensity, lack of handling equipment, and prolonged handling methods (Eleria & Vargas, 2021). Most utilization techniques are in the early stages and may be chemical, energy, or labor-intensive. As a result of the limited utilization of rice straw, farmers prevalently burn 76% of harvested land area in the open field for convenience (Mendoza, 2015).

Rice straw has similar higher heating value (HHV), proximate, and ultimate analyses to other biomass, making thermochemical conversion feasible for the complete energy utilization of rice straw, including lignin (Maguyon-Detras et al., 2020). Additionally, renewable energy, its direct use, and renewable energy electrification have the potential to cut energy-related CO_2 emissions by up to 75% and agriculture, after forestry, has the second highest share of mitigation potential in agriculture, forestry, and other land use (AFOLU) (IRENA, 2019; Shukla et al., 2022). However, the conversion of rice straw to energy, particularly thermochemical conversion, produces a significant amount of CO_2. As a form of renewable energy, bioenergy with carbon capture and utilization (BECCU) is emissions-neutral or --negative and a market-driven approach to produce energy without increasing land use or decreasing food sources (Babin et al., 2021; Global CO_2 Initiative, 2016). Rice straw-based BECCU could cut energy-related CO_2 emissions as well as agricultural GHG emissions from rice agriculture, deliver emissions-neutral or -negative products, promote sustainable agricultural waste management, and valorize second-generation biomass and captured CO_2.

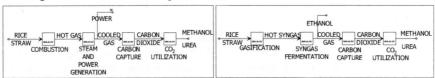

Figure 1: Hierarchy block flow diagram of BECCU systems

This study aims to quantify the environmental impacts of rice straw BECCU in the Philippines, to determine the total capital investment, operating cost, and the cost per liter of ethanol and kilogram of urea, and to compare the environmental impacts and economic performance of BECCU systems. In this study, a simulation of electricity generation and ethanol production coupled with carbon capture is performed using Aspen Plus®, whose processes are separated into hierarchy blocks as shown in Figure 1. Because of potential opportunities to limit carbon emissions, technological advancement, economic potential, and large predicted market sizes by 2030 (Global CO_2 Initiative, 2016), the use of CO_2 in methanol, and urea production are considered in this study. Process simulation results are used in the environmental and techno-economic assessment of rice straw-based BECCU using life cycle assessment (LCA) and cost analysis.

2. Methods

2.1. Goal and Scope

This study evaluates the environmental and economic impacts of producing power and ethanol from rice straw in the BECCU scheme through combustion and syngas fermentation. The functional unit is the processing of 1 ton of rice straw from fields. The system boundaries are rice straw collection, biomass-to-energy conversion, and carbon capture and utilization. Thermochemical conversions of rice straw are highly considered because of cheaper capital cost, lower operational cost, complete utilization of rice straw, and elimination of costly and energy-intensive pretreatment (Maguyon-Detras et al., 2020). Thus, in this study, there are four system boundaries considered, namely, 1) urea from combustion, 2) urea from gasification, 3) methanol from combustion, and 4) methanol from gasification.

2.2. Life Cycle Inventory

The foreground data are drawn from different literature sources, and inputs, outputs, and emissions from the process simulation in Aspen Plus®, while the background data are drawn from the Ecoinvent database (Ecoinvent Association, 2020).

Techno-Economic and Environmental Sustainability Assessment of
Rice Straw-Based Bioenergy with Carbon Capture and Utilization
2205

2.2.1. Process Simulation

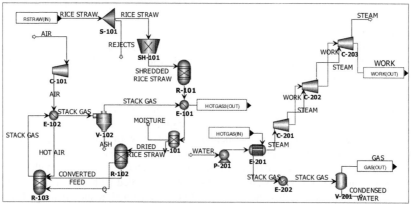

Figure 2: Process simulation of power generation from rice straw combustion

The rice straw is shredded and dried to remove the moisture. The dryer is simulated with RYield, which is linked with a calculator block and yields 25% of the biomass component to water, HeatX, and Sep blocks. The furnace is modeled using RYield, which is coupled with a calculator block converting the nonconventional properties of biomass into its ultimate and proximate analysis by assuming the devolatilization products, and RGibbs block under Gibbs free energy minimization and chemical equilibrium assumptions (Almena et al., 2022). The combustion product passes through a cyclone to separate the ash from high-temperature flue gas. The hot flue gas enters a HeatX block coupled with design specs in the power generation hierarchy block. Water is pumped to the heat exchanger producing a superheated steam of 565°C and 164bar. Based on a vapor fraction of 1, the design spec function calculated the water flow rate entering the pump. The steam passes to a series of isentropic high-pressure (HP), medium-pressure (MP), and low-pressure (LP) turbines. The CO_2 in the combustion gas is then captured in the CO_2 capture system hierarchy block.

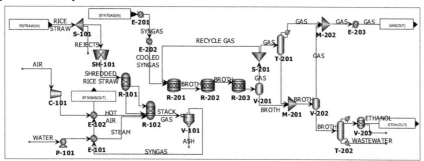

Figure 3: Process simulation of ethanol production through syngas fermentation

Similar to the combustion path, as shown in Figure 3, rice straw in the gasification undergoes physical pretreatment, and nonconventional properties of the biomass were converted to ultimate, proximate, and sulfate analysis. However, the RGibbs block is modeled at restricted equilibrium, specifying a temperature approach for the entire system at 700°C and 335 bar. The air-to-biomass ratio is 1.21 and the steam-to-biomass ratio is 0.57 (Im-Orb et al., 2016). The produced syngas are cooled and sent to the three RStoic reactor blocks in series. The fermentation model operates at atmospheric pressure and

38°C in which 70% and 5% of carbon monoxide and 50% and 2% of hydrogen gas is converted to ethanol and acetic acid, respectively (Safarian et al., 2021). The fermentation product is sent to a Flash2 block to separate the broth and gas mixture. A recycle stream is used to reintroduce some gas mixture to the reactor block such that 88kg/hr of carbon monoxide is exiting to the carbon capture system. The gas mixture from the FSplit block is fed to a stripping column to recover the ethanol broth. The final broth is distilled in a RadFrac block and passes through a molecular sieve to purify the ethanol.

The cooled and compressed gas from power generation and ethanol production enters the carbon capture system. The process simulation of the CO_2 capture system is adapted directly from Aspen Plus® and is modified to maintain the stage pressure of stage 1 at 37°C. The captured CO_2 is fed in the methanol synthesis with hydrogen gas or the urea synthesis with ammonia. The process simulation for the synthesis of methanol is adapted from the study of Kiss et al. (2016) and is modified to achieve Grade AA methanol. The distillation column is modeled using a RadFrac block coupled with design specifications varying the boilup ratio, reflux ratio, and distillate vapor fraction such that the distillate contains 99.85% methanol, the bottom product contains 99.99% water, and the stage temperature in the first stage is 32°C. The process simulation for the urea production is adapted from Aspen Plus® but is modified such that the feed CO_2 is pure. The reaction occurring in the RPlug block is modeled based on the chemical reaction kinetics studied by Chinda et al., 2019.

2.3. Life Cycle Impact Assessment and Techno-Economic Assessment

The LCA modeling is performed using openLCA software v2.0 and the impacts are assessed using the hierarchist perspective of ReCiPe v1.13 (Huijbregts et al., 2017). The environmental impacts considered in this study are agricultural land occupation (ALOP), fossil depletion (FDP), global warming (GWP), and water depletion potential (WDP). The costs of equipment in the techno-economic assessment are evaluated within Aspen Plus® Economics. The economic indicators considered in this study are capital cost, operating cost, and cost per unit product.

3. Results and Discussion

Table 1: Power, ethanol, methanol, and urea production from 50,000kg/h rice straw

Process Option	Main Product	Secondary Product
Methanol from combustion	28,706 kWh power generation	35,878 kg/h methanol
Urea from combustion		80,091 kg/h urea
Methanol from gasification	6,554 kg/h ethanol	28,261 kg/h methanol
Urea from gasification		63,271 kg/h urea

Process simulation results showed a gross 28,706 kilowatts of power or 9,553 liters of ethanol is produced from 50,000 kilograms of rice straw while producing 45,724 or 36,016 liters of methanol and 80,092 or 63,272 kilograms of urea, respectively, as shown in

Table **1**. The steam generation from gasification routes is 8,664 kilowatts higher than combustion routes because the heat from the flue gas of combustion is harnessed to electricity, drying of rice straw, and preheating of air. The CO_2, however, in the combustion route is 10,000 kilograms higher as the carbon in gasification participated in the synthesis of ethanol. The percent conversion of CO and H_2 in the three-series reactor are 98 and 89%.

Techno-Economic and Environmental Sustainability Assessment of
Rice Straw-Based Bioenergy with Carbon Capture and Utilization

2207

The environmental impacts of rice straw BECCU systems are shown in Figure 4. Per ton of rice straw, emissions of 382.4 kg CO_{2e} are avoided from the open field burning based on the carbon content of the rice straw (Jenkins et al., 1998). Net negative GWP of 396.0823 kg CO_{2e}, ALOP of 23.57 m^2a, and FDP of 112.75 kg oil-equivalent is credited from electricity generation, and a GWP of 142.8050 kg CO_{2e}, ALOP of 231.36 m^2a, and FDP of 35.98 kg oil-equivalent is avoided from ethanol production.

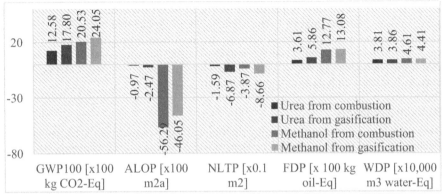

Figure 4: Cradle-to-grave life cycle environmental impacts of rice straw BECCU systems [Multiplied by factors on the x-axis per ton of rice straw.]

Credits from the co-production of electricity, steam, ethanol, methanol, and urea have a negative contribution to global warming potential (19.3-31.48%, 8.63-14.08%, 5.94-8.02%, 15.66-23.30%, and 118.18-211.65%, respectively). However, the production of ammonia, hydrogen, and steam for the carbon capture process outweighs the credits resulting in a net positive life cycle GWP. Agricultural land occupations and natural land transformation potential show a net negative impact in all BECCU systems. The net negative impacts in ALOP are mainly derived from credited co-products. The co-production of electricity, ethanol, methanol, and urea credited net-negative fossil depletion potential, but is outweighed by the process requirements in the carbon capture block. Water depletion potential is mainly caused by the carbon capture system, but production of methanol and urea avoided 6.23-7.91 and 109.46-138.56 m^3 water-equivalent, respectively.

Table 2: Techno-economic indicators of rice straw BECCU

	Capital Cost	Operating Cost
Urea from combustion	USD 230,447,498.54	USD 99,881,206.63
Urea from gasification	USD 152,189,663.13	USD 13,435,071.36
Methanol from combustion	USD 233,944,464.06	USD 142,776,734.74
Methanol from gasification	USD 151,672,565.63	USD 46,824,092.25

The capital and operating expenses of rice straw BECCU systems are shown in Table 2. Fifty percent of the purchased equipment cost in the combustion route is incurred in the combustion of rice straw, while 36% of the equipment cost in the gasification route is from syngas fermentation and ethanol purification. The cost of the raw materials ammonia and hydrogen constitute 75-82% of the operating expense. The production cost per kilowatt-hour of power is USD 0.09, and the cost per kilogram of ethanol is 0.34. The steam generated is used for internal steam consumption. The production cost of per kilogram of urea is USD 0.20-0.21 and methanol is USD 0.59-0.61.

4. Conclusion

This work has evaluated the techno-economic and environmental sustainability of rice straw BECCU systems. The results suggest that generated electricity has greater environmental impact savings in terms of GWP and FDP. The net GWP, FDP, and WDP of urea from combustion have the least impact among the cases because of avoided emission primarily from urea production. However, the economic indicators state otherwise. The capital cost is higher for the combustion route mainly because of the purchased cost of the compressor. The operating expenses incurred mainly in purchasing raw materials such as ammonia in urea production and hydrogen in the production of methanol. The current study can be extended to the incorporation of ammonia and hydrogen synthesis to probe the opportunities for environmental impact and economic savings from the purchase of ammonia and hydrogen.

Acknowledgments

This work is supported and funded by the Engineering Research and Development for Technology (ERDT) of the Philippine Department of Science and Technology (DOST).

References

Almena, A., Thornley, P., Chong, K., & Röder, M, 2022, Carbon dioxide removal potential from decentralised bioenergy with carbon capture and storage (BECCS) and the relevance of operational choices, Biomass and Bioenergy, 159.

Chinda, R. C., Pessoa, F. L. P., Yamamoto, C. I., & Alves, T. L. M., 2019, Process Intensification Applied to Urea Production Process, Universidade Federal Do Rio De Janeiro.

Climate Transparency, 2020, Philippines Climate Transparency Report.

Ecoinvent Association, 2020, Ecoinvent, 3.7.1, https://ecoinvent.org/the-ecoinvent-database/data-releases/ecoinvent-3-7-1/.

Huijbregts, M. A. J., Steinmann, Z. J. N., Stam, G., Verones, F., Vieira, M. D. M., Hollander, A., Zijp, M., & van Zelm, R, 2017, ReCiPe 2016 v1.1: A harmonized life cycle impact assessment method at midpoint and endpoint level, Report I: Characterization.

Im-Orb, K., Simasatitkul, L., & Arpornwichanop, A., 2016, Analysis of synthesis gas production with a flexible H2/CO ratio from rice straw gasification. Fuel, 164, 361–373.

Jenkins, B. M., Baxter, L. L., & Miles, T. R., 1998, Combustion properties of biomass, In Fuel Processing Technology, 54.

Kiss, A. A., Pragt, J. J., Vos, H. J., Bargeman, G., & de Groot, M. T, 2016, Novel efficient process for methanol synthesis by CO2 hydrogenation, Chemical Engineering Journal, 284, 260–269.

Logeswaran, J., Shamsuddin, A. H., Silitonga, A. S., & Mahlia, T. M. I., 2020, Prospect of using rice straw for power generation: a review, In Environmental Science and Pollution Research, 27, 21, 25956–25969, Springer.

Maguyon-Detras, M. C., Migo, M. V. P., Van Hung, N., & Gummert, M, 2020, Thermochemical Conversion of Rice Straw, In Sustainable Rice Straw Management, 43–64, Springer International Publishing.

Philippine Statistics Authority, 2021, Palay Production in the Philippines, 2018-2020.

Safarian, S., Unnthorsson, R., & Richter, C., 2021, Bioethanol production via herbaceous and agricultural biomass gasification integrated with syngas fermentation, Fermentation, 7, 3.

Flavio Manenti, Gintaras V. Reklaitis (Eds.), Proceedings of the 34th European Symposium on Computer Aided Process Engineering / 15th International Symposium on Process Systems Engineering (ESCAPE34/PSE24), June 2-6, 2024, Florence, Italy
© 2024 Elsevier B.V. All rights reserved. http://dx.doi.org/10.1016/B978-0-443-28824-1.50369-0

Surrogate Based Mixed Integer Linear Programming Model for Decarbonization of an Integrated Gas-Oil Separation Network

Abdullah Bahamdan[a], Nilay Shah[a], Antonio del Rio-Chanona[a*]

[a]*Sargent Centre for Process Systems Engineering, South Kensington.*
London, SW7 2AZ, United Kingdom
Corresponding author: a.del-rio-chanona@imperial.ac.uk

Abstract

Energy companies seek to decarbonize their business operations and reduce emissions. However, achieving this goal while maintaining a solid financial performance is challenging. This research focuses on the upstream sector of the oil and gas industry, where a cluster of producing wells supply a network of interconnected gas-oil separation (GOSP) facilities. Existing methods in literature exhibit several key limitations, such as lack of sustainability objectives, utilization of simplified approaches, or adoption of computationally expensive models to optimize network operations. To overcome such challenges, a novel data-driven approach is proposed. It employs artificial neural networks within a multi-objective mixed integer linear programming (MILP) framework to optimize feed allocation and equipment utilization while reducing emissions across the network. Moreover, the surrogate models are trained using a high-fidelity model to capture possible feed uncertainties. The proposed framework is tested using real-world industrial production scenarios. The solution demonstrated acceptable capabilities in reducing greenhouse gas emissions while maximizing profitability.

Keywords: upstream processing, machine learning, multi-objective optimization, enterprise-wide optimization, supply chain.

1. Introduction

Since the Paris Agreement came into effect, the pressure on the energy industry to achieve sustainability objectives has escalated. This is mainly attributed to the conflict between minimizing emissions and maximizing the profitability required to finance capital-intensive energy transition projects. Accordingly, this work is proposed to support practitioners in optimizing the trade-off between sustainability and profitability metrics.

This project focuses on the upstream and midstream sectors of the oil and gas industry. In particular, the interface between the production wells and gas-oil separation facilities (GOSP). In a conventional oil and gas reservoir that is spread across a vast geographical space, production wells are clustered into groups, while each group of wells supplies wet crude oil to a network of GOSPs. The GOSPs are interconnected via swing pipelines, typically used during maintenance shutdowns and operational disturbances to divert feed flow from one facility to another.

Figure 1 illustrates a block flow diagram of a typical GOSP configuration. The feed, which consists of crude oil, oily water, and natural gas, is fed into the high-pressure production trap (HPPT) and low-pressure production trap (LPPT) in series to separate the three phases. The gas streams are mixed, compressed in the high and low-pressure compressors, and transferred to downstream facilities for further processing. Meanwhile, the crude oil stream is dehydrated, desalted, and transferred to either refining for further processing or terminals for export. The oily water stream is collected throughout the system and processed in the water-oil separation section (WOSEP) to remove hydrocarbon traces before being injected into the reservoir to maintain its pressure profile.

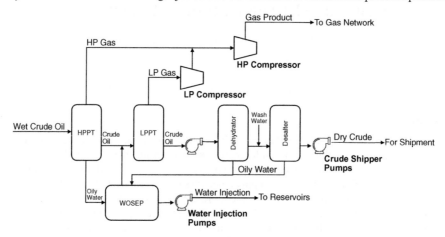

Figure 1: Block flow diagram of a typical GOSP

The literature covers numerous contributions from academics and practitioners in applying legacy chemical engineering tools to improve the efficiency and performance of processing industries. This includes optimizing unit process parameters, retrofitting equipment, and upgrading technologies. In recent years, enterprise-wide optimization (EWO) has emerged as an exciting research field within process systems engineering (PSE). It seeks to achieve higher combined rewards by expanding the envelope and solving complex optimization problems considering several supply chain functions (Grossmann, 2012). Consequently, researchers have explored improving the overall performance of a network of GOSPs by utilizing swing pipelines during normal operations to optimally allocate loads between the facilities. The first effort was instigated by developing a mixed-integer linear programming (MILP) model to minimize the network's overall operating expenditure (OPEX) (Liu et al., 2016). Each facility was modeled using a state-task network (STN) approach, whereas simplified linear equations were used to model the nonlinear equipment behaviour. However, this work only considers a profit-driven objective and the simplified linear equations cannot fully capture process nonlinearity. Leveraged by this work, researchers explored the possibility of utilizing a mixed-integer nonlinear programming (MINLP) model to minimize OPEX (Al-Ghazal et al., 2020). In contrast, physics-based simulations were used to model each facility and achieve higher savings. However, this approach presents drawbacks, primarily due to utilizing a profit-driven objective and hindering scalability due to expensive computational costs.

This work aspires to overcome the drawbacks by proposing a generalizable and robust framework that couples machine learning algorithms in a multi-objective MILP model to maximize profitability while minimizing emissions. The paper is structured as follows: in section 2, the proposed methodology is thoroughly explained; in section 3, the case study is introduced; in section 4, the results are discussed; in section 5, the work is concluded with a research outlook.

2. Methodology

This work aims to maximize profitability and minimize emissions by solving a multi-objective optimization problem. According to domain knowledge expertise, the profitability objective is achieved by minimizing OPEX, resulting mainly from power consumption. Meanwhile, the emissions objective is realized by minimizing emissions from energy consumption tasks and minimizing/eliminating process venting and flaring events. The latter occurs when the gas feed flow rate exceeds the facility's maximum capacity.

Given the goal of this work, the proposed methodology consists of four main phases: the development of high-fidelity models, the training and selection of surrogate models, the formulation of the optimization problem, and solving and validating the results. Figure 2 demonstrates and summarizes the four phases in a visual format.

The first phase of the methodology concerns the development of high-fidelity models to capture the complexity of an operating facility. Equipment items highly correlated with the objective function are rigorously modeled, while others are simplified for computational ease. Process simulation software is then used to generate an appropriately large dataset for a variety of operating scenarios to ensure information-rich data. In the second phase, the dataset is used to train and test several machine learning algorithms. A suitable surrogate model is selected following several iterations of training/testing and hyperparameters tuning according to predefined performance metrics (van de Berg et al., 2022). In the third phase, the case study is formulated as a multi-objective optimization problem consisting of an objective function, constraints, and binary and continuous variables. In the fourth phase, the problem is solved using a MILP approach, which requires linearization techniques for problem reformulation (Grossmann, 2021). The results are then generated and validated.

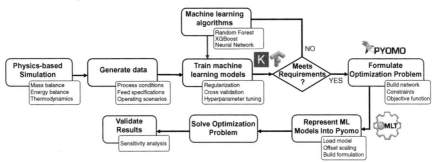

Figure 2: Flowchart of the proposed methodology

3. Case Study

An abstract network consisting of three interconnected facilities (A, B, C) is employed to demonstrate the performance of the proposed methodology. The network specifications are based on a real-world example presented in (Liu et al., 2016). The facilities are assumed to have identical layout configurations and component capacities according to the following: crude oil is 330 "kbdoe", water is 160 "kbdoe", gas is 30 "kbdoe". Moreover, they are assumed to operate at a steady state, with optimal operating conditions.

Starting with the high-fidelity model, Aspen HYSYS was used to simulate the flowsheet. According to domain knowledge expertise, approximately 80 % of the facility's OPEX is attributed to the power consumed by rotating equipment. This includes the five major types: high and low-pressure compressors, dry crude shipper pumps, and sour water injection pumps. Major equipment has been rigorously modeled using historical data and power consumption curves from a real-world facility to capture the nonlinearity. The case study feature in Aspen HYSYS was used to generate a rich dataset of 18,479 data points. The dataset covers 25 feed quality scenarios by varying the gas-to-oil ratio and water cut percentages. This is essential to ensure the robustness of the solution, as data-driven models, or surrogate models in this case, perform optimally when interpolating. To overcome the imbalanced dataset resulting from the gas flow rate values being magnitudes higher than the liquid component flow rates, the dataset values were rescaled to meet the characteristics of the standard normal distribution. This will significantly enhance the efficiency and accuracy of the machine learning-based surrogate models. This standardization, given in Eq. (1), uses the z-score normalization method and was applied to the dataset:

$$x' = \frac{x - \mu}{\sigma} \tag{1}$$

Where x' is the normalized value, μ is the mean, and σ is the standard deviation. In selecting the surrogate model type, three machine-learning algorithms have been investigated. The first is the Artificial Neural Network (ANN) with a rectified linear unit (ReLU) activation function to ease computational cost-effectively and support complex pattern recognition. The second algorithm is RandomForest. Which is based on the bagging method, a statistical technique used in machine learning to reduce variance and improve prediction accuracy by combining multiple models trained on different subsets of the available data. The third algorithm is based on a boosting method called XGBoost. It uses a numerical technique to minimize the model's loss function by adding weak learners using gradient descent. Each of the three potential surrogate models was trained and tested according to a five-fold cross-validation technique. In this work, TensorFlow/Keras was used to develop the surrogate models for software compatibility purposes. After that, the three models were compared and evaluated according to the following four metrics: mean absolute error (MAE), mean squared error (MSE), root mean squared error (RMSE), and the coefficient of determination (R^2). Given the results, the artificial neural network was selected as the surrogate model to represent GOSPs in the optimization problem.

The optimization problem is formulated using an open-source Python-based package, Pyomo (Bynum et al., 2021). Pyomo aligns with the notation used in mathematical optimization and adopts an object-oriented approach for modeling elements such as parameters, decision variables, objectives, and constraints. To overcome the complexity of translating the trained machine learning-based surrogate models into Pyomo's environment, we used a Python-based package called OMLT: Optimization & Machine Learning Toolkit (Ceccon et al., 2022). It provides the flexibility of formulating the activation functions differently based on the application needed.

The optimization problem features two sets of binary decision variables: X_{sd} denotes the selection of swing pipeline originating from source s and terminating in destination d; the second binary variable is X_f, which denotes the selection of facility f in the network. Additionally, the optimization problem includes a set of continuous decision variables

$V_{c,sd}$ representing the flow rate of component c in swing pipeline sd. The multi-objective function of the optimization problem is formulated as given below in Eq. (2):

$$\min \{OPEX, Emm\}$$

$$OPEX = \sum_f \sum_{e \in E^R} \sum_{i \in I_{fi}} Pc_{fei} \tag{2}$$

$$Emm = (\sum V_f \cdot X_f) + (\sum_f \sum_{e \in E^R} \sum_{i \in I_{fi}} Pm_{fij})$$

Where $OPEX$ is the total operating expenditure cost of the entire network and calculated by adding the power consumption value of each equipment ei in facility f. Emm is the total emissions generated from the whole network and calculated by adding the emissions produced by power generation activities from equipment ei in facility f with the surplus gas feed flow rate in facility f. The optimization problem is subject to several constraints; however, this paper will highlight the major ones. Eq. (3) demonstrates the first set of constraints related to the design capacities of the facilities and swing pipelines:

$$\min\{DC_{fc}\} \; X_f \leq FV_{fc} \leq \max\{DC_{fc}\} \; X_f \quad \forall f \in F, c \in C \tag{3}$$

$$\min\{SC_{c,sd}\} \; X_{sd} \leq V_{c,sd} \leq \max\{SC_{c,sd}\} \; X_{sd} \quad \forall s, d \in G_{sd}$$

Where DC_{fc} is the design capacity of facility f, and $SC_{c,sd}$ is the design capacity of swing pipeline sd. Eq. (4) defines a constraint that ensures the selection of a single flow direction in bi-directional swing pipelines. Furthermore, Eq. (5) describes the mass balance constraint, which calculates the material balances across each facility in the network.

$$X_{sd} + X_{ds} \leq 1 \quad \forall s \in G_s, \; d \in G_d \tag{4}$$

$$FV_{fc} = IV_{fc} + (X_{sd} V_{c,sd}) - (X_{sd} V_{c,sd}) \tag{5}$$

Meanwhile, the flow composition ratios of each component in the swing pipelines were reformulated from a division of continuous variables to a linear expression as given in Eqs. (6):

$$0.3 = \frac{V_{w,sd}}{V_{w,sd} + V_{o,sd}} \quad \text{to} \quad 0.3\, V_{o,sd} = 0.7\, V_{w,sd}$$

$$\tag{6}$$

$$700 = \frac{V_{g,sd}}{V_{o,sd}} \quad \text{to} \quad 700\, V_{o,sd} = V_{g,sd}$$

Similarly, the product of binary variable X_{sd} with continuous variable $V_{c,sd}$ in the mass balance constraint results in a nonlinear term that was linearized using the big-M method, as per the following:

$$
\begin{array}{ll}
M_X = constant & \text{(maximum capacity)} \\
Z \leq M_X & \text{(upper bound)} \\
Z \geq V_{c,sd} - M_X(1 - X_{ij}) & \text{(lower bound)} \\
Z \geq 0 &
\end{array}
\tag{7}
$$

4. Results

Following the description of section 3, a large optimization problem is formulated. The problem features 727 constraints, 126 binary variables, and 333 continuous variables. In Pyomo, the IBM CPLEX optimizer was used to solve the model. Accordingly, the proposed methodology has contributed to a total reduction of 6.3 % in OPEX and 10.7 %

in total emissions by shifting loading between facilities using swing pipelines. The magnitude of the results depends on the initial planning feed flow rates. However, the solution confirms the results are directionally correct. Figure 3 summarizes the difference between the current and proposed operating scenarios once swing pipelines are utilized.

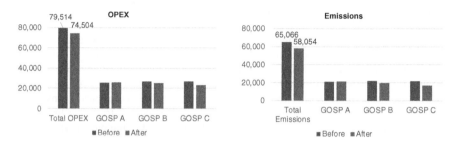

Figure 3: Difference of objective function values between current and proposed methods

5. Conclusion and Outlook

In this work, we proposed a multi-objective MILP optimization framework to maximize profitability and minimize emissions of an integrated network of GOSPs in the oil and gas industry. Embedding machine learning-based surrogates in a multi-objective optimization framework alleviates the drawbacks of alternative methods in the literature. The presented case study demonstrates the framework's capability to yield robust results for the desired objectives. Future work will pursue expanding the formulation into a complete real-world application while exploring alternative multi-objective methods.

6. References

a.   Al-Ghazal, A. H., He, Y., Al-Hurai, M. A., & White, R. J. (2020). A Rigorous Mixed Integer Nonlinear Programming Model to Optimize the Operations of an Integrated Gas-Oil Separation Network. The Aramco Journal of Technology.

b.   Bynum, M.L., Hackebeil, G.A., Hart, W.E., Laird, C.D., Nicholson, B., Siirola, J.D., Watson, J.-P., Woodruff, D.L. (2021). Pyomo – Optimization Modeling in Python. Third Edition. Springer.

c.   Ceccon, F., Jalving, J., Haddad, J., Thebelt, A., Tsay, C., Laird, C. D., & Misener, R. (2022). OMLT: Optimization & Machine Learning Toolkit. In Journal of Machine Learning Research (Vol. 23).

d.   Grossmann, I. E. (2012). Advances in mathematical programming models for enterprise-wide optimization. Computers and Chemical Engineering, 47, 2–18.

e.   Grossmann, I. E. (2021). Advanced Optimization for Process Systems Engineering. Cambridge University Press.

f.   Liu, S., Alhasan, I., & Papageorgiou, L. G. (2016). A mixed integer linear programming model for the optimal operation of a network of gas oil separation plants. Chemical Engineering Research and Design, 111, 147–160.

g.   van de Berg, D., Savage, T., Petsagkourakis, P., Zhang, D., Shah, N., & del Rio-Chanona, E. A. (2022). Data-driven optimization for process systems engineering applications. Chemical Engineering Science, 248.

Flavio Manenti, Gintaras V. Reklaitis (Eds.), Proceedings of the 34th European Symposium on Computer Aided Process Engineering / 15th International Symposium on Process Systems Engineering (ESCAPE34/PSE24), June 2-6, 2024, Florence, Italy

Using CFD to calculate the heat transfer effectiveness of a particle curtain heat transfer device for an atmospheric pressure gas with high effectiveness and extremely low pressure drop

Marko Trifunović[a], Mark Latham[a], Andrew Hoadley[a], David Frederick Fletcher[b], Caecilia Potter[a]

[a]Venso Pty Ltd, 106 Church Street, Melbourne , Australia
[b]School of Chemical and Biomolecular Engineering, The University of Sydney, NSW 2006, Australia
cpotter@vensogrow.com

Abstract

Recovering heat from an atmospheric gas stream and transferring this heat into another atmospheric gas stream is a relatively common, but challenging operation. Traditional heat exchangers such as shell and tube, plate and plate and fin are unable to do this effectively without costing more in compression than the energy recovered. An alternative is to use a solid intermediate for heat storage between two gas streams, such as a crossflow gas-particle system. The advantage of these systems is that the heat transfer surface area can be equivalent or greater than a traditional heat exchanger whilst having a much lower pressure drop. In the context of heat recovery, the use of CFD is important for predicting the heat transfer in gas-particle interactions as well as the hydrodynamics of the bulk system, as CFD can consider the gases influence on each particle and vice versa, which is more difficult to predict with the use of analytical methods. Additional to providing a calculation method for heat transfer effectiveness of scaled up crossflow systems, CFD was also found to identify relationships in pressure drop when scaling up to total heat recovered. Our findings indicate that on a complete gas-gas heat exchanger basis, the use of a solid particle crossflow medium for heat transfer results in orders of magnitude smaller pressure drop than conventional technologies.

Keywords: CFD, Gas-particle interaction, Low pressure drop, Heat recovery

1. Introduction

Typically, recovering heat from gases at atmospheric pressure has proven to be difficult. An option is to use a fluid intermediate, such as steam or hot oil system, but both require significant infrastructure and maintenance to support them despite dealing with the issue of pressure drop (Mitra, 2015). Alternatively, a solid device such as a Ljungstrom heat exchanger can deal with heat recovery at or near atmospheric pressure, however leakage is common and can impact on the heat transfer effectiveness and the process operation in air preheating applications (Maharaj et al., 2015).

Gas-particle contact can also provide a very high heat transfer surface area which is formed by a particle curtain and provides a reasonable heat transfer effectiveness, at very low pressure drops (Ouyang et al., 2003). Asfar and Sheehan (2013) incorporated CFD into their hydrodynamic and heat transfer analysis of a curtain of particles free falling in air. They obtained good agreement between the experiment and the CFD model for small particle sizes using the Eulerian-Eulerian approach. Wardjiman and Rhodes (2009) investigated heating silica sand in a horizontal stream of warm air and identified a non-uniform horizontal velocity profile following the curtain, leading to a need for better understanding of the pressure profiles and path of the gas streamlines inside and outside the particle curtain. Potter (2013) also investigated the performance of crossflow particles of silica sand using a computational model that relied on estimating the residence time, surface area and overall heat transfer coefficient using analytical methods in estimating the number of gas heat transfer units necessary as an input into the model. He calculated the heat transfer effectiveness on an equal heat capacity flowrate basis, and from this, analytically determined the Number of Transfer units, NTUs, by iterating through a matrix of cells describing the gas-particle interactions. However, his simplified computational model did not consider the drag effects of the particles on the direction of the gas flow and the impact on the magnitude and distribution of the residence time, nor the implication on the gas temperature mixing nor the effect of the slip velocity on each particle.

From the investigations mentioned above, the pressure drop was assumed to be very low, but was not studied in detail or quantitatively determined, particularly for large systems where heat recovery would be economically viable. Furthermore, the drag effects on the gas in one crossflow curtain and its effect on proceeding curtains was not investigated.

In this study, CFD is used to provide a calculation method for assessing the overall heat transfer effectiveness and resultant pressure drop required for a scale-up crossflow heat recovery system. Furthermore, the CFD is used to determine the effectiveness and pressure drop relationships during scale up for different orientations of particle curtains used as a solid intermediate in heating ambient air using hot air. A crossflow system using three curtains in each duct is shown in Figure 1. The study extrapolates a scaled-up crossflow system for recovering heat into ambient air to a maximum of 5.05 MW. Assessing the suitability for atmospheric heat recovery, the crossflow system is compared with a duty-equivalent shell and tube heat recovery system.

2. Methodology

The schematic shown in Figure 1 describes the interaction of air at 200°C interacting with silica sand in the sand heating duct and ambient air at 15°C interacting with the resultant hot sand in the air heating duct. For this investigation, it is important to approximate the system based on an equalized heat capacity flowrate between the solids and gases, such that temperature changes between all interactions are equal.

$$Z = \frac{m_{hot}C_{p,hot}}{m_{cold}C_{p,cold}} = 1 \qquad (1)$$

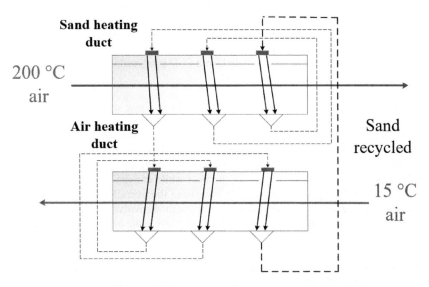

Figure 1 Schematic of 3-curtain looping crossflow heat recovery device heating sand using 200 °C air in the sand heating duct, then heating up 15 °C air in the air heating duct with the resultant sand, with sand being recycled between both individual ducts.

Ansys Fluent 2022R2 commercial CFD software is used to simulate the moving particle moving gas system. The gas side is solved with the Navier-Stokes equations and the $k - \omega$ SST turbulence model. The particles are modelled using Lagrangian discrete particle tracking to consider trajectories, residence time analysis and reinjection (Jadhav and Barigou, 2022). The simulation considers a two-way coupling between each particle and the continuous phase of air while calculating the heat transfer coefficient according to Ranz-Marshall. The exchange of momentum between the particles and gas is also modelled. The particles were assumed to exhibit no internal temperature profile, as well as thermal equilibration consistent with low Biot numbers. The inlet air flow is assumed to enter the simulation with a turbulence intensity of 5% and a turbulent viscosity ratio of 10. Except for the final curtain, particles reaching the bottom wall are reinjected into the proceeding curtain/s with the same temperature and size properties, assuming no heat losses.

Due to the computationally expensive nature of large Lagrangian simulations, the methodology relies on a base simulation described by a 1 m × 1 m cross-section processing 1 kg/s of sand and the mass flow rate of hot air to satisfy eq. (1) for 1, 2 and 3 curtains. Only the sand heating duct is simulated using CFD to determine the heat transfer effectiveness and pressure drop of the interaction. The base simulation assumes the sand is entering at 15 °C. The overall gas-gas heat transfer effectiveness is then calculated according to the following steps:

1. The same heat transfer effectiveness value is assumed in the air heating duct due to similar NTU value and $Z = 1$ mixture of the resultant air and sand are then calculated based on this value.
2. The resultant sand is recycled back into the sand heating duct, changing the theoretical maximum heat transfer in the sand heating duct. The resultant

temperatures are then recalculated by assuming the same heat transfer effectiveness as determined by CFD.

3. Steps 1 and 2 are repeated iteratively until the solution converges and the overall gas-gas heat transfer effectiveness is found.
4. The same pressure drop calculated from CFD produced in the sand heating duct is assumed for the air heating duct.

Different particle sizes of sand are simulated first for the base simulation to emphasize the effect on the heat transfer effectiveness and pressure drop based on differing available surface areas, residence times and heat transfer coefficients associated with different slip velocities produced by fluid drag effects. The base simulation using 200-micron particles is then used to scale up the target heat duty given to the ambient air in two different ways. The first relies on a geometric scaling of the duct while conserving the mass fluxes of both the solids and the gases, subsequently increasing the overall heat transfer based on the increase in flow rates. The second scaling up method involves scaling up both sand and air flow rates within the same duct geometry, increasing the overall duty and pressure drop.

Both scaling up methods are investigated individually using CFD to identify the effect on the overall heat transfer effectiveness and pressure drop. The resultant data are used to extrapolate a pressure drop estimate for the target duty of 5.05 MW to be compared with a shell and tube heat exchanger with the same duty. For comparison purposes, a network of 1-2 shell and tube heat exchanger designs are also included. These designs calculated using Kern's method are based on a pressure drop fixed at 10 kPa on both hot and cold air sides (Sinnot and Towler, 2009). This pressure drop was chosen to ensure a reasonable heat transfer effectiveness without requiring excessive compression. However, both streams are compressed/recompressed to satisfy atmospheric operation.

3. Results

Figure 2 shows the impact of particle size on the resultant heat transfer performance of the base case heat recovery system and the impact of exhibiting larger NTU values for 1, 2 and 3 curtain systems. For example, more heat can be exchanged to the ambient air in one curtain of 200-micron particles, than three curtains of 1 mm particles or two curtains of 600-micron particles. Although the pressure drop did differ for different particle sizes for all 3 curtain combinations, the total pressure drop did not exceed 7 Pa for the base simulation, regardless of the particle size. Figure 3 shows the effect of the smaller particle size inducing a downward flow in each curtain for the 200-micron particle size but allowing the air to pass through each curtain horizontally for the 1 mm particle size. The hydrodynamic impact of particles on the horizontal flow of the gas stream introduces opportunities for further study and design with the use of CFD, to ensure the flow is as perpendicular to the particles as possible, thereby increasing the slip velocity.

The NTU vs Effectiveness relationship was compared with conventional 1-2 shell and tube heat exchanger with a fixed pressure drop of 10 kPa on both sides. Although the effectiveness relationship is slightly higher for the shell and tube heat exchanger, this is due to additional heat coming from compressing the air back to one atmosphere. The cost of this compression is approximately 25% in work of the heat recovered.

Using CFD to calculate the heat transfer effectiveness of a particle curtain heat transfer device for an atmospheric pressure gas with high effectiveness and extremely low pressure drop

2219

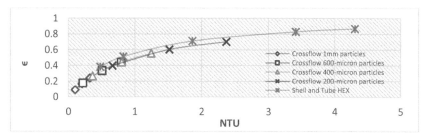

Figure 2 NTU vs Effectiveness values for 1, 2 and 3 curtains in crossflow heat recovery system for different particles sizes compared with shell and tube heat exchanger with fixed 10 kPa pressure drop on both sides.

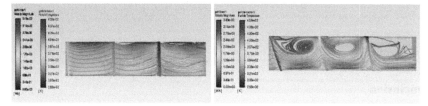

Figure 3 CFD simulations of the air path-lines interacting with 3 curtains in the sand heating duct for 1 mm particles (left) and 200-micron particles (right) in the base simulation.

Figure 4 describes the pressure drop relationship for 1, 2 and 3 curtain systems when increasing the cross-section and feeder sizes while conserving the mass fluxes of the sand and air as well as the pressure drop relationship when the solids and gas flows are multiplied by some factor in the same duct. While the square scale factor did have an impact on the pressure drop induced by the curtain, the pressure drop was still of the same order or magnitude despite increasing the heat transfer duty by approximately a factor of 4 and 9, for the 2 squared and 3 squared scale ups, respectively. The small increase is likely due to the exaggerated vortex generated from a taller curtain and its effect on subsequent curtains. It was also found that the heat transfer effectiveness did increase for all 3 curtain formations with a quadratic relationship, likely due to the increase in residence time per kilo of particles, due to the taller duct. The taller duct allowed the particles to have more time to heat up and increased the scaled total surface area. For example, the 3-curtain heat transfer effectiveness of the base simulation was 0.703, while the simulation involving a 3 m × 3 m cross section processing 9 kg/s of sand was 0.719.

When scaling up both flows within the same geometry, it was found that a general linear increase in pressure drop occurred when increasing the number of curtains, reflecting a linear relationship between the pressure drop and NTU for each scaling up factor. However, the increase in total pressure drop when scaling up both flows showed a general polynomial relationship, where the increase in pressure drop from a larger number of curtains increases with the scale factor. This is largely due to an improvement in the perpendicular nature of the interaction for increased flow scale factors, resulting in a higher particle slip velocity leading to a higher pressure drop. Despite this, the heat transfer effectiveness was relatively constant.

The scaled-up heat recovery system with a target duty provided to the ambient air of 5.05 MW was considered in a 3 m × 3 m horizontal duct with a flow scale factor of 4.1 exhibiting a heat transfer effectiveness of 0.719 and an extrapolated pressure drop of

115 Pa. This is orders of magnitude smaller than the shell and tube heat exchanger case with the same effectiveness value and a 10 kPa pressure drop. The crossflow heat recovery system can therefore be considered for atmospheric operation without the need for compression.

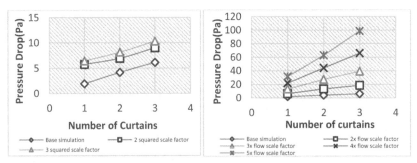

Figure 4 Pressure drop relationship for 1, 2 and 3 curtains when square scaling up (left) and flow scaling up (right).

4. Conclusion

In conclusion, this work has provided a calculation method for determining the heat transfer effectiveness and pressure drop for crossflow curtain systems using CFD for a system involving two crossflow ducts with looping particle curtains for heating ambient air using hot air at near atmospheric pressure. The CFD determined an insignificant increase in pressure drop occurs when scaling up the geometry of the system while conserving mass fluxes of both solids and gases while slightly improving the heat transfer effectiveness. The scaling up of heat duty due to scaling up the flows within the same duct showed a relatively constant heat transfer effectiveness while showing a general polynomial increase in the pressure drop based on 1, 2 and 3 curtain systems. Furthermore, the crossflow system was determined to have orders of magnitude lower pressure drop when compared with a duty-equivalent shell and tube heat exchanger system exchanging 5.05 MW of heat, demonstrating its suitability for atmospheric heat recovery. This paper has also introduced a need for better understanding and management of the impact of particles on the horizontal flow path of the gas in subsequent curtains.

References

Afshar, S., Sheehan, M., 2013. CFD and experimental study of convectional heat transfer in free-falling particle curtains. 11th International Conference of Numerical Analysis and Applied Mathematics, AIP Conf. Proc., 1558, 2005-2008.

Jadhav, A., Barigou, M., 2022. Eulerian-Lagrangian modelling of turbulent two-phase particle-liquid flow in a stirred vessel: CFD and experiments compared. International Journal of Multiphase Flow, 155, 104191.

Maharaj, A., Schmitz, W., Naidoo, R., 2015. A numerical study of air preheater leakage. Energy, 92(1), 87-99.

Mitra, S., 2015. Design of hot oil system: A technical report. The University of Newcastle, Australia, DOI: 10.13140/RG.2.1.4159.0882.

Ouyang, S., Mao, Q.M., Rhodes, M., Potter, O.E., 2003. Short contact time gas-solid systems. Reviews in Chemical Engineering, 19(2), 133-228.

Potter, O., 2013. Crossflow gas-particle heat and mass transfer and chemical reaction. Chemical Engineering Research and Design, 91(2), 244-253.

Sinnott, R., Towler, G., 2009. Chemical Engineering Design (5th ed.). SI edition.

Wardjiman, C., Rhodes, M., 2009. Heat transfer in a particle curtain falling through a horizontally-flowing gas stream. Powder Technology, 191(3), 247-253.

Flavio Manenti, Gintaras V. Reklaitis (Eds.), Proceedings of the 34th European Symposium on Computer Aided Process Engineering / 15th International Symposium on Process Systems Engineering (ESCAPE34/PSE24), June 2-6, 2024, Florence, Italy

Scale-bridging Optimization Framework for Desalination Integrated Produced Water Networks

Sakshi Naik[a], Miguel Zamarripa[b], Markus Drouven[c], Lorenz T. Biegler[a*]

[a]*Carnegie Mellon University, Pittsburgh, PA, 15232, USA*
[b]*National Energy Technology Laboratory, Pittsburgh, PA, 15236, USA*
[c]*NETL Support Contractor, Pittsburgh, PA, 15236, USA*
Corresponding Author: lb01@andrew.cmu.edu

Abstract

Produced water (PW) management poses a major challenge to U.S. oil and gas development. Due to freshwater scarcity and PW injection curtailments, desalination may become a necessity in some parts of the country. Integrating rigorous desalination process models within a produced water network for co-optimization of desalination design and network operation can be challenging to scale-up due to computational complexity. In this work we use the trust region filter framework to decompose the integrated optimization problem into an optimization master problem consisting of the network model and simplified surrogates for the desalination units and an optimization sub problem for the rigorous desalination unit model. The approach is demonstrated on a multiperiod produced water network from the PARETO library (Drouven et al., 2022) with thermal desalination units.

Keywords: Optimization, Surrogate Models, Sustainability, Energy.

1. Introduction

Hydraulic fracturing has become crucial to U.S. oil & gas development, and it involves the pumping of large amounts of water and some chemicals into the subsurface to extract oil and natural gas from unconventional reservoirs. Along with oil and gas, brackish water - both injected and natural formation water containing high amounts of total dissolved solids (TDS) surfaces back to the earth as PW which needs to be managed efficiently. Large volumes, disposal constraints, and the high salinity of PW serve as strong incentives for integrating desalination technologies into the produced water infrastructure to introduce desalinated water into the water cycle. Thermal desalination technologies like mechanical vapor recompression (MVR) have shown promise to desalinate high TDS produced water (Onishi et al., 2017). Optimizing desalination design and operation in-sync with PW management can yield significant environmental and economic benefits. A framework for integrating rigorous MVR models into a multi-period produced water network optimization has been developed (Naik et al., 2023). For larger networks and complex desalination units, the direct integration of rigorous models into network optimization can be computationally challenging to solve. It is therefore desirable to use shortcut models or simple data driven surrogates which can emulate the original rigorous desalination model for computational efficiency. The main disadvantage of directly replacing the rigorous model using surrogates/shortcut models is the lack of convergence guarantees to the optimum of the rigorous problem. In this work, we use the trust region filter (TRF) proposed by Yoshio and Biegler (2020) approach to decompose the integrated network optimization problem into a master problem consisting of the network equations along with a reduced order model (ROM) to approximate the desalination outputs and trust region constraints. The ROM is updated in each iteration by solving the rigorous desalination optimization problem maintaining the accuracy of the ROM within the trust region. The TRF approach provides guaranteed convergence to the optimum of the rigorous problem. This work supports the development of PARETO, a DOE-sponsored, free, and open-source optimization tool for onshore PW management (www.project-pareto.org), by integrating detailed desalination models into the existing PW management framework.

2. Trust Region Filter Formulation

Given an optimization problem of the form shown in *(a)*, the trust region problem can be written by substituting the rigorous model $d(w)$ with a simplified corrected surrogate model $r_k(w)$ and a trust region constraint on the degrees of freedom u, shown in *(b)*.

a) Optimization problem

$$\min_x f(x)$$
$$\text{s.t. } h(x) = 0$$
$$g(x) \leq 0$$
$$y = d(w)$$

b) Trust region problem (TRP)

$$\min_x f(x)$$
$$\text{s.t. } h(x) = 0$$
$$g(x) \leq 0$$
$$y = r_k(w)$$
$$|u - u_k| \leq \Delta_k$$

The corrected surrogate model in each iteration is given by:

$$r_k(w) = \hat{r}(w) + \big(d(w_k) - \hat{r}(w_k)\big) + \big(\nabla d(w_k) - \nabla \hat{r}(w_k)\big)(w - w_k)$$

where $\hat{r}(w)$ is the surrogate model without any correction for inputs w, $d(w_k) - \hat{r}(w_k)$ is the zero order correction and $(\nabla d(w_k) - \nabla \hat{r}(w_k))(w - w_k)$ is the first order correction. At $w = w_k$ the corrected surrogate is exact i.e., $r_k(w_k) = d(w_k)$ and $\nabla r_k(w_k) = \nabla d(w_k)$. Hence, any choice of $\hat{r}(w)$ converges to the optimum of the original problem. The zero and first order corrections are obtained by solving the rigorous model at fixed inputs w_k. The trust region constraint bounds the degrees of freedom u of the master problem to stay in the trust region Δ_k. The TRF algorithm is given in Figure 1.

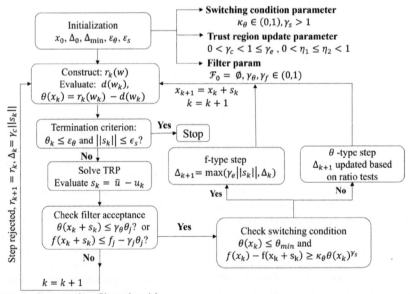

Figure 1. Trust region filter algorithm

An integrated model formulation for optimization of produced water networks with the rigorous desalination models embedded at desalination sites has been developed in Naik et al. (2023). For completeness the integrated formulation is given below:

$$\min C_{net} + \sum_{n \in \mathcal{N}^{T,In}} \sum_{t \in \mathcal{T}} (CAPEX_{\Delta t}^n + \overline{OPEX_{\Delta t}^{nt}}) \Delta t \quad \left.\right\} \quad \begin{array}{l}\text{Sum of network costs and} \\ \text{MVR CAPEX and OPEX}\end{array}$$

$$\text{s.t} \quad F_{nt}^{in} = \bar{F}_{nt}^{in} \qquad \forall n \in \mathcal{N}^{T,In}, t \in \mathcal{T}$$
$$C_{nt}^{in} = \bar{C}_{nt}^{in} \qquad \forall n \in \mathcal{N}^{T,In}, t \in \mathcal{T}$$
$$\alpha_{nt} = \bar{\alpha}_{nt} \qquad \forall n \in \mathcal{N}^{T,In}, t \in \mathcal{T}$$

Linking inlet (flows, concentrations) and outlets (water recovery fractions) from the network model desalination sites to rigorous MVR models

$$CAPEX_n^{(i)g,ev} \geq \overline{CAPEX_{nt}^{(i)ev}} \quad \forall i \in I, n \in \mathcal{N}^{T,In}, t \in \mathcal{T}$$
$$CAPEX_n^{g,ph} \geq \overline{CAPEX_{nt}^{ph}} \qquad \forall n \in \mathcal{N}^{T,In}, t \in \mathcal{T}$$
$$CAPEX_n^{g,comp} \geq \overline{CAPEX_{nt}^{comp}} \qquad \forall n \in \mathcal{N}^{T,In}, t \in \mathcal{T}$$

Global capacity constraints on CAPEX in every period.

$$CAPEX_{\Delta t}^n = \sum_{i \in I} CAPEX_n^{(i)g,ev} + CAPEX_n^{g,ph} + CAPEX_n^{g,comp} \quad \forall n \in \mathcal{N}^{T,In}$$

Network mass balances with concentration tracking

Rigorous steady state MVR models in each period

The variables with an overbar represent the ones from the rigorous desalination models. A detailed description of the variables is given in Table 1. The objective is to minimize the MVR capital cost (from evaporator, compressor, and preheater) and operating cost (from electricity consumption in compressor) along with network cost consisting of transportation, storage, disposal and credits for desalination and removal of water from storage. The flows and concentrations of produced water into the desalination nodes in the network model are linked to the inlet flows and concentrations of the rigorous steady state MVR models in each period. The water recovery fraction from the rigorous desalination models is linked with the water recovery fraction from the desalination site in the network model. To ensure that the built desalination unit has feasible operation in every period of the planning horizon, global capacity constraints are written for the capital cost of evaporators, compressor, and preheater in the MVR model. The TRF master problem in iteration k can be written as:

$$\min C_{net} + \sum_{n \in \mathcal{N}^{T,In}} \sum_{t \in \mathcal{T}} (CAPEX_{\Delta t}^n + OPEX_{\Delta t}^{nt}) \Delta t$$

$$\text{s.t} \quad w_{nt} = [F_{nt}^{in}, \ C_{nt}^{in}] \qquad \forall n \in \mathcal{N}^{T,In}, t \in \mathcal{T} \quad \longrightarrow \quad \text{Input variables}$$
$$\alpha_{nt} = y_{nt}^{\alpha} = r_k^{\alpha}(w_{nt}) \quad \forall n \in \mathcal{N}^{T,In}, t \in \mathcal{T}$$
$$OPEX_{\Delta t}^{nt} = y_{nt}^{Opex} = r_k^{Opex}(w_{nt}) \quad \forall n \in \mathcal{N}^{T,In}, t \in \mathcal{T}$$
$$y_{nt}^{(i)C_{ev}} = r_k^{(i)C_{ev}}(w_{nt}) \quad \forall i \in I, n \in \mathcal{N}^{T,In} \ t \in \mathcal{T}$$
$$y_{nt}^{C_{ph}} = r_k^{C_{ph}}(w_{nt}) \qquad \forall n \in \mathcal{N}^{T,In}, t \in \mathcal{T}$$
$$y_{nt}^{C_{comp}} = r_k^{C_{comp}}(w_{nt}) \quad \forall n \in \mathcal{N}^{T,In}, t \in \mathcal{T}$$

Surrogate constraints

$$CAPEX_n^{(i)g,ev} \geq y_{nt}^{C_{ev}} \qquad \forall i \in I, n \in \mathcal{N}^{T,In}, t \in \mathcal{T}$$
$$CAPEX_n^{g,ph} \geq y_{nt}^{C_{ph}} \qquad \forall n \in \mathcal{N}^{T,In}, t \in \mathcal{T}$$
$$CAPEX_n^{g,comp} \geq y_{nt}^{C_{comp}} \quad \forall n \in \mathcal{N}^{T,In}, t \in \mathcal{T}$$

Global capacity constraints

$$CAPEX_{\Delta t}^n = \sum_{i \in I} CAPEX_n^{(i)g,ev} + CAPEX_n^{g,ph} + CAPEX_n^{g,comp} \quad \forall n \in \mathcal{N}^{T,In}$$
$$||u - u_k|| \leq \Delta_k \qquad \longrightarrow \quad \text{Trust region constraint}$$

Network mass balances with concentration tracking

The degrees of freedom u in the master problem, such as flowrates at the splitter nodes, inventory levels in storage units, fresh water sourced in each period, produced water sent to disposal, and water recovery fractions from the desalination units are bounded to stay within the trust region Δ_k by the trust region constraint. A linear ROM given by: $\hat{r}(w_{nt}) = 0.01w_{nt}^{(1)} + 0.001w_{nt}^{(2)}$ is used in the master problem to ensure that the outputs are scaled; the master problem only has bilinear terms and hence is a quadratically constrained program (QCP). The surrogate models are updated from the optimal solution of the rigorous MVR unit subproblems at desalination site n at period t, with fixed inputs w_{nt}^* obtained from the optimal solution of the master problem. The MVR subproblem is given by:

$$\min \overline{CAPEX}_{\Delta t}^n + \overline{OPEX}_{\Delta t}^{nt}$$

$$\text{s.t.} \quad \bar{F}_{nt}^{in} = w_{nt}^{*(1)}$$

$$\bar{C}_{nt}^{in} = w_{nt}^{*(2)}$$

$$\overline{CAPEX}_{\Delta t}^n = \sum_{i \in I} \overline{CAPEX}_n^{(i)ev} + \overline{CAPEX}_n^{ph} + \overline{CAPEX}_n^{comp}$$

Rigorous steady state MVR model in period t at desalination site n

Table 1. Descriptions of sets and variables

Sets		Variables	
$\mathcal{N}^{T,In}$	Desalination inlet node in the network	$CAPEX$	Global CAPEX for evaporator stage (i) at node n
$\mathcal{T}$	Time periods	$CAPEX$	Global CAPEX for preheater at node n
I	Evaporator stages in the MVR unit	$CAPEX$	Global CAPEX for compressor at node n
Variables		F_{nt}^{in}	Inlet flow to MVR unit at node n at time t
C_{net}	Sum of network costs (kUSD)	C_{nt}^{in}	Inlet concentration to MVR unit at node n at time t
$CAPEX_{\Delta t}^n$	Capital cost (kUSD/Δt) of MVR unit at node n	α_{nt}	Water recovery fraction from node n at time t
$OPEX_{\Delta t}^{nt}$	Operating cost (kUSD/Δt) of MVR unit at node n at time t	w_{nt}	Inputs to the MVR subproblem at node n at time t

3. Case study

In this section we demonstrate the TRF approach on a case study from the PARETO network library (Drouven et al., 2022). The planning horizon is 52 weeks, with one week time periods. The test network consists of four production pads producing water, two disposal sites, two fresh water sources, a single storage site, and a prospective desalination site as shown in Figure 2. The network

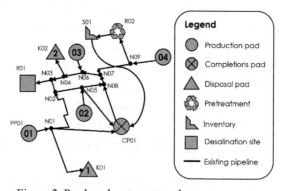

Figure 2. Produced water network case

also has one completion pad with a water demand between weeks 1 to 12 and weeks 45 and 52 and in the remaining time there is completion flowback which means there is no demand for water in the network. At desalination site R01, a single stage MVR unit is installed. The TRF master problem has 4,477 variables and 3,624 constraints and the sub problems in each period have 51 variables and 49 equality constraints. The case study is relatively simple and can be solved using both the TRF formulation and the integrated formulation to validate the results. The models are developed in Pyomo (Hart et al., 2011), solved using the open source NLP solver IPOPT (Wächter and Biegler, 2004) and the Pyomo TRF package is used to implement the TRF approach.

The TRF method converges in 3 iterations and the optimal flow profiles are shown in Figure 3. The optimal desalination unit built has an evaporator with area $372 \ m^2$, a preheater with area $73.8 \ m^2$ and a 2,750 Hp compressor. The optimal solution obtained by using the TRF method matches closely with the optimal solution from the integrated model as shown in Table 2. The overall solution time for the TRF method is about 40% more than the integrated formulation. However, the sensitivity calculation and output computation from the rigorous models can be parallelized for each period. We estimate that this would reduce the overall TRF solution time by a factor of two.

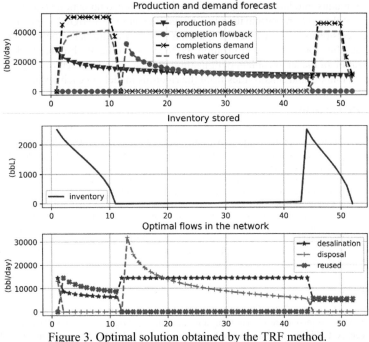

Figure 3. Optimal solution obtained by the TRF method.

Table 2. Optimal costs obtained by the TRF approach and the integrated approach.

Solution approach → Costs ↓	TRF formulation (kUSD)	Integrated formulation (kUSD)
Objective value	9,884.5	9,884.46
Piping cost	370.05	370.04
Disposal	917.56	917.56
Storage	6.58	6.57
Fresh water sourcing	12,684	12,684
Desalination CAPEX	405.93	405.93

Desalination OPEX	2,144.37	2,144.37
Storage credit	0.50	0.50
Desalination credit	6,643.51	6,643.53

Table 3. Computational times

Method	Total time		
Integrated formulation	111 s		
TRF formulation	158 s	⎰ 101 s – Sensitivity calculation ($\nabla d(w_k)$) 12.5 s – Output calculation ($d(w_k)$) ⎱ 44.8 s – Other	

4. Conclusions and Future Work

The TRF approach is applied to co-optimize rigorous desalination unit design and produced water network operation. The TRF method decomposes the integrated problem into a computationally efficient QCP and smaller NLP subproblems without loss of solution accuracy. The approach provides a scalable framework to integrate rigorous desalination units into larger network case studies. The decomposition also allows for an extension of the network formulation to a mixed integer QCP (MIQCP) to make discrete strategic decisions such as capacity expansion, building additional pipelines, etc. while solving desalination design optimization as NLP subproblems. Future work involves parallelization of the sub-problem optimization in each period to decrease the time taken to compute outputs and sensitivities from the rigorous models in each period.

Acknowledgements

We gratefully acknowledge support from the U.S. Department of Energy, Office of Fossil Energy and Carbon Management, through the Environmentally Prudent Stewardship Program.

Disclaimer: This project was funded by the Department of Energy, National Energy Technology Laboratory an agency of the United States Government, through a support contract. Neither the United States Government nor any agency thereof, nor any of their employees, nor the support contractor, nor any of their employees, makes any warranty, express or implied, or assumes any legal liability or responsibility for the accuracy, completeness, or usefulness of any information, apparatus, product, or process disclosed, or represents that its use would not infringe privately owned rights. Reference herein to any specific commercial product, process, or service by trade name, trademark, manufacturer, or otherwise does not necessarily constitute or imply its endorsement, recommendation, or favoring by the United States Government or any agency thereof. The views and opinions of authors expressed herein do not necessarily state or reflect those of the United States Government or any agency thereof.

References

A. Wächter, L.T. Biegler, 2004, On the implementation of an interior-point filter line-search algorithm for large-scale nonlinear programming, Math. Programming, vol 106, pp. 25-57

M. Drouven, A. Caldéron, M. Zamarripa, K. Beattie 2022, PARETO: An open-source produced water optimization framework, Optimization and Engineering, vol 24. pp. 2229-2249

N. Yoshio, L. T. Biegler, 2020, Demand-based optimization of chlorobenzene process with high-fidelity & surrogate reactor models under trust region strategies, AIChE J., vol 67, e17054

S. Naik, M. Zamarripa, M. Drouven, L.T. Biegler, 2023, Integrating the design of desalination technologies into produced water network optimization, Systems & Control Transactions (Accepted - FOCAPD 2024)

V. Onishi, A. C. Parreño, J. R. Labarta, R. R. Femenia, R. S. Díaz, E. Fraga 2017, Shale gas flowback water desalination: Single vs multiple-effect evaporation with vapor recompression cycle and thermal integration, Desalination, vol. 404, pp. 230–248.

W. Hart, J. P. Watson, and D. Woodruff 2011, Pyomo: modeling and solving mathematical programs in Python, Mathematical Programming Computation, vol.3, no. 3, pp. 219-260.

Flavio Manenti, Gintaras V. Reklaitis (Eds.), Proceedings of the 34th European Symposium on Computer Aided Process Engineering / 15th International Symposium on Process Systems Engineering (ESCAPE34/PSE24), June 2-6, 2024, Florence, Italy

Electrification in the Petrochemical Industry: Can Flexibility Enable Low-Carbon Utility Systems?

Svenja Bielefeld,[a*] Miloš Cvetković,[b] Andrea Ramírez Ramirez [c]

[a]*Engineering Systems and Services Department, Faculty of Technology, Policy and Management, Delft University of Technology, Jaffalaan 5 2628 BX Delft, the Netherlands*
[b]*Electrical Sustainable Energy Department, Faculty of Electrical Engineering, Mathematics & Computer Science, Delft University of Technology, Mekelweg 4 2628 CD Delft, the Netherlands*
[c]*Department of Chemical Engineering, Faculty of Applied Sciences, Delft University of Technology, Van der Maasweg 9 2629 HZ Delft, the Netherlands*
s.e.bielefeld@tudelft.nl

Abstract

Electrifying the utility supply of existing petrochemical processes is a potential measure for CO_2 emission reduction in the chemical industry. With an increasing share of variable renewable energy sources in the electricity grid, electricity price fluctuations will become more frequent. However, most existing petrochemical processes operate continuously and, therefore, require a constant supply of utilities. In this paper, we model an electrified utility system that includes different types of storage units to explore how a constant utility demand could be supplied under fluctuating electricity prices. To achieve this, we model a utility system that provides electricity and heat to an olefins plant in the Port of Rotterdam and use mathematical optimisation to capture optimal hourly operations of the plant under fluctuating prices. We find that the cost-optimal utility system consists of electric boilers, integrated thermal energy storage, and technologies for storing and using hydrogen produced on-site. With data for prices of the Dutch electricity grid in 2022, the electrified utility system results in higher costs than a fossil-based system. Increasing price fluctuation levels would lead to lower operational costs as the system's flexibility enables shifting the electricity consumption to the hours with the lowest electricity prices.

Keywords: Electrification, utility system, flexibility, olefins, optimisation

1. Introduction

Climate change and increasing regulation of greenhouse gas (GHG) emissions drive the need for speeding up emission reduction efforts in the chemical industry. The production of olefins like ethylene, propylene, and butadiene from fossil feedstock via steam cracking is currently the most energy-intensive process in the chemical industry (Layritz et al., 2021). Ethylene is a base chemical and building block in about 60 % of global polymer production (Layritz et al., 2021), leading to a demand of 177 million tons in 2022 (Statista, 2023). This demand is expected to continue growing in the coming years in line with the expected growth of the demand for plastics (Layritz et al., 2021). Therefore, emission reduction in ethylene production would have a large impact on the overall emissions of the chemical industry. A promising option is decarbonising the utility supply of olefin plants through electrification as the carbon emission intensity of the electricity grid is decreasing due to a rising share of renewable energy sources (RES) in the electricity generation mix. However, a rising share of renewables is also causing larger electricity price fluctuations due to the intermittent nature of RES, which makes balancing generation and demand more challenging.

CO_2 emission reduction in utility systems of the petrochemical industry has been a research topic for many years. Exergy efficiency enhancement (Luo et al. (2014)), process integration (Han & Lee (2014), Ghiasi et al. (2022)) and Carbon Capture and Storage (CCS) (Han & Lee (2014)) are measures that have been proposed and analysed. Partial fuel switching from fossil sources to renewable energy sources like wind energy, solar power and biomass in combination with thermal energy storage or batteries has also been considered (Qian et al. (2021), Hwangbo et al. (2022), Su et al. (2023)). However, only one study was found that proposed to rely only on electricity and avoid fossil energy use completely. This study (Kim (2022)) considered different possibilities for using heat integration and electrified heating for two chemical processes. The author considered the electrification of the process and utility systems together by using heat pumps, Organic Rankine Cycles, e-heaters and e-furnaces. However, the study assumes steady-state conditions of the electricity supply and focuses on utility systems for (novel) electrified processes and not for existing thermal-based processes. Therefore, it remains unclear what a complete electrification of utility systems of existing fossil-based plants could look like under fluctuating conditions of the electricity supply. It is also unknown whether such a system could be financially viable under current electricity prices and how an increase in price fluctuations impacts the techno-economic performance.

Our study addresses these knowledge gaps by presenting a fully electrified utility system for an existing olefins plant. We explore different types of storage units to cope with electricity price fluctuations. Further, we assess different electricity price curves and present insights into the impact of increasing price fluctuations on the techno-economic performance of fully electrified utility systems.

2. Methods

Our utility system model is connected to the national power grid and has to supply the power and steam demand of an existing olefins plant for each hour of the operational year. To supply the steam demand, the model can choose between an electric boiler (ElB) or a hydrogen boiler (H2B) together with an electrolyser (H2E) that supplies hydrogen on-site. To make the utility system flexible, the model can install different types of storage units: electricity (Bat), thermal energy (TES), and hydrogen storage tanks (H2S). The thermal energy storage is an integrated unit of power-to-heat conversion and sensible heat storage in solid material. Since many combinations of these technologies are possible, mathematical optimisation was used to find the combination with the least investment and operating costs. The model is formulated as an LP to ensure fast solving times. Figure 1 shows the potential configurations of the technologies. The energy demand data (steam, electricity, cooling, chilling) for the olefins plant is taken from an ASPEN Plus model developed in-house. The plant is modelled for a yearly ethylene production capacity of 900 kilotons and mimics the current conditions of an ethylene production plant in the Port of Rotterdam. The optimisation was run for electricity prices of the Dutch Day-Ahead Market in 2022 with a price cap at 0 EUR/MWh for all negative prices.

The objective function is given in Eq. (1) and solved for the operational year of the plant (8000 hours). Capex is the sum over the annualised investment costs of all installed technologies, where s_i is the size of technology i, c_i the cost per unit capacity of technology i, and AF_i the annualisation factor of technology I (Eq. (2)).

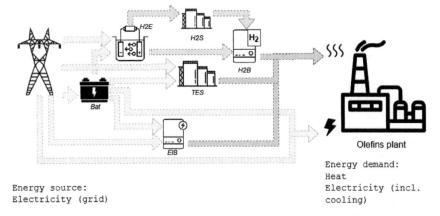

Energy source:
Electricity (grid)

Energy demand:
Heat
Electricity (incl.
cooling)

Figure 1. Design options for a fully electrified utility system. Yellow lines indicate potential electricity flows, red lines show potential steam flows and blue lines potential hydrogen flows.

Opex is calculated as the grid consumption at a given moment $P_{gr}(t)$ of all grid-connected units, multiplied by the cost of electricity at the same moment, pel, grid(t) (Eq. (3)).

$$\min \text{Capex} + \sum_{t=0}^{t=8000} \text{Opex(t)} \tag{1}$$

$$\text{Capex} = \sum s_i * c_i * \text{AF}_i \tag{2}$$

$$\text{Opex(t)} = \text{pel, grid(t)} * \sum P_{gr}(t) * 1h \tag{3}$$

The electric boiler, hydrogen boiler and electrolyser are modelled with an equality constraint that determines the energy flow balance (including conversion efficiencies). Their size constrains their maximum energy outflow. The hydrogen storage tank, battery and thermal energy storage are modelled with an equality constraint that describes their state of energy (SoE) as a function of their SoE of the previous time step, the energy inflow, the energy outflow and charge or discharge efficiencies. The maximum SoE is constrained by the size of the unit. Since there are spatial limitations for the utility systems, the sum of the spatial footprint of all units is constrained by the space available in the plant (75 hectares (Wong & Van Dril, 2020)). An equality constraint ensures that the utility system supplies the low-pressure steam and power demand of the olefins plant at every hour of the operational year. Lastly, the total power flow from the grid to the plant is limited to the capacity of the plant's electricity grid connection. Since the plant requires roughly 400 MW to run, the grid connection capacity is assumed to be 400 MW. The result of the model is the design of the plant's utility system comprising the capacities of each technology, as well as the performance in terms of total cost (investment cost and operational cost) and CO_2 emissions (scope 1 and scope 2). Scope 1 emissions are calculated based on the amount of natural gas used and the emission factor of natural gas in the Netherlands. Scope 2 emissions are calculated every hour by multiplying the grid electricity consumption per hour from the grid with its respective emission intensity for the period of the optimisation (i.e., from 01.01.2022 to 01.12.2022). The grid emission intensity data was retrieved from (Electricity Maps, 2023).

The performance of the new system is compared to the performance of a fossil fuel-based utility system, which consists of a 450 MW_{th} combined heat and power plant (CHP) fueled by natural gas and a connection to the national electricity grid. The CHP and the grid connection are assumed to exist already (mimicking the current situation in the Port of Rotterdam), and hence, only operational costs are considered. The operational costs of the fossil-based system are calculated with a scheduling optimisation model, which includes natural gas prices from the Dutch TTF market. All remaining assumptions are the same as in the first model.

To investigate the performance of the CHP and the electrified system in a scenario of higher electricity price fluctuations, we created electricity price curves with higher peaks and lower valleys using Eq. (4), where k determines the increase of the price peaks and valleys. The values applied for k are within a range starting at k = 1.025 and ending at k = 1.2, with a stepwise increase of 0.025. Since price peaks go up to 1000 EUR/MWh for k = 1.2, no higher values were tested. Alike to the original price data (k=1), negative prices were capped at 0 EUR/MWh. The impact of the new price curves on the systems' performance was found by optimising the operation of the systems under the new price conditions and comparing the resulting costs to those under the original price conditions.

$$p_{el, grid, new}(t) = p_{el, grid, old, mean} \tag{4}$$
$$+ k \left(p_{el, grid, old}(t) - p_{el, grid, old, mean} \right)$$

3. Results and discussion

Figure 2 shows the energy flows in the electrified system, which relies on 1.25 GWh (integrated) thermal energy storage, 181 MW electric boiler capacity, 22 MW electrolyser capacity, 55.4 GWh of hydrogen storage and 162 MW hydrogen boiler capacity. No batteries are installed. For comparison, Figure 3 shows the energy flows in the fossil-based utility system.

Table 1 presents the costs and CO_2 emissions of the fossil-based and the electrified utility systems. With the price data for 2022, the electrified system is still more expansive than the fossil-based system. Note that the results change when other values for the grid connection capacity (and hence maximum power flow from the grid to the plant) are assumed. The dependency of the costs on the grid connection capacity will be the subject of further research. While scope 1 emissions are reduced to 0, scope 2 emissions remain high due to the CO_2 emission intensity of the Dutch electricity grid in 2022. However, the emission intensity of the electricity supply in the Netherlands is expected to decrease rapidly in the coming years (Rijksoverheid, 2019).

Table 1. Costs and CO_2 emissions of fossil-based and electrified utility system

	Cost [Million euro]			CO2 Emissions [kilotonnes]		
	Capex	Opex	Total	Scope 1	Scope 2	Total
Fossil-based system	0	620	620	723	90	813
Electrified system	5	654	659	0	776	776

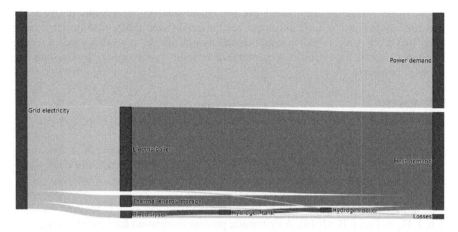

Figure 2. Energy flows in the electrified utility system of the Olefins plant.

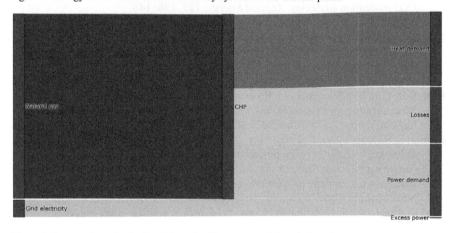

Figure 3. Energy flows in the fossil-based utility system of the Olefins plant.

With increasing price peaks and valleys, the operational cost of the electrified system declines because the system's flexibility allows shifting electricity consumption to hours with lower prices and avoiding hours with higher prices.

Table 2. Operational costs of the electrified system in cases of increased price peaks and valleys

k in Eq. (4)	1	1.025	1.05	1.075	1.1	1.125	1.15	1.175	1.2
Opex [Million euro]	654	642	641	640	639	638	638	637	636

4. Conclusion

We modelled a fully electrified utility system for an olefins plant with a constant low-pressure steam and electricity demand. The cost-optimal system design includes electric boilers, thermal energy storage, electrolyser capacity, hydrogen tanks and hydrogen boilers. With electricity and natural gas price data for the Netherlands in 2022, the electrified system is 6% more expensive than a fossil-based utility system but reduces scope 1 CO_2 emissions to 0. Increasing electricity price peaks and valleys would reduce operational costs in the electrified system due to its ability to shift electricity consumption to low-price hours.

References

Electricity Maps. (2023, July 1). *Data Portal*. https://www.electricitymaps.com/data-portal

Ghiasi, M., Manesh, M. H. K., Lari, K., Salehi, G., & Azad, M. T. (2022). A New Algorithm for the Design of Site Utility for Combined Production of Power, Freshwater, and Steam in Process Industries. *Journal of Energy Resources Technology, Transactions of the ASME, 144*(1). https://doi.org/10.1115/1.4050879

Han, J. H., & Lee, I. B. (2014). A systematic process integration framework for the optimal design and techno-economic performance analysis of energy supply and CO2 mitigation strategies. *Applied Energy, 125*, 136–146. https://doi.org/10.1016/j.apenergy.2014.03.057

Hwangbo, S., Heo, S. K., & Yoo, C. K. (2022). Development of deterministic-stochastic model to integrate variable renewable energy-driven electricity and large-scale utility networks: Towards decarbonization petrochemical industry. *Energy, 238*. https://doi.org/10.1016/j.energy.2021.122006

Kim, J.-K. (2022). e-Site Analysis: Process Design of Site Utility Systems With Electrification for Process Industries. *Frontiers in Thermal Engineering, 2*. https://doi.org/10.3389/fther.2022.861882

Layritz, L. S., Dolganova, I., Finkbeiner, M., Luderer, G., Penteado, A. T., Ueckerdt, F., & Repke, J. U. (2021). The potential of direct steam cracker electrification and carbon capture & utilization via oxidative coupling of methane as decarbonization strategies for ethylene production. *Applied Energy, 296*. https://doi.org/10.1016/j.apenergy.2021.117049

Luo, X., Hu, J., Zhao, J., Zhang, B., Chen, Y., & Mo, S. (2014). Multi-objective optimization for the design and synthesis of utility systems with emission abatement technology concerns. *Applied Energy, 136*, 1110–1131. https://doi.org/10.1016/j.apenergy.2014.06.076

Qian, Q., Liu, H., He, C., Shu, Y., Chen, Q. L., & Zhang, B. J. (2021). Sustainable retrofit of petrochemical energy systems under multiple uncertainties using the stochastic optimization method. *Computers and Chemical Engineering, 151*. https://doi.org/10.1016/j.compchemeng.2021.107374

Statista. (2023). *Ethylene demand and production capacity worldwide from 2015 to 2022*. https://www.statista.com/statistics/1246694/ethylene-demand-capacity-forecast-worldwide/

Wong, L., & Van Dril, A. W. N. (2020). *Decarbonisation options for large volume organic chemicals production, Shell Moerdijk*. www.pbl.nl/en.

Flavio Manenti, Gintaras V. Reklaitis (Eds.), Proceedings of the 34th European Symposium on Computer Aided Process Engineering / 15th International Symposium on Process Systems Engineering (ESCAPE34/PSE24), June 2-6, 2024, Florence, Italy

An efficient EMS for aggregated energy systems including renewables, storages, CHP units and heat pumps

Filip Sobic,[a] Lavinia Ghilardi,[a] Hilal Bahlawan,[b] Lapo Cheli,[b] Alessandro Innocenti,[b] Emanuele Martelli[a,*]

[a]*Politecnico di Milano, Department of Energy, Via Lambruschini 4, Milano 20156, Italy*
[b]*Yanmar R&D Europe, Viale Galileo 3/A, Firenze 50125, Italy*
*emanuele.martelli@polimi.it

Abstract

The need to reduce man-made greenhouse gas emissions leads to the ever larger importance of exploiting operational synergies of Aggregated Energy Systems. Mixed Integer Linear Programming (MILP) based Energy Management Systems (EMS) are state-of-the-art tools for exploiting these synergies by determining the optimal operation of different units over the desired time horizon. This work presents two EMSs evaluated through a two-month case study. The performance of these two EMSs is compared against the ideal operation of the system assuming perfect forecasts, as well as heuristic strategies. Results showed that using EMS can yield monthly cost savings of up to 14.7% compared to heuristic strategies. The EMS shows also a very good robustness to the uncertainty of input forecasts. The solutions derived remain feasible, with only 1.1% suboptimality compared to the scheduling solution obtained under perfect forecast conditions.

Keywords: energy management systems, energy districts, MILP, microgrids, rolling-horizon.

1. Introduction

Improvements in energy efficiency have been identified as one of the key actions for achieving required emission reductions that will put the energy sector on the pathway to limit the global average surface temperature increase below 1.5 °C above pre-industrial levels (IEA, 2023). One of the ways to achieve an increase in energy efficiency is to leverage synergies between energy sources. They can be exploited by including different energy sources in an Aggregated Energy System (AES) that can use different techniques for determining their operation that allows the system to satisfy user's energy demand. HOMER (Lambert et al., 2005) is a widely known commercial software used for determining the design and operation of off-grid microgrids. For determining the operation of the system, it uses two heuristic strategies, Load Following (LF) and Cycle Charging (CC), as described in Barley & Winn, 1996. However, due to their inability to see the future, these approaches provide suboptimal solutions. This problem can be solved by means of adopting an Energy Management System (EMS) that uses systematic optimization approaches and forecasts of the energy demand, production of intermittent renewables, and ambient conditions, to determine the optimal operation of the system.

There are numerous works in literature adopting MILP models for the EMS of Combined Heat and Power (CHP) systems, multi-energy systems and microgrids. For example, Bischi et al., 2014 developed a detailed MILP model for the short-term operational optimization of CHP units, that was later extended to optimize the long-term yearly operation (Bischi et al., 2019), and uncertainty of the input forecasts (Moretti et al., 2020, Castelli et al., 2023). Further examples include work by Fang & Lahdelma, 2016 in which they developed an EMS that optimizes the operation of a CHP plant, coupled with the heat storage, under inaccurate forecast, and work by Hellmers et al., 2016 in which the operation of the AES, consisting of CHP plant and wind farm, was optimized on the day-ahead and balancing markets.

This work presents two EMSs developed by Politecnico di Milano throughout the years, tailored specifically for AES featuring CHP units, energy storages, and intermittent renewables. These EMSs are applied in collaboration with Yanmar R&D to determine the optimal operation of AES that incorporates their products, in particular CHP engines and Heat Pumps (HPs). The EMSs employ a rolling-horizon approach, utilizing forecasts of the energy demand, intermittent renewables production (PV and ST), and ambient conditions (ambient temperature and irradiation) to determine optimal unit commitment, loads of dispatchable generators (CHP engines, HPs, boilers, etc.), storage management, and electricity import/export from/to the grid. The EMSs are based on a rigorous and accurate formulation of the optimization problem as a MILP that is solved using Gurobi.

2. Methodology

Both EMSs are an adaption of the one originally proposed by Moretti et al., 2020 for off-grid microgrids. They are implemented using the rolling horizon framework with an optimization horizon of 24 hours. Moreover, the performance maps of the units are linearized using the convex hull approach considering the effect of the ambient temperature. EMS 1 is a single-layer rolling-horizon approach which uses a forecast correction strategy for the transition from the current measured data to the forecasted ones. EMS 2 consists of two layers, its first layer employs only the forecasts and therefore its time resolution is equal to one hour. Meanwhile, the second layer works only with the measured data resulting in a time resolution of 15 minutes. Figure 1 shows a schematic representation of the two EMSs (i.e., EMS 1 and EMS 2) proposed in this work.

2.1. EMS 1: Single-layer EMS

EMS 1 combines both measurements and forecasts by taking the measured values in the first timestep of the optimization horizon, while taking the forecasted values for the rest. It is formulated as a MILP, where the real variables are used to characterize the production and consumption of the machines, renewables production, storage charge/discharge and State of Charge (SOC), and import/export from/to the grid. On the other hand, binary variables are used to define the machines on/off state, and machine start-up.

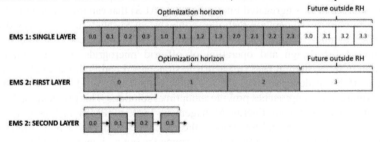

Figure 1: Schematic representation of EMS 1 and EMS 2

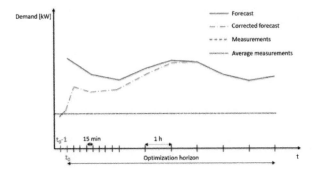

Figure 2: Example of forecast correction and variable time discretization.

Forcing a value of storage SOC at the end of the day might lead to suboptimal solutions for tomorrow. Therefore, to improve the management of the storage system, it is decided to impose SOC value after two days to reduce its impact on the scheduling solutions during the first day. In the case that forecasts are available only for the first 24 hours, the proposed approach can be realized by repeating the same forecast. If the fine time discretization, required to include measured values results in MILP being too large, it is possible to adopt an adaptive time mesh. It consists of adopting finer discretization in the timesteps close to the present, while coarser time resolution is used for the future. Finally, as the forecasts can have a significant impact on the results of the EMS, this work applies a forecast correction strategy. The idea is to make the weighted average between the average of the measured values in the last two timesteps and forecasted values. To ensure that the correction made is more significant in the timesteps closer to the present, a weight vector that starts from a defined value at the current timestep and then linearly reduces to zero, is considered. Figure 2 shows a schematic representation of adaptive time mesh and forecast correction.

2.2. EMS 2: Two-layer EMS

It is a two-layer EMS in which each of the two layers is formulated as a MILP. The role of the first layer is to determine the optimal operation of the system across a day using the forecasts of energy demands, ambient temperature (which influence the efficiency of the engines, refrigeration cycles and heat pumps) and renewables productions. It is formulated exactly as the single layer of the EMS 1, with the only difference being that it uses forecasts also in the first timestep. The second layer is used on a real-time basis to correct the solution of the first layer in light of the actual energy demands and renewables production. Since it carries out optimization only in the present timestep, without considering the future, without an additional constraint it would shut down the machines and discharge the storage to meet energy demands. Therefore, an additional cost term, that imposes the desired behavior of the storage, is added to the objective function as shown in Eq. (1). It includes a fictitious revenue ($\tilde{c}_{st}^{surplus} E_{st}^{surplus}$) obtained by charging the storage above the setpoint indicated by the first layer, and a fictitious cost ($\tilde{c}_{st}^{deficit} E_{st}^{deficit}$) associated with discharging the storage below it.

$$OF = OF + \sum_{st \in \mathcal{S}} \left(\tilde{c}_{st}^{deficit} E_{st}^{deficit} - \tilde{c}_{st}^{surplus} E_{st}^{surplus} \right) + \sum_{m \in \mathcal{M}} \tilde{c}_{m}^{dispatch} \delta_{m}^{dispatch} \qquad (1)$$

Unmet demand, that can arise due to the error in the forecasts, is avoided by including a binary variable in the second layer that allows it to turn on the machines. However, this allows the second layer to turn off the machines if the demand is lower than expected, which can result in frequent on/off of the machines. Therefore, an additional cost term $(\tilde{c}_m^{dispatch} \delta_m^{dispatch})$ is added to the objective function that penalizes the divergence in the dispatching decisions of the first and second layers that is expressed through a binary variable $\delta_m^{dispatch}$ defined for every machine.

2.3. Benchmark Control Strategies

In addition to the widely adopted heuristic strategies such as LF and CC, this work also proposes the single timestep MILP (here called LF-MILP) as the benchmark for the EMS performance (for each timestep, the LF-MILP minimizes the operational cost without taking into account the future timesteps). While the LF-MILP uses the units that minimize the current operational cost, the LF case uses the units according to an efficiency priority order (set by the user).

3. Case Study and Computational Results

To assess the effectiveness of the two EMSs, they are used for optimizing the operation of the case study shown in Figure 3 for the months of January and March of 2017. The case study consists of the following components: TESS, 2 CHP engines, boiler, HP, ST panels, and PV panels. Its hourly demand values for electricity and heating are taken from the National Renewable Energy Laboratory, 2014 data set for a full-service restaurant, while ambient condition data are taken from the TMY provided by PVGIS (Huld et al., 2012). Values for the forecast are obtained using the persistence method on the aforementioned data, where for the demand, weekends are forecasted using the data of the previous weekend. In the case of electricity demand forecast, Mean Average Percentage Error (MAPE) and Mean Average Deviation (MAD) are equal to 5.6 % and 1.7 kW, respectively. On the other hand, the forecast for the heat demand is much less reliable, with MAPE and MAD equal to 200.4 % and 19.1 kW, respectively. Table 1 reports the performance of the two EMSs and the comparison with the two heuristic strategies and LF-MILP. Moreover, the table reports the minimum possible operating cost (lower bound) which could be achieved with perfect forecasts (no forecast uncertainty) and optimizing the operation with a single large-scale MILP. Such an ideal case is referred to as "omniscient EMS". It is evident that management of the AES using two proposed EMSs is not far away from the perfect operation described by the omniscient. As expected, EMS 1 provides the best performance as it can avoid suboptimal second-layer corrections and its operating cost is only 1.1 % higher compared to that of the lower bound. This also indicates that the EMS is very robust to the uncertainty of the forecasts.

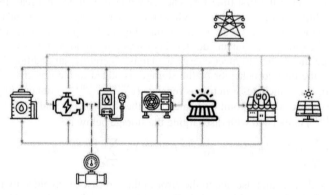

Figure 3: Configuration of the AES used in the test case.

Table 1: Performance summary of the different EMSs.

	Total cost [€]	Cost increase [%]	Average run time [s]
Lower bound (Omniscient EMS)	7,792	/	1.87
EMS 1	7,881	1.1	2.29
EMS 2	7,993	2.6	0.61
LF-MILP	8,264	6.1	0.02
LF	8,477	8.8	$<10^{-5}$
CC	9,239	18.6	$<10^{-5}$

On the other hand, LF-MILP and heuristic strategies are extremely fast, however, this comes at the expense of their performance, having significant deviation from the omniscient. For the sake of brevity and easier interpretation, only plots presenting the results of EMS 1 and omniscient in the case of thermal energy demand for the first day of January are reported in Figure 4. Before commenting on the differences in the results, it is important to note that the forecast for January 1st significantly underestimates thermal demand during the largest part of the day, especially in the morning. However, for January 2nd the situation is the other way around, with the forecast that significantly overestimates actual thermal demand. These two factors are a driving force behind the differences in EMS 1 and omniscient operation which can be seen in Figure 4. Omniscient, due to its perfect knowledge, is aware that the load is significantly higher than forecasted and therefore dispatches both CHP 2 and HP during the morning to fill the storage that, together with the HP, will be used during morning hours to meet the demand. On the other hand, EMS 1 is unaware of the forecast error and therefore is not able to prepare the storage and instead uses CHP 2 to cover most of the demand during early morning. The second main difference is the energy content of the storage at the end of the day. EMS 1 sees high demand for the following day and therefore completely fills the storage. On the contrary, as omniscient is aware that the forecast is overestimating actual demand, it fills storage only up to 60 % of its maximum energy content.

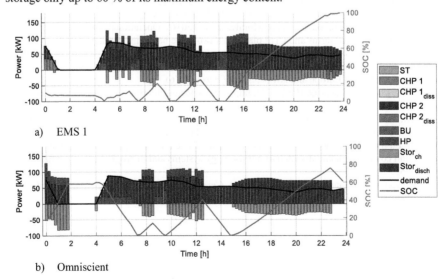

Figure 4: Comparison between operation of EMS 1 and omniscient for January 1st

In terms of cost savings, EMS 1 performs better than EMS2 because the second layer corrections of EMS2 are made without knowledge of the future.

4. Conclusions

This work presented two different EMSs developed by Politecnico di Milano used for determining optimal operation of the AESs with combined heat and power units, heat pumps, energy storages, and intermittent renewables. These two EMSs were employed in collaboration with Yanmar R&D for a case study considering the AES employing their CHP engines along with other machines (i.e., HP and boiler) and renewable energy generators (i.e., PV and ST panels). Operation of the AES was simulated during the months of January and March and the results showed that the single-layer EMS is particularly effective, with a total operating cost of only 1.1 % higher than the perfect operation. Compared to benchmark heuristic algorithms, it allows reducing the operational cost in the range 5-15 %. Therefore, the proposed EMS is very promising for the optimal operation of aggregated energy systems.

References

Barley, C. D., & Winn, C. B. (1996). Optimal dispatch strategy in remote hybrid power systems. *Solar Energy, 58*(4–6). https://doi.org/10.1016/S0038-092X(96)00087-4

Bischi, A., Taccari, L., Martelli, E., Amaldi, E., Manzolini, G., Silva, P., Campanari, S., & Macchi, E. (2014). A detailed MILP optimization model for combined cooling, heat and power system operation planning. *Energy, 74*(C).

Bischi, A., Taccari, L., Martelli, E., Amaldi, E., Manzolini, G., Silva, P., Campanari, S., & Macchi, E. (2019). A rolling-horizon optimization algorithm for the long term operational scheduling of cogeneration systems. *Energy, 184*.

Castelli, A. F., Moretti, L., Manzolini, G., & Martelli, E. (2023). Robust optimization of seasonal, day-ahead and real time operation of aggregated energy systems. *International Journal of Electrical Power & Energy Systems, 152*, 109190. https://doi.org/10.1016/J.IJEPES.2023.109190

Fang, T., & Lahdelma, R. (2016). Optimization of combined heat and power production with heat storage based on sliding time window method. *Applied Energy, 162*.

Hellmers, A., Zugno, M., Skajaa, A., & Morales, J. M. (2016). Operational strategies for a portfolio of wind farms and CHP plants in a two-price balancing market. *IEEE Transactions on Power Systems, 31*(3). https://doi.org/10.1109/TPWRS.2015.2439060

Huld, T., Müller, R., & Gambardella, A. (2012). A new solar radiation database for estimating PV performance in Europe and Africa. *Solar Energy, 86*(6).

IEA. (2023). *World Energy Outlook 2023*. https://www.iea.org/reports/world-energy-outlook-2023

Lambert, T., Gilman, P., & Lilienthal, P. (2005). Micropower system modeling with HOMER. In *Integration of Alternative Sources of Energy*. John Wiley & Sons.

Moretti, L., Martelli, E., & Manzolini, G. (2020). An efficient robust optimization model for the unit commitment and dispatch of multi-energy systems and microgrids. *Applied Energy, 261*.

National Renewable Energy Laboratory. (2014). *Commercial and Residential Hourly Load Profiles for all TMY3 Locations in the United States*. [Data Set].

Flavio Manenti, Gintaras V. Reklaitis (Eds.), Proceedings of the 34th European Symposium on Computer Aided Process Engineering / 15th International Symposium on Process Systems Engineering (ESCAPE34/PSE24), June 2-6, 2024, Florence, Italy

Electric Heat Pumps and Combined Heat and Power Systems for the Optimal Decarbonisation of the Integrated UK Energy System

Matthias Mersch,[a,b,c] Andreas V. Olympios,[a,c,d] Christos N. Markides,[a,c] Niall Mac Dowell[b,c]*

[a]*Clean Energy Processes (CEP) Laboratory, Department of Chemical Engineering, Imperial College London, London SW7 2AZ, UK*
[b]*Centre for Environmental Policy, Imperial College London, London SW7 2AZ, UK*
[c]*Sargent Centre for Process Systems Engineering, Department of Chemical Engineering, Imperial College London, London SW7 2AZ, UK*
[d]*PV Technology Laboratory, FOSS Research Centre for Sustainable Energy, Department of Electrical and Computer Engineering, University of Cyprus, Nicosia, 2109, Cyprus*
niall@imperial.ac.uk

Abstract

Electric heat pumps and combined heat and power (CHP) systems are potentially key technologies to decarbonise heating, which currently accounts for over a third of the UK's carbon emissions. In this work, we use an integrated energy system optimisation model to investigate the role of both in the energy system transition, studying interactions between the heating and power sectors. To increase the robustness of the analysis, a Monte Carlo approach is used to account for uncertainties in key model input parameters, such as fuel costs and capital costs of key technologies. Results show that heat pumps provide 40 to 80 % of all heat in the UK in 2050, while CHP systems are especially valuable as intermediate technology in the 2030s.

Keywords: Energy system optimisation, heat decarbonisation, heat pump, combined heat and power, integrated energy systems

1. Introduction

Heating accounts for about 37 % of UK carbon emissions (BEIS, 2018) and urgently needs to be decarbonised to meet ambitious climate targets. Currently, heating is mainly provided by natural gas boilers. Low-carbon alternatives such as heat pumps, hydrogen boilers, and CHP systems result in a strong integration of different sectors of the energy system, especially heating and power generation. In this work, we use an integrated energy system optimisation model (Mersch, 2023) to assess the role of heat pumps and CHP systems in the decarbonisation of the UK energy system, considering both individual solutions and district heating networks. Hydrogen boilers are also considered as an alternative, and hydrogen can also be used to power CHP systems.

In their meta-analysis of UK energy system decarbonisation pathways, Dixon et al. (2022) found that in 6 of the 7 reviewed pathways air-source heat pumps (ASHPs) and district heating are the dominant low-carbon heating technologies, while the last one mainly relies on hydrogen boilers. The share of individual heat pumps in UK homes ranges from 27 % to 74 %, while district heating shares range from 10 % to 42 %.

Aunedi et al. (2022) soft-linked an electricity system model with a heating model to study optimal heat decarbonisation options for the UK. The authors found a strong role for hybrid heating systems consisting of ASHPs and hydrogen boilers. However, the sectors are only soft-linked, CHP systems are not considered, and no uncertainty analysis is performed. Pavičević et al. (2020) investigated decarbonisation pathways for integrated energy systems and the benefits of sector-coupling in Europe by soft-linking a capacity-expansion and a unit-commitment model. The results showed that in the optimal system about 30 % of heat is provided by biomass and natural gas-fired CHP systems, about 50 % from ASHPs and electric heaters, and the rest from backup gas boilers. Hydrogen heating options are not considered, and no uncertainty analysis is performed. Charitopoulos et al. (2023) used a spatially explicit optimisation model to analyse the impact of fully electrifying domestic heating in the UK on the power sector. The authors showed that if thermal energy storage (TES) is utilised, only a 30 % increase of power generation capacity is required to fully electrify domestic heating, while without TES the required power generation capacity is another 40 % higher. Furthermore, Olympios et al. (2020) compared the deployment of heat pumps and gas-fired CHP systems at household level and in district heating networks. The findings indicated that heat pumps can provide high emission reductions even when powered by the UK electricity grid of 2020 (55 to 62 %), while gas-fired CHP systems integrated within district heating networks are the most cost-effective option in areas with high energy density. Then, Olympios et al. (2022) compared ASHPs and hydrogen heating technologies from a household and whole-energy system perspective, concluding that ASHPs are the least-cost pathway for both, but hydrogen in the context of CHP systems was not considered. In a related study, Hoseinpoori et al. (2022) demonstrated the significant role of ASHPs in UK heat decarbonisation, with hydrogen boilers being identified as a supplementary option. CHP systems at building or district-heating level were not examined.

In this paper, we investigate the role of different low-carbon heating technologies in the UK energy system decarbonisation, using an integrated whole-energy system model that explicitly links the heating, electricity, and hydrogen sectors. The focus lies hereby on heat pumps and CHP systems, which were both shown to have great heat decarbonisation potential. We explicitly account for uncertainties in technology costs and fuel prices, thus providing a more robust analysis that allows for a direct and comprehensive comparison of these technologies within the broader context of the whole energy system.

2. Methodology

The Energy System Optimisation (ESO) model used for the analysis is described in detail in Mersch et al. (2023). The model performs a simultaneous optimisation of capacity expansion from 2020 to 2050, allowing investment decisions every 5 years, and technology dispatch with hourly resolution, using a representative-day approach. This approach allows the model to account for seasonal effects, such as changing demand patterns. Electricity, hydrogen, and CO_2 removal sectors as well as domestic, commercial, and industrial heat are explicitly represented in the model, while for the transport sector assumptions on the uptake of electric vehicles and the corresponding electricity demand are made. The model performs a cost minimisation assuming perfect foresight.

For this work, CHP systems and a representation of district heating networks have been added to the model. Modelled CHP systems are natural gas and hydrogen internal combustion engines (ICEs), which can be deployed either at household, commercial building, or industrial site level, or in district heating networks. Other generation technology options for district heating are ground-source heat pumps (GSHPs), natural gas boilers and hydrogen boilers, while hot water tanks are considered as a TES option. CHP systems are assumed to be able to feed any generated electricity into the grid.

The cost and performance of heating technologies are modelled based on the data collected by Olympios et al. (2021). Key parameters for small-scale household level systems are shown in Table 1, while parameters of larger assets for *e.g.*, district heating systems are shown in Table 2. Note that these are only the baseline parameters. Some parameters are varied during the Monte Carlo study to account for uncertainties, as described below. Efficiencies of ASHPs and GSHPs are calculated using a correlation based on the ambient air and ground temperature, respectively.

Table 1. Key cost and performance parameters of domestic heating technologies.

Technology	Size [kW_{th}]	CAPEX [£]	OPEX [£/y]	Efficiency
Gas boiler	30	2,560	100	0.9
H_2 boiler	30	2,560	100	0.9
Small ASHP	5	6,860	240	variable
Large ASHP	10	8,230	240	variable
GSHP	10	18,190	240	variable
Electric backup	3	110	0	1
Gas ICE	25	37,130	100	0.67 thermal, 0.27 electric
H_2 ICE	25	37,130	100	0.67 thermal, 0.27 electric
District heat	30	5,930	0	0.94

Table 2. Key cost and performance parameters of district heating technologies.

Technology	CAPEX [£/kW]	OPEX [£/kW/y]	Efficiency
Gas boiler	32	6.25	0.9
H_2 boiler	32	6.25	0.9
GSHP	299	6.67	variable
Gas ICE	207	10.3	0.67 thermal, 0.27 electric
H_2 ICE	207	10.3	0.67 thermal, 0.27 electric

District heating is only viable in areas with a high heat demand density. Based on analysis from the UK Department of Business, Energy & Industrial Strategy (BEIS) (2021), district heating is constrained to a maximum of 20 % of domestic and commercial properties. The cost of district heating connections is estimated based on data from a Finnish district heating scheme (Helen, 2023), while the cost of the pipe network is estimated based on the annual delivered heat, using data from the BEIS (2021) report.

2.1. Monte Carlo Analysis

A Monte Carlo analysis is used to account for uncertainties in key model input parameters, such as capital costs, fuel prices and the interest rate. The uncertain input parameters and respective bounds considered in the sampling are shown in Table 3. The gas price bounds cover the variation seen in the UK since 2021. The biomass availability is included as parameter to account for cases where emission offsetting is much more expensive, while the interest rate influences the trade-off between CAPEX and OPEX.

Table 3. Uncertain input parameters and respective bounds considered in the analysis.

Parameter	Lower bound	Upper bound
Gas price	10 £/MWh	150 £/MWh
Biomass availability	0 % of baseline	100 % of baseline
Heat pump CAPEX	-50 %	+50 %
CHP CAPEX	-50 %	+50 %
District heating network cost	-50 %	+50 %
Interest rate	0 %/y	10 %/y

A Latin hypercube sampling approach is used to effectively cover the parameter space. For the analysis presented here, the optimisation is performed for 100 sets of input parameters to limit the computational complexity.

3. Results and Discussion

Figure 1 shows the share of heat provided by heat pumps across all sectors, including domestic, commercial, and industrial demand as well as district heating, for the different Monte Carlo runs, while Figure 2 shows the share of heat provided by CHP systems.

Not shown in the figures is the degree of district heating deployment, as in every scenario the maximum amount of district heating, corresponding to 20 % of domestic and commercial heat demand, is deployed, regardless of fuel prices and network costs. This highlights the strong potential role for such solutions, which benefit from economies of scale and the ability to easily integrate multiple heating technologies. Results show that in many cases district heating is powered by a combination of both GSHPs and CHP systems, responding to changes in demand in the wider electricity sector.

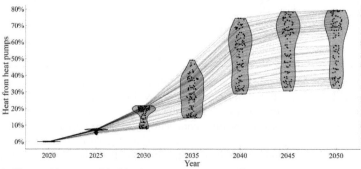

Figure 1. Share of heat provided by heat pumps across all sectors.

Heat pumps play a significant role in every scenario, providing 40 to 80 % of total heat in 2050. As shown in Figure 3, the amount of heat pump deployment is strongly correlated with the natural gas price (Pearson correlation coefficient $r = 0.92$), as the gas price strongly affects the operating costs of alternative heating solutions. A breakdown of heat pump deployment by sector reveals that in every run all of the low-temperature industrial heat is provided by ASHPs. Due to the assumed flat demand profile and economies of scale, heat pumps appear to be especially cost-effective there. The same applies to district heating and commercial buildings, where the demand profile is not flat, but economies of scale are still strong. GSHPs supply 52 to 97 % of heat for district heating, while ASHPs cover 32 to 72 % of the commercial demand in all scenarios. Deployment in domestic buildings depends strongly on the natural gas price. In scenarios with gas prices near the lower bound no domestic heat pumps are deployed, while in others up to 80 % of the domestic heating demand is supplied by ASHPs.

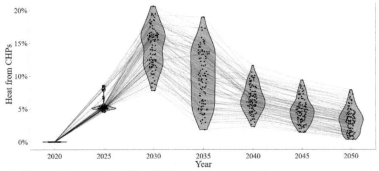

Figure 2. Share of heat provided by CHP systems across all sectors.

CHP systems appear to be especially valuable as transitional technology, as the share of heat provided from CHP systems peaks in 2030 before decreasing towards 2050. Hydrogen ICEs are not competitive; therefore, CHP systems rely mostly on natural gas and are thus associated with emissions, which need to be offset as emission constraints become tighter. Especially for district heating, in most scenarios the heat supply gradually shifts from initially a larger share of CHP systems towards a larger share of heat from GSHPs in 2050. Domestic CHP systems are too expensive and therefore not deployed in any scenario, while larger CHP systems show potential for industrial, commercial and district heating applications. In 2030, natural gas ICE CHP systems provide 16 to 61 % of industrial heat, 5 to 46 % of district heat, and 0 to 22 % of commercial heat. The natural gas price also has the biggest single impact on the degree of CHP deployment (Pearson correlation coefficient r = -0.88, see Figure 3).

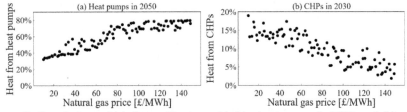

Figure 3. Correlations of (a) share of heat provided by heat pumps in 2050; and (b) share of heat provided by CHPs in 2030 with natural gas prices.

3.1. Integration between heat and power sectors

The deployment of heat pumps and CHP systems results in a significant integration of the heating and power sectors. The additional annual electricity demand due to heat electrification reaches 100 to 230 TWh in 2050, with peak electricity demands of 17 to 86 GW. To put this into context, the current annual peak electricity demand in the UK is about 50 GW. On the other hand, CHP systems co-generate a maximum of 8 to 15 GW of electricity in 2030, and 19 to 47 TWh annually.

The district heating sector is a good indicator for the interaction between heating and power sectors, as both heat pumps and CHP systems are utilised and can satisfy the same heat demand. CHP systems are primarily used during times of high system electricity demand, while heat pumps primarily operate at off-peak times, and at times with a high availability of renewable energy technologies.

Additionally, 31 to 136 GWh of TES capacity is deployed for district heating alone, which allows shifting electricity demand further. This is especially valuable towards the end of the time horizon when the share of CHP systems in the system is lower.

4. Conclusions

Optimal whole-energy system decarbonisation pathways for the UK have been studied using an integrated energy system optimisation model that explicitly considers the heating, electricity, and hydrogen sectors, as well as negative emission technologies. Both long-term investment decisions and short-term dispatch schedules were optimised simultaneously. A Monte Carlo approach was used to account for uncertainties in key model input parameters, such as fuel costs and capital costs of key technologies.

Heat pumps play a key role in the energy system transition, supplying 40 to 80 % of all heat in 2050. The degree of deployment mainly depends on the natural gas price, though especially for low-temperature industrial heat deployment is consistently high. CHP systems on the other hand are mainly useful during the transition, with utilisation peaking in 2030 before then declining again. District heating is consistently highly deployed.

Heat pumps and CHP systems result in a significant integration of heating and power sectors. District heating networks using both, as well as TES, provide valuable flexibility.

Acknowledgements

This work was supported by the UK Engineering and Physical Sciences Research Council (EPSRC) [grant numbers EP/R045518/1, EP/V042149/1, and EP/T033940/1]. For the purpose of Open Access, the authors have applied a CC BY public copyright licence to any Author Accepted Manuscript version arising from this submission.

References

M. Aunedi, M. Yliruka, S. Deghan, A.M. Pantaleo, N. Shah, G. Strbac, 2022, Multi-model assessment of heat decarbonisation options in the UK using electricity and hydrogen, Renewable Energy, 194, 1261-1276

V.M. Charitopoulos, M. Fajardy, C.K. Chyong, D.M. Reiner, 2023, The impact of 100% electrification of domestic heat in Great Britain, iScience, 26, 11, 108239

Department for Business, Energy & Industrial Strategy (BEIS), 2018, Clean Growth – Transforming Heating. Overview of Current Evidence.

Department for Business, Energy & Industrial Strategy (BEIS), 2021, Opportunity areas for district heating networks in the UK.

J. Dixon, K. Bell, S. Brush, 2022, Which way to net zero? a comparative analysis of seven UK 2050 decarbonisation pathways, Renewable and Sustainable Energy Transition, 2, 100016

Helen, 2023, District heat prices, https://www.helen.fi/en/heating/district-heat/district-heat-prices

P. Hoseinpoori, A.V. Olympios, C.N. Markides, J. Woods, N. Shah, 2022, A whole-system approach for quantifying the value of smart electrification for decarbonising heating in buildings, Energy Conversion and Management, 268, 115952

M. Mersch, C.N. Markides, N. Mac Dowell, 2023, The impact of the energy crisis on the UK's net-zero transition, iScience, 26, 4, 106491

A.V. Olympios, A.M. Pantaleo, P. Sapin, C.N. Markides, 2020, On the value of combined heat and power (CHP) systems and heat pumps in centralised and distributed heating systems: Lessons from multi-fidelity modelling approaches, Applied Energy, 274, 115261

A.V. Olympios, M. Mersch, P. Sapin, A.M. Pantaleo, C.N. Markides, 2021, Library of price and performance data of domestic and commercial technologies for low-carbon energy systems, Zenodo, https://zenodo.org/doi/10.5281/zenodo.4692648

A.V. Olympios, M. Aunedi, M. Mersch, A. Krishnaswamy, C. Stollery, A.M. Pantaleo, P. Sapin, G. Strbac, C.N. Markides, 2022, Delivering net-zero carbon heat: Technoeconomic and whole-system comparisons of domestic electricity- and hydrogen-driven technologies in the UK, Energy Conversion and Management, 262, 115649

M. Pavičević, A. Mangipinto, W. Nijs, F. Lombardi, K. Kavvadias, J.P. Jiménez Navarro, E. Colombo, S. Qoilin, 2020, The potential of sector coupling in future European energy systems: Soft linking between the Dispa-SET and JRC-EU-TIMES models, Applied Energy, 267, 115100

Flavio Manenti, Gintaras V. Reklaitis (Eds.), Proceedings of the 34th European Symposium on Computer Aided Process Engineering / 15th International Symposium on Process Systems Engineering (ESCAPE34/PSE24), June 2-6, 2024, Florence, Italy

Economic Analysis of Liquid Air Energy Storage Systems

Shaylin A. Cetegen[a], Truls Gundersen[b], Paul I. Barton[a]

[a]*Process Systems Engineering Laboratory, Dept. of Chemical Engineering, Massachusetts Institute of Technology, Cambridge, MA 02139, United States*
[b]*Department of Energy and Process Engineering, Norwegian University of Science and Technology (NTNU), Kolbjørn Hejes Vei 1B, NO-7491, Trondheim, Norway*
pib@mit.edu

Abstract

Liquid air energy storage (LAES) is a clean and scalable long-duration energy storage technology capable of delivering multiple GWh of energy storage. The inherent locatability of LAES systems unlocks nearly universal siting opportunities for grid-scale energy storage, which were previously unavailable with traditional technologies such as pumped hydro energy storage (PHES) and compressed air energy storage (CAES). While the technical viability of LAES systems has been demonstrated [1], its economic viability has not yet been established across a broad range of electricity markets. In this work, we perform a high-level economic analysis of LAES systems across various United States domestic and international markets under current levels of renewable energy penetration to provide baseline estimates of LAES economic viability. By simultaneously optimizing the design and operation of LAES systems to maximize their net present value over the project lifespan, we can deliver a yes/no indication of the economic viability of these systems. Our results enable comparison of the economic viability of LAES systems operating in different regions and provide detailed insights into their economic dynamics that can aid in the development of supportive policy and economic incentives to encourage further adoption of LAES. A sensitivity analysis is also performed to provide a better understanding of the potential economic benefit of co-locating LAES systems with other processes to boost LAES round-trip efficiencies by making efficient use of otherwise wasted heating/cooling resources.

Keywords: energy storage, grid-scale energy storage, liquid air energy storage, mixed-integer linear programming, optimization

1. Introduction

Grid-scale energy storage demand is increasing due to the growing adoption of renewable energy sources, which are intermittent and require reliable storage solutions to ensure a continuous and stable power supply [2]. PHES and CAES currently supply over 96% of global grid-scale energy storage capacity; however, due to their location constrained nature, both PHES and CAES face severely limited expansion opportunities moving forward. Thus, alternative grid-scale energy storage solutions, such as LAES, are sought to meet growing demand.

2. Background

LAES is a thermo-mechanical grid-scale energy storage technology that serves to balance supply and demand of the electric grid while generating revenue via arbitrage. LAES systems charge when the energy supplied to the grid exceeds demand (i.e., when electricity prices are low) and discharge when demand exceeds supply (i.e., when electricity prices are high). LAES systems operate by intaking ambient air from the atmosphere, cleaning and drying it, compressing it to high pressure through a multi-stage compression train, and cooling it to a liquid state using one or more multi-stream heat exchangers. The liquid air is then stored in insulated tanks at atmospheric pressure and very low temperature (~ 90 K), typically for durations of several hours to days with negligible losses over these periods. Later, when energy demand exceeds supply, the liquid air is pumped out of storage, evaporated/heated, and passed through a multi-stage expansion train with reheating, which drives a generator to recover power. The round-trip efficiency (RTE) of standalone LAES systems currently stands at around 60 %. Hot and cold thermal storages, which recycle compression heat released during charging and high-grade cold generated from exchange with cold air during discharging, are critical to achieving LAES efficiencies over 50 % and thus, are an essential feature of all practical LAES system designs. A high-level flowsheet of the LAES process is shown in Figure 1.

Several key features of LAES make it an attractive grid-scale energy storage solution. First, unlike other energy storage technologies, such as Li-ion batteries and CAES, no rare-earth minerals or carbon emissions are required by or produced through the operation of LAES systems. Second, the unique locatability of LAES unlocks, for the first time, nearly universal siting opportunities for grid-scale energy storage. Third, there exist significant opportunities to co-locate LAES systems with other processes (e.g., waste industrial heat and LNG regasification) to make efficient use of otherwise wasted heating/cooling resources, which can significantly boost LAES RTEs. While the technical viability of LAES has been established in the literature, with reported RTEs of up to 68.2 %, the economic viability of LAES systems has yet to be rigorously established across the broad range of markets in which it could theoretically be implemented [1, 3]. To this end, we perform an economic assessment of LAES systems in several United States (US) domestic and international markets. The sensitivity of LAES economic performance to improvements in RTE resulting from co-location with liquefied natural gas (LNG) regasification is also explored to elucidate the potential value of LAES-LNG co-location.

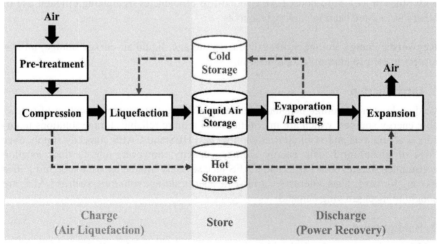

Figure 1: A standalone liquid air energy storage system with hot and cold thermal recycle.

3. Methods

To perform long-term economic optimization of LAES systems in several US domestic and international electricity markets, a mixed-integer linear program (MILP) was formulated to maximize the net present value (NPV) of an LAES system over its expected lifespan. Hourly locational marginal price (LMP) profiles were derived from historical data obtained from the official source for each considered load zone of all US independent system operators (ISOs) or European/Asian transmission system operators (TSOs) and supplied to the optimizer to calculate revenue generation from arbitrage - the strategic buying and selling of electricity over time for profit. The generated electricity price profiles, which contain hourly LMPs for a representative day of each month of the year, are repeated annually over the project horizon. This is likely to yield a conservative estimate of the economic viability of LAES systems because it does not consider an increasing supply of renewables over time, which is expected to result in increased opportunities for arbitrage profitability.

In the optimization formulation, the design and operation of LAES systems are simultaneously optimized to maximize the NPV of the LAES system. The decision variables for this problem were the power rating of the system and the operating schedule of the system over its expected lifespan. A RTE of 60 % was assumed for all systems considered herein, unless otherwise noted, as this efficiency is presently achievable for LAES. A storage capacity of 8 hours (i.e., 800 MWh of storage for a 100 MW system) was used for all systems in this study; however, this can be changed easily by manipulating a parameter in the optimization model. The capital expense (CAPEX) model used for all systems is given by Eq. (1), where v_l is the lth element of a user-defined vector of feasible system power ratings and y_l is a binary variable used for capacity selection.

$$CAPEX(y_l) = 5.2307\left(\sum_{l=1}^{n_l} v_l y_l\right)^{0.76532} \tag{1}$$

This model, which delivers reasonable CAPEX values of 30 - 178 million US dollars (USD) for 10 - 100 MW LAES systems, respectively, was derived from CAPEX estimates available in the literature and was linearized for use in the MILP [1]. Annual operating expenses (OPEX) were set, based on literature estimates, to equal 3 % of the CAPEX for all systems [4]. The MILP formulation contains constraints enforcing single-mode operation, over-cycling prevention, and feasible operation at all times. The objective function is the NPV of the project. This function accounts for CAPEX and OPEX, revenue generation via arbitrage, corporate taxes, tax credits (assumed 30% investment tax credit on all systems) depreciation (5-year modified accelerated cost recovery system depreciation schedule), and cashflow discounting. In order to compare systems of equivalent size across markets, in cases when the optimal NPV was initially found to be nonpositive, the design was fixed at a power rating of 100 MW for the power recovery unit (PRU) and the operating schedule was optimized to obtain the highest possible NPV.

4. Results

The optimization results for LAES systems in 19 load zones across three US ISOs, 27 European TSOs, and two load zones of the Korean TSO are summarized in Figure 2. All NPVs are reported in 2023 US dollars. The best-performing system identified in this study was the system in the WEST load zone of the ERCOT market, located in Texas, which had an NPV of $10.4 million. The positive NPV for this system is likely due to the

Table 1: Optimal solution of LAES system in the WEST load zone of the ERCOT market.

Parameter	Value
Optimal NPV	$10,429,900
PRU Power Capacity	100 MW
ALU Power Capacity	50 MW
Storage Capacity	800 MWh
CAPEX	$177,498,800
Annual OPEX	$5,325,000
Annual Revenue	$20,325,400
Installed Cost	$222/kWh
Levelized Cost of Storage (LCOS)	$119/MWh

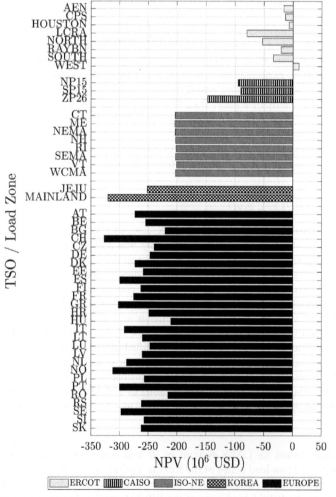

Figure 2: Optimal NPVs of 100MW/800MWh LAES systems in multiple load zones of three US ISOs, two load zones of the Korean TSO, and 27 European TSOs.

combined effects of a deregulated market and high penetration of wind energy in the ERCOT-WEST load zone. The positive NPV indicates that LAES is presently economically viable in this location. The optimal solution for this system is summarized in Table 1 and the levelized cost of storage (LCOS) for this system is $119/MWh, which is within range of the 100 – 150 $/MWh estimates reported by Highview Power, a UK-based company leading LAES implementation efforts. It is interesting to note that the LCOS of the ERCOT-WEST system is lower than the $150/MWh LCOS of Li-ion batteries, which agrees with the recent findings of Vecchi and Sciacovelli (2023).

While the optimal NPVs of a 100 MW / 800 MWh LAES system were negative in all but one of the studied locations, it is important to note that significant increases in NPV are expected to result when an increasing supply of renewables over time is considered in such an analysis. Nevertheless, useful insights can still be gained from these results. For instance, the large range of optimal NPVs identified in the ERCOT, CAISO, KOREA, and EUROPE markets highlight the importance of informed load zone selection. Based on our results, if a US ISO wanted to build an LAES system within their network, informed load-zone selection could result in up to a 39 % or 113 % increase in NPV in the CAISO and ERCOT markets, respectively, compared to a system operating in the worst performing load zone of that market. Each of the markets considered herein has a unique mix of renewables with different levels of renewable penetration at the market and load-zone levels. However, overall, throughout this study, it was observed that locations with high levels of renewable supply are generally best-suited for LAES implementation and that the positive economic influence of any improvements in RTE or potential economic incentives such as CAPEX subsidies are amplified in these regions.

While RTEs above 60 % may be challenging to achieve for standalone LAES systems presently, RTEs of over 100% are theoretically achievable for this technology through co-location with other processes. A unique feature of the Korean market considered in this study is that Korea currently has seven LNG regasification terminals – six on the mainland and one on Jeju Island. The concept of utilizing high-grade cold exergy that is released during LNG regasification to reduce the energy requirement of air liquefaction for LAES has been studied in the literature. Several studies of proposed co-located LAES-LNG systems report RTEs of roughly 70 - 190 % [1, 5].

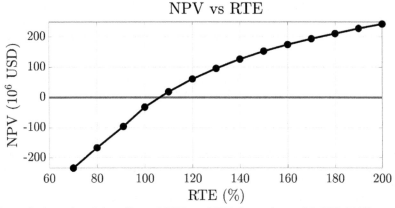

Figure 3: A study of the effect of RTE on NPV for co-located LAES-LNG systems in South Korea's Jeju Island load zone.

A sensitivity analysis on co-located LAES-LNG systems located in Korea was performed to gain a better understanding of the economic benefits of LAES-LNG co-location. Optimization was performed for 100 MW / 800 MWh LAES-LNG systems with RTEs ranging from 70 - 200 %, as shown in Figure 3. A 10 % increase in CAPEX was included for these systems to account for the added cost of LAES-LNG system interconnections. The air liquefaction unit (ALU) power rating was also adjusted to satisfy a charging time to discharging time ratio of 2:1, as there are typically twice as many hours per day available for charging. A \$1250/kW increase/decrease in CAPEX was made based on the deviation of the ALU power rating from the 50 MW ALU for which the original CAPEX function was formulated. As expected, the increased RTEs of co-located LAES-LNG systems results in higher NPVs. Interestingly, while a 60 % RTE standalone LAES system is not presently economically viable in Korea based on our results, a 110+ % RTE co-located LAES-LNG system is. Since achieving these efficiencies is viable today, further investigation into LAES-LNG co-location, including an updated analysis accounting for an increased supply of renewables over time should be explored.

5. Conclusions

In this study, economic optimization of LAES systems was performed across a broad range of US domestic and international markets to gain insights into LAES on both the global (i.e., market) and local (i.e., load zone) levels. Through this study, the economic viability of LAES was established for the WEST load zone of the ERCOT market in Texas. The ability of our approach to serve as a useful planning tool to inform LAES siting was also demonstrated by up to 113 % improvements in NPV achieved through informed load-zone selection. Our results also showed that while standalone LAES systems may not presently be economically viable in Korea, co-located LAES-LNG systems with RTEs above 110 % are, indicating that significant RTE increases attributable to efficient use of otherwise wasted heating/cooling resources from a variety of processes are likely to merit further inquiry.

References

[1] A. Vecchi, Y. Li, Y. Ding, P. Mancarella, & A. Sciacovelli, (2021). Liquid air energy storage (LAES): A review on technology state-of-the-art, integration pathways and future perspectives. *Advances in Applied Energy*, *3*, 100047.

[2] O. Edenhofer, R. Pichs-Madruga, Y. Sokona, K. Seyboth, S. Kadner, T. Zwickel, ... & P. Matschoss, (Eds.). (2011). *Renewable energy sources and climate change mitigation: Special report of the intergovernmental panel on climate change*. Cambridge University Press.

[3] Z. Liu & T. Gundersen. (2022, November 18). Liquid Air Energy Storage – Optimization Opportunities. Presentation presented at 2022 American Institute of Chemical Engineers Annual Meeting, Phoenix, AZ.

[4] T. Liang, T. Zhang, X. Lin, A. Tafone, M. Legrand, X. He, ... & Y. Ding. (2022). Liquid air energy storage technology: a comprehensive review of research, development and deployment. *Progress in Energy*.

[5] J. Park, S. Cho, M. Qi, W. Noh, I. Lee, & I. Moon (2021). Liquid air energy storage coupled with liquefied natural gas cold energy: Focus on efficiency, energy capacity, and flexibility. *Energy*, *216*, 119308.

[6] A. Vecchi, & A. Sciacovelli, (2023). Long-duration thermo-mechanical energy storage–Present and future techno-economic competitiveness. *Applied Energy*, *334*, 120628.

Flavio Manenti, Gintaras V. Reklaitis (Eds.), Proceedings of the 34th European Symposium on Computer Aided Process Engineering / 15th International Symposium on Process Systems Engineering (ESCAPE34/PSE24), June 2-6, 2024, Florence, Italy

Prospective life-cycle design of regional resource circulation applying technology assessments supported by CAPE tools

Yasunori Kikuchi,[a,b,c*] Hideaki Kurishima,[d] Yuichiro Kanematsu,[b]

Takuya Kasai,[a,e] Shoma Fujii,[a,c] Yuko Oshita,[a] Tetsuya Ishida,[a] Satoshi Ohara[a,c]

[a]*Institute for Future Initiatives, The University of Tokyo, 7-3-1 Hongo, Bunkyo-ku, Tokyo 113-8654, Japan*
[b]*Presidential Endowed Chair for "Platinum Society", The University of Tokyo, 7-3-1 Hongo, Bunkyo-ku, Tokyo 113-8656, Japan*
[c]*Department of Chemical System Engineering, The University of Tokyo, 7-3-1 Hongo, Bunkyo-ku, Tokyo 113-8656, Japan*
[d]*Research Center for Regional Co-creation Basis (ReCoBa), Shibaura Institute of Technology, 3-7-2 Toyoshu, Koto-ku, Tokyo 135-8548, Japan*
[e]*Regional Revitalization Business Department, Solution Marketing Section, Idemitsu Kosan Co., Ltd. 1-2-1 Otemachi, Chiyoda-ku, Tokyo 100-8321, Japan*
ykikuchi@ifi.u-tokyo.ac.jp

Abstract

In this study, we examine regional transformation by applying carbon-neutral technologies as a springboard. Unutilized renewable resources can be recovered in some regions, for example as surplus variable renewable energy or as residues from agriculture and forestry. To link such locally available resources with energy systems consisting mainly of fossil resources, technologies for their procurement, transfer, storage, and operation need to be systematically selected and integrated into the system pre-emptively. Simulation-based design support is needed to identify possible solutions, taking into account multiple energy requirements, such as low-carbon resources, high stability, and high economic efficiency. As case studies of such regional transportation, computer-aided process engineering (CAPE) tools are employed in the technology assessments. The candidate solutions for the design of regional energy systems are generated through the characterization of the regional availability of renewable and waste resources. As the technologies utilize such resources, electric vehicles powered by local surplus photovoltaic, biomass conversion through torrefaction, biomass-derived combined heating and power, and thermal energy storage and transport are considered. Some of the options are now demonstrated in Tanegashima, an isolated Japanese island.

Keywords: microgrid decarbonization, lignocellulosic biomass, circular economy, pre-emptive life-cycle synthesis.

1. Introduction

The design of energy systems has become a global issue and necessitates regionally customized solutions to foster technological and social changes that revitalize local industries and resources. Well-coordinated, multifaceted actions including a shift from fossil to locally available renewable resources and empowering of regions are vital in addressing this challenge. Technology assessments such as life-cycle assessment (LCA), material flow analysis (MFA), and regional input–output analysis (IOA) can visualize the future potential in regions, including the implementation of emerging technologies such as biomass conversions (Corradini et al., 2023). For engaging stakeholders, such a visualized future vision is key information (Kikuchi et al., 2020). When we generate alternative candidates for future regional systems, however, the appropriate combination of applicable technologies in a region must be addressed as the life-cycle design of regional resource circulation. Because various technology options seem to be available in a region, process systems must be devised considering regional characteristics.

In this study, we examine the regional transformation through the application of carbon-neutral technologies as a springboard. Prospective thinking inevitable in such transformation can be supported by CAPE tools developed for process systems synthesis, simulation, assessment, and optimization. This study proposes a prospective life-cycle design through a case study of regional system design and assessment in Tanegashima, a remote island in Japan.

2. Materials and method

2.1. Prospective life-cycle design of regional resource circulation with CAPE tools

Prospective life-cycle design requires the steps of PSE, e.g., alternative generation, analysis, evaluation and optimization, and sensitivity analysis. Considering regional resource circumstances, adequate alternative candidates must be generated for regional transformations. Figure 1 illustrates a prospective thinking to generate the alternatives of circulating resources preemptively.

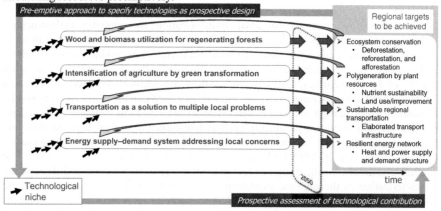

Figure 1 Preemptive thinking for alternative generation in prospective life-cycle design toward regional sustainability.

Forward-looking LCA has become an important tool for examining the future applicability of emerging technologies considering the scenarios in line with shared socioeconomic pathways (van der Giesen et al., 2020). Conventional LCA does not consider changes in technology level and social infrastructure such as power mix. Conducting a strategic LCA of emerging technologies and systems for the 30-year time horizon up to the target year, e.g., carbon neutral in 2050, is important. Toward regional real sustainability, carbon neutrality is just one of the issues; it must address ecosystem conservation, implementation of stable food production, intensification of regional industries, construction of reliable transporting infrastructure, and realization of resilient energy systems. For such long-term visions beyond carbon neutral, prospective life-cycle design should be able to synthesize emerging technologies into regional systems. Emerging technologies, as defined by Rotolo et al. (2015), are characterized as innovative, rapid growth, consistent, significant impact, and uncertain, making technology assessment difficult because of the lack of existing data and knowledge. The mechanisms developed in PSE can be applied to such system design problems.

2.2. Case study in a region: Tanegashima, a remote island in Japan

Well-coordinated, multifaceted actions, including a shift from imported fossil to locally available renewable resources and empowering rural areas, are vital to solving social challenges such as resource security, sustainable food production, and forest management. The co-learning approach to practice multifaceted actions with a case study on Tanegashima, an isolated Japanese island, was applied to move society toward sustainability. (Kikuchi et al., 2020) In these actions, knowledge of the feasible technologies, locally available resources, and socioeconomic aspects of the local community should be shared among the stakeholders to motivate change. In addition to the technoeconomic analysis, several other analyses were conducted to reveal the concerns of respective stakeholders, share the possibilities of technology options, and their socioeconomic implications on local sustainability. Tools such as the LCA, input–output analysis, and choice experiments based on questionnaire surveys on residents' preferences are used for the analyses. The stakeholders were provided with the results. These opportunities gradually converted the concerns of local stakeholders about their future regional energy systems into expectations and yielded constructive alternatives in technology implementation that can use locally available resources. PSE basics were employed in simulating and visualizing possible future visions achieved by feasible technologies and available resources. Several systems design, assessment, and demonstration projects were launched and conducted through preemptive life-cycle management (Research Center for "Co-JUNKAN" Platform towards Beyond "Zero-Carbon," 2023). Parts of the projects were taken up as case studies of prospective life-cycle design.

3. Results and discussion

3.1. Demonstration of prospective life-cycle design by technology implementation

Figure 2 schematically shows three demonstration tests conducted in Tanegashima. The following sections describe the background of prospective thinking demonstrations on regional targets.

3.1.1. Regional transportation as a solution to multiple local problems

Problems are progressively emerging in remote island regions, which have difficulties in spreading electrification of transport because of issues such as a declining population, high energy prices, and the limited number of users. The introduction of variable renewable energies has been promoted, but the share of renewable energies in the power supply mix is not increasing because of inadequate microgrid adjustment capacity. Electrification of transport can be a means of stabilizing electricity demand and utilizing local variable renewable energy (Ravi and Aziz, 2022), but the situation is that there are few early adopters. In this study, four electric vehicles and three quick chargers were introduced to Tanegashima Island in 2021 as a social demonstration test (Idemitsu Kosan Co. Ltd., 2022). Because of the small number of users, the environmental impact of infrastructure development in the LCA tended to be high, and depending on the fuel consumption of the internal combustion engines, greenhouse gases may have increased. However, it was possible to achieve electrification of the transport infrastructure in the region through discussions with the public transport sector in the region to provide a first opportunity for electrification initiatives to strengthen the transport infrastructure. In addition, a regional power supply configuration model (Kikuchi et al., 2014) was implemented, although only in small quantities, and simulations found the possibility of regulating variable renewable energy in the region (Igarashi et al., 2022). In this demonstration, the transformation of regional transportation concerns not only vehicles and their infrastructure; it also involves a transformation of lifestyles regarding transportation on the island. Electrification of vehicles can thus serve to help address various local issues.

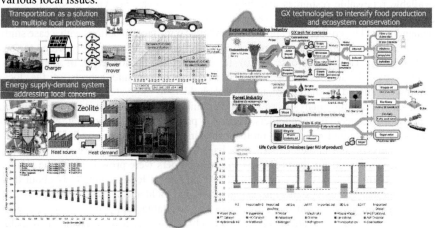

Figure 2 Demonstration tests conducted in Tanegashima based on prospective life-cycle design (Research Center for "Co-JUNKAN" Platform towards beyond "Zero-Carbon," 2023)

3.1.2. Green transformation technologies to intensify food production and ecosystem conservation

Various industries of agriculture, forestry, and livestock exist on Tanegashima. Sugarcane is a particularly strong part of regional culture, and the sugarcane industry, which produces raw sugar from local sugarcane, is one of the core industries. Sugarcane bagasse has long been used as fuel in the sugar mill in Tanegashima, and previous studies have shown that there is potential for more bagasse-derived energy than is needed for sugar production as an unutilized resource (Kikuchi et al., 2016). Also, forests in Tanegashima are in an unhealthy state because the trees are aging, even after the harvesting age, and have a small ratio of high-quality timbers suitable for sawmilling, so expanding their energy use could help to simultaneously replace fossil fuels and improve forest health. (Kanematsu et al., 2017) Industrial symbiosis is proving to be a regional innovation for fossil-free resources in agricultural and forestry regions. The combined application of bagasse and woody biomass could become a stable biomass resource in Tanegashima for producing fuels through torrefaction. (Corradini et al., 2022) Additionally, the cultivar breeding of sugarcane can also increase the potential of the sugarcane industry (Ouchida et al., 2023), as confirmed by sophisticated checking of adverse effects on sugar production (e.g., Ohara et al., 2023). Such green transformations (GX) enable the intensification of local agriculture and forestry by replacing fossil fuels.

3.1.3. Energy supply–demand systems addressing local concerns on energy

In addition to higher fuel prices compared to mainland areas, microgrids in remote island regions are subject to risks such as power outages and supply disruptions. The introduction of regional mechanisms such as industrial symbiosis into the energy infrastructure can not only make it more resilient but also can lead to de-fossilization.

In this study, a mobile thermal energy storage system is demonstrated in Tanegashima for industrial use using a zeolite water vapor adsorption and desorption cycle that can utilizes waste heat. A numerical model was developed to predict the performance of the system using a moving bed indirect heat exchange system as the heat-discharging system and a moving bed countercurrent contact system as the heat-charging system, coupled with mass, energy, and momentum conservation equations for obtaining the foreground data for the prospective LCA (Fujii et al., 2022). The results demonstrated that the unused energy derived from regional renewable resources has not been effectively distributed and has the potential to replace fossil fuels. This means that the regionally available resources can be substituted for imported resources.

3.2. Preemptive approach to regional resource circulation by CAPE tools

Geels and Schot (2007) argue that transitions occur through interactions among niche innovations, sociotechnical regimes, and the sociotechnical landscape. To grow the seeds of niche innovation, niche actors should be involved and motivated by technology assessments (Geels et al. 2017). Also, the social embeddedness of emerging technology options should be addressed through the holistic application of scientific technology assessments into co-learning. The main questions are whether systematic technology assessments could contribute to the bridging of the valley of death between research development and actual implementation, how the settings of assessment, i.e., boundary, indicators, and raw data could be defined through co-learning for mitigating concerns of stakeholders, and how the assessment results can help stakeholders understand the necessity of implementing the technology options.

Unutilized renewable resources can be recovered in some regions, for example as surplus variable renewable energy or as residues from agriculture and forestry. To link such locally available resources with energy systems consisting mainly of fossil resources, technologies for their procurement, transfer, storage, and operation need to be systematically selected and integrated into the system as alternative generation. Simulation-based design support is needed to identify possible solutions, taking into account multiple energy requirements, such as low-carbon resources, high stability, and high economic efficiency. Based on the simulation results, forward-looking assessments should be conducted. When we design an applicable solution for regional systems, specific conditions should be considered for resource demand and supply (e.g., Shimizu et al., 2015). The CAPE tools must be usable for region-specific designs of resource circulation.

4. Conclusions

Prospective life-cycle design can be conducted by applying an adequate combination of CAPE tools enabling alternative generation, analysis, evaluation and optimization, and sensitivity analysis. PSE can manage such regional systems development preemptively. The basics of PSE, i.e., mathematical modeling and simulation of changes to understand the impact on mass and heat balances, are essential for appropriate technology and system assessments. The obtained information applying PSE can become the essential information for the social changes that involve various stakeholders. The elaborated interpretation for those who are not experts in PSE is needed to accurately convey the quantitative and qualitative essences clarified by PSE.

Acknowledgments

This work was supported by MEXT/JSPS KAKENHI (JP21H03660, JP23K11521, JP21K12336, JP22K18061, and JP21K17919), JST COI-NEXT JPMJPF2003, JST PRESTO (JPMJPR2278), JST-Mirai Program (JPMJMI19C7), the Environment Research and Technology Development Fund (JPMEERF20213R01) of the Environmental Restoration and Conservation Agency of Japan, and the Nippon Foundation. Activities of the Presidential Endowed Chair for "Platinum Society" at the University of Tokyo are supported by Mitsui Fudosan Corporation, Sekisui House, Ltd., East Japan Railway Company, and Toyota Tsusho Corporation.

References

L.L. Corradini, A. Heiho, Y. Kanematsu, R. Shimono, S. Ohara, Y. Kikuchi. 2023. Simulation-based design of regional biomass thermochemical conversion system for improved environmental and socio-economic performance, Comput. Aided Chem. Eng., 52, 2361–2366

S. Fujii, T. Nakagaki, Y. Kanematsu, Y. Kikuchi. 2022. Prospective life cycle assessment for designing mobile thermal energy storage system utilizing zeolite, J. Clean. Prod., 365, 132592

F.W. Geels, J. Schot, 2007. Typology of sociotechnical transition pathways. Res. Policy, 36, 399–417.

F.W. Geels, B.K. Sovacool, S. Sorrell, 2017. Sociotechnical transitions for deep decarbonization. Science, 357, 1242–1244.

C. van der Giesen, S. Cucurachi, J. Guinée, F.J. Kramer, A. Tukker, 2020. A critical view on the current application of LCA for new technologies and recommendations for improved practice, J. Clean. Prod., 259, 120904

Idemitsu Kosan Co. Ltd., 2022. Idemitsu Integrated Report 2022. https://sustainability.idemitsu.com/en/themes/204

K. Igarashi, H. Kurishima, Y. Kikuchi. 2022. Evaluation of Vehicle-to-Grid System Using Renewable Energy in Tanegashima, Papers Environ. Inform. Sci., 36, 87–92.

Y. Kanematsu, K. Oosawa, T. Okubo, Y. Kikuchi. 2017. Designing the scale of a woody biomass CHP considering local forestry reformation: a case study of Tanegashima, Japan, Appl. Energ., 198, 160–172

Y. Kikuchi, Y. Kanematsu, M. Ugo, Y. Hamada, T. Okubo. 2016. Industrial Symbiosis Centered on a Regional Cogeneration Power Plant Utilizing Available Local Resources: A Case Study of Tanegashima, J. Ind. Ecol., 20(2), 276–288.

Y. Kikuchi, S. Kimura, Y. Okamoto, M. Koyama. 2014. A scenario analysis of future energy systems based on an energy flow model represented as functionals of technology options, Appl. Energ., 132, 586–601

Y. Kikuchi, M. Nakai, Y. Kanematsu, K. Oosawa, T. Okubo, Y. Oshita, Y. Fukushima, 2020. Application of technology assessments into co-learning for regional transformation: A case study of biomass energy systems in Tanegashima, Sustain. Sci., 15, 1473–1494.

S. Ohara, Y. Hamada, Y. Terajima, T. Ishida, Y. Kikuchi, Y. Fukushima, A. Sugimoto, 2023. Effect of single-boiling crystallization of high-yielding sugarcane KY01-2044 on sugar and molasses production, Food Sci. Technol. Res., https://doi.org/10.3136/fstr.FSTR-D-23-00158

K. Ouchida, Y. Kanematsu, Y. Fukushima, S. Ohara, A. Sugimoto, T. Hattori, Y. Terajima, T. Okubo, Y. Kikuchi. 2023. Coordinated Integration of Agricultural and Industrial Processes: A Case Study of Sugarcane-Derived Production, Process Integra. Optim. Sustain., 7, 1191–1209.

Research Center for "Co-JUNKAN" Platform towards beyond "Zero-Carbon" at Institute for Future Initiatives, the University of Tokyo, https://coinext.ifi.u-tokyo.ac.jp/en/index.html

S.S., Ravi, M. Aziz. 2022. Utilization of Electric Vehicles for Vehicle-to-Grid Services: Progress and Perspectives. Energies. 15(2):589.

D. Rotolo, D. Hicks, B.R. Martin. 2015. What is an emerging technology? Res. Policy, 44(10), 1827–1843.

T. Shimizu, Y. Kikuchi, H. Sugiyama, M. Hirao. 2015. Design method for a local energy cooperative network using distributed energy technologies, Appl. Energ., 154, 781–793

Flavio Manenti, Gintaras V. Reklaitis (Eds.), Proceedings of the 34th European Symposium on Computer Aided Process Engineering / 15th International Symposium on Process Systems Engineering (ESCAPE34/PSE24), June 2-6, 2024, Florence, Italy

Hydrogen strategic planning for heat decarbonisation under uncertainty

Margarita E. Efthymiadou, Vassilis M. Charitopoulos and Lazaros G. Papageorgiou*

The Sargent Centre for Process Systems Engineering, Department of Chemical Engineering, University College London (UCL), Torrington Place, London WC1E 7JE, UK

l.papageorgiou@ucl.ac.uk

Abstract

Heat decarbonisation is indispensable to meet Net-Zero emission target by 2050. The UK, as a world leader in reducing greenhouse gas emissions, needs to explore alternative pathways and energy carriers for the heat sector such as hydrogen. In this concept, a multi-period spatially-explicit two-stage stochastic mixed-integer linear programming (MILP) optimisation framework for hydrogen infrastructure is proposed to meet hydrogen heating demand in Great Britain. The mathematical framework aims to minimise the total cost accounting for investment and operational decisions considering 10-year steps 2030-2050 and typical days with hourly resolution. 10 scenarios are taken into account, which are selected using backward selection in GAMS-SCENRED. The results show that the stochastic approach provides a cost-efficient risk neutral infrastructure strategy to decarbonise the heat sector in the UK.

Keywords: Net-Zero; MILP Model; Two-stage Stochastic; Uncertainty; Hydrogen Infrastructure Planning;

1. Introduction

Over the last decade, there has been an important increase in the frequency of extreme weather events, largely attributed to climate change. Thus, there is a growing urgency to establish and pursue Net-Zero target, aimed at greenhouse gas emissions reduction and mitigation of adverse effects of climate change. Heating sector accounts for one third of the UK's emissions while residential heating is responsible for 17% of the carbon footprint (Industrial Strategy Committee, 2022). Therefore, heat decarbonisation constitutes a key element to achieve Net-Zero target by 2050. Taking into account that the wide use of gas boilers is responsible for the majority of greenhouse gas emissions, the exploitation of low-carbon alternatives is crucial. In this concept, hydrogen boilers are considered as an efficient alternative low-carbon heat source (HM Government, 2021). Consequently, strategic decisions for the role of hydrogen in the heat sector will be required. Therefore, it is crucial to investigate hydrogen infrastructure planning and the uncertainties related to the energy transition in low-carbon hydrogen investments.

Over the last decades, the employment of uncertainty in hydrogen supply chain has received significant by the PSE community. Kim et al. (2008) introduced a two-stage stochastic spatially-explicit framework for hydrogen demand uncertainty. A three-stage stochastic multi-period spatial-explicit model with uncertainty in hydrogen transportation demand was proposed by Almansoori and Shah (2012). Dayhim et al. (2014) based their multi-period two-stage model in the aforementioned works adding emission, energy consumption and risk costs in the framework. A case study with hydrogen transportation uncertainty in the UK using a two-stage stochastic model was proposed by Nunes et al. (2015). Moreover, uncertainty in primary energy sources was studied by Camara et al. (2019). The authors developed a ε-constraint method with lexicography optimisation framework to minimize total system cost and global warming potential and meet hydrogen transportation demand in Portugal. A fuzzy programming multi-objective approach was suggested by Robles et al. (2020). In this work, uncertainty was incorporated in hydrogen demand while genetic algorithms are used for the multi-objective formulation. Yang et al. (2020) proposed a spatially-explicit hydrogen supply chain model for a typical day while uncertainty was introduced in hydrogen demand and wind availability. A five-stage stochastic multi-period spatially explicit model was demonstrated by Ochoa Bique et al. (2021). Their study included 81 scenarios for hydrogen transportation demand uncertainty in Germany. In his work, a multi-period spatially-explicit two-stage stochastic framework is developed for hydrogen infrastructure planning while uncertainty is considered in heat demand, natural gas price and technologies costs. The applicability of the model is demonstrated through a case study for residential heat demand in Great Britain.

2. Problem Statement

The goal of this work is to design optimal hydrogen supply chain investments over the planning horizon to meet hydrogen residential demand and satisfy GHG emission targets. **Given:** (i) H2 heating demand and renewables availability in each region, year, cluster, hour and scenario, (ii) capital and operating costs for production technologies, storage sites, hydrogen and CO2 pipelines and road transportation modes, (iii) minimum and maximum capacity and ramp rates as well as the lifetime of production plants and storage sites, (iv) minimum and maximum flowrate in pipelines, (v) capacity of H2 caverns and CO2 reservoirs, (vi) H2 import price, (vii) carbon tax and capture rates for CO2 emissions as well as CO2 emission targets
Determine the optimal: (i) location and capacity of production technologies, storage sites and renewable farms, (ii) H2 production and storage rate in each region, year, cluster, hour and scenario, (iii) H2 and CO2 transmission investments between regions, (iv) H2 and CO2 flowrates between regions in year, cluster, hour and scenario, (v) hydrogen and natural gas penetration in each region, year and scenario, (vi) electricity generation of renewables (vii) H2 import rates in each year, cluster, hour and scenario
So as to minimise the total system cost and satisfy greenhouse gas emissions trajectory.

3. Optimisation Framework

3.1. Problem Description

The proposed framework aims at the decarbonisation of residential heat sector taking into account two energy carriers (hydrogen and natural gas). Strategic decisions for hydrogen infrastructure are determined including hydrogen production, storage and transmission technologies as well as a carbon capture and storage (CCS) system. Fig. 1 illustrates the superstructure of the studied system. Hydrogen can be produced through Water Electrolysis (WE), Biomass Gasification (BG) with Carbon Capture and Storage (CCS) and Reforming with CCS including Steam Methane Reforming (SMR) and Autothermal Reforming (ATR). The electricity, which is required for WE, is generated from renewable technologies to reduce the environmental footprint of the system. Solar, Wind Onshore and Wind Offshore farms are considered in this work. Regarding hydrogen storage, two types of storage vessels, High Pressure and Storage Vessel (HPSV) and Medium Pressure

Storage Vessel (MSPV), are incorporated. Hydrogen can be transmitted between regions through pipelines while 3 diameter options are available (0.5m / 0.8m /1.0m). CO_2 emissions which are captured from the production units, are transmitted to CO_2 reservoirs, located in North and Irish Sea. Finally, hydrogen and gas boilers can be used to satisfy the residential heat demand.

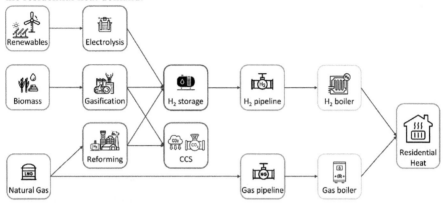

Figure 1: Model superstructure

The multi-period optimisation framework takes into consideration three 10-year time bins from 2030 to 2050. Hourly resolution is incorporated to explore operating decisions. Due to the high combinatorial complexity of the model, k-means clustering method is employed to reduce the model size. To preserve the peak heat day, it is excluded from clustering, and added in the final stage (Charitopoulos et al., 2023). In this study, 4 typical days which represent each season, and the peak demand day are considered. Moreover, Great Britain is divided into 13 regions according to local gas distribution zones (LDZ).

3.2. Mathematical Modelling
The cost optimal hydrogen infrastructure planning framework is formulated as a multi-period spatially-explicit two-stage stochastic mixed integer linear programming (MILP) model based on the work of Efthymiadou et al. (2023). The objective function of the problem is the minimisation of the system cost (SC) formulated as in Eq. (1):

$$\min SC = \sum_{k \,\epsilon K} pb_k \cdot TC_k \tag{1}$$

where pb_k is the probability of occurrence of each scenario k and TC_k is the total cost in each scenario k. The total cost consists of hydrogen production, storage and transmission capital and operating costs, hydrogen boiler installation cost, hydrogen import cost, carbon emission cost and natural gas transmission cost. The objective function is minimised in respect with mass and energy balances, production, storage and transmission, emissions, renewable generation and import constraints.

The heat demand can be met by hydrogen or natural gas. The energy balances are demonstrated in the following Eq. (2)-(4):

$$HD_{gtchk} = L^H_{gtk} \cdot TD_{gtchk} \tag{2}$$
$$GD_{gtchk} = L^G_{gtk} \cdot TD_{gtchk} \tag{3}$$
$$L^H_{gtk} + L^G_{gtk} = 1 \tag{4}$$

where TD_{gtchk} stands for the total demand for each region g, time period t, cluster c, hour h and scenario k. HD_{gtchk} and GD_{gtchk} are the hydrogen and gas demand for each region g, time period t, cluster c, hour h and scenario k. L^H_{gtk} and L^G_{gtk} constitute the demand penetration of hydrogen and natural gas, respectively.

3.3. Uncertainty

In this work, uncertainty is modelled using a two-stage stochastic approach. First stage decisions, which are common in all scenarios, include the optimal capacity and location of production plant, storage sites as well as H_2 and CO_2 pipeline connections. On the other hand, all the other variables constitute second stage decisions (e.g. production rates, flowrate between regions). These variables are different from scenario to scenario.

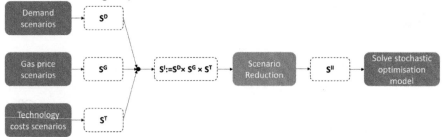

Figure 2: Scenario reduction steps.

Uncertainty is incorporated into heating demand, natural gas price and techno-economic data. More specifically, 3 (low, base, high) scenarios (S^T) for Water Electrolysis, Solar, Wind Onshore and Wind Offshore capital and operating costs are obtained from BEIS (Department for Business, Energy & Industrial Strategy, 2021 & 2023). Moreover, 10 gas price scenarios (S^G) are considered based on Future Energy Scenarios gas price (National Grid ESO, 2023). Future energy carriers for domestic heat are forecasted to be a mix of hydrogen, electricity and natural gas (National Grid ESO, 2023). In this study, only hydrogen and natural gas are taken into account and thus 4 different

Table 1: Scenario probability

Scenario	Probability
(1)	0.060
(2)	0.060
(3)	0.100
(4)	0.100
(5)	0.300
(6)	0.100
(7)	0.085
(8)	0.055
(9)	0.085
(10)	0.055

penetration rate scenarios (S^D) of the total heat demand are considered varying from 10% to 50%. A combination of the aforementioned uncertainties results in 120 scenarios. Due to the combinatorial complexity of the model, scenario reduction to 10 scenarios is conducted through backward selection using GAMS-SCENRED (GAMS Documentation, 2023). Table 1 showcases the probability of the reduced scenarios.

4. Results & Discussion

The proposed model was implemented in GAMS 38.2.1 and solved in monolithic fashion with Gurobi 10.0.3, using a Dell workstation with Intel® Core™ i9-10980XE CPU @ 3.00 GHz and 128 GB RAM. Optimisation termination criteria were 18 h CPU time limit or 5% optimality gap.

Fig. 3 illustrates the optimal technology mix for the deterministic (mean case) and stochastic (10 scenario case) approaches. The installed capacity of deterministic approach is

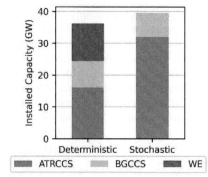

Figure 3: Technology mix.

36.1 GW consisting of ATRCCS, BGCCS and WE investments, while stochastic approach optimal design includes ATRCCS and BGCCS of 39.5 GW.

The optimisation results are summarised in Table 2. The quality of each solution is tested in the 120 scenarios set fixing the first stage decisions of each approach to get the expected system cost (ESC). As illustrated in Table 2, deterministic approach provides a lower system cost (SC) than the stochastic approach. However, there is a 33% increase in the ESC of the deterministic case when comparing to the corresponding SC. On the other hand, the stochastic approach provides a more realistic strategy as ESC is increased by 4% comparing to the stochastic SC.

Table 2: Computational statistics

	Deterministic Approach	**Stochastic Approach**
No. of continuous variables	119,801	1,155,694
No. of discrete variables	582	582
No. of equations	186,582	1,856,639
Optimality gap (%)	4.88	5.81
CPU time (h)	4	18
System Cost (£b)	34.1	37.9
Expected system cost (£b)	45.6	39.5

Fig. 4a demonstrates that stochastic solution results in a narrow distribution of ESC. Moreover, in most scenarios, stochastic approach grants a more cost-effective solution as illustrated in the Fig. 4b.

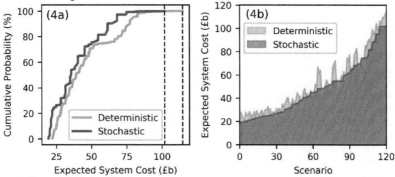

Figure 4: Expected System Cost.

A breakdown of the system costs and the expected system cost for the 120-scenario set is depicted in Fig. 5. ESC hydrogen facilities operating and production feedstock (gas, biomass) costs are significantly augmented for the deterministic approach while there is a slight increase in the stochastic approach. Moreover, hydrogen imports are surged comparing ESC and SC for the deterministic approach. Thus, stochastic case, which is more risk-neutral approach, reduces cost considering cost and demand uncertainties.

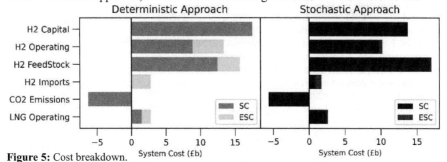

Figure 5: Cost breakdown.

5. Concluding Remarks

A stochastic, multi-period spatially-explicit MILP modelling framework is presented for the optimal design of hydrogen infrastructure applied to a case study for heat decarbonisation in the UK. Uncertainty in heat demand, gas price and technology costs is considered while a scenario reduction is used to reduce to decrease the combinatorial complexity of the stochastic model. The results indicate that the stochastic approach leads to a more cost-effective strategy. Future work includes the investigation of tailored solution approaches and integration of electrification and power sector in the framework.

Acknowledgements

The financial support from Engineering and Physical Sciences Research Council (EPSRC) under the project EP/T022930/1 is gratefully acknowledged. Authors appreciate collaborators Prof David Reiner, Dr Carmen Li and Dr Saheed Bello for providing gas price scenarios.

References

A. Almansoori, N. Shah, 2012, Design and operation of a stochastic hydrogen supply chain network under demand uncertainty, Int. J. Hydrogen Energy, 37, 3965–3977

D. Camara, T. Pinto-Varela, A. P. Barbosa-Povoa, 2019, Multi-objective optimization approach to design and planning hydrogen supply chain under uncertainty: A portugal study case. Comput. Aided Chem. Eng., 46, 1309–1314

V. M. Charitopoulos, M. Fajardy, C. K. Chyong, D. M. Reiner, 2023, The impact of 100% electrification of domestic heat in Great Britain, iScience, 26 , 108239

M. Dayhim, M. A. Jafari, M. Mazurek, 2014, Planning sustainable hydrogen supply chain infrastructure with uncertain demand, Int. J. Hydrogen Energy, 39, 6789–6801

Department for Business, Energy & Industrial Strategy, 2021, Hydrogen production costs 2021, https://assets.publishing.service.gov.uk/government/uploads/system/uploads/attachment_data/file/1011506/Hydrogen_Production_Costs_2021.pdf

Department for Business, Energy & Industrial Strategy, 2023, Electricity Generation Costs 2023, www.gov.uk/government/publications/electricity-generation-costs-2023

M. E. Efthymiadou, V. M. Charitopoulos, L. G. Papageorgiou, 2023, Hydrogen infrastructure planning for heat decarbonisation in Great Britain, Comput. Aided Chem. Eng., 52, 3025–3030

GAMS, 2023, SCENRED, www.gams.com/latest/docs/T_SCENRED.html

HM Governemnt, 2021, Heat and Buildings Strategy, assets.publishing.service.gov.uk/government/uploads/system/uploads/attachment_data/file/1044598/6.7408_BEIS_Clean_Heat_Heat__Buildings_Strategy_Stage_2_v5_WEB.pdf

Industrial Strategy Committee, 2022, Decarbonising heat in homes Seventh Report of Session 2021-22 Report. committees.parliament.uk/publications/8742/documents/88647/default/

J. Kim, Y. Lee, I. Moon, 2008, Optimization of a hydrogen supply chain under demand uncertainty, Int. J. Hydrogen Energy, 33, 4715–4729

National Grid ESO, 2023, Future Energy Scenarios, www.nationalgrideso.com/document/283101/download

P. Nunes, F. Oliveira, S. Hamacher, A. Almansoori, 2015, Design of a hydrogen supply chain with uncertainty, Int. J. Hydrogen Energy, 40, 16408–16418

A. Ochoa Bique, L. K. K. Maia, I. E. Grossmann, E. Zondervan, 2021, Design of hydrogen supply chains under demand uncertainty – a case study of passenger transport in germany, Phys. Sci. Rev., 6, 000010151520200052

J. O. Robles, C. Azzaro-Pantel. A. Aguilar-Lasserre, 2020, Optimization of a hydrogen supply chain network design under demand uncertainty by multi-objective genetic algorithms, Comput. Chem. Eng., 140, 106853

G. Yang, Y. Jiang, S. You, 2020, Planning and operation of a hydrogen supply chain network based on the off-grid wind-hydrogen coupling system, Int. J. Hydrogen Energy, 45, 20721–20739

Flavio Manenti, Gintaras V. Reklaitis (Eds.), Proceedings of the 34th European Symposium on Computer Aided Process Engineering / 15th International Symposium on Process Systems Engineering (ESCAPE34/PSE24), June 2-6, 2024, Florence, Italy

A Solar and Wind Energy-based Biomass-to-Methanol System with Coupling of Different Electrolyzers

Guanxin Xu,[a] Yan Wu,[a,b] Yufei Wang,[a,*] Xiao Feng,[c]

[a]*School of Chemical Engineering and Environment, China University of Petroleum (Beijing), 18 Fuxue Road, Changping, Beijing, 102249, China*
[b]*China Huanqiu Contracting & Engineering CO., LTD, No.1 Chuangda 2nd Road, Laiguangying Hi-tech Industrial Park, Chaoyang District, Beijing, 100012, China*
[c]*School of Chemical Engineering and Technology, Xi'an Jiaotong University, Xi'an, Shaanxi 710049, China*
wangyufei@cup.edu.cn

Abstract

The concepts of renewable energy and low-carbon economy are rapidly emerging. Considering the randomness and volatility of renewable energy sources (RESs), hydrogen production system of water electrolysis could be used. Biomass-to-methanol technology can be combined with solar and wind energy-based water electrolysis system. Between different kinds of electrolyzers, alkaline (ALK) electrolysis is the most common and mature technology with the lowest capital cost. Besides, proton exchange membrane (PEM) electrolyzers have higher sensitivity of response to input power and wider power regulation range, meaning it could make a fuller use of the electricity. In this paper, a method is proposed to design an optimal water electrolysis and methanol production system, taking into account the hourly solar and wind power generation capacity. The operation states of electrolyzer are also considered. In the case study part, a HPS consisting of 72 ALK electrolyzers and 8 PEM electrolyzers was designed, with an annual methanol production of 30.03×10^4 t/y. According to the result, the annual revenue of the coupling system is 62.6% higher than that of the PEM system. Compared with the ALK system, the scale of hydrogen and energy storage systems decrease significantly. The result shows promise in adapting to the fluctuations in renewable energy generation. Furthermore, the combined environmental and economic performance of the new system indicates its potential for long-term viability and positive impact.
Keywords: Coupling of Electrolyzers, Biomass-to-Methanol, Water Electrolysis, Renewable Energy

1. Introduction

The global air temperature has continuously increased in nearly two centuries. Climate change and global warming are considered as the most pressing issues (Dogan et al., 2023). Besides, the energy crisis also contributed to the concept of renewable energy sources (RESs) and a low-carbon economy. Thus, developing renewable energy technologies to reduce carbon emissions is crucial (Kojima et al., 2023). In recent decades, renewable energy generation capacity is continually increasing. However, compared to fossil energy sources generation, RESs has the characteristics of randomness, intermittence and fluctuation (Xiong et al., 2023). Thus, energy abandonment generally occurs when RESs power generation exceeds the electricity demand or transmission capacity. This problem could lead to energy resources and economic losses. Therefore, RESs generation is generally combined with hydrogen production system (HPS) of water electrolysis to prevent curtailment. Recently, energy production from biomass has gained interest as a suitable approach for agricultural countries. Combining biomass-to-methanol technology with the HPS of wind and solar power generation can not only increase the utilization of the carbon in the biomass, but also deal with the randomness, intermittence and fluctuation of RESs (Poluzzi et al., 2022).

Electrolyzing water could be carried out via several electrolyzer types, including alkaline (ALK) electrolyzer, proton exchange membrane (PEM) electrolyzer, anion exchange membrane (AEM) electrolyzer, and solid oxide (SO) electrolyzer (Gado & Hassan, 2023). Among them, the ALK and PEM electrolyzers have been applied in industrial production. ALK electrolysis is the most common and mature technology with the lowest capital cost. However, ALK electrolyzers cannot operate at low loads (Squadrito et al., 2023). Although the cost of a PEM electrolyzer is more expensive, the current density rate is higher and the gas crossover rate is lower, leading to higher sensitivity of response to input power. Besides, the operating range and capability is wider than that of ALK ones, meaning they could make a fuller use of the electricity (Mucci et al., 2023).

Recently, many researchers have done many studies on the combination of biomass-to-methanol and hydrogen production through RESs generation. Herdem et al. (2020) proposed a novel non-combustion heat-carrier biomass gasification system, coupled with a solar power plant and ALK water electrolysis system for MeOH production. Fournas and Wei (2022) demonstrated the economic viability of a MeOH production technology combining biomass gasification and PEM electrolysis for decarbonization. However, these studies only used one kind of electrolyzer. In this paper, a method is proposed for designing an optimal water electrolysis and MeOH production system. A HPS coupling ALK and PEM electrolyzers can be developed according to the hourly solar and wind power generation capacity, equipped with the corresponding hydrogen storage and energy storage modules. The model shows the differences between the two electrolyzers from multiple parameters. The operation state is also considered. The hydrogen produced by this system is used for biomass-to-methanol production.

2. Mathematical model

2.1. System structure

In this paper, the whole system consists of several components: a wind power generation system (WS), a PV power generation system (PVS), a power grid (PG), an energy storage system (ESS), a hydrogen storage system (HSS), a hydrogen production system (HPS) with two types of electrolyzers, a biomass gasification and purification system (BGPS), and a methanol production system (MPS). The electrolyzers operate in groups, and the operating loads of electrolyzers within the same group are set to be consistent. The overall system structure is depicted in Figure 1.

The electricity power could be obtained from WS, PVS and PG. Part of the electricity is able to be stored in the ESS while the electricity price is lower or the renewable energy resources are abundant. Similarly, HSS is applied to ensure the stability of MPS.

2.2. Biomass-to-methanol processing

Through treatment, gasification and desulfurization of 1 t biomass, 1,020 Nm^3 dry gas could be generated. The volume percentages of CO, CO_2, H_2 and CH_4 are 30.22%, 32.69%, 26.93% and 9.8%. CH_4 is transported to Partial Oxidation (POX) processing. Half of the CH_4 is burned and the other half produces CO and H_2 (Ugwu et al., 2020).

For treated gas transported back for MeOH production, the volume percentages of CO, CO_2 and H_2 (φ_{CO}^{Gas}, $\varphi_{CO_2}^{Gas}$ and $\varphi_{H_2}^{Gas}$) are 33.48%, 31.16% and 35.01%. 750 Nm³ CO or CO_2 can be used to produce 1 t MeOH. And 2,100 Nm³ hydrogen is required to produce 1 t MeOH from pure CO_2 and 1,400 Nm³ is required for pure CO. To ensure sufficient hydrogen supply, 105% of the above data is taken as the calculated value. The relationship between MeOH production and hydrogen supply is as follows:

$$V_t^{H_2} = 1.05\left(1400\,\text{Nm}^3/\text{t} \cdot \frac{\varphi_{CO}^{Gas} \cdot V_t^{Gas}}{750\,\text{Nm}^3/\text{t}} + 2100\,\text{Nm}^3/\text{t} \cdot \frac{\varphi_{CO_2}^{Gas} \cdot V_t^{Gas}}{750\,\text{Nm}^3/\text{t}}\right) - \varphi_{H_2}^{Gas} V_t^{Gas}, t \in T \tag{1}$$

where, $V_t^{H_2}$ is the volume of hydrogen supplied by HPS and HSS at time t (Nm³); V_t^{Gas} is the volume of treated gas used for MeOH production at time t (Nm³); T is the total annual operating hours of the system.

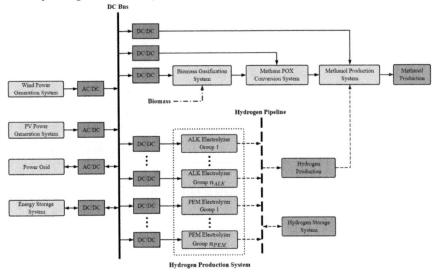

Figure 1. MeOH production system structure

2.3. Hydrogen production system with coupling electrolyzers

The ALK and PEM electrolyzers are coupled in the HPS and operate in groups. A binary variable L determined by input load is introduced as state parameters to describe the operation state. When the operation load is above the lower limit of the hydrogen production load range, $L = 1$ and the electrolyzer could be qualified to produce hydrogen.

$$\frac{P_{t,n}}{P_{max,n}} - \varphi_{min,n} \le L_{t,n} < 1 + \frac{P_{t,n}}{P_{max,n}} - \varphi_{min,n}, t \in T, n \in N \tag{2}$$

where, $L_{t,n}$ and $p_{t,n}$ are the state parameter and operation loads (kW) of the electrolyzer group n at time t; $P_{max,n}$ and $\varphi_{min,n}$ are respectively the maximum operation loads (kW) and the lowest hydrogen-producing workload ratio of the electrolyzer group n; N is the number of electrolyzer groups.

ALK electrolyzers consume several minutes as start-up time while changing from the UPS to the PS (Buttler & Spliethoff, 2018). By contrast, PEM electrolyzers have higher sensitivity of response to input power, and the starting time can be negligible. To show the difference in the starting speed, a binary variable i is proposed. $i = 1$ while the ALK group changing from UPS to PS. Start-up interval takes effect in the model as a penalty on the electrolyzer availability, that is, the hydrogen production capacity.

3. Case study

In this case, the data of wind and solar generation capability is taken from Changling County, Jilin Province, China. The scales of WS and PVS are 500 MW and 100 MW respectively. And the scale of MPS is 350,000 t/y. Electricity purchase is allowed, while selling is not allowed. Different parameters of electrolyzers provided by a commercial electrolyzer supplier are shown in Table 1.

Table1. Parameters of the two kinds of electrolyzers

Electrolyzer type	ALK	PEM
Maximum operation load (kW)	5	4.5
Hydrogen production efficiency (Nm^3/kW)	0.2	0.22
Lowest hydrogen-producing workload ratio	0.3	0.05
Upper load-extended limit	-	1.2
Investment cost of an electrolyzer (10^6 CNY)	7.5	30
Hydrogen production capacity penalty (Nm^3)	640	-
Proportion of the investment cost to the total installment cost	0.5	0.8

Table 2. Optimal results for the different systems

System type	ALK+PEM	ALK	PEM
Number of ALK groups × Number of electrolyzers in each group	9×8	11×8	-
Number of PEM groups × Number of electrolyzers in each group	2×4	-	15×4
Scale of ESS (MW)	12.20	39.11	12.28
Scale of HSS (10^4 Nm3)	142.76	155.53	122.47
Annual total generation capacity (10^8 kW·h)	18.16	18.16	18.16
Annual total power consumption (10^8 kW·h)	17.98	18.45	16.69
Annual total electricity purchase (10^8 kW·h)	1.42	1.48	1.34
Curtailment rate (%)	4.32	1.83	11.23
Investment cost (10^8 CNY)	76.28	76.49	84.37
Annual total MeOH production (10^4 t/y)	30.03	30.11	30.11
Carbon emissions (gCO_2/kg MeOH)	389.03	398.22	360.24
Annual total hydrogen production (10^8 Nm^3/y)	2.95	2.97	2.97
Annual earnings (10^8 CNY/y)	1.74	1.75	1.07

The systems of coupling ALK and PEM electrolyzers, single ALK and single PEM electrolyzers are designed for comparison. The results are shown in Table 2.

The optimized results indicate that the annual earnings of the coupling system are slightly lower than those of the pure ALK system but significantly higher than those of the pure PEM system. On the other hand, the carbon emissions of the MeOH product from the coupling system are higher than that of the ALK system but lower than that of the PEM system. These results can be attributed to the different characteristics of the electrolyzers. The high investment cost of the pure PEM system, due to the expensive PEM electrolyzers, contributes to its lower earnings. The ALK electrolyzer has a lower cost, but its smaller adjustment load range requires a larger scale of hydrogen storage systems HSS and ESS, affecting its profitability. The coupling system takes advantage of both electrolyzers, resulting in favorable environmental and economic performance. Furthermore, the curtailment rate of the coupling system is within 5%. For the annual MeOH production, the operation load ratio of the MPS is not less than 80% in about 2/3 of the whole year with the minimum one of 69.75%. Thus, the operation of the biomass-to-methanol system is basically stable. This demonstrates that the system is capable of adapting to the volatility of RESs.

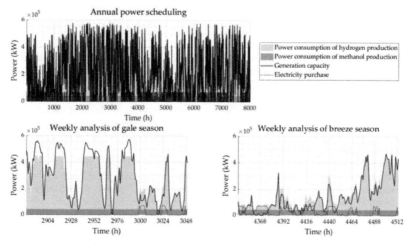

Figure 2. Diagram of annual and weekly power scheduling

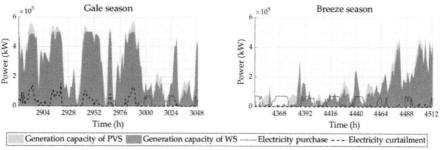

Figure 3. Weekly power sources and abandon

Figure 2 illustrates that the electricity purchase during the gale season is significantly lower than during other seasons. Figure 3 further explains that electricity purchases are primarily used to maintain system operation at night when there is no PV power generation during the breeze season. On the other hand, during the gale season, when there is sufficient PV power generation during the day, there is a noticeable phenomenon of power abandonment. This is likely due to the high cost of the batteries used in the ESS. Instead of increasing the scale of the ESS to store the excess power generated during the gale season and use it during the breeze season, it is more economical to abandon the excess power and purchase electricity when RESs are insufficient.

4. Conclusion

The proposed method for designing an optimal integrated system of biomass-to-methanol and green hydrogen appears to be innovative and promising. The coupling of both ALK and PEM electrolyzers allows for the combination of their respective advantages. In the case study part, the method is applied to design a system, with an annual revenue of 1.738 $\times 10^8$ CNY/y and the carbon emission of 398.03 gCO$_2$/kg MeOH. The ability of the system to adapt to fluctuations in RESs power generation is also a significant advantage according to the annual operating status of MPS.

In future studies, it would be interesting to consider other downstream processes of hydrogen production in order to further optimize the system. Additionally, the existing model could be combined with heuristic algorithms for even greater optimization.

References

A. Buttler, & H. Spliethoff, 2018, Current status of water electrolysis for energy storage, grid balancing and sector coupling via power-to-gas and power-to-liquids: A review, Renewable and Sustainable Energy Reviews, 82

E. Dogan, T. Luni, M. T. Majeed, and P. Tzeremes, 2023, The nexus between global carbon and renewable energy sources: A step towards sustainability, Journal of Cleaner Production, 416

N. D. Fournas, & M. Wei, 2022, Techno-economic assessment of renewable methanol from biomass gasification and PEM electrolysis for decarbonization of the maritime sector in California, Energy Conversion and Management, 257

M. G. Gado, & H. Hassan, 2023, Potential of prospective plans in MENA countries for green hydrogen generation driven by solar and wind power sources, Solar Energy, 263

M. S. Herdem, D. Mazzeo, N. Matera, J. Z. Wen, J. Nathwani, & Z. Hong, 2020, Simulation and modeling of a combined biomass gasification-solar photovoltaic hydrogen production system for methanol synthesis via carbon dioxide hydrogenation, Energy Conversion and Management, 219

H. Kojima, K. Nagasawa, N. Todoroki, Y. Ito, T. Matsui, & R. Nakajima, 2023, Influence of renewable energy power fluctuations on water electrolysis for green hydrogen production, International Journal of Hydrogen Energy, 48, 4572-93

S. Mucci, A. Mitsos, & D. Bongartz, 2023 Power-to-X processes based on PEM water electrolyzers: A review of process integration and flexible operation, Computers & Chemical Engineering, 175

A. Poluzzi, G. Guandalini, S. Guffanti, C. Elsido, S. Moioli, P. Huttenhuis, G. Rexwinkel, E. Martelli, G. Groppi, & M. C. Romano, 2022, Flexible Power & Biomass-to-Methanol plants: Design optimization and economic viability of the electrolysis integration, Fuel, 310

G. Squadrito, G. Maggio, & A. Nicita, 2023, The green hydrogen revolution, Renewable Energy, 216

A. Ugwu, A. Zaabout, J. R. Tolchard, P. I. Dahl, & S. Amini, 2020, Gas Switching Reforming for syngas production with iron-based oxygen carrier-the performance under pressurized conditions, International Journal of Hydrogen Energy, 45, 1267-82

K. Xiong, W. Hu, D. Cao, S. Li, G. Zhang, W. Liu, Q. Huang, & Z. Chen, 2023, Coordinated energy management strategy for multi-energy hub with thermo-electrochemical effect based power-to-ammonia: A multi-agent deep reinforcement learning enabled approach, Renewable Energy, 2141, 216-32

Flavio Manenti, Gintaras V. Reklaitis (Eds.), Proceedings of the 34th European Symposium on Computer Aided Process Engineering / 15th International Symposium on Process Systems Engineering (ESCAPE34/PSE24), June 2-6, 2024, Florence, Italy

Municipal Solid Waste Treatment Processes: Identification and Comparison of Performance Indicators

Júlia P. Oliveira,[a]* Ana Mehl,[a] Argimiro R. Secchi,[b] Flávia C. Alves,[a]

[a]*School of Chemistry, Universidade Federal do Rio de Janeiro, Rio de Janeiro, Brazil*
[b]*Chemical Engineering Program, COPPE, Universidade Federal do Rio de Janeiro, Rio de Janeiro, Brazil*
juliapancini@eq.ufrj.br

Abstract

Selecting the most appropriate process or a combination of them to treat municipal solid waste (MSW) is a challenge due to cultural and structural aspects of collecting segregated waste and the high investment and operational costs, since each technology has different requirements, such as typical capacity ranges, fractions of MSW that can be treated, among others. There is a gap in the literature about decision tools that simultaneously consider technical-economic, environmental, and social aspects. The main objective of this work is to propose indicators for a tool to help make decisions on how to treat MSW, encompassing the sustainability tripod. The identified economic indicators were: net present value and technology readiness level. Environmentally: global warming potential (GWP), energy and water intensity, land use, ozone depletion, photochemical smog, and acidification. On the social side: job creation, salary with the absorption of waste pickers, the population served, and the reduction in MSW sent to landfills. A database was drawn up with information collected from the literature to calculate the indicators and an analysis of the social and environmental indicators was carried out for a specific case: an MSW incineration plant with a capacity of 400 kt/year. The analysis identified the need to remove some environmental indicators: ozone layer depletion and photochemical smog, due to the lack of data available in the literature; and the social one: salary with absorption of waste pickers, since this indicator would not differentiate technologies, i.e., it is not relevant for decision-making. The result of the other indicators were job creation: 79 people; population served: 950,872 people; reduction in MSW sent to landfill: 92%; GWP: 0.45 kg CO_{2eq}/kg MSW; energy intensity: 241.7 GWh/y; water intensity: 62 m³; land use: 15,735 m²; acidification: 53.8 t SO_{2eq}/y. The importance of a database of plants with different capacities and compositions was also noted, so it would be possible to cover various scenarios that waste management agents might want to evaluate.

Keywords: waste-to-energy, sustainability, MSW incineration.

1. Introduction

The Brazilian National Solid Waste Policy (Brasil, 2010) defines an order of priority for waste management: non-generation, reduction, reuse, recycling, treatment of solid waste, and environmentally appropriate final disposal of waste. However, the actual scenario in Brazil is different, with around 98 % of municipal solid waste (MSW) going to landfills and dumps and only 2 % to recycling and composting (Brasil, 2021), despite the fact that there are already different treatments for MSW, such as anaerobic digestion, incineration, pyrolysis, and gasification. The inadequate disposal of waste can lead to various environmental impacts, such as water and soil contamination, air pollution, and greenhouse gas emissions (Kaza et al., 2018); and social impacts, as the proliferation of disease vectors and risk to human health (Gouveia, 2012).

The available technologies to treat MSW can convert waste into energy or other valuable products, such as biogas, synthesis gas, ethanol, among others. Anaerobic digestion uses organic matter from MSW, highlighting the need for segregation (Pinasseau, 2018). It is converted into biogas, which can generate electricity, heat, or chemicals, and digestate, which can be used as fertilizer or soil structuring material in the civil construction sector (Pinasseau, 2018). Anaerobic digestion is an established technology for MSW treatment (Neehaul et al., 2020). Incineration is the thermal process that converts MSW into thermal or electrical energy most used worldwide (Kalogirou, 2018). Other thermal processes are pyrolysis and gasification. The first one generates a 3-phases product: synthesis gas, pyrolysis oil and char (Neuwahl et al., 2019), it is still an emerging technology (Neehaul et al., 2020), and there are no large-scale plants in operation (Saveyn, 2016). Gasification generates synthesis gas and ash; synthesis gas must go through a cleaning process and can be used to generate electricity or as a raw material for other chemicals (Chan et al., 2019), and it is a technology validated in full scale (Neehaul et al., 2020).

There are some MSW treatment processes assessments in the literature. Diaz-Barriga-Fernandez et al. (2018) carried out a multi-objective optimization to support the decision-making in the MSW management, considering the financial risk involved as an objective function. Morero et al. (2017) proposed a mathematical formulation to find the optimal process design for the co-digestion of MSW and sludge, using net present value (NPV) as the objective function. Santibañez-Aguilar et al. (2014) proposed a model for optimal planning for the reuse of MSW considering economic, environmental and safety aspects, such as annual net profit, the amount of reused waste and fatalities generated, respectively. Pereira et al. (2018) presented a methodological proposal for building indicators for MSW management, encompassing the social aspect with indicators such as diseases related to environmental sanitation, the existence of collectors in dumps and on the streets.

However, although there are the assessments mentioned above, they are of specific scenarios, and many consider only one or two aspects. There is, therefore, a gap in the literature regarding decision-making tools that simultaneously consider technical-economic, environmental, and social aspects, and that can be applied to different scenarios. The main objective of this work is to propose indicators for a tool to help make decisions on how to treat MSW, encompassing the sustainability tripod.

2. Methodology

2.1. Technical-economic aspects

This work considers that economic development is related to technical aspects (Sikdar, 2003). The NPV is a widely used technical-economic indicator, such as in the analysis of the potential economic viability of implementing MSW incineration plants in Brazil (Silva et al., 2020) and economic analysis of MSW gasification and incineration with generation of energy (Rodrigues et al., 2020).

To calculate the NPV, it is possible to account for a premium received from the public authorities for treating MSW as revenue, the costs of land use, and revenue for the CO_2 mitigation, based on carbon credits (Araya, 2019). It is also important to consider the technology readiness level (TRL), related to data availability and the risk linked to technology (Klar et al., 2016).

2.2. Environmental aspects

The indicators were identified in line with the main environmental impacts of the MSW treatment sector: leaching, air pollution, and greenhouse gas emissions (Kaza et al., 2018), and are presented in Table 1.

Table 1 – Environmental indicators

Indicator	Calculation form	Unit
GWP	Ratio between the total mass of CO_{2eq} and the amount of MSW treated.	kg CO_{2eq}/ kg MSW
Ozone depletion	Ratio between the total mass of $CFC\text{-}11_{eq}$ and the amount of MSW treated.	kg $CFC\text{-}11_{eq}$/ kg MSW
Energy intensity	Ratio between net energy (difference between produced and consumed) and the amount of MSW treated.	MJ/ kg MSW
Water intensity	Ratio between the mass of water consumed and the amount of MSW treated.	kg water/ kg MSW
Land use	Ratio between the area used and the amount of MSW treated.	m^2/ kg MSW
Photochemical smog	Ratio between the total mass of $ethylene_{eq}$ and the amount of MSW treated.	kg $ethylene_{eq}$/ kg MSW
Acidification	Ratio between the total mass of SO_{2eq} and the amount of MSW treated.	kg SO_{2eq}/ kg MSW

2.3. Social aspects

This aspect is sometimes neglected due to its subjectivity, and it is not yet consolidated (Interlenghi et al., 2017). Critical points for identifying the indicators, presented in Table 2, were the generation of employment and income, and reduction in the amount of MSW sent to landfill, which reduces the population's potential exposure to disease vectors (Gouveia, 2012). The authors emphasize the existence of waste pickers in South America who informally collect, separate, classify and market recyclable wastes.

Table 2 – Social indicators

Indicator	Calculation form	Unit
Job creation	Number of jobs generated with the implementation of the process	People
Salary with the absorption of waste pickers	Difference between the average received by the waste pickers and the average paid by companies	USD
Population served	Population served	People
Reduction in MSW sent to landfill	Quantity of MSW treated / quantity of MSW generated	%

2.4. Analysis of the social and environmental indicators

A database was drawn up with information collected from the literature to calculate the indicators and an analysis of the social and environmental indicators was carried out for a specific case: an MSW incineration plant with a 400 kt/year capacity. The MSW composition was assumed as: 53.03 % of organic matter; 19.69 % of plastic; 16.57 % of paper and cardboard; 2.95 % of glass; 1.49 % of metal; and 6.27 % other recyclables as presented for the Rio de Janeiro State Solid Waste Plan Report (Rio de Janeiro, 2013) for medium-sized cities, between 100,001 and 1,000,000 inhabitants. Since a plant with the studied capacity serves cities of this size, considering the per capita generation of 1.1 kg/day also presented in the report (Rio de Janeiro, 2013).

This database – a compilation developed by the authors based on data from different plants – contains the necessary information to calculate the indicators, such as the number of employees, average emission of CO_{2eq} and SO_{2eq} per ton of MSW, water and energy consumption, and the area occupied by the plant. In this database, the averages of each indicator will be identified for plants similar to the one studied, and this value is identified as the result of that indicator.

3. Results

The TRL 9 was identified for incineration technology, since there are several MSW incineration plants in the world (Kalogirou, 2018). For reference purpose, anaerobic digestion (Neehaul et al., 2020) and sanitary landfill (Kaza et al., 2018) also have TRL 9, gasification presents TRL 8, since it is also validated in full scale, but not as long as incineration and anaerobic digestion (Neehaul et al., 2020), and pyrolysis is validated in pilot facilities, presenting TRL 6 (Saveyn et al., 2016). The social and environmental indicators were evaluated for the proposed scenario as presented in Table 3.

Table 3 – Result of social and environmental indicators

Indicator	Result	Unit	Validated
Job creation	79	People	Yes
Salary with the absorption of waste pickers	94.03	USD	No
Population served	950,872	People	Yes
Reduction in MSW sent to landfill	92%	-	Yes
GWP	0.45	kg CO_{2eq} /kg MSW	Yes
Ozone depletion	-	-	No
Energy intensity	241.7	GWh/y	Yes
Water intensity	62	m^3	Yes
Land use	15,735	m^2	Yes
Photochemical smog	-	-	No
Acidification	53.8	t SO_{2eq}/y	Yes

The social indicators job creation, population served and reduction in MSW sent to landfill were validated, as there is data available for their calculations, and each technology will present different values, making it possible to differentiate the technologies through these indicators. On the other hand, the salary with the absorption of waste pickers indicator did not prove to be effective, since the average value received by collectors and that paid to operators by companies do not vary from technology to technology, so this indicator does not differentiate between technologies, and is not relevant for the decision-making tool.

Two of the environmental indicators were not validated for use in the decision-making tool. They are ozone depletion and photochemical smog. This occurred because there is no data available in the literature to calculate these indicators, leading to the need to remove them from the tool. The ozone depletion indicator is not relevant in the decision-making as its impact is important in the case of a landfill, but there is little variation among treatment alternatives (Arafat et al., 2015).

On the other hand, photochemical smog is an interesting indicator for decision-making, since it is a local measure of environmental impact, unlike other indicators such as GWP which is a global one. Therefore, the possibility of compensating for the lack of data with a calculation proposal must be assessed. For example, the maximum emission allowed by regulatory agencies for emission plants, such as incineration and gasification plants, can be used, as emission occurs in high-temperature exhaust systems (Rani et al., 2011).

All other environmental indicators were validated, since there is data available for their calculations, and the technologies can be differentiated between them, for example: anaerobic digestion will not have the same CO_{2eq} emission as incineration, therefore, this indicator helps in the decision-making between technologies.

4. Conclusions

This work identified the main technologies used to treat MSW, and the indicators that make it possible to compare them to select the most appropriate process (or a combination of them) in different scenarios, considering the sustainability tripod. With the TRL analysis it was found that pyrolysis is the only one of the technologies analyzed that is not globally consolidated. Although all the other technologies are already in operation on a large scale, gasification is the most recent one, with fewer plants in operation.

The analysis identified the need to remove some environmental indicators: ozone layer depletion and photochemical smog, due to the lack of data available in the literature; and the social one: salary with absorption of waste pickers, since this indicator would not differentiate technologies, i.e., it is not relevant for decision-making. The importance of a database of plants with different capacities and compositions was also noted, so that it would be possible to cover various scenarios that waste management agents might want to evaluate.

References

H. A. Arafat, K. Jijakli, A. Ahsan, 2015, Environmental performance and energy recovery potential of five processes for municipal solid waste treatment, Journal of Cleaner Production, 105, 233–240.

V. A. Araya, 2019, Should the chilean government encourage waste-to-energy facilities for municipal solid waste? Columbia University, USA.

Brasil, 2010, Lei No 12.305, de 2 de agosto de 2010. Presidência da República, Brasil.

Brasil, 2021, Diagnóstico temático: manejo de resíduos sólidos urbanos – visão geral – ano de referência 2020, Ministério do Desenvolvimento Regional, Brasil.

W. P. Chan, A. Veksha, J. Lei, W. D. Oh, X. Dou, A. Giannis, G. Lisak, and T.T. Lim, 2019, A novel real-time monitoring and control system for waste-to-energy gasification process employing differential temperature profiling of a downdraft gasifier, J. Environ. Manage., 234, 65-74.

A. D. Diaz-Barriga-Fernandez, J. E. Santibañez-Aguilar, J. B. González-Campos, F. Nápoles-Rivera, J. M. Ponce-Ortega, M. M. El-Halwagi, 2018, Strategic planning for managing municipal solid wastes with consideration of multiple stakeholders, Computer Aided Chemical Engineering, 44, 1597-1602.

N. Gouveia, 2012, Resíduos sólidos urbanos: impactos socioambientais e perspectiva de manejo sustentável com inclusão social, Ciên. Saúde Coletiva, 17, 6, 1503-1510.

S. F. Interlenghi, P. A. Bruno, O. Araujo, J. L. Medeiros, 2017, Social and environmental impacts of replacing transesterification agent in soybean biodiesel production: multi-criteria and principal component analyses, J. Clean. Prod., 168, 3, 149-162.

E. N. Kalogirou, 2018, Waste-to-Energy technologies and global applications, CRC Press, USA.

S. Kaza, L. C. Yao, P. Bhada-Tata, and F. van Woerden, 2018, What a waste 2.0: a global snapshot of solid waste management to 2050, World Bank, USA.

D. Klar, J. Frishammar, V. Roman, and D. Hallberg, 2016, A technology readiness level scale for iron and steel industries, Ironmak. Steelmak., 43, 7, 494-499.

B. Morero, A. F. Montagna, E. A. Campanella, D. C. Cafaro, 2017, Integrated Process Design Optimization Accounting for Co-Digestion of Sludge and Municipal Solid Waste, Computer Aided Chemical Engineering, 40, 853-858.

N. Neehaul, P. Khadoo-Jeetah, and P. Deenapanray, 2020, Energy recovery from municipal solid waste in Mauritius: opportunities and challenges, Environ. Dev., 33, 100489.

F. Neuwahl, G. Cusano, J. G. Benavides, S. Holbrook, and S. Roudier, 2019, Best Available Techniques (BAT) reference document for waste incineration: industrial emissions directive 2010/75/EU (Integrated Pollution Prevention and Control), Joint Research Centre – European Commission, Luxembourg.

S. S. Pereira, R. C. Curi, W. F. Curi, 2018, Use of indicators in urban solid waste management: a methodological proposal of construction and analysis for cities and regions, Engenharia Sanitaria e Ambiental, 23, 3, 471–483.

A. Pinasseau, B. Zerger, J. Roth, M. Canova, and S. Roudier, 2018, Best Available Techniques (BAT) reference document for waste treatment: industrial emissions directive 2010/75/EU (Integrated Pollution Prevention and Control), Joint Research Centre – European Commission, Luxembourg.

B. Rani, U. Singh, A. K. Chuhan, D. Sharma, R. Maheshwari, 2011, Photochemical Smog Pollution and Its Mitigation Measures, Journal of Advanced Scientific Research, 2, 4, 28-33.

Rio de Janeiro, 2013, Plano estadual de resíduos sólidos do Rio de Janeiro (PERS): relatório síntese, Secretaria de Estado do Ambiente (SEA) – Rio de Janeiro, Brasil.

L. F. Rodrigues, I. F. S. Santos, T. I. S. Santos, R. M. Barros, and G. L. Tiago Filho, 2022, Energy and economic evaluation of MSW incineration and gasification in Brazil, Renew. Energy, 188, 933-944.

J. E. Santibañez-Aguilar, J. Martínez-Gómez, J. M. Ponce-Ortega, F. Nápoles-Rivera, M. Serna-González, M.M. El-Halwagi, 2014, An Optimal Planning for the Reuse of Municipal Solid Waste Considering Economic, Environmental and Safety Objectives, Computer Aided Chemical Engineering, 33, 1027-1032.

H. Saveyn, P. Eder, M. Ramsay, G. Thonier, K. Warren, and M. Hestin, 2016, Towards a better exploitation of the technical potential of waste-to-energy, Joint Research Centre – European Commission, Luxembourg.

S. K. Sikdar, 2003, Sustainable development and sustainability metrics, AIChE J., 49, 8, 1928-1932.

L. J. V. B. Silva, I. F. S. Santos, J. H. R. Mensah, A. T. T. Gonçalves, and R. M. Barros, 2020, Incineration of municipal solid waste in Brazil: an analysis of the economically viable energy potential, Renew. Energy, 149, 1386-1394.

Flavio Manenti, Gintaras V. Reklaitis (Eds.), Proceedings of the 34th European Symposium on Computer Aided Process Engineering / 15th International Symposium on Process Systems Engineering (ESCAPE34/PSE24), June 2-6, 2024, Florence, Italy

A data visualization tool for biomass valorization in Brazil

Roger Sampaio Bif,[a] Larissa Thais Bruschi,[a] Moisés Teles dos Santos,[a*]

aDepartment of Chemical Engineering, Polytechnic School, University of São Paulo, Av. Prof. Luciano Gualberto, Trav. 3, 380, São Paulo, 05508-900, Brazil
moises.teles@usp.br

Abstract

Brazil's diverse climate zones, vast territory, varied soils, and abundant water resources contribute to its rich biodiversity, making it ideal for biomass exploitation. This work deals with the creation of a user-friendly, interactive data visualization tool for biomass valorization. This involves collecting georeferenced data on biomass production and availability and developing an ontology to represent the Brazilian biomass supply chain. The Python programming language with libraries like Pandas, Matplotlib, and Streamlit, are used for data analysis, mapping, and creating web-based visualization applications. The proposed tool provides dynamic maps, showing biomass distribution and availability, highlighting regional resource disparities, assisting in region-specific planning and decision-making. This tool will be further integrated into optimization frameworks, helping to identify opportunities and to develop effective strategies for biomass valorization in Brazil, supporting the decision-making process.

Keywords: data visualization, biomass valorization, ontology.

1.   Introduction

Brazil presents natural competitive advantages for biomass exploitation, such as the presence of various climatic zones, vast territory, a wide range of soils, and abundant water resources, reflecting in its biodiversity. These aspects demonstrate the Brazilian potential for the development of economic activities based on renewable resources. It also highlights the perspective to generate employment, income, and technological advancements in decentralized regions, where biomass can be harvested or cultivated. In the last ten years, Brazil has increased its participation in the global food market, rising from US$ 20.6 billion to US$ 100 billion (CEPEA/ESALC, 2020). Projections indicate that by 2030, approximately one-third of globally traded agricultural products will originate from Brazil (Forster-Carneiro et al., 2013). To produce biofuels, the biomass production, harvesting, and preprocessing can represent 44 % of the selling prices (Roni et al., 2019), presenting the dependence of the biorefinery success in the efficient supply chain management for biomass valorization projects. In this context, the valorization of the agricultural waste through science, technology, and innovation can contribute to the minimization of environmental impacts, promotion of the circular economy, enhancement of the economic performance of the sectors involved, and social development in associated rural communities.

The decision-making process on the entire supply chain requires a laborious data gathering procedure on collecting, transforming, and evaluating several data sources from different domains, such as engineering, accounting, agriculture, economics, and others.

These complex datasets also need to be converted to standards that can be used by an optimization model, which increases the complexity of the data gathering process. To assist this process, the model input parameters and decisions variables can be ontologically represented. The ontology specifies the components in classes, that are characterized by attributes, only shared by the individuals of the class. Classes can interact with each other for relations, that define the properties (Marquardt et al., 2010). Ontology development can be found in different domains, as in the study of Okibe et al. (2023) for the valorization of sugarcane bagasse with different uses in the world largest's sugarcane producers. In conceptual design, the ontology can also be used, for screening and selection of ingredients of cosmetics based on its properties, and to evaluate the formulation proposed (Gabriel et al., 2023). Hazard and operability studies can also be beneficiated by ontology, since these processes are laborious and depend on large quantities of data, algorithms based on ontologies can infer hazard and its propagation, not susceptible to human errors (Single et al., 2020).

In complex systems that depend on strategic and tactics decisions, data mining, visualization and ontology are crucial for computational decision-making tools, and can enhance efficient planning, particularly in systems involving renewable resources like biomass. Therefore, the objectives of this work are to gather georeferenced data about biomass production and availability, to create a data visualization tool for biomass, that is interactive and user friendly, and to formulate an ontology that represents the Brazilian supply chain of biomass uses, to support decision-making and to assist future optimization studies about agricultural wastes valorization.

2.   Methodology

The data visualization tool was developed by data collection and user interface programming. Relevant and up-to-date biomass data from Brazil was collected and analyzed, creating a comprehensive database. The biomass types added to the database were: crops such as maize, sugarcane, soybean, palm, sunflower and agricultural residues from rice, potato, sugarcane, orange, maize, soybean and wheat. The data regarding crops were obtained from the Municipal Agricultural Production research (IBGE, 2021). To estimate the amount of residue produced for each of these crops, the production was multiplied by a residue coefficient, described by Ferreira-Leitao et al. (2010).

2.1.   *Visualization tool development*

The Brazilian territory is divided into federative units, mesoregions, microregions and municipalities (IBGE, 2021). The Instituto Brasileiro de Geografia e Estatística (IBGE) provides the files for the regions, in a shapefile format, widely used in Geographic Information Systems (GIS). After downloading the files, the PyShp library (Lawhead, 2022) was used to convert them from shapefile to json format, which is understandable to humans. However, the maps obtained can lead to a high level of detail, which means heavy files and low performance for the visualization software. For this reason, the Ramer–Douglas–Peucker algorithm (Douglas and Peucker, 1973) was used to reduce the map resolution and generate lighter files. Given that the boundaries of a region are represented by a polygon, the algorithm reduces the number of points of that polygon while keeping its general shape, this makes curves look more jagged and generates smaller files.

Afterwards, using Python's object-oriented functionality, the *BiomassMap* class was created. Its function is to associate the biomass production in a region to its geographical position by joining the production dataset to the map dataset (json) using Pandas (Mckinney, 2015). A color scale was created based on the production values, and the

BiomassMap class creates a Matplotlib figure (Hunter, 2007) that displays a biomass production map; the color of each region is related to the amount of biomass produced, defined by the color scale.

Similarly, the classes *DynamicUnits* and *StaticUnits* were created to display strategic points on the map, including storage units, regional capitals, and consumer centers. The difference between the classes is the fact that *DynamicUnits* has an associated magnitude (such as storage capacity) and the *StaticUnits* does not. Matplotlib (Hunter, 2007) was used to plot the points on the figure previously created by the *BiomassMap* class. Finally, the Streamlit library (Streamlit, 2023) was used to create an interactive graphical user interface (GUI) on the web, allowing the user to select the biomass type, the region to be displayed, the dynamic and static units of interest. Streamlit can identify the selections and interact with the classes described, updating the map based on the user's choices.

2.2. *Ontology development*

In the proposed ontology, classes were created to represent biomass, purchase sites, technologies, production and storage units, products, residues and consumer centers. The ontology created is presented in the class diagram of Figure 1.

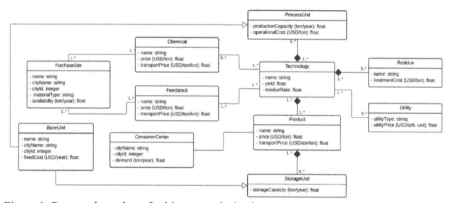

Figure 1: Proposed ontology for biomass valorization

The core of the ontology is the *Technology* class; it represents the conversion technology used in a process, such as transesterification and fermentation, objects of the class. *Technology* has a composition relationship with three classes: *ProcessesUnit*, *Residue* and *Product*. For example, if transesterification is a *Technology* object, biodiesel could be a *Product* object and glycerol a *Residue* object, any biodiesel plant could be a *ProcessUnit* object. The class *Utility* is also associated with *Technology* and electrical energy could be one of its objects.

The classes *Chemical* and *Feedstock* are related to *Technology* and its objects could be methanol and soybean oil, respectively, considering the biodiesel production scenario.

Both *Chemical* and *Feedstock* classes are related to a *PurchaseSite*, which represents geographically where these goods can be purchased. Likewise, the class *ConsumerCenter* is related to *Product*. The *StorageUnit* class has a composition relationship with *Product* and, like *ProcessUnit*, inherits the attributes from *BaseUnit*.

3.   Visualization tool demonstration

The application interface developed allows the user to select the feedstock, as well as to select a single region to get a detailed vision of the feedstock distribution. The biomass availability is presented in the map by a color scale, representing the quantity produced, shown in Figure 2. The use of color scales offers an intuitive and quick visual comprehension of the data. The flexibility to choose the biomass enables the user to assess the availability and potential of each feedstock type, making informed choices about which sources to prioritize based on factors like distance to storage and consumer centers.

Figure 2: Production of soybean waste in Brazil

The option to select a single region or visualize the whole Brazilian territory provides an understanding of biomass distribution and availability across different areas, which helps to identify regional disparities in resources and enables planning for each region based on its characteristics, as shown in Figure 3, for São Paulo region.

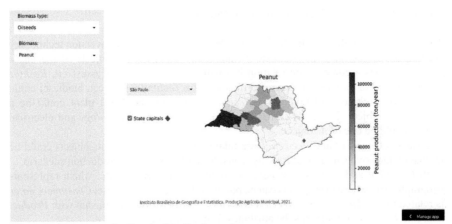

Figure 3: Peanut production in São Paulo region

The availability of peanuts in the state of São Paulo is more concentrated in the north and west of the state, far from the capital as shown in the Figure 3. To implement projects to valorize wastes from this production chain, knowing the location of the largest producers and the consumer market for a possible product is very important in the strategic decisions of these projects.

4.   Case study for ontology application

An example for the developed ontology use is the production of orange essential oil through steam distillation (Ortiz-Sanchez, et al. 2024). As shown in Figure 4, steam distillation is a *Technology* object, the feedstock used is orange peel, steam is used as a utility and the product is orange essential oil. The exemplified purchase site is an industrial orange juice plant, located in Matão (region of São Paulo) – Brazil, which is one of the largest plants in the country (CitroSuco, 2023), and has orange peel as a residue of the orange juice production.

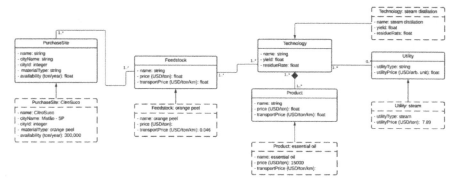

Figure 4: Ontology for orange essential oil production from orange peel

Process and Storage units locations and capacities should be determined by solving a supply chain optimization problem, using the aforementioned classes. Data such as transportation costs and the geographical position of the possible purchase sites, consumer centers, production costs and yields should be used as input in an optimization framework, to obtain deterministic results for a supply chain problem. However, it is important to note that the detailed resolution of this optimization problem is not part of this study.

5.   Conclusions

The data visualization tool supports decision-making by providing a comprehensive view of biomass availability, operational capacity, and regional distribution. It assists decision-makers to identify opportunities, make informed choices, and develop effective strategies for biomass utilization, thereby contributing to sustainable and efficient resource management. In addition, the data visualization tool helps in interpreting the results of an optimization problem, as it allows the upload of these data into the database and visualization of the origins of the raw materials, which operational centers are used, and which consumer centers can buy the products. Furthermore, the presented ontology organizes and structures Brazil's biorefinery sector and divides it into defined categories. The proposed data visualization tool and ontology will be further used integrated to optimization models, to assist decision-makers to identify opportunities, make informed choices, and develop effective strategies for biomass valorization in Brazil.

6.   Acknowledgments

The authors thank the financial support from FAPESP agency (projects 2022/02809-0, 2023/05420-0 and 2023/12377-3).

References

A. Gabriel, J. Serna, V. Plantard–Wahl, A. Le Jemtel, V. Boly, V. Falk, 2023, Decision making software for cosmetic product design based on an ontology, Computer Aided Chemical Engineering, 52, 1987-1992.

CEPEA/ESALC, 2020, PIB Do Agronegócio, Série Histórica Do PIB Do Agronegócio Brasileiro.

CitroSuco, 2023, A CitroSuco. Available at: < https://www.citrosuco.com.br/a-citrosuco/#governanca> Accessed in 28/07/2023.

D. H. Douglas, T. K. Peucker, 1973, Algorithms for the reduction of the number of points required to represent a digitized line or its caricature, Cartographica: the international journal for geographic information and geovisualization, University of Toronto Press, 10, 2, 112–122.

IBGE - Instituto Brasileiro de Geografia e Estatística, 2021, Malha Municipal. Available at: <https://www.ibge.gov.br/geociencias/organizacao-do-territorio/malhas-territoriais/15774-malhas.html?=&t=acesso-ao-produto>. Accessed in 09/02/2023.

J. D. Hunter, 2007, Matplotlib: A 2d graphics environment, Computing in Science & Engineering, 9, 3, 90–95.

J. I. Single, J. Schmidt, J. Denecke, 2020, Computer-Aided Hazop: Ontologies and Ai for Hazard Identification and Propagation, Computer Aided Chemical Engineering, 48, 1783-1788.

J. Lawhead, 2022, PyShp. Available at: <https://github.com/GeospatialPython/pyshp>. Accessed in 09/02/2023.

M. C. Okibe, M. Short, F. Cecelja, M. Bussemaker, 2023, Ontology Modelling for Valorisation of Sugarcane Bagasse, Computer Aided Chemical Engineering, 52, 3363-3368.

M. Ortiz-Sanchez, J. C. Solarte-Toro, P. J. Inocencio-García, C. A. C. Alzate, 2024, Sustainability analysis of orange peel biorefineries, Enzyme and Microbial Technology, 172, 110327.

M. S. Roni, D. N. Thompson, D. S. Hartley, 2019, Distributed biomass supply chain cost optimization to evaluate multiple feedstocks for a biorefinery, Applied Energy, 254, 113660.

Streamlit, 2023, Streamlit Documentation. Available at: <https://docs.streamlit.io/>. Accessed in 09/02/2023.

T. Forster-Carneiro, M. D. Berni, I.L. Dorileo, M. A. Rostagno, 2016, Biorefinery study of availability of agriculture residues and wastes for integrated biorefineries in Brazil. Resources, Conservation and Recycling,77, 78-88.

V. Ferreira-Leitão, L.M.F. Gottschalk, M. A. Ferrara, A. L. Nepomuceno, H. B. C. Molinari, E. P. S. Bon, 2010, Biomass Residues in Brazil: Availability and Potential Uses, Waste Biomass Valor, M. Ortiz-Sanchez, J. C. Solarte-Toro, P. J. Inocencio-García, C. A. C. Alzate1, 2024, Sustainability analysis of orange peel biorefineries, Enzyme and Microbial Technology, 172, 110327.

W. Marquardt, J. Morbach, A. Wiesner, A. Yang, 2010, OntoCAPE A Re-usable Ontology for Chemical Process Engineering, Springer, In RWThedition.

W. Mckinney, 2015, Pandas, python data analysis library. Available at:< http://pandas.pydata.org>. Accessed in 09/02/2023.

Flavio Manenti, Gintaras V. Reklaitis (Eds.), Proceedings of the 34th European Symposium on Computer Aided Process Engineering / 15th International Symposium on Process Systems Engineering (ESCAPE34/PSE24), June 2-6, 2024, Florence, Italy

Evaluation of different water sources for electrolysis: a study case of the priority regions for green hydrogen production in the state of Bahia

Leonardo O. S. Santana,[a] Gustavo S. dos Santos,[a] Chrislaine B. Marinho,[a] Artur S. Bispo,[a] José Almeida,[a] Fernando L. P. Pessoa[a,b]

[a] *SENAI CIMATEC university center, Avenida Orlando Gomes, Salvador 41650-010, Brazil*
[b] *Federal University of Rio de Janeiro (UFRJ), Av. Athos da Silveira Ramos, Rio de Janeiro 21941-909, Brazil.*
leosantana049@gmail.com

Abstract

Green hydrogen is progressively being recognized as a crucial component in the extended process of reducing carbon emissions from the worldwide energy framework. Water usage in the hydrogen economy is gaining importance in literature, thus, a proper analysis must include four dimensions of sustainability criteria (environmental, social, technical, and economic). This work evaluates the suitability of water sources (WS) for green hydrogen production based on a Multi-Criteria Decision Making (MCDM) Model for Water Assessment in Green Hydrogen Production. The approach was applied to three different sites (A, B, and C) in the Brazilian state of Bahia. As a result, the most suitable water sources were different for each site (seawater, Rainwater, and treated urban wastewater), regarding the different characteristics of each location.

Keywords: Green Hydrogen, Electrolysis, Water Sources, Analytic Hierarchy Process, Decision support system.

1. Introduction

Green hydrogen is progressively being recognized as a crucial component in the extended process of reducing carbon emissions from the worldwide energy framework. This emergence highlights substantial inquiries about sustainability, concerning its creation and global trade in countries where it is produced. Beswick et al. (2021) highlight the potential to significantly reduce carbon emissions by meeting a substantial hydrogen demand in a renewable future. Newborough and Cooley (2021) underscore the substantial water requirements for this transition. Cremonese et al. (2023), determined that issues about freshwater availability carry paramount importance both environmentally and socioeconomically.

In addition, the study of alternative water sources, such as seawater or industrial wastewater, gains prominence due to their potential to alleviate stress on conventional freshwater resources and support large-scale green hydrogen production. This necessitates a comprehensive assessment that considers quantitative metrics and qualitative factors, aligning environmental sustainability with the imperative for water security, as emphasized by Woods et al. (2022) and Winter et al. (2022).

This paper presents a decision support system based on a Multi-Criteria decision-making (MCDM) Model for Water Assessment in Green Hydrogen Production (Santana, et al. 2023) to evaluate from an economic, environmental, and social point of view, the water's resources for green hydrogen production. The approach is implemented using three different sites in the Brazilian state of Bahia, the fifth-largest state in terms of territory. The State of Bahia is energetically strategic, being Brazil's second generator of wind energy and eighth in solar PV, according to Santos et al. (2023).

2. Methodology

The methodology presented herein is based on the multi-criteria approach of sustainable value methodology proposed by Simões (2021) and Santana (2023). A computational model based on MS Excel was developed for the sustainable assessment of water sources for electrolysis. It was developed by integrating different concepts from distinct subjects such as value analysis, ecoefficiency, energy efficiency, and cleaner production.

The choosing locations of the clusters were based on the green hydrogen map of the state of Bahia (Figure 1): a semi-urban location along the Atlantic coast with cooler summers (site A); a rural area far from the coast with slightly hotter summers (site B); and a semi-urban location far from the coast with intermediated summers (site C). The model uses the analytical hierarchy process to define the weight of each criterion. The weights of each sustainable dimension are determined according to the water exploitation index (WEI+) of the study area.

Figure 2 shows an overview of the approach. The first step was to identify and map all potential water sources (WS) that can input the electrolyzer which was available around the green hydrogen cluster, and then information about distance and elevation (between the water source and the hydrogen plant) and treatment needs were summarized. Then the cost calculations were run, followed by the qualitative evaluation.

Figure 1 – Site locations in the Bahia's GH2 Map

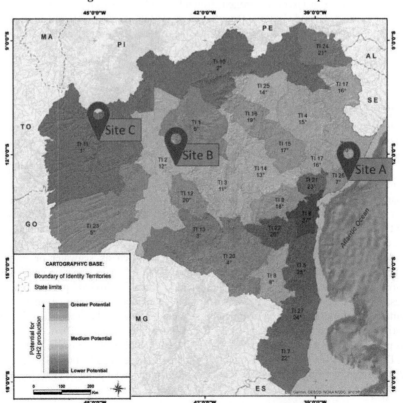

Evaluation of different water wources for electrolysis: a study case of the priority regions for green hydrogen production in the state of Bahia

2283

Figure 2 – Overview of considered approach for assessing potential water sources for electrolysis.

1º	• Definition of localization and electrolysis plant size. • Identify the water sources (WS) for electrolysis.
2º	• Mass and energy balance of plant. Definition of hydric footprint. • Evaluate water availability in terms of quantity (supply>demand)
3º	• Costs calculations (CAPEX e OPEX) of the hydrogen plant and all steps of water supply.
4º	• Perform each criteria • Sum the performance of each criteria and find the sustainable value

A total of seven potential WS were identified (grid "Tap" water (TW), treated industrial wastewater (IW), Treated Urban wastewater (UW), Surface "river/lakes" water (SFW), seawater (SW), rainwater (RW), and groundwater (GW)). The CAPEX and OPEX information were calculated considering water abstraction, transport, and treatment, as in our previous work, Santana et al. (2023a). The hydrogen site capacity was 60MW and the electricity cost considered was R$ 0.575/kWh (CNI, 2021).

For site A, a semi-urban location along the Atlantic coast with cooler summers, all potential WS are available; for the rural area plant, far from the coast with slightly hotter summers (named site B) only three WS were available (SFW, GW, RW); for the site C, the semi-urban location far from the coast with intermediated summers, TW, UW, SFW, GW and RW are available.

Table 1 – Water sources and distances (m) /elevation (m) for each site

Site	A	B	C
Groundwater (GW)	On-site	On-site	On-site
Industrial wastewater (IW)	5,247/13	NA	NA
Seawater (SW)	4,686/40	NA	NA
Rainwater (RW)	On-site	On-site	On-site
Water grid (TW)	On-site	NA	On-site
Urban wastewater (UW)	10,000/10	NA	5,247/13
Surface water (SFW)	5,000/10	On-site	4,686/40

Table 2 – Treatment and collection costs

WS	Treatment train	W. loses	Process CAPEX (€)	Energy consumption kWh/m3	Collection (€)	Collection OPEX kW/m3
UW	FS→MF→RO	25%	701,000.00	4.5635	25,000.00	-
SFW	FS→Chempre→MF	15%	281,000.00	0,1135	50,000.00	-

The considered distance between the local water collection and the electrolysis plant is listed in Table 1. These data are crucial to quantify the capex and Opex related to water in the electrolysis process. Table 2 presents the treatment train and collection costs for the urban wastewater, and surface water. The other water sources costs are listed in our previous work, Santana et al. (2023a).

After cost calculations, each of the potential WS was qualitatively assessed for each site, adopting a functional value approach (equation 1), where W is the weight, and C is the criterion's performance level), each measure is divided into 4 performance levels, being level 1 the lowest, and 4 the highest level, as mentioned by Santana et al. (2023b), where the function is to supply water for hydrogen production. For this, the following criteria, presented in Table 1, were identified.

$$SV \; \alpha \; Performance \; \alpha \; \sum_1^n (W_i \cdot C_i) \; (1)$$

The weight for each criterion described in Table 1 depends on the water exploitation index (WEI+) of the region of study. This index is presented by Baldinelli et al. (2022) as the pressure on the region's available water, with a maximum limit of 40% (severe scarcity of water resources). Thus, this study classified the regions into five types (Figure 3), depending on the WEI+, regions with water exploitation greater than 40% can't afford an electrolysis plant. The WEI+ is defined in equation 2, where ABS is the abstraction of water, RET is the return to water sources, and LAAW is the long-term average available water at a given time and place. For this study, the WEI+ considered were 20%, 30%, and 30% for sites A, B, and C respectively.

$$WEI+= {ABS - RET}/_{LAAW} \; (2)$$

The criteria for Sustainable Value analysis of water sources. The used and their respective weights for each WEI+ level are listed in Figure 3. The criteria description (A to L) can be found in the literature (Santana et al. 2023a) except for "ecological impact" (M-ecological impact on the environment, effect on flora and fauna, related to ecosystem health) and "regulatory compliance" (N- Water usage and disposal regulations. Understanding of local regulations regarding water usage and disposal to ensure compliance).

Figure 3 – Criteria weight for each WEI+ value

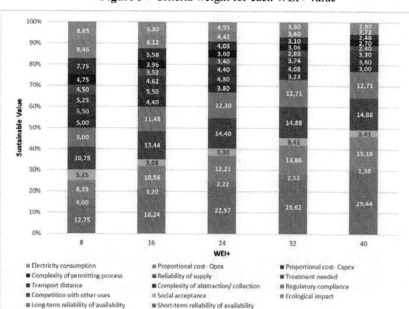

Table 3 – Criteria for Sustainable Value analysis of water sources.

Criteria	Performance Level			
	1	**2**	**3**	**4**
M	High ecological impacts at the abstraction level	Medium ecological impacts at the abstraction level	Low ecological impacts at the abstraction level	No ecological impacts at the abstraction level
N	High difficulty of environmental licensing and water use granting; involvement of multiple entities with complex procedures and lengthy approval timelines	Moderate difficulty of environmental licensing and water use granting; involvement of a few entities with relatively streamlined procedures and reasonable approval timelines.	Low difficulty of environmental licensing and water use granting; involvement of a single entity with straightforward procedures and efficient approval timelines.	The minimal difficulty of environmental licensing and water use granting; no involvement of additional entities or regulatory hurdles.

3. Results and discussions

After performing each criterion for the water sources of all the sites, the results obtained are presented in Table 4, and Figure 3. It's possible to visualize the performance of each WS divided into the four sustainable dimensions of the study. The better WS for each criterion is underlined in Table 4.

Table 4 – Sustainable Value analysis of water sources.

		TW	IW	UW	SFW	GW	RW	SW
Site A	*Envir*	19	28	25	24	28	20	36
	Social	15	17	20	24	17	30	24
	Tech	12	20	20	16	20	13	8
	Econ	8	5	5	9	8	11	8
Site B	*Envir*	–	–	–	22	32	23	–
	Social	–	–	–	16	17	31	–
	Tech	–	–	–	10	17	11	–
	Econ	–	–	–	8	6	8	–
Site C	*Envir*	29	–	42	22	32	23	–
	Social	21	–	28	16	17	31	–
	Tech	17	–	6	10	17	11	–
	Econ	6	–	6	8	6	8	–

Figure 3 shows the overall performance of the water sources. Presenting the results of this study. Comparing them it's possible to note that the higher sustainable value is for the urban wastewater in site C. For each site, however, the most suitable WS is seawater for site A, Rainwater (site B), and Urban wastewater for site C. The results show that the most suitable WS depends on the plant capacity and local issues. Still, overall analysis shows that rainwater is a promising water source regarding availability in medium-scale plants even in locals with higher water scarcity. This type of evaluation is extremely necessary when a hydrogen hub is being built.

Figure 3 – Results of water sources evaluation for each Site

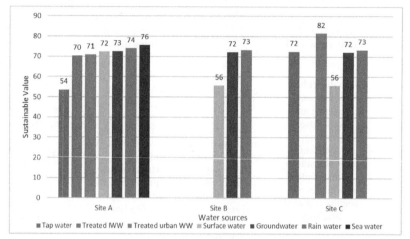

3. Conclusion

A sustainable value indicator allows a relative quantitative comparison of the performance of different water sources for electrolysis. The approach provides elements to support decision-making regarding the most suitable water inputs for H_2 production from water electrolysis: quality and reliability of water sources, treatment needs, the complexity of the permitting process, and associated costs. As a result, the most suitable water sources were different for each site (seawater, rainwater, and treated urban wastewater), regarding the different characteristics of each location.

References

A. Baldinelli, G. Cinti, L. Barelli, G. Bidini, 2022, Hydrogen production from low-quality water: challenges and perspectives, Journal of physics: conference series, 2385,012048.

CNI. (2021). Perfil da industria da Bahia. Retrieved from Portal da industria: https://perfildaindustria.portaldaindustria.com.br/estado/ba

G. S. Santos, C. B. Marinho, L. O. S. Santana, A. S. Bispo, F. L. P. Pessoa, J. L. G. Almeida, E. E. S. Calixto, 2023, Hydrogen production using renewable energy: solar PV and offshore wind power – An economic evaluation in Bahia, Computer aided chemical engineering, 52, 2947-2957.

L. Cremonese, G.K. Mbungu, R. Quitzow, 2023, The sustainability of green hydrogen: An uncertain proposition, International journal of hydrogen energy, 48, 51, 19422-19436.

L. O. S. Santana, A. S. Bispo, G. S. Santos, C. B. Marinho, E. E. S. Calixto, J. L. G. Almeida, F. L. P. Pessoa, 2023, Water sources evaluation for green hydrogen production: a case study in Brazil, Computer aided chemical engineering, 52, 2923-2928.

L. O. S. Santana, J. L. G. Almeida, F. L. P. Pessoa, 2023, Sustainable value approach to evaluate water sources for electrolysis, 24º congresso brasileiro de engenharia química.

M. Newborough & G. Cooley, 2021, Green hydrogen: water use implications and opportunities, Fuel Cells Bulletin, Volume 2021, Issue 12, p 12-15.

P. Woods, H. Bustamente, K. Zinsou, 2022, The hydrogen economy- where is the water? Energy nexus, volume 7.

R. Beswick, A. Oliveira, Y. Yan, 2021, Does the green hydrogen economy have a water problem? ACS Energy Letters, 6, p 3167-3169.

S. Simoes, J. Catarino, A. Picado, T. Lopes, S. di Berardino, F. Amorim, F. Gírio, C. Rangel, T. Ponce de Leão, 2021, Water availability and water usage solutions for electrolysis in hydrogen production, Journal of Cleaner Production, 315, p 128124.

Flavio Manenti, Gintaras V. Reklaitis (Eds.), Proceedings of the 34th European Symposium on Computer Aided Process Engineering / 15th International Symposium on Process Systems Engineering (ESCAPE34/PSE24), June 2-6, 2024, Florence, Italy

Design of a Reverse Supply Chain Network for Photovoltaic Panels

Funda Iseri[a,b], Halil Iseri[b,c], Natasha J. Chrisandina[a,b], Shivam Vedant[c,d], Eleftherios Iakovou[b,c,d], Efstratios N. Pistikopoulos[a,b,*]

[a] *Artie McFerrin Department of Chemical Engineering, Texas A&M University, 3122 TAMU, 100 Spence St., College Station, TX, 77843, USA*

[b] *Texas A&M Energy Institute, Texas A&M University, College Station, TX, 77843, USA*

[c] *Department of Multidisciplinary Engineering, Texas A&M University, College Station, TX, 77843, USA*

[d] *Department of Engineering Technology and Industrial Distribution, Texas A&M University, College Station, TX, 77843, USA*

* *stratos@tamu.edu*

Abstract

The global energy transition towards sustainable energy sources has triggered a significant increase in photovoltaic (PV) panel investments. This remarkable growth has led solar PV to reach the highest generation expansion among all renewable technologies, surpassing wind power. This global surge underscores the urgency of innovating end-of-life (EoL) management for solar panels. Effective EoL management is crucial to ensure that the lifecycle of PV panels is sustainable and environmentally friendly. An effective policy would have to involve the responsible disposal, recycling, and repurposing of solar panels at the end of their service life. This work proposes an efficient, sustainable, and environmentally responsible PV panel recycling system. The Resource-Task-Network (RTN)-based network model, PV recycling, enables strategic decision making for recycling technology selection, resource allocation and location selection for collection and processing facilities within the reverse supply chain. In this manner, this structured framework offers overall reverse supply chain network optimization and scenario-based analysis under different market considerations. The developed decision-making framework would be a vital tool for current and future investment decisions and targeted inventories.

Keywords: End-of-Life Management of photovoltaic panels, supply chain optimization, Resource-Task-Network, decision-making tool

1. Introduction

In the global transition towards sustainable energy, solar energy is a key contributor. However, the surge in PV installations brings a significant challenge regarding managing the increasing volume of solar panel waste. Projections suggest that by 2030, the global waste could reach 1.7 million tons under regular loss scenario, and these figures could escalate to 60 million tons by 2050 (Weckend et al., 2016).

A typical PV solar panel is composed of aluminum, glass, silver, copper, silicon, and polymer. While glass is the component carrying the most weight in a typical PV panel, silver and aluminum constitute the components with the most value. The potential for value creation through raw material recovery from PV recycling is highly remarkable. The value of this recovered material, if fully incorporated back into the economy, is estimated to be around $450 million by 2030, and $15 billion by 2050 (Weckend et al., 2016). Recycling and upcycling materials derived from PV panels presents an effective solution to the escalating volume of EoL panels. The incorporation of these recovered materials can broaden the spectrum of critical resources required for PV manufacturing or other supply chains. This diversification enhances resilience and strengthens these crucial supply chains (Bechtsis et al., 2022).

There has been growing interest and emphasis on the need for EoL management of solar PV panels (Heath et al., 2020 & Salim et al., 2019). However, there is a noticeable lack of quantitative assessments regarding the effectiveness of policies aimed at increasing recycling adoption rates, indicating a need for further research in this area. It is also worth to mention that more research is needed to gather practical insights from industry stakeholders to identify next-generation reverse supply chain management practices, which will help bridge the gap between academic research and industrial practice. This study highlights the necessity for innovative systematic modeling frameworks that should be capable of encapsulating the dynamics among various components of the supply chain. Such a capability would facilitate "what-if" analyses under various market conditions and regulatory structure by optimizing the reverse supply chain system under diverse scenarios and objectives. The proposed methodology is demonstrated through a case study for planning and scheduling of a PV value chain.

2. Methodology

2.1. Decision making tool designed for PV recycling market

The surge in PV market expansion has triggered a pivotal moment for the industry, where the dominant practice of disposing of PV waste in landfills, primarily driven by cost considerations, poses a substantial challenge to the establishment of a truly sustainable PV market. This economic gap underscores the pressing need for optimized, integrated, cost-competitive, and sustainable solutions within the dynamic PV recycling domain. It is crucial for these solutions to consider potential regulations and incentives, as well as environmental considerations, thereby aligning with the broader objectives of fostering a circular economy within the PV industry. Navigating this dynamic landscape requires a structured framework, a strategic decision-making tool for the optimization of the PV reverse supply chain, focusing on the sustainable and economical recycling of critical materials from PV panels, such as aluminum, silver, copper, glass, and silicon. These materials have the potential to be reintegrated into manufacturing facilities to produce new PV components, or alternatively, be directed to other supply chains to boost the cost competitiveness and create optionality to enhance resilience. As illustrated in Figure 1, an ideal PV reverse supply chain should be modelled with respect to the key pillars as sustainability, sensitivity to incentives/regulations, and cost competitiveness, and the impact of them should be examined on the design and operation of the PV network.

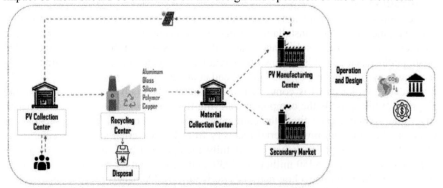

Figure 1. Schematic overview of the investigated PV recycling system

In response to the identified challenges, this study proposes a mathematical model based on an RTN representation, a unified framework for the representation and solution of process scheduling problems where resources and tasks are shown in an interconnected network to transform material and/or energy resources into other resources. The proposed model aims to determine tactical and operational decisions, including facility site, facility, capacity, route, and transport mode selections along with options for recycled materials, for the reverse supply chain network for PVs. Criteria such as cost, the complexities of regulatory compliance, incentives, and environmental considerations under different market settings such as cooperative and competitive environments can be considered in the model, which results in a mixed-integer program (MIP) using *energiapy* (Kakodkar et al., 2023), and the details of the model will be described in the following section.

2.1.1. Nomenclature

The nomenclature used in the rest of this section is outlined below.

Table 1: Sets

$\mathcal{R}$	Set of resources	$\mathcal{T}$	Set of temporal periods
$\mathcal{L}$	Set of facility locations l	$\mathcal{F}$	Set of transport modes f
$\mathcal{P}$	Set of processes		

Table 2: Parameters

$Cap_{l,p,t}^{max}, Cap_{l,p,t}^{min}$	Max and min production capacity of process p in location l at time t
$Capex_{l,p,t}$	Capital expenditure of process p in location l at time t
$Vopex_{l,p,t}$	Variable operational expenditure of process p in location l at time t
$Price_{l,r,t}$	Purchase Price for resource r in location l at time t
$Revenue_{l,r,t}$	Revenue obtained from sales of resource r in location l at time t
$Demand_{l,r,t}$	Demand for resource r in location l at time t
$Distance_{l,l'}$	Distance between location l and l'
$conv_{p,r}$	Conversion ratio of resource r in process p
$Tcost_f$	Transportation cost for transport mode f
$TCap_{f,r}^{max}$	Maximum transportation capacity of transport mode f for resource r
$Tmode_{f,l,l'}$	1 if transport mode f is available between location l and l'

Table 3: Continuous and Binary Variables

Notation	Description	Notation	Description
$P_{l,p,t}$	Production of process p in location l at time t	$S_{l,r,t}$	Discharge of resource r in location l at time t
$C_{l,r,t}$	Consumption of resource r in location l at time t		
$Cap_{l,p,t}^{P}$	Installed production capacity for process p in location l at time t	$x_{l,p,t}^{P}$	1 if process p is chosen for location l at time t, 0 otherwise
$Tr_{f,l,l',r,t}$	Amount of resource r transported by f from location l to l' at time t	$x_{f,l,l',r,t}^{F}$	1 if resource r is transported by f from location l to l' at time t, 0 otherwise

2.1.2. Constraints

- Inventory balance: at every time period $t \epsilon \mathcal{T}^{sch}$, the amount of resource r produced and transported into location l needs to be equal to the amount discharged out of the l.

$$\sum_{p \in \mathcal{P}} P_{l,p,t} \, conv_{p,r} + C_{l,r,t} + \sum_{f \in F} \sum_{l' \in L \cap l} Tr_{f,l,l',r,t} = \sum_{f \in F} \sum_{l' \in L \cap l} Tr_{f,l,l',r,t} + S_{l,r,t} \qquad (1)$$

- Production level cannot exceed capacity

$$P_{l,p,t} \leq Cap^P_{l,p,t} \quad \forall p\epsilon\mathcal{P}, t\epsilon\mathcal{T}^{sch} \tag{2}$$

- Production capacity cannot exceed maximum capacity allowable

$$Cap^P_{l,p,t} \leq Cap^{max}_{l,p,t} * x^P_{l,p,t} \quad \forall l\epsilon\mathcal{L}, p\epsilon\mathcal{P}, t\epsilon\mathcal{T}^{sch} \tag{3}$$

- Production capacity at time *t* cannot be lower than capacity at time *t-1*

$$Cap^P_{l,p,t} \leq Cap^P_{l,p,t-1} \quad \forall l\epsilon\mathcal{L}, p\epsilon\mathcal{P}, t\epsilon\mathcal{T}^{sch} \tag{4}$$

- Consumption of resource *r* cannot exceed the maximum availability of the resource

$$C_{l,r,t} \leq C^{max}_{l,r,t} \quad \forall l\epsilon\mathcal{L}, r\epsilon\mathcal{R}, t\epsilon\mathcal{T}^{sch} \tag{5}$$

- Amount of resource discharged cannot exceed the demand for that resource

$$\sum_{l\epsilon L} Demand_{l,r,t} \geq \sum_{l\epsilon L} S_{l,r,t} \quad \forall r\epsilon\mathcal{R}, t\epsilon\mathcal{T}^{sch} \tag{6}$$

- Amount of resource transported by transport mode *f* cannot exceed the capacity of *f*

$$\text{Tr}_{f,l,l',r,t} \leq Tr^{max}_{f,r} * x^F_{f,l,l',r,t} \; x^P_{l,p,t} \quad \forall l, l'\epsilon\mathcal{L}, r\epsilon\mathcal{R}, t\epsilon\mathcal{T}^{sch}, f\epsilon\mathcal{F} \tag{7}$$

2.1.3. Objective function

The objective of this problem is to create an optimal network design and schedule for the recycling of solar panels, with a focus on minimizing the overall cost, encompassing both *capital* and *operational* expenditures as well as *transportation cost* and *raw material cost*.

$$min \sum_{l\epsilon L}\left(\sum_{t\epsilon\mathcal{T}^{net}} \sum_{p\epsilon\mathcal{P}} Capex_{l,p,t} \; Cap^P_{l,p,t} \right) + \sum_{l\epsilon L}\left(\sum_{t\epsilon\mathcal{T}^{sch}} \sum_{r\epsilon\mathcal{R}} Vopex_{l,r,t} \; P_{l,r,t} \right)$$
$$+ \sum_{l\epsilon L}\sum_{f\epsilon\mathcal{F}}\left(\sum_{t\epsilon\mathcal{T}^{sch}} \sum_{l'\epsilon L} Tcost_f \; \text{Tr}_{f,l,l',r,t} \; Distance_{l,l'} \right) + \sum_{l\epsilon L}\left(\sum_{t\epsilon\mathcal{T}^{sch}} \sum_{r\epsilon\mathcal{R}} C_{l,r,t} \; Price_{l,r,t} \right) \tag{8}$$

3. Case study

3.1. Setup

To illustrate the practical application of the proposed mathematical model formulation for decision-making in the PV recycling supply chain, a case study is presented based on the state of Arizona (see Figure 2). The study considers locations of different facilities within the PV recycling ecosystem: i) *Collection Centers (CC1, CC2, CC3)*: These serve as primary points for collecting PV modules from end users, are strategically located based on the existing places of PV installment companies. ii) *Recycling Centers (RC1, RC2, RC3)*: These are located across the state. iii) *Central Manufacturing Center (MC)*: It acts as a potential purchaser for the recycled materials from these recycling centers to produce PV. iv) *Aluminum Collection (AC) and Glass Collection (GC) Centers:* These

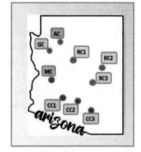

Figure 2. Representation of PV Ecosystem in Arizona

demonstrate additional demand sites for aluminum and glass.

Figure 3 shows the RTN representation of the PV recycling ecosystem, illustrating all potential connections between locations. Each collection center (CC1, CC2, and CC3) is strategically linked to three distinct recycling centers (RC1, RC2, and RC3), thereby offering a variety of options for processing PV waste. Three structured recycling technologies are considered in this case study. Within these designated recycling centers, one of three process technologies as FRELP, ASU, and Hybrid (Curtis et al., 2021) (referred to as P1, P2, and P3 in Figure 3), can be chosen and utilized for the recycling process. Each recycling center could operate at either low or high capacity, allowing for an exploration of the impact of economies of scale. The case study also investigates the recovery and reuse of specific materials such as glass and aluminum, focusing on down-cycling and recycling possibilities. Material collection centers (AC for aluminum and GC for glass) are designed as demand sites for aluminum and glass with low purity and economical prices, while the PV manufacturing center (MC) demands high-purity glass, aluminum, silver, silicon, polymer, and copper at higher costs to produce new PVs.

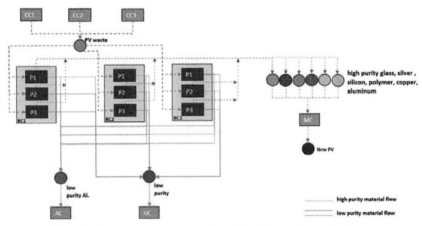

Figure 3. Superstructure representation of the PV recycling network

3.2. Results and Discussion

The results derived from the RTN model reveal that the locations RC2 and RC3 have been selected as the optimal recycling centers as depicted in Figure 4. RC2 is equipped with a high-capacity hybrid process, while RC3 operates a high-capacity FRELP process. These selections were made to achieve elevated production levels, which are based on the demand satisfaction for glass, aluminum, and new PV installments as well as price of the materials by minimizing the total cost involving capital, variable, and fixed costs.

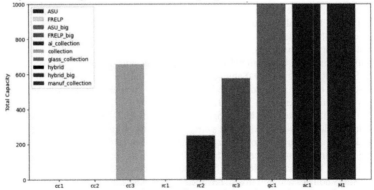

Figure 4. Total production capacity at each location by the selected process

As represented in Figure 5, when the model is given the option to generate additional demand for certain materials (as glass and aluminum), even at a slightly lower selling price, the overall cost does not show a significant increase with the chosen facilities with the same design as shown in Figure 4. Different case studies are investigated including scenarios with no additional material demand (MD), as well as low, medium, and high demand for glass and aluminum, as shown in Figure 5. The findings show that the model helps maximize capacity utilization while minimizing cost for the increased material demand and leading to the efficient use of resources. Therefore, the model exhibits both optionality in its strategic selection of materials, and flexibility in its ability to adapt to varying demand levels without substantial additional costs. The model's characteristics of optionality and flexibility align well with the principles of sensitivity analysis.

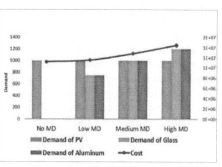

Figure 5. Demand vs Cost for different

4. Conclusion

Significant rise in solar PV panel installations and manufacturing brings the challenge of managing EoL PV panels. The key to a sustainable reverse supply chain network for solar PV panels lies in cost optimization efforts supported by enabling policies. In this work, a systematic decision-making modeling framework is proposed as a vital tool for examining different possibilities and scenarios for optimizing solar PV reverse supply chain networks. This framework allows for "what-if" analyses under various market conditions. It captures the dynamics between different components of the supply chain and aids in selecting the optimal location and technology. The RTN-based model is represented as a case study of such a framework, demonstrating its application and benefits in optimizing the reverse supply chain system under different scenarios.

Acknowledgments

This research was supported by the NSF Convergence Accelerator Program under the Grant titled "Securing Critical Material Supply Chains by Enabling Photovoltaic Circularity (SOLAR)" with Grant No49100423C0005. The authors also gratefully acknowledge support from Texas A&M University, Texas A&M Energy Institute.

References

S. Weckend, A. Wade, and G. A. Heath. End-of-life management: solar photo-voltaic panels. Technical report, IEA and International Renewable Energy Agency, 2016.

D. Bechtsis, N. Tsolakis, E. Iakovou, and D. Vlachos. Data-driven secure, resilient and sustainable supply chains: gaps, opportunities, and a new generalised data sharing and data monetisation framework. International Journal of Production Research, 60(14):4397–4417, 2022.

H. K. Salim, R. A. Stewart, O. Sahin, and M. Dudley. Drivers, barriers and enablers to end-of-life management of solar photovoltaic and battery energy storage systems: A systematic literature review. Waste Management, 537–554, 2019.

G. A. Heath, T. J. Silverman, M. Kempe et al. Research and development priorities for silicon photovoltaic module recycling to support a circular economy. Nature Energy, 5(7): 502–510, 2020.

R. Kakodkar, E. Pistikopoulos. Energiapy-an Open Source Python Package for Multiscale Modeling & Optimization of Energy Systems. AIChE Annual Meeting, 2023.

T. L. Curtis, H. Buchanan, G. Heath, L. Smith, and S. Shaw. Solar photovoltaic module recycling: A survey of US policies and initiatives. Technical report, NREL, US, 2021.

Flavio Manenti, Gintaras V. Reklaitis (Eds.), Proceedings of the 34th European Symposium on Computer Aided Process Engineering / 15th International Symposium on Process Systems Engineering (ESCAPE34/PSE24), June 2-6, 2024, Florence, Italy

Determining competition between LCA environmental impact categories through MILP single objective optimization - A case study on green hydrogen

Diego Larrahondo Chavez*[a,b] , Catherine Azzaro-Pantel[b] , Florent Montignac[a] , Alain Ruby[a]

[a]*Univ. Grenoble Alpes, CEA, Liten, DTCH, 38000 Grenoble, France*
[b]*Laboratoire de Génie Chimique, Université de Toulouse, CNRS, INPT, UPS, Toulouse France *diego.larrahondochavez@cea.fr*

Abstract

As the world faces the urgent need for sustainable energy solutions, understanding and mitigating the environmental impact of energy systems is critical. This involves considering several environmental factors, some of which may compete with each other, by either antagonism, correlation or co-benefit. This study presents a methodology, based on single objective optimization using mixed-integer linear programming (MILP). Its aim is to comprehensively assess and optimize various environmental impact categories derived from life cycle assessment (LCA) within energy systems, with the goal of minimizing them individually. The case study of a green hydrogen supply chain illustrates the proposed methodology using the PERSEE tool, developed at CEA. The results showed that minimizing climate change impact category could generate substantial co-benefits in areas related to energy resources and other impacts. However, conflicts might arise with other impacts, such as land use. Additionally, the study identified a high correlation between certain impacts such as land use and material resources. These outcomes can significantly facilitate downstream processes, including multi-objective optimizations and decision-making, for the deployment of hydrogen ecosystems.

Keywords: Optimization, LCA, MILP, Hydrogen

1. Introduction

As the quest for sustainable energy systems progresses, the interplay between technology, economics and the environmental impact of these systems requires a holistic understanding. Energy system simulation plays a key role in modeling and analyzing the intricate interactions of complex energy infrastructures. In addition, integrating Life Cycle Assessment (LCA) into the simulation of energy systems enables the quantification of environmental impacts throughout their entire life cycle. This sheds light on the overall ecological footprint, rendering it an indispensable tool for informed decision-making in strategies for transitioning energy.

In the field of energy systems, considering various categories of environmental impacts is increasingly essential. These impacts extend beyond carbon emissions, providing a comprehensive perspective of the environmental footprint associated with energy production. For example, eutrophication underscores the need to minimize the release of nutrients into water bodies, thus mitigating harmful algal blooms that endanger aquatic ecosystems. Acidification contributes to the degradation of soil and water quality, affecting biodiversity and ecosystem resilience. Ecotoxicity assesses the potential harm that energy-related substances pose to organisms, highlighting the significance of choosing materials and processes that minimize adverse effects on living systems. Depletion of energy and material resources informs us about the long-term availability of essential resources, urging the adoption of renewable and efficient energy sources. Assessing land and water use helps to safeguard natural habitats and freshwater resources, while analyzing ionizing radiation and ozone depletion highlights risks to human health and the atmosphere. The formation of particulate matter and photochemical ozone underscores the need to reduce atmospheric pollutants for human well-being, emphasizing the need for cleaner energy technologies.

Nevertheless, while energy transition strategies aim to be climate-friendly, they may overlook the broader scope of environmental protection. This oversight risks developing energy systems where climate friendliness comes at the expense of increasing other environmental impacts (Vandepaer et al. 2020). Hence, there is a crucial need to assess various environmental impacts of energy systems, to avoid unintended environmental consequences and devise strategies that are both climate and environmentally friendly.

Hydrogen emerges as a pivotal strategy in this context, serving as a versatile energy carrier with widespread recognition for its potential to mitigate environmental impacts across diverse energy sectors, particularly when produced via electrolysis. However, even in that case, hydrogen generated from electrolysis is associated with indirect carbon emissions (Mashi et al. 2023), through the way the electricity it uses is produced. This, in turn, has the potential to amplify other environmental impacts (Vandepaer et al. 2020).

For this purpose, a new methodological framework is proposed to integrate diverse environmental indicators based on the LCA method into single-objective MILP-based optimization of energy systems. Compared to existing tools, the novelty of this approach relies on a point that tends to be overlooked in LCA integration in optimization processes: how does the minimization of one specific environmental impact affect the other environmental impacts? This methodology is exemplified through the case study of a hydrogen supply chain. The aim is to identify a streamlined and representative set of environmental indicators in competition with each other to facilitate the downstream processes, including multi-objective optimizations and decision-making for the deployment of hydrogen ecosystems.

2. Methodology

This section outlines the process of integrating LCA indicators into the simulation of energy systems, to subsequently perform the individual optimization of each environmental objective and economic optimization. First, a detailed description of the primary tools utilized in this study is provided. Then, the case study and its parameterization are described. Next, the calculation of the different optimizations is presented. Finally, an analysis of the trade-offs between distinct environmental objectives is discussed. Figure 1 illustrates the sequential steps and the corresponding supporting tools.

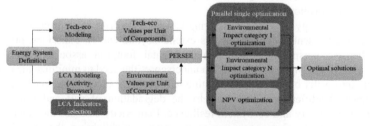

Figure 1. Methodology framework

2.1. Main Tools

2.1.1. LCA tool

To assess all components of the energy system, an Environmental Life Cycle Assessment (LCA) must be conducted. LCA, a standardized methodology (ISO 14040), evaluates the environmental impacts of products, processes, or systems. Brightway version 2, an open-source software tool based on Python, alongside its graphical interface Activity-Browser, is a widely used tool in the research community for LCA calculations. This software has been chosen for this study because of its flexibility to build parameterized environmental impact models.

2.1.2. PERSEE optimization tool

The optimization process presented in this paper is carried out with PERSEE software developed at CEA by members of LSET laboratory in Grenoble, France (Cuisinier et al. 2021). PERSEE is a tool for optimizing the sizing and management of multi-vector energy systems, using MILP formulation. This software allows the modeling and single optimization of energy systems based on either economic or environmental criteria. Upon user input, PERSEE creates a system of equations containing the objective function and all problem constraints. Subsequently, this system of equations is solved using a commercial solver, such as Cplex.

2.2. Case Study

2.2.1. System description

The case study is a theoretical small-scale hydrogen system based on some of the characteristics of the GreenHysland EU deployment project in Mallorca (Spain). This scenario involves solar and grid-powered PEM electrolysis, gas compression, and transportation to end applications (injection into the natural gas grid and refueling of hydrogen buses), as shown in Figure 2. Dynamic optimization is employed to accommodate variable inputs and outputs, considering flexible injection of hydrogen into Mallorca's natural gas grid up to 4%$_{vol}$. Additionally, the analysis includes the consideration of the environmental impacts of existing technologies (such as natural gas combustion and diesel buses) to quantify the benefits of optimal hydrogen solutions. The optimization criteria encompass the sizing of the PV system and hydrogen storage, as well as the operational control of the entire system, including grid usage, PEM electrolyzer operating hours, hydrogen transport, and the amount of hydrogen injected into the natural gas grid. A comprehensive description of the case study, with model data and references, can be found in (Montignac et al. 2023).

2.2.2. Environmental modelling

The environmental boundaries considered for the case study are summarized in Figure 2. Here, "avoided emissions" refer to reductions in various environmental burdens or adverse effects compared to a baseline situation, specifically the fossil fuel scenario. The impacts from the production and use of diesel and natural gas that would have been emitted are included in these avoided emissions (the manufacturing of diesel buses, hydrogen buses, and gas generators is out of scope). The functional unit serves as the benchmark for comparing different solutions from an LCA perspective. The functional unit considered involves two uses: one for the buses and the other for the gas and hydrogen mixture, totaling 778,666 km of service per year and 178,109 GJ per year, respectively, as depicted in Figure 2. The impact assessment method selected is Environment Footprint (EF 3.1, covering 14 out of 19 impact categories, detailed in Figure 3.

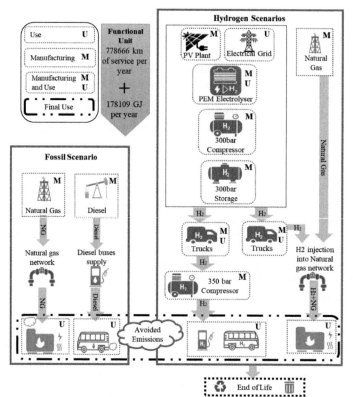

Figure 2.Case study description

3. Results

This section presents some significant results obtained from optimizing each environmental impact. Figure 3 showcases the diverse environmental impacts calculated for each optimal solution. Considering all assumptions, the results showed that all solutions except the economic one, yield negative NPV (Net Present Value), which means non profitable architectures. Notably, the scenario that optimized the economic aspect by maximizing the NPV exhibited the highest values across all impact categories (the magnitude of the environmental criteria is so high that it out of range of the figure's scale). For example, concerning Global Warming Potential, it recorded 345,000 tonsCO$_2$-eq compared to the highest value of 18,100 tonsCO$_2$-eq generated by any other optimization based on environmental criteria. This underscores that, in this case study, optimizing any specific environmental impact coincides with reductions in other impacts, portraying the economic objective as a primary antagonist to each environmental objective.

Nevertheless, minimizing a single environmental objective does not mean optimal conditions for all other impacts or equal benefits. For instance, Figure 3 illustrates how the optimal solution for global warming also optimizes energy resource use, acidification, ozone depletion, and photochemical ozone creation. Moreover, impacts such as eutrophication, ecotoxicity, particulate matter, ionizing radiation and non-carcinogenic human toxicity are notably reduced but not optimized. Conversely, in the same optimization scenario, impacts related to water use, land use, material resources and carcinogenic human toxicity were considerably high.

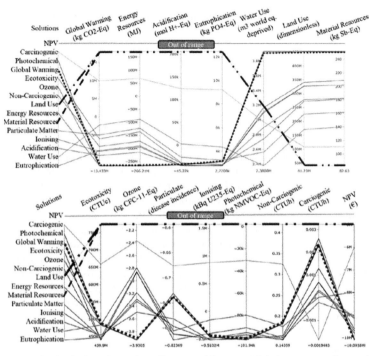

Figure 3. Optimal solutions for each environmental impact and their corresponding trade-offs
with other impacts

Another significant aspect is illustrated in Figure 3 is the conflict between different optimal solutions. For example, the optimization of land use conflicts with various impacts linked to global warming solutions, and conversely, global warming optimization conflicts with various impacts linked to land use solutions. For instance, optimizing for global warming leads to a tenfold increase in land use impact (due to the maximization of PV plant size) compared to the optimization of land use impact itself. This highlights a significant point since there is a common tendency to solely prioritize global warming, often neglecting its antagonistic relationship with land use.

In addition, some instances showcase optimal solutions that overlap, such as the scenarios for land use and material resources. This is due to high degree of correlation between these impacts, meaning that optimizing one automatically yields the optimal solution for the other. This is highly relevant since it allows simplifying the computational processes by removing one environmental objective without losing its optimal solution, thereby streamlining the case study and reducing computational costs.

Another outcome analysed was the identification of key components contributing to various environmental impacts. These included the use of the electrical grid, PV plant, and hydrogen injection into natural gas grid. Across all optimizations of the environmental criteria, there was a consistent trend toward reducing grid reliance, attributed to the high fossil fuel content in Mallorca's current grid. Meanwhile, PV optimal size tended to vary depending on the environmental criteria. For instance, material resource optimization led to no PV plant (0 MWp) compared to energy resource optimization leading to 8.56 MWp (upper bound of the optimization domain). Regarding hydrogen injection, substituting natural gas by hydrogen does not generate similar reduced impacts across different environmental criteria. For example, while it significantly addressed particulate matter in some scenarios, its effect on others, such as ecotoxicity, was negligible.

4. Conclusions

The framework presented here provides a better understanding of the potential environmental and economic capabilities of energy systems. The results highlight the risk of designing a hydrogen system solely optimized from an economic viewpoint. Therefore, adopting a life-cycle perspective becomes essential when developing energy systems.

Furthermore, minimizing climate change can generate substantial co-benefits in areas related to energy resources, acidification, ozone depletion, and photochemical ozone creation. However, such minimization also involves environmental trade-offs, leading to increased impacts in terms of land use, water use, and material resources, requiring careful consideration. Additionally, the strong correlation between some impacts can simplify these issues without losing accuracy, thereby aiding in multi-objective optimization processes and decision-making. The methodology was rather easy to implement using existing tools, and without particular link to our test case, which shows good ability for further applications. Several perspectives can enhance the robustness of these approaches. This includes conducting end-of-life and prospective analysis for all components in the environmental inventory information. Additionally, uncertainties regarding all input types should be incorporated and managed in energy system optimization problems.

Acknowledgments

The authors acknowledge specially the University of Balearic Islands, in particular Dr. Vincent Canals for providing local grid data, as well as Calvera Hydrogen Company for providing equipment data. The authors thank the GreenHysland EU project. This project has received funding from the Fuel Cells and Hydrogen 2 Joint Undertaking (now Clean Hydrogen Partnership) under Grant Agreement No 101007201. This Joint Undertaking receives support from the European Union's Horizon 2020 Research and Innovation programme, Hydrogen Europe and Hydrogen Europe Research. The content of this publication reflects only the authors' view, and the JU is not responsible for any use that may be made of the information it contains.

References

Cuisinier, Etienne, Cyril Bourasseau, Alain Ruby, Pierre Lemaire, and Bernard Penz. 2021. "Techno-Economic Planning of Local Energy Systems through Optimization Models: A Survey of Current Methods." *International Journal of Energy Research* 45(4):4888–4931.

Mashi, Rocky, Yohan Vincotte, Sofía De-León Almaraz, and Catherine Azzaro-Pantel. 2023. "Optimization of Hydrogen Systems for Prospective Life Cycle Assessment: Well-to-Tank Approach." Pp. 3211–17 in *Computer Aided Chemical Engineering*. Vol. 52, *33 European Symposium on Computer Aided Process Engineering*, edited by A. C. Kokossis, M. C. Georgiadis, and E. Pistikopoulos. Elsevier.

Montignac, Florent, Maria-Candelaria Arpajou, Diego Larrahondo Chavez, and Alain Ruby. 2023. "Multi-Criteria Optimization of Hydrogen Energy Supply Chains Considering Economic and Environmental Impacts: Theoretical Case Study in the Context of Balearic Islands." *Proceedings.Com.* doi: https://doi.org/10.52202/069564-0096.

Vandepaer, Laurent, Evangelos Panos, Christian Bauer, and Ben Amor. 2020. "Energy System Pathways with Low Environmental Impacts and Limited Costs: Minimizing Climate Change Impacts Produces Environmental Cobenefits and Challenges in Toxicity and Metal Depletion Categories." *Environmental Science & Technology* 54(8):5081–92. doi: 10.1021/acs.est.9b06484.

Flavio Manenti, Gintaras V. Reklaitis (Eds.), Proceedings of the 34th European Symposium on Computer Aided Process Engineering / 15th International Symposium on Process Systems Engineering (ESCAPE34/PSE24), June 2-6, 2024, Florence, Italy

Solving Combined Sizing and Dispatch of PV and Battery Storage for a Microgrid using ADMM

Robert Steven,[a] Oleksiy Klymenko,[a] Michael Short[a,b*]

[a]*School of Chemistry and Chemical Engineering, University of Surrey, Guildford, Surrey, GU2 7XH, UK.*
[b]*Institute for Sustainability, University of Surrey, Guildford, Surrey, GU2 7XH, UK.*
*m.short@surrey.ac.uk

Abstract

This paper presents results for solving a mixed-integer linear programming-based optimal microgrid design problem in a distributed fashion using the alternating direction method of multipliers (ADMM). A 7-bus network, with options for installing photovoltaic panels, boilers and battery storage, is considered. A representative-season, multi-year formulation is presented and, when solved in a distributed fashion, was decomposed temporally. It is shown that when a sufficiently large number of years are considered, assuming the ADMM iterations are computed in parallel, then the overall solve time can be less than that of the same problem solved in a centralised manner, whilst still producing near-optimal results. When considering a time period of 50 years, a reduction of 43 % in overall solve time is achieved. This highlights the potential use of this technique to enable the design of microgrids at scales where centralised methods may struggle.

Keywords: Distributed Energy Systems, Renewable Energy, Distributed Optimisation, ADMM

1. Introduction

To meet the pressing need of net-zero carbon emissions, electrical grids have been undergoing a recent radical process of decarbonisation. One of the keys to enabling this has been distributed energy resources such as photovoltaic (PV) panels and battery storage which can be co-located at electrical loads to form connected or islanded microgrids.

The optimal design problem of determining the optimal placement and sizing of these assets to jointly minimise the capital (CAPEX) and operational (OPEX) expenditure, over a fixed time period, can be formulated as a mixed-integer linear programming (MILP) problem. Problems of this form can be decomposed and solved in a distributed manner using ADMM, described by Boyd et al. (2011) as a means of solving convex optimisation problems containing separable objective functions, using a "decomposition-coordination" process. The objective terms for the original problem are decomposed into smaller subproblems, solved in parallel, with coordination steps to ensure a uniform overall solution (Boyd et al., 2011). Whilst a well-known drawback of ADMM is its slow convergence rate (Boyd et al., 2011), with a sufficient level of parallelisation, the overall solve time for other problem formulations using ADMM has been shown to be reduced below that of the equivalent centralised problem formulation (Guo et al., 2017). The literature shows that ADMM has been applied extensively to problems relating to microgrids, such as energy trading (Paudel and Gooi, 2019), economic dispatch (Chen and Yang, 2018) and optimal power flow (Wang et al., 2020) but has not, to the authors knowledge, previously been used for microgrid design problems. This is further evidenced by the fact that design problems are not referenced as a considered application area in a recent survey examining the use of ADMM in smart power grids (Maneesha and Swarup, 2021).

2. Methodology

2.1. Main Problem Formulation

An MILP formulation is used, employing the modelling elements presented by De Mel et al. (2024). These include PV panels, boilers and battery storage, as well as electrical and heat energy balance. To preserve the linearity of the formulation, the DC-OPF power flow approximation (Frank and Rebennack, 2016) was used. The original formulation used a representative seasonal approach, whereby a single 24-hour period of averaged electrical and heat load, with a 1-hour temporal resolution, was considered for each season (De Mel et al., 2024). This was extended to multiple years by adding additional linking constraints for the three decision variables, shown below in Eq. (4). The objective function for each individual season is defined as the total seasonal cost (TSC) in Eq. (1).

$$
\begin{aligned}
\text{TSC}_m = C_m^{\text{OPEX,grid}} &+ C_m^{\text{OPEX,PV}} + C_m^{\text{OPEX,boiler}} + C_m^{\text{OPEX,batt}} \\
&- \left(C_m^{\text{export,income}} + C_m^{\text{FIT,income}} \right), m \in \mathbf{M}
\end{aligned}
\tag{1}
$$

The terms in Eq. (1) include the operational costs for the PV, boiler and battery technologies considered here, as well as the cost of purchasing power from the main grid ($C^{\text{OPEX,grid}}$), income from selling excess power back to the grid ($C^{\text{export,income}}$) and income from a feed-in-tariff scheme ($C^{\text{FIT,income}}$). The reader is encouraged to refer to De Mel et al. (2024) for further details.

Only a single investment, made at the start of the overall time period, is considered, and so the overall objective function, the total cost (TC), becomes the sum of this CAPEX and the TSC across all seasons and years, defined in Eq. (2).

$$
\text{TC} = C^{\text{CAPEX,PV}} + C^{\text{CAPEX,boiler}} + C^{\text{CAPEX,batt}} + \sum_{m \in \mathbf{M}} \text{TSC}_m
\tag{2}
$$

The subscript m denotes the time period index, with M being the set of all considered time periods, namely 4 seasons in each of the considered years. Extending the considered time period here allows the model to take into account trends and changes in parameters such as electricity pricing, grid carbon intensity and electrical load.

2.2. Problem Decomposition

The problem formulation is decomposed temporally, with a single subproblem for each m, using the consensus version of ADMM (Boyd et al., 2011). The consensus formulation given by Boyd et al. (2011) is as follows:

$$
\min \sum_{i=1}^{N} f_i(x_i) \text{ s.t. } x_i - z = 0, i = 1, \dots, N
\tag{3}
$$

For this problem, the consensus variables are given as:

$$
x_m = \begin{bmatrix} n_m^{\text{panel,PV}} \\ H_m^{\text{gen,max}} \\ \text{Cap}_m^{\text{batt}} \end{bmatrix} = z, m \in \mathbf{M}
\tag{4}
$$

Where $n^{\text{panel,PV}}$ is the number of PV panels on each roof, $H^{\text{gen,max}}$ is the maximum boiler heat generation and Cap^{batt} is the installed battery capacity. Here, x_m defines the copy of the consensus variables in each subproblem m whilst z is defined globally as the "central collector" (Boyd et al., 2011). The addition of the consensus constraint, shown generally in Eq. (3) and specifically for this problem in Eq. (4), gives the formulation a separable objective function, tied together with complicating constraints, suitable for solving using ADMM (Boyd et al., 2011).

The augmented Lagrangian for the problem then becomes:

$$\min \sum_{m \in M} \left[TSC_m + y_m^T(x_m - z) + \left(\frac{\rho}{2}\right) \|x_m - z\|_2^2 \right] \tag{5}$$

Here, y_m is the Lagrange multiplier associated with the consensus constraint and ρ is the ADMM penalty parameter (Boyd et al., 2011). The reader is referred to Boyd et al. (2011) for the corresponding ADMM algorithmic steps. These steps are carried out iteratively until either the maximum number of iterations is reached or convergence is declared by reducing the primal gap below the given threshold. The threshold is defined as ε, with the corresponding primal gap convergence criteria across all subproblems for iteration k:

$$\left\| x_m^k - z^k \right\|_\infty \leq \varepsilon, \forall m \in \mathbf{M} \tag{6}$$

2.3. Test Network

The network used for the results presented here is the 7-bus network from De Mel et al. (2022). Data for only a single year is provided, to extrapolate this to multiple years the electrical load, heat load and irradiance values were multiplied by a uniformly distributed random value between 0.5 and 1.5. Whilst this is not expected to be representative of a real-world scenario, it provides appropriate datasets for each considered year.

2.4. Experiments

The performance of ADMM in terms of convergence is known to depend on the chosen value of the penalty parameter, ρ, that is used (Boyd et al., 2011). Here, we start with an exploratory set of computational experiments with values of ρ between 1000 and 0.01, number of years considered between 1 and 50 and note the results for required primal gap convergence thresholds, ε, of 1, 0.1 and 0.01. The problem was also solved in a centralised manner and CPU solve times for both centralised and ADMM formulations were recorded, along with optimality gaps. The optimality gap here is simply taken as the difference between the overall objective value of the two formulations:

$$obj_{gap} = obj_{ADMM} - obj_{central} \tag{7}$$

Here, a positive value for the optimality gap indicates that the ADMM formulation returned a sub-optimal result.

To determine the solve time for the ADMM solution, it is assumed that each of the subproblems are being solved in parallel (the x^{k+1} update step in Boyd et al. (2011)) and the time taken for any communication of the x^{k+1} values, as well as the updates for z and y are negligible. As this is a synchronous implementation, the total solve time for the ADMM solution is taken as the maximum x^{k+1} solve time for all subproblems in each iteration, summed over all iterations. The solve times are presented as a ratio, where a ratio value larger than 1 indicates that the ADMM formulation took longer to solve compared to the centralised formulation and vice versa.

2.5. Implementation

All problems were implemented with the Julia programming language (Bezanson et al., 2017) using the JuMP modelling language (Lubin et al., 2023) and solved using the

Gurobi solver (Gurobi, 2023). All results were computed on a Dell Latitude 7420 laptop with an Intel i5-1135G7 processor running at 2.40 GHz and 16 GB of RAM.

3. Results

3.1. Initial Centralised Results

The objective value and CPU solve time for the centralised formulation are shown in Figure 1.

Figure 1: Centralised Solution CPU Solve Time and Objective Value

The objective value here is presented as the overall cost (including CAPEX, OPEX and income), normalised by the number of years considered, to give the total cost per year. These results correspond to the following values for the decision variables highlighted in the previous section, a subset of which are shown below in Table 1.

Table 1 Optimal Decision Variables for 1 and 50 Years

	1 year			50 years		
Load	No. of PV Panels	Max Heat Gen (kWh)	Battery Capacity (kWh)	No. of PV Panels	Max Heat Gen (kWh)	Battery Capacity (kWh)
1	85	6.67	0.00	85	14.85	7.11
2	400	31.84	0.00	400	70.87	33.60
3	342	18.10	0.00	342	40.30	25.62
4	85	4.25	0.00	85	9.47	6.79
5	314	20.96	0.00	314	46.65	22.16

The number of installed PV panels selected remains the same for both the minimum and maximum number of years considered, this number is the maximum possible number of panels for the given load roof areas. Batteries on the other hand are only installed when the investment cost is spread over more years and is outweighed by export income.

3.2. ρ Value Sweep

The following plot shows the optimality gap for the ADMM formulation and CPU solve time ratio, for a primal gap convergence threshold of 1. From the plot in Figure 2, a value of $\rho=0.1$ is selected as an optimal trade-off between both the optimality gap and the CPU solve time ratio.

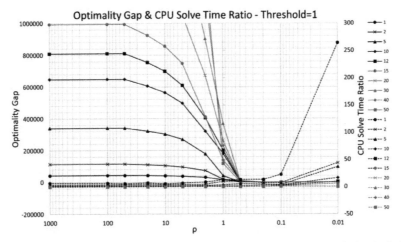

Figure 2: ρ Value Sweep – Optimality Gap (Solid Line) & CPU Solve Time Ratio (Dashed Line)

3.3. Performance Across No. of Considered Years

The plot shown in Figure 3 gives the performance of the ADMM formulation with ρ=0.1 in terms of CPU solve time ratio and optimality gap, considering a number of years between 1 and 50. The final point for 50 years and a threshold of 0.01 is omitted as ADMM did not converge within the iteration limit.

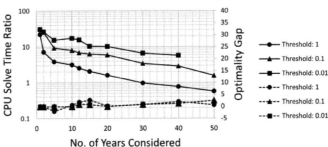

Figure 3: CPU Solve Time Ratio (Solid Line) and Optimality Gap (Dashed Line) for ρ =0.1

4. Discussion

In the initial results in Figure 1 and Table 1, whilst the number of PV panels remains constant, battery storage is only selected for a longer considered time period, reflecting the larger investment that this entails. Due to the ability to sell energy back to the grid, objective values become increasingly attractive for longer timescales, paying back the up-front investment costs in PV and batteries. The time taken to solve the formulation in a centralised manner scales with the problem size, from <1 CPUs to 14 CPUs for 50 years. For the ADMM formulation, when sweeping the value of ρ, a clear region exists affording both a low optimality gap, which increases if ρ is set too high, and a minimal CPU solve time ratio, which increases if ρ is set too low. With ρ set to 0.1, the plot in Figure 3 demonstrates a low optimality gap, implying that the solution mimics that of the centralised formulation, with a decreasing CPU solve time ratio as more years are considered. For a primal gap convergence threshold of 1, there is a "break-even" point at 30 years, when considering more years than this, the overall solve time for the ADMM solution is lower than that of the centralised solution when decomposed temporally into each considered time period. This demonstrates the enhanced ability of the ADMM formulation to provide solutions in a timely manner when considering more time periods.

5. Conclusions

The results presented here highlight the potential for ADMM to speed-up the solving of MILP microgrid design problems, whilst still providing results that closely match those calculated in a centralised fashion. When considered over 50 years, use of the ADMM formulation resulted in a reduction in CPU solve time of 43 %, assuming parallel computation. Care must be taken however, as these time savings from use of the parallel formulation are only seen with sufficiently large problem sizes.

Further work will involve adding additional objective function terms, such as asset lifetimes and associated maintenance and disposal costs, and adding the ability for capital expenditure to be made at different points throughout the considered time period. Testing with the larger Modified IEEE EU LV Network and using the AC-OPF power flow formulation, as presented in De Mel et al. (2024) will also be completed. The formulation presented above can be extended to include elements such as heat pumps, electric vehicle charging, and demand response and further research will also look at incorporating spatial decomposition into the formulation and comparing the results obtained from ADMM with other decomposition methods.

References

J. Bezanson, A. Edelman, S. Karpinski and V. B. Shah, 2017, Julia: A fresh approach to numerical computing, SIAM review, 59, 1, 65-98

S. Boyd, N. Parikh, E. Chu, B. Peleato and J. Eckstein, 2011, Distributed optimisation and statistical learning via the alternating direction method of multipliers, Foundations and Trends in Machine Learning, 3, 1, 1-122

G. Chen and Q. Yang, 2018, An ADMM-Based Distributed Algorithm for Economic Dispatch in Islanded Microgrids, IEEE Transactions on Industrial Informatics, 14, 9, 3892-3903

I. De Mel, O. Klymenko and M. Short, 2022, Optimal Design of Distributed Energy Systems Considering the Impacts on Electrical Power Networks, arxiv

I. De Mel, O. V. Klymenko and M. Short, 2024, Complementarity reformulations for the optimal design of distributed energy systems with multiphase optimal power flow, International Journal of Electrical Power & Energy Systems, 155, B, 109610

S. Frank and S. Rebennack, 2016, An introduction to optimal power flow: Theory, formulation, and examples, 48, 12, 1172-1197

J. Guo, G. Hug and O. K. Tonguz, 2017, A Case for Nonconvex Distributed Optimization in Large-Scale Power Systems, IEEE Transactions on Power Systems, 32, 5, 3842-3851

Gurobi Optimization, LLC, 2023, Gurobi Optimizer Reference Manual

M. Lubin, O. Dowson, J. Dias Garcia, J. Huchette, B. Legat and J. P. Vielma, 2023, JuMP 1.0: Recent improvements to a modeling language for mathematical optimization, Mathematical Programming Computation

A. Maneesha and K. S. Swarup, 2021, A survey on applications of Alternating Direction Method of Multipliers in smart power grids, Renewable and Sustainable Energy Reviews, 152, 111687

A. Paudel and H. B. Gooi, 2019, Pricing in Peer-to-Peer Energy Trading Using Distributed Optimization Approach, 2019 IEEE Power & Energy Society General Meeting (PESGM)

Y. Wang, T. L. Nguyen, C. Ju, Y. Xu, B. Wang and X. Feng, 2020, A Distributed Secondary-Tertiary Coordinated Control Framework for Islanded Microgrids, 2020 IEEE 18th International Conference on Industrial Informatics (INDIN), 1, 603-608

Flavio Manenti, Gintaras V. Reklaitis (Eds.), Proceedings of the 34th European Symposium on Computer Aided Process Engineering / 15th International Symposium on Process Systems Engineering (ESCAPE34/PSE24), June 2-6, 2024, Florence, Italy

Screening of solvents for perovskite solar cells using reverse engineering approach

Luis Eduardo Ramirez Cardenas[a]*, Rachid Ouaret[b], Lea Schwersenz[c], Vincent Gerbaud[b], Markus Kohlstädt[c], Sophie Thiebaud-Roux[a], Ivonne Rodríguez Donis[a]

[a]*Laboratoire de Chimie Agro-Industrielle, Université de Toulouse, INRAE, INP, France*
[b]*Laboratoire de Génie Chimique, Université de Toulouse, CNRS, INP, UPS, France*
[c]*University of Freiburg, Freiburg Materials Research Center, Stefan Meier Str 21, D-79104, Germany.*
luiseduardo.ramirezcardenas@toulouse-inp.fr

Abstract

Perovskite solar cells are a promising technology in the field of photovoltaics but the use of dimethylformamide, a highly toxic solvent, to solubilize all type of precursors, still limits their production to larger solar modules. The search of alternative solvents relies primarily on trial-and-error approaches due to the complex relationship between solvent and device performance. In this work we propose a Computer-Aided Molecular Design reverse engineering to find substitutes for dimethylformamide using COSMO-RS. Solubility experiments of the best candidates suggest an effect from steric hindrance of the solvent molecule and the degree of polarization around the molecule.

Keywords: Reverse engineering, COSMO-RS, Perovskite solar cells

1. Introduction

Perovskite solar cells (PSC) are a promising alternative to current silicon based solar cells due to its increase in power conversion efficiency (PCE) over the last two decades and all-solution based fabrication (NREL, 2023). Existing technologies depend greatly on dimethylformamide (DMF), in spite of its good performance, having a high toxicity makes their use in the industry dangerous under standard conditions (Gardner et al., 2016). The process to build PSC is composed by two steps. First, the perovskite precursors are solubilized by the solvent, usually via the formation of complexes. Then, the second step concerns deposition of PSCs active layer through a controlled crystallization process by solvent evaporation. The search of alternative solvents requires an understanding of the interactions between solvents and perovskite precursors.

Most studies aimed at replacing these toxic solvents have used the classic "trial and error" methodology, based on the researcher's expertise consuming time and resources (Ying et al. 2023). Solvent screening can be improved by using a Reverse Engineering approach based on Computer Aided Molecular Design (CAMD) for many applications in chemical engineering fields. The CAMD methodology starts by defining a set of physicochemical properties and target values related to the main solvent functionalities. It is then followed by the screening of existing solvents or the design of new molecular structures which better meet these requirements. In this work, Reverse Engineering is used for the substitution of DMF in the solubilization step of the triple cation lead perovskite $Cs_{0.05}FA_{0.85}MA_{0.10}PbI_{2.90}Br_{0.10}$. Identification of solvents having similar solvency power to DMF is done using the σ-potential profile computed by COSMO-RS and FPCA to assess similarity. Further solvent screening is based on Lewis basicity of best solvents via the Gutmann's donor number (DN). Physicochemical properties related to the crystallization step are then considered. To discriminate potential solvents, a global performance function aggregating difference between property values and requirements is used and helps establish a list of solvents that are further tested for the solubilization of the perovskite precursors.

2. Methodology

2.1. Reverse Engineering

Reverse Engineering is a 3-phase process (Heintz et al., 2014). The first phase, the intelligence phase, consists of an in-depth understanding of the mechanisms involved in the process enabling the definition of a list of solvent functionalities, which will be further described by target physico-chemical properties. Compliance with these requirements by the solvent candidates is assessed using a global performance function ($GlobPerf$). In the next search phase, two steps can be considered: 1) assessing the global performance of existing molecules; 2) designing molecular structures using a CAMD tool where the properties are calculated using predictive models. Performance functions for a large database of existing molecules are computed during the assessment step, allowing the identification of chemical families and groups having a beneficial impact on matching the target properties. These groups can be further used in the design step using the CAMD tool. The last phase encompasses the selection of the reverse engineering most promising solvents to be tested experimentally, and deals with the selection of the best candidates, either pure components or mixtures.

For this work the search of substitution solvents for DMF is done using the evaluation of existing molecules. In the intelligence phase, a database including ~ 5000 molecules was created taking COSMO-RS' database as reference. Furthermore, the list of solvent functionalities is defined along with the related physicochemical properties. In the search phase, comparison of each molecule's solvency power to DMF is done thanks to the reduction of the entire σ-potential computed with COSMOtherm into a 2D space using Functional Principal Component Analysis (FPCA). The distance of each molecule from DMF into the 2D space is then combined with the Donor Number (DN) allowing the preliminary identification of the best candidates. The solvent choice phase for further experimental test is based on the molecules having the better $GlobPerf$ (max is 1). It depends on a performance function for each target property $Perf_P$, depending of the property value x and the target value P. *Tol* parameter helps accounting for uncertainty of predicted values (Heintz et al., 2014). Performance equals *val* value when $P-x = tol$.

$$GlobPerf = \frac{\sum_{p=1}^{np} W_P * Perf_P}{\sum_{p=1}^{np} W_P} \quad (1) \qquad \text{where:} \quad Ln(Perf_P) = \ln(val) * \left(\frac{P-x}{tol}\right)^2 (2)$$

2.2. COSMO-RS σ-potential dimensionality reduction with FPCA

COSMO-RS is a predictive model, able to calculate interactions between molecules in a fluid state, combining statistical thermodynamics and quantum mechanics to predict thermodynamic properties without experimental data (Eckert and Klamt, 2002). COSMO-RS takes as input a COSMO file generated from a geometrical optimization of a molecule in a cavity surrounded by a virtual perfect conductor. The surface polarization of the cavity is obtained. This surface is then divided into several segments, which are stored as a histogram, called σ-profile, representing the number of segments as a function of the surface charge. Positive polarizations (red zones) are caused by the presence of electronic density around an atom. From the σ-profile, interactions between all the segments can be calculated resulting in a molecular descriptor curve called σ-potential, which indicates how likely a molecule is to have a good interaction with certain surface charge value. Molecules having similar σ-potential curves have comparable solvency power. This characteristic is used to identify substitution solvents for DMF. Comparison of the σ-potential curve of the molecules with that of DMF is done with FPCA (Ramsay, 2009). The results of FPCA are obtained using FPCA package implemented in R (Gajardo and B. Satarupa, 2021).

2.3. Gutmann's Donor Number

The Gutmann's donor number (DN) indicates the Lewis basicity of a solvent, and is defined as the negative enthalpy value for the formed adduct between a Lewis base and a standard Lewis acid. Experimental measurement of DN is expensive and time-consuming. For the purposes of solvent screening, we have implemented the DN calculation method proposed by Smiatek (2019) based on molecular orbital LUMO and HOMO energy values of the molecules, computed with Turbomole (2019).

2.4. Experimental testing of solvent candidates for perovskite precursors

The solubility tests were carried out by mixing precursor salts with the respective test solvents to yield 1.45 M solutions. The mixtures were stirred at room temperature for one hour and further diluted with solvent to 1.2 M and further to 0.15 M and 0.1 M by adding the suitable volume when the mixtures were not fully dissolved. Additionally, mixtures set to 0.1 M concentration were heated and stirred at 90°C for 1 h. All solutions were visually inspected for complete dissolution of the precursor salts.

3. Results and Discussion

3.1. Parametrization of the evaluation of existing molecules

Table 1 displays the list of technical functionalities of the ideal solvent along with the associated physico-chemical properties. Target values "P" in Eq. (2) were set based on the best solvent's properties reported in literature for different perovskites (Jiang et al., 2023). A smooth decrease of $Perf_P$ is allowed by "tol" when the computed value of the property "x" is outside of the target range (Table 1). The weight of the property in the $GlobPerf$ Eq. (1) is considered *via* the weighting parameter W_P. In this work, good candidates were identified by comparing the σ-potential curves taking that of DMF as reference. DN is also considered for this functionality due to its strong relationship with the solvent's ability to form adducts. COSMO-RS is the only computational tool used for computing all physico-chemical properties reported in Table 1.

Table 1. Solvent properties, target values and used models

Functionality	Property	Target value (P)	W_P (eq.2)	Parameters
Solvency power	Distance of σ-potential curve	D < 50	4	Val =0.8 Tol=25
	Gutmann's donor number	18 < DN <30	4	Val =0.5 Tol=1
Liquid state	Boiling temperature (K)	333 < BP <473	2	Val=0.8, Tol=10
	Vapor pressure (mbar)	0.8<VP < 120	2	Val=0.5, Tol=5
	Density (kg/m³)	800 < ρ < 1300	1	Val=0.5,Tol=0.1
Transport property	Viscosity (cP)	0.8< μ < 2	1	Val=0.5,Tol=0.2
	Surface tension (Mn/m)	35 < ST < 45	1	Val=0.8, Tol=2

3.2. Parametrization of the evaluation of existing molecules

3.2.1. Comparison of candidates using the of σ-potential curves and DN

The σ-potential curves are represented in a multidimensional space corresponds to a matrix having 5000 molecules (rows) × 61 columns (values ranging between -0.03 to +0.03 e/Å²). The data reduction of original data space using FPCA captures 99.5% of the total variation in a 2D space. Display of all molecules in the FPCA 2D space creates a simple visual categorization, that allows to differentiate them according to their polarity more easily than the σ-potential curves. Figure 1 displays the position of the best 15 solvents having a low distance with respect to the DMF position. Their respective σ-potential curves appear in figure 2.

Table 2 displays the best candidates having a *GlobPerf* > 0.5 and ranks them by the distance values. NMP and N,N-Dimethylacetamide candidates have been cited in literature for PSC manufacturing as good solvents for precursors solubilization. Pure dimethyl sulfoxide (DMSO) is not capable to dissolve organic-inorganic perovskites (Jiang et al., 2023). Indeed, only binary mixtures DMSO-DMF have shown good PCE values. New substitution solvents were found from our study, with lower distance than DMSO to DMF and a suitable DN. Most of the new candidates contain similar atoms to DMF mainly nitrogen and oxygen in a linear or cyclic molecular structure. Substitution of nitrogen atom by sulphur atom has also been explored but studied molecules, for instance, Dimethylthioformamide, is not suitable to be used as solvent but as additives to retard the crystallization phase of the active layer (Hamill et al., 2020). Other new candidates contain only nitrogen or oxygen atoms belonging to a different chemical family. Due to confidential reasons, only the main atoms (type and number) are reported in table 2 for the new candidates. Candidate C5-N2 has *GlobPerf* = 1 as DMF. NMP is the second better solvent reported in literature but its main drawback, apart its high toxicity, is its high boiling point, which alongside of low vapor pressure, are the main cause of low *GlobPerf* for candidates with distance < 50.

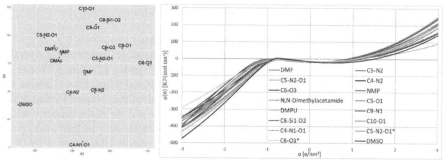

Figure 1 Candidate solvents position in the FPCA space.   Figure 2 σ-potential curves of the candidate solvents

3.2.2. Solubility experiments with the perovskite $Cs_{0.05}FA_{0.85}MA_{0.10}PbI_{2.90}Br_{0.10}$

Ten solvents (italic) were selected in Table 2 for the solubility tests. Among the top three *GlobPerf* candidates (C5-N2, C5-O1, C4-N1-O1), only one, C5-N2, dissolved the perovskite precursors, questioning the relevance of the *GlobPerf* ranking. Even so, this methodology is well suited for an initial solvent screening from a large database although other less performant candidates passed the solubility test.

Experimental observations could be explained by considering extra atomic features of the chemical structures, that were not considered during reverse engineering, like steric access to polarized areas. Typical precursor solubilizing solvents are small molecules (DMF, NMP, DMSO) providing an accessible red zone (fig 3 a), b), c)) with polarization values superior to 0.01 e/Å². Three other molecules could solubilize the perovskite precursors at different concentrations. The highest concentration was achieved by N,N-dimethylacetamide (DMAc) at 1.2 M. DMAc has a small size, comparable to DMF, with an exposed red zone which facilitates the electronic interaction with the perovskite precursors. The second highest concentration was obtained for C5-N2-O1*, with a value of 0.3 M. The lower concentration can be explained by a more hindered red zone (Fig.3e)). The best candidate, C5-N2, resulted in the lowest concentration of 0.1 M. Two red zones are found in C5-N2 (Fig 3f)) but only the most outer nitrogen could interact with the perovskite precursors. Nevertheless, this most accessible nitrogen generates a weak surface charge of 0.01 e/Å² around it (Fig4), decreasing its solubilization power.

Table 2. Results of the search phase

Solvent candidates	D	DN	BP (K)	VP (bar)	P (kg/m³)	μ (Cp)	ST (Mn/m)	GlobPerf
DMF	0	25.1	153	5.16	948	0.92	35.8	1
C5-N2	20	29.3	444	0.77	862	1.77	35.1	**1**
C5-N2-O1	22	30.8	494	0.3	1068	4.08	41	0.7419
C4-N2	27	24.8	400	5.4	1012	2.19	38	**0.9678**
C6-O3	34	25.4	435	3.15	969	6.80	29.5	**0.9324**
NMP	36	27.8	475	0.11	1048	2.67	41.4	0.9304
N,N-dimethylacetamide	37	28.0	438	0.72	904	2.16	36.6	**0.9751**
C5-O1	46	28.2	351	129	887	0.76	36.6	**0.9954**
DMPU	48	31.7	519	0.08	1063	6.09	43.8	0.5656
C9-N1	54	19.2	443	1.34	907	2.87	36.6	0.8457
C8-Si1-O2	54	2.8	431	2.66	904	6.16	39.7	**0.9314**
C7-N2-S1	56	23.4	498	0.12	1105	8.55	35.4	0.7944
C10-O1	56	29.3	449	1.44	948	2.80	36.6	**0.9292**
C4-N1-O1	59	22.8	350	53.9	1064	1.46	41.2	**0.9882**
C5-N2-O1 *	64	30.6	449	1.4	927	2.98	36.6	**0.9163**
C6-O3 *	84	19.6	431	5.37	995	6.28	27.6	**0.8561**
DMSO	93	29.8	189	1.45	1.135	2.89	43.5	0.8688

The remaining tested solvents were not capable to solubilize the precursors even at high temperature. Four different atomic features were identified for these solvents. Case 1: C5-N2-O1 and C8-Si-O2 have inaccessible red zones hindered by methyl groups around them (Fig.3k) and Fig.3h)) which makes it impossible for these molecules to correctly interact with the salts and solubilize them. Case 2: C5-O1 (Fig3i)) and C4-N1-O1 (Fig.3m)), have small, slightly flat, in-cycle red zones reducing their field of interaction with the precursors. Case 3: C6-O3* has an accessible red zone but the big size of the molecule would hinder other solvent molecules approaching the precursors decreasing its solubility power. Case 4: two candidates, C6-O3 (Fig.3g)) and C4-N2 (Fig.3j)), formed a solution of both dissolved and not dissolved perovskite precursors. C6-O3 is a long chain that has 17 conformers, from which 6 of them have a long red zone that would be capable of surrounding some of the perovskite precursors allowing C6-O3 to dissolve them to some extent. C4-N2 has an in-cycle red zone that, unlike C5-O1 and C4-N1-O1, has a higher electronic density due to the inductive effect of its methyl group, and the mesomeric effect of the neighbor N, less electronegative than an oxygen.

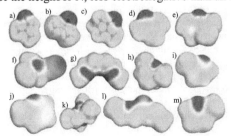

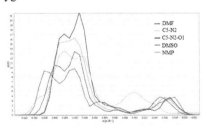

Figure 3. COSMO surface of candidate molecules

Figure 4. σ-profiles of candidate molecules

According to the experimental results, neither the FPCA distance nor the calculated DN correlate with the solubility power. But they remain useful as initial screening criteria. Accessibility and polarity of the solvent's red zone seems to be a decisive factor for the perovskite precursor solvation. The inclusion of these two criteria could improve the solvent screening specially for solubilisation process without the formation of complexes. That is the case of gama-valerolactone, which has been recently reported as capable to solubilize MAPbI$_3$ (Chalkias et al., 2023). To further test this hypothesis, a combination of FPCA distance and red zone availability is being tested.

4. Conclusions

We proposed a reverse engineering methodology to find alternative solvents for a triple-cation perovskite using COSMO-RS σ-potential and an in-silico calculation of the DN. Using reverse engineering on a database of ~5000 molecules helped screening candidates for further experimental solubility testing of 10 molecules. A 2D visual representation of solvents from the σ-potential indicative of their polarity was produced. Experiments found three suitable solvents, not proposed previously for this system, which will be further tested in the fabrication step of solar cells. Access to polarized areas and steric hindrance were shown to impact the solubilization process of perovskite precursors. Further work will be carried out to determine the contribution of solvent red zone availability to the dissolution of the perovskite precursors. Proven right this methodology could then be easily extended any molecule.

Acknowledgments

This work has benefited from state aid managed by the French National Research Agency (ANR) under the project ANR-21-CE05-0031-01 as well as the "Investissements d'Avenir" program with the reference ANR-18-EURE-0021.

References

Best Research-Cell Efficiency Chart https://www.nrel.gov/pv/cell-efficiency.html (2023)

BIOVIA COSMOtherm, Release 2022; Dassault Systèmes. http://www.3ds.com

D.A. Chalkias, A. Mourtzikou, G. Katsagounos, A.N. Kalarakis, E. Stathatos, 2023, Development of Greener and Stable Inkjet-Printable Perovskite Inks for All-Printed Annealing-Free Perovskite Solar Mini-Modules Manufacturing, Small Methods, 7, 2300664

J. C. Hamill, O. Romiluyi, S. A. Thomas, J. Cetola, J. Schwartz, M. F. Toney, P. Clancy et Y.-L. Loo, 2020, Sulfur-Donor Solvents Strongly Coordinate Pb^{2+} in Hybrid Organic-Inorganic Perovskite Precursor Solutions, J. Phys. Chem., 124, 14496-14502

F. Eckert, A. Klamt, 2002. Fast solvent screening via quantum chemistry: COSMO-RS approach. AIChE Journal 48, 369–385

A. Gajardo, B. Satarupa, 2021, fdapace: Functional Data Analysis and Empirical Dynamics

K.L. Gardner, J.G. Tait, T. Merckx, W. Qiu, U.W. Paetzold, L. Kootstra, M. Jaysankar, R. Gehlhaar, D. Cheyns, P. Heremans, J. Poortmans, 2016, Nonhazardous Solvent Systems for Processing Perovskite Photovoltaics, Adv. Energy Mat., 6, 1600386

J. Heintz, J.-P. Belaud, N. Pandya, M. Teles Dos Santos, V. Gerbaud, 2014. Computer aided product design tool for sustainable product development. Computers & Chemical Engineering 71, 362

Z. Jiang, B. Wang, W. Zhang, Z. Yang, M. Li, F. Ren, T. Imran, Z. Sun, S. Zhang, Y. Zhang, Z. Zhao, Z. Liu, W. Chen, (2023), Solvent Engineering Towards Scalable Fabrication of High-Quality Perovskite Films for Efficient Solar Modules, Journal of Energy Chemistry, 80, 689

J.O. Ramsay, G. Hooker, S. Graves, 2009, Functional Data Analysis with R and MATLAB, Springer New York

J. Smiatek, 2019, Enthalpic contributions to solvent–solute and solvent-ion interactions: Electronic perturbation as key to the understanding of molecular attraction, J. Chem. Phys., 150, 174112

TURBOMOLE V7.4 2019, a development of University of Karlsruhe and Forschungszentrum Karlsruhe GmbH, 2007, TURBOMOLE GmbH, since 2007; available from turbomole.com.

Flavio Manenti, Gintaras V. Reklaitis (Eds.), Proceedings of the 34th European Symposium on Computer Aided Process Engineering / 15th International Symposium on Process Systems Engineering (ESCAPE34/PSE24), June 2-6, 2024, Florence, Italy

Towards CO_2 Reduction in Middle East: A Techno-Environmental Assessment

Nasser Al-Malki, Mohammed Yaqot, Brenno C. Menezes[*]

Division of Engineering Management and Decision Sciences, College of Science and Engineering, Hamad Bin Khalifa University, Doha, Qatar Foundation, Qatar

bmenezes@hbku.edu.qa

Abstract

Greenhouse gases (GHGs) are emitted mainly by countries heavily dependent on coal and with high population such as China and USA, responsible, respectively, for 30% and 15% of the global amounts of CO_2-equivalent and close to this numbers of related combustion-made emissions, such as CO, NO_x, SO_2, particulate matter (PM), etc. Then, there is a direct correlation on CO_2 emissions from fossil-fuels to the non-CO_2, since the latter occurs by the imperfect combustion of the carbonic components (CO and PM) or presence of heteroatoms in the fuel (NO_x and SO_2). Particularly NOx is also formed by N_2 and O_2 reaction at high temperature. Heavily polluted per capita (PPC), figuring all six Gulf Cooperation Council (GCC) countries among the 10 first PPC positions, these wealthy countries in the Middle East have presented in the last years one of the worst qualities of air worldwide. This is a consequence of high PPC levels localized in these countries that cannot be solved without changes towards fossil fuels consumption regardless of the climate change issues by the CO_2 excess globally. To combat climate changes and air quality localized, the Middle East Energy Policy launched sustainable development strategies in the series of so-called National Vision 2030 and beyond. As an example of these sustainable initiatives, this work calculates the CO_2 reduction from national projects such as subway lines, electrical buses, solar panel farms, etc., for Qatar's National Vision 2030 towards CO_2 reduction considering the baseline as the year before the COVID-19 pandemic. Widespread greener transportation systems and electricity from renewables for the visioned CO_2 reduction may not suffice for the intended projects and changes in energy policies and housing consumer behavior in the country or in the region are fundamental to reach the reduction targets.

Keywords: Sustainability, CO_2 emissions, greener transportation, GHG, GCC countries

1. Introduction

CO_2-equivalent emissions are unequally distributed worldwide. It depends on countries' population size and wealth, energy matrix on fossil-fuels, transportation networks, industrial capacities and capabilities, energy diversification towards renewables, awareness and behavior of the communities on housing energy savings and impacts on health of exhausted gases (emissions) from fossil-fuel combustion. Policymakers, academics, and industrial experts develop nationwide plans or international agreements to mitigate by several means the footprint of any kind of under-monitoring and control (UMC) activities of the interdependent energy-emission flows (EIA Outlook, 2022).

Globally, Middle Eastern countries pollute 4% (GCC 3.23%) in total amount. Locally, the quality of the air in its higher levels, at 4 or 5 (of a scale from 1 to 5), is found most of the time in certain GCC regions. Although the CO_2-equivalent is the subject under discussion in this paper, other emissions related to the combustion processes emitted together when burning fossil-fuel derivatives (coal, natural gas, fuel oil, bunker, gasoline, jet-fuel, diesel, etc.) are NOx, SO_2, CO, PM, etc. Adding to the CO_2-equivalent bulk, countries where methane (CH_4) to the atmosphere is prominent, the GHG concerns are more complex such as in Brazil for its huge production of livestock (CH_4 from animal manure) and in Qatar with escaping of CH_4 throughout the liquid natural gas (LNG) production and supply chain networks.

Technical solutions towards GHG reduction typically consider (1) sustainable design, operation, control, and monitoring of current or new assets, (2) phasing down or out of fossil fuels, (3) carbon capture processes, and (4) use of renewables. However, all these options present pitfalls and risks inherent to their expansion. In some GCC countries, their *National Vision Programs* are counting on these solutions to achieve GHG reduction. However, many of these programs are taken as initiatives or intentions rather than being considered as mandates or new legislation.

On the other hand, non-technical solutions, related to the energy end-user must count on society's *glocal* management by acting locally to achieve a global (or regional) outcome. In the case of the Middle East, particularly in GCC, the high regional consumption of energy per capita can potentially cause more health issues than other regions in the globe. This is directly related to other exhausted gases (not CO_2) and particulate matter (PM) generated mainly by the combustion of fossil-fuel derivatives in transportation systems. Efficient energy systems and adequate policies are necessary for the development of viable projects towards the sustainable reduction of GHGs, whereby techno-economic assessments must evaluate the trade-offs between technology, economics, and sustainability in a systematic way. It includes energy system design and integration, greener energy production considering the transition to renewables, technologies for energy savings and storage, carbon capture, among others.

2. Problem statement

The Middle East, GCC countries, faces significant challenges related to high levels of GHG emissions, particularly CO_2. Despite regional efforts outlined in national development plans, there is a pressing need to assess the feasibility and effectiveness of current strategies aimed at reducing CO_2 emissions. The study focuses on Qatar's National Vision 2030 as a case study, evaluating the impact of sustainable initiatives such as subway lines, electrical buses, and solar panel farms purposed for CO_2 or, broadly, GHG/CO_2-eq reduction. However, there is a growing concern that the envisioned greener transportation systems and renewable energy sources may not be sufficient to achieve the targeted reduction. The key issues towards CO_2 reduction in the GCC are as follows:

1. The high per capita energy consumption in the region, leading to severe air quality issues, primarily caused by emissions from fossil-fuel combustion in transportation systems.

2. The inadequacy of technical solutions, including sustainable design, carbon capture processes, and renewable energy use, to fully address the complex challenges of GHG reduction.
3. The discrepancy between the intentions outlined in National Vision Programs and the lack of mandatory regulations or legislation to enforce the implementation of GHG reduction initiatives.

The study will primarily focus on the GCC countries, with a special emphasis on Qatar, using quantitative data and techno-economic assessments to analyze the current state of GHG emissions, the impact of sustainable initiatives, and the challenges faced in achieving GHG reduction targets. Understanding the challenges and limitations in the current approach towards GHG/CO_2-eq reduction in the Middle East is crucial for policymakers, researchers, and industrial experts. The findings of this study will contribute valuable insights to guide the development of more effective and enforceable strategies for achieving sustainable GHG/CO_2-eq reduction in the region.

3. GHG/CO_2-eq emissions in Gulf Cooperation Council (GCC) countries

Sustainable development has been one of the major concerns of many countries recently and has attracted the attention of policymakers. Protection of environment has been identified as one of the major pillars of achieving sustainable development goals for the GCC countries. For example, Qatar's National Vision 2030 addresses "environmental management" as one of the major challenges (General secretariat for development planning, 2008). A mixture of abrupt economic expansion and population growth has fuelled a massive energy demand in the GCC countries recently (World Bank, 2022).

GCC countries have seen a 74% growth in population since 2000 (Our World in Data, 2022). Hence, these countries are on one hand facing enhanced domestic energy demand and on the other are challenged with emissions' control (Bekhet et al., 2017). This recent growth in demand for energy production in both fuels and electricity can be directly linked to the rising CO_2 emissions and localized air quality has become a global concern. This sought for the adoption of technologies for carbon-reduction and alternative energy sources in implementing significant energy efficiency measures. If these measures are not implemented CO_2 emissions will continue to increase.

The total GCC countries population is 57.3 million which is 0.73% of the global population of 7.8 billion, however contributes with 1198.28 million tonnes (3.23%) of the global CO_2 emissions of 37.12 billion tonnes (Our World in Data, 2022). In Figure 1, the CO_2-eq emissions per capita is presented. The GCC countries are all among the 10 most polluted per capita with Qatar showing the highest value, almost double than the avarege for GCC amd 10 times the world numbers.

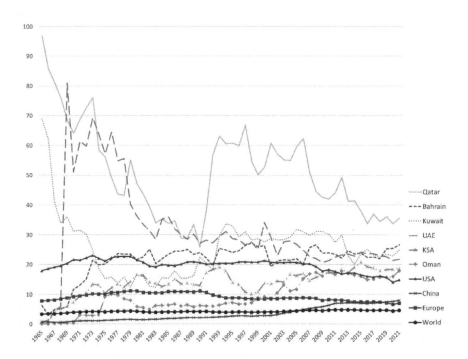

Figure 2: CO_2-eq emission per capita (Our World in Data, 2022)

Zmami and Ben-Salha (2020) conduct a study on the determinants of CO_2 emissions in GCC countries and revealed that energy consumption and foreign direct investments (FDI) have been major causes of environmental degradation in the GCC countries but found urbanization to have a positive impact on the environment. This study argued that FDI has been positively related to less environmental pollution, whereas energy consumption has been found to be an important factor affecting the environment. Praveen et al. (2020) conduct a study on the utilization of renewable energy (RE) of GCC countries that highlighted the social, political, and economic factors towards RE adoption. The study investigates the scope, methods, and feasibility of generating energy from solar and wind resources and guides how GCC countries would be able to achieve their 2030 RE goals by proactively utilizing their abundant RE reserves.

However, the GCC countries would need to strategize some infrastructural and policy options to reach their CO_2 emission goals of 25% reduction by 2030. Zmami and Ben-Salha (2020) recommend that policymakers in GCC countries should focus on developing renewable energy sources (e.g., solar energy sources) investing in the development of renewable energy technologies. GCC countries should also emphasize strengthening environmental regulations enforcing and controlling the implementation of environmental laws. Praveen et al. (2020) suggest to utilize the solar and wind adopting solar photovoltaic technology because concentrated solar power plants with thermal energy storage systems would be able to offer fir power to the grid. Besides, generating energy from the wind in Oman, Kuwait, and Saudi Arabia more favorable both economically and in terms of return on investment (ROI). These options would not only contribute towards the reduction of CO_2 emission but also these would help in curbing climate change and sustainable development goals in the region. The GCC policymakers would need to be united and work collectively while focusing on the reforms and innovative strategies at social and political levels in order to be successful in reaching their sustainable development goals by 2030.

4. Results

Focusing on CO_2 reduction in Qatar this study has found some results which is worth mentioning. The study has analyzed data on CO_2 emission in Qatar 2019 to 2022 CO_2 which is presented as follows:

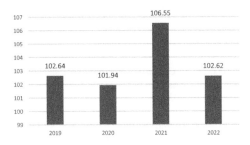

Figure 2: CO_2 Emission (in million metric tons) (Our World in Data, 2022)

The country is working towards CO_2 emission to adhere to the targets in the Qatar's Vision 2023, which is aimed at bringing CO_2 emission down to 76.97 million metric tons by 2030. This means Qatar would have to reduce 25.66 million metric tons of CO_2 emissions by the next 8 years. Nevertheless, by the open-data sources and projects raised in this work, Qatar will be able to reduce:

- 1.04 million metric tons of CO_2 emissions from 4000 electric buses operation in the public sector by 2030 (Atatullah, 2022), which accounts 4% of the total target emission of 25.66 million metric tons.

- 0.47 million metric tons CO_2 emission from 3 Metro lines by 2030, which is around 2% of the total target emission reduction (Al-Thawadi and Al-Ghamdi, 2019).

- From the solar panels the country is currently producing 800MW of electricity, which would be able to reduce 14400 metric tons of CO_2 emission by 2030, which is 0.45% of the total target emission (Ataullah, 2022).

All these adds up to 6.3% of the total emission until 2030, which leaves the country to achieve a staggering 93.7% to achieve from other means of CO_2 emission.

4. Conclusion

This study highlights the pressing issue of greenhouse gas (GHG) emissions in the Gulf Cooperation Council (GCC) countries, notably Qatar. Rapid economic growth and population increase have surged energy demands, significantly elevating CO_2 emissions. Despite Qatar's sustainable initiatives like electric buses, subway lines, and solar farms, they represent only 6.3% of the 25% CO_2 reduction goal by 2030. The country faces a substantial 93.7% gap to meet its target. To bridge this gap, GCC policymakers must prioritize collaborative renewable energy investments, especially solar and wind power, reinforce environmental regulations, and foster collaborations. Achieving significant reductions hinges on comprehensive strategies, including technological advancements, robust policies, and a united front for sustainable development and emission mitigation in the region. Changes in energy policies and housing consumer behavior in the country or in the region are fundamental to reach the reduction targets.

References

Al-Thawadi, F. E., & Al-Ghamdi, S. G. (2019). Evaluation of sustainable urban mobility using comparative environmental life cycle assessment: A case study of Qatar. Transportation research interdisciplinary perspectives, 1, 100003.

Ataullah, S. (2022). *Electric vehicles help reduce 1.6 million kg CO2.* Available at: https://thepeninsulaqatar.com/article/11/12/2022/electric-vehicles-help-reduce-16-million-kg-co2#:~:text="During%20the%20first%20part%20of,the%20Ministry%20of%20Transport%20tweeted.

Bekhet, H.A., Matar, A. and Yasmin, T., (2017). CO2 emissions, energy consumption, economic growth, and financial development in GCC countries: Dynamic simultaneous equation models. Renewable and sustainable energy reviews, 70, pp.117-132.

General Secretariat For Development Planning (2008). Qatar National Vision 2030. Available at: https://www.gco.gov.qa/en/about-qatar/national-vision2030/. Last Accessed:

Our world in Data (2021). Annual Co2 emission. Available at: https://ourworldindata.org/grapher/annual-co2-emissions-per-country. Last accessed:

Praveen, R.P., Keloth, V., Abo-Khalil, A.G., Alghamdi, A.S., Eltamaly, A.M. and Tlili, I., (2020). An insight to the energy policy of GCC countries to meet renewable energy targets of 2030. Energy Policy, 147, p.111864.

World   bank   (2022).   Population   growth   (annual   %).   Available   at: https://data.worldbank.org/indicator/SP.POP.GROW. Last Accessed:

Zmami, M. and Ben-Salha, O., (2020). An empirical analysis of the determinants of CO2 emissions in GCC countries. International Journal of Sustainable Development & World Ecology, 27(5), pp.469-480.

IEA   (2022).   https://www.iea.org/reports/world-energy-outlook-2022/an-updated-roadmap-to-net-zero-emissions-by-2050

Flavio Manenti, Gintaras V. Reklaitis (Eds.), Proceedings of the 34th European Symposium on Computer Aided Process Engineering / 15th International Symposium on Process Systems Engineering (ESCAPE34/PSE24), June 2-6, 2024, Florence, Italy

Multiscale Modeling of Solid Oxide Fuel Cells Using Various Microscale Domains Across the Length of the Cell

Hamid Reza Abbasi,[a] Masoud Babaei,[a] Constantinos Theodoropoulos,[a*]

[a]*Department of Chemical Engineering, The University of Manchester, Manchester, M13 9PL, United Kingdom*

Abstract

This study presents a multiscale modelling approach for solid oxide fuel cells (SOFCs), focusing on the interplay between macroscopic and microscopic features. Our investigation delves into the electrochemical performance of SOFCs, using a microscale solver that models electrochemical reactions and mass/charge transport within porous anode microstructure and a macroscale model that only solves mass/charge transport equations. The multiscale model is responsible for communicating information between a single macroscale model representing the entire cell and multiple microscale models of the anode microstructure. This multiscale model offers valuable insights into how both the macro and micro aspects of cell design collectively influence overall electrochemical performance. Applicability of the current multiscale framework lies in its capacity to eliminate the necessity for model calibration with experimental measurements. This is achieved by employing lineal exchange current density that remains independent of porous microstructure topology. Consequently, novel configurations incorporating distinctive attributes at both macro and microscales may be explored without preliminary calibration with experimental measurements. Results of multiscale model indicate that it can predict the polarization curve with higher accuracy, compared to an exclusively macroscale model that has undergone calibration with experimental measurements.

Keywords: Solid Oxide Fuel Cell, Multiscale model, Microstructure, Porous media

1. Introduction

Solid oxide fuel cell (SOFC) offers promising technology for clean and efficient power generation. SOFCs provide high energy efficiency, low emissions, and versatility in fuel sources, making them an attractive option for a wide range of applications, from portable power generation to large-scale industrial processes.

Various numerical models, characterized by varying degrees of precision, have been formulated to predict the operational characteristics of SOFCs. Frequently employed in capturing cell performance, macroscopic scale models (Tseronis, Kookos, and Theodoropoulos 2008; Tseronis et al. 2012; 2016; Fu et al. 2021) are subject to versatility limitations. Specifically, alterations in the microstructure of porous electrodes are inadequately represented within the confines of such macroscopic models. Conversely, microscale models have been employed to address the phenomena of transport and electrochemical reactions within an individual porous microstructure (Hsu et al. 2022; 2020; T. A. Prokop et al. 2020; T. Prokop 2020). However, microscale models are limited in their ability to represent the entire cell with the refined numerical resolution required, which leads to enormous computational costs.

This work aims to build a computationally efficient multiscale numerical framework that facilitates the efficient information exchange between macro and microscale models. This framework addresses transport equations in both macro and microscale domains, with electrochemical reactions solely being modelled within the microscale domain, at spatially resolved triple phase boundaries. The newly developed multiscale model can be used in predicting the characteristics of new SOFC configurations without necessitating experimental calibration. This framework is built based on previous SOFC work performed by the same group of authors (Abbasi et al. 2023). Nevertheless, the previous method disregards the spatial variation of the porous microstructure across the length of the cell. The recently developed method may be considered an extension of its predecessor considering spatial microstructure variation across the length of the cell, through a multiple microstructure representation, which allows the multiscale solver to be more accurate particularly in scenarios characterized by substantial variations in field variables along the length of the SOFC.

2. Methodology

Macroscopic and microscopic scale computational domains are schematically depicted in Figure 1. The macroscale domain consists of fuel/air channel, porous electrode, and electrolyte, whereas the microscale domain only consists of an electrochemically *active* thin layer of porous anode microstructure in the vicinity of the electrolyte. This is where electrochemical reactions involving hydrogen oxidation take place; therefore, the microscale model can facilitate the use of a microlevel description of kinetics of electrochemical reactions. In the macroscale model, kinetics of electrochemical reactions is described using area-specific exchange current density, $J_{0,M}$:

$$J_M \left[\frac{A}{m^2} \right] = J_{0,M} \left[\frac{A}{m^2} \right] \times f_{BV} \left(\eta_{act,M} \right) \tag{1}$$

Where J_M is the current density, η_{act} is the activation overpotential, and f_{BV} the Butler-Volmer operator that describes the rate of electrochemical reaction with respect to bulk voltage difference between the electrode and the electrolyte. $J_{0,M}$ has units of (A/m^2), which is inconsistent with the true nature of the electrochemical reactions that take place on triple phase boundary (TPB) sites that are lines in space. It provides an area-averaged way of reporting the kinetics of electrochemical reactions in each microstructure and, hence, it depends on the topological properties of the microstructure. A more precise way of reporting the exchange current density would be to express it per length (A/m). This approach eliminates the reliance on the topological characteristics of microstructure when describing the kinetics of electrochemical reactions and consequently is more versatile. The lengthwise exchange current density, $J_{0,m} [A/m]$, should be used in a microscale domain where TPB sites have been resolved. In microscale model, the current density is defined as:

$$J_m \left[\frac{A}{m} \right] = J_{0,m} \left[\frac{A}{m} \right] \times f_{BV} \left(\eta_{act,M} \right) \tag{2}$$

Lengthwise exchange current density, $J_{0,m}$, does not depend on the intricacies of the microstructure; it only depends on the macroscale descriptors such as material, temperature, and pressure. Therefore, experimentally measured lengthwise exchange current densities can be used to solve the rate of electrochemical reactions in any microstructure with any set of topological properties.

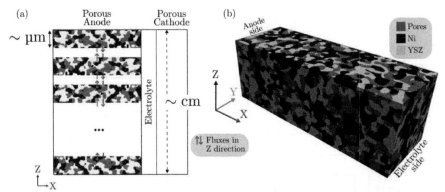

Figure 1 – *Computational domain for macro and microscale simulations*

Our multiscale method uses a microscopic description of the electrochemical reactions that take place on triple phase boundaries in vicinity of anode/electrolyte interface. It also solves the mass/charge transport at a larger scale within the entire cell, consisting of fuel/air channels, porous electrodes, and electrolyte.

The flowchart of our multiscale methodology is schematically described in Figure 2. It starts with a macroscale description of the kinetics of electrochemical reactions (exchange current density, $J_{0,M}$) as an initial guess to conduct macroscale simulations. The distribution of field variables across the length of the cell in Z direction at the anode/electrolyte interface is then used to run different microscale simulations with different boundary conditions. Boundary conditions of microscale patches are linked to the results obtained from the macroscale simulation:

$$BC_{m,1}, BC_{m,2}, \dots, BC_{m,N} \propto \Phi_M(z) \tag{3}$$

Here, $BC_{m,i}$ denotes the boundary conditions used in i_{th} patch at microscale, and $\Phi_M(z)$ represents the distribution of field variables at macroscale. Separate values of current density at different microscale patches are then used to calculate the interpolated current density at the macroscale:

$$J_{m\rightarrow M}(z) = f_{int}\big(J_{m,1}(z_1), J_{m,2}(z_2), \dots, J_{m,N}(z_N)\big) \tag{4}$$

Here, the function f_{int} denotes a simple spatial interpolation operator. The interpolated current density at the microscale is then compared to that of the macroscale ($J_{m\rightarrow M}$ and J_M, respectively) to measure the error of the iteration. In the first iterations of the described algorithm, these two values differ greatly; therefore, a correction step is needed to improve the macroscale description of electrochemical reactions ($J_{0,M}$) with respect to the difference in current densities obtained from micro and macroscale simulations. The correction formula shown in Figure 2 is the simplest approach to correct $J_{0,M}$ that assumes a first-order convergence. This iterative approach continues until the current density obtained from micro and macroscale simulations agrees within an acceptable tolerance.

Both macro and microscale models use finite volume method to discretize equations in space. Tolerance of the microscale, macroscale, and multiscale models are set to 1E-5, 1E-6, and 1E-4, respectively. It was observed that convergence beyond 1E-4 is especially difficult for the multiscale model.

3. Results and discussion

Results of the multiscale model are presented in this section, focusing on the distribution of mole fractions and current density across different length scales within the fuel cell.

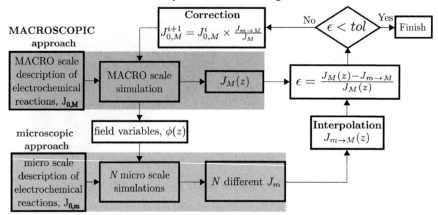

Figure 2 *– Flowchart of the multiscale method used in this study*

Mole fractions of hydrogen and oxygen in fuel and air channels, as well as in porous electrodes, are shown in Figure 3. The studied SOFC is anode-supported; therefore, the thickness of the electrolyte and porous cathode is too small to be visualized properly when the entire cell is shown.

As hydrogen and oxygen diffuse through the porous electrodes from the fuel/air channel inlets to the outlets, their concentration reduces due to electrochemical reactions that consume these components at both sides of the electrolyte. The mole fraction of hydrogen drops from 0.95 at the inlet to approximately 0.86 at the anode/electrolyte interface close to the outlet. For oxygen, it reduces from 0.21 at the inlet to 0.16 in the vicinity of the cathode/electrolyte interface, which is close to the outlet.

Figure 4 shows the polarization curve of the SOFC predicted with two different numerical frameworks, namely a fully macroscopic and the multiscale one. Both models are compared with experimental data points of (Rogers et al. 2003). As seen, the multiscale model can make more accurate predictions, especially at higher current densities, where the interplay between different physical phenomena becomes more pronounced. It should be noted that SOFCs are normally designed to operate at higher ranges of current density to provide maximum efficiency. It should be highlighted that the macroscopic model in Figure 4 has been initially calibrated with experimental measurements (Rogers et al. 2003). In contrast, multiscale model does not necessitate any calibration with experimental setups.

The variation of current density across different patches in the Z-direction is shown in Figure 5. Ten different microstructure patches are evenly distributed in the Z-direction from the fuel channel inlet (Z=0) to the outlet (Z=16 mm).

Each patch is an anode microstructure with length 50x10x10 microns in X, Y, and Z directions, respectively. The X=0 line is aligned with the anode/electrolyte interface. Current density across the length of each patch varies from zero to a maximum value at the interface. The maximum current density predicted in each patch corresponds to the current density that is calculated by the macroscale model at that exact location in Z direction. As mentioned before, the error of the multiscale model is defined as the difference between current density calculated by the multiscale model and the macroscale model at specific locations throughout the cell length. Electrochemical reactions only take place at a noticeable rate at the electrochemical active layer in vicinity of the anode/electrolyte interface. As seen from the microscale results presented in Figure 5 (a), the length of the electrochemical active layer is approximately 25 microns, and it does not change significantly throughout the length of the cell from the inlet to the outlet.

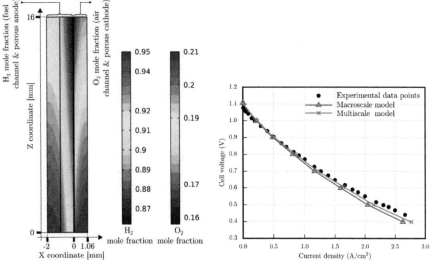

Figure 3 – *Mole fraction of hydrogen and oxygen in the entire cell consisting of fuel/air channels, and porous electrodes. Operating voltage V_{op}=0.4 V.*

Figure 4 – *SOFC Polarization curve. Comparison of multiscale and macroscale models with experimental data (Rogers et al. 2003)*

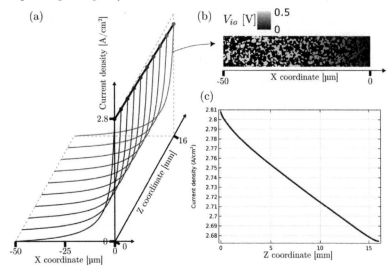

Figure 5 – *Distribution of current density for V_{op}=0.4 V. (a) Current density variation across each microscale patch. (b) Variation of ionic potential in one of the microscale patches. (c) Current density variation across the length of the SOFC*

In Figure 5 (a) and (c), a slight variation in the maximum current density (from 2.81 to 2.67 A/cm^2) can be observed from the inlet to the outlet of the fuel cell in both macro and multiscale models when the operating voltage of the cell is 0.4 V. A higher current density at Z=0 can be attributed to local higher concentrations of H_2 and O_2 at the anode/electrolyte and cathode/electrolyte interfaces, respectively, as depicted in Figure 3.

4. Conclusions

A multiscale model has been developed to address mass/charge transport and electrochemical reactions within SOFCs. The applicability of the current multiscale model lies in predicting SOFC performance without any previous calibration with experimental setups. It can be used to predict the performance of new SOFC configurations with new features both at the macroscopic and microscopic scales. In addition, the multiscale model shows better agreement with experimentally measured polarization curves in comparison with a macroscale model that has already been calibrated with an experimental setup.

References

Abbasi, Hamid Reza, Masoud Babaei, Arash Rabbani, and Constantinos Theodoropoulos. 2023. 'Multi-Scale Model of Solid Oxide Fuel Cell: Enabling Microscopic Solvers to Predict Physical Features over a Macroscopic Domain'. In *Computer Aided Chemical Engineering*, 52:1039–45. Elsevier.

Fu, Quanrong, Zhiyi Li, Wei Wei, Fengxia Liu, Xiaofei Xu, and Zhijun Liu. 2021. 'Performance Degradation Prediction of Direct Internal Reforming Solid Oxide Fuel Cell Due to Ni-Particle Coarsening in Composite Anode'. *Energy Conversion and Management* 233 (April): 113902. https://doi.org/10.1016/j.enconman.2021.113902.

Hsu, Tim, Hokon Kim, Jerry H. Mason, Rubayyat Mahbub, William K. Epting, Harry W. Abernathy, Gregory A. Hackett, Shawn Litster, Anthony D. Rollett, and Paul A. Salvador. 2022. 'High Performance Finite Element Simulations of Infiltrated Solid Oxide Fuel Cell Cathode Microstructures'. *Journal of Power Sources* 541 (September): 231652. https://doi.org/10.1016/j.jpowsour.2022.231652.

Hsu, Tim, Rubayyat Mahbub, Jerry H. Mason, William K. Epting, Harry W. Abernathy, Gregory A. Hackett, Anthony D. Rollett, Shawn Litster, and Paul A. Salvador. 2020. 'High Performance Modeling of Heterogeneous SOFC Electrode Microstructures Using the MOOSE Framework: ERMINE (Electrochemical Reactions in MIcrostructural NEtworks)'. *MethodsX* 7: 100822. https://doi.org/10.1016/j.mex.2020.100822.

Prokop, Tomasz. 2020. 'Three-Dimensional Numerical Analysis of Transport Phenomena in a Positive-Electrolyte-Negative Assembly of a Solid Oxide Fuel Cell'. PhD Thesis.

Prokop, Tomasz A., Grzegorz Brus, Shinji Kimijima, and Janusz S. Szmyd. 2020. 'Thin Solid Film Electrolyte and Its Impact on Electrode Polarization in Solid Oxide Fuel Cells Studied by Three-Dimensional Microstructure-Scale Numerical Simulation'. *Energies* 13 (19): 5127. https://doi.org/10.3390/en13195127.

Rogers, William A, Randall S Gemmen, Christopher Johnson, Michael Prinkey, and Mehrdad Shahnam. 2003. 'Validation and Application of a CFD-Based Model for Solid Oxide Fuel Cells and Stacks', 4.

Tseronis, K., I. Bonis, I.K. Kookos, and C. Theodoropoulos. 2012. 'Parametric and Transient Analysis of Non-Isothermal, Planar Solid Oxide Fuel Cells'. *International Journal of Hydrogen Energy* 37 (1): 530–47. https://doi.org/10.1016/j.ijhydene.2011.09.062.

Tseronis, K., I.S. Fragkopoulos, I. Bonis, and C. Theodoropoulos. 2016. 'Detailed Multi-Dimensional Modeling of Direct Internal Reforming Solid Oxide Fuel Cells'. *Fuel Cells* 16 (3): 294–312. https://doi.org/10.1002/fuce.201500113.

Tseronis, K., I.K. Kookos, and C. Theodoropoulos. 2008. 'Modelling Mass Transport in Solid Oxide Fuel Cell Anodes: A Case for a Multidimensional Dusty Gas-Based Model'. *Chemical Engineering Science* 63 (23): 5626–38. https://doi.org/10.1016/j.ces.2008.07.037.

Flavio Manenti, Gintaras V. Reklaitis (Eds.), Proceedings of the 34th European Symposium on Computer Aided Process Engineering / 15th International Symposium on Process Systems Engineering (ESCAPE34/PSE24), June 2-6, 2024, Florence, Italy

Sustainable Transformation of Polystyrene Waste through Pyrolysis

Maria V. Colombo[a], Jorge A. Ressia[b,c], Alejandra S. Diez[a], Patricia M. Hoch[b,d*]

[a]*Depto. de Quimica, Universidad Nacional del Sur, 8000 Bahia Blanca, Argentina*
[b]*Depto. de Ing. Quimica, Universidad Nacional del Sur, 8000 Bahia Blanca, Argentina*
[c]*Comision de Investigaciones Cientificas de la Provincia de Buenos Aires CIC*
[d]*PLAPIQUI – UNS – CONICET - 8000 Bahia Blanca, Argentina*

Corresponding author email: p.hoch@plapiqui.edu.ar

Abstract

The escalating issue of single-use plastic waste accumulation demands innovative solutions that can transform environmental liabilities into economic assets. Pyrolysis of polystyrene waste offers a promising route to address this challenge by converting discarded plastics into valuable products. The objective is to develop a sustainable and economically viable PS pyrolysis process. By doing so, a circular approach to managing plastic waste is obtained, thereby reducing the environmental burden and dependency on virgin plastic production. A model for the combination pyrolysis reactor-separation of liquids is proposed, and the net present value considering a time span of 10 years is calculated as 4.85 MMU$S resulting in a potentially feasible process at this stage.

Keywords: Pyrolysis, Polystyrene, Depolymerization, Circular Economy.

1. Introduction

Urban solid waste (USW) is a mixture of various solid wastes generated by human activities. The components of USW include food waste, paper, biomass, glass, metals, plastics, rubber, and textiles (Lu *et al.*, 2020). Currently it is possible to manage this waste through landfills, composting and incineration. The annual global USW production rate is currently over two billion tons and will increase to four billion tons before the next century. Sustainable Development Goal number 11 "Sustainable cities and communities" establishes that for a sustainable development of modern societies, the components of USW are a significant raw material to obtain new products. Sustainable processes must manage to transform waste and value it, promoting the idea of obtaining new added-value products. Within the framework of the "Circular Economy" (Ismail and Dincer, 2023), plastic waste, like any other waste, constitutes a great opportunity for the development of new technologies. In the sustainable future, new economic models will maximize the value of raw materials by encouraging practices such as reuse and remanufacturing. The recycling of polystyrene, a widely used plastic polymer known for its versatility and lightweight properties, has gained increasing attention due to the environmental concerns associated with plastic waste. PS is used in packaging, disposable products, and various industries. However, the inherent difficulties in recycling PS (Thakur *et al.*, 2018) have contributed to its significant presence in landfills and the environment. While research aims to make efforts towards finding effective methods to manage plastic waste, pyrolysis has emerged as a promising approach, offering the potential to transform discarded PS materials by depolymerization.

Pyrolysis, a thermal decomposition process conducted in the absence of oxygen, allows for converting waste and residues into valuable products such as liquid fuels, platform chemicals, and feedstocks. In recent years, research efforts have focused on optimizing the pyrolysis process parameters, understanding the kinetics of PS decomposition, and evaluating the quality and potential applications of the pyrolytic products. Pyrolysis takes place at high temperatures, between 400-800 °C and energy is required to raise the feedstock temperature to the temperature of the endothermic parallel reactions.

The pyrolysis process allows for the thermal degradation of the waste, and products obtained have a wide range of liquid and gaseous hydrocarbons that can be recovered, guaranteeing the reduction of the volume of waste and the generation of new products with added-value (Xue, Johnston and Bai, 2017). Products are a liquid fraction or pyrolytic oil, a solid fraction or carbon, and a fraction of non-condensable combustible gases. Pyrolytic oil is usually composed of a complex mixture of hydrocarbons ranging from light alkanes to heavy oils, naphtha, aromatics, and paraffins (Al-Salem *et al.*, 2017). Plastic waste, such as polyethylene (PE), polypropylene (PP) and polystyrene (PS), are suitable materials to produce fuels or chemical raw materials with high added-value, through a catalytic pyrolysis process. The use of catalysts could selectively convert plastic waste into aromatic compounds such as benzene, toluene, ethylbenzene, xylene, and naphthalene. These chemical compounds are widely used as raw materials, solvents, and additives in the chemical, pharmaceutical, cosmetic, transportation, and various other industries (Mangesh *et al.*, 2020). It was experimentally determined that the β cleavage of the final PS chain is the main mechanism for the formation of styrene monomers (Park *et al.*, 2020), which could be used again in the formulation of new plastic materials, aligning the process with the circular economy.

The objective of this work is to obtain a mathematical model for the PS pyrolysis-separation process, which would allow to perform a preliminary economic analysis to decide about the feasibility of this method for the depolymerization of polystyrene.

2. Experimental

2.1. Materials and methods

Experimental work was needed for model parameters estimation. A pyrolysis reactor on a laboratory scale was created and assembled, comprising a heating module and a condensation module. The reactor has an entry point for plastic and N_2 gas at one end, while the other end features a reduction zone for placing the catalyst. This design allows the gases produced during the thermal degradation of plastic to pass through both the catalyst and the condensation module. To enhance pyrolysis efficiency, the following experiments were conducted:

2.1.1. Pyrolysis of polystyrene (PS) without catalyst:

The reaction occurred at temperatures of 400, 450, and 500 °C, establishing a temperature-dependent model for control purposes. The sample was introduced into the reactor, heated at a rate of 100 °C/min (fast pyrolysis) until reaching the reaction temperature. After reaching the desired temperature, the sample underwent a 4-minute reaction at a constant temperature. Cooling down was uncontrolled, and the resulting pyrolysis gases were condensed to obtain the liquor.

2.1.2. Pyrolysis of PS with various catalysts:

Different catalysts were tested for the catalytic pyrolysis of PS. The catalysts included CeO_2 synthesized through the combustion method and commercial Al_2O_3. Additionally, modified Co/CeO_2 and $Co/\gamma Al_2O_3$ supports were obtained through the wet impregnation method.

The catalysts underwent characterization using XRD and BET area measurements. Reaction conditions were optimized, and the resulting liquids were analyzed using a Gas Chromatograph coupled to a Perkin Elmer GC/MS mass spectrometer, specifically the Clarus 500 MS TurboMass software with the NIST 14 spectral library.

3. Pyrolysis model

The kinetics of the pyrolysis of polystyrene (PS) is a critical aspect that governs the thermal degradation process and the formation of pyrolytic products. Understanding the kinetics is essential for optimizing the pyrolysis process, designing efficient reactors, and predicting the yield and composition of the resulting products. Several models have been proposed to describe the kinetics of PS pyrolysis, with varying degrees of complexity and accuracy. One such model is the Distributed Activation Energy Model (DAEM), which has been widely used to characterize the pyrolysis kinetics of polymers, including PS, and considers that the pyrolysis reaction involves a distribution of activation energies, accounting for the different types of chemical bonds present in the polymer matrix. This model assumes that the rate of reaction is determined by the distribution of activation energies across the polymer structure. The DAEM equation can be expressed as follows:

$$\frac{d\alpha}{dt} = A \sum_{i=1}^{n} g_i(\alpha) f_i(T) e^{-\frac{E_i}{RT}} \tag{1}$$

Where α is the extent of reaction , t is time, A is the pre-exponential factor, n is the number of reaction pathways, $g_i(\alpha)$ is the distribution function of the extent of reaction, $f_i(T)$ is the distribution function of the temperature, E_i is the activation energy for each pathway, R is the gas constant, T is the temperature

The DAEM provides a more realistic representation of the complex pyrolysis process by accounting for the different activation energies associated with the various bonds present in the molecule of polystyrene. This allows for a better prediction of the reaction rate and product distribution across different temperature ranges.

To determine the parameters of the DAEM, experimental data from thermogravimetric analysis (TGA) or other pyrolysis experiments are typically used. These data are fitted to the model using parameter estimation techniques to obtain the values of pre-exponential factors, activation energies, and distribution functions. By incorporating the resulting kinetic parameters into the simulation software, it is possible to predict the behavior of the pyrolysis process under different conditions.

In recent years, research efforts have been directed towards improving the accuracy of kinetic models for PS pyrolysis by considering more sophisticated mechanisms and reaction pathways. For example, particle size of the polystyrene has influence on the speed of the pyrolysis process and so in the DAEM model (Jiang *et al.*, 2020). Additionally, the coupling of experimental data with advanced computational techniques, such as molecular dynamics simulations, has provided deeper insights into the pyrolysis process and its kinetics (Potnuri *et al.*, 2022).

4. Results

4.1. Experimental results

From the experiences conducted, it was found that commercial Al_2O_3 was the catalyst of choice, as it gave the highest yield of styrene. Chromatographic profile for this experience is shown in Figure 1, showing the styrene peak in the second position of the profile. This was used as the case of study for the modeling and simulation of the process.

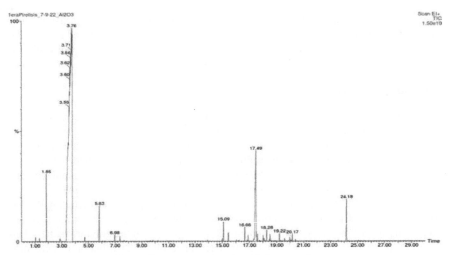

Figure 1: Chromatographic profile for pyrolysis using Al₂O₃ as catalyst

4.2. Pyrolysis simulation results

Using the results of the experiences conducted, a model as shown in Section 3 was obtained for the extent of the main reactions for the catalyst Al_2O_3. It was used as a base for estimating the volume of the pyrolysis reactor at a larger scale, assuming that the conditions are such that the reactions take place as in the experimental setup. The model obtained is proprietary and cannot be disclosed. The pyrolysis liquid composition resulting from the simulation is used for the separation step and shown in Table 1.

4.3. Separation results

For the separation of the pyrolysis liquid, distillation is the process of choice. The thermodynamic behavior of the mixture was predicted using data from ASPEN® databank, with binary parameters derived from APV10 VLE-RK. Additionally, binary interaction parameters involving styrene with α-methylstyrene and toluene were sourced from (Dahal *et al.*, 2023). The significance of the binary interaction parameter between styrene and toluene lies in ensuring simulation results align with experimental values.

For the simulation it was considered a feed comprising the main components present in the pyrolysis liquid. A distillation column with side extraction was simulated to yield styrene with a purity of approximately 97% w/w. Heavy components were represented as a single pseudo component for simulation purposes. The primary objective was to obtain pure styrene, contributing to the circular economy by serving as feedstock to produce new polystyrene (PS). Detailed data and simulation results are presented in Tables 1, 2, and 3. Styrene is withdrawn from a side stream, while lighter components are collected in the distillate stream, and heavier components in the bottom stream. To estimate the cost of obtaining pure styrene through distillation in $/t, a feed rate of 1 t/h with the composition outlined in Table 1 was utilized as the basis. This composition results from the simulation of PS pyrolysis at 450 °C using Al_2O_3 as the catalyst, with DAEM model including all the reactions to obtain the products present in the chromatography results. The net present value of the whole process for this basis was computed using data from Aspen Economics, it is shown in Table 3. It indicates that the current stage renders the process economically feasible. The IRR is 43% and the investment was calculated using a conservative approach while the price of styrene was reduced 25% with respect to global price.

Table 1: Feed composition (F) – Pyrolysis simulation.

Component	Mass %	Component	Mass %
Acetone	0,05	α-ethylstyrene	0,05
Benzene	0,04	2-methylindene	0,04
Toluene	1,69	Naphthalene	0,04
Ethylbenzene	0,27	Diphenylmethane	0,05
Styrene	83,04	(E)-stilbene	0,1
Cyclopropylbenzene	0,2	s-diphenylethane	0,77
α-methylstyrene	1,98	1,2 diphenylpropane	0,32
Benzene derivative	0,27	1,3 diphenylpropane	0,47
Indene	0,21	(E)-1-Phenyl-1-butene	8,41
		Heavier -Pseudo component	2,00

Table 2: Column simulation data and NRTL parameters for the pairs Toluene/Styrene and Styrene/ α-methylstyrene, to be used for the equations

$$\tau_{ij} = a_{ij} + \frac{b_{ij}}{T} + e_{ij}\ln(T) + f_{ij}T; \; \alpha_{ij} = c_{ij} + d(T - 273.15)$$ as shown in Dahal et. al, (2023b).

Number of stages (top-bottom)	20
Feed flow rate F [kg/h]	1000
Feed location	14
Distillate flow rate (D) [kg/h]	6
Sidestream flow rate (S) [kg/h]	830
Sidestream (S) location	8
Reflux ratio [mass]	200
Condenser pressure [bar_abs]	0.05
Interstage pressure drop [bar]	0.0001
NRTL model parameters	
Toluene/Styrene b_{ij}/K	-227.0
Toluene/Styrene b_{ji}/K	275.9
Toluene/Styrene c_{ij}/K	0.2
Styrene/ α-methylstyrene B_{ij}/K	606.5
Styrene/ α-methylstyrene B_{ji}/K	-469.7
Styrene/ α-methylstyrene c_{ij}/K	0.2

Table 3: Simulation results (only main components are shown, but all components shown in table 1 were used for the simulation)

Main Components mass fraction	Distillate	Sidestream	Bottom
Toluene	0.7513	0.0017	0.0000
Styrene	0.0336	0.9950	0.0034
α-methylstyrene	0.0179	0.0000	0.1456
Acetone	0.0381	0.0000	0.0000
Benzene	0.1758	0.0000	0.0000
Ethylbenzene	0.0010	0.0031	0.0000
Cyclopropylbenzene (Phenylcyclopropane)	0.0000	0.0000	0.0150
Total flow rate [kg/h]	20.00	830.00	150.00
Styrene recovery	0%	99.9%	>0.1%
NPV MM$ 4.85			

5. Conclusions

The amount of liquid obtained at the experimental step depends strongly on the condensation setup. Future work will be directed towards improving this stage. To do so, online gas chromatography is used to analyze online the composition of the pyrolysis gas to find if the recovered amount of styrene could be higher by using an improved condensation stage. This would improve the parameter estimation in the pyrolysis model. However, the pyrolysis model represents appropriately the experimental results.

Distillation was found as a suitable method for conducting the separations although a high reflux ratio is required. As an alternative, the distillation process can be coupled with a pervaporation membrane or with an adsorption process to further improve the separation and/or reduce the column size. This will be subject of further investigation, as well as the optimization of the process. This product has a benefit, since it can be used as a platform molecule or in the manufacture of new plastic materials, managing to add value to a polluting residue difficult to dispose of. In this way, the process is aligned with the principles of sustainable development. The process is potentially feasible as the Net Present Value for a time horizon of 10 years is 4.85 MMU$S.

References

Al-Salem, S.M. *et al.* (2017) 'A review on thermal and catalytic pyrolysis of plastic solid waste (PSW)', *Journal of environmental management*, 197, pp. 177–198. Available at: https://doi.org/10.1016/J.JENVMAN.2017.03.084.

Dahal, R., Uusi-Kyyny, P., Pokki, J.-P., *et al.* (2023) 'Conceptual design of a distillation process for the separation of styrene monomer from polystyrene pyrolysis oil: experiment and simulation', *Chemical Engineering Research and Design*, 195, pp. 65–75. Available at: https://doi.org/10.1016/J.CHERD.2023.05.039.

Dahal, R., Uusi-Kyyny, P., Pokki, J.P., *et al.* (2023) 'Isobaric Vapor-Liquid Equilibrium of the Binary Mixtures Toluene + Styrene and Styrene + α-Methylstyrene', *Journal of Chemical and Engineering Data*, 68(3), pp. 654–663. Available at: https://doi.org/10.1021/ACS.JCED.2C00662

Ismail, M.M. and Dincer, I. (2023) 'Development and evaluation of an integrated waste to energy system based on polyethylene plastic wastes pyrolysis for production of hydrogen fuel and other useful commodities', *Fuel*, 334. Available at: https://doi.org/10.1016/j.fuel.2022.126409.

Jiang, L. *et al.* (2020) 'Pyrolytic Kinetics of Polystyrene Particle in Nitrogen Atmosphere: Particle Size Effects and Application of Distributed Activation Energy Method', *Polymers 2020, Vol. 12, Page 421*, 12(2), p. 421. Available at: https://doi.org/10.3390/POLYM12020421.

Lu, J.S. *et al.* (2020) 'Slow pyrolysis of municipal solid waste (MSW): A review', *Bioresource Technology*, 312, p. 123615. Available at: https://doi.org/10.1016/J.BIORTECH.2020.123615.

Mangesh, V.L. *et al.* (2020) 'Experimental investigation to identify the type of waste plastic pyrolysis oil suitable for conversion to diesel engine fuel', *Journal of Cleaner Production*, 246, p. 119066. Available at: https://doi.org/10.1016/J.JCLEPRO.2019.119066.

Park, K.B. *et al.* (2020) 'Two-stage pyrolysis of polystyrene: Pyrolysis oil as a source of fuels or benzene, toluene, ethylbenzene, and xylenes', *Applied Energy*, 259. Available at: https://doi.org/10.1016/j.apenergy.2019.114240.

Potnuri, R. *et al.* (2022) 'Understanding the role of modeling and simulation in pyrolysis of biomass and waste plastics: A review', *Bioresource Technology Reports*, 20, p. 101221. Available at: https://doi.org/10.1016/J.BITEB.2022.101221.

Thakur, S. *et al.* (2018) 'Recent developments in recycling of polystyrene based plastics', *Current Opinion in Green and Sustainable Chemistry*, 13, pp. 32–38. Available at: https://doi.org/10.1016/J.COGSC.2018.03.011.

Xue, Y., Johnston, P. and Bai, X. (2017) 'Effect of catalyst contact mode and gas atmosphere during catalytic pyrolysis of waste plastics', *Energy Conversion and Management*, C(142), pp. 441–451. Available at: https://doi.org/10.1016/J.ENCONMAN.2017.03.071.

Flavio Manenti, Gintaras V. Reklaitis (Eds.), Proceedings of the 34th European Symposium on Computer Aided Process Engineering / 15th International Symposium on Process Systems Engineering (ESCAPE34/PSE24), June 2-6, 2024, Florence, Italy

Wine effluents valorization through a biorefinery scheme

Carlos Eduardo Guzmán Martínez [1], Araceli Guadalupe Romero Izquierdo [1], Sergio Iván Martínez Guido [1], Salvador Hernández [2], Claudia Gutiérrez Antonio [1]*

[1] Universidad Autónoma de Querétaro, Querétaro, Querétaro, 76010, México
claudia.gutierrez@uaq.mx
[2] Universidad de Guanajuato, Guanajuato, Guanajuato, 36000, México

Abstract

The wine industry produces a large amount of highly polluting wastewater; its inadequate disposal has become a social and environmental problem. At the same time, these effluents are characterized by having a high content of carbohydrates and alcohols; these compounds can be used in the generation of bioenergy, a priority to ensure energy sovereignty in Mexico. Current technology does not take advantage of the energy potential of this type of wastewater. Thus, the valorization of wine effluents is proposed through a biorefinery scheme that generates biofuels and value-added products. For this, the composition and pretreatment of the wastewater are determined, and the products of interest in the biorefinery are selected. A case study is defined, which process is designed and simulated into the Aspen Plus simulator. For comparative purposes, a conventional treatment scheme consisting of an anaerobic digester to produce methane gas is developed. As a result, the production of levulinic acid, sustainable aviation fuel, electrical energy, green diesel, naphtha, light gases, glycols, and bioethanol is obtained. In addition, the biorefinery reduces the Chemical Oxygen Demand (COD) of the effluent by 99.99% allowing it to generate water that meets the quality necessary for human use according to Official Mexican Standards (NOM-001-SEMARNAT-2021, NOM-127-SSA1-2021). On the other hand, the conventional treatment process, which is constituted by biodigester, has a COD reduction of 18.79%; this decrement is not enough to achieve national standards of water for human use. In conclusion, both the biorefinery and conventional treatment schemes are feasible technically. However, biorefinery can offer a wide variety of biofuels and value-added products, such as those aforementioned; in contrast to the conventional treatment process which only can produce methane. Besides, according to the COD reduction obtained for each process, the conventional procedure must be complemented with other operation units to reach the required level for Mexico authorities.

Keywords: Biorefinery, wine effluent, sustainable aviation fuel, simulation, valorization.

1. Introduction

The wine industry generates from 0.2 to 4 wastewater liters per liter produced. In México, 400,000 hectoliters of wine are manufactured annually. The main composition of this effluent includes glucose, ethanol, and lignocellulosic material, in smaller quantities, as well as some polyphenols, and carboxylic acids. The inadequate disposal of this type of wastewater may cause damage to ecosystems (Buitron et al. 2019).

There are several treatments to achieve discharge standards and recovery of value-added products from distillery wastewater; this kind of wastewater is similar to wine effluent due to its organic content (alcohol, glucose, carboxylic acids). Some treatments include physical-chemical methods (adsorption, coagulation, oxidation, ozonation, electrolysis, reverse osmosis, ultrafiltration, and nanofiltration), biological processes (aerobic and anaerobic), as well as a combination of them (Ratna S et al., 2021). For instance, Wagh et al. (2020) performed a reduction of 94.88 % Chemical Oxygen Demand (COD) by using electrocoagulation; Wilk et al. (2019) eliminated 62 % color in vinasse by employing *Lactobacillus* and *Pediococus*; in the field of bioenergy, Buitron et al. (2019) generated biogas from wine effluent by working with methanogenic microorganisms.

All the reported works related to the treatment of this wastewater involve the methods aforementioned. Indeed, Kopsahelis et al. (2018) proposed a biorefinery scheme to obtain polyphenols, tartaric salts, and ethanol from grape lees, which are represented by dead yeast, and whey. However, no one has employed the concept of biorefinery to valorize wine effluents, to obtain add-value products, and to produce a wide variety of biofuels, simultaneously. Therefore, the research aim is to valorize wine effluents through a biorefinery scheme to generate biofuels and value-added products.

2. Methodology

The second column of Table 1 shows the composition of the wine effluent considered as case study, which represents a possible scenario in Baja California State (the main wine producer in México). It is important to mention that solids are represented by cellulose ($C_6H_{10}O_5$), hemicellulose ($C_5H_8O_4$), lignin, and lees (dead yeast, $CH_{1.83}O_{0.56}N_{0.17}$) (Wooley, et al. 1996).

Table 1.- Comparison between feed stream for both schemes, treated water from biorefinery and digestor.

Parameter	Wine effluent	Treated water III (Biorefinery)	Treated water (Digestor)
Mass flow (kg/h)	10,000	4,922	8,959.76
Water (% mass)	71.76	100	77.94
Ethanol (% mass)	7.39	0	4.47
Glucose (% mass)	5.26	0	0.33
Solid (% mass)	15.59	0	6.96
COD (PPM)	210,052	29.42	206,105

Figure 1 represents the conceptual biorefinery. To simulate the process in Aspen Plus, it was used BK-10 (for DC-05 to DC-07), Peng-Robinson (for R-01 and R-02), and NRTL for the other equipment as thermodynamic models (Carlson, 1996). Besides, for all distillation columns, including the reactive ones, module Rad Frac is used. In the biorefinery scheme, solids are separated from wine effluent in CN-01. Inside RD-01, glucose reacts to form 5-Hydroxymethyl Furfural (5-HMF), Eq. (1), and then, 5-HMF is converted to levulinic acid and formic acid, Eq. (2) (Solis, et al. 2022). These products, coming from RD-01 bottom, are separated by DC-01 and DC-02.

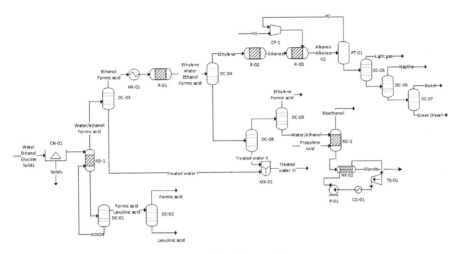

Figure 1.- Biorefinery scheme

Where CN= Centrifuge, RD= Reactive distillation column, DC= Distillation column, R= reactor, FT= Flash tank, MX= Mixer, Tb=Turbine, CD= condenser, P= Pump, CP= Compressor, HX= Heat exchanger.

DC-03 separates all formic acid traces and ethanol/water mixture, 1:1, for sending them to R-01; from the bottom, it obtains the first treated water stream (TW1). In R-01, ethanol dehydration occurs to get ethylene, Eq. (3). The ethylene coming from the DC-04 top reacts in R-02 to form alkenes (C_2 to C_{20}) by oligomerization; this is summarized by Eq. (4). After that, alkanes are developed by hydrogenation process in R-03, Eq. (5) (Romero et al., 2022). It is important to mention that the module employed in these reactors is R-Stoic. The H_2 excess is recirculated by using FT-01 and the biofuels are separated by distillation arrangement DC-05, DC-06, and DC-07. The biofuels are defined as light gas (C_2 to C_4), naphtha (C_5-C_8), biojet fuel (C_9-C_{16}), and green diesel (C_{17}-C_{20}).

Water coming from the mixture of DC-04 bottom stream is separated by DC-08 to form treated water II (TW2). Treated water III (TW3) is constituted by the sum of TW1 and TW2. The remaining components are sent to DC-09. A mixture of ethanol/water, obtained from the DC-09 bottom, feeds RD-02; where bioethanol, propylene glycol, and dipropylene glycol are produced by using propylene oxide, Eq. (6) and Eq. (7). This process is known as bioethanol reactive dewatering (Guzmán et al., 2019). Finally, the thermal potential of glycols is taken advantage of by using the organic Rankine cycle.

$$C_6H_{12}O_6 \xrightarrow{H_2SO_4} C_6H_6O_3 + 3H_2O \tag{1}$$

$$C_6H_6O_3 + 2H_2O \rightarrow C_5H_8O_3 + CH_2O_2 \tag{2}$$

$$C_2H_6O \rightarrow C_2H_4 + H_2O \tag{3}$$

$$XC_2H_4 \rightarrow C_{2X}H_{4X} \tag{4}$$

$$C_nH_{2n} + H_2 \rightarrow C_nH_{2n+2} \tag{5}$$

$$C_3H_6O + H_2O \rightarrow C_3H_8O_2 \tag{6}$$

$$C_3H_6O + C_3H_8O_2 \rightarrow C_6H_{14}O_3 \tag{7}$$

Figure 2 represents biogas production, which corresponds to the conventional treatment process. The wine effluent gets into BR-01 where polymers are hydrolyzed by enzymes. The reactions involved correspond to cellulose, hemicellulose, and dead yeast decomposition, Eq. (8-10) respectively; it is important to mention that lignin is inert in this stage. This operation unit is modeled by the R-Stoic module. In BR-02, it is carried out the steps involved in anaerobic digestion: amino acid degradation, Eq. (11), acidogenic, Eq. (12), acetogenic, Eq. (13), methanogenic, Eq. (14) (Rajendran et al., 2014); the lignin keeps inert. Once digestion has concluded, the mixture is sent to FT-01 for phase separation, where treated water is obtained from the flash tank bottom. The wet biogas is dried by FT-02.

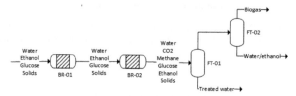

Figure 2.- Conventional process. Anaerobic digestion

Where BR=Bioreactor, FT= Flash tank.

$$C_6H_{10}O_5 + H_2O \rightarrow C_6H_{12}O_6 \tag{8}$$

$$C_5H_8O_4 + H_2O \rightarrow C_5H_4O_2 + H_2O \tag{9}$$

$$135.294CH_{1.83}O_{0.56}N_{0.17} + 53.8235H_2O \rightarrow GLY + ALA + VAL + LEU + ILEU + PHE +$$
$$TYR + TRY + ASP + GLU + HIS + LYS + ARG + PRO + 45.2941CO_2 + 97.6176H_2 \tag{10}$$

$$A.A. + WATER \rightarrow Carboxilic\_Acid + NH_3 + CO_2 + H_2 \tag{11}$$

$$C_6H_{12}O_6 + NH_3 \rightarrow Biomass + Carboxilic\_Acid + CO_2 + H_2O \tag{12}$$

$$Carboxilic\_Acid + NH_3 + H_2O \rightarrow Biomass + C_2H_4O_2 + CH_4 + CO_2 + H_2 \tag{13}$$

$$C_2H_4O_2 + NH_3 \rightarrow Biomass + CH_4 + CO_2 + H_2O \tag{14}$$

For the biorefinery scheme and biogas process, a literature search is made for collecting the thermodynamic and chemical kinetic data, followed by the Aspen Plus V11 simulation. Once the processes have been modeled, parametric analysis is performed to adjust the manipulable variables by sensitivity analysis. Finally, both processes are evaluated and compared between themselves. The manipulable variables employed in parametric analysis are stage number, feed stage, reflux ratio, distillation rate, hold-up, reactive stages, reactant inlet flow, and pressure for reactive/conventional distillation columns (according to the case); temperature and pressure for flash tanks; finally, temperature and reactor volume for bioreactors.

To perform the evaluation and comparison, the next parameters are considered: COD, which is calculated by Aspen Plus, total heat duty, reactant conversion, and product yield. Eq. (15) and Eq. (16) show how conversion and product yield are defined.

$$cv = \frac{r_{in} - r_{out}}{r_{in}} \tag{15}$$

$$Yd = \frac{pms}{rms} \tag{16}$$

Where: cv =conversion, r_{in} = reactant input to process (mol/h), r_{out} = reactant output to process (mol/h), Yd = Yield, pms = desired product mass (kg), rms = reactant mass (kg).

3. Results

The product obtained, from anaerobic digestion, is 864.76 kg biogas/h, where 44.28 % mol is methane, 35.37 % mol is CO_2 and 18.13 % mol is H_2. About biorefinery, Table 2, summarizes all products. Although it might seem that digester get more biofuels, it is important to remember that the concentration of methane in gas is only 44.28 %mol; besides, this methane biogas has lower energy than those products obtained from biorefinery, because it has a longer carbon chain.

Table 1 compares the quality of water. The water produced from the digestor still having a COD value elevated, unlike biorefinery. Table 3 shows the values for those parameters selected to perform the comparison. In this sense, the digestor $Yd_{treated-water}$ is better than the biorefinery one; however, it does not achieve with limits in Mexican Law about COD. On the other side, although the anaerobic digestor has employed solids to generate more quantity of biofuels, biorefinery can get better $Yd_{biofuels}$ without using those solids. Finally, 93 % of energy employed for biorefinery comes from the energy contained in RD-01; it is important to highlight that heat integration is not considered. Indeed, the application of heat integration tools could reduce the heat duty for the refinery.

Table 2.- Biorefinery products

Product	Mass flow (kg/h)
Propylene glycol / dipropylene glycol	47.66
Levulinic Acid	221.57
Bioethanol	4.56
Formic Acid	96.4
Light Gas (C_1-C_4)	86.32
Naphtha (C_5-C_7)	73.03
Sustainable aviation fuel (C_8-C_{16})	103.83
Green diesel (C_{17}-C_{20})	26.03

Table 3.- Process comparison

Parameter	Biorefinery	Digestion
Heat duty (kW)	64,829.44	519.45
$CV_{glucose}$	65.7 %	94.32 %
$CV_{ethanol}$	65.08 %	37.59 %
CV_{solids}	0 %	58.96 %
$Yd_{biofuels}$	2.94 %	2.71%
$Yd_{add-value\ mol}$	2.68 %	0%
$Yd_{Treated-water}$	49.22 %	89.6%

4. Conclusions

In this research, the technical feasibility of obtaining biofuels is presented and confirmed, such as light gases, naphtha, sustainable aviation fuel, green diesel, and bioethanol through the simulation of a biorefinery for the processing of wine effluents. Additionally, the technical feasibility of the production of value-added molecules such as levulinic acid and glycols is verified. With the proposed scheme, it is feasible to obtain water with the quality required for human use according to the COD reduction achieved (99.98%) and the Official Mexican Standards (NOM-001-SEMARNAT-2021 and NOM-127-SSA1-2021). Finally, even though this biorefinery presents a promising alternative to substitute the conventional process (anaerobic digestion), further investigations are needed such as mass/heat integration and economic aspects.

5. Acknowledgment

The authors appreciate the financial support provided by CONAHCyT through the Carlos Eduardo Guzmán Martínez postdoctoral scholarship (Call: 2022 (1). Project: 2397403).

6. References

G. Buitrón, F. Martínez, & F. Ojeda, 2019, Biogas production from a highly organic loaded winery effluent through a two-stage process, BioEnergy Research, 12, 714-721.

E. Carlson, 1996, Don't gamble with physical properties for simulations, Chemical engineering progress, 92(10), 35-46.

C. Guzmán, A. Castro, & F. Nápoles, 2019, Economic and environmental comparison of bioethanol dehydration processes via simulation: reactive distillation, reactor–separator process and azeotropic distillation, Clean Technologies and Environmental Policy, 21, 2061-2071.

N. Kopsahelis, C. Dimou, A. Papadaki, E. Xenopoulos, M. Kyraleou, & S. Kallithraka, 2018, Refining of wine lees and cheese whey for the production of microbial oil, polyphenol-rich extracts and value-added co-products, J Chem Technol Biotechnol, 93.

G. Romero, C. Gutiérrez, F. Gómez, & S. Hernández, 2022, Synthesis and intensification of a biorefinery to produce renewable aviation fuel, biofuels, bioenergy, and chemical products from Jatropha Curcas fruit, IET Renewable Power Generation, 16(14), 2988-3008.

K. Rajendran, H. Kankanala, M. Lundin, & M Taherzadeh, 2014, A novel process simulation model (PSM) for anaerobic digestion using Aspen Plus. Bioresource Technology, 168, 7-13.

S. Ratna, S. Rastogi, & R. Kumar, 2021, Current trends for distillery wastewater management and its emerging applications for sustainable environment, Journal of Environmental Management, 290, 112544.

J. Solis, H. Alcocer, E. Sanchez, & J. Segovia, 2022, Innovative reactive distillation process for levulinic acid production and purification, Chemical Engineering Research and Design, 183, 28-40.

M. Wagh, P. Nemade, P. Jadhav, 2020, Continuous electrocoagulation process for the distillery spent wash using Al electrodes, Techno-Societal, 41–49.

M. Wilk, M. Krzywonos, D. Borowiak, P. Seruga, 2019, Decolourization of sugar beet molasses vinasse by lactic acid bacteria-the effect of yeast extract dosage, J. Environ, 28, 385–392.

R. Wooley, & V. Putsche, 1996, Development of an ASPEN PLUS physical property database for biofuels components (No. NREL/TP-425-20685), National Renewable Energy Lab. (NREL), Golden, CO (United States).

Flavio Manenti, Gintaras V. Reklaitis (Eds.), Proceedings of the 34th European Symposium on Computer Aided Process Engineering / 15th International Symposium on Process Systems Engineering (ESCAPE34/PSE24), June 2-6, 2024, Florence, Italy

Circular Economy Assessment of Viable for Fuels for Mobility

Kenneth J. Martinez[a], Paola A. Munoz-Briones[a], Styliani Avraamidou[a,*]

[a]University of Wisconsin – Madison, 1415 Engineering Dr, Madison, WI 53706
avraamidou@wisc.edu

Abstract

The continuous rise in greenhouse gas (GHG) emissions and the potential lithium scarcity imposed by the increase in battery electric vehicles is escalating the need for alternative sustainable transportation options. There is a lack of holistic environmental assessments, considering the array of trade-offs between these technologies. In this work, we utilize a Circular Economy assessment framework, MICRON, to analyze and identify sustainable transportation fuel options based on five principal metrics: Waste, Energy, Emissions, Water, and Procurement. Based on this analysis, among Hydrogen (H_2) production technologies, H_2 from wind electrolysis is the most sustainable, resulting in a score of 0.63 for overall circularity. Among methanol production technologies, methanol produced by Biogas is the most sustainable, with a circularity score of 0.52.

Keywords: energy carriers, circular economy, circularity index, sustainability index

1. Introduction

The transportation sector is primarily dominated by internal combustion engine (ICE) vehicles, which rely on gasoline as their primary fuel source, contributing significantly to GHG emissions. The rest of the vehicles are mainly battery electric vehicles (BEVs), the largest consumers of lithium. Lakhani N, et al. (2023) predicted that by 2040, the global demand for lithium is predicted to rise over 40 times, leading to environmental and social instability. The escalating threats of climate change and resource depletion emphasize the urgent need for transitioning to more efficient and sustainable transportation fuels.

Methanol stands out as a prominent alternative in today's market to reduce global emissions in the transportation sector. Its production from captured carbon dioxide (CO_2) helps counterbalance the CO_2 emissions during vehicle use. Additionally, methanol burns cleaner than gasoline when used in internal combustion engines and offers flexibility in blending with other fuels across various air-fuel ratios. Hydrogen (H_2), another promising energy carrier, is gaining traction, particularly in public transportation buses. Due to its zero emissions at its point of use in fuel cell vehicles (FCVs) and its high energy efficiency, H_2 is a promising alternative for the near future. Ammonia also holds potential as a transportation fuel. Its ability to store hydrogen in greater quantities than other fuels addresses a significant challenge faced by hydrogen due to its low density. This feature positions ammonia as a viable candidate in the evolving fuel mix for the transportation sector. However, the sustainability of these fuels for transportation is highly contingent on their production processes. Some production pathways may generate more waste and emissions, and they often consume significant resources (energy, water, and other natural materials). For that reason, a holistic metric that considers these factors when assessing technologies is fundamental to determining their viability as transportation fuels.

Despite various efforts to assess the viability of these energy carriers, including life cycle assessments (Bouillass et al., 2021), life cycle inventory, and social life cycle assessments (Ahmed et al., 2023), a comprehensive, unified framework for their environmental comparison is still lacking. Circular economy (CE) represents a sustainability assessment tool that enables the assessment of different technologies to determine the most circular technology among them. In this work, a CE assessment is conducted to assess holistically the sustainability of different production methods for these low-carbon fuels.

2. Methodology

Determining the most circular vehicle technology would require a comprehensive revaluation of its use and disposal, along with the fuel production process. As the first step, this work contemplates a cradle-to-gate scope, as shown in Figure 1, for the fuel synthesis of some of the most promising fuels: renewable gasoline, hydrogen, methanol, and ammonia. All the emissions, along with an array of other CE metrics, are evaluated for the stages of feedstock extraction, transportation, and production of the fuel.

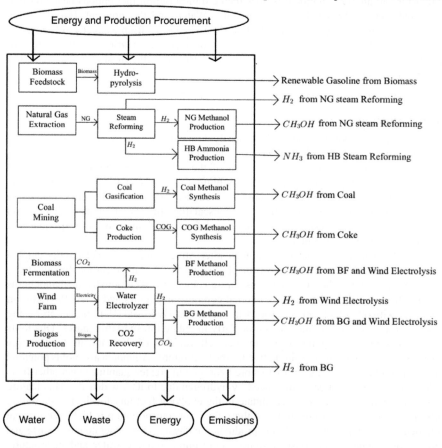

Figure 1. Circularity Assessment Scope: A cradle-to-gate analysis of different fuel production pathways

Baratsas et al, (2022) proposed a CE assessment tool to evaluate the circularity of companies. The CE impact scores range from 0 to 1, where zero represents linear operations and 1, circular operations. The calculator was designed based on the five circular economy goals identified. The goals encompass: i) minimizing waste and pollutants, ii) decreasing the utilization of natural resources, iii) boosting the proportion of renewable resources, iv) lowering emissions, and v) increasing the durability of products. Therefore, the impact principal categories of waste, water, procurement, energy, and emissions were defined according to the CE goals. These principal categories are scored based on metrics derived from GRI standards (standards commonly used in sustainability reports) and LCA.

In the present work, this calculator is adapted to analyze the production of fuels for powertrains with the final intention of determining the most circular transportation fuel. A table with the metrics utilized in the current study is presented in **Table 1**. A weight is assigned to the metric of each indicator so a score for each category can be computed. An overall index can be obtained from the linear average of the different categories.

Table 1. Principal indicators and metrics of the circular economy calculator.

Principal Category	Metric
Waste	**1a.** % Hazardous Waste over Total Waste Generated
	1b. % Diverted Waste over Total Generated Waste
	1c. Waste generated [kg] / kg of fuel produced
Water	**2.** Total volume of water recycled and reused as a percentage of the total water withdrawal [%]
	2b. % of water consumed per water withdrawn
	2c. Water consumed per kg of fuel produced
Procurement	**3.** % of renewable material
Energy	**4a.** % of Renewable over Total Energy Consumed
	4b. Total Energy Consumed per kg of fuel produced [MJ]
GHG Emissions	**5a.** Net Total Emissions per kg of fuel produced [$kgCO_2e$/ kg]
	5b. NO_x, SO_x etc. over kg of fuel produced [kg/kg]

3. Discussion and Results

Given the established scope, the manufacturing of the fuel and production of the inputs are studied. The Overall "Circularity" Index, along with the sub-indices is calculated here for the considered fuels and available data on production technologies. An extensive literature review was carried out to collect the data needed for the calculator indicators, and a normalized value from 0 to 1 was calculated for each metric, as shown in Table 2.

Table 2. Circularity metric values and literature review for each technology.

Technology	Waste			Water			Proc.	Energy		GHG Emissions	
	1a	1b	1c	2a	2b	2c	3	4a	4b	5a	5b
H$_2$ from Elec. Wind (Mann et al. , 2004)	1.00	1.00	0.00	0.36	0.00	0.75	0.0	1.00	0.00	1.00	0.92
H$_2$ Biogas (Hajjaji et al., 2016)	1.00	1.00	0.97	0.00	0.00	0.79	1.0	0.40	0.88	0.00	1.00
H$_2$ from NG SMR (Spath et al., 2001)	1.00	0.00	0.98	0.00	0.00	0.47	0.0	0.01	0.00	0.00	0.00
Methanol by NG (Li et al., 2018)	0.00	1.00	1.00	0.00	0.00	0.69	0.31	0.02	0.66	0.72	0.91
Methanol by Ethanol fermentation (Demirel, 2016)	1.00	0.00	0.94	0.00	0.00	0.00	0.0	0.33	0.66	0.85	0.94
Methanol by BG using H$_2$ wind Elec. (Eggemann et al., 2020)	1.00	1.00	0.00	0.00	0.01	0.00	0.57	0.11	0.60	1.10	0.92
Methanol by Coal (Li et al., 2018)	0.14	0.14	0.98	0.00	0.00	0.72	0.89	0.02	0.55	0.58	0.98
Methanol by Coke (Li et al., 2018)	0.96	1.00	0.59	0.09	0.00	0.70	0.63	0.01	0.45	0.64	0.59
Renewable Gasoline (Zupko, 2019)	0.95	0.95	0.96	0.00	0.00	0.00	1.0	0.00	0.29	0.45	0.77
NH$_3$ by HB with H$_2$ SMR, US grid (Biçer et al., 2017)	1.00	0.00	0.98	0.89	0.06	0.93	0.0	0.13	0.59	0.43	0.00

Figure 2 presents the sub-index circularity scores for each evaluated technology. Among the methanol production methods, methanol derived from coke demonstrates the highest waste recycling rate, achieving a perfect score in the waste sub-index. This efficiency significantly offsets its emissions, positioning it as the methanol technology with the highest circularity. Excluding hydrogen produced via wind electrolysis, the remaining hydrogen production methods utilizing the same type of energy: the U.S. energy mix. Nevertheless, biogas production stands out due to its superior efficiency, leading to higher circular sub-index values in three out of four categories and trailing closely in the fourth. Despite its renewable production, gasoline production remains a predominantly linear technology. The overall circularity indices for these technologies are further illustrated in **Figure 3**.

Figure 2. Circularity indicator metrics for each technology

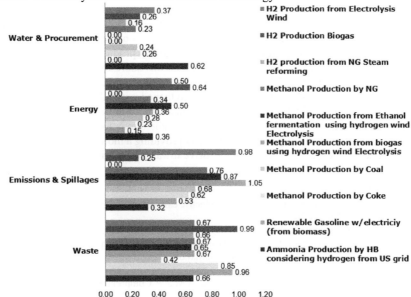

Figure 3. Overall circularity for all the considered production pathways ranked by most circular most linear.

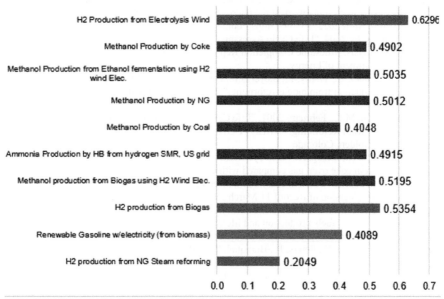

4. Conclusions

This study successfully leveraged the MICRON CE framework to quantify the circularity indices of various fuel production technologies. Our findings revealed that hydrogen generated through wind electrolysis emerged as the leading circular technology, while methanol production via biogas outperformed in terms of circularity for methanol technologies. These insights underscore the need for a strategic shift towards these more circular technologies in order to meet greenhouse emission reduction goals sustainably. In addition, the current trajectory of renewable methanol production, characterized by its linearity, raises concerns over its feasibility in the short to medium term without substantial advancements. While the assessments conducted were thorough, the breadth and depth of the analysis could be further strengthened with additional data on a wider range of ammonia and hydrogen production technologies. Future research endeavors will aim to enhance the framework by integrating considerations for fuel transportation and storage, as well as their usage in FCVs, thereby providing a more comprehensive view of the vehicle's life cycle and supporting the drive towards a sustainable energy economy.

References

Lakhani, N., "Revealed: how US transition to electric cars threatens environmental havoc," The Guardian, 24 January 2023

Bouillass, G., Blanc, I., Perez-Lopez, P., "Step-by-step social life cycle assessment framework: a participatory approach for the identification and prioritization of impact subcategories applied to mobility scenarios," The International Journal of Life Cycle Assessment, Vol. 26, pp. 2408–2435, 2021.

Ahmed, A.A., Nazzal, M.A., Darras, B.M., Deiab, I.M., "A Comprehensive Sustainability Assessment of Battery Electric Vehicles, Fuel Cell Electric Vehicles, and Internal Combustion Engine Vehicles through a Comparative Circular Economy Assessment," Sustainability, Vol. 15(1), 171, 2023.

Baratsas, S.G., Pistikopoulos, E.N., Avraamidou, S., "A quantitative and holistic circular economy assessment framework at the micro level," Computers & Chemical Engineering, Volume 160, April 2022, 107697, https://doi.org/10.1016/j.compchemeng.2022.107697.

Mann, M., Spath, P., 2004, "Life Cycle Assessment of Renewable Hydrogen Production via Wind/Electrolysis: Milestone Completion Report," National Renewable Energy Lab., Golden, CO, US Department of Energy.

Hajjaji, N., Martinez, S., Trably, E., Steyer, J.P., Helias, A., 2016, "Life cycle assessment of hydrogen production from biogas reforming," International Journal of Hydrogen Energy, 41 (14), pp.6064-6075.

Spath, P.L., Mann, M.K., February 2001, "Life Cycle Assessment of Hydrogen Production via Natural Gas Steam Reforming," NREL/TP-570-27637, National Renewable Energy Laboratory, Golden, Colorado

Li, J., Ma, X., Liu, H., Zhang, X., "Life cycle assessment and economic analysis of methanol production from coke oven gas compared with coal and natural gas routes," Received 7 September 2017, Revised 8 February 2018, Accepted 9 February 2018, Available online 12 February 2018, Version of Record 11 March 2018.

Matzen, M., Demirel, Y., "Methanol and dimethyl ether from renewable hydrogen and carbon dioxide: Alternative fuels production and life-cycle assessment," Journal of Cleaner Production, 2016, https://doi.org/10.1016/j.jclepro.2016.08.163.

Eggemann, L., Escobar, N., Peters, R., Buraquel, P., Stolten, D., "Life cycle assessment of a small-scale methanol production system: A Power-to-Fuel strategy for biogas plants," Journal of Cleaner Production, Volume 271, 20 October 2020, 122476, https://doi.org/10.1016/j.jclepro.2020.122476.

Zupko, R., "Life cycle assessment of the production of gasoline and diesel from forest residues using integrated hydropyrolysis and hydroconversion," The International Journal of Life Cycle Assessment, Vol. 24, pp. 1793–1804, 2019.

Biçer, Y., Dinçer, I., Vezina, G., Raso, F., "Impact Assessment and Environmental Evaluation of Various Ammonia Production Processes," Environmental Management, Vol. 59, pp. 842–855, 2017.

Flavio Manenti, Gintaras V. Reklaitis (Eds.), Proceedings of the 34th European Symposium on
Computer Aided Process Engineering / 15th International Symposium on Process Systems
Engineering (ESCAPE34/PSE24), June 2-6, 2024, Florence, Italy

Optimum Green Clean Water Solution for Remote Islands

Aggelos Kaldellis[a], Christofis Koroneos[b], Emilia. Kondili[c], John K. Kaldellis[a]

[a]*Soft Energy Applications & Environmental Protection Lab., UNIWA, Greece*
[b]*Nisyros Municipality, Nisyros, Greece*
[c]*Optimisation of Production Systems Lab., UNIWA, Greece*
email for correpondence: jkald@uniwa.gr

Abstract

Water and energy are two fundamental resources with the supply of one highly dependent
on the availability of the other. The recognition that their scarcity underpins socioeconomic development has resulted in a growing interest of policy makers in the so-called
"Water-Energy Nexus". The water-energy supply problem affects all types and sizes of
contemporary communities around the world due to the spatial characteristics of the water
availability, also challenged by the availability and the security of energy supply. Remote
islands' communities in the Mediterranean area suffer from significant water scarcity on
top of their electricity generation problems due to the utilization of expensive thermal
power stations. These problems are much more intense during the summer-touristic
period, where the total islands population increases by almost one order of magnitude,
strongly testing the capacity of the corresponding infrastructures. On the other hand, the
entire Mediterranean region possesses excellent solar potential. In this context, the current
paper investigates the opportunities for the autonomous operation of a clean water
production scheme using only the available solar potential and an appropriate energy
storage unit, paying also special attention in order to stabilize the operation of the water
production sub-system. For this purpose, a reliable and user-friendly numerical model is
developed to optimize the parameters of the proposed solution. The applied optimization
procedure is based on scenarios' analysis targeting maximum clean water production,
uninterrupted operation of the desalination unit and minimum installation/operation cost,
based on exclusive solar potential exploitation.

Keywords: Desalination, RES exploitation, energy storage, energy-water nexus.

1. Introduction

The existence of more than 85,000 islands consists a particular trait of the global
geography. Focusing on the East Mediterranean region, the Aegean Archipelagos is an
area of great interest, where one may find an extensive number of islands, 7% of them
being inhabited. A semi-arid climate (Pnevmatikos and Katsoulis, 2006), the lack of local
conventional energy resources (Kaldellis et al., 2007) as well as the relatively long
distance from the mainland consist the main characteristics of most of these remote
islands. Moreover, due to the specific climate type, significant water resources scarcity
for both domestic and agricultural use is present for the vast majority of these islands,
deteriorating the life quality of inhabitants and visitors, especially during the summer.
Actually, in most remote islands electricity generation problems exist due to the
utilization of expensive and heavily polluting outdated autonomous thermal power
stations (APS). Actually, the water and electricity demand maximizes from June to

August, strongly testing the performance of the corresponding infrastructures. The problem becomes much more severe in cases of electricity generation black out, since the existing desalination units will also stop their operation. Fortunately, the Mediterranean region possesses high solar potential, which is almost unexploited for various reasons.

In this context, the present work investigates the opportunities of an autonomous clean water solution including one photovoltaic (PV) generator and an appropriate energy storage device in order to fulfil the electricity demand of a typical desalination unit, paying also special attention in order to stabilize the operation of the water production system. For this purpose, a reliable and user-friendly numerical model has been developed to optimize the parameters of the proposed solution. The applied optimization procedure is based on scenarios' analysis targeting maximum clean water production, uninterrupted operation of the desalination unit and minimum installation/operation cost, based on exclusive solar potential exploitation. According to the results obtained from the application of the proposed solution to a representative medium-sized Aegean Sea island, the continuous operation of the desalination unit is obtained by an appropriate combination of photovoltaics and battery storage units, providing green clean water quantities mainly during the high touristic season at a rational first installation cost.

2. Problem Description

The problem to be analyzed concerns the optimum sizing of a PV-battery based system able to provide the necessary electricity input for a reverse osmosis (RO)-desalination plant supporting its continuous (uninterrupted) operation. In figure (1) the proposed installation is schematically described. Note that for every cubic meter of clean water produced the energy required is "ε" (kWh/m^3), depending mainly on the pressure and the water volume flow rate "Q" of the high-pressure pumps and on the feed water salinity.

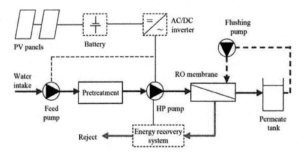

Figure 1: Schematic presentation of the proposed PV-battery water desalination solution

At the same time the renewable energy based solution selected -as the most appropriate (Kaldellis et al., 2007)- for very small islands is the exploitation of the existing solar potential via high efficiency photovoltaic panels. For this purpose, one needs data concerning the available solar irradiance and the ambient temperature time series. Furthermore, the PV panels output depends also on their inclination (tilt) angle in relation to the horizontal plane and the cleanliness index of the PV surface. Finally, the battery bank is characterized by its maximum useful energy to be provided to the consumption, its maximum depth of discharge (DOD$_{max}$) and its maximum charging and discharging rate as well as its charging and discharging efficiency (Kaldellis et al., 2009). In view of the configuration of figure (1), one may face the following operation cases (Table I):

R1	Operation	The solar potential is high enough to provide the appropriate power and energy in order to operate the desalination plant, while any energy excess is forwarded to the system batteries. The desalination plant operates at its maximum flow rate "Q_{max}".
R2	Operation	The solar potential is not high enough to provide the appropriate energy in order to operate the desalination plant, hence any additional energy is complemented by the battery bank, assuming that the DOD of the battery is lower than the DOD_L. This limit is lower than the DOD_{max}, (e.g. DOD_L=65% vs. DOD_{max}=80%) in order to protect the batteries and prolong their service period, normally is provided by the battery manufacturer. The desalination plant operates at maximum flow rate "Q_{max}".
R3	Partial Operation	The solar potential is not high enough to provide the appropriate energy in order to operate the desalination plant, however the battery bank DOD is higher than a first security limit (DOD_L) but it is still lower than the DOD_{max}. The desalination plant continues its operation but at a lower flow rate than "Q_{max}", being however higher than the minimum flow rate "Q_{min}" of the installation (technical minimum).
R4	Non-operation	The solar potential is not high enough to provide the appropriate power and energy in order to operate the desalination plant and the battery bank DOD is higher or equal to DOD_{max}. The desalination plant suspend its operation for the rest of the day. Any energy yield of the PV panels is used to charge the installation batteries and to decrease the corresponding DOD value. Finally, in case of total clean water shortage the desalination plant may be connected to the local electrical grid.

Table I: Available operational modes of the proposed clean water production solution

The proposed operation strategy is definitely a sustainable green solution, since the entire energy consumption of the desalination process is provided by the exploitation of solar potential. Hence, the target is to maximize the potable water production without jeopardizing the service period of the desalination plant components, i.e. by eliminating the successive start and stop orders, protecting at the same time the system battery.

3. Proposed Methodology

For the estimation of the necessary PV panels' number and the appropriate capacity of the battery bank, in view of the sustainable operation of existing desalination unit, a new optimization model has been developed, taking into consideration the local water consumption needs, the land availability and the available budget or equivalently the corresponding clean water production cost vs. the elimination of CO_2 emissions.

3.1. Model Development

The approach that is implemented here is to operate a RO desalination plant in order to cover the water needs of an arid remote region integrating sustainability principles into traditional fossil fuels based applications and addressing complex interdependencies between various energy production components. The proposed model has been developed to address the complex interactions between various elements of solar energy exploitation -solar irradiance utilization, ambient temperature impact, battery bank depth of discharge (DOD) and uninterrupted operation- all under the sustainability strategy. The first step is to identify the critical elements affecting the uninterrupted sustainable operation of a desalination unit, maximizing the clean water production without the consumption of fossil fuels. Then a large number of scenarios (i.e. combinations of PV panels peak power P_{pv} and battery storage "E_{ss}") have been examined using long-term time series of solar irradiance along with ambient meteorological parameters (temperature, seawater salinity, etc.). Based on these input parameters and taking into account the existing constraints, the model defines several potential solutions that can be evaluated on the basis of minimum life cycle water production cost, minimum greenhouse gas emissions, maximum clean water production or any combination of all these criteria.

3.2. The Objective function

The optimization model developed combines the PV generator power output, the battery bank DOD in the course of time and the clean water production by the RO-desalination unit. The objective function is to achieve an optimal balance between cost, sustainability and clean water production. At the core of the model is a multi-objective function, as given in Eq. (1), including three primary objectives, i.e.: minimizing the water production cost "c_w", the CO_2 emissions "e" and the water deficit between the society needs and the desalination yield "d"(=Demand-Clean Production). The objective function is expressed:

$$\text{Minimize } \Phi = \alpha c_w + \beta e + \gamma d \qquad (1)$$

In this context, "Φ" symbolizes the total weighted impact of the RES-based autonomous clean water production. The water production cost takes into account the PV-battery autonomous power system turnkey cost as well as the operation and maintenance cost of the proposed installation in present values divided by the clean water production volume of life cycle basis. Regarding the carbon dioxide emissions "e", these depend on the specific emissions coefficients per energy unit consumed (gr/kWh$_e$) by the desalination plant (e.g. 750 gr CO_2/kWh$_e$ produced by oil vs. 35 gr CO_2/kWh$_e$ by the PV panels) along with CO_2 emissions related with the battery bank and the necessary auxiliary equipment.

Additionally "d", as defined in Eq. (2), describes the maximum clean water production throughout the RO process, thus the minimum deficit between clean water demand "D" of the local society and the capability of the proposed solution "S" to fulfil the water demand. Thus, the corresponding water balance is investigated on daily basis "j".

$$d = \sum (D_j - S_j) \quad (j = 1,365) \qquad (2)$$

The weighting factors (α, β and γ) included in Eq. (1) indicate the varying significance of distinct factors aligned with the strategic priorities and policy decisions for any remote consumer. These factors underline the importance of water production cost, local market decarbonization and local society clean water needs fulfilment. They are determined based on objectives related to sustainability within the EU and national policy decisions, regulatory requirements and local society standard of living.

3.3. Variables and Constraints

For every optimization model it is important to define the variables and acknowledge the major constraints. Normally, variables include decision variables such as the clean water production quantities "Q", the PV generator peak power "P_{pv}", the battery capacity "E_{ss}" (and the permitted DOD$_{max}$), as well as operational variables. Constraints are formulated to enclose the limitations and requirements like the land availability, the maximum budget available, the maximum clean water demand on a monthly basis "D_{mo}" and the maximum existing water reservoirs capacity. The variables and constraints are designed to balance cost-efficiency, decarbonisation performance and clean water production.

3.3.1. Constraints

First, the constraint of land availability is introduced. This constraint aims for optimal use of the available land. Following that, the constraint of the available budget is also introduced since the initial investment cost should not exceed the capital availability. Finally, the clean water production should not exceed the corresponding clean water demand, including the local water storage potential, especially during low demand periods. Summarizing the above mentioned constraints may be summarized as follows:

$$A_c(P_{pv}) \leq Available \ Land \tag{3}$$

$$IC_o \leq Available \ Initial \ Capital \tag{4}$$

$$Smo_i \leq Dmo_i \quad i = 1,12 \ for \ every \ month \tag{5}$$

3.3.2. Variables

The main variables of the problem under investigation are the photovoltaic generator peak power "P_{pv}", the battery bank energy capacity "E_{ss}" and the clean water production "Q" of the desalination unit. In this context, the PV generator characteristics along with the solar irradiance, the PV panels tilt angle and the other meteorological parameters define the energy yield available for the desalination unit at every moment. Moreover, the battery bank capacity along with the corresponding DOD determine (Kaldellis et al., 2009) the opportunity to support the desalination plant operation during low solar potential periods (eliminating the unnecessary stop and start operation) and absorb any energy surplus due to the PV generator operation. Finally, the potable water production is based (Papapostolou et al., 2019) on the green energy availability and scopes to cover the everyday clean water demand of the local society, including the high tourism periods.

4. Results and Discussion

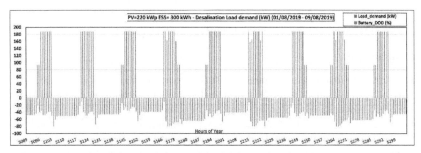

Figure 2: Operational characteristics vs. time for the proposed PV-battery based solution

The model developed is applied to a medium sized island of approximately 1000 permanent habitants, possessing high solar potential ($\approx$1800 kWh/m^2/year) and covering its total energy needs up to now using diesel oil ($\sim$500 MWh$_e$ per year for the desalination units), Kaldellis et al., 2022. In order to estimate the optimum solution of equation (1) under the constraints of section three, a detailed scenarios analysis has been carried out, testing a large number of combinations (P_{pv} and E_{ss}). The resulting clean water quantity "Q" as well as the carbon dioxide emissions savings "e" and the corresponding clean water production cost "c_w" are estimated on an annual basis. Thus, by selecting a pair of (P_{pv} and E_{ss}) the hourly PV generator power output is calculated and compared with the power demand of the desalination unit on the basis of Table I operation modes. If the R4 situation appears, the proposed combination is excluded from the potential solutions. In figure (2) one may find the desalination plant load demand fulfilled by the operation of a 220 kW$_p$ (i.e. P_{pv}=220 kW$_p$) solar generator and the corresponding Li-ion batteries (E_{ss}=300 kWh$_e$, DOD$_{max}$=80%) along with the (DOD) value of the system proposed batteries vs. time.

In figure (3) one may find the summary of the calculation results, concerning the annual clean water production for several combinations of (P_{pv} and E_{ss}) that guarantee the non-stop and start operation of the existing desalination plant on a daily basis. According to the results obtained it is clear that the existence of even a small battery bank remarkably increases the clean water production. However, after the 200 kWh$_e$ of battery capacity the clean water production increase is minimal. Moreover, the gradual increase of PV generator peak power leads to an analogous increase of the clean water production and the corresponding carbon dioxide emissions reduction. At the same time, the first installation (turnkey) cost is also increasing, while the continuous increase in the PV generator size may raise land availability issues. Recapitulating, the optimum clean energy solution for each case study investigated depends strongly on the solar potential and the water demand profile of each candidate island as well as on the value of coefficients "α", "β" and "γ" selected by the local authorities and the local community.

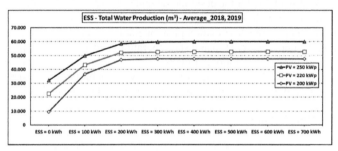

Figure 3: Potential energy autonomous optimal configurations based on scenarios analysis

5. Conclusions

The present work investigates the possibility of covering the energy requirements of remote arid islands' desalination units in a sustainable manner, proposing the installation of photovoltaic power stations. For this purpose an optimization model has been developed offering a comprehensive approach for policy makers and local authorities to address the complexities of clean-green production, balancing financial, decarbonization and water demand considerations to achieve the most sustainable and efficient configurations. This optimization model is adaptable to different island cases and can be applied to prioritize specific targets, with the aim of guiding local societies to select more environmental friendly and lower production cost solutions. In any case, the proposed model may serve as a decision making tool and determines the foundations for encouraging clean green water production solutions in areas of similar specifications in the wider Mediterranean region.

References

Kaldellis J.K., Kavadias K.A., Koronakis P.S., 2007, "Comparing Wind and Photovoltaic Stand-Alone Power Systems Used for the Electrification of Remote Consumers", Journal of Renewable and Sustainable Energy Reviews, Vol.11(1), pp.57-77.

Kaldellis J.K., Koroneos Chr., Triantafyllou P., Kaldellis A., Kollas P., 2022, " Clean energy solution for remote islands. The case of Nisyros island", Int. Journal of Sustainable Energy.

Kaldellis J.K., Zafirakis D., Kavadias K., 2009, "Techno-economic comparison of energy storage systems for island autonomous electrical networks", Renewable and Sustainable Energy Reviews, Vol. 13(2), pp.378-392.

Papapostolou Chr., Kondili E., Tzanes G., 2019, Optimisation of the integrated water - energy systems: a review with a focus in Process Systems Engineering, Computer Aided Chemical Engineering, 2019, 46, Pages 1621-1626

Pnevmatikos, J.D. and Katsoulis, B.D. (2006). The changing rainfall regime in Greece and its impact on climatological means. Meteorol Appl, 13(4), pp. 331-345.

Flavio Manenti, Gintaras V. Reklaitis (Eds.), Proceedings of the 34th European Symposium on Computer Aided Process Engineering / 15th International Symposium on Process Systems Engineering (ESCAPE34/PSE24), June 2-6, 2024, Florence, Italy

A Novel Vapor Recompressed Batch Extractive Distillation for Ethanol Dehydration

Sidharth Sankar Parhi[a], Gade Pandu Rangaiah[b] and Amiya K Jana[a*]

[a]Department of Chemical Engineering, Indian Institute of Technology Kharagpur, India−721302

[b]Department of Chemical and Biomolecular Engineering, National University of Singapore, Singapore-117585

* Corresponding author. *E-mail address*: akjana@che.iitkgp.ac.in (A. K. Jana).

Abstract

This work proposes a novel batch extractive distillation (BED) by introducing vapor recompression in selected stages of batch operation, for ethanol dehydration using ethyl glycol. To optimize BED for multiple conflicting objectives related to economics, production and environmental impact, a mixed-integer nonlinear multi-objective optimization problem is formulated and solved using the elitist non-dominated sorting genetic algorithm. One optimal design from the generated Pareto-optimal front is selected by multi-criteria decision making. Then, a novel selective vapor recompressed BED (S-VRBED) is developed for BED. Retrofitting BED to S-VRBED lowers energy consumption and CO_2 emissions by 58%, and the investment made for the compressor is recovered in 5.7 years.

Keywords: Batch extractive distillation, Retrofitting, Selective vapor recompression, Multi-objective optimization, Ethanol dehydration

1. Introduction

Despite very low thermodynamic efficiency, distillation is widely used for separating liquid mixtures. Among various technologies for improving efficiency of distillation, heat integration of reboiler and condenser via a motor-driven vapor recompression (VRC) heat pump is attractive. However, reported studies are mostly on separation of liquid mixtures in a continuous column. Recently, our group has successfully employed VRC for batch distillation (BD) (Parhi et al., 2019). Distillation is dominant for ethanol recovery from fermentation broth to ≈ 95 wt% ethanol; then, azeotropic distillation with cyclohexane, extractive distillation (ED) with ethyl glycol (EG) or adsorption with molecular sieves is used for subsequent dehydration to > 99.5 wt% ethanol (Singh and Rangaiah, 2017). ED offers versatility with a range of entrainers (solvents). There are studies on batch ED (BED) for ethanol dehydration; but, VRC is uncommon in BEDs, due to its high capital cost (CAPEX) despite high energy savings. To reduce the investment, this work proposes different VRC schemes; they avoid operation at a high compression ratio. Hence, they will be beneficial from both economic and environmental perspectives.

Design of any process including BED should be optimized. BED optimization is a mixed-integer nonlinear programming problem with continuous (reboiler duty, reflux ratio, RR etc.) and integer variables (number of trays, feed tray etc.). Further, optimization of an unsteady process like BED is challenging, complex and requires a robust global optimizer like genetic algorithm (GA). Thanks to advancements, e.g., elitist non-dominated sorting

GA (NSGA-II), and computational power, multi-objective optimization (MOO) of BD has been studied recently (Parhi et al., 2019). However, MOO of BED has not been explored extensively. Barreto et al. (2011) reported this considering only continuous variables to maximize profit while minimizing environmental impact, for the separation of chloroform and methanol with water as the entrainer. We suggested a MOO strategy to optimize BED and vapor recompressed BED (VRBED) for separating azeotropic mixture of acetone and methanol using water as the entrainer (Parhi et al., 2020). These studies on MOO and VRC for BED are limited to separating mixtures of two products using a cheaper entrainer such as water.

However, for dehydration of a desirable component (ethanol in this case) using a suitable but expensive entrainer such as EG, a different strategy is required considering objectives related to economics, environment, production and entrainer recovery. This is because both product and entrainer recovery are equally important in ethanol dehydration. Moreover, the same type of VRC cannot be used for all BEDs; because of high CAPEX, traditional VRC may not be economical. To address this issue, the present work proposes a novel selective VRC. **In summary**, main contributions and novelty of this study are as follows. Firstly, a unique MOO problem is articulated considering competing objectives of economics, production, entrainer recovery and CO_2 emissions for ethanol dehydration in BED. Secondly, a variable speed VRC is introduced to retrofit the optimal BED and assess its benefits for ethanol dehydration. Thirdly, a novel selective VRBED (S-VRBED) is suggested to reduce CAPEX for VRC.

2. Working Principle and Process Modeling

A typical BED (Fig. 1a) has a reboiler at the bottom, a distillation tower in the middle and a total condenser with a reflux drum at the top. The working procedure of BED, its modeling and simulation, associated thermodynamic model and operating conditions are described elsewhere (Parhi et al., 2020). Proposed VRBED schemes are developed below.

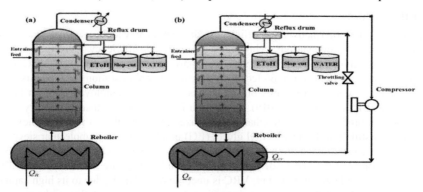

Figure 1. Schematic diagram of BED (plot 1a) and VRBED (plot 1b)

VRBED: VRC, one effective solution for reducing CO_2 emissions, uses internal heat to minimize external energy requirement. As shown in Fig. 1b, column overhead vapor stream (at T_{NT}) is compressed to increase both pressure and temperature, and then it is used to vaporize the liquid in the reboiler (at T_B). Driving force (ΔT) for heat transfer in the reboiler was taken as 15°C. The compressed vapor condenses in the reboiler, giving its latent heat for boiling the reboiler content. A throttling valve depressurizes the condensed vapor before channelling it to the reflux drum. Thus, latent heat of the overhead vapor is used to reduce the hot utility required at the reboiler. Compressor duty (Q_{Comp}) in VRC is computed using Eq. 1 in Parhi et al. (2020).

A ***variable speed operating policy*** is formulated for VRBED for optimum utilization of internal heat. Inputs and outputs of BED (i.e., reboiler duty, feed composition and product purity) are same for both VRBED and BED. Complete condensation of compressed vapor in the reboiler is assumed provided that the required thermal driving force is maintained during the operation. For this, two operating criteria, namely, constant thermal driving force and constant reboiler duty (Q_R) are proposed; to satisfy them, an open-loop control policy that computes three manipulated variables, namely, compression ratio (CR), V_{NT} and external heat input to the reboiler (Q_E), is devised. ***First operating criterion:*** A variable-speed compressor is used to ensure column operation at $\Delta T_T = T_{NTC} - T_B = 15°C$ during the entire batch process. For this, the compressor is operated below or at maximum CR (by varying CR at every time step of 0.0008 h with the change in top and reboiler temperatures). ***Second operating criterion:*** In BED, the entire heat input to the reboiler is supplied externally. In VRBED, latent heat, $Q_{CV} = \lambda V_{NT}$ of the compressed overhead vapor reduces Q_E to the reboiler according to: $Q_R = Q_E + Q_{CV}$. Here, there are two scenarios. In the *First Scenario* ($Q_{CV} > Q_R$), overhead vapor is split into two fractions. One fraction (V_{NTC}) is fed to the compressor and then condensed in the reboiler, and the other fraction (V_{NTI}) is sent to the condenser, which is operated with reduced coolant flow rate, and no external steam is needed in the reboiler. In the *Second Scenario* ($Q_{CV} < Q_R$), all the overhead vapor (V_{NTC}) is compressed for use in the reboiler. The deficit heat ($Q_R - Q_{CV}$) is provided by steam to the reboiler, and the condenser operation is not required. Thus, VRC reduces steam required in the reboiler and coolant needed in the condenser; but, it requires a compressor that is typically operated by a motor. This raises a query whether VRBED saves total energy or not compared to BED. Another important issue is the compressor's high CAPEX that can make retrofitting a BED with VRC uneconomical. To address this, a novel **S-VRBED** is proposed and investigated later in this paper.

3. Quantitative Performance Assessment and Optimization Strategy

Total annual cost (TAC) and total annual production (TAP) (Parhi et al., 2020) are implemented for techno-economic analysis of the considered schemes. TAC is the sum of operating cost, OPEX ($/a) and 20% (i.e., payback period, PBP = 5 years) of CAPEX ($) that includes additional 10% for working capital. For BED, both TAP of required product and entrainer recovery are often important. Hence, TAP of the desired product and total annual entrainer recovery (TAER) are included for performance analysis. TAP is the product collected per batch multiplied by number of batch cycles per annum (based on 8000 working hours and 30 minutes of batch setup time). Similarly, TAER is computed based on the amount of entrainer recovered per batch in the reboiler. Efficiency of entrainer usage ($EoEU$), equal to molar ratio of total ethanol collected to total entrainer used, and CO_2 emissions are also included as objectives in MOO. In BED, steam is employed in reboiler; VRBED additionally uses electricity for compressor. CO_2 emissions in steam generation are based on equations in Parhi et al. (2020) and it is 51.1 kg CO_2/GJ of electricity.

Optimization Strategy: Due to the nonlinearity and presence of both continuous and discrete decision variables, BED optimization is challenging. Hence, a 3-step procedure is developed for BED optimization. In the first step, significant decision variables impacting objectives are identified by sensitivity analysis and then MOO problem is formulated. The second step deals with optimizing BED using NSGA-II in MATLAB. This gives a set of non-dominated solutions. Such sets obtained from several runs of NSGA-II are pooled and subjected to non-dominated sorting to find the 'true' Pareto-optimal front. In the final step, one optimal solution from this front is selected by a multi-criteria decision making (MCDM) method, namely TOPSIS (Technique for Order of Preference by Similarity to Ideal Solution), available in an MS Excel program. Weights required for TOPSIS are found by the entropy method (Parhi et al., 2019).

4. Case Study, BED Optimization and Retrofitting

The case study is separation of ethanol and water that form a minimum-boiling azeotrope with 89.4 mol% ethanol at 78.28°C and 1 atm. For BED, a MOO problem is formulated to minimize CAPEX ($), OPEX ($/a) and CO_2 emissions (t/a), while maximizing TAP of ethanol (kmol/a), *EoEU* and TAER (kmol/a). Constraints are: purity of ≥ 99.5% for both ethanol and water, and ≥ 99.9% for EG. Decision variables with their lower/upper bounds are: no of trays (20/80), feed tray (15/75), reboiler duty (0.3/30 GJ/h), RR during ethanol production (0.01/10), RR during slop-cut discharge (0.01/10), RR during water collection (0.01/30), entrainer feed rate (1/500 kmol/h) and weir height (25.4/101.6 mm).

MOO problem along with model equations for BED (Parhi et al., 2020) was solved 4 times using NSGA-II. Each optimization run generated 50 non-dominated solutions after 200 generations. The 200 solutions thus obtained are subjected to non-dominated sorting to find the "true' Pareto-optimal front having 68 non-dominated solutions. Trends of objectives and decision variables are not discussed here due to space constraint. TOPSIS with entropy weights for objectives is used for selecting one optimal solution from the Pareto-optimal front. The optimal configuration of BED, thus chosen, is: 20 trays (plus reboiler and condenser), RR of 0.184, 0.304 and 0.185 during ethanol production, slop-cut discharge and water collection, respectively, constant reboiler duty of 2.02 GJ/h throughout batch operation, 5.52 kmol/h of EG entering at tray 17 and weir height of 76.2 mm. The transient composition profile for the optimal BED is presented in Fig. 2a. A quasi-steady state under total reflux (Step 1) is achieved in 0.94 h; ethanol in the reflux drum reached 99.984 mol% at the end of start-up phase (Step 1). In Step 2, ethanol is continuously collected in the product tank for 0.364 h, and this is halted when the average ethanol purity in the tank no longer exceeds 99.5 mol%. Then, slop-cut (Step 3) starts and continues for 0.223 h. With the progression of this step, ethanol concentration in the column decreases, and water concentration in the top section increases gradually. Finally, in Step 4, highly concentrated water is collected in the tank at the top having a maximum concentration of 99.97 mol% and then it reduces due to the removal of water from the column. This final step proceeds for 0.17 h till the concentration of water in its tank is more than 95 mol%. Taking the total batch time of 1.693 h for 4 steps and 0.5 h for batch preparation, unloading and cleaning, 3,648 (= 8,000/(1.693+0.5)) batches can be performed in one year. This means BED is operated for only 6176 (= 1.693×3648) h annually with TAP of 28.96×3648 = 105,655 kmol/a. Difference between T_B and T_{NT} (Fig. 2b) is ≈ 20°C for half the batch operation and attains a maximum of 98.33°C at 1.52 h (in Step 3). Saturation temperature of steam should be 15°C more than the maximum reboiler temperature of 198°C; that is, it should be 213°C.

Retrofitting BED to VRBED and S-VRBEDs: Optimal BED is retrofitted to VRBED and five S-VRBEDs. All these schemes are such that dynamics of product quantities, purities and annual operational hours are the same as those of the optimum BED. VRBED is formulated based on two operating criteria: $\Delta T_T = 15°C$ and $Q_R = 2.02$ GJ/h, stated earlier. Following the CR profile (Fig. 2c), a variable speed compressor is operated to maintain $\Delta T_T = 15°C$. Providing fixed Q_R is met by supplying the requisite Q_E according to the profile (Fig. 2d) for retrofitted VRBED; second scenario ($Q_{CV} < Q_R$) occurs during the first half of the batch operation, and first scenario ($Q_{CV} > Q_R$) occurs in ethanol production phase. Further, in VRBED case (Fig. 2c), CR of 8.62 reached at 1.28 h significantly increases compressor's CAPEX and TAC that make retrofitting BED to VRBED is uneconomical. This inspired us to propose different S-VRBEDs, which involve selective use of VRC in one or more steps of BED operation. Based on this, five S-VRBEDs are proposed and assessed; these are added to the optimal BED, selected by TOPSIS with entropy weights. As shown in Fig. 2c, maximum CR is in Step 2, and so VRC addition in this step is unlikely to be economical. Five S-VRBEDs are: S1-VRBED with VRC in only Step 1 of the batch operation; S2-VRBED with VRC in Steps 1, 3 and 4; S3-VRBED with VRC based on average CR of 2.97 (Fig. 2c) in all steps; S4-VRBED with VRC based on average CR of 4.03 (Fig. 2c) in product withdrawal Steps 2 to 4; and S5-VRBED with VRC based on average CR of 3.12 (Fig. 2c) in the last two Steps of 3 and 4. Thus, S3-, S4- and S5-VRBED are based on average CR of VRBED. When the required CR goes beyond the average, these schemes work like a BED.

Figure 2. Transient profiles of distillate composition (plot 2a for BED & VRBED), temperature difference (plot 2b for BED & VRBED), CR (plot 2c for VRBED), Q_{CV}, Q_R & Q_E of VRBED (plot 2d), Q_{CV}, Q_R & Q_E for S5-VRBED (plot 2e) and overhead vapor split to compressor for S5-VRBED (plot 2f).

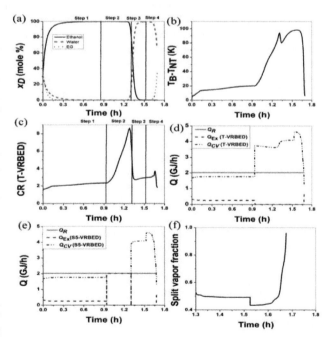

5. Selection of Retrofitting and Performance Assessment

Three criteria: reduction in CO_2 emissions, PBP and amount of product (ethanol) per dollar (PPD), are considered for selecting the best scheme out of the proposed ones. This is because TAP of ethanol, *EoEU* and TAER are same for the schemes. Reduction in CO_2 emissions, PBP and PPD of six retrofitted schemes (VRBED and five S-VRBEDs) are compared in Fig. 3, which clearly shows the trade-off among these criteria. Hence, one of these schemes is chosen using TOPSIS with entropy weights. The chosen scheme is S5-VRBED with VRC based on the average CR of 3.12 in Steps 3 and 4. For this scheme, Q_{CV} and Q_E profiles are in Fig. 2e. Like VRBED, first scenario

($Q_{CV} > Q_R$) occurs in Steps 3 and 4, and it requires splitting overhead vapor according to the profile in Fig. 2f.

Figure 3. Performance indicators of six retrofitted schemes.

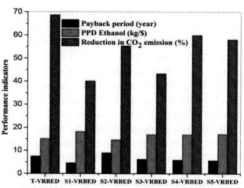

Results show that substantial CAPEX for compressor addition in VRBED (i.e., 116.2% of CAPEX for optimal BED) is the main obstacle to using traditional VRC. This is overcome in the proposed selective VRCs. For the chosen S5-VRBED, CAPEX is 20% lower than that of VRBED (although it is higher for both VRBED and S5-VRBED than that of BED). OPEX is reduced for both VRBED (by 68%) and S5-VRBED (by 56.4%) compared to optimal BED. Further, retrofitting optimal BED to VRBED or S5-VRBED lowers CO_2 emissions by 68.7% or 58.1%, respectively. VRC, however, incurs an additional investment as reflected in TAC increase and lower PPD of ethanol. Hence, PPD of ethanol for VRBED and S5-VRBED is reduced by 15.5 and 4.1%, respectively, over BED. The chosen S5-VRBED has PBP of 5.7 years for compressor's CAPEX, which seems high, but it reduces CO_2 emissions by 58.1%. Enterprises are actively addressing environmental concerns to improve their sustainability and not just economics. Hence, PBP of 5.7 years for S5-VRBED is acceptable.

6. Conclusions

This work proposes a novel way to retrofit BED by selective VRC in some steps of batch operation, to reduce CO_2 emissions without compromising economics. It is illustrated for the dehydration of ethanol using EG entrainer. For this, BED is optimized for six objectives. From the "true" Pareto-optimal front found, one optimal solution is selected using TOPSIS with entropy weights. Then, to improve sustainability, 5 different retrofits (S-VRBEDs) of optimal BED are proposed along with VRBED. The best retrofit is chosen by TOPSIS with entropy weights considering three criteria. All the retrofitted VRBEDs reduce both OPEX and CO_2 emissions. VRBED requires substantial CAPEX for the compressor, which is addressed by S-VRBEDs. The chosen retrofitting of BED to S5-VRBED requires 62.9% of CAPEX of VRBED for compressor. It reduces CO_2 emissions by 58.1% with a PBP of 5.7 years for compressor's CAPEX but increases TAC by 4.3%. Proposed S-VRBEDs can be applied to any existing or new BD systems.

References

A.A. Barreto, I.R. Donis, V. Gerbaud, X. Joulia, Multi-objective optimization of three-phase batch extractive distillation, Computer Aided Chem. Eng., 29, 562 (2011).

S.S. Parhi, A. Pramanik, G.P. Rangaiah, A.K. Jana, Evolutionary algorithm based multi-objective optimization of vapor recompressed batch extractive distillation: Assessing economic potential and environmental impact, Ind. Eng. Chem. Res., 59, 5032 (2020).

S.S. Parhi, G.P Rangaiah, A.K. Jana, Optimizing reboiler duty and reflux profiles of vapor recompressed batch distillation, Sep. Purif. Technol., 213, 553 (2019).

A. Singh, G.P. Rangaiah, Review of technological advances in bioethanol recovery and dehydration, Ind. Eng. Chem. Res., 56, 5147 (2017).

Flavio Manenti, Gintaras V. Reklaitis (Eds.), Proceedings of the 34th European Symposium on Computer Aided Process Engineering / 15th International Symposium on Process Systems Engineering (ESCAPE34/PSE24), June 2-6, 2024, Florence, Italy

Optimal design supply chain for agricultural waste-based biofuels

Dulce María Aguilar-Murguía [a], Sergio Iván Martínez-Guido [a], Claudia Gutiérrez-Antonio [a], Salvador Hernández [b*]

[a] *Universidad Autónoma de Querétaro, El Marqués, Querétaro, 76265, Mexico*

[b] *Universidad de Guanajuato, Guanajuato, Guanajuato, 36050, Mexico*

hernasa@ugto.mx

Abstract

Nowadays, biofuels are an attractive alternative to reducing environmental impact on transport and power production sectors. Nevertheless, in the production of biofuels, the main factor that contributes to the cost is the raw material. Due to this, agricultural wastes derived from harvesting and processing crops are considered an attractive raw material for biofuel production. A common strategy is choosing some agricultural waste to produce a specific biofuel. Nevertheless, these wastes have differences in their composition. In addition, the availability of each type of residue, the temporality, collection, distribution, and storage are other concerns that must be considered to obtain optimal management and revalorization of these residues. Hence, this work has proposed the conversion of the agricultural wastes generated by the production of the food crops from Querétaro, Mexico (858,504 t/y), into biofuels, such as green diesel, bio-jet fuel, bioethanol, and fuel pellets; in this case, the composition of each kind of residue is considered to define the final produced biofuel. Moreover, environmental impact, the linked cost, and social benefits can determine the entire supply chain configuration. Therefore, a mathematical optimization model was performed and codified in GAMS® to obtain the optimal revalorization waste supply chain, which included all the steps and activities associated with the primary process, residues availability, collection, distribution, storage, hubs and plants installation, transformation, and final use of each considered biofuel. The main results show that it is possible to transform 98.54% of the total agricultural wastes used only for pellet production. The other biofuel conversion pathways are not the best alternative considering all the criteria defined. Also, an economic income of US\$ 42,515,076/y is generated, and 2,264,720 t of CO_2 is not released into the atmosphere.

Keywords: waste management, circular economy, supply chain, optimization, mathematical model.

1. Introduction

In recent decades, population growth, escalating energy demand, and finites resource depletion have become critical global challenges (EEA, 2023). This has led to the exploration of sustainable solutions by researchers and scientists to meet the growth of global energy demand. According to Chen et al. (2009), biomass is the third-largest primary energy in the world and contributes 1,250 million tons of fuel (oil equivalent), 14% of the world's annual energy consumption. Mainly, agro-industrial waste valorization into biofuels represents the transition towards the circular economy. Biofuels promise energy security worldwide because of their renewability and capability to reduce and fix carbon emissions (Rame *et al.*, 2023). Therefore, agro-industrial waste has become an alternative raw material available worldwide for energy generation (Donato-Rocha *et al.*, 2023; Tomé *et al.*, 2023). On the other hand, biofuels, such as green diesel, bioethanol, bio-jet, and pellets, offer a renewable and cleaner alternative to conventional fossil fuels, reducing greenhouse gas emissions and mitigating climate change (Aguilar-Murguía et al., 2022; Escudero-Enríquez et al., 2023). Nevertheless, comparing conventional and bioenergy sources is necessary to assess the environmental benefits of energy from bioproducts. Therefore, process optimization is crucial in increasing the efficiency and effectiveness of agro-industrial waste treatment and organic production. Through research and technological advances, process optimization can minimize energy consumption, reduce waste generation, and optimize product performance (Bala et al., 2023; Murillo-Alvarado & Flores Russell, 2022). However, the composition versatility and the variety of these residues represent more significant challenges in the biofuel's final yields. These residues typically comprise various organic and inorganic compounds, including carbohydrates, proteins, lipids, lignin, cellulose, and hemicellulose. Consequently, this work aims to valorize agro-industrial residues for the generation of biofuels, taking into consideration the range of composition variation of residues, promoting a circular economy that allows us to contribute to the reduction of CO_2 emissions, and increase the economic and social benefits in the state of Querétaro in Mexico.

2. Problem Statement

One region grappling with the challenges of population growth, energy demand, and dwindling resources is Querétaro, a state in central Mexico. Querétaro has witnessed remarkable economic development and urban expansion in recent years, leading to increased agricultural and industrial activities. It boasts a thriving agro-industrial sector that contributes significantly to the local economy. With these activities, the generation of agro-industrial waste has become a significant concern because with this growth comes the age of substantial amounts of agro-industrial waste, which may have adverse environmental and economic impacts. Thus, the problem is obtaining the optimal supply chain design for different bioenergetics production using different agro-industrial waste generated in Querétaro State, Mexico. As a first instance, 57 kinds of waste were considered, produced in the 18 municipalities that conform to Querétaro. The waste flux is proposed to be collected weekly from each municipality ($i=1$-18) and sent to the installed hub. If wastes aren't used as raw material during biofuel production, then these are burned in the fields. In each hub, the residues are characterized according to three main biomolecules: carbohydrates, lipids, and lignin ($n=3$). Depending on the biomolecule proportion of each waste, these are sent to the biorefinery as raw material ($k=1$-18). In each biorefinery, are considered the installation of four different technologies to obtain one of the four biofuels (ethanol, bio-jet, green diesel, and pellets). The proposed model allows the installation of a single biorefinery per municipality. Therefore, if one biofuel is not produced, the energy demand will be satisfied by a conventional fuel obtained from an oil refinery ($s=2$). Finally, the flow of each bioenergetic generated is sent to each demand site.

3. Methodology

The research began studying the types and chemical composition of waste generated in Querétaro and the production technologies of the biofuels considered (ethanol, green diesel, bio-jet, and pellets). Later, a mathematical model was developed, which includes collecting, managing, processing, producing, and distributing biofuel.

Mathematical model. Equation one calculates the waste flux $\left(FRA_{i,j,t}\right)$ generated in each municipality (i) and from each crop (j), obtained from the crop area harvested $\left(FPC_{i,j,t}\right)$, a constrain which is multiplied by the respective percentage yield factor $\left(RG_j\right)$. Afterward, Equation 2 shows the balance for the generated residues in which the produced flux is equal to the residues sent to the biorefinery $\left(FRA_{i,j,t}^u\right)$, or to a landfill $\left(FRST_{i,j,t}\right)$. The residues sent to the biorefinery are received in a hub if this is installed as Equations 3 and 4 describes. In Equation 5 is described how the hubs can be installed with the use of a binary variable $\left(x_{c,m}^1\right)$; this is multiplied by the variable $\left(SCA_{c,j,m,t}\right)$ and fixed $\left(CF_{c,m}^{hub}\right)$ costs to obtain the total cost $\left(Cost_{c,m}^{hub}\right)$ by the installation of each hub.

$$FRA_{i,j,t} = FPC_{i,j,t} * RG_j, \ \forall \, i \in I, j \in J, t \in T \tag{1}$$

$$FRA_{i,j,t} = FRA_{i,j,t}^u + FRST_{i,j,t}, \ \forall \, i \in I, j \in J, t \in T \tag{2}$$

$$FRA_{i,j,t}^u = \sum_m FRA_{i,j,m,t}^{Rec}, \ \forall \, i \in I, j \in J, t \in T \tag{3}$$

$$FRA_{j,m,t}^a = \sum_i FRA_{i,j,m,t}^{Rec}, \ \forall \, j \in J, m \in M, t \in T \tag{4}$$

$$\begin{bmatrix} x_{c,m}^1 \\ x_{c,m}^1 ICA_{c,j,m,t} \leq FRA_{j,m,t}^a \leq x_{c,m}^1 SCA_{c,j,m,t} \\ Cost_{c,m}^{hub} = CF_{c,m}^{hub} + CV_{c,m}^{hub} * FRA_{j,m,t}^a \end{bmatrix} \forall \, c, m \tag{5}$$

Once with the residues in storage, they are characterized (see Equation 6), in terms of which is the percentage of each biomolecule $\left(YB_{j,b,t}^a\right)$ in all the residues $\left(FRA_{j,m,t}^a\right)$. Then the flux of carbohydrates, lipids, lignin $\left(FBM_{b,k,t}^b\right)$ is sent to the respective biorefinery (Equations 7 and 8) if this is installed, the biochemical composition is another constrain that limits the flux of biofuel produced. In Equation 9 is described how is calculated the installation of each biorefinery, with the use of a binary variable $\left(y_{c,k}^1\right)$; similarly, as was used for the hub installation.

$$FBM_{b,m,t}^a = \sum_j FRA_{j,m,t}^a * YB_{j,b,t}^a, \forall \, b \in B, j \in J, t \in T \tag{6}$$

$$FBM_{b,m,t}^a = \sum_k FBB_{b,m,k,t}^{sent}, \ \forall \, b \in B, m \in M, t \in T \tag{7}$$

$$FBM_{b,k,t}^b = \sum_m FBB_{b,m,k,t}^{sent}, \ \forall \, b \in B, k \in K, t \in T \tag{8}$$

$$\begin{bmatrix} y_{c,k}^1 \\ y_{c,k}^1 ICB_{c,b,k,t} \leq FBM_{b,k,t}^b \leq y_{c,k}^1 SCB_{c,b,k,t} \\ Cost_{c,b,k}^{Biore} = CF_{c,b,k}^{Biore} + CV_{c,b,k}^{Biore} * FBM_{b,k,t}^b \end{bmatrix} \forall \, c, b, k \tag{9}$$

After carbohydrates, lipids, lignin arrives to the biorefinery this is transformed into the respective biofuel bio-jet, green diesel, ethanol and pellets $\left(BioF_{f,k,t}^b\right)$, multiplying the received flux $\left(FBM_{b,k,t}^b\right)$ per the respective conversion factor $\left(FCB_{b,f}^{YB}\right)$, as Equation 10 indicates.

$$BioF_{f,k,t}^b = \sum_b FBM_{b,k,t}^b * FCB_{b,f}^{YB}, \forall \, f \in F, k \in K, t \in T \tag{10}$$

In Equation 11 is calculated the flux of conventional fuel $\left(FCF_{f,k,t}^{Conv}\right)$ used to produce the bio-blend $\left(FBLE_{f,k,t}^{Mix}\right)$, using the respective biofuel obtained in Equation 10. The balance shown by the Equation 12 represent the bio-blend calculation of each energetic fuel, obtained by conventional fuel flux $\left(FCF_{f,k,t}^{Conv}\right)$ plus the biofuel flux $\left(BioF_{f,k,t}^{b}\right)$. The demand of each energetic fuel in each municipality $\left(DFu_{f,k,t}^{tot}\right)$ is calculated with Equation 13, multiplying the amount of population $\left(PM_{k,t}^{mun}\right)$ per the respective factor of fuel required $\left(FFu_{f,k,t}^{tot}\right)$. The fuel demand calculated with Equation 13 must be equal or higher to the produced bio-blend of fuel, as Equation 14 shown. Then the current demand $\left(DFu_{f,k,t}^{tot}\right)$ must be satisfied by the conventional fuel $\left(CFD_{f,k,t}^{CF}\right)$ plus the produced bio-blend $\left(FBLE_{f,k,t}^{Mix}\right)$ of fuel (see Equation 15).

$$FCF_{f,k,t}^{Conv} = \sum_e BioF_{f,k,t}^{b} * \frac{\alpha_e}{\beta_f}, \forall\, f \in F, k \in K, t \in T \tag{11}$$

$$FBLE_{f,k,t}^{Mix} = FCF_{f,k,t}^{Conv} + BioF_{f,k,t}^{b}, \forall\, f \in F, k \in K, t \in T \tag{12}$$

$$DFu_{f,k,t}^{tot} = PM_{k,t}^{mun} * FFu_{f,k,t}^{tot}, \forall\, f \in F, k \in K, t \in T \tag{13}$$

$$DFu_{f,k,t}^{tot} \geq FBLE_{f,k,t}^{Mix}, \forall\, f \in F, k \in K, t \in T \tag{14}$$

$$DFu_{f,k,t}^{tot} = FBLE_{f,k,t}^{Mix} + CFD_{f,k,t}^{CF}, \forall\, f \in F, k \in K, t \in T \tag{15}$$

The total cost (TC) was calculated with the Equation 16, in which are included the installation of hubs $\left(Cost_{c,m}^{hub}\right)$, and biorefineries $\left(Cost_{c,b,k}^{Biore}\right)$, the biofuel production cost $\left(Cost_{f,k,t}^{Biofuel}\right)$, the waste transportation to hub $\left(Cost_{j,i,m}^{Tra-Hub}\right)$ and to the biorefinery $\left(Cost_{b,m,k}^{Tra-Bior}\right)$, and lastly the biofuel transportation cost $\left(CTBLE_{f,k,t}^{FBLE}\right)$. In Equation 17 profit $(Profit)$ is calculated using the balance between the total cost (TC) and the earnings (Gan). Lastly, the objective function is shown by Equation 18, in which the goal is to maximize the Profit.

$$TC = \sum_{c,m} Cost_{c,m}^{hub} + \sum_{c,b,k} Cost_{c,b,k}^{Biore} + \sum_{f,k,t} Cost_{f,k,t}^{Biofuel} +$$
$$\sum_{j,i,m} Cost_{j,i,m}^{Tra-Hub} \sum_{b,m,k} Cost_{b,m,k}^{Tra-Bior} + \sum_{f,k,t} CTBLE_{f,k,t}^{FBLE} \tag{16}$$

$$Profit = Gan - TC \tag{17}$$

$$OF = max\ Profit \tag{18}$$

4. Results

According to the results, the profits obtained are a total of US$ 42,515,076/y with a generation of CO_2 emissions of 105,938,000 t/y, which are the CO_2 emissions still produced by the main chain, which includes in this analysis only the use of conventional fuels to meet all the demand and emissions generated by waste not used during the chain. Within the proposed process, the number of emissions generated is 2,264,722 t/y, mainly due to the exchange of flows between municipalities and fuel generation. The total amount of waste considered is 858,504 t/y, of which this model uses 98.54%, while the remaining 1.46% is sent to the final disposal sites or burned in the same cultivation places. It should be mentioned that in all municipalities, a warehouse plant is installed, as well as a biorefinery of the maximum proposed capacity, which means that 1.46% of the land is untreated due to the limitation of the maximum permitted capacity. The municipality with the highest waste exchange is San Juan del Río since it has the most increased waste generation, with a value of 232,690 t/y.

The type of biofuel generated from the four proposed for this analysis was the pellet; this may be due to the production yields for the other three types of biofuels contemplated and the costs of the technologies used to produce this. The pellet flow obtained was 84,600 t/y. Since the pellet is not mixed explicitly with conventional fuel, the flow of the blended biofuel is the same. While profits from the sale of biofuel are reported, all municipalities present the same profits. In contrast, the San Juan del Río municipality is positioned first in waste management earnings, followed by the Pedro Escobedo, El Marqués, and Colón municipalities. Each municipality installed a biorefinery and a hub, as Table 1 indicates, with an annual capacity of 47,000 t. Table 2 shows only a flux interchange between the production sites and the hubs, but not from hubs to biorefinery.

Table 1. Sites selected for the hub and biorefinery installation.

Max Profit
Municipalities selected as hub (18)
Amealco de Bonfil, Arroyo Seco, Cadereyta de Montes, Colón, Corregidora, El Marqués, Ezequiel Montes, Huimilpan, Jalpan de Serra, Landa de Matamoros, Pedro Escobedo, Peñamiller, Pinal de Amoles, Querétaro, San Joaquín, San Juan del Río, Tequisquiapan, Tolimán. All of them have a capacity of 47,000 t/y.
Municipalities selected as sites for the biorefinery installation (18)
Amealco de Bonfil, Arroyo Seco, Cadereyta de Montes, Colón, Corregidora, El Marqués, Ezequiel Montes, Huimilpan, Jalpan de Serra, Landa de Matamoros, Pedro Escobedo, Peñamiller, Pinal de Amoles, Querétaro, San Joaquín, San Juan del Río, Tequisquiapan, Tolimán. All of them have a capacity of 47,000 t/y.

Table 2. The flux of biomass distribution.

From the production site to the hub		
Municipality that sent	Municipality that receives	Flux (t/y)
Colón	Tolimán	8,759
El Marqués	Querétaro	33,421
Ezequiel Montes	San Joaquín	8,617
Jalpan de Serra	Landa de Matamoros	34,862
Pedro Escobedo	Huimilpan	34,739
Querétaro	Corregidora	3,976
San Juan del Río	Amealco	21,094
San Juan del Río	Arroyo Seco	44,230
San Juan del Río	Cadereyta de Montes	43,280
San Juan del Río	Ezequiel Montes	47,000
San Juan del Río	Jalpan de Serra	47,000
San Juan del Río	Landa de Matamoros	44,632
San Juan del Río	Peñamiller	27,732
San Juan del Río	Pinal de Amoles	46,232
San Juan del Río	San Joaquín	37,984
San Juan del Río	Tequisquiapan	21,545
San Juan del Río	Tolimán	36,881

5. Conclusions

Challenges of population growth, energy demand, and dwindling resources have driven the exploration of alternative energy sources and the efficient use of waste materials. Querétaro, with its essential generation of agro-industrial waste, has the potential to establish sustainable waste management and generate bioenergy products, as is the case with this analysis. Pellets, which are among the four types of biofuels contemplated, are the ones that will allow the most waste to be treated and obtain significant profits that can help to increase the economy in Queretaro, in addition to helping meet a portion of the energy demand required in this state. In particular, the results obtained show that biofuels are an economic and environmental solution for the energy transition currently required in our society. However, investments are needed to remedy waste that today ends up in landfills or is incinerated. This strategy is doubly beneficial for the environment as it avoids generating emissions from untreated matter and creates products that integrate with sustainable energy production. By adopting a circular economy, comparing the environmental impacts of conventional and bio-based energy, and optimizing processes, Querétaro could take significant steps towards a more sustainable and environmentally friendly future. Thus, the optimal design solution obtained can be valuable information for developing public policies to implement a circular economy through biological alternatives.

6. Acknowledgements

The authors acknowledged the financial support the Faculty of Engineering, Universidad Autónoma de Querétaro, provided for the scholarship to D.M. Aguilar-Murguía for her postgraduate studies.

7. References

A. G. Tomé, E. A. M. Ribeiro, M. Lima, R. F. Brocemschi, L. N. M. Ribeiro, F. A. Amaral, 2023, Biorefinery of peanut shell agroindustrial lignocellulosic waste for the synthesis of a natural coagulant applied in the treatment of dairy wastewater, *Jourunal of Environmental Chemical Engineering*, 111535, https://doi.org/10.1016/j.jece.2023.111535

D. H. Donato-Rocha, F. R. Sousa-Freitas, I. Kimiko-Sakamoto, E. Luis-Silva, M. B. Amâncio-Varesche, 2023, Co-digestion of solid-liquid waste from citrus agroindustrial: Effect of hydraulic retention time and organic loading rate on H2 production in a long-term continuous operation leach bed reactor, *International Journal of Hydrogen Energy*, https://doi.org/10.1016/j.ijhydene.2023.10.289

D. M. Aguilar-Murguía, S. I. Martínez-Guido, J. F. García-Trejo, S. Hernández, C. Gutiérrez-Antonio, 2022, Optimal configuration of a biodiesel production network using oil from black soldier fly larvae, *Computer Aided Chemical Engineering*, 51, 901–906, https://doi.org/10.1016/B978-0-323-95879-0.50151-X

E. Escudero-Enríquez, O. D. Lara-Montaño, S. I. Martínez-Guido, Gutiérrez-Antonio, 2023, Bagazo de agave, la otra cara (valiosa) de la producción de tequila, available on: http://www.naturalezaytecnologia.com/index.php/nyt/article/view/488/Guti%C3%A9rrez-Antonio

EEA European Enviroment Agency, 2023, Sustainability challenges, available on: https://www.eea.europa.eu/en/topics/in-depth/sustainability-challenges

L. Chen, L. Xing, L. Han, 2009, Renewable energy from agro-residues in China: Solid biofuels and biomass briquetting technology, *Renewable and Sustainable Energy Reviews*, 13, 2689-2695, https://doi.org/10.1016/j.rser.2009.06.025

P. E. Murillo-Alvarado, E. Flores Russell, 2022, Optimization approach for bioethanol production from agro-industrial waste. *Frontiers in Energy Research*, 10, https://doi.org/10.3389/fenrg.2022.975133

R. Rame, P. Purwanto, S. Sudarno, 2023, Biotechnological approaches in utilizing agro-waste for biofuel production: An extensive review on techniques and challenges, *Bioresources Technolgy Reports*, 24, 101662, https://doi.org/10.1016/j.biteb.2023.101662

S. Bala, D. Garg, K. Sridhar, B. S. Inbaraj, R. Singh, S. Kamma, M. Tripathi, M. Sharma, 2023, Transformation of Agro-Waste into Value-Added Bioproducts and Bioactive Compounds: Micro/Nano Formulations and Application in the Agri-Food-Pharma Sector. *Bioengineering*, 10(2), 152, https://doi.org/10.3390/bioengineering10020152

Flavio Manenti, Gintaras V. Reklaitis (Eds.), Proceedings of the 34th European Symposium on Computer Aided Process Engineering / 15th International Symposium on Process Systems Engineering (ESCAPE34/PSE24), June 2-6, 2024, Florence, Italy

Performance Assessment of Waste and Biomass Two-stage Pyrolysis/Split Product Oxy-gasification (PSPOG) Using Aspen Simulation

Juma Haydary*

Slovak University of Technology in Bratislava, Radlinského 9, 812 37 Bratislava, Slovakia, juma.haydary@stuba.sk

Abstract

Air blowing gasifiers produce syngas with low heating value, which can limit its application. The use of pure oxygen increases the gas heating value, however, in a single-stage gasification process, total carbon conversion is reached at relatively high equivalence ratio (ER), which results in high oxygen requirement. A two-stage pyrolysis/split product oxy-gasification (PSPOG) combined with steam reforming can reduce the required ER for complete carbon conversion at high cold gas efficiency (CGE) and high gas heating value. A laboratory scale PSPOG unit was used to determine suitable gasification conditions. In the next step, Aspen Plus simulation was employed to simulate an industrial scale PSPOG process. As a reference, a single-stage gasifier model was simulated. Carbon conversion in the PSPOG process was completed at ER of 0.11 which is almost 2.5 times lower than the value required in a single-stage gasifier for the same raw material. Theoretical CGE at this ER was 0.93, while for a single-stage gasifier it was 0.52 and reached the maximum value of 0.89 at ER of 0.25. Gas lower heating value (LHV) at complete carbon conversion was 15 MJ/Nm^3 versus 12 MJ/Nm^3 for a single-stage gasifier. Recycling of 22% of the produced raw gas back to the char gasification reactor helped to maintain the required reactor temperature.

Keywords: gasification, two-stage, oxy-gasification, equivalence ratio, Aspen Plus.

1. Introduction

Most solid waste streams are in form of mixed waste, the mechanical recycling of which is inconvenient. Based on OECD 2022 report, only 9% of plastic waste were recycled during the period of 2000–2019 (Zheng and Watanabe, 2022). Currently, most of this waste is disposed of in landfills or incinerators. Thermochemical methods like gasification and pyrolysis are considered as better alternatives as they enable energy recovery and recovery of valuable chemicals at the cost of much lower environmental side effects. Gasification can convert mixed plastic waste into syngas containing mainly CO, H_2, CO_2, H_2O, and CH_4. In addition to these major components, syngas can also contain impurities like solid particles, tars, compounds of sulfur, chlorine, etc. (Antoiou et.al, 2014). Syngas composition, heating value, and conversion efficiency depend on raw material composition, used gasification technology, process conditions, and on the type of gasification agent used (Ahmad, et.al, 2016). Air, pure oxygen, oxygen enriched air, and steam are the most often used gasification agents.

Air blowing gasifiers produce syngas with low heating value, which can significantly limit its application. The use of pure oxygen or oxygen enriched air increases the gas heating value. However, process operational cost also increases; therefore, the amount of oxygen required is very important. Syngas composition and overall performance of a gasifier are mainly affected by the equivalence ratio (ER) defined as the ratio of actual amount of oxygen used to the stoichiometric mount of oxygen needed for combustion (Jangsawang, et.al, 2015). Overall performance of the gasification process (Kuo et.al. 2014) is given by carbon conversion (CConv) and cold gas efficiency (CGE), which represent the yield of raw material energy content transferred to syngas and carbon conversion efficiency (CCE), which is defined as the ratio of carbon transferred to syngas to total carbon present in raw material.

Gasification technologies with fixed bed, fluidized bed, and entrained flow reactors commercialized in coal gasification use a single-stage process for the gasification of solid raw materials. In a single-stage gasification process, total carbon conversion is reached usually at ER above 0.3-0.5. At lower ER, the conversion is not complete, gasification temperature is low, and the gas tar content is high. However, at higher ER, the gas is diluted by CO_2 and cold gas efficiency (CGE) is low as a large amount of combustible matter is used to ensure suitable conditions for the gasification process.

A two-stage gasification unit consisting of a pyrolysis stage and two gasification reactors for separate pyrolysis product gasification was developed and tested in a previous work (Šuhaj et.al, 2022). The unit is flexible for the use of different oxidizing agents and can work under any pyrolysis, gasification, or oxy-gasification conditions. By splitting the pyrolysis products and oxidizing agents, the system can work at significantly lower ER. In this work, gasification performance parameters (CConv, CGE, CCE), gas composition, and gas lower heating value (LHV) are investigated at different ER, oxygen split ratio (OSR), steam split ratio (SSR), and process gas recycling ratio (PGRR) in a two-stage pyrolysis/split product oxy-gasification (PSPOG) unit.

2. Materials and methods

A plastic mixture consisting of high-density polyethylene (HDPE, 7.95 wt. %), polypropylene (PP, 49.37 wt. %), and polyethylene terephthalate (PET, 42.68 wt. %) was considered in this work. Composition of the feed corresponded with average yields of individual plastic types in lithium-ion batteries (Dunn et.al, 2014). Each type of plastic material was characterized by thermogravimetric analysis (TG), elemental analysis (EA), and calorimetric analysis (CA). Using thermogravimetric data obtained by a STA 409 PC Luxx (NETZSCH, Germany) thermogravimeter, the content of moisture, volatile mater (VM), fixed carbon (FC), and ash was determined. The content of carbon, hydrogen, nitrogen, and sulfur was determined by a Vario Macro Cube® (Elementar, Germany) CHNS analyzer. Results of proximate and elemental analyses of all types of plastics present in the waste mixture, feed, and char from pyrolysis stage are shown in Table 1.

Table 1: Proximate and elemental analyses of individual plastics, waste mixture, and pyrolysis char

Waste	Moisture	VM	FC	Ash	C	H	O*	N	S
HDPE	0	96.5	0.76	2.74	85.3	13.8	0.72	0.12	0.06
PP	0	98.45	1.54	0.01	83.5	14	2.4	0.02	0.08
PET	0.75	88.21	11.79	0	62.9	4.27	32.79	0.04	0
Feed	0.32	93.92	5.85	0.22	74.85	9.83	15.24	0.04	0.04
Pyrolysis char	0	47.29	43.42	9.29	84.54	5.72	0	0.36	0.09

* Wt% O = 100-(Wt % C + Wt % H + Wt %N + Wt % Cl + Wt % S + Wt % ASH)

Lower heating value of plastics was measured using a bomb calorimeter (Fire Testing Technology Ltd, United Kingdom). For LHV /values of 40.2 MJ/kg, 44.1 MJ/kg, and 24.4 MJ/kg were measured for HDPE, PP, and PET, respectively.

A two-stage laboratory scale pyrolysis/split product gasification (PSPG) unit, described in (Šuhaj et.al. 2022), was used to determine suitable gasification conditions, i.e., pyrolysis stage temperature, secondary catalytic reactor temperature, char gasification reactor temperature, product yield, and gas tar content.

In the next step, Aspen Plus simulation was employed using experimental data to simulate the industrial scale two-stage pyrolysis/split product oxy-gasification process shown in Figure 1. As a reference, a single-stage gasifier model was simulated. The feed of 10 t/h of feedstock into an industrial scale PSPOG unit was considered. The feedstock is pyrolyzed at 740 °C in the first stage. The yields of gas, liquid, and solid products obtained from the laboratory experiments were 49.7 %, 39.64%, and 10.66 %, respectively.

The composition of pyrolysis gases at 740 °C was derived from the composition of the pyrolysis gas of HDPE, PP, and PET obtained from literature (Jung et al. 2010). The liquid pyrolysis product was modeled according to four representative components (naphthalene, ethylbenzene, toluene, and benzenediol).

The thermodynamic equilibrium model for gasification was employed to analyze the performance of the PSPOG system. The solid pyrolysis product is gasified in a char gasification reactor (CHGR); produced gas from CHGR is used together with additional oxygen and steam as gasifying agents in the secondary catalytic reactor (SCR). A portion of raw syngas is recycled to CHGR to maintain the reactor temperature. Raw gas is cooled and cleaned in a gas cleaning unit. A fraction of clean gas is used to heat the pyrolysis reactor. The equivalence ratio (ER), oxygen split ratio (OSR), steam split ratio (SSR), carbon conversion (CConv), cold gas efficiency (CGE), and carbon conversion efficiency (CCE) are calculated by Eqs. 1-6.

$$ER = \frac{(O_2)_1 + (O_2)_2}{O_{stechiometric}} \tag{1}$$

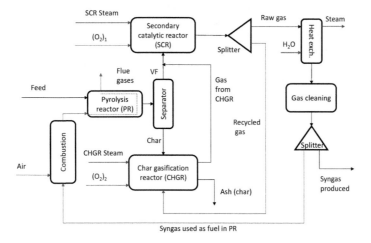

Figure 1. Process flow diagram of two-stage pyrolysis/split product oxy-gasification

$$OSR = \frac{(O_2)_1}{(O_2)_1 + (O_2)_2} \tag{2}$$

$$SSR = \frac{SCR_{steam}}{SCR_{steam} + CHGS_{steam}} \tag{3}$$

$$CConv = \frac{C_{in} - C_{out}}{C_{in}} \tag{4}$$

$$CGE = \frac{m_{syngas} HHV_{syngas}}{m_{feed} HHV_{feed}} \tag{5}$$

$$CCE = \frac{C_{syngas}}{C_{feed}} \tag{6}$$

Where $(O_2)_1$ and $(O_2)_2$ represent the oxygen flow to SCR and CHGR, respectively, C_{in} is flow of carbon entering the gasifier, C_{out} the flow of carbon in the remining solid residue, m_{syngas} is the mas flow of syngas, m_{feed} the mass flow of feed, HHV_{syngs} is higher heating value of syngas, and HHV_{feed} is higher heating value of feed.

3. Results and discussion

The effect of ER on gasification performance parameters and gas composition is shown in Figure 2. Carbon conversion was completed at ER of 0.11. At this point, a theoretical CGE of 0.93 and CCE of 0.87 were reached, gas LHV was 14.8 MJ/Nm³, and the equilibrium content of H_2, CO, and CH_4 reached 43, 44, and 11 mole %, respectively. Compared to one-stage gasification, ER for complete carbon conversion was almost 2.5 time lower. As it results from Figure 3a, carbon conversion was completed at ER of 0.25 in one stage gasification process. Theoretical CGE at this ER was 0.89 (Figure 3b), while at ER of 0.11 it was only 0.52. Gas LHV at complete carbon conversion was 11.8 MJ/Nm³ (Figure 3c) versus 14.8 MJ/Nm³ in the PSPOG process. However, in case of the PSPOG process, less gas is produced because lower amount of oxygen is used. The reason for high LHV of syngas at 100% carbon conversion in PSPOG is the much higher concentration of methane, 11 vol. %, compared to its practically zero content in case of one-stage gasification (Figure 3d). Carbon conversion efficiency in case of the one-stage gasification process is higher than in the PSPOG process. The reason is that in PSPOG, a portion of the gas is used to heat the pyrolysis reactor. Optimal value of gas fraction used to heat the pyrolysis reactor was found to be 0.11, at which the required temperatures of all three reactors are obtained.

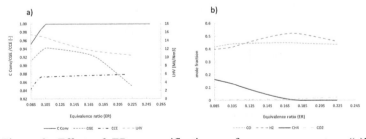

Figure 2: Effect of ER on gasification performance parameters "a)" and syngas equilibrium composition "b)"

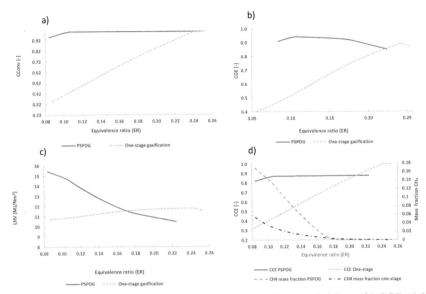

Figure 3: Comparison of PSPOG with one-stage gasification a) CConv, b) CGE, c) LHV d) CCE and methane concentration in syngas

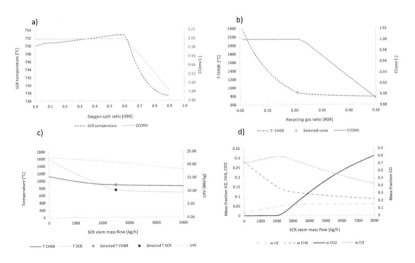

Figure 4: a) Effect of OSR, b) Effect of RGR, c) and d) Effect of SCR steam mass flow on reactor temperatures and gas composition at CHGR reactor mass flow of 500 kg/h

PSPOG enables slitting oxygen and steam to SCR and CHGR, which can affect both gasification reactor's temperature and gas composition and gasification performance parameters. It was found that maximum reactor temperature is reached at OSR of 0.6

(Figure 4a). At higher value of OSR, the SCR temperature decreases because of the decreasing CConv. Reactor temperature is maintained by the recycling gas ratio (RGR) (fraction of raw syngas returned to CHGR) and mass flow of steam used in SCR. The optimal RGR was found to be 0.22 (Figure 4b) and steam mass flow to SCR 2500 kg/h (Figure 4c) at the CHGR steam mass flow of 500 kg/h. At these conditions, carbon conversion was completed, CHGR was 890 °C, SCR temperature was 752 °C, and maximum CO/CO_2 ratio was reached.

4. Conclusion

Pyrolysis/Split Product Oxy-gasification (PSPOG) process is efficient in increasing the gas LHV, CGE, and CCE at much lower ER than conventional one-stage gasification. Combination of a pyrolysis reactor with two gasification reactors for separate pyrolysis product gasification and their mutual integration has been proven as a convenient way to improve waste and biomass gasification performance. For a mixture of HDPE, PP, and PET plastics at ER of 0.11 and steam to feed ratio of 0.3, a gas with LHV of 14.8 MJ/Nm^3 can be produced with the theoretical CGE of 93% and CCE of around 89%. This ER was almost 2.5 times lower than that for the one-stage gasification process. Combustion of around 11 % of produced gas covered the energy requirements of the pyrolysis stage. These results were achieved based on the thermodynamic equilibrium model and laboratory scale experiments, the effect of scale-up is not reflected.

Acknowledgement

This work was supported by Grant APVV-19-017 provided by the Slovak Research and Development Agency

References

A. A. Ahmad, N. A. Zawawi, F. H. Kasim, A. Inayat, A., A. Khasri, 2016, Assessing the gasification performance of biomass: A review on biomass gasification process conditions, optimization and economic evaluation, Renewable and Sustainable Energy Reviews, 53, 1333-1347.

N. Antoniou, G. Stavropoulos, A. Zabaniotou, 2014, Activation of end of life tyres pyrolytic char for enhancing viability of pyrolysis–Critical review, analysis and recommendations for a hybrid dual system, Renewable and sustainable energy reviews, 39, 1053-1073.

J. B. Dunn, L. Gaines, M. Barnes, J. L. Sullivan, M. Wang, 2014, Material and energy flows in the materials production, assembly, and end-of-life stages of the automotive lithium-ion battery life cycle (No. ANL/ESD/12-3 Rev.), Argonne National Lab.(ANL), Argonne, IL ,United States.

W. Jangsawang, K. Laohalidanond, S. Kerdsuwan, 2015, Optimum equivalence ratio of biomass gasification process based on thermodynamic equilibrium model, Energy Procedia, 79, 520-527

S. H. Jung, M. H. Cho, B. S. Kang, J. S. Kim, 2010, Pyrolysis of a fraction of waste polypropylene and polyethylene for the recovery of BTX aromatics using a fluidized bed reactor, Fuel processing technology, 91(3), 277-284.

P. C. Kuo, W. Wu, W.H. Chen, 2014, Gasification performances of raw and torrefied biomass in a downdraft fixed bed gasifier using thermodynamic analysis, Fuel, 117, 1231-1241.

J. Scheirs, W. Kaminsky, 2006, Feedstock recycling and pyrolysis of waste plastics, Chichester, UK; Hoboken, NJ: J. Wiley & Sons.

P. Šuhaj, J. Husár, J. Haydary, J. Annus, 2022, Experimental verification of a pilot pyrolysis/split product gasification (PSPG) unit, Energy, 244, 122584.

Q., Li, Z., Zheng, M. Watanabe, 2022, Production of solid fuels by hydrothermal treatment of wastes of biomass, plastic, and biomass/plastic mixtures: A review, Journal of Bioresources and Bioproducts, 7(4), 221-244.

Flavio Manenti, Gintaras V. Reklaitis (Eds.), Proceedings of the 34th European Symposium on Computer Aided Process Engineering / 15th International Symposium on Process Systems Engineering (ESCAPE34/PSE24), June 2-6, 2024, Florence, Italy

Green Hydrogen Production from Solar-powered Electrolysis: A Novel Optimization Methodology

Andrea Isella, Davide Manca*

PSE-Lab, Process Systems Engineering Laboratory, Dipartimento di Chimica, Materiali e Ingegneria Chimica "Giulio Natta", Politecnico di Milano, Piazza Leonardo da Vinci 32, 20133 Milano, Italy
davide.manca@polimi.it

Abstract

Today, hydrogen production still relies primarily on fossil fuels. Indeed, over 99% of the hydrogen produced in 2022 was synthesized via highly carbon-intensive processes such as steam methane reforming and coal gasification (IEA, 2023). This represents a primary problem in the chemical engineering scenario as hydrogen is the raw material of a plethora of commodities that are produced in tremendous amounts every year. Thus, hydrogen production is accountable for the vast majority of chemical industry carbon dioxide emissions along with the oil refining sector (Isella and Manca, 2022). In this perspective, being ever closer to entering a fully green economy, renewable-powered water electrolysis represents an increasingly valid alternative to produce hydrogen. However, properly sizing the renewable power plant (*e.g.*, a solar or wind farm) and the electrolyzer may be challenging since many features should be considered. Facilitating such a task is the main aim of this work, which proposes a novel methodology to optimally design green hydrogen production facilities. Specifically, starting from renewable energy availability time profiles in the location of interest, this criterion allows for the optimal evaluation of the installed capacities of both renewable power plant and electrolyzer which minimize the plant's total costs (both capital and operative expenditures).

Keywords: photovoltaics, electrolyzers, renewable energy, environmental sustainability, climate change mitigation.

1. Introduction

In 2022, about 95 Mt/y of hydrogen were produced globally. Like the previous year, low-emission hydrogen was less than 1% and almost entirely based on conventional fossil routes combined with carbon capture, storage, and utilization (CCUS) technologies. Water electrolysis, instead, simply accounts for 0.1% of current hydrogen production worldwide (IEA, 2023), but installed capacity and industrial facilities are rapidly increasing. That is the case of the REPowerEU Plan by the European Commission, which set the objective to deliver 65 GW of electrolysis capacity in Europe by 2030, plus 41 GW of wind and 62 GW of solar in additional capacity for the related renewable electricity supply (European Commission, 2022). Producing hydrogen through renewable-powered electrolyzers is indeed the only available-to-date synthetic pathway that allows total decoupling of hydrogen production from fossil feedstocks. This allows for eliminating at the same time both upstream Scope 3 (*i.e.* corporate value chain) emissions associated with fossil fuel extraction and all Scope 1 (*i.e.* direct) and 2 (*i.e.* indirect) emissions, given that renewable sources and electricity are used for meeting the energy demand of the whole process (MPP, 2022). The primary drawback of entirely renewable-based (*i.e.*

"green") processes, however, relies upon their complete dependence on renewable power generation (such as solar, wind, hydropower, etc.). Indeed, being these energy sources generally strongly subject to daily (even hourly) fluctuations and seasonal behavior, they tend to convey such discontinuous trends to the whole process they are connected to. Feeding green (*i.e.* intermittent) electric power to an electrolyzer results in fact in equally intermittent green hydrogen mass flows generated from such a unit. Moreover, the overall trends provided by renewable energy sources can also vary from year to year, causing even more difficulties in properly estimating essential sizes such as the power capacities for the renewable power plant and the electrolyzer. This work introduces a new criterion to design green hydrogen production facilities both optimally (*i.e.* providing the installed capacities that minimize the levelized cost of hydrogen, LCOH, or of the final product, LCOX, for a specific location and time horizon) and robustly (*i.e.* providing the installed capacities needed to satisfy the same requirements throughout several years of operation).

2. Methodology

Solar-powered green hydrogen production facilities (*i.e.* renewable power from solar energy only), which represent the control volume of our methodology, call for a solar power plant to produce the renewable energy needed for electrolysis; an electrolyzer to convert the renewable electric energy harvested by the solar farm into green hydrogen mass flows; and a hydrogen buffer storage to provide the produced hydrogen to downstream processes/utilizations.

Consequently, to optimally design green hydrogen production facilities, the following optimization procedure is proposed:

$$\text{Minimize}_{P_{PV}^{\text{inst}},\, P_{EL}^{\text{inst}}} \Phi_{\text{obj}} = \left(CapEx{+}OpEx\right)_{PV} + \left(CapEx{+}OpEx\right)_{EL} + \left(CapEx{+}OpEx\right)_{ST} \tag{1a}$$

$$s.t. \int_0^{t_{tot}} P_{EL}(t)\, dt = P_{EL}^{\text{target}}\, t_{tot} \tag{1b}$$

$$\int_0^{t_{tot}} \dot{m}_{H_2}^{ST,\text{out}}(t)\, dt = \dot{m}_{H_2}^{\text{target}} \cdot t_{tot} \tag{1c}$$

$$\text{with: } P_{EL}(t) = \min\left(P_{EL}^{\text{inst}}, P_{PV}(t)\right) \tag{1d}$$

Namely, P_{PV}^{inst} and P_{EL}^{inst} are the installed capacities of the solar plant and the electrolyzer, respectively; $P_{PV}(t)$ is the instantaneous renewable power generated by the solar plant while $P_{EL}(t)$ is the instantaneous power consumed by the electrolyzer, that corresponds to the electricity generated by the solar plant but is bounded above by the nominal capacity of the electrolyzer itself; $\dot{m}_{H_2}^{\text{target}}$ and P_{EL}^{target} are the target green hydrogen production rate and the electric power required by the electrolyzer to generate it, respectively; $\dot{m}_{H_2}^{ST,\text{out}}$ is the green hydrogen mass flow withdrawn from the storage for downstream utilization, and t_{tot} is the total timespan covered by the optimization procedure (*e.g.*, one year). Finally, $\left(CapEx{+}OpEx\right)_{PV}$, $\left(CapEx{+}OpEx\right)_{EL}$, and $\left(CapEx{+}OpEx\right)_{ST}$ are the capital and operative costs of the solar plant, the electrolyzer, and the hydrogen storage system, respectively, whose sum constitutes the objective function to minimize.

Few input data are needed: namely, the power generation solar profiles from the location of interest (and the installed capacity of such a reference dataset), and techno-economic data regarding the costs (*i.e.* CapEx and OpEx) and the operative requirements of solar plants, electrolyzers, and hydrogen storage systems to be installed. To solve the optimization problem, one may simply consider a grid search minimization within an arbitrarily defined investigation domain of solar plant installed capacities (*i.e.* ranging from the minimum to the maximum installed capacity values defined by the user) and according to the physical limit of non-negative installed capacities. Specifically, for each point of the grid (*i.e.* for each different configuration of solar plant installed capacity): (i) the corresponding power generation profile is estimated by scaling up/down the reference solar power profiles to the actual solar plant installed capacity; (ii) the corresponding electrolyzer size is estimated through Equation (1b) and, if no solution is found, it means that the solar plant installed capacity of such a configuration cannot produce the sufficient amount of electric energy required by the electrolyzer to meet the target specifications (*i.e.* it falls into the unfeasibility region and must be discarded); (iii) the power consumption profile of the electrolyzer is then estimated through Equation (1d); (iv) the green hydrogen profile originating from the electrolyzer is evaluated from the electrolyzer consumption profile and its operating specifications given as input data; (v) The green hydrogen storage size and its outlet mass flow profile are estimated according to Equation (1c); and (vi) the CapEx and OpEx of the corresponding solar plant, electrolyzer, and hydrogen storage are estimated. Precisely, for each process unit, such costs are evaluated by multiplying the intensive input costs data (*e.g.*, CapEx and OpEx per MW installed, or per t_{H2} stored) by the computed sizes. At the end of the whole procedure, once every single solar plant installed capacity scenario has been assessed, the optimal configuration is the one satisfying Equation (1a), *i.e.* resulting in the lowest total costs.

3. Case study

Our methodology is now validated by performing a feasibility study of a green hydrogen production plant in California, USA. As we want to estimate the lowest LCOH attainable with our criterion, we consider the system depicted in Figure 1, which refers to the green hydrogen generation section and neglects any further downstream utilization feature (that is why no hydrogen storage has been included neither in the system nor in the objective function, as its operation completely depends on the user's requirements).

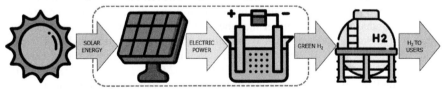

Figure 1: System and control volume of the case study.

Specifically, an average yearly target production rate equal to 1 t_{H2}/h is assumed, and Californian solar hourly profiles from 2022 (CAISO, 2023) are considered as input data. Furthermore, Table 1 reports the reference techno-economic data for the (photovoltaic, PV) solar plant and the (alkaline) electrolyzer.

Table 1: Techno-economic data for the case study. From DEA (2022) and Nel Hydrogen (2021).

	Life [y]	CapEx [€$_{2020}$/MWe]	OpEx [€$_{2020}$/MWe/y]	Power consumption [kWh/Nm^3$_{H2}$]
Solar plant	20	520,000	9,700	–
Electrolyzer	10	700,000	2% of [CapEx/y]	4.5

Thus, we apply the optimization procedure described by Equation (1) by implementing it on MATLAB™ R2022a and selecting an investigation region ranging from $P_{PV}^{\min} = 0$ MW to $P_{PV}^{\max} = 300$ MW. Moreover, to directly estimate the LCOH values corresponding to each solar installed capacity, the objective function (*i.e.* Equation (1a)) is divided by the target hydrogen production rate. Panels A and B of Figure 2 show the final results of the assessment.

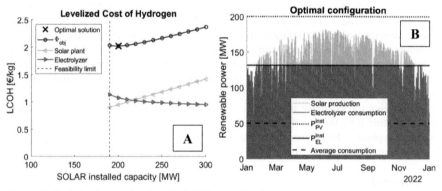

Figure 2: Optimization results. (Panel A) Objective function. (Panel B) Optimal configuration.

Focusing on Panel A, the objective function predictably interrupts way before $P_{PV}^{\min}$ (*i.e.* 0 MW), as too small installed capacities of the solar plant cannot produce the sufficient amount of electric energy required by the electrolyzer to meet the 1 t$_{H2}$/h yearly average production rate specification (see step (ii) in the previous section): precisely, 190 MW is the smallest feasible solar plant installed capacity. However, that is not the optimal point as smaller solar plants typically call for bigger electrolyzers: indeed, when less renewable energy is produced, the electrolyzer must be oversized to consume the highest possible fraction of it. Such a trade-off leads to an optimal configuration corresponding to a solar plant installed capacity of 200 MW, which calls for an electrolyzer installed capacity equal to 131.67 MW and ensures an LCOH of 2.02 €/kg, *i.e.* the cheapest one. By focusing on Panel B, instead, the effect of Equation (1b) within the optimization routine becomes evident. Indeed, the winning configuration shows an average electrolyzer consumption rate equal to 50.06 MW (*i.e.* P_{EL}^{target}), that is (considering the power consumption specification of the electrolyzer as reported in Table 1) the required electric power input for a production rate of 1 t$_{H2}$/h. Interestingly, such an optimal configuration calls for an electrolyzer sized to fully accommodate the solar production profiles in the off-season (*i.e.* winter) while curtailing the high-season (*i.e.* summer) production peaks.

4. Sensitivity analysis

To give more robustness to the results reported in the preceding section, the same case study was assessed by also considering Californian solar hourly profiles from the previous 4 years (*i.e.* since 2018). By doing so, the proposed optimization methodology gives the optimal values for each one of the investigated years, allowing the user to compare them and evaluate how the final installed capacities should change from year to year to minimize the overall production costs. Indeed, due to the high variability that characterizes renewable power generation, the design of renewable-based plants strongly reflects (and suffers from) such an undesirable behavior. As an example, the capacity factor of renewable power plants (CF, *i.e.* the dimensionless ratio of the actual electrical energy output over a certain time to the electrical energy output if theoretically operating at full capacity over the same period) might change considerably over the years. However, it is reasonable to expect that it should oscillate around a characteristic value according to the geographical location.

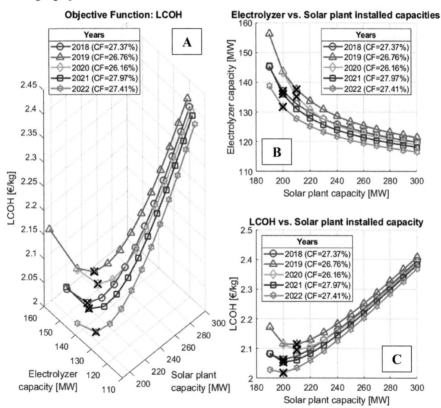

Figure 3: (Panel A) Objective function profiles resulting from the 2018-to-2022 assessment (the corresponding yearly solar capacity factors are reported within the legend); (Panel B) Investigated solar plant installed capacities and corresponding electrolyzer installed capacities; (Panel C) Objective function dependence on solar plant installed capacities. Black crosses refer to the minima points, *i.e.* the economically optimal configuration for each year.

Figure 3 shows the results of such a 5-year assessment: precisely, Panel A displays the topology of the multiple objective functions concerning both solar plant and electrolyzer installed capacities; Panel B focuses on the trade-off between the required solar plant and electrolyzer installed capacities; and Panel C highlights the objective function dependence on the solar plant installed capacity (analogously to Panel A of Figure 2). As expected, the variability of the input solar power profiles (as it can be partially verified from the different capacity factors associated with each investigated year, as they are an index of how much renewable power has been harvested over a certain time frame but do not give any information concerning the distribution of the power production throughout that period) reflects on the optimal results. Indeed, the optimal solar plant installed capacity is 200 MW for 2018, 2021, and 2022 but rises to 210 MW for 2019 and 2020. Analogously, different electrolyzer installed capacities have been obtained: 137.11 MW in 2018; 137.52 MW in 2019; 135.21 MW in 2020; 136.04 MW in 2021; and 131.67 MW in 2022. This implies that a lower-than-average solar power availability occurred in 2019 and 2020 (as it could also be inferred *a priori* from their respective capacity factors, which are the smallest ones provided), and therefore higher installed solar plant capacities are needed to meet the specified production requirements.

5. Conclusions

By entering the so-called "green economy", the manufacturing sector increasingly pushes for decarbonization. Green hydrogen might then represent the key raw material for many processes that currently depend heavily on fossil fuels in procuring hydrogen feedstocks. This work presented a novel methodology to design green hydrogen production facilities both optimally (*i.e.* providing the installed capacities that currently minimize the levelized cost of hydrogen or other downstream chemicals, if any) and robustly (*i.e.* also providing the optimal results referring to multiple years of operation). It requires just a few input data: namely, the input solar power profiles from the location of interest and the techno-economic data (such as the costs and the operative variables) of the main process units to be installed (*i.e.* the solar plant and the electrolyzer). In this regard, a case study was assessed, first considering a 1-year time frame and then a 5-year one. By doing so, more conservative estimations for the installed capacity requirements for both the solar plant and the electrolyzer were made possible, as the methodology was able to consider the different solar power availability of each year.

References

CAISO (2023). California Independent System Operator. Available at: http://www.caiso.com/Pages/default.aspx (accessed Nov 7th, 2023).

DEA (2022). Technology Data for Generation of Electricity and District Heating. Danish Energy Agency. Available at: https://ens.dk/en/our-services/projections-and-models/technology-data/technology-data-generation-electricity-and (accessed Oct 30th, 2023).

European Commission (2022). REPowerEU: Affordable, secure and sustainable energy for Europe. European Commission. Available at: https://commission.europa.eu/strategy-and-policy/priorities-2019-2024/european-green-deal/repowereu-affordable-secure-and-sustainable-energy-europe_en (accessed Dec 13th, 2023).

IEA (2023). Global Hydrogen Review 2023. International Energy Agency. Available at: https://www.iea.org/reports/global-hydrogen-review-2023 (accessed Oct 19th, 2023).

Isella, A., & Manca, D. (2022). GHG Emissions by (Petro)Chemical Processes and Decarbonization Priorities—A Review. Energies, 15(20), 7560.

MPP (2022). Making Net-Zero 1.5°C-Aligned Ammonia Possible. Mission Possible Partnership. Available at: https://www.energy-transitions.org/publications/making-net-zero-ammonia-possible/ (accessed Oct 20th, 2023).

Nel Hydrogen (2021). Nel Hydrogen Electrolyzers The World's Most Efficient and Reliable Electrolysers. Available at: https://nelhydrogen.com/wp-content/uploads/2020/03/Electrolysers-Brochure-Rev-D.pdf (accessed Oct 30th, 2023).

Flavio Manenti, Gintaras V. Reklaitis (Eds.), Proceedings of the 34th European Symposium on Computer Aided Process Engineering / 15th International Symposium on Process Systems Engineering (ESCAPE34/PSE24), June 2-6, 2024, Florence, Italy

Estimating the potential of sustainable aviation fuel enabled aviation decarbonization in China: An integrated resource-technology-economy-environment analysis framework

Wubin Yan[a,b], Fangwei Cheng[c], Xiaonan Wang[d], Chuan Zhang[a,e*]

[a]*Institute of Energy, Peking University, Beijing 100871, China*
[b]*College of engineering, Peking University, Beijing 100871, China*
[c]*Andlinger Center for Energy and the Environment, Princeton University, Princeton, NJ 08544, USA*
[d]*Department of Chemical Engineering, Tsinghua University, Beijing 100084, China*
[e]*Institute of Carbon Neutrality, Peking University, Beijing 100871, China*
czhang@pku.edu.cn

Abstract

The decarbonization of aviation sector has aroused extensive attention in China. Sustainable aviation fuel is widely considered as a promising strategy for aviation decarbonization. However, a realistic estimation of China's sustainable aviation fuel enabled decarbonization potential has not been achieved so far. In order to fill this gap, system analysis including resource potential evaluation, conversion process simulation, techno-economic analysis, and environmental impact assessment are conducted to evaluate the decarbonization potential of sustainable aviation fuel in China's aviation sector. In this study, sustainable aviation fuel is produced from six conventional crop straws in China via Gasification-Fischer-Tropsch conversion pathway. Among these straws, cotton straw and corn straw are promising feedstocks for sustainable aviation fuel production from the perspective of decarbonization cost. Considering their reserves in China, cotton straw is suitable for early industrial production of sustainable aviation fuel, while corn straw can support future large scale sustainable aviation fuel application. When the blending ratio of sustainable aviation fuel reaches 50 %, about 60 Mt CO_2e emission can be reduced, which accounts for 43 % of the emission for China's aviation sector in 2023, showing the huge decarbonization potential of sustainable aviation fuel.

Keywords: sustainable aviation fuel, agricultural biomass, Fischer-Tropsch synthesis, techno-economic analysis, decarbonization potential.

1. Introduction

Aviation is one of the most difficult-to-decarbonize sectors among the net-zero energy transitions. China's 2060 carbon neutrality commitment, plus the likely increasing aviation demand in the long run, further emphasizes the importance of aviation decarbonization. Replacing petroleum jet fuel (PJF) with sustainable aviation fuel (SAF) is widely considered as a promising aviation decarbonization pathway(Cavalett and Cherubini, 2018), while other strategies, such as electric and hydrogen fuel cell commuter aircrafts, are limited in their short range and technical challenges(Vardon et al., 2022).

Currently, several SAF production pathways have been certified by ASTM standards, e.g., gasification and Fischer-Tropsch (G-FT), hydroprocessed esters and fatty acids (HEFA), alcohol to jet (ATJ), and sugar to jet (STJ)(Okolie et al., 2023). Among these strategies, researchers paid constant attention to G-FT synthesis method due to its universal adaptability to feedstocks and larger life cycle CO_2 mitigation effect(Vardon et al., 2022). Besides the investigation of SAF production pathways, the assessments of SAF from environmental and economical perspectives are also meaningful, since they can help researchers understand the prospects and challenges of SAF manufacture in the future. However, previous studies mostly focused on single biomass feedstock (Alherbawi et al., 2021; Lee et al., 2023; Li et al., 2019), and there is a limited work on the comparative evaluation of SAF production from different feedstocks.

In this study, we conduct an integrated resource-technology-economy-environment analysis (RTEEA) framework to evaluate the decarbonization of SAF in China's aviation sector, as shown in Figure 1. Six conventional crop straws, e.g., rice straw, wheat straw, corn straw, peanut straw, cotton straw, and beans straw, are selected as the feedstocks to produce SAF via G-FT synthesis pathway. By combining the results of crop straws investigation, chemical process simulation, technology-economy analysis, and life cycle emission analysis, crop straws suitable for SAF production are recommended. Finally, the decarbonization potential of SAF can be evaluated under such optimal straw feedstocks.

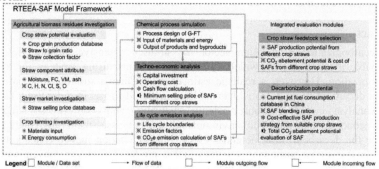

Figure 1. Framework of the integrated resource-technology-economy-environment analysis (RTEEA) for evaluating the decarbonization potential of sustainable aviation fuel (SAF).

2. Methods

2.1 Resource investigation

Resource investigation is the first step in the RTEEA framework, since it can provide necessary databases to support the following chemical process simulation, technology-economy analysis, and life cycle emission analysis, as shown in Figure 1. In this section, we focus on the investigation of major agricultural biomass residues in China, e.g., rice straw, wheat straw, corn straw, peanut straw, cotton straw, and beans straw. The crop straw collection potential can be calculated using Eq. (1):

$$Straw\ collection\ potential = \sum GY_i * STG * CF \qquad (1)$$

Where i is the province in China, GY is the corresponding grain yield (taken from China Statistical Yearbook 2022), STG is the straw to grain ratio(Gao et al., 2016), and CF is the collection factor of crop straw(Gao et al., 2016).

The component attributes of investigated crop straws are summarized from published literatures, and they are important parameters for the proximate and ultimate analysis in process simulation. The straw selling price database is built according to the current straw market condition in China. The crop farming investigation mainly focuses

Estimating the potential of sustainable aviation fuel enabled aviation decarbonization in China: An integrated resource-technology-economy-environment analysis framework

2373

on the materials input and energy consumption during the farming process(Chen et al., 2021).

2.2 Process simulation

The production process of SAF from crop straws via G-FT synthesis is simulated on Aspen Plus software. Straws are defined as non-conventional components, and their proximate and ultimate attributes are listed in Table 1. The whole simulation process is mainly divided into 4 parts, including straw drying step, straw gasification to syngas, syngas cleaning up, and SAF production from regulated and cleaned syngas via Fischer-Tropsch reaction.

In the drying step, the moisture content of straws is regulated to 5 wt.%. Steam gasification, which has a higher exergy efficiency and can provide an optimum H_2/CO ratio for FT synthesis(Alherbawi et al., 2021), is selected to conduct the gasification of dry straws in this study. Besides CO and H_2, raw syngas usually contains H_2O (g), HCl, H_2S, NH_3, and CO_2, which may be not conducive to the following FT reaction. In the cleaning up step, HCl and H_2S are absorbed by Na_2CO_3 and ZnO respectively, NH_3 is decomposed into N_2 and H_2 catalyzed by dolomite, CO_2 is captured via organic amine solvents, and H_2O (g) is removed via condensation. Finally, the cleaned syngas $(n(H_2)/n(CO) \approx 2)$ is converted into hydrocarbons via FT reaction catalyzed by Co/γ-Al_2O_3. The distribution of hydrocarbons is simulated based on the Anderson-Schulz-Flory (ASF) model(Alherbawi et al., 2021).

Table 1. Proximate and ultimate analysis of different crop straws in China

Content (wt.%)	Rice straw	Wheat straw	Corn straw	Peanut straw	Cotton straw	Beans straw
Moisture	8.11	8.63	9.31	8.56	7.66	9.34
Fixed carbon	16.91	16.37	16.35	17.12	20.11	17.23
Volatile matter	66.49	70.00	69.18	72.90	72.95	76.06
Ash	16.60	13.63	14.47	9.97	6.94	6.71
C	37.81	40.37	39.35	39.28	43.91	41.93
H	6.02	6.26	5.68	7.00	6.52	6.70
N	0.68	0.56	0.91	2.01	1.04	0.92
Cl	0.05	0.05	0.05	0.05	0.05	0.05
S	0.28	0.31	0.19	0.27	0.25	0.19
O	38.56	38.83	39.35	41.42	41.29	43.49

2.3 Techno-economic analysis

In the techno-economic analysis (TEA) of SAF, we build a virtual biomass refinery factory with a typical 0.25 Mt/y of feedstock processing capacity. The net present value (NPV) method is applied to calculate the minimum selling price (MSP) of SAF product. NPV calculation relies on the investigation of cash flow (Wang et al., 2022).

2.4 Life-cycle assessment

The life-cycle assessment (LCA) of SAF is conducted on GREET software and some emission factors are adjusted to the context of China according to China Products Carbon Footprint Factors Database (CPCD). A typic well-to-wheel (WTW) LCA boundary contains well-to-pump (WTP) stage and pump-to-wheel (PTW) stage. As shown in Figure 2, the whole LCA boundary of SAF can be divided into 6 processes: crop farming and harvesting process, straw collection and transportation process, straw pretreatment process, straw conversion to SAF via G-FT synthesis, transportation of SAF to refueling station, and SAF combustion in aero-engine (PTW). In the transportation of straws, we assume that the straws are transported to the biorefinery 60 km away by means of the heavy-duty truck with a loading capacity of 25 t. It should be noted that CO_2 emission from combustion of biomass-derived fuels is offset by CO_2 uptake from the atmosphere by plants, so CO_2 emission in PTW stage can be ignored in the LCA of SAF.

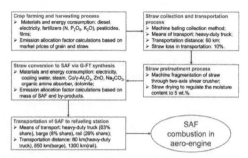

Figure 2. Life-cycle analysis boundary of sustainable aviation fuel from crop straws via G-FT synthesis.

3. Results and Discussion

The province-level distribution of major crop straws collection potential in China is shown in Figure 3a. Heilongjiang, Henan, and Shandong are the three provinces with the highest collection potential of straw biomass, since they are major agricultural provinces in China. Besides, straw collection potential in Jinlin, Xinjiang, Anhui, Hebei, Inner Mongolia, and Jiangsu province, is also considerable (over 30 Mt/y). Overall, the northern provinces produce more corn straw and wheat straw, while rice straw is the major crop straw in southern provinces. From the national perspective, corn straw accounts for the largest proportion, followed by rice straw and wheat straw, while the other crop straws occupy much smaller proportion, as shown in Figure 3b.

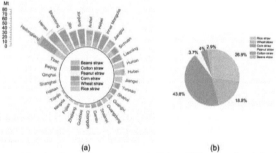

(a)   (b)

Figure 3. Resource potential estimation of six crop straws in China. (a) Province-level distribution of crop straw resource potential in China (lacking the data of Taiwan, Hong Kong, and Macao); (b) The amount proportion of different crop straws in China.

Furtherly, Figure 4a shows that SAF from different crop straws also have different TEA and LCA performance. SAF produced from cotton straw has the lowest MSP, while the MSP of SAF from peanut straw is the highest. The MSP order is similar to the rank of straw price, indicating that the feedstock price may be a major factor affecting the cost-effectiveness of SAF. The life cycle GHG emission of SAF from these crop straws is ranked as: wheat straw > rice straw > peanut straw > cotton straw > corn straw > beans straw. Overall, the MSPs of SAF from these crop straws are all higher than that of conventional petroleum jet fuel (PJF) ($ 393/t), while the LCA GHG emission of SAF is much lower than that of PJF (3.8 t CO_2e/t PJF). A single-point sensitivity analysis of critical parameters in TEA and LCA models is conducted, and Figure 4b-c show the results with corn straw as the feedstock. Improving the SAF production yield can

Estimating the potential of sustainable aviation fuel enabled aviation
decarbonization in China: An integrated resource-technology-economy-
environment analysis framework
2375

significantly reduce the MSP and enhance the decarbonization capacity of SAF simultaneously. Besides, the feedstock price and steam cost also have great impacts on the MSP calculation of SAF, and the consumption of fertilizer and electricity in the farming process plays an influential role in the LCA model. The sensitivity analysis of SAF from other crop straws also shows similar trends. In order to increase the comparability of TEA and LCA performance, a comprehensive analysis is proposed to calculate the decarbonization cost of SAF from different crop straws, as shown in Eq. (2):

$$Decaronization\ cost = \frac{MSP_{SAF} - MSP_{PJF}}{LCA_{PJF} - LCA_{SAF}} \tag{2}$$

As shown in Figure 4d, the decarbonization cost of SAF from straws is ranked as: peanut straw > rice straw > beans straw > wheat straw > corn straw > cotton straw. Combining the SAF production potential of these straws, cotton straw can be applied as a promising feedstock for the early industry application of SAF when the demand of SAF is not high.

With the support of the above analysis results, the decarbonization potential of SAF in China's aviation sector can be estimated. Figure 4e shows annual PJF consumption and GHG emission in China's aviation sector from 2005 to 2022. The consumption of PJF increased dramatically until 2019, but plummeted subsequently due to the strike of the COVID-19. Fortunately, now China's aviation industry is gradually recovering from the impact of the epidemic and is expected to return to or even exceed the pre-epidemic level in the next few years. Therefore, we assume the jet fuel consumption in 2023 is comparable to that of 2019 to calculate the decarbonization potential in China under different SAF blending ratios. According to the ASTM D7566 standards, the blending ratio of SAF produced via G-FT method is no more than 50 %, so 50 % is set as the highest blending ratio scenario. As shown in Figure 4f, at low blending ratio (<10 %), SAF is mainly produced from cotton straw due to the lowest decarbonization cost. With the further increase of blending ratio, corn straw has become the major feedstock for SAF production owing to the abundant reserves and moderate decarbonization cost. If the SAF blending ratio reaches 50 %, about 60 Mt CO_2e emission can be reduced, accounting for 43 % of the emission for China's aviation sector in 2023.

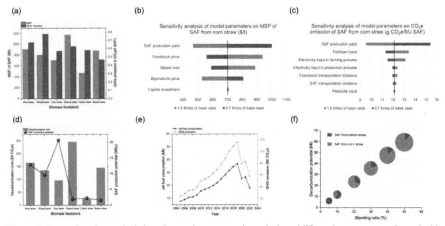

Figure 4. Comprehensive analysis based on techno-economic analysis and life cycle assessment of sustainable aviation fuel (SAF) from different crop straws. (a) Minimum selling price (MSP) and greenhouse gas (GHG)

emission of SAF from different crop straw feedstocks; (b) Sensitivity analysis of model parameters on MSP of SAF from corn straw; (c) Sensitivity analysis of model parameters on GHG emission of SAF from corn straw; (d) Decarbonization cost and SAF production potential from different crop straw feedstocks; (e) Annual petroleum jet fuel consumption and GHG emission in China's aviation sector from 2005 to 2022; (f) Cost-effective straw-to-SAF production strategies and decarbonization potential under different SAF blending ratios, the area of the pie represents the demand of SAF under corresponding SAF blending ratio, blue and orange parts represent the proportion of SAF produced from cotton straw and corn straw respectively.

4. Conclusions

An integrated resource-technology-economy-environment analysis (RTEEA) framework is conducted to evaluate the decarbonization of sustainable aviation fuel (SAF) in China's aviation sector. The minimum selling price (MSP) and greenhouse gas (GHG) emission of SAF from six crop straws in China have been calculated via techno-economic analysis (TEA) and life cycle assessment (LCA) respectively. Compared with conventional petroleum jet fuel (PJF), SAFs from crop straws via G-FT synthesis have higher MSP and much lower GHG emission. Comprehensive analysis shows that cotton straw is an ideal feedstock for the early industrial production of SAF due to the lowest decarbonization cost, but its low reserves may be difficult to support large scale SAF production. In the long run, corn straw, which has abundant reserves and moderate decarbonization cost, is a promising biomass feedstock to produce SAF. When the SAF blending ratio reaches 50 %, about 60 Mt CO_2e emission can be reduced, which accounts for 43 % of the emission for China's aviation sector in 2023, showing the huge decarbonization potential of SAF from straws via G-FT synthesis.

References

Alherbawi et al., 2021, A novel integrated pathway for Jet Biofuel production from whole energy crops: A Jatropha curcas case study, Energy Conversion and Management 229: 113662.

Cavalett et al., 2018, Contribution of jet fuel from forest residues to multiple Sustainable Development Goals. Nature Sustainability 1: 799-807.

Chen et al., 2021, Identifying the main crops and key factors determining the carbon footprint of crop production in China, 2001–2018. Resources, Conservation and Recycling 172: 105661.

Gao et al., 2016. An integrated assessment of the potential of agricultural and forestry residues for energy production in China. GCB Bioenergy 8: 880-893.

Lee et al., 2023, Life cycle analysis of gasification and Fischer-Tropsch conversion of municipal solid waste for transportation fuel production. Journal of Cleaner Production 382: 135114.

Li et al., 2019, Comprehensive Life Cycle Evaluation of Jet Fuel from Biomass Gasification and Fischer–Tropsch Synthesis Based on Environmental and Economic Performances. Industrial & Engineering Chemistry Research 58: 19179-19188.

Okolie et al., 2023, Multi-criteria decision analysis for the evaluation and screening of sustainable aviation fuel production pathways. iScience 26: 106944.

Vardon et al., 2022, Realizing "net-zero-carbon" sustainable aviation fuel. Joule 6: 16-21.

Wang et al., 2022, Techno-economic analysis of renewable jet fuel production: The comparison between Fischer-Tropsch synthesis and pyrolysis. Energy 239: 121970.

Flavio Manenti, Gintaras V. Reklaitis (Eds.), Proceedings of the 34th European Symposium on Computer Aided Process Engineering / 15th International Symposium on Process Systems Engineering (ESCAPE34/PSE24), June 2-6, 2024, Florence, Italy

Dynamic simulation and optimisation of water and energy consumption in a ceramic plant: Application of the customised ThermWatt computational tool

Miguel Castro Oliveira [a,b], Rita Castro Oliveira [c], Henrique A. Matos [b]

[a] *Low Carbon & Resource Efficiency, R&Di, Instituto de Soldadura e Qualidade, 2740-120 Porto Salvo, Portugal*

[b] *Department of Chemical Engineering, Instituto Superior Técnico, Universidade de Lisboa, Avenida Rovisco Pais 1, 1049-001 Lisboa, Portugal*

[c] *Department of Computer Science and Engineering, Instituto Superior Técnico, Universidade de Lisboa, Avenida Rovisco Pais 1, 1049-001 Lisboa, Portugal*

Abstract

In this work, complex models developed for the project of Water and Energy Integration Systems (WEIS) in a ceramic industry plant are presented. The WEIS is an innovative concept of systems that consider the recirculation of water and energy streams in a plant to produce overall water and energy efficiency improvement-related benefits. These models have been created in the scope of the development of a computational tool and derivate Engineering service designated as ThermWatt (using both the Modelica and Python languages). A post-processing assessment to the results of the final simulation model allowed the estimation of 2 years and 10 months payback time and a reduction of 1.76 kton $CO_{2,eq}$/ year, which are highly favourable results compared to the benchmarks defined for the European.

Keywords: Water and energy integration systems, water-energy nexus, thermal energy storage, Python NLP-model, Modelica DP-model.

1. Introduction

The whole production process in manufacturing plants requires the use of significant quantities of natural resources, with water and energy being two of the most relevant categories of these resources (Walsh et al., 2015). The recirculation of resources, for instance, through waste heat recovery and water recirculation, constitutes a set of measures that may solve the issues related to the overuse of resources. One of the challenges related to such measures' implementation is the existence of intermittent operations.

Most recently, researchers have proposed the implementation of new conceptual systems designated as Water and Energy Integration Systems (WEIS), which contemplate water and waste heat stream recirculation (Castro Oliveira et al., 2022). These studies have been supported by the use of simulation and optimisation models, namely with a customised tool named ThermWatt (Castro Oliveira et al., 2022a, 2023). Although these systems have been proved to be successful in the fulfilment of the aims related to water and energy use reduction and all the economic and environmental benefits thereof, the WEIS have only been conceptualized and analysed in a steady-state based perspective, not considering a transient-based perspective, such as with the presence of intermittent combustion-based processes and the installation of thermal energy storage (TES) units.

In this work, a set of computational models using the overall capabilities of the ThermWatt tool are developed for a WEIS set to be installed in a ceramic plant, in which

TES are conceptually set to be installed to reduce the energy use in intermittent combustion-based processes. The goal of this work is to obtain a final dynamic simulation model, to achieve water and energy use reduction-related economic and environmental benefits.

2. Characterization of the Case-study

The case-study is set in a sanitaryware plant installed in Portugal, containing three water-using lines (three water-using processes, three heaters and three coolers), two tunnel kilns (continuous combustion-based processes) and two intermittent kilns (intermittent combustion-based processes). All the combustion-based processes use natural gas as fuel. The water-using processes make use of a water stream to remove determinate quantities of three non-identified salts (designated by the indexes 1, 2 and 3). Each outlet wastewater (saline water) stream is associated to determinate minimum and maximum concentrations for each salt. The baseline scenario of the plant encompassing the identified processes is characterized in the sequence of Figures 1 and 2.

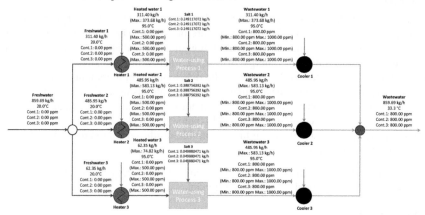

Figure 1. Flowsheets of the water-using lines

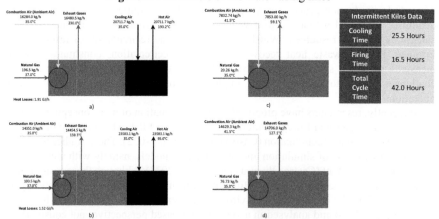

Figure 2. Flowsheets of combustion-based processes: Kilns a) 1, b) 2, c) 3, d) 4

The conceptualized WEIS for the approached case-study may be characterized by the following sequence of steps:

- The superstructure configuration considers the processes presented in Figures 1 and 2 as baseline, in addition to several recirculation points and technologies, as described in the points below;
- Each one of the two tunnel is characterized by having two waste heat streams: exhaust gas streams and hot air streams;
- An Organic Rankine cycle (ORC) is considered for electricity generation from enthalpy withdrawal from a mixed gas (hot air and exhaust gas mixture) stream;
- A MED unit is considered as the wastewater treatment unit (treatment of the saline water stream at the outlet of the water-using processes);
- An Electrolysis unit is considered for the generation of green hydrogen from the discharge water stream from the water system;
- The hydrogen produced in the Electrolysis unit is distributed to the fuel inlet of each one of the tunnel kilns so to produce hydrogen-enriched natural gas (HENG);
- A PCM-based heat exchanger is used for enthalpy withdrawal from a mixture of part of the hot air from both tunnel kilns (during the cooling phase of the intermittent kilns, which is enthalpy charge phase to the TES unit) and to supply additional enthalpy to the ambient air streams at the inlet of each one of the combustion-based processes kilns (during the firing phase of the intermittent kilns, which is enthalpy discharge phase to the TES unit);
- During the cooling cycle of the kilns, the respective part of the mixture hot air streams from each one of the tunnel kilns is recirculated to the ORC
- The hot air streams from each one of the two tunnel kilns are recirculated to the respective tunnel kiln and to the HRSG unit of the ORC;
- The remaining quantities of the hot air streams from each one of the two tunnel kilns are mixed and recirculated to three water-gas heat exchangers (economisers) installed to heat up the inlet water stream at each one of the water system's heaters and the first effect of the MED unit;
- The hot air streams at the outlet of the water-gas heat exchangers and the MED unit are then conjoined and furtherly recirculated to be mixed with the conjoined exhaust gas streams, so then the mixed gas stream to be recirculated to the ORC.

3. Simulation and Optimisation Models

A complex modelling framework has been developed in the scope of this work. A total of three models have been created: a non-linear programming (NLP) model for the water system developed in Python, a dynamic programming (DP) model developed for the thermal process system in Modelica and a final dynamic simulation model (which integrates the results of the two optimisation models) also developed in Modelica. Since the final simulation model is the ultimate end of the work in terms of modelling, the numerical results obtained by the two counterpart optimisation models had to be allocated to the final model. For the water system NLP model, the results may be allocated from the Python-NLP model to the Modelica model using the OpenModelica Python API. However, a similar API does not exist for the allocation of results between the two Modelica models, and it is impossible to run the two models within the same script due to need of different solvers for each one (*optimization* solver for the DP model and DASSL for the final model). Although that is not considered an issue in respect to the objectives of the work, which are based on the obtention of water and energy use-related benefits, such may be a challenge to be attended in further developments of the ThermWatt tool. In the sequence of these, Tables 1 and 2 shows the model characterization with only the equality constraints of interest, with thew whole set of equations characterizing a WEIS (including trivial ones) have already delineated for a similar case-study in a previous work (Castro Oliveira et al., 2023). The considered inequality constraints are only defined as the lower and upper limit values for variables, as defined in Figures 1 and 2. In Figure 3, the final simulation model is presented, in the form of the flowsheet of the optimal WEIS configuration (considering the values of the parameters characterizing each stream of interest and only the streams and technologies making part of the final optimal scenario, and not the whole superstructure). In relation to the constant values presented in Tables 1 and 2, is to note:

- 1/4 refers to the splitting of the water stream from the MED unit condenser to each one of the four effects;
- 418.896 (with kJ/kg units) refers to the specific enthalpy of saturated liquid water;
- 2675.43 (with kJ/kg units) refers to the specific enthalpy of saturated steam;
- 999 (with kg/ m3 units) refers to the density of liquid water.
- 0.0422 refers to the thermal-to-electric conversion efficiency associated to the ORC;
- 3600 (with kJ/kWh units) refers to the factor of conversion of kWh to kJ energy units;
- 0.15 (with W/(m.°C) units) refers to the thermal conductivity of the considered PCM;
- 890 (with kg/m3 units) refers to the density of the considered PCM;
- 225000 (with J/kg units) refers to the latent enthalpy associated to the melting/ solidification of PCM (as required as a parameter on the apparent specific heat capacity determination equation);
- 3.1416 is an approximation of pi;
- 0.1626 (with °C units) refers to the temperature constant for the PCM microstructure;
- 72 (with °C units) refers to lower bound for the temperature range of phase change of the PCM;
- 2200 (with J/(°C.kg) units) refers to the specific heat capacity for the solid phase of the PCM.

Table 1. Characterization of the non-linear programming (NLP) model

Decision Variables		
• Freshwater mass flow rate ($\dot{M}_{FW}$)	• Each water stream contaminant concentration (C_W)	
• Each water stream mass flow rate ($\dot{M}_W$)	• Consumption of hot utilities ($q_{Hot.Ut.}$) and cold utilities ($q_{Cold.Ut.}$)	
• Each water stream specific enthalpy (h_W)/ temperature (T_W)	• Heat transfer area of economisers ($A_{Econ.}$)	
	• Heat transfer area of MED Effect 1 ($A_{Eff1.}$)	

Equality Constraints	
$\dot{M}_{W,in,Eff} \cdot 1/4 = \dot{M}_{TW,Eff} + \dot{M}_{Concentrate,Eff}$	(1)
$q_{with.,MED} - \dot{M}_{TW,Eff1} \cdot (h_{V,Eff1} - 418.896) = \dot{M}_{W,in,Eff} \cdot 1/4 \cdot (418.896 - h_{w,in,Eff})$	(2)
$\dot{M}_{TW,Eff\,k-1} \cdot (h_{V,Eff1} - 418.896) = \dot{M}_{TW,Eff\,k} \cdot (h_{V,Eff\,k} - 418.896) + \dot{M}_{W,in,Eff\,k} \cdot 1/4 \cdot (418.896 - h_{w,in,Eff})$	(3)
$\dot{M}_{TW,Effect} \cdot (2675.43 - 418.896) = \dot{M}_{W,in,Eff} \cdot 1/4 \cdot (h_{Vapour,Eff1} - 418.896)$	(4)
$q_{with.} = U \cdot A \cdot \left((T_{Air,in} - T_{w,out}) \cdot (T_{Air,out} - T_{w,in}) \cdot ((T_{Air,in} - T_{w,out}) + (T_{Air,out} - T_{w,in})) \cdot 0.5 \right)^{1/3}$	(5)

Objective-Function (Unitary water and energy prices for Portugal)	
$\min \left(1.8499(€/m^3) \cdot 1/999\,(m^3/kg) \cdot \dot{M}_{FW}(kg/h) + 23.66(€/GJ) \cdot q_{Hot.Ut.}(GJ/h) + 0.1459(€/kWh) \cdot 1/0.95 \right.$ $\left. \cdot 1/3600\,(kWh/GJ) \cdot q_{Cold.Ut.}(GJ/h) \right) (€/h)$	(6)

Table 2. Characterization of the dynamic programming (DP) model

Decision Variables		
• Natural gas flow rates ($\dot{M}_{Fuel}$)	• Recirculated air flow rates ($\dot{M}_{Rec.Air}$)	
• Ambient air flow rates ($\dot{M}_{Amb.Air}$)	• Recirculated air specific enthalpies ($h_{Rec\,Air}$) and temperatures ($T_{Rec\,Air}$)	
• Exhaust gases flow rates ($\dot{M}_{Ex.}$)	• Generated electricity ($Elec_{Eff}$)	
• Exhaust gases specific enthalpies ($h_{Ex.}$)	• Thermal storage material temperature (T_{PCM})	
• Hot air flow rates ($\dot{M}_{Hot\,Air}$)	• Thermal storage material apparent specific heat capacity (C_{PCM})	
• Hot air specific enthalpies ($h_{Hot\,Air}$)/ temperatures ($T_{Hot\,Air}$)	• External (r_{ext}) and internal radius (r_{int}) of the TES unit	

Relevant Start Values	
Temperature of the PCM within the TES unit (T_{PCM}) (°C)	41.5

Equality Constraints		
Thermal Process System (Stream Recirculation)		
	$\dot{M}_{Comb.Air} = \dot{M}_{Rec.Air} + \dot{M}_{Amb.Air}$	(7)
	$\dot{M}_{C.Air} \cdot h_{Comb.Air} = \dot{M}_{Rec.Air} \cdot h_{Recyc.Air} + \dot{M}_{Amb.Air} \cdot h_{Amb.Air}$	(8)
	$\dot{M}_{Fuel} + \dot{M}_{C.Air} = \dot{M}_{Ex.}$	(9)
	$\dot{M}_{Fuel} \cdot AF = \dot{M}_{C.Air}$	(10)
	$\dot{M}_{gas,in,ORC} \cdot (h_{gas,in,ORC} - h_{gas,out,ORC}) \cdot 0.0422 = Elec \cdot 3600$	(11)
Thermal Energy Storage-Related		
Charge Phase	$\dfrac{dT_{PCM}}{dt} = \dfrac{0.15}{890 \cdot C_{PCM}} \cdot \dfrac{1}{(r_{ext} + r_{int}) \cdot 0.5} \cdot \left(\left(\dfrac{T_{PCM,N} - T_{PCM,1}}{r_{ext} - r_{int}} \right) + \left(\dfrac{T_{PCM,N} - 2 \cdot T_{PCM} + T_{PCM,1}}{(r_{ext} - r_{int})^2} \right) \right)$	(12)
Discharge Phase	$\dfrac{dT_{PCM}}{dt} = \dfrac{0.15}{890 \cdot C_{PCM}} \cdot \dfrac{1}{(r_{ext} + r_{int}) \cdot 0.5} \cdot \left(\left(\dfrac{T_{PCM,1} - T_{PCM,N}}{r_{ext} - r_{int}} \right) + \left(\dfrac{T_{PCM,1} - 2 \cdot T_{PCM} + T_{PCM,N}}{(r_{ext} - r_{int})^2} \right) \right)$	(13)
	$C_{PCM} = \dfrac{225000}{(2 \cdot 3.1416)^{0.5} \cdot 0.1626} \cdot \exp\left(\dfrac{-(T_{PCM} - 72)^2}{2 \cdot 0.1626^2} \right) + 2200$	(14)

Objective-Function (Unitary water and energy prices for Portugal)	
$OBJ = \left((23.66(€/GJ) \cdot 0.0453(GJ/kg) \cdot \dot{M}_{Fuel}(kg/h) - 0.1459(€/kWh) \cdot Elec_{Eff}(kWh/h)) \cdot 1/3600\,(s/h) \right) (€/s)$	(15)
$OBJ(€/s) = \left(\dfrac{d}{dt}(OBJEff(€)) \right) (€/s)$	(16)
$\min(OBJEff\,(t = 151200\,s)\,(€)), OBJEff\,(t = 0\,s) = 0\,€$	(17)

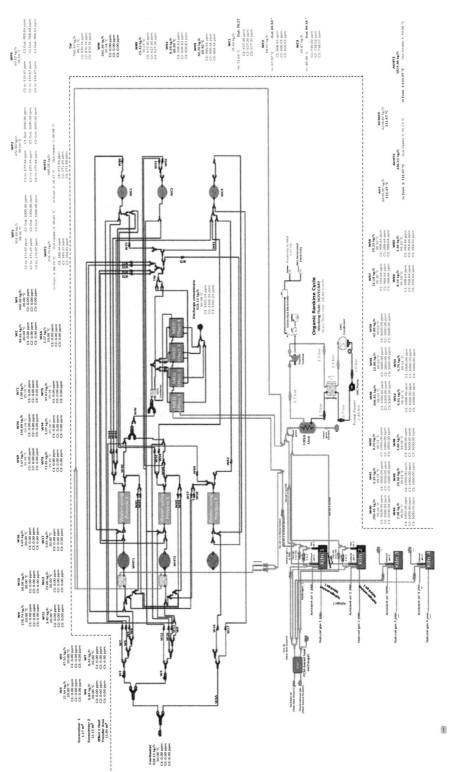

4. Post-processing – Economic and Environmental Impact Assessment

The obtained results for stream allocation must be analysed at the light of economic and environmental impact reduction-related benefits. In Table 3, the results for economic and environmental impact assessment are presented.

Table 3. Economic and Environmental Impact Reduction Assessments

Process	Initial	Improved	Relative Savings Share	Savings (€/cycle)
Natural gas consumption (kg/cycle)				
Kiln 1	5355.00	4530.38	15.40%	879.92
Kiln 2	5044.20	3529.69	30.02%	1616.08
Kiln 3	334.29	318.18	4.82%	17.19
Kiln 4	1266.05	1230.65	2.80%	37.78
Hot and Cold utilities consumption (GJ/h)				
Process	Initial	Improved	Relative Savings Share	Savings (€/h)
Heaters (3)	0.338		100.00%	7.998
Coolers (3)	0.235		100.00%	9.502
Water consumption (m³/h)				
Initial		Improved	Relative Savings Share	Savings (€/h)
0.861		0.529	38.57%	0.61
Electricity Balances (kWh/h)				
Net Electricity Generation (kWh/h)				Savings (€/h)
771.89				112.62

Final assessment				
Energy Savings	CAPEX (k€)	Savings (k€/year)	Payback Time (Years)	CO₂eq emissions reduction (kton/year)
6.88%	1802.81	637.91	2.83	1.76

The results are highly favourable compared to industrial benchmarks defined for the European industry (2 – 3 years payback time and 0.775 kton $CO_{2,eq}$/ year reduction).

5. Conclusions

This work approaches the assessment of potential improvements of the overall water and energy efficiencies in a ceramic industry plant through the development and further use of a complex modelling framework (encompassing a set of simulation and optimisation models), as part of a customised tool designated as ThermWatt. The models were developed with the aim to apply the newly created methodology of Water and Energy Integration Systems (WEIS). The developed models proved to be valuable for the achievement of the proposed objectives. A set of indicators were assessed in post-processing, having been obtained a payback period of about of 2 years and 10 months and an emission reduction level of 1.76 kton $CO_{2,eq}$/year, which are highly favourable compared to industrial benchmarks defined for the European industry, associated to 6.88% overall energy savings and 38.57% water savings.

Acknowledgements

This work and conference participation was funded through the base funding component of the Center for Technology and Innovation – ISQ, under the terms defined in AAC nº 03/C05-i02/2022, and CERENA under grant UIDB/04028/2020_UIDP/04028/2020.

References

M. Castro Oliveira, M. Iten, H.A. Matos, 2023, Simultaneous optimisation of energy recovery and water recirculation in a ceramic plant. Comput. Aided Chem. Eng. 52, 2785–2790.

M. Castro Oliveira, M. Iten, H.A. Matos, 2022, Simulation and assessment of an integrated thermal processes and Organic Rankine Cycle (ORC) system with Modelica. Energy Reports 8, 764–770.

M. Castro Oliveira, M. Iten, H.A. Matos, 2022a, Review on Water and Energy Integration in Process Industry: Water-Heat Nexus. Sustain. 14.

B.P. Walsh, S.N. Murray, D.T.J. O'Sullivan, 2015. The water energy nexus, an ISO50001 water case study and the need for a water value system. Water Resour. Ind. 10, 15–28.

Flavio Manenti, Gintaras V. Reklaitis (Eds.), Proceedings of the 34th European Symposium on Computer Aided Process Engineering / 15th International Symposium on Process Systems Engineering (ESCAPE34/PSE24), June 2-6, 2024, Florence, Italy

Pioneer Options for Sustainable Energy Storage: A Comparative Study of 25 Alternatives Using Data Envelopment Analysis

Fatemeh Rostami, Richard Cabrera, Laureano Jiménez, Carlos Pozo*

Departament d'Enginyeria Quimica, Universitat Rovira i Virgili, Av. Països Catalans 26, 43007 Tarragona, Spain
corresponding author: carlos.pozo@urv.cat

Abstract

This work examines 25 energy storage alternatives, categorized into medium and long-term options. We evaluate their sustainability level considering economic, environmental, and social aspects, including crucial indicators, such as the levelized cost of energy, energy and water usage, global warming potential, and employment opportunities. We employ Data Envelopment Analysis to rank these options based on their efficiency score. Among medium-term options, nickel-cadmium battery stands out as the most efficient choice, while in the long-term options, green hydrogen and green ammonia, powered by renewable sources, take the lead. The study provides improvement targets for alternatives deemed inefficient. The results offer valuable guidance for policymakers and energy planners seeking the most promising options for energy storage.

Keywords: Data Envelopment Analysis, Energy Storage, Grid Flexibility, Sustainability.

1. Introduction

Historically, electricity, an essential part of modern lifestyle, came from reliable grids relying on dispatchable sources like fossil fuels and nuclear energy. However, increasing environmental awareness has shifted the focus to cleaner yet intermittent and unpredictable energy sources, such as solar and wind, which challenge grid stability if extensively used. Energy storage offers a promising solution to bridge the gap between intermittent renewables and energy demand.

Energy storage technologies convert, store, and release electricity, boosting grid efficiency and reliability. These technologies differ in function, duration, and stored energy form, with "*no one-option-fits-all need*". These technologies need to meet economic, environmental, and technical criteria to foster their development.

Several studies have assessed energy storage technologies, focusing solely on economic, technical, or environmental aspects. For example, some studies examined life cycle costs, highlighting the impact of power conversion components (Zakeri and Syri, 2015). Others evaluated storage technologies based on energy density, cycle efficiency, and lifetime (Akram et al., 2020), while the rest shifted the attention to environmental concerns through a life cycle assessment approach (Fernandez-Marchante et al., 2020).

This contribution aims to comprehensively evaluate a range of energy storage alternatives considering all the economic, environmental, and social dimensions. We employ Data Envelopment Analysis (DEA) to combine these dimensions and report a single efficiency score. To do so, we first categorize storage alternatives as medium-term and long-term options and then fairly compare them in separate analyses. The findings identify preferred options within each category and present improvement targets for the less efficient ones.

2. Methodology

Initially, we categorize energy storage options into medium-term and long-term groups, as detailed in Table 1.

Table 1. Energy storage alternatives and their classifications.

Medium-term		Long-term	
Alternatives	Symbol	Alternatives	Alternatives
Lead acid	LA	H_2, Hydropower[gr]	
Lithium-ion	Li-ion	H_2, Solar[gr]	Alternatives
Lithium iron phosphate	LiFePh	H_2, Wind[gr]	H_2, CG[4, g]
Lithium nickel manganese cobalt	LiNiMnCo	NH_3, Hydropower[gr]	H_2, Grid mix[g]
Nickel-cadmium	NiCd	NH_3, Solar[gr]	H_2, SMR[4, g]
Sodium nickel chloride	NaNiCl	NH_3, Wind[gr]	H_2, WSCL[3, g]
Sodium sulphide	NaS	H_2, SMR-CCS[1, 2, b]	H_2, CG-CCS[2, 4, g]
Vanadium redox flow battery	VRFB	NH_3, SMR-CCS[1, 2, b]	NH_3, Grid mix[g]
Zinc bromine flow battery	ZBFB	NH_3, WSCL[3, b]	NH_3, SMR[4, g]

1: Steam methane reforming, 2: Carbon capture and storage, 3: Water splitting by chemical looping, 4: Coal gasification. gr: Green, the used energy source is from renewable energies; b: Blue, the used energy source is from fossil fuels combined with carbon capture and storage, g: Grey, the energy source is from fossil fuels (or the grid, sometimes referred to as yellow).

We then employ DEA to assess the sustainability performance of energy storage alternatives. DEA is a linear programming method that helps evaluate the relative efficiency of a set of so-called Decision-Making Units (DMUs) by comparing their ability to convert inputs into outputs. It assigns an efficiency score to each DMU: higher efficiency achieves when more outputs are generated with fewer inputs (Fernández et al., 2018). Note that when there are specific undesirable outputs, attaining lower levels of these outputs is preferable. DMUs with an efficiency score of one are considered efficient, while inefficient DMUs receive a score between 0 and 1.

In this context, we consider energy storage technologies as DMUs, which consume inputs and yield both desired and undesired outputs. We evaluate five indicators for each group. Additionally, we consider energy density as an input for medium-term technologies due to their size sensitivity, particularly in portable applications. These indicators, covering the three sustainability pillars, are:

- Energy consumption [GJ] (*input*): represents emissions and is viewed as an environmental indicator (Mukelabai et al., 2021).
- Energy density [GJ/kg] (*input*): provides insights into material requirements and the size of the technology. It is used for medium-term alternatives. Note that we use its inverse term (i.e., 1/energy density) as an input to be minimized (Zakeri and Syri, 2015).
- Employment [FTEJ] (*desired output*): it reflects the creation of full-time equivalent jobs needed to develop the options within each group. It serves as a social indicator (Rostami et al., 2022).
- Global warming potential, GWP [CO_2-eq emissions] (*undesired output*): it is an environmental indicator that reflects the CO_2-eq emissions resulting from the development of storage alternatives (Siddiqui and Dincer, 2019).
- Levelized cost of energy, LCOE [€] (*input*): for medium-term options, it reflects initial, variable, and end-of-life costs (Zakeri and Syri, 2015). For long-term options, it presents the cost of producing one kilogram of hydrogen or ammonia (Thengane et al., 2014).
- Water usage [m^3] (*input*): it is used as an environmental indicator, representing the water used for the development of each medium-term option, or one kg H_2 or NH_3 (Chisalita et al., 2020).

Finally, a non-oriented, undesired output slack-based model combines these indicators and returns a single efficiency score for each technology within each group (i.e., medium-term, or long-term), as presented in Eqs. (1) – (6).

$$\tau^* = \min t - \frac{1}{m} \sum_{i=1}^{m} \frac{S_i^-}{x_{io}} \tag{1}$$

$$\text{s.t.} \qquad 1 = t + \frac{1}{s_1+s_2} \left(\sum_{r=1}^{s_1} \frac{S_r^g}{y_{ro}^g} + \sum_{r=1}^{s_2} \frac{S_r^b}{y_{ro}^b} \right) \tag{2}$$

$$x_o t = X\Lambda + S^- \tag{3}$$

$$y_o^g t = Y^g \Lambda - S^g \tag{4}$$

$$y_o^b t = Y^b \Lambda + S^b \tag{5}$$

$$S^- \geq 0,\ S^g \geq 0,\ S^b \geq 0,\ \Lambda \geq 0,\ t > 0. \tag{6}$$

Here, τ^* represents the efficiency score of DMU under assessment. Variable t denotes the Charnes-Cooper linear transformation coefficient, which is necessary to convert the original nonlinear undesired output SBM model into a linear model like the one presented above. Also, m, s_1, and s_2 represent the numbers of inputs, desired outputs, and undesired outputs, respectively, for DMUs in that cluster. Subscript i refers to inputs, while subscript r relates to outputs. Slack variables S_i^-, S_r^g, and S_r^b quantify the distance from each DMU to the efficient frontier. For efficient DMUs, these values will be zero, while for inefficient DMUs, they provide the improvements required for this DMU to become efficient. Parameters x_{io}, y_{ro}^g, and y_{ro}^b refer to the input, the desired output, and the undesired output of DMU o, respectively. X is the inputs matrix, while Y^g and Y^b are the corresponding matrices for desired and undesired outputs. Λ represents weights that combine efficient DMUs to form the so-called virtual DMU of the assessed DMU. The virtual DMU is an efficient version of the evaluated DMU, obtained by projecting the inefficient DMU onto the efficient frontier. We also used a super-efficiency model that allows efficiency scores above one and ranking efficient DMUs in case that there is more than one efficient DMU. Due to space constraints, the details of the super-efficiency model are not presented here, but they can be found elsewhere (Fang et al., 2013) .

Additionally, we employed uncertainty distributions to handle data variability arising from simplifications and regional differences among storage options. These distributions, generated through Monte Carlo sampling, produced one hundred scenarios for each indicator (Frutiger et al., 2018). This approach broadens the range of potential values, enhancing the robustness of our findings.

3. Results and discussion

3.1. Efficiency scores and ranking of technologies in each group

Figures 1 and 2 display the distribution of efficiency scores for each medium-term and long-term energy storage alternative across the scenarios considered. The lowest score in this set represents the DMU's worst-case scenario, while the highest indicates its best performance. In each violin plot, the wider sections correspond to efficiency scores that are more likely to occur.

Among medium-term options, NiCd, Li-ion, NaS, and LiFePh batteries have median efficiencies above one. NiCd and NaS technologies are promising because of their job creation potential (i.e., employment indicator). However, deploying them in high-wage regions may pose challenges to their LCOE. Li-ion and LiFePh also benefit from the employment along with the energy density indicator to ensure their efficiency. Lithium-ion batteries have varying efficiency, with some scenarios below 0.5 for LiNiMnCo and LiFePh. However, their median efficiency is close to or above one, indicating acceptable sustainability levels for these batteries. In contrast, VRFB, ZBFB, LA, and NaNiCl have median efficiencies below 0.5, needing further improvements.

Among the long-term options, green ammonia from solar energy consistently exhibits high efficiency (i.e., above one) due to employment and energy consumption indicators. It is followed by green hydrogen from solar and wind, and green ammonia from hydropower and wind, all with median efficiencies higher than one. While they all rely on the employment indicator to get their relatively high efficiency score, green hydrogen from solar is also strongly benefited by its relatively lower energy consumption, and green ammonia from wind is partially benefited by its relatively lower LCOE. In contrast, grey and blue options have lower median efficiencies due to high global warming potential and energy consumption.

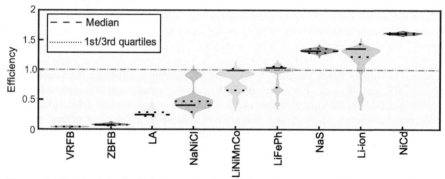

Figure 1. Distribution of efficiency score for medium-term energy storage technologies. Technologies are sorted in increasing order of their median efficiency score.

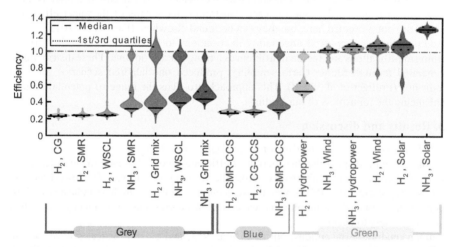

Figure 2. Distribution of efficiency score for long-term energy storage options. Technologies in each group are sorted in increasing order of their median efficiency score. A dashed line is added in efficiency equal to one to facilitate the comparison.

3.2. Improvement targets

In Figure 3, we provide improvement targets for inefficient medium-term and long-term energy storage alternatives by comparing the value of their indicators with those of their corresponding virtual DMU.

Flow batteries need over 80 % improvement to become efficient, i.e., a reduction in their input or undesired output indicators. Lead acid batteries require a 100 % reduction in water use and about 40-60 % improvement in other input indicators and GWP. NaNiCl needs around an 80 % decline in water use and GWP. All these alternatives need further research and development to become competitive, and it will require time.

Two lithium battery types, LiFePh and LiNiMnCo, efficient in 70 % and 50 % of the 100 scenarios, have low average improvement targets of 8.5 % and 13.5 %. Similarly, Li-ion batteries, efficient in 93 % of the scenarios, have small improvement targets. NaS and NiCd batteries are always efficient (Figure 1) and have a zero-improvement target.

Figure 3 also highlights that while the levelized cost of energy is not critical for long-term alternatives, energy consumption, water use, and GWP need attention, especially for grey and blue options. Grey hydrogen alternatives like coal gasification, water splitting using chemical looping, and steam methane reforming have high improvement targets in energy consumption (over 80 %), water use (over 95 %), and GWP (over 80 %). This shows the need for significant improvements in these options to enhance efficiency.

Ammonia alternatives have lower improvement targets, with ammonia from steam methane reforming requiring 60-75 % improvements and ammonia produced by water splitting using chemical looping needing less than 80 % improvements.

As expected, blue alternatives have smaller improvement targets on GWP compared to grey options (less than 70 % compared to more than 80 %). While CCS can reduce environmental impacts, it presents challenges in other areas, such as energy consumption and cost-effectiveness. Technologies relying on renewable energy sources like solar, wind, and hydropower have lower average improvement targets, indicating their relative efficiency or fewer required enhancements in the indicators used in this study.

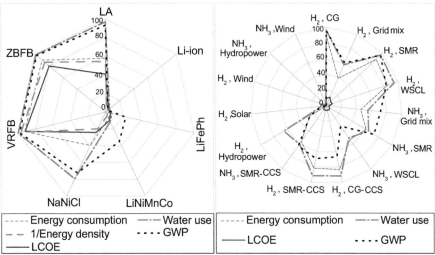

Figure 3. Improvement targets obtained for inefficient medium-term (left-side) and long-term (right-side) energy storage alternatives. Note that the values are in percentage. LCOE: levelized cost of energy, GWP: global warming potential.

4. Conclusions

This study assessed 25 energy storage alternatives, categorizing them as medium-term and long-term options. Employing Data Envelopment Analysis, we evaluate their economic, environmental, and social sustainability. The findings emphasize the importance of sustainability assessment in transitioning to renewable energies.

Medium-term options like NiCd and NaS batteries demonstrate potential in sustainability, while others, such as VRFB batteries need significant improvements. In the long-term category, renewable energy-powered options are efficient and sustainable, while grey and blue alternatives need important improvements. Variations in efficiency scores indicate the importance of considering regional factors such as the availability of renewable energy resources.

Noteworthy, even an inefficient option may be irreplaceable in some applications. Furthermore, many of these options are still evolving, and further innovation can help reduce their need for drastic improvements. In this regard, the reported improvement targets provide insights into making energy storage technologies more efficient. For example, flow batteries stand out, requiring 90 % reduction in input indicators to enhance efficiency. Researchers can use these results to identify the extent to which efforts should be concentrated to improve the overall efficiency of each energy storage option.

References

U. Akram, M. Nadarajah, R. Shah, F. Milano, 2020, A review on rapid responsive energy storage technologies for frequency regulation in modern power systems, Renewable and Sustainable Energy Reviews, 120, 109626, https://doi.org/10.1016/j.rser.2019.109626.

D.A. Chisalita, L. Petrescu, C.C. Cormos, 2020, Environmental evaluation of european ammonia production considering various hydrogen supply chains, Renewable and Sustainable Energy Reviews, 130, 109964, 10.1016/j.rser.2020.109964.

H.H. Fang, H.S. Lee, S.N. Hwang, C.C. Chung, 2013, A slacks-based measure of super-efficiency in data envelopment analysis: An alternative approach, Omega, 41, 4, 731-734, https://doi.org/10.1016/j.omega.2012.10.004.

D. Fernández, C. Pozo, R. Folgado, L. Jiménez, G. Guillén-Gosálbez, 2018, Productivity and energy efficiency assessment of existing industrial gases facilities via data envelopment analysis and the Malmquist index, Applied Energy, 212, 1563-1577, 10.1016/j.apenergy.2017.12.008.

C. Fernandez-Marchante, M. Millán, J. Medina-Santos, J. Lobato, 2020, Environmental and Preliminary Cost Assessments of Redox Flow Batteries for Renewable Energy Storage, Energy Technology, 8, 11, 1900914, 10.1002/ente.201900914.

J. Frutiger, M. Jones, NG. Ince, G. Sin, 2018, From property uncertainties to process simulation uncertainties – Monte Carlo methods in SimSci PRO/II process simulator, Computer Aided Chemical Eng., 44, 10.1016/B978-0-444-64241-7.50243-3.

M.D. Mukelabai, JM. Gillard, K. Patchigolla, 2021, A novel integration of a green power-to-ammonia to power system: Reversible solid oxide fuel cell for hydrogen and power production coupled with an ammonia synthesis unit, International Journal of Hydrogen Energy, 46, 35.

F. Rostami, Z. Kis, R. Koppelaar, L. Jiménez, C. Pozo, 2022, Comparative sustainability study of energy storage technologies using data envelopment analysis, Energy Storage Materials, 48, 412–438, https://doi.org/https://doi.org/10.1016/j.ensm.2022.03.026.

O. Siddiqui, I. Dincer, 2019, A well to pump life cycle environmental impact assessment of some hydrogen production routes, International Journal of Hydrogen Energy, 44, 12, 5773-5786.

S.K., Thengane, A. Hoadley, S. Bhattacharya, S. Mitra, S. Bandyopadhyay, 2014, Cost-benefit analysis of different hydrogen production technologies using AHP and Fuzzy AHP, International Journal of Hydrogen Energy, 39, 28, 15293-15306.

B. Zakeri, S. Syri, 2015, Electrical energy storage systems: A comparative life cycle cost analysis, Renewable and Sustainable Energy Reviews, 42, 569-596, 10.1016/j.rser.2014.10.011.

Flavio Manenti, Gintaras V. Reklaitis (Eds.), Proceedings of the 34th European Symposium on Computer Aided Process Engineering / 15th International Symposium on Process Systems Engineering (ESCAPE34/PSE24), June 2-6, 2024, Florence, Italy

Comparing the sustainability level of biofuels with Data Envelopment Analysis

Richard Cabrera[a], Fatemeh Rostami[a], Laureano Jiménez[a], Carlos Pozo[a]

[a]Departament d'Enginyeria Quimica, Universitat Rovira i Virgili, Av. Països Catalans 26, 43007 Tarragona, Spain.

corresponding author: carlos.pozo@urv.cat

Abstract

Liquid biofuels are an alternative to a more sustainable transport sector, providing an interim solution before the required infrastructure for electric vehicles is in place. With a myriad of biofuel production options available today, decisions regarding fuel type, blend, conversion process, and carbon source significantly impact the cost and environmental footprint of the final product. Hence, a comprehensive multi-criteria decision-making approach is essential to identify the most suitable biofuels, considering economic, environmental, and social dimensions.

This study combines life cycle assessment with Data Envelopment Analysis (DEA) to assess the performance of 72 biofuel routes using 12 sustainability metrics. DEA allows to systematically combine the 12 sustainability metrics into a single efficiency score, facilitating the ranking of the biofuel alternative routes, and avoiding the need to predefine subjective weights between the indicators.

Our findings reveal that among the biofuel routes analysed, 35 perform more efficiently, with renewable diesel proving superior to ethanol-based blends or biodiesel. Waste biomass stands out as a preferable choice over cellulosic biomass or bio-oil. The selection of the carbon source emerges as a critical decision, emphasizing the need to consider regional factors like soil and climate conditions.

Overall, this work provides a powerful framework for holistic assessments that could help policymakers develop better-informed regulations and achieve, in this way, the emission reduction targets of current environmental policies for the transportation sector.

Keywords: Sustainable development, Data envelopment analysis, Life cycle assessment, Transport, Biofuels.

1. Introduction

The continued growth of global population and increased living standards have driven energy demand to unprecedented heights. Transport, a dominant energy-consuming sector reliant on fossil fuels (92% of fuel demand), stands as the third major contributor to greenhouse gas emissions, emphasizing the unsustainable nature of current transport sector. In 2018, less than 4% of transport fuel demand was met by renewable energy, predominantly biofuels (93%). Biofuels like biodiesel and bioethanol are considered pivotal for sustainable development, aligning with environmental policies such as the Paris Agreement and the European Green Deal(European Commission, n.d.).

In the current landscape, a plethora of alternatives exist for biofuel production, each influenced by critical decisions regarding fuel type, blend, conversion process, and carbon source. These decisions wield substantial influence over the final cost and environmental impact of the biofuel product.

This contribution evaluates the sustainability of 72 biofuels routes, considering their entire life cycle from cultivation to combustion in vehicles (cradle-to-wheel). To address the sustainability of biofuels comprehensively. A multi-criteria decision-making tool, DEA, is employed. DEA is chosen for its ability to integrate multiple indicators into a single performance score, providing a holistic assessment of biofuels. During the last years, some authors have combined Life Cycle Assessment (LCA) with DEA to assess the overall level of sustainability of alternatives, enabling the identification of efficient processes with a focus on their sustainable performance for different applications, including: the production of liquid fuels (Rodríguez-Vallejo et al., 2019) energy storage alternatives (Rostami et al., 2022) or bioenergy systems (González-García et al., 2012) among others.

2. Methodology

2.1. Data acquisition

We first obtain the data required to compute the indicators that will be used to assess the sustainability performance of the biofuels. This requires the collection of different types of data, from mass and energy balances for biofuel production processes to traditional LCA data and complementary information such as costs.

Specifically, 19 types of biological feedstocks are considered as carbon sources, together with four types of biofuel production processes. The resulting biofuels can be used in five different blends: ethanol (blended with gasoline in 10-90% (E10) or 85-15% (E85) proportions), biodiesel (blended with diesel in a 20-80% fuel (BD20)), and two types of renewable diesel, one based on the super cetane process (RDI) and another based on fluid catalytic cracking technology (RDII). RDI and RDII can be used as standalone fuel in compression ignition direct injection engines, avoiding blends with fossil fuels.

For each of these 72 biofuels, 12 performance metrics covering the three sustainability dimensions from a cradle-to-wheel approach are considered as follows. The economic dimension is assessed through the cost and the distance that can be traveled with the biofuel; the environmental dimension is evaluated through eight life-cycle impacts; and the performance in the social dimension is based on water use and land occupation since the shortage of these resources can trigger social conflicts(Pozo et al., 2020).

We next describe how these data from the performed LCA and complementary information are used in DEA to benchmark the sustainability performance of the different biofuels studied.

2.2. Data envelopment analysis model

Data Envelopment Analysis (DEA) is a mathematical programming technique (Charnes et al., 1978), with the aim of comparing and evaluating a homogeneous set of decision-making units (DMUs) in a production system with multiple inputs and multiple outputs.

DEA stands out from other multi-criteria assessment methods due to its ability to combine various indicators into one performance score without the need to establish subjective weights between the indicators. This is particularly useful in sustainability assessments that always create controversy. Also, it enables the integration of indicators covering all three sustainability dimensions into a single metric, allowing for easy identification of efficient and inefficient alternatives.

In this contribution, each of the 72 biofuel alternatives is modelled as a DMU whose relative performance is evaluated based on the 12 sustainability indicators and classified as either inputs or outputs. These sustainability indicators are depicted in Figure 1.

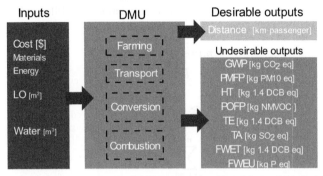

Figure 1. Inputs and (desirable and undesirable) outputs considered for each biofuel (DMU).. LO: land occupation; Water: water used in farming plus water depletion; GWP: global warming potential; PMFP: particulate matter formation potential; HT: human ecotoxicity; POFP: photochemical oxidant formation potential; TE: terrestrial ecotoxicity; TA: Terrestrial acidification; FWET: freshwater ecotoxicity; PMFP: fine particulate matter formation; FWEU: freshwater eutrophication.

Among the different DEA models available, we opt for a non-oriented slack-based model (SBM), as presented in Eq. (1), to combine the sustainability indicators into a single performance score (i.e., efficiency score). This score lies between 0 and 1, so that DMUs (i.e., biofuels) with a score of 1 are referred to as efficient, while DMUs with a score strictly lower than 1 are considered inefficient.

$$\rho^* = \min \frac{1 - \frac{1}{m}\sum_{i=1}^{m}\frac{s_i^-}{x_{i0}}}{1 + \frac{1}{k}\sum_{r=1}^{k}\frac{s_r^+}{y_{r0}}} \qquad \text{Eq. (1)}$$

s.t.
$$\sum_{j=1}^{n} \lambda_j x_{ij} + s_i^- = x_{i0} \qquad i = 1, 2, \dots, m$$

$$\sum_{j=1}^{n} \lambda_j y_{rj} - s_r^+ = y_{r0} \qquad r = 1, 2, \dots, k$$

$$s^- \geq 0, s^+ \geq 0$$

$$\lambda_j \geq 0 \qquad j = 1, 2, \dots, n$$

In this model, ρ is the SBM-efficiency score, x_{ij} is the value of input i of DMU j, y_{rj} is the value of output r of DMU j, and x_{io} and y_{ro} are the values of input i and output r of the DMU o under evaluation. In turn, s_i^- and s_r^+ are the input and output slacks, providing the distance from the DMU assessed to the so-called efficient frontier (i.e., the multi-dimensional frontier that would be obtained by linearly combining efficient DMUs).

Slack variables in non-oriented SBM models provide information regarding the degree of inefficiency attained by each input and output individually (Tone, 2001).

In addition to the SBM model, we employ a super-efficiency DEA model (Tone, 2002), which assigns efficiency scores above one to efficient alternatives, thus providing an additional option to distinguish among efficient DMUs. DMUs assigning to each of them efficiency scores beyond one. This is obtained by assuming that the DMU to be evaluated is excluded from the reference set. The model formulation is as follows:

$$\delta^* = min \frac{\frac{1}{m}\sum_{i=1}^{m}\frac{\bar{x}_i}{x_{i0}}}{\frac{1}{k}\sum_{r=1}^{k}\frac{\bar{y}_r}{y_{r0}}} \qquad \text{Eq.(2)}$$

s.t.
$$\bar{x} \geq \sum_{j=1,\neq 0}^{n} \lambda_j x_j$$

$$\bar{y} \leq \sum_{j=1,\neq 0}^{n} \lambda_j y_j$$

$$\bar{x} \geq x_0, \bar{y} \leq y_0, \lambda \geq 0$$

3. Results and discussion

3.1. Efficiency assessment

Fig. 2 provides the combined results for the efficiency and super-efficiency DEAs, with inefficient biofuels being represented based on their efficiency score and efficient biofuels depicted based on their super-efficiency score. Results reveal that 48% of the 72 biofuels analyses are efficient. The highest efficiency score, standing at 1.61, is achieved by the blend using 85% of ethanol from municipal solid waste (MSW), owning to different factors such as its low cost, and the water and land use requirements attributed to MSW compared to other raw materials. On the contrary, the lowest efficiency score (0.26) is achieved by a blend using 85% of ethanol derived from corn (E85) from combined dry and wet milling corn. This outcome can be attributed to its low mileage efficiency (8.63 km per litre, compared to 14.57 km for any renewable diesel), and increased requirements for water use and land occupation.

When comparing the five types of fuel studied (E10, E85, BD20, RDI, RDII), it becomes evident that there is, at least, one efficient biofuel for each. However, this does not imply equal performance across all fuel types: while almost all BD20, RDI, and RDII fuels demonstrate efficiency, only 30% of ethanol-based fuels (15 out of 50) achieve this status. This underscores the importance of considering, not only the fuel type, but also the carbon source for comprehensive sustainability assessments.

On average, both renewable diesel exhibits the highest efficiency scores at 1.03, outperforming biofuels based on lignocellulosic biomass (e.g., sorghum, standing at 0.91 average efficiency score) and first-generation biomass (e.g., corn, 0.56). These results are attributed to the lower fuel consumption of engines using E10 and E85 blends, compared to those fuelled by BD20, RDI or RDII.

In conclusion, these findings advocate for promoting the use of renewable diesel (RDI and RDII) over bioethanol (E10 and E85) due to its lower GWP under a cradle-to-wheel LCA, owing mainly to reduced fuel consumption per km. The continuous evolution of enzymes for the degradation of lignocellulosic materials into simple fermentable sugars is making them more competitive, to the point that they achieve better performance and lower costs than first regeneration ethanol feedstocks (e.g., corn).

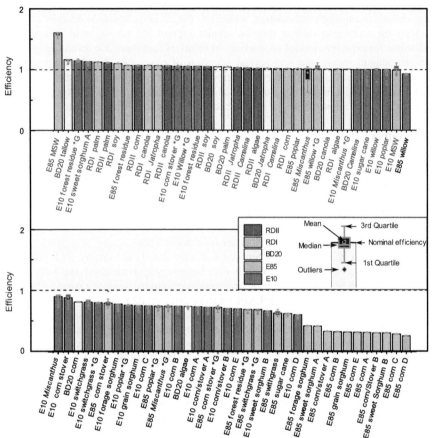

Figure 2. Efficiency scores for biofuels. (Super)efficiency scores for the 72 biofuels routes are provided as vertical bars in subplot, with biofuels sorted in decreasing order of efficiency and efficient biofuels depicted with a green label. Corn A: Dry mill corn without oil extraction; Corn B: Dry mill corn with oil extraction; Corn C: Wet milling corn; Corn D: combined dry and wet milling corn; Corn/stover A: integrated corn/stover ethanol (associated with corn); Corn/stover B: integrated corn/ stover ethanol (associated with stover); Corn E: Gen dry milling corn with oil extraction; Sweet sorghum A: Conventional; Sweet sorghum B: Integrated; *G: ethanol produced by gasification. BD20: Diesel fuel with up to 20 %v/v FAME content; E10: Gasoline fuel with up to 10 %v/v bioethanol content; E85: Gasoline fuel with up to 85 %v/v bioethanol content; RDI: Renewable Diesel Production Based on SuperCetane; RDII: Renewable Diesel Production Based on fluid catalytic cracker technology.

4. Conclusions

Multi-criteria approaches, exemplified in this contribution by combining LCA with DEA, provide a robust framework for conducting sustainability studies. Such methodologies have the capacity to minimize burden-shifting episodes and offer valuable insights to policymakers for the development of well-informed and effective policies. In this contribution, we used such an approach to assess the performance of 72 biofuels based on 12 sustainability indicators, to identify trends that can be used to inform policymakers.

The biofuel alternative with the highest efficiency score was based on MSW, which suggests that residues should be prioritized among carbon sources. Fuels from natural oils also show a promising performance, with 20 of the 22 units analysed deemed efficient. Among the remaining carbon sources, results support the recent trend of promoting cellulosic material for ethanol production. In terms of fuel type, our results suggest that policies should favour the widespread adoption of renewable diesel over traditional ethanol or biodiesel, since the former achieved the best performance thanks to a higher fuel economy and a higher biogenic carbon content in the fuel. The fuel type, however, was not found as impactful as the carbon source in achieving high efficiency scores.

References

Charnes, A., Cooper, W. W., & Rhodes, E. (1978). Measuring the efficiency of decision making units. *European Journal of Operational Research*, *2*(6), 429–444. https://doi.org/10.1016/0377-2217(78)90138-8

European Commission. (n.d.). *Sustainable transport | Mobility and Transport*. Retrieved February 11, 2021, from https://ec.europa.eu/transport/themes/sustainable_en

González-García, S., Iribarren, D., Susmozas, A., Dufour, J., & Murphy, R. J. (2012). Life cycle assessment of two alternative bioenergy systems involving Salix spp. biomass: Bioethanol production and power generation. *Applied Energy*, *95*, 111–122. https://doi.org/10.1016/J.APENERGY.2012.02.022

Pozo, C., Galán-Martín, A., Cortés-Borda, D., Sales-Pardo, M., Azapagic, A., Guimerà, R., & Guillén-Gosálbez, G. (2020). Reducing global environmental inequality: Determining regional quotas for environmental burdens through systems optimisation. *Journal of Cleaner Production*, *270*, 121828. https://doi.org/10.1016/J.JCLEPRO.2020.121828

Rodríguez-Vallejo, D. F., Galán-Martín, Á., Guillén-Gosálbez, G., & Chachuat, B. (2019). Data envelopment analysis approach to targeting in sustainable chemical process design: Application to liquid fuels. *AIChE Journal*, *65*(7), e16480. https://doi.org/10.1002/AIC.16480

Rostami, F., Kis, Z., Koppelaar, R., Jiménez, L., & Pozo, C. (2022). Comparative sustainability study of energy storage technologies using data envelopment analysis. *Energy Storage Materials*, *48*, 412–438. https://doi.org/10.1016/J.ENSM.2022.03.026

Tone, K. (2001). Slacks-based measure of efficiency in data envelopment analysis. *European Journal of Operational Research*, *130*(3), 498–509. https://doi.org/10.1016/S0377-2217(99)00407-5

Tone, K. (2002). A slacks-based measure of super-efficiency in data envelopment analysis. *European Journal of Operational Research*, *143*(1), 32–41. https://doi.org/10.1016/S0377-2217(01)00324-1

Flavio Manenti, Gintaras V. Reklaitis (Eds.), Proceedings of the 34th European Symposium on Computer Aided Process Engineering / 15th International Symposium on Process Systems Engineering (ESCAPE34/PSE24), June 2-6, 2024, Florence, Italy

A Multi-Parametric Optimization Approach for Bi-Level Decision-Making Strategies in Energy-Water Nexus Supply Systems

Elizabeth J. Abraham,[a,b,c] Marcello Di Martino,[a,b] Dustin Kenefake, [a,b] Dhabia M. Al-Mohannadi,[c] Efstratios N. Pistikopoulos [a,b]

[a]*Artie McFerrin Department of Chemical Engineering, Texas A&M University, 3122 TAMU, College Station, TX 77843, USA*
[b]*Texas A&M Energy Institute, Texas A&M University, 1617 Research Pkwy, College Station, TX 77845, USA*
[c]*Department of Chemical Engineering, Texas A&M University at Qatar, Education City, PO Box 23874, Doha, Qatar*
stratos@tamu.edu

Abstract

The demands for energy and water continue to increase amid depleting natural resource availability and rising sustainability concerns. To address these exigent challenges, systematic shifts are expected to take place in global energy and water supply systems. Therefore, it is pivotal to understand how these two resource supply systems are interconnected for the generation of synergistic systems solutions based on an energy-water nexus (EWN) approach. Effective trade-offs between minimizing cost and maximizing resource utilization, among other objectives, can be identified through this approach for sustainable resource management. In these instances, it is customarily assumed that the decisions made by both systems are dictated at the same level, where there is effectively one single decision-maker to simultaneously satisfy the energy system's water requirements and the water system's energy requirements. However, these systems are typically in competition with one another to meet their respective objectives and true synergy can only be achieved in an ideal case. With these antagonistic objectives, the priorities of the involved systems naturally assume a hierarchical structure. To account for such structured decision-making, we present a bi-level programming framework for EWN supply systems based on a multi-parametric programming approach to optimize system design and operation.

Keywords: Multi-parametric optimization, Bi-level mixed-integer optimization, Mixed-integer programming, Energy-water nexus

1. Introduction

The rapid growth of the population is accompanied with increasingly prevalent economic, environmental, and social concerns that have a profound impact on the global demand for energy and water. To meet the rising demands of these resources and to adapt to the far-reaching challenges of these changing times, it is important to encapsulate the complexity of energy and water supply systems (Di Martino et al., 2023). A fundamental factor that contributes to this intricacy is the interconnected nature of these resources and their supply systems. For instance, 15% of the global water harnessed is distributed for energy use, while 8% of the global energy generated is allocated for water use (Garcia and You,

2016). Therefore, these systems must be analyzed from a holistic perspective using nexus approaches to explore the synergies and trade-offs that exist between them (Liu et al., 2018). When energy and water resources are shared to gain collective benefits in this manner, the two systems must work together to achieve set objectives in an integrated system, specifically referred to as the energy-water nexus (EWN).

The energy transition is a pressing matter for the EWN. For the energy system, the shift towards renewable energy comes with a myriad of challenges such as the intermittency of these resources in addition to the need for new infrastructure and the extreme stresses they exert on land and water resources (Cook et al., 2022). For the water system, water scarcity is a major challenge given that natural resources are depleting and that demands to meet energy generation are expected to increase drastically (Di Martino et al, 2023). To address these challenges, works such as those of Martin and Grossman (2015) and Panagopoulos (2021) harness trade-offs using nexus modeling and optimization approaches for the development of renewable energy infrastructure. The decisions made in these works by each system to meet these objectives are accustomed to hold the same level of priority. Since the decisions are taken at the same level, the nexus approach effectively analyzes the sub-systems as a single integrated system with a single decision maker. In other words, there is a coordinated effort in state-of-the-art approaches to enable synergy without information asymmetry where different systems are considered from a single level of decision-making without different levels. However, it is well-established that external and internal factors of this nature have a more considerable effect on the decisions made by some sub-systems than others. Therefore, the decisions made and the sub-systems they are associated with naturally fall into hierarchical order, for which a structured decision-making framework is essential.

Within the EWN, the incorporation of more renewable technologies in the energy system takes precedence over alleviating strains on resources in the water system, as it not only provides an opportunity to produce clean energy but can also ultimately provide relief to the water system through the deployment of less water-intensive energy production technologies. Therefore, there is a need to enable multi-level decision-making within the EWN to analyze the trade-offs that exist from prioritizing one sub-system over the other. Hierarchical decision-making of this manner, especially from a bi-level perspective within the nexus has already been investigated in literature through the use of multi-level programming. In bi-level programming, there are two different hierarchical levels of decision makers, namely, the upper level decision maker and the lower level decision maker. The works of Avraamidou et al. (2018) using a data-driven solution algorithm and Chen et al. (2022) using graph theory are some instances that enable structured decision-making under nexus considerations.

In this work, we introduce a bi-level optimization framework to leverage prioritized decision-making of a single sub-system on the EWN for the design of renewable energy systems. In this way, the impact of competition and subsequent information access on the design on these systems can be evaluated. The bi-level formulation presented is based on multi-parametric programming. Through this approach, the feasible solution space of an optimization problem with uncertain parameters is represented as critical regions that define the optimal solution in terms of the uncertain parameters offline (Avraamidou and Pistikopoulos, 2022). Therefore, by formulating the lower level problem as a multi-parametric problem, its optimal solutions in term of the uncertain parameters can be integrated as constraints in the upper level problem before its solution. Section 2 provides the framework and Section 3 presents the model and describes the multi-parametric programming approach used to enable the design of these renewable energy systems under EWN considerations. Section 4 illustrates its application to a case study and Section 5 concludes this work.

2. EWN Framework

The framework enables the design of renewable energy systems by integrating decisions from the energy and water systems in a hierarchical manner to meet specified resource demands over a time horizon. The decisions effectively describe energy supply through the selection of the optimal renewable energy sources and water supply through the characterization of the operation of the reverse osmosis (RO) desalination plant. Essentially, the energy system provides the energy necessary for the operation of the water system, while the RO system provides the water required for farming maize in the energy system. Therefore, to enable effective decision-making within the components of the EWN, the interconnections that exist between them must be carefully considered.

To account for the interactions within the integrated system, the EWN must be examined as a collective whole of the two sub-systems. Therefore, the integrated energy-water supply system can be considered as the upper level decision maker as it will decide the optimal design and operation of the energy and water systems. The overall objective of the energy system is to maximize the power generated while meeting energy and water demands. The lower level decision maker can then be assigned to the water system, where it will optimize its operation to minimize its energy consumption. Therefore, hierarchical decision-making is embedded in this framework to maximize the total power generated while considering the operational profiles of the water system as illustrated in Figure 1.

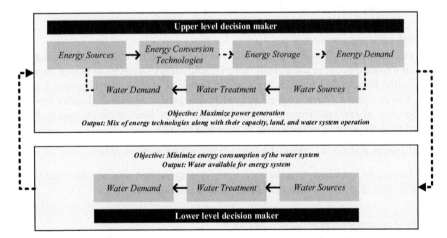

Figure 1: Proposed framework with the interactions between system decision makers

3. Mathematical Model

The development of the EWN optimization model used, which involves the integration of two independent models that define the energy and water systems, is detailed in this section.

3.1. Energy supply sub-system

The energy system is defined by a set of energy sources (solar, wind, and biomass), energy conversion technologies (fixed angle and single axis tracking solar panels, turbines, and maize), and energy storage technologies (pumped storage hydropower and compressed air energy storage) to meet a predefined demand target. Model equations pertaining to the energy sub-system resulted in a linear programming model and was simplified based on the mixed integer linear programming model which details the system operation in Cook et al. (2022). The objective of the energy system is to maximize power generation by determining the optimal set of renewable energy sources and technologies that meet energy demands which include those of the water system as well.

3.2. Water supply sub-system

The water system considered here is a RO desalination unit defined by its feed flow (FF), permeate flow (PF), energy consumption (EC), and water recovery (WR), in addition to its capital and operating costs. The model equations that describe it resulted in a non-linear programming (NLP) model and is a simplified version of the RO unit described in Di Martino et al. (2023). The objective of the water system here is to minimize its energy consumption as shown in Eq. (1) and is defined as a linear expression of its other operational characteristics based on the analysis performed in Di Martino et al. (2022).

$$EC = a + b \times FF + c \times PF + d \times WR \tag{1}$$

As the water system is designated as the lower level decision maker in this case, this equation is the objective function of the optimization problem of the lower level decision maker, herein referred to as the lower level problem. The water system therefore determines the amount of water that is available to meet water demands, which includes those of the energy system as well.

3.3. EWN optimization model

The model equations of the energy and water systems are integrated by introducing their respective requirements in the overall material and energy balances to obtain the EWN optimization model using insights from Di Martino et al. (2023). The objective function of the energy system which maximizes total power generated, which thereby serves as the objective of the optimization problem of the upper level decision maker, herein referred to as the upper level problem, as shown in Eq. (2).

$$Total\ power\ output\ =\ Sum\ of\ power\ from\ all\ energy\ sources \tag{2}$$

Other extensions, particularly in the investment and operating costs, are also made to the energy system model to include the operation of the desalination unit.

3.4. Multi-parametric optimization approach

To implement hierarchical decision-making in the EWN, the lower level problem here is treated as a multi-parametric programming problem, whose resulting explicit solutions are then integrated into the upper level problem to be subsequently solved as single-level programming problems (Avraamidou and Pistikopoulos, 2022). The water recovery of the RO unit, a variable in the upper level problem, is considered the parameter in the lower level problem to enable its reformulation into a multi-parametric problem.

4. Case Study

To illustrate the hierarchical decision-making capabilities of the proposed framework, we consider a case study based on an energy-water supply system in Texas. The aim of this system is to meet the energy and water demands of a metropolitan region where hourly energy and water demands must be satisfied for a period of one year. The upper level decision maker will decide the design of the energy system based on lower level decision maker that will determine the optimal operational profile for the water system. For the energy system, data pertaining to the power output of the renewable energy sources, namely, the solar direct normal irradiation and wind speeds, was obtained from the National Renewable Energy Laboratory (NREL), while the biomass power output was determined using crop and net energy yields (Cook et al., 2022). Moreover, the land available to the energy system is set at 10 Mha and is allotted for harvesting maize and installing solar panels and wind turbines. For the water system, it is assumed that the water recovery of the desalination unit is constrained to operate between 45% and 85%, while it's permeate flow should be at least 227 m³/h. To analyze the impact of prioritizing the operation of the RO unit, three cases are considered where the feed flows of water to this unit are varied as shown in Table 1. For each case, the solution of lower level multi-parametric problem yields one critical region, and therefore, one explicit function that defines the energy consumption of the water system in terms of its water recovery. After this solution was incorporated into the upper level problem, the total power generated by all renewable energy sources is maximized to determine the design and operation of the energy-water supply systems. The optimization results of the integrated energy-water supply systems are detailed in Table 1.

Table 1: Optimization results for annual operation of integrated energy-water supply systems

Case	RO Feed flow (m³/h)	Total Costs (Billion USD)	Total Power Available (TWh)	RO Water Recovery (%)	RO Energy Consumption (MW)
1	1,703.44	151.98	1,260.541	47	1,359
2	1,362.75	151.93	1,260.539	59	2,276
3	1,022.06	161.02	1,260.646	78	3,193

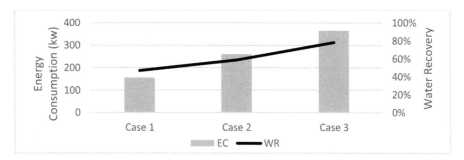

Figure 2: Results of varying feed flow of the RO unit on the operations of the water system

The energy system in all three cases comprised primarily of single axis tracking solar panels and some wind turbines to produce 1,259 TWh in each case by utilizing the maximum land available for the deployment of the renewable energy infrastructure.

Biomass was not deployed for energy generation due to the water system's objective of minimizing energy consumption. As such, only the water necessary to meet the metropolitan demands at 800 m^3/h are produced. However, as the feed flow of water to the RO decreased, its water recovery and subsequently its energy consumption increases across the three cases as illustrated in Figure 2. Therefore, the total power available, or in other words, the energy available after meeting the demands of the water system also subsequently varied in each case as shown in Table 1 to meet the overall demands which remained constant.

5. Conclusion

In this work, a framework for developing bi-level decision strategies in hierarchical energy-water supply systems was presented. The proposed framework was applied to a case study in Texas, where the optimal mix of renewable energy sources and technologies, along with the land utilization and desalination requirements were determined to meet preset energy and water demands. Future work will aim to incorporate dynamic RO operational profiles and assess the impact of competing and non-competing objectives among multiple levels of hierarchy in a system.

6. Acknowledgments

This publication was made possible by support from the TAMUQ PhD Fellows Program and the Texas A&M Energy Institute, for which the authors are sincerely grateful. The work presented is solely the responsibility of the authors.

References

S. Avraamidou, B. Beykal, I. P. E. Pistikopoulos, E. N. Pistikopoulos, 2018, A hierarchical food-energy-water nexus (FEW-N) decision-making approach for land use optimization, Computer Aided Chemical Engineering, 44, 1885-1890.

S. Avraamidou, E. N. Pistikopoulos, 2022, Multi-Level Mixed-Integer Optimization, De Gruyter, Germany.

C. Chen, X. Zhang, H. Zhang, Y. Cai, S. Wang, 2022, Managing water-energy-carbon nexus in integrated regional water network planning through graph theory-based bi-level programming, Applied Energy, 328, 120178.

J. Cook, M. D. Martino, R. C. Allen, E. N. Pistikopoulos, S. Avraamidou, 2022, A decision-making framework for the optimal design of renewable energy systems under energy-water-land nexus considerations, Science of the Total Environment, 827, 154185.

M. D. Martino, P. Linke, E. N. Pistikopoulos, 2023, Towards Optimal Energy-Water Supply System Operation for Agricultural and Metropolitan Ecosystems, arXiv preprint arXiv:2303.13599

M. D. Martino, S. Avraamidou, E. N. Pistikopoulos, 2022, A Neural Network Based Superstructure Optimization Approach to Reverse Osmosis Desalination Plants, Membranes, 12, 2, 199.

D. J. Garcia, F. You, 2016, The water-energy-food nexus and process systems engineering: A new focus, Computers & Chemical Engineering, 91, 49-67

J. Liu, V. Hull, H.C.J. Godfray, D. Tilman, P. Gleick, H. Hoff, C. Pahl-Wostl, Z. Xu, M. Gon Chung, J. Sun, S. Li, 2018, Nexus approaches to global sustainable development, Nature Sustainability, 1, 466-476.

M. Martina, I. E. Grossmann, 2015, Water–energy nexus in biofuels production and renewable based power, Sustainable Production and Consumption, 2, 96-108.

A. Panagopoulos, 2021, Water-energy nexus: desalination technologies and renewable energy sources, Environmental Science and Pollution Research, 28, 21009-21022.

Flavio Manenti, Gintaras V. Reklaitis (Eds.), Proceedings of the 34th European Symposium on Computer Aided Process Engineering / 15th International Symposium on Process Systems Engineering (ESCAPE34/PSE24), June 2-6, 2024, Florence, Italy

A Systematic Analysis of Economic and Environmental Trade-Offs in Hydrogen Supply Chains with Resilience Considerations

Yasir Ibrahim[a,b], Elizabeth J. Abraham[a,c,d], Dhabia M. Al-Mohannadi[a]

[a]*Department of Chemical Engineering, Texas A&M University at Qatar, Education City, PO Box 23874, Doha, Qatar*
[b]*Department of Multidisciplinary Engineering, Texas A&M University, College Station, 77843 TX, United States*
[c]*Artie McFerrin Department of Chemical Engineering, Texas A&M University, 3122 TAMU, College Station, TX 77843, USA*
[d]*Texas A&M Energy Institute, Texas A&M University, 1617 Research Pkwy, College Station, TX 77845, USA*
dhabia.al-mohannadi@qatar.tamu.edu

Abstract

The global impacts of climate change have necessitated a shift in the production, distribution, and consumption of energy. To facilitate this transition in energy that will replace fossil fuels with more renewable sources, it is key to understand the role of energy storage in supply chains of the future energy mix. Due to the intermittent nature of renewable energy, hydrogen is gaining traction to store this energy and thereby plays a major role towards achieving greener energy systems. As multiple segments within the hydrogen supply chain are presently being investigated extensively to enable deployment at larger scales, there is considerable uncertainty associated with the progress of the supply chain as a whole. Furthermore, these supply chains will not only need to account for the uncertainties that come with the energy transition, but those that inherently exist for all supply chains. Accordingly, there is a need to incorporate resilience into the design and optimization of hydrogen supply chain networks that account for such uncertainties. Through this work, an optimization-based model is presented to analyze the trade-offs that exist between economic and environmental decision objectives when resilience is considered. In this manner, strategies for managing disruptions within the context of energy security and sustainable development can be developed to adapt to changing circumstances.

Keywords: Resilience, Hydrogen supply chain networks, Multi-objective optimization

1. Introduction

Hydrogen supply chain networks (HSCN) have become an integral part of global discussions on the energy transition. As a cleaner alternative to traditional energy sources, the drive to utilize hydrogen is reinforced by its ability to connect various energy sectors, enhancing the flexibility of systems through diverse transportation and distribution networks (Li et al, 2019). Hydrogen's adaptability with other forms of energy, such as ammonia, methanol, and liquid organic hydrogen carriers, further diversifies the energy sector. The range of sources for hydrogen production, from fossil fuels to renewables, and the associated technologies at various maturity levels, present a complex landscape for conversion technologies and transportation options, including ships, pipelines, and trucks. This complexity necessitates a holistic analysis of the different components of HSCNs, each with its unique functionalities.

In this work, we concentrate specifically on technology failure scenarios within HSCNs. Our analysis identifies technology failure as a prevalent and impactful uncertainty. These failures, ranging from total system shutdowns to gradual recoveries, effectively mirror a spectrum of real-time operational disruptions commonly encountered in the industry. While acknowledging the existence of various uncertainties in HSCNs, our focused approach on technology failures allows for a nuanced exploration of resilience strategies. This specificity enables a realistic assessment of critical conditions and resilience measures in response to technological disruptions. As HSCNs evolve to meet climate targets, uncertainties related to their implementation, influenced by a myriad of internal and external factors, become increasingly significant. To address these challenges, our study embraces the concept of resilience. The ability of HSCNs to anticipate, withstand, and recover from disruptive events, particularly technology failures, is crucial for maintaining system integrity. This resilience is assessed through both qualitative and quantitative approaches (Gasser et al., 2018), aiming to minimize adverse impacts and restore performance.

This paper introduces a novel superstructure-based optimization approach to design resilient HSCNs. We specifically address the vulnerabilities arising from the diverse and time-variant factors affecting HSCN's production and utilization pathways. This approach equips decision-makers to evaluate economic and environmental impacts under various disruption scenarios, aiming to identify optimal network configurations. The subsequent sections will detail our methodology, present a case study applying this approach, and conclude with our findings and directions for future work.

2. Methodology

The superstructure-based multi-objective optimization approach used in this work is adopted from Ibrahim and Al-Mohannadi (2023). Through their approach, the selection of the optimal production, storage, and transportation technologies can be determined, where each technology is represented as an input-output module. The selection of the technologies that can be considered for the design of the HSCN is based on the stage-gate process presented in Abraham et al. (2021). Each module is associated with operational capacities, capital and operating costs, and further is defined by a unique set of resources with given specifications. These resources can then be exchanged between different technologies to meet a set hydrogen demand target and carbon dioxide reduction targets for the HSCN, which are set as constraints. In the face of disruptive events, the impact is essentially on the capacity of the system. Either the system stops performing entirely or partially. To introduce resilience considerations in this model, we introduce a parameter called the operation phase, given by θ, which essentially defines the operational capacity of a unit as defined by Eq. (1).

$$\text{Operational capacity} = \theta \times \text{Maximum operational capacity} \qquad (1)$$

At different rates of the operation phase, ranging from complete outage (0.0) to full operation (1.0), the multi-objective optimization model will decide the optimal pathways to meet the set demand targets while accounting for economic and environmental trade-offs when disruptions in performance defined by capacity changes occurs.

Central to our approach is the concept of diversification, which is favored over redundancy as a resilience strategy. Diversification, in this context, refers to the integration and utilization of a wide array of technologies and resources within the HSCN.

By embracing diversification, our model does not solely rely on redundant capacities (duplicate systems for backup) but rather explores a variety of pathways and technologies that can be activated or adjusted in response to disruptions. This diversification approach enhances the HSCN's robustness by enabling it to adapt to various disruptions without relying on a limited set of solutions. The model evaluates different production, storage, and transportation options to determine the most resilient network design. It also assesses the feasibility and impact of switching between energy sources, technologies, or logistical routes in response to changing conditions. This ensures that the HSCN remains functional and efficient under operational challenges, securing a sustainable and reliable energy supply.

3. Case Study

In pursuit of considering resilience in the design of the HSCN, we employed the proposed multi-objective optimization model to analyze the impact of imposing CO_2 emission reduction targets with technology failures and subsequent recovery phases. The HSCN is set to export 30,000 t of hydrogen. The data pertaining to the economic parameters was established from the works of Ibrahim and Al-Mohannadi (2023) and Ahmed et al. (2020). 3D Pareto surface plots were then obtained to illustrate the relationship between unit operational phases, total costs of producing and distributing hydrogen, and carbon reduction goals. The impact of disruptions was analyzed on units that represent production, transportation, and storage.

3.1. Pipeline Disruptions

In the first case, the impacts of disruptions on the transportation mode, namely, pipelines were analyzed. The Pareto plot obtained in this case is shown in Figure 1.

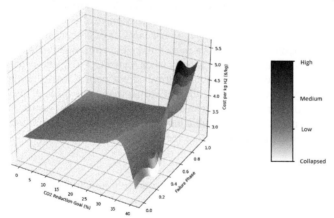

Figure 1: Pareto plot for the operational phases of the pipeline

For lower CO_2 reduction goals (0% to approximately 15%), the cost of hydrogen production and distribution decreases as the operational performance of the pipeline recovers. This is due to a gradual recovery in the pipeline mode as it is more cost-effective than other expensive alternative transportation means (such as trucks in this case). As the CO_2 reduction goal increased beyond 15% the cost became more volatile as more technologies for carbon capture needed to be deployed. There is a significant peak in cost associated with the most restrictive CO_2 reduction goal of 40% reaching 5.31 \$/kg. Moreover, the plot shows collapsing phases (as highlighted in white) when the CO_2

reduction goal is at its maximum and the pipeline's operational performance ranges from 0 to 40% operational phase. This highlights the network is more vulnerable to pipeline failures when it strives for aggressive CO_2 reduction goals.

3.2. Storage Disruptions

3.2.1. Hydrogen Storage

The Pareto plot in Figure 2 provides insights on the impact of disruptions on gaseous hydrogen storage when coupled with economic and environmental considerations.

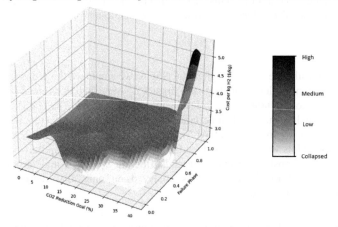

Figure 2: Pareto plot for the operational phases of hydrogen storage

In the early phases of operational recovery, the cost exhibits significant variability, which can be attributed to the reliance on more expensive hydrogen storage alternatives, such as liquid vessels, to compensate for the reduced operational capacity of gaseous hydrogen storage. Figure 2 shows that hydrogen storage is a more vulnerable portion of the HSCN due to the presence of more collapsing phases especially when higher CO_2 reduction goals need to be achieved. These white areas pinpoint critical stress points where urgent recovery actions are necessary to avoid system collapse. Furthermore, as expected, there is a gradual increase in the cost per kg of hydrogen as the CO_2 reduction goal increases. However, the cost initially remains relatively stable but spikes to \$5.31/kg for ambitious targets due to the need for costlier carbon capture technologies or cleaner production methods.

3.2.2. Carbon Storage

As the carbon reduction targets of the HSCN play a pivotal role in achieving climate targets, the impact of disruptions on carbon storage which is vital to achieving these targets is analyzed. The Pareto plot indicating the influence of these disruptions is presented in Figure 3. At relaxed CO_2 reduction targets, the system is stable even at lower operational phases or capacities or higher performance losses. This suggests that the network relies on low-cost carbon emission mitigation technologies (i.e. SMR accompanied by carbon capture). As the CO_2 reduction goal intensifies, the graph shows an increase in the cost per kg of H_2, particularly at higher levels of operational impairment in CO_2 storage until the system collapses. However, the valleys or lower-cost areas in the operational phase axis indicate that there are levels of resilience built into the network, allowing for some degree of flexibility and cost control. These points correlate with the network's ability to leverage other CO_2 reduction measures that are less dependent on storage, such as low-carbon hydrogen production or enhanced utilization of CO_2.

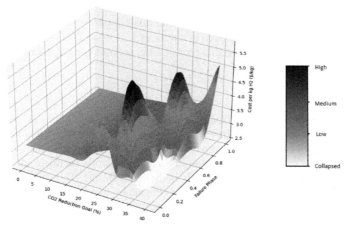

Figure 3: Pareto plot for the operational phases of carbon storage

Despite the inherent resilience and cost control mechanisms within the network, the observed white areas represent collapsing phases and signify critical points where the system fails to meet hydrogen demands under extreme CO_2 reduction goals. The inability to rely solely on carbon storage necessitates the activation of more costly carbon mitigation strategies. However, the increasing frequency and breadth of these collapsing phases suggest that the network's current flexibility does not suffice when faced with the duality of extensive CO_2 storage outages and rigorous environmental standards.

3.3. Production disruptions
To understand the impact imposed by disruptions on production units, Figure 4 depicts the failure of the SMR, which showcases a twofold challenge for the HSCN.

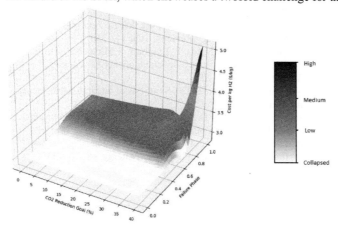

Figure 4: Pareto plot for the operational phases of the SMR

On one hand, the initial absence of SMR's operational capacity (from 0 to almost 60%) and subsequent collapse of the system as shown by the expansive white region indicate the network's substantial dependence on this technology to meet the hydrogen demand. Moreover, this further indicates that without the SMR, the network cannot meet production demand by solely depending on existing green and white production technologies, namely electrolysis and natural gas pyrolysis (Kvaerner process). On the other hand, the pursuit of more stringent CO_2 reduction goals further exacerbates the situation, as it drives the cost per kg of hydrogen to a peak of 5.31 \$/kg. This rise in cost can be attributed to the network's shift towards more CCUS technologies to adhere to stricter CO_2 emissions regulations.

4. Conclusions

This study presents a multi-objective optimization model for a HSCN that prioritizes cost efficiency, CO_2 emission thresholds, and network resilience. The model highlights the importance of integrating diverse hydrogen production technologies and demonstrates that while each component's operational disruption impacts the network, there are some components that are more critical than others, such as the SMR in this. The network's resilience, as evidenced by its ability to recover and maintain functionality despite disruptions, underscores the need for robust and adaptable system designs that can withstand individual plant failures that still meet environmental and economic objectives. For future work, it is essential to extend the model's capabilities by incorporating recovery time metrics to provide a more nuanced understanding of system resilience. Additionally, measuring system reliability to predict the likelihood and timing of future failures will be a critical step forward to enhance the sustainability and reliability of HSCNs.

5. Acknowledgments

The authors gratefully acknowledge the support of Qatar National Research Fund (QNRF) grant NPRP14C-0920-210017 and the TAMUQ PhD Fellows Program.

References

E. J. Abraham, F. Ramadan, D. M. Al-Mohannadi, 2021, Synthesis of Sustainable Carbon Negative Eco-Industrial Parks, Frontiers in Energy Research, 9.

L. Li, H. Manier, M. Manier, 2019, Hydrogen supply chain network design: An optimization-oriented review, Renewable and Sustainable Energy Reviews, 103, 342-360.

P. Gasser, P. Lustenberger, M. Cinelli, W. Kim, M. Spada, P. Burgherr, S. Hirschberg, B. Stojadinovic, T. Y. Sun, 2019, A review on resilience assessment of energy systems, Sustainable and Resilient Infrstructure, 6, 5, 273-299.

R. Ahmed, S. Shehab, D. M. Al-Mohannadi, P. Linke, 2020, Synthesis of integrated processing clusters, Chemical Engineering Science, 227, 115922.

S. Cutter, 2018, Compound, Cascading, or Complex Disasters: What's in a Name?, Environment: Science and Policy for Sustainable Development, 60, 6, 16-25.

Y. Ibrahim, D. M. Al-Mohannadi, 2023, Optimization of low-carbon hydrogen supply chain networks in industrial clusters, International Journal of Hydrogen Energy, 48, 36, 13325–13342.

Flavio Manenti, Gintaras V. Reklaitis (Eds.), Proceedings of the 34th European Symposium on Computer Aided Process Engineering / 15th International Symposium on Process Systems Engineering (ESCAPE34/PSE24), June 2-6, 2024, Florence, Italy

Sustainability analysis of a large-scale calcium looping plant coupled with concentrated solar energy

Ricardo N. Dias[a], Rui M. Filipe[b,c], Carla I.C. Pinheiro[a], Henrique A. Matos[c]

[a]*Centro de Química Estrutural, IMS, Department of Chemical Engineering, Instituto Superior Técnico, Universidade de Lisboa, Av. Rovisco Pais 1, 1049-001 Lisboa, Portugal*
[b]*Instituto Superior de Engenharia de Lisboa, Instituto Politécnico de Lisboa, R. Conselheiro Emídio Navarro 1, Lisboa 1959-007, Portugal*
[c]*Centro de Recursos Naturais, Department of Chemical Engineering, Instituto Superior Técnico, Universidade de Lisboa, Av. Rovisco Pais 1, 1049-001 Lisboa, Portugal*

ricardo.n.dias@tecnico.ulisboa.pt

Abstract

Concentrated solar energy represents one potential solution for the energy transition of energy-intensive industries, including the cement industry, wherein temperatures exceeding 800 ºC are required. The present study provides a sustainability analysis of a calcium looping plant coupled with a thermochemical energy storage system. Three process alternatives were evaluated: V0, which used CO_2 as the fluidization fluid, and V1 and V2, were CO_2 is replaced by water vapor as the fluidization fluid and different calciner temperatures are used (800 ºC and 900 ºC). The sustainability of each option was evaluated using the GREENSCOPE analysis tool and the four metrics provided by GREENSCOPE were analysed in detail. To determine the most sustainable alternative, TOPSIS was used and V2 was found to be the best alternative overall. V1 had a similar sustainability to V2 due to both using water vapor as the fluidization fluid, which was found to be the primary factor in improving sustainability. However, using water vapor to achieve fluidization instead of CO_2 has some drawbacks, as significant process changes are necessary, which increase energy consumption and capital costs.

Keywords: LCA, Ca-Looping, Thermochemical Energy Storage, Sustainability

1. Introduction

Concentrated solar energy (CSE) when coupled with a power generation facility, offers a viable alternative to mainstream solar harvesting technologies such as photovoltaics. However, this technology is dependent on a highly intermittent energy source, the sun. There are many factors influencing the performance of CSE units, with cloud coverage being one of the most influential. Yet, when CSE is capable of operating at optimal conditions, temperatures higher than 1000 ºC can be achieved. These temperatures make it a viable solution for many energy intensive industries struggling to achieve a clean energy transition (Marques et al., 2023).

The cement industry is one of the largest contributors to carbon emissions, accounting for 8 % of worldwide emissions. These emissions result from the combustion of fossil fuels used to achieve the high temperatures required for the calcination endothermic reaction and clinkerization, as well as the inherent CO_2 produced by the calcination reaction.

Therefore, replacing the fossil fuels with a clean energy source could reduce emissions by approximately 40 %. It would also enable an easier capture of the CO_2 produced, since the effluent is not diluted with the air used in the combustion with fossil fuels. An example of such technology is solar calcination of calcium carbonate, which has several projects demonstrating the feasibility of this technique (SoCaLTES, 2019). A pure CO_2 stream can be used to achieve fluidization during calcination, making the capture of this greenhouse gas straightforward. Another solution has been presented, with the use of water vapor has fluidization fluid (Rodrigues et al., 2023a), where a separation unit for water/CO_2 is required. However, this separation is easier than the capture from a flue gas stream.

The reversibility of the calcination reaction makes it suitable for a looping process, where the products of the calcination reaction store energy in chemical form (Teixeira et al., 2021). This process is termed calcium looping for thermochemical energy storage (CaL-TCES) and has been demonstrated at pilot scale. Yet, some hurdles must be addressed before full scale implementation, namely the deactivation of the sorbent (calcium oxide, the product of the calcination reaction). As proposed by Rodrigues et al. (2023b), the deactivation of the sorbent can be addressed by purging it, making the CaL an open cycle, where the calcium carbonate is 100 % converted to CO_2 and CaO, and later these products are reacted together to produce back the calcium carbonate in the carbonator, where an 81 % conversion is achieved. The effluent stream from the carbonator is purged, forcing a make-up of fresh calcium carbonate to be fed to the calciner.

This work presents a sustainability analysis of a CaL-TCES plant using GREENSCOPE. Several process alternatives have been evaluated, including the use of CO_2 and water vapor as fluidization fluids, and different calciner temperatures. This work further elaborates on the sustainability analysis of the process (Dias et al., 2023b), presenting a detailed analysis of the GREENSCOPE metrics. The sustainability results obtained from GREENSCOPE (global and by metric) were evaluated using TOPSIS to choose the most sustainable process alternative and demonstrate the advantage of an integrated analysis.

2. Calcium Looping for Thermochemical Energy Storage

The case study used in this work is a CaL-TCES plant, that has been previously modelled in Aspen Plus® (Rodrigues, et al., 2023a). The process was designed with a focus on thermochemical energy storage. Therefore, the optimal operating conditions were defined to maximize the energy conversion of the process, the solar to electrical efficiency. A solar field of 100 MJ was considered as the energy source for the calciner. Three process alternatives from the base process were evaluated: use of CO_2 as the fluidization fluid (V0), use of water vapor as the fluidization fluid (V1), and a reduced temperature in the calciner prompted by the use of water vapor (V2). Table 1 outlines the different process alternatives considered.

Table 1 – Evaluated CaL-TCES process alternatives, adapted from (Dias et al., 2023b).

Alternative	Purge (%)	Fluidization Fluid	Calciner temperature (ºC)
V0		CO_2	900
V1	100	Water vapor	
V2			800

3. Methodology

The sustainability analysis presented evaluated the impact of proposed process design changes on the sustainability of the CaL-TCES plant model. As the models used are not representative of a real plant and the alternatives compared are conceptual models, the assessment boundaries were set at the "gates" of the model. Therefore, the supply chain of raw materials and the subsequent use of system products are not considered. These boundaries are the most appropriate for comparing process changes (Smith et al., 2015).

3.1. GREENSCOPE

Gauging Reaction Effectiveness for the ENvironmental Sustainability of Chemistries with a Multi-Objective Process Evaluator (GREENSCOPE) is a sustainability analysis tool developed by Gonzalez and Smith (2003), that focus on evaluating process design changes. A total of 139 sustainability indicators are considered, distributed across 4 metrics, as shown in Table 2.

Table 2 – GREENSCOPE metrics and the total number of indictors in each.

Metrics	N° of indicators
Mass Efficiency	26
Environment	66
Energy	14
Economy	33

Each indicator is computed with a specific equation (Ruiz-Mercado et al., 2012), which leads to an absolute indicator value (x_i), for each indicator i. The upper ($x_{i,upper}$) and lower ($x_{i,lower}$) possible values for each indicator are defined based on heuristics (e.g. water consumption limits) or inherent to the indicator (e.g. reaction yield). A maximum-minimum normalization, Eq. (1), is then applied to all indicators, yielding a score ($\%G_j(i)$), for each alternative j, that facilitates comparison and graphical representation, where n is the number of indicators and V the number of alternatives.

$$\%G_j(i) = \frac{|x_i - x_{i,lower}|}{|x_{i,upper} - x_{i,lower}|} , i \in \{1,2, \dots, n\}, j \in \{1,2, \dots, V\} \qquad (1)$$

3.2. TOPSIS

Technique for Order of Preference by Similarity to Ideal Solution is a multi objective decision making (MODM) method presented by Yoon and Hwang (1981) It determines the best option based on Euclidean distances of each alternative to the others (relative distance to the best performance) in each indicator. In this work, TOPSIS is used to decide on which process alternative assessed with GREENSCOPE is the more sustainable. TOPSIS implementation method was previously described by Dias et al. (2023).

4. Results

The GREENSCOPE results for the assessment of the CaL-TCES alternatives are presented, firstly the results for each metric, secondly, the TOPSIS analysis of the GREENSCOPE results.

4.1. Spider graphs from each metric

The sustainability results obtained using GREENSCOPE for the CaL-TCES plant indicate that the three evaluated alternatives have a similar sustainability performance. As shown in Figure 1, deciding which alternative is the most sustainable, just based on the spider graphs obtained, is inaccurate. If the decision on which alternative is the most sustainable was to be made from the energy indicators (Figure 1c), alternative V0 was to be selected as the most sustainable, as it has a similar performance to the other alternatives, except in indicator four, where it outperforms the other ones. Conversely, in economic indicators (Figure 1d) alternative V0 was to be selected as worst performing one, because of a similar performance of the alternatives in all but one indicator. In

Figures 1a and 1b there is no difference between the three alternatives, so these do not allow for a solid decision on which alternative is the most sustainable.

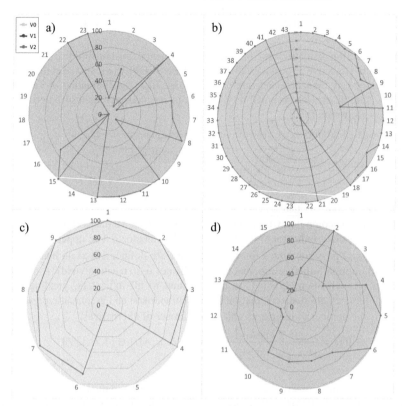

Figure 1 - GREENSCOPE results for each metric. a - Efficiency, b - Environment, c - Energy, d - Economy.

The differences identified between alternatives in Figures 1c and 1d can be attributed to the introduction of water vapor as the fluidization fluid (alternatives V1 and V2), which significantly improves the calcination reaction efficiency (Rodrigues et al., 2023a). However, this change introduces a more complex process with the need for a water/CO_2 separation unit, leading to an energy penalty, as compressors and coolers are required to carry out the separation. Therefore, in Figure 1c, alternative V0 outperforms the remaining alternatives.

The introduction of the separation unit also affects the economic indicators, due to the increased expenditure on equipment and operational costs. The increase in the costs is not easily noticeable from Figure 1d, as the three alternative scores are almost overlayed. Hence, a variation in the economic indicators between the alternatives was expected.

4.2. TOPSIS results

The data presented in Figure 1 was fed to the TOPSIS algorithm, allowing it to rank each alternative, as described in section 3.2. The results obtained for an overall assessment (considering all indicators) can be found in Table 3. From the overall evaluation is possible to observe a clear difference between the three process alternatives considered. These results are contrasting with the ones in Figure 1, and clearly show that V0 as an inferior alternative to V1 and V2. V2 is elected as the most sustainable alternative, with a score obtained from TOPSIS of 0.9213. Which means that in almost every indicator, V2 has the highest GREENSCOPE score.

Table 3 – TOPSIS results for the three alternatives evaluated using GREENSCOPE results.

	V0	V1	V2
TOPSIS	0.0787	0.9036	0.9213
Rank	3	2	1

V1 has a TOPSIS result similar to alternative V2, as expected, since these two alternatives feature the use of water vapor as fluidization fluid in the calciner, which allows for a more efficient calcination reaction. However, V2 was modelled with a lower calcination temperature (800 °C), which increases its sustainability performance.

The results for the metrics assessment using TOPSIS are presented in Table 4 were obtained. These used the same indicator split as for the results shown in Figure 1. As seen in Table 4, TOPSIS ranks each alternative in each metric, which was not possible to obtain with the GREENSCOPE results shown in Figure 1. Alternatives V1 and V2 are similar, but use different calciner temperatures tied, which justifies the very close, but not equal, values obtained for the efficiency metric. V1 and V2 are closely matched in the environment metric, but V2 is still the best performing alternative.

Table 4 – TOPSIS results split into metrics for the three alternatives evaluated using GREENSCOPE results.

	V0	V1	V2
Efficiency			
TOPSIS	0.0074	0.9926	0.9926
Rank	3	2	1
Environment			
TOPSIS	0.0001	0.9249	0.9999
Rank	3	2	1
Energy			
TOPSIS	0.9762	0.0781	0.0229
Rank	1	2	3
Economy			
TOPSIS	0.2716	0.7306	0.7294
Rank	3	1	2

In the energy metric alternative V0 is clearly the best performing alternative, as expected, since this alternative does not feature the energy consuming of the water/CO_2 separation unit. The economic results from GREENSCOPE are more evenly distributed across the alternatives, with V1 and V2 being closely matched. In this simpler configuration V1 was the best performing alternative.

5. Conclusions

A sustainability analysis was performed on a calcium looping plant coupled with thermochemical energy storage using GREENSCOPE. To facilitate the decision-making process and determine the most sustainable option, TOPSIS was used because the results obtained from GREENSCOPE did not provide a straightforward decision. Thus, the use of TOPSIS was essential in distinguishing between the alternatives under consideration. When considering an overall evaluation of all alternatives using TOPSIS, the alternative using steam as fluidization fluid and 800 °C in the calciner (V2) proved to be more sustainable. However, a closer analysis of each metric gave a clearer understanding of the impact of the proposed process changes. It was found that, although V2 is the best alternative, it is the worst performing in the energy metric. These results show that considering only one metric may lead to wrong decisions on the selection of the more sustainable alternative.

The use of water vapor to achieve fluidization is shown to increase the sustainability of the CaL-TCES system, which will be further investigated in the future with a detailed techno-economic analysis.

6. Acknowledgements

The present work was financed by the Portuguese Foundation for Technology and Science (FCT) PTDC/EAM-PEC/32342/2017, CQE strategic project FCT-UIDB/00100/2020, CERENA strategic project FCT-UIDB/04028/2020 and PhD grant PRT/BD/154409/2023, this support is gratefully appreciated.

References

R. N., Dias, R. M., Filipe & H. A., Matos (2023a). Decision-making based on sustainability analysis using GREENSCOPE. Clean Technologies and Environmental Policy, https://doi.org/10.1007/s10098-023-02647-4

R. N., Dias, R. M., Filipe & H. A., Matos (2023b). Sustainability analysis of a solar-driven calcium looping plant for thermochemical energy storage. Journal of Cleaner Production, 139551. https://doi.org/10.1016/J.JCLEPRO.2023.139551

M. A., Gonzalez & R. L., Smith (2003). A Methodology to Evaluate Process Sustainability. Environmental Progress, 22(4). https://doi.org/10.1002/ep.670220415

C.-L., Hwang & K., Yoon (1981). Multiple Attribute Decision Making Methods and Applications A State-of-the-Art Survey. Lecture Notes in Economics and Mathematical Systems, 186.

L. M., Marques, S. M., Mota, P., Teixeira, C. I. C., Pinheiro, & H. A., Matos (2023). Ca-looping process using wastes of marble powders and limestones for CO_2 capture from real flue gas in the cement industry. Journal of CO_2 Utilization, 71, 102450. https://doi.org/10.1016/J.JCOU.2023.102450

D., Rodrigues, C. I. C., Pinheiro, R. M., Filipe, L. F., Mendes, & H. A., Matos (2023a). Optimization of an improved calcium-looping process for thermochemical energy storage in concentrating solar power plants. Journal of Energy Storage, 72, 108199. https://doi.org/10.1016/J.EST.2023.108199

D., Rodrigues, M., Alvarez Rivero, C. I. C., Pinheiro, J. P., Cardoso, & L. F., Mendes (2023b). Computational model of a Calcium-looping fluidized bed calcination reactor with imposed concentrated solar irradiance. Solar Energy, 258, 72–87. https://doi.org/10.1016/J.SOLENER.2023.04.018

G. J., Ruiz-Mercado, R. L., Smith, & M. A., Gonzalez (2012). Sustainability indicators for chemical processes: II. Data needs. Industrial and Engineering Chemistry Research, 51(5). https://doi.org/10.1021/ie200755k

R. L., Smith, G. J., Ruiz-Mercado, & M. A., Gonzalez (2015). Using GREENSCOPE indicators for sustainable computer-aided process evaluation and design. Computers and Chemical Engineering, 81. https://doi.org/10.1016/j.compchemeng.2015.04.020

SoCaLTES. (2019). SoCaLTES Project Solar-driven Ca-Looping Process for Thermochemical Energy Storage. https://socaltes.net/

P. Teixeira, A., Fernandes, F., Ribeiro, & C. I. C., Pinheiro (2021). Blending wastes of marble powder and dolomite sorbents for calcium-looping CO_2 capture under realistic industrial calcination conditions. Materials, 14(16). https://doi.org/10.3390/ma14164379

Flavio Manenti, Gintaras V. Reklaitis (Eds.), Proceedings of the 34th European Symposium on Computer Aided Process Engineering / 15th International Symposium on Process Systems Engineering (ESCAPE34/PSE24), June 2-6, 2024, Florence, Italy

Real Time Optimization of Sour Gas Processing Unit via Sulfur Dioxide Emissions Predictive Model

A. Eren Vedin[a,*], Pelin Dologlu[a], Mert Akcin[a] , Aygul Karimova[b] , Kemal Burçak Kaplan[a], Aysegul Sener[c], Osman Karan[c]

[a]*SOCAR Turkey, Data Science and Analytics, Istanbul 34485, Türkiye*
[b]*SOCAR STAR Oil Refinery, Process Engineering, Aliaga, Izmir 35800, Türkiye*
[c]*SOCAR STAR Oil Refinery, Process Excellence, Aliaga, Izmir 35800, Türkiye*
eren.vedin@socar.com.tr

Abstract

Sour gas processing in refineries, for the separation of H_2S from off-gases, is an important process in terms of environmental concerns. Thus, combustion fuel can be used in furnaces as energy source, after processing. However, disturbances such as sulfur content fluctuations in crude-oil feed, plant operating policy updates such as operating capacity, and process related variations in the plant variables such as absorber temperature and pressures cause sudden SO_2 emission peaks in the furnaces. This is avoided by excess amine supply, resulting in higher steam consumption in amine regeneration unit (ARU), eventually leading to economic losses. This study focuses on the development of a real-time optimization architecture to calculate optimum amine flow rate both to account for plant constraints and profitability issues. Based on the architecture, decision tree based predictive model for refinery furnace emissions has been established to deliver in-advance warning for feedforward plant control tasks. The architecture also employs several empirical sub-models to estimate sulphur fraction in the streams, for the real-time integration by eliminating the laboratory analysis at high frequency. The approach is implemented on the actual plant through Python Programming Language and implements the control actions at 30 minute frequency, which is significantly smaller than the time constant of the plant, by changing amine feed after the algorithm predicts the emission increase. It has been observed that the model predicts an emission increase from 1 hour to 4 hours in advance.

Keywords: Decision Tree Algorithm; Emission Reduction; Real Time Optimization; Sour Gas Processing; Amine Reduction Unit.

1. Introduction

The fuel gas in the refinery is composed of a mixture of off-gases and natural gas. The mixture is primarily used as the energy source for the furnaces and boilers. In line with the growing emphasis on the environmental and the economic concerns, it is of paramount importance to monitor the chemical content of the fuel within this system to ensure acceptable emission rates. A major pollutant from the process is sulphur dioxide (SO_2) and caused by emissions from furnace stacks when hydrogen sulphide (H_2S) is burnt, unless removed from the off-gas by sour gas processing plant. Thus, the performance and the management of the plant is important for environmental concerns. Studies indicate localized increase in environmental SO_2 concentration in the atmosphere which can even contribute to acid rain when those plants fail to achieve their task properly. Therefore, continuous monitoring of emissions and optimization of related proceses are crucial for human health (Abdelrasoul et al, 2010) to ensure production under legal constraints. A significant fraction of the studies in the literature employ thermodynamic and kinetic equations (Feng et al., 2023) for the optimization tasks. On the other hand, those are limited to a narrow operating regime or dynamic optimization for small-scale processes. These algorithms are feasible, especially in systems where all components entering and exiting the absorber system can be tracked. In such solutions, optimization can be solved by kinetic equations or mass-energy balance equations by using physicochemical information of all streams which are entering or leaving the absorber system (Nordenkampf et al., 2003).

Machine learning based algorithms, benefiting from historical patterns and plant management policies, on absorber column and amine regeneration column show a promising tool for the task. In parallel with more sophisticated mechanistic formulations, the optimization computations are carried out by considering important column variables including composition, pressure, and temperature of streams entering and leaving the units. These methods are generally effective for optimizing processes composed of several units. While this approach is practical, the prediction accuracy is highly dependent on measured variables and increases once higher number of sensors are implemented, in general (Curreri et al., 2021).

This study, a novel optimization architecture, benefiting from advanced machine learning algorithms at different temporal scales, for the implementation to the actual plant is proposed. The architecture is operationally desirables as it ensures a coordinating decision making through integrating several small scale subprocesses with individual inferential sensors and local control and management architectures. The approach is implemented on the sour gas processing plant to process the off-gases from Crude Distillation Unit (CDU), Hydrocracking Unit (HCU), Diesel Hydrotreating Unit (DHT) and Delayed Coking Unit (DCU) which are processed in a SGP and UGP.

2. Materials and Methods

2.1. Refinery Sour Gas Process Description

In the refinery, crude oil distillation, hydrocracking and thermal cracking are major sources H_2S emission. Off-gases from those are processed in SGP and UGP units, where H_2S are separated for emission management. In the former, gases from the CDU, HCU, and DHT undergo a purification process using MDEA in the amine scrubber column to eliminate H_2S from sour off-gas; whereas the latter employs the off-gas from DCU with a similar process flow diagram and plant objective. All rich MDEA which have absorbed sulphur content of off-gasses is processed in Amine Reduction Unit (ARU) and recycled as lean MDEA. A simplified flow diagram is shown in the Figure 1.

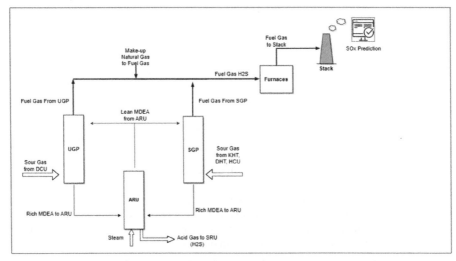

Figure 1: Simplified process flow diagram of sour gas process and furnaces

2.2. Inferential Sensor Design and Integration

With current limitations in laboratory analysis of H_2S and many other streams in the plant, due to few sample collection locations, oscillations in plant variables in daily routine, and delayed feedback with few measurement capabilities under work load, a real-time decision making policy development based on laboratory measurements is practically challenging. Moreover, H_2S analysis for petroleum fractions with high sulphur content is a difficult task, in our case. Thus, an inferential approach, integrated to large scale optimization problem, has been developed to avoid aforementioned issues through development of empirical formulations including the variables shown in Fig. 2.

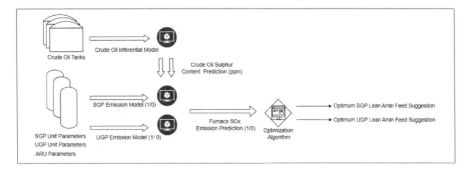

Figure 2: Inferential sensor and optimization architecture

2.2.1 Crude Oil Sulphur Inferential

An inferential sensor is designed to estimate the inlet sulphur content, which has been driven by the crude oil sulphur fraction. However, crude oil is a mixture from several tanks whose sulphur contents are included in the formulation to account for the blending effect.

2.2.2 Furnace Emission Models of SGP and UGP Units

Decoupled emission models were developed for the SGP and the UGP units as they might operate at different regimes despite similar process architecture. Those models predict whether absorber column operations in these two plants will suffer from an increase in emissions in the furnaces. In the modeling phase, a binary decision tree architecture was used to forecast the existence of emission increase.

2.3. Unbalanced Data and Decision Tree Model Selection

Due to the high emission data scarcity, several data sampling formulations have been implemented to avoid typical problems arising from training on an imbalanced data. Moreover, MDEA nutrition was mostly consumed in excess. To eliminate the effect of excess MDEA feeding over the optimization model, emission models progressed through the classification methods. In this way, furnace emissions were modeled to predict their occurrence rather than their quantity in ppm levels. These models were then incorporated into an integrated optimization model to find the optimal MDEA feed. Oversampling and undersampling methods under such a complex dataset delivered a small prediction accuracy with high number of false alarms, in our case.

A decision tree algorithm is trained based on one-year of historical data. Models were trained to predict the occurrence of emissions in real-time by examining the historical process data from the past year, through defining a binary target to represent emission increase in all furnaces. MDEA properties like temperature, concentration, flow, crude oil properties like sulphur, capacity, and absorber columns properties as temperature and pressure were used in models. During model training progress, to prevent incorrect learning caused by the post-increase process conditions and the increased MDEA feed in response to high emissions data cleaning was applied. The data 4 hours prior to the emission increase and the first 8 hours data which includes higher MDEA feed due to increased emission levels, were excluded from the training dataset.

To stay on the safe side in optimization, regulatory limits of furnace emissions were not used during the model training phase. Distribution curves of SO_2 emission levels of all furnaces have been calculated and statistical process limits have been set for each furnace, which are significantly below the legal limits.

2.4. Decision-making architecture

High emission alarm forecasts which are generated in a decentralized manner from SGP and UGP furnace emission models were progressed in the coordinated decision-making architecture in Fig. 3. The control actions are implemented on the plant with a 30 minute frequency, which is calculated based on the average time constant of process variables and their interactions, in order to calculate optimum MDEA feed for these units.

The optimization algorithm operates in three decomposed stages. In the first stage, the directions of MDEA flow change based on emission predictions are calculated. In the second stage, the decision to implement at current time step or the next one is calculated to balance the control action frequency considering the impact of the previously implemented decisions. Thus, a wiser decision might be probable after delayed impacts are settled in the plant although 30-minute calculation frequency is required when delayed impact is not the case. Finally, the last stage calculates the extent of change to deliver optimal MDEA flow rate. Overall decision making information flow diagram is shown in Figure 3.a and real time optimization timing as in figure 3.b.

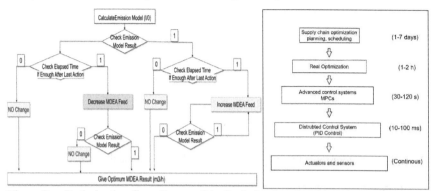

Figure 3.a: Optimization flow diagram 3.b: Optimization algorithm time scales

3. Results and Discussion

Sulfur emissions have consistently posed a concern in refinery processes. Additionally, given the growing emphasis on sustainability, the removal of sulfur from refinery processes has become notably sensitive in the current era. Consequently, numerous articles in the literature address sulphur prediction and amine optimization processes. On the other hand, this study differs from other articles in the way it deals with optimization.

In Figure 4, one of the emission increase and recommendations from the optimization model regarding amine increase and decrease are observed. The number of consolidated furnaces with high emissions can be seen instantly at the top of the chart. It is observed that emissions increased three times in all furnaces during this period. The lower graph illustrates the calculated optimal MDEA flow during this timeframe. Optimal MDEA values show an increase before emission spikes and a subsequent decrease after the emissions drop. This graph represents the period when the optimization models were activated but their results were not yet implemented. As a result, the model's performance could be tested, demonstrating its ability to predict emissions.

Figure 5 shows the actual MDEA flows and MDEA optimization results for 2 months after the optimization model was put into operation. When the results are examined, it is seen that there is general parallelism between MDEA flow and optimization. Additionally, when examining the trends, it's noticeable that the model consistently advises reducing the actual MDEA during long-term decreasing trends of MDEA.

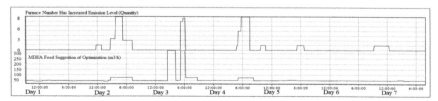

Figure 4: Optimization algorithm results in case of high emission period

Conversely, during periods when MDEA needs to increase, the model promptly recommends a rapid rise in MDEA.

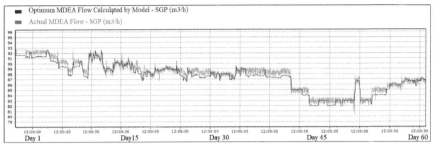

Figure 5: Optimum and actual MDEA feed results

4. Conclusion

In this article, the sour gas processing system, has been optimized through the amine feed. The optimization model was developed based on three inferential models: the crude oil sulfur prediction inferential model, and SGP and UGP furnace emission prediction models. By developing these models independent of the analysis results, that enabled the real-time optimization of the amine feed, allowing for an instant response to observed increases in sulphur levels in the system. As a result of monitoring it has been that furnace emission increase can be detected in 1-4 hours in advance.

References

Guerreiro, C. B., Foltescu, V., & De Leeuw, F. (2014). Air quality status and trends in Europe. *Atmospheric environment*, *98*, 376-384. https://doi.org/10.1016/j.atmosenv.2014.09.017.

Bolhàr-Nordenkampf, M., Friedl, A., Koss, U., & Tork, T. (2004). Modelling selective H2S absorption and desorption in an aqueous MDEA-solution using a rate-based non-equilibrium approach. Chemical Engineering and Processing, 43(8), 701–715.

Abdelrasoul, A., Al-Hadad, A., Khan, A. R., & Khan, A. R. (2010). Oil Refineries Emissions Impact on Urban Localities Using AERMOD. American Journal of Environmental Sciences, 6(6), 505-515. https://doi.org/10.3844/ajessp.2010.505.515.

Li, Z., Feng, X., & Yang, M. (2023). Absorption mechanism-based approach for synthesis of refinery desulfurization solvent network. *Journal of Chemical Engineering*, 27(3), 123-145.

Curreri, F., Patanè, L., & Xibilia, M.G. (2021). "Soft Sensor Transferability between Lines of a Sulfur Recovery Unit." IFAC-PapersOnLine, 54(7), 535-540. https://doi.org/10.1016/j.ifacol.2021.08.415.

Flavio Manenti, Gintaras V. Reklaitis (Eds.), Proceedings of the 34th European Symposium on Computer Aided Process Engineering / 15th International Symposium on Process Systems Engineering (ESCAPE34/PSE24), June 2-6, 2024, Florence, Italy

Design and planning green hydrogen supply chains: characterization and optimization

Filipa Braz Silva,[a*] Cátia da Silva,[a] Ana Paula Barbosa-Póvoa[a]

[a]CEG-IST, Instituto Superior Técnico, University of Lisbon, Av. Rovisco Pais, 1049-001 Lisboa, Portugal
filipa.b.silva@tecnic.ulisboa.pt

Abstract

Society faces urgent challenges requiring collaboration between energy and climate policies, especially in industry and transport. Green Hydrogen (GH2) is a key component of the European Union's strategy for a hydrogen-based, carbon-neutral economy, promoting sustainable growth, job creation, and energy security. Successful integration of hydrogen (H2) into the future energy landscape depends on reducing costs and optimizing infrastructure. However, the environmental benefits of the hydrogen economy are hindered by a lack of infrastructure and significant capital investments. Establishing a future hydrogen supply chain efficiently necessitates a strategic model accounting for changing requirements and cost-effective infrastructure design. This study addresses these challenges by developing a multi-period Mixed-Integer Linear Programming (MILP) model for GH2 supply chain design and planning, aiming to minimize overall costs while meeting industrial demand using renewable sources. The research provides insights into choosing renewable feedstock sources, centralized or decentralized production, and hydrogen storage, evaluating liquid and gaseous hydrogen forms. Diverse scenarios cover GH2 options, transportation modes, storage, penetration rates, and economies of scale, offering a comprehensive framework. Applied in a Portuguese case study, the model contributes practically to implementing a sustainable GH2 supply chain in Portugal focused on the Industrial sector needs.

Keywords: green hydrogen, supply chain, renewable energy source, design and planning

1. Introduction

Climate change, environmental pollution, and biodiversity loss have far-reaching economic, social, and quality of life implications. The European Commission has introduced "Fit for 55," a comprehensive set of legislative proposals aimed at achieving carbon neutrality by 2050, with an interim target of at least a 55% reduction in greenhouse gas emissions by 2030 (European Commission, 2021). In this context, the shift from fossil fuels to renewable energies, particularly green hydrogen, is of considerable importance. Many European Union member states, including Portugal, have unveiled their national energy and climate plans, emphasizing their national hydrogen strategies. Portugal, favored with abundant renewable energy resources, holds a strategic position in the European hydrogen landscape. Its commitment to renewable energy aligns seamlessly with the EU's hydrogen strategy, making it an ideal candidate to explore hydrogen's potential as a sustainable energy carrier. Portugal has set ambitious goals to reduce emissions and promote renewable energy sources, recognizing hydrogen's promise as a clean energy alternative. In line with these plans, Portugal has also adopted its National Strategy for Hydrogen (EN-H2), aiming to position the country as a major player in the global hydrogen industry. EN-H2's macro-objectives for 2030 include deploying 2% to 5% of green hydrogen in the industrial energy consumption sector. This paper emerges in this context, aiming to analyze and assist decision-makers in designing and planning green hydrogen supply chains (GHSC), particularly for the Portuguese case, to meet the future hydrogen demand of the industrial sector. Such supply chains are instrumental in Portugal's pursuit of carbon neutrality. This paper is pivotal in advancing the development of a sustainable and environmentally friendly energy ecosystem in Portugal, in harmony with broader European clean energy objectives.

2. Literature Review

Supply chain (SC) integrates business processes to acquire raw materials, transform them, distribute products, and share information, aiming for operational efficiency and competitiveness. Decision-support tools categorize SC decisions as strategic, tactical, and operational. Hydrogen supply chain design (HSCD) involves investment and operational decisions to meet demand, covering facility types, locations, capacities, and transportation networks (Sgarbossa et al., 2023). A holistic view across all processes proves effective for optimization. HSCD optimization falls into single-objective (cost minimization) and multi-objective categories, with emerging trends emphasizing sustainability (Cantú et al., 2021). Literature predominantly focuses on grey hydrogen production, but some studies explore green hydrogen with renewable sources. Moreno-Benito et al. (2017) developed an optimisation-based approach for hydrogen infrastructure and emphasised the needs for further works. Câmara et al. (2019) considers solar, wind, hydroelectric, and biomass in Portugal to meet hydrogen demand in the transportation sector by producing hydrogen only in liquified form. The physical form of hydrogen (liquid or gaseous) influences transportation and storage decisions, with trade-offs differing for each that needs future research. Additionally, research often concentrates on the transportation sector, overlooking comprehensive supply chain design for industrial clusters. Despite these contributions, literature gaps persist, including the lack of research focused on hydrogen supply chain deployment. In this work, we address this gap and develop a comprehensive model for Green H2 supply chain, where H2 penetration over time should be explored considering both liquid and gas forms.

3. Problem description and model characterization

This study considers the design and planning of Green Hydrogen Supply Chains, exploring a multiperiod context and different hydrogen penetration levels, which is generically represented in Figure 1. In this framework, the main stages correspond to: (i) the distribution of energy from suppliers to plant facilities, (ii) the production and storage of hydrogen, and, finally, (iii) the distribution of hydrogen to the demand points. Given: (i) locations of potential or existing entities in the supply chain; (ii) capacity of energy source suppliers; (iii) capital and operating costs for hydrogen transportation, production, and storage facilities; (iv) time horizon in study; (v) distance between entities; (vi) product demand by each industry cluster in each period considered; (vii) H2 product form. The objective is to obtain: (i) the structure of the SC network; (ii) the transport network between entities; (iii) the flow of energy and H2 transported between entities; (iv) production and storage levels; (v) the capacity of production and storage facilities over time. In order to minimize total discounted costs while meeting the potential future industrial H2 demand.

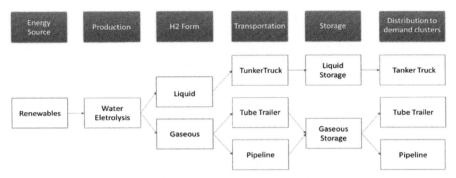

Figure 1: Green Hydrogen Supply Chain

To solve this problem, it is developed an optimisation model (MILP), based on Forghani et al. (2023) by adding new relevant considerations. The model was extended to incorporate the availability and logistics of energy sources for hydrogen production, and it only focuses on the production of GH2. Additionally, H2 was analysed not only on its gaseous form but also on its liquid form. It focuses on the most eco-friendly hydrogen production method, ignoring carbon emissions constraints. Lastly, this work intends to satisfy the demand of H2 from the industry sector. The objective function is represented in Equation (1) and intends to minimize the total discounted costs (TDC) of the GHSC while meeting demand requirements during different periods. Costs for each period are discounted back to the present time at a certain discount rate to account for the time value of money. The costs related to the construction of GHSC are applied over time by considering the specific capital costs incurred in each period, as production and storage facilities can be extended gradually over periods – costs incur in the previous year of each period, so that infrastructures are ready to operate for the whole period. Additionally, it considers daily operating, transportation, and energy source related costs – incur for each one of the years.

$$\min TDC = \sum_{t \in T} \left(\frac{TI_t}{(1+\beta)^t} + N(TO_T + TT_t + ESC_t) \times \sum_{a=1}^{y} \frac{1}{(1+\beta)^{yt-(y-a)}} \right) \qquad (1)$$

The TDC minimization can be divided in the following components: (i) TI_T represents the total capital cost associated with the production plants, storage facilities, and pipelines; (ii) TO_T corresponds to the total operating cost of the production plants, storage facilities, and pipelines; (iii) TT_T represents the total transportation cost associated with the pipeline and tube trailer transport modes; (iv) ESC_t denotes the total costs for the energy source consumed in each period of time and represents an innovative constrain compared to basis model. The regular equations for demand fulfilment, material balance, transportation and capacity limitations are among the defined constraints.

4. Case Study

To validate the effectiveness of the model, it is applied to the Portuguese context with the aim of assisting stakeholders in choosing the most appropriate configurations based on the evolution of the Hydrogen adoption level, need that was recently identified in Portugal. The 18 districts of Portugal are the subsets of locations or possible locations in which entities are located. The time frame is of 25 years and divided in periods of 5 each one representing 5 years to analyse the evolution of hydrogen demand from 2025 to 2050 – aligning with the year set by the International Energy Agency for achieving net-zero emissions. The model is demand-driven and the need for hydrogen is predetermined by estimating the potential hydrogen demand for energy-intensive industries in Portugal within the main sectors: Chemical industry; Iron and steel; Non-ferrous metals; Non-metallic minerals; Paper and printing; and Refineries. The penetration rate was defined based on the targets/ indicative trajectories to be met defined by the national Portuguese H2 strategy. For the renewable energy sources availability, data from the 3 more relevant sources in this category are considered: hydroelectric, wind, and solar. Water electrolysis as the technology to produce GH2 was considered. Three different sizes of H2 production plants are studied: small, medium, and large. Each type of plant and storage facility has sets of data to produce/ store gaseous hydrogen and liquid hydrogen. The storage time of H2 is assumed to be 10 days. The tanker trucks have been chosen for the transportation of liquid hydrogen on roads, while the tube trailers and a pipeline system have been explored for hydrogen in its gaseous form. Only distances between districts were considered, while local distances were not.

5. Results Analysis

Results obtained through scenario analysis and sensitivity analysis are presented. The scenarios analysed are: i) Case A – includes a penetration profile that meets the average values for the targets/ indicative trajectories; ii) Case B – includes a penetration profile that meets the maximum values for the targets/ indicative trajectories; iii) Case C - includes a penetration profile that meets the minimum values for the targets/ indicative trajectories; iv) Case D - includes the benefits of economies of scale in production and storage facilities. For each one of these scenarios, hydrogen is assessed in its liquid and gaseous form. However, detailed results for both forms are only presented for Case A, as it is revealed as the most representative case: (i) Case A.1 - represents hydrogen in its liquid form; (ii) Case A.2 - represents the gaseous form of H2 with only on-road transportation; (iii) Case A.3 – represents hydrogen in its gaseous form with on-road transportation and a pipeline system. For the other cases (B, C and D) the results presented concern only liquid hydrogen as it resulted always in the less expensive supply chain structure between the 3 different options. Additionally, Case D.1 is an extension of Case

Table 1 - Results for main scenarios.

Scenario	TDC (M€)	Centralization Degree	No of Plants	No of storage facilities (capacity in t)	Transportation units
A.1	17,006	78% - 91%	5 medium 9 small	4 (100), 4(250), 7(1000)	64 tanker trucks
A.2	17,732	79% - 81%	5 medium 10 small	4(100), 2(250), 5(500), 5(1000)	224 tube trailers
A.3	17,613	82% - 89%	5 medium 9 small	1(50), 1(100), 1(250), 4(500), 6(1000)	53 tube trailers + 727 km pipeline
B	20,504	87% - 96%	6 medium 4 small	1(100), 1(250), 4(500), 7(1000)	76 tanker trucks
C	13,086	87% - 96%	5 medium 3 small	1(50), 2(100), 3(250), 1(500), 6(1000)	52 tanker trucks
D	14,517	100%	2 large	1(50), 1(100), 1(250), 4(500), 6(1000)	90 tanker trucks
D.1	14,457	100%	2 large	1(50), 1(100), 1(250), 2(4000)	35 tanker trucks

D by considering the possible installation of a higher storage capacity. From the analysis of these cases, the obtained values are stated in Table 1.

The key finding from the scenario analysis indicates that liquid hydrogen appears to be the more cost-effective choice for deploying an H2 supply chain. The scenario with the lowest costs, 13,086 M€, involves a lower penetration of H2 (Case C), where lower production rates contribute to reduced overall costs, particularly when production costs hold a significant share of the total costs. Conversely, the optimistic scenario (Case B), characterized by the highest values of TDC, 20,504 M€, emerges as the most expensive. The moderate scenario (Case A.1) has an overall TDC of 17,006 M€ and is represented in Figure 2. The second least expensive scenario is Case D.1 with a TDC of 14,457 M€. This scenario considers economies of scale in production plants and the potential installation of higher storage capacity. Notably, as the main entities of this SC configuration are presented in Figure 2, this scenario strategically designates Setúbal and Coimbra as the primary hydrogen production hubs, minimizing the need for tanker trucks due to centralized storage facilities and large consumers having plants with large capacities within their districts. Higher centralization degrees are observed in scenarios linked to economies of scale (see Table 1 and Figure 2), with liquid hydrogen displaying higher centralization rates compared to compressed hydrogen.

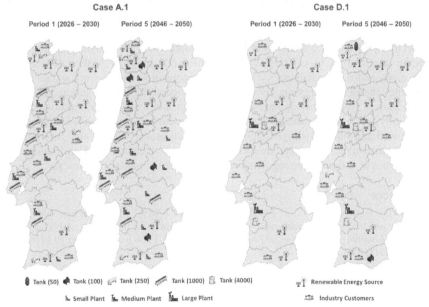

Figure 2: SC design for periods 1 and 5 of Case A.1 and Case D.1

Additionally, a sensitivity analysis was performed on the discount rate, storage time of hydrogen, electricity costs and capital cost of liquid hydrogen production plants. The study found that variations in electricity cost and discount rate significantly affect the overall TDC but not the SC structure. The average number of days H2 is stored significantly impacts the SC's structure and storage facility dimensions (see Figure 3). Therefore, it is crucial to consider this factor when planning the SC design. Also, it was verified that until a 75% increase in capital cost of liquid H2 plants, liquid hydrogen SC is the preferred option, supporting again the idea of a liquid hydrogen SC (see Figure 3).

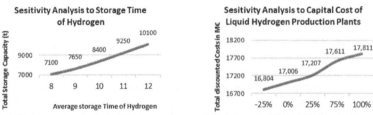

Figure 3: Sensitivity analysis to H2 storage time and capital cost of liquid H2 production plants

6. Conclusions

This work defines an optimization tool for designing green hydrogen supply chains, focusing on Portugal. The aim is to assist key investors and/or politicians in developing a sustainable energy ecosystem aligned with European clean energy objectives. Results are expected to inform infrastructure and technology decisions for each supply chain component, considering the availability of renewable energy resources and potential industrial hydrogen demand while minimizing total discounted costs. Optimal solutions consistently favour liquid hydrogen over gaseous one for the chosen scenarios, even with a 75% increase in the capital cost of liquid hydrogen plants. The study questions the suitability of a pipeline system for H2 distribution in Portugal, favouring tanker trucks, possibly due to the country's size. Moreover, the importance of considering factors such as electricity cost, discount rates, and H2 storage duration in SC design is highlighted.

Despite contributing to existing literature, the work suggests further development, particularly addressing challenges related to data acquisition. Future work should include assessing renewable energy deployment near production facilities to ensure sustainable power sources and addressing uncertainties in solar and wind power. Additionally, the availability of water resources for hydrogen production and detailed research on compressed and liquid hydrogen storage are crucial aspects to explore. Incorporating political incentives, utilizing multicriteria analysis methods and accounting for uncertainties in various chain segments would enhance the model's accuracy.

References

Câmara, D., Pinto-Varela, T., & Barbósa-Povoa, A. P. (2019). Multi-objective optimization approach to design and planning hydrogen supply chain under uncertainty: A Portugal study case. *Computer Aided Chemical Engineering, 46*, 1309–1314. https://doi.org/10.1016/B978-0-12-818634-3.50219-8

Cantú, V. H., Azzaro-Pantel, C., & Ponsich, A. (2021). A Novel Matheuristic based on bi-level optimization for the multi-Objective design of hydrogen supply chains. *Computers and Chemical Engineering, 152*. https://doi.org/10.1016/j.compchemeng.2021.107370

European Commission. (2021). *"Fit for 55": delivering the EU's 2030 Climate Target on the way to climate neutrality.*

Forghani, K., Kia, R., & Nejatbakhsh, Y. (2023). A multi-period sustainable hydrogen supply chain model considering pipeline routing and carbon emissions: The case study of Oman. *Renewable and Sustainable Energy Reviews, 173*. https://doi.org/10.1016/j.rser.2022.113051

Moreno-Benito, M., Agnolucci, P., & Papageorgiou, L. G. (2017). Towards a sustainable hydrogen economy: Optimisation-based framework for hydrogen infrastructure development. *Computers and Chemical Engineering, 102*, 110–127. https://doi.org/10.1016/j.compchemeng.2016.08.005

Sgarbossa, F., Arena, S., Tang, O., & Peron, M. (2023). Renewable hydrogen supply chains: A planning matrix and an agenda for future research. *International Journal of Production Economics, 255*. https://doi.org/10.1016/j.ijpe.2022.108674

Flavio Manenti, Gintaras V. Reklaitis (Eds.), Proceedings of the 34th European Symposium on Computer Aided Process Engineering / 15th International Symposium on Process Systems Engineering (ESCAPE34/PSE24), June 2-6, 2024, Florence, Italy

Life Cycle Assessment (LCA) of Dimethyl Ether (DME) Production: Fossil Fuels vs. Biogas

Matteo Fedeli[a,b], Alessandro di Pretoro[b], Ludovic Montastruc[b], Flavio Manenti[a*]

[a] *Politecnico di Milano,Dipartimento di Chimica, Materiali ed Ingegneria Chimica "Giulio Natta", Piazza Leonardo da Vinci 32, Milano, 20133, Italy*
[b] *Laboratoire de G´enie Chimique, Universit´e de Toulouse, CNRS/INP/UPS, 4 All. Emile Monso, 31030, Toulouse, 31030, France*
*flavio.manenti@polimi.it

Abstract

This study conducts a comprehensive Life Cycle Assessment (LCA) to compare the environmental impacts of two alternative pathways for producing dimethyl ether (DME): one utilizing conventional fossil fuel-based processes and the other relying on biogas feedstocks. LCA is employed as a robust tool for evaluating the sustainability of these fuel production methods. The authors meticulously quantify resource inputs and outputs for both production routes in the inventory analysis phase. For conventional fossil fuel-based production, the value of the impact categories is retrieved from SimaPRO database. On the other hand, for biogas-based production, Aspen HYSYS is utilised to perform process simulations. The results of these are used as input for LCA analysis. Our findings reveal significant disparities between the two production pathways. Biogas-derived DME exhibit lower greenhouse gas emissions and reduced dependence on finite fossil resources. The biogas route also provides valuable co-benefits, such as organic waste valorization and potential improvements in soil quality through feedstock cultivation. However, it is essential to recognize that biogas-based production requires more land and water resources than fossil fuel-based. Therefore, trade-offs between reduced carbon emissions and increased resource use should be carefully considered, particularly in regions with limited land and water availability.

Keywords: Methanol, Di-methyl-ether, Biogas feedstock, LCA, Process sustainability

1. Introduction

The heightened global interest in renewable energy sources has been spurred by growing apprehensions regarding climate change and the conventional exploitation of fossil fuels. Among the prospective alternatives, biogas emerges as an auspicious solution owing to its sustainable attributes, capacity for waste management, and minimal ecological footprint. Presently, the European Commission is actively engaged in advancing the utilization of biogas employing an all-encompassing regulatory framework, investment incentives, and initiatives in research and development [1]. Biogas finds primary application in Combined Heat and Power (CHP) and Biomethane Injection Plants (BIP). CHP represents a conventional cogeneration cycle designed for the simultaneous generation of heat and electricity. BIP, on the other hand, involves the purification of biogas from CO_2 and other impurities to yield biomethane. Specifically, as outlined by the International Energy Agency (IEA), biomethane must possess a minimum methane content of 97%. Initially, the heightened attractiveness of CHP utilization was attributed to financial incentives extended by European governments during the 2007-2020 period. However, after the expiration of these economic advantages, the biogas market witnessed a notable decline in investor interest. The utilization of biogas to produce advanced fuels, including methanol and dimethyl ether (DME), holds paramount importance in the pursuit of sustainable energy solutions. This technological approach is referred to as Heat, Power, and Chemicals (HPC) [2]. In this work, a Life Cycle Assessment (LCA) analysis is performed to assess and compare two different production routes of the dimethyl ether. The difference between the two processes lies in the feedstock type. The first one is the conventional production of biofuel from natural gas, while the latter employs biogas as a raw material. The aim is to evaluate the environmental impact of the upcoming and more sustainable technology, compared to the conventional one. Process simulations are rigorously simulated in Aspen HYSYS v11 to retrieve LCA data input for biogas-to-bio-DME processes. LCA is computed through the software SimaPro.

2. Materials and methods

The biogas to biofuel process is rigorously simulated in Aspen HYSYS and Aspen PLUS to collect process data for the subsequent environmental assessment. Biogas properties are retrieved from the work of Fedeli and Manenti, which analysed a feedstock from energy crops. The average H_2S content in the gaseous mixture is 200 ppm [3].

Biogas is treated with caustic scrubbing first in order to remove H_2S impurities that could damage the downstream units by means of corrosion and catalyst poisoning [4]. Figure 1 illustrates the streamlined diagram of the scrubbing unit, meticulously simulated in Aspen Plus using the Electrolyte Non-Random Two Liquid (ELECNRTL) thermodynamic model. Gas phase behavior was characterized using the Soave-Redlich-Kwong (SRK) model. The choice of ASPEN Plus software was motivated by its enhanced suitability for managing electrolytic systems compared to Aspen HYSYS. Subsequently, the simulation outcomes were employed as input parameters in Aspen HYSYS.

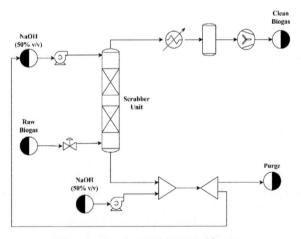

Figure 1 Flowsheet of biogas purification

DME production section is rigorously simulated in Aspen HYSYS v11. In the proposed layout three different sections can be distinguished: (i) biogas reforming, (ii) DME production, and (iii) purification section. The introduction of biogas into the system precedes its compression through a three-stage compressor, increasing the pressure to 1.5 MPa. Subsequently, the pressurized stream is amalgamated with medium-pressure steam from an internal loop. This composite stream undergoes pre-heating in a process-process heat exchanger before entering the steam reforming tubes. The modeling of this unit is achieved utilizing the Aspen HYSYS isothermal Plug Flow Reactor (PFR) module with Xu-Froment kinetics [5]. The operating conditions of the reformer unit are 950°C and 1.5 MPa. The syngas exiting the system imparts heat to the biogas-water mixture, followed by cooling through a heat exchanger. Within this unit, the thermal energy is harnessed to produce medium-pressure (MP) steam (at 1.5 MPa) from the pumped water. The cooled syngas undergo dewatering in a separator, and the resulting condensed water is returned to the water loop for steam generation. Additionally, the dehydrated reformate is directed to a dual-stage compressor (at 6 MPa) for subsequent synthesis stages. The initial portion of this stage remains consistent across both synthesis processes. The dehydrated syngas undergo pre-heating via two heat exchangers before being introduced into methanol reactor tubes at 235°C. This unit is modelled as catalytic PFR with the Graaf refitted kinetics model from the work of Bisotti et al. (2021) [6]. Pressure drops of 200 kPa are estimated with the Ergun equation. However, the produced methanol is rich in water and light gases such as CO, H_2, CH_4, and CO_2. The uncondensable gases are separated in a water-cooled vessel and recycled back to the reactor to enhance the overall conversion. Regarding DME synthesis, following the purification stage, methanol is pressurized to 1 MPa and heated to 230 °C before entering the DME reactor, where methanol dehydration occurs. Even in this instance, the elevated temperature of the resultant products proves beneficial for pre-heating the reacting mixture. From a simulation standpoint, this unit was modeled as an Aspen Gibbs reactor to predict the equilibrium behaviour of the system. The Aspen Gibbs reactor module is designed to establish equilibrium conditions while accounting for thermodynamic non-idealities. This selection is well-established in the literature, as evidenced by Merkouri et al. (2022), who evaluated DME production using an Aspen equilibrium reactor [7], and Moura et al. (2023), where DME production through sugarcane bagasse gasification was analyzed [8]. In the process simulation, the effluent from the DME converter primarily consists of DME, water, and unreacted methanol. The DME purification column, operating at 160°C and 1 MPa, separates DME, meeting ASTM D7901-14 standard specifications, from the other compounds. Specifically, DME is collected from the top of the unit, while the water-methanol mixture is recycled back to the methanol column. Figure 2 illustrates the process simulation flowsheet for methanol and DME production, respectively. Despite the utilization of two distinct software platforms for this section, consistency in the results, especially in the context of methanol/DME separation, is ensured by maintaining the same NRTL thermodynamic model and SRK equation for gas phase behavior.

The outputs of this process simulation are used as input for the LCA analysis concerning the DME production from biogas. Input values for the fossil-based process are directly retrieved from SimaPRO inventories. Based on the simulations, the LCA analysis of the three processes was then performed employing SimaPRO 9.3 software. A cradle-to-gate lifecycle model was selected as the method to analyse the systems. 1 kg of produced DME is selected as the functional unit of the assessment. The results of each impact category were normalised for each section to facilitate the comparison.

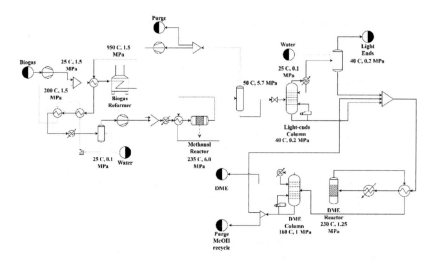

Figure 2 Flowsheet of biogas to bio-DME production

3. Results and discussions

The analysis of the chemical synthesis involves assessing the molar conversion of biogas, molar conversion of H_2, and chemical yield. Key performance indicators for DME production, including distillation column design, are presented in Table 4. Notably, these indicators are not provided for biogas cogeneration, as it lack relevant reactions and purification steps. The reforming unit yields a methane conversion of 93% in the process. This value aligns well with existing literature [9]. Furthermore, the hydrogen conversion is consistent between the two processes, as they share the same methanol reactor. In DME production, methanol is further converted in DME with a conversion of 89%. Although this value was obtained because of thermodynamic equilibrium instead of a proper kinetic model, it is still coherent with literature works assessing methanol conversion to DME on silica or zeolite catalysts.

Table 1 Main key performance indicators of bio-DME synthesis

Biogas reforming	
χCH_4	92.8%
Chemical synthesis	
χH_2 per pass	20,7%
χCO_x per pass	32,6%
χMethanol per pass	88,6%
Purification section	
DME column	35 trays; RR 1.5

Figure 3 depicts the LCA comparison assessment. DME-biogas based shows less impact in most of the impact categories. The values of the bio-DME production are five times lower. 0.18 kgCO2eq is the climate change factor related to the bio-DME production. In their work, Barati et al. (2023) evaluated the environmental impact assessment of electrified CO2 to methanol process. The global warming value reported for this analysis is equal to 2 kgCO2eq, i.e. more than the LCA outcome of this research [10]. As concerns DME, Karittha Im-orb et al. (2023) showed a total GWP of about 1.2 kgCO2eq to produce bio-DME via biomass gasification [11]. The only indexes where fossil fuel-based DME performs better are related to water consumption, water eutrophication, and land usage. The second one describes the gradual increase in the concentration of phosphorus, nitrogen, and other plant nutrients and water ecosystems. Results of water use stand for 21 m^3/h and 0.76 m^3/h for bio and fossil-DME processes respectively. Thus, it is a greater deviation mainly because the biogas treating, purification, and reforming are water high-demanding steps. The CO_2 content in the biogas led to higher impurities in the downstream section, increasing the cooling water utilizations. The above-mentioned considerations are applied also for the eutrophication since this category is strictly related to the water consumption. Land use categories represents the environmental impacts of occupying, reshaping, and managing land for human purposes. In the context of bio-DME production, this value is larger than the fossil fuel-based production. This outcome is mainly related to the footprint are needed to build, manage, and process several steps such as: (i) biogas digestors, (ii) biogas purification, (iii) biogas reforming, (iv) bio-DME synthesis, and (vi) downstream section. The conventional way to produce DME requires only the latter three sections. However, potential solution could be developing the "biogas to bio-X" supply chain. The main limitation of the biogas context is the plant capacity since the average digestor production stands for 500 Nm^3/h in the European scenario. The optimization of the space, with bigger plants for digestion and processing, for this technology is still not implemented, and it will be beneficial in terms of land use.

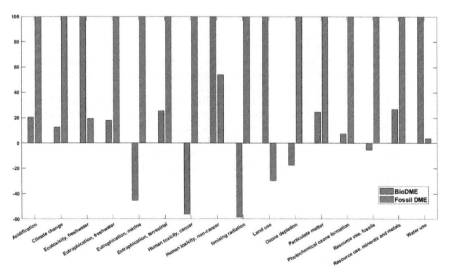

Figure 3 LCA comparison assessment

4. Conclusions

In conclusion, the conducted Life Cycle Assessment (LCA) has systematically compared the environmental ramifications associated with dimethyl ether (DME) production from divergent sources fossil fuel-based processes and biogas feedstocks. The analysis delineates huge disparities between these two processes, highlighting the commendable environmental attributes of biogas-based DME. Biogas-derived DME manifests as a superior alternative, characterized by diminished greenhouse gas emissions and a mitigated reliance on finite fossil resources. Furthermore, the biogas trajectory proffers auxiliary merits, encompassing organic waste valorization and conceivable enhancements in soil quality. However, it is imperative to underscore that biogas-driven production necessitates a more pronounced allocation of land and water resources in comparison to fossil fuel-based counterparts, thereby obligating a judicious calibration of trade-offs. The findings underscore the imperativeness of fine-tuning water management and land utilization to optimize the sustainability quotient of biogas-centric DME production.

5. References

[1]   N. Scarlat, J.F. Dallemand, F. Fahl, Biogas: Developments and perspectives in Europe, Renew. Energy. 129 (2018) 457–472. https://doi.org/10.1016/J.RENENE.2018.03.006.

[2]   M. Fedeli, A. di Pretoro, L. Montastruc, F. Manenti, Conventional vs. alternative biogas utilization: An LCA-AHP based comparative study, Clean. Environ. Syst. 11 (2023) 100150. https://doi.org/https://doi.org/10.1016/j.cesys.2023.100150.

[3]   M. Fedeli, F. Manenti, Assessing process effectiveness with specific environmental and economic impact of heat, power & chemicals (HPC) option as future perspective in biogas, Clean. Chem. Eng. 2 (2022) 100016. https://doi.org/10.1016/J.CLCE.2022.100016.

[4]   L. Chen, R. Case, L. Liu, S. Xiang, H. Castaneda, Assessment of sulfide corrosion cracking and hydrogen permeation behaviour of ultrafine grain high strength steel, Corros. Sci. 198 (2022) 110142. https://doi.org/10.1016/J.CORSCI.2022.110142.

[5]   J. Xu, G.F. Froment, Methane steam reforming, methanation and water-gas shift: I. Intrinsic kinetics, AIChE J. 35 (1989) 88–96. https://doi.org/10.1002/aic.690350109.

[6]   F. Bisotti, M. Fedeli, K. Prifti, A. Galeazzi, A. Dell'Angelo, M. Barbieri, C. Pirola, G. Bozzano, F. Manenti, Century of Technology Trends in Methanol Synthesis: Any Need for Kinetics Refitting?, Ind. Eng. Chem. Res. 60 (2021) 16032–16053. https://doi.org/10.1021/acs.iecr.1c02877.

[7]   L.P. Merkouri, H. Ahmet, T. Ramirez Reina, M.S. Duyar, The direct synthesis of dimethyl ether (DME) from landfill gas: A techno-economic investigation, Fuel. 319 (2022). https://doi.org/10.1016/j.fuel.2022.123741.

[8]   C.P.C. Moura, M.A. De Araujo, H.G.D. Villardi, R.M. Cavalcante, F. Young, Process simulation and economic evaluation of an integrated production plant for methanol , acetic acid and DME synthesis via sugarcane bagasse gasification, 286 (2023). https://doi.org/10.1016/j.enconman.2023.117051.

[9]   J. Chen, W. Song, D. Xu, Compact Steam-Methane Reforming for the Production of Hydrogen in Continuous Flow Microreactor Systems, (2019). https://doi.org/10.1021/acsomega.9b02063.

[10]   K. Barati, Y. Khojasteh-Salkuyeh, O. Ashrafi, P. Navarri, Electrified combined reforming of methane process for more effective CO2 conversion to methanol: Process development and environmental impact assessment, Energy Convers. Manag. 287 (2023) 117096. https://doi.org/10.1016/J.ENCONMAN.2023.117096.

[11]   K. Im-orb, P. Piroonlerkgul, Sustainability analysis of the bio-dimethyl ether (bio-DME) production via integrated biomass gasification and direct DME Synthesis Process, Renew. Energy. 208 (2023) 324–330. https://doi.org/10.1016/J.RENENE.2023.03.092.

Flavio Manenti, Gintaras V. Reklaitis (Eds.), Proceedings of the 34th European Symposium on Computer Aided Process Engineering / 15th International Symposium on Process Systems Engineering (ESCAPE34/PSE24), June 2-6, 2024, Florence, Italy

Computer-Aided Drug Screening Based on the Binding Site Selectivity of ACE2: Machine Learning, Docking, and Molecular Dynamics Simulations

Xinhao Che,[a] Qilei Liu,[a] Fang Yu,[a] Lei Zhang[a,*]

[a]*Frontier Science Center for Smart Materials Oriented Chemical Engineering, Institute of Chemical Process Systems Engineering, Dalian University of Technology, Dalian 116024, China.*
Corresponding Author's E-mail: keleiz@dlut.edu.cn

Abstract

Since the outbreak of COVID-19, much scientific effort has been made to discover small molecule drugs targeting various stages of the infection of SARS-CoV-2. As the host-cell receptor of SARS-CoV-2, ACE2 is also an important regulatory factor in the human renin-angiotensin system. However, the selectivity of compounds for the two functional sites of ACE2 are not considered in the virtual screening process targeting ACE2. In this work, a virtual screening framework based on the binding site selectivity is developed. The framework integrates two machine learning models, molecular docking, and molecular dynamics simulation methods, which can be used to screen for candidate inhibitors with better pharmaceutical properties and binding site selectivity, so as to reduce potential drug side effects of in humans. Five compounds with better pharmaceutical properties and selectivity than the reported inhibitors are finally selected for experimental assays in future according to the screening results.

Keywords: Virtual screening, Binding site selectivity, Machine learning model, Molecular docking, Molecular dynamics simulation

1. Introduction

The outbreak of Corona Virus Disease in late 2019 (COVID-2019) (Zhou et al., 2020) has had an unprecedented impact on human society, especially on human health and economic development. Much scientific effort has been made to target various stages of the infection process of the severe acute respiratory syndrome coronavirus 2 (SARS-CoV-2) (Lu et al., 2020). In this process, the host-cell receptor, angiotensin converting enzyme 2 (ACE2), is of great significance and potential for the reason that it is the "gateway" for SARS (Kuba et al., 2010) and SARS-CoV-2 (Benton et al., 2020) to infect human cells. In March 2020, Yan et al. (2020) determined the full-length structure of the human ACE2 receptor for the first time, which makes it possible to discover small molecule drug targeting ACE2 based on the structure.

Different from vaccines or large molecule drugs, small molecule drugs usually have long development periods, high costs and low success rates (Bhutani et al., 2021). Thus, how to accelerate the development process of lead drugs is a pressing issue at present. Compared to traditional experiment-based exploration of active compounds, computer-aided drug design (CADD) methods, such as virtual screening, can quickly identify a group of promising compounds for focused experiment validation at the early stage of an outbreak of disease. For example, Terali et al. (2020) screened a clinically approved drug library to find drug candidates targeting the catalytic site of ACE2 for stabilizing the closed conformation of ACE2, thereby shifting relative positions of critical exterior residues in ACE2 recognized by SARS-CoV-2. However, inhibitors for ACE2 obtained in this way may cause a potential side effect risk because the catalytic function of ACE2 is essential for the human cardiovascular system. Targeting the binding interface of ACE2 and the receptor binding domain (RBD) to block the binding of SARS-CoV-2 can be a better strategy (Razizadeh et al., 2021). It's necessary to consider the selectivity of inhibitors to different binding sites on/in the target protein during the virtual screening process, especially for multifunctional targets such as ACE2.

In order to minimize the negative influence of candidate compounds in the early stage of drug discovery, a virtual screening framework based on the binding site selectivity is proposed in this paper, which can be used for small molecule drug discovery targeting those proteins with multiple functional sites.

2. Materials and methods

The virtual screening framework proposed in this paper is shown in Figure 1. Details of the steps in the framework are discussed in the following sections.

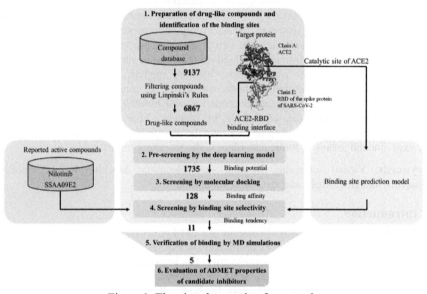

Figure 1. The virtual screening framework

2.1. Preparation of drug-like compounds and identification of the binding site

The DrugBank database (v5.1.8, released 2021.01.03) containing 9,137 3D structures of small molecule compounds is used for virtual screening in this work. The compounds that do not meet Lipinski's Rules are filtered out using RDKit tool (https://www.rdkit.org). The complex of ACE2 and the RBD of the spike protein of SARS-CoV-2 (PDB ID: 6M0J) is selected as the target for virtual screening. The binding site at ACE2-RBD binding interface is determined by Razizadeh et al. (2021). The conserved catalytic site of ACE2 is determined by Towler et al. (2004).

2.2. Pre-screening by the deep learning model

A deep learning model based on the binding site level is developed to predict which compounds have the binding potential to the specific binding site of a target protein, to quickly and effectively pre-screen a large number of compounds. The model construction steps are shown in Figure 2. By calculating the matrix descriptors of the compounds (active compounds and decoys) from DUD-E database and their binding sites as input to a 2D-convolutional neural network (CNN), the deep learning model is trained and the virtual screening performance of the model is evaluated (given in section 3.1). Then, the drug-like compounds obtained in section 2.1 and the binding site at ACE2-RBD binding interface are used as input to the model. The compounds that are more likely to bind to ACE2-RBD binding interface according to the model prediction results are selected for subsequent molecular docking.

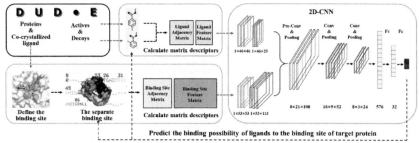

Figure 2. The construction steps of the deep learning model

2.3. Screening by molecular docking

Molecular docking is performed using Autodock Vina 1.2.3 (Eberhardt et al., 2021). Two different scoring functions, Vina (Eberhardt et al., 2021) and Vinardo (Quiroga and Villarreal, 2016), are selected to cross-validate the pre-screening results. The compounds with binding potential predicted by the developed CNN model are docked to ACE2-RBD binding interface. Then, the top compounds ranked by docking scores, which represent the strength of the binding affinity between the compound and the target protein, are used for binding site selectivity screening.

2.4. Screening by binding site selectivity

Besides the binding tendency of the compounds evaluated by the binding potential prediction model developed in section 2.2 and two affinity scores in section 2.3, an artificial neural network (ANN) model for binding site prediction (Che et al., 2022) is also used for binding tendency analysis. The ANN model can predict the possibility of a compound in its true binding site, which provides an additional complement to the reliability of the above binding potential prediction model and affinity scores. The screening steps are shown in Figure 3. By comparing and analyzing the above four binding metrics, the compounds with higher selectivity to ACE2-RBD binding interface are obtained.

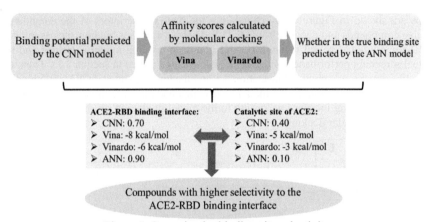

Figure 3. Screening by binding site selectivity

2.5. Verification of bind by MD simulations

The complexes consist of the docking conformation of each potential compound screened in section 2.4 and ACE2-RBD binding interface are used for MD simulations. MD simulations are performed using *Desmond* module in the Schrödinger software package. The possible inhibitory mechanism of the compounds as candidate inhibitors and binding process are analyzed using *Simulation interactions diagram* module. In addition, to quantitatively evaluate the dynamic binding strength of compounds to a target protein, binding free energy is calculated using the MM-GBSA method.

2.6. Evaluation of ADMET properties of candidate inhibitors

In order to further evaluate the pharmaceutical properties, the properties of absorption, distribution, metabolism, excretion, and toxicity (ADMET) of the 5 candidate inhibitors selected in section 2.5 are evaluated using the PharmaMind platform of Infinite Intelligence Pharma (http://www.iipharma.com.cn).

3. Results and discussion

3.1. Performance of the developed CNN model

The virtual screening performance of the developed CNN model is given in Table 1, which shows the excellent early enrichment capability of the model.

Table 1. The virtual screening performance of the developed CNN model

Adjusted logAUC			ROC enrichment (RE)			Early hit rate (Hit)	Boltzmann-enhanced discrimination of ROC (BEDROC)	Enrichment factor (EF)
Adjusted $logAUC_{0.5\%}$	Adjusted $logAUC_{1\%}$	Adjusted $logAUC_{2\%}$	$RE_{0.5\%}$	$RE_{1\%}$	$RE_{2\%}$	$Hit_{2\%}$	$BEDROC_{80.5}$	$EF_{2\%}$
0.62	0.64	0.65	89.2	55.6	34.5	52.8%	0.673	27.0

3.2. Virtual screening

6,876 drug-like compounds are obtained by filtering the DrugBank database with Lipinski's Rules. Then, 1,735 compounds with high binding potential according to the prediction results of the CNN model are docked to ACE2-RBD binding interface. 128 compounds ranked in the top 300 by the CNN model, at the same time, with a Vina score below -6.4 kcal/mol and a Vinardo score below -4.8 kcal/mol are used for binding site selectivity screening. Next, their binding tendency to ACE2-RBD binding interface and the catalytic site of ACE2 is evaluated. 11 compounds with better binding site selectivity for ACE2-RBD binding interface are finally selected. Detailed selectivity metrics are given in Table 2. The binding site selectivity of two reported active compounds, Nilotinib and SSAA09E2 (Razizadeh et al., 2021), are also evaluated for comparison.

Table 2. Detailed selectivity metrics of the 11 compounds from screening and two reported active compounds

DrugBank ID	Prediction values of the two deep learning models and the docking scores of Vina & Vinardo							
	For the catalytic site of ACE2				For the ACE2-RBD binding interface			
	CNN	ANN	Vina	Vinardo	CNN	ANN	Vina	Vinardo
DB06837	0.002	0.086	-7.5	-5.674	0.959	0.660	-8.5	-5.725
DB08029	0.017	0.404	-6.6	-5.322	0.949	0.662	-7.1	-5.559
DB08409	0.128	0.103	-5.8	-4.817	0.946	0.575	-6.8	-5.254
DB04371	0.031	0.091	-6.6	-5.261	0.924	0.584	-7.3	-5.394
DB07579	0.152	0.112	-6.4	-4.544	0.923	0.543	-8.2	-5.492
DB08394	0.384	0.060	-5.8	-4.587	0.910	0.550	-7.2	-5.826
DB12574	0.030	0.131	-7.2	-5.745	0.907	0.528	-7.9	-5.961
DB08302	0.317	0.231	-6.4	-5.362	0.903	0.526	-7.9	-6.392
DB03313	0.019	0.015	-6.6	-5.045	0.891	0.720	-7.3	-5.547
DB01139	0.054	0.144	-6.5	-4.486	0.884	0.678	-7.2	-5.142
DB08397	0.050	0.072	-6.3	-5.167	0.873	0.528	-7.4	-5.586
Nilotinib	0.008	0.068	-8.8	-6.862	0.000	0.698	-9.2	-5.868
SSAA09E2	0.056	0.739	-6.8	-4.836	0.391	0.193	-7.3	-4.907

3.3. Verification of bind and final inhibitor selection

The possible inhibitory mechanism and binding process of the above 11 compounds are analyzed according to the MD simulation results. Four main aspects are as follows: (1) protein-compound RMSD analysis. RMSD analysis not only indicates if a simulation has equilibrated, but also gives insights into conformation changes of the compound and its target protein throughout the simulation. (2) protein RMSF analysis. RMSF characterizes the flexibility of different amino acid residues in a protein, which is used to compare the conformational differences of the protein before and after the binding of compounds. (3) protein-compound interaction analysis. By calculating the non-bonding interactions of binding between compounds and the protein, possible inhibitory mechanism of the compounds as candidate inhibitors is analyzed. (4) protein-compound binding free energy (ΔG). ΔG is used to quantitatively evaluate the dynamic binding strength between different compounds and the target protein. Besides the above verification of bind, the binding tendency of compounds to different binding sites are also analyzed according to the visualization of MD simulation trajectories. Finally, the five most promising candidate inhibitors are selected and their ADMET properties are given in Table 3.

Table 3. ADMET properties of the 5 candidate inhibitors

Compound drugBank ID	Adsorption			Distribution		Metabolism	Excretion		Toxicity
	Human oral Bioavailability (F20)	Caco2 cell permeability	Human intestinal absorption	Plasma protein binding	Volume of distribution at steady state	CYP Substrate/ Inhibitor	Clearance in Hepatocyte	Half-life	LD50
	probability	Log cm/s	probability	%	L/kg		uL/(min · 10^6 cells)	h	Mg/kg
DB06837	0.80	-6.10	0.80	76.65	1.14	CYP2C19 inhibition CYP3A4 inhibition CYP3A4 substrate	29.28	7.95	902.94
DB08029	0.88	-5.26	0.90	71.65	4.07	-	37.34	14.26	2519.97
DB07579	0.53	-5.73	0.47	63.40	5.83	-	30.26	17.89	1708.90
DB01139	0.74	-5.84	0.49	66.03	0.59	CYP3A4 inhibition	19.55	1.33	16118.83
DB08397	0.84	-5.12	0.83	91.75	1.69	-	22.29	15.53	468.84

4. Conclusions

In this paper, a virtual screening framework based on the binding site selectivity is developed to discover small molecule inhibitors targeting ACE2-RBD binding interface. The binding potential, binding affinity, and binding tendency of the candidate inhibitors are evaluated. Five compounds with better pharmaceutical properties and selectivity than the reported inhibitors are finally selected for experimental assays in future according to the screening results.

Acknowledgements

This work was supported by the NSFC [22278053, 22078041]. The authors are grateful for the University of Minnesota for their generous assistance of the Schrödinger software package used for molecular dynamics simulation in this paper.

References

D.J. Benton, A.G. Wrobel, P. Xu, C. Roustan, S.R. Martin, P.B. Rosenthal, J.J. Skehel, S.J. Gamblin, 2020. Receptor binding and priming of the spike protein of SARS-CoV-2 for membrane fusion. Nature 588, 327-330.

P. Bhutani, G. Joshi, N. Raja, N. Bachhav, P.K. Rajanna, H. Bhutani, A.T. Paul, R. Kumar, 2021. US FDA Approved Drugs from 2015-June 2020: A Perspective. Journal of medicinal chemistry 64, 2339-2381.

X.H. Che, S.Y. Chai, Z.Z. Zhang, L. Zhang, 2022. Prediction of ligand binding sites using improved blind docking method with a Machine Learning-Based scoring function. Chemical Engineering Science 261, 10.

J. Eberhardt, D. Santos-Martins, A.F. Tillack, S. Forli, 2021. AutoDock Vina 1.2.0: New Docking Methods, Expanded Force Field, and Python Bindings. J Chem Inf Model 61, 3891-3898.

K. Kuba, Y. Imai, T. Ohto-Nakanishi, J.M. Penninger, 2010. Trilogy of ACE2: a peptidase in the renin-angiotensin system, a SARS receptor, and a partner for amino acid transporters. Pharmacol Ther 128, 119-128.

R. Lu, X. Zhao, J. Li, P. Niu, B. Yang, H. Wu, W. Wang, H. Song, B. Huang, N. Zhu, Y. Bi, X. Ma, F. Zhan, L. Wang, T. Hu, H. Zhou, Z. Hu, W. Zhou, L. Zhao, J. Chen, Y. Meng, J. Wang, Y. Lin, J. Yuan, Z. Xie, J. Ma, W.J. Liu, D. Wang, W. Xu, E.C. Holmes, G.F. Gao, G. Wu, W. Chen, W. Shi, W. Tan, 2020. Genomic characterisation and epidemiology of 2019 novel coronavirus: implications for virus origins and receptor binding. The Lancet 395, 565-574.

R. Quiroga, M.A. Villarreal, 2016. Vinardo: A Scoring Function Based on Autodock Vina Improves Scoring, Docking, and Virtual Screening. PLoS One 11, e0155183.

M. Razizadeh, M. Nikfar, Y. Liu, 2021. Small molecule therapeutics to destabilize the ACE2-RBD complex: A molecular dynamics study. Biophys J 120, 2793-2804.

K. Terali, B. Baddal, H.O. Gulcan, 2020. Prioritizing potential ACE2 inhibitors in the COVID-19 pandemic: Insights from a molecular mechanics-assisted structure-based virtual screening experiment. Journal of Molecular Graphics & Modelling 100, 10.

P. Towler, B. Staker, S.G. Prasad, S. Menon, J. Tang, T. Parsons, D. Ryan, M. Fisher, D. Williams, N.A. Dales, M.A. Patane, M.W. Pantoliano, 2004. ACE2 X-ray structures reveal a large hinge-bending motion important for inhibitor binding and catalysis. J Biol Chem 279, 17996-18007.

R. Yan, Y. Zhang, Y. Li, L. Xia, Y. Guo, Q. Zhou, 2020. Structural basis for the recognition of SARS-CoV-2 by full-length human ACE2. Science 367, 1444-1448.

Q.A. Zhou, J. Kato-Weinstein, Y. Li, Y. Deng, R. Granet, L. Garner, C. Liu, D. Polshakov, C. Gessner, S. Watkins, 2020. Potential Therapeutic Agents and Associated Bioassay Data for COVID-19 and Related Human Coronavirus Infections. ACS Pharmacol Transl Sci 3, 813-834.

Flavio Manenti, Gintaras V. Reklaitis (Eds.), Proceedings of the 34th European Symposium on Computer Aided Process Engineering / 15th International Symposium on Process Systems Engineering (ESCAPE34/PSE24), June 2-6, 2024, Florence, Italy

Modelling Liver Preservation

Angelo Lucia[a], Korkut Uygun[b]

[a]*Department of Chemical Engineering, E. Alumni Ave., Kingston,RI 02881 USA*
[b]*Center for Engineering in Medicine & Surgery, 51 Blossum St., Boston, MA 02114 USA*
alucia@uri.edu

Abstract

Liver preservation has obvious healthcare implications in treating liver diseases. With the continuing shortage of viable livers and other organs for transplantation, methods of organ preservation have progressed over the last 40 years from static cold storage to include machine perfusion in many clinical settings. However, modelling organ preservation has been slow to be accepted by the medical community. The objective of this paper is to present an overview of a novel approach to metabolic network modelling based on Nash equilibrium. An example of liver preservation consisting of static cold storage followed by machine perfusion is described. Monte Carlo (MC) optimization of the perfusion chamber temperature protocol and antioxidant supplementation for controlling the effects of reactive oxygen species (ROS) from reperfusion are also presented. Results show that the Nash equilibrium/Monte Carlo approach can predict fluxes, concentrations, pH, temperature policies, supplementation protocols, and other properties of a complex metabolic network.

Keywords: Static cold storage, machine perfusion, Nash equilibrium, Monte Carlo.

1. Introduction

The only current solution to liver disease (e.g., non-alcoholic fatty liver disease or NAFLD) is transplantation. Livers harvested from cardiac death are typically preserved on ice at 4 °C (i.e., static cold storage, or SCS) until a suitable patient is identified. While SCS has been the gold standard for organ preservation for many years, it is time limited because it results in ATP depletion, which if continued long enough can result in cell injury or cell death. Since the 1980's clinical researchers have investigated ways of extending organ viability using machine perfusion (MP). MP is an engineered system in which an organ is placed in a perfusion chamber and continuously supplied with nutrients and oxygen for some length of time to generate ATP and to put the organ in an improved energy state. However, MP is not without drawbacks. Re-introducing nutrients and oxygen can generate reactive oxygen species (ROS) like superoxide and hydrogen peroxide and cause oxidative stress and inflammation (Sies, 2017).

Most studies of machine perfusion have been experimental, which is expensive and time consuming because of the large space of decision variables (i.e., temperature, nutrients, medicinal additives, etc.). Analysis and liver viability determinations are also limited because not all concentrations of metabolites can be measured. In our opinion, static cold storage followed by MP represents an application where metabolic network modeling, simulation and optimization have the potential to make significant contributions in evaluating organ viability, guiding experiments in the short term, and providing personalized medicine in the long term.

Unfortunately, numerical modelling has been poorly received by the medical community for two reasons: (1) initial modeling studies using flux balance analysis over-promised what could be delivered and (2) many medical professionals are not trained in numerical methods and are not comfortable relying on numerical simulations. In this paper a Nash Equilibrium/Monte Carlo framework for modeling/optimizing metabolic networks along with numerical results for liver preservation are presented.

1.1 A Nash Equilibrium Model for Metabolic Networks

Metabolic networks consist of pathways, biochemical reactions, organ specific intra- and inter-pathway transport, regulatory constraints, feedback inhibition, etc.
The Nash equilibrium approach to modeling metabolic networks proposed by Lucia and DiMaggio (2016, 2018) is based on competitive game theory and three simple ideas:

1) Enzymes are the players in a multi-player game.
2) Each enzyme minimizes the Gibbs free energy of the reaction(s) it catalyzes subject to constraints.
3) The network goal is to find the best solution given enzyme competition for nutrients.

2. Modeling, Simulation and Optimization of Liver Preservation

The metabolic network model used in this work contains many of the major pathways in any cell and was used for both SCS and MP.

2.1 A Metabolic Network Model of the Liver

The specific metabolic network model of the liver consisted of:

1) 5 cellular compartments (i.e., cytosol, mitochondria, membrane, endoplasmic reticulum, and peroxisome).
2) 27 metabolic pathways (e.g., glycolysis, Kreb cycle, fatty acid synthesis/oxidation, urea cycle, etc.).
3) 80 biochemical reactions.
4) 428 metabolites and cofactors (i.e., the unknown flux variables, some of which are also transport variables).
5) 271 mass balance constraints, most of which involve charged species.
6) 21 active inter-pathway transport variables.
7) 92 model parameters (standard state Gibbs free energy and enthalpies).

Figure 1 is a schematic of the metabolic network which. also accounts for liver specific metabolic functions. For example, the liver does not produce the amino acid serine because the enzyme 3-phosphoglycerate dehydrogenase (3-PGDH) is not present to any great extent in the liver. Also, ammonia and ammonium are toxic to the liver; normal levels are 0.5 mM to 1 mM for ammonia and 100 µM for ammonium.

The unknown variables in the model are the fluxes and are determined by a two-level algorithm in which Gibbs free energy minimizations for all reactions in each pathway are solved sequentially for fluxes in an inner loop and any inter-pathway transport fluxes are converged in an outer loop. See Lucia and DiMaggio (2019) for algorithmic details such as problem formulation, temperature effects via the van't Hoff equation, charge balancing, the prevalence of linear dependence in mass balance constraints, etc.

2.2 Static Cold Storage

When a liver is harvested from cardiac death it is flushed with University of Wisconsin (UW) solution (Southard et al., 1990, Lucia and Uygun, 2022) and placed on ice at 4 °C. Under these conditions the liver is receiving no nutrients and is in a hypoxic state, which results in several metabolic changes including (1) a shift at the pyruvate hub causing an

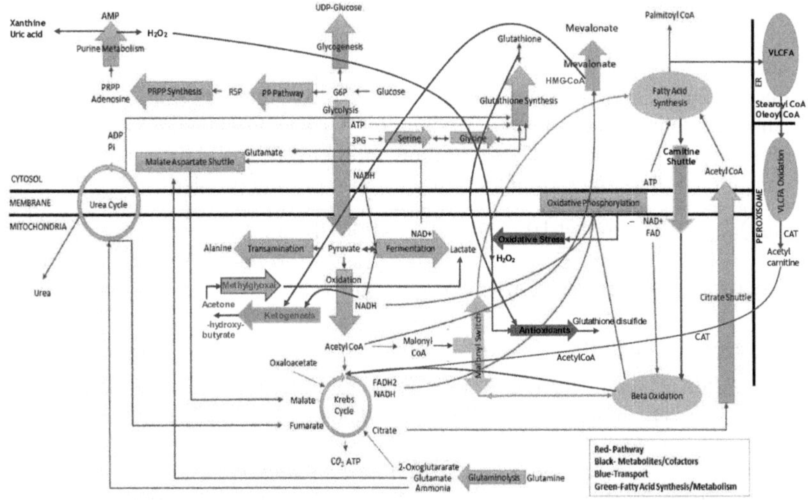

Figure 1: Metabolic Network of the Liver

increase in lactic acid production, (2) an increase in hydrogen peroxide synthesis from purine metabolism, (3) accumulation of succinate due to the reversal of the succinate to fumarate reaction in the Krebs cycle, and (4) a loss of function in the electron transport chain. These and other metabolic changes result in the depletion of ATP and a decrease in the energy charge (EC) of the cells, where energy charge is defined as

$$EC = \frac{[ATP] + \frac{1}{2}[ADP]}{[ATP] + [ADP] + [AMP]} \tag{1}$$

where ATP is adenosine triphosphate, ADP is adenosine diphosphate, AMP is adenosine monophosphate, and [ ] denotes concentration. Normal EC is in the range [0.6, 0.95].

2.3 Machine Perfusion
During machine perfusion, the liver was supplied with glucose, amino acids, and oxygen.

2.4 Optimization Formulations
A constrained multi-objective formulation was used for temperature policy optimization while antioxidant supplementation was posed as a nonlinear programming problem. A two-stage optimization approach was used by first determining the best temperature protocol for MP and then determining a glutathione supplementation protocol needed to keep hydrogen peroxide concentration in the normal range (i.e., $10^{-9} - 10^{-8}$ M).

2.4.1 Temperature Policy Optimization
Following a base case SCS + MP simulation, Monte Carlo optimization was used to adjust the temperature at any time interval to improve the multi-objective function given by

$$\max_{T(t)} R : [\text{lactate}] \leq 2.3 \text{ mM}, \text{pH} > 7.3; \max E = \frac{net\ ATP}{|Glc|} \tag{2}$$

where $T(t) = \{T_1, T_2, ..., T_N\}$ is discrete and the return function is given by

$$R = w_1|Glc| + w_2 ATP + w_3 Mev + w_4 EC \tag{3}$$

where R is a return function formulated from criteria given in Laing et al. (2017), E is network efficiency, Glc is glucose consumption, ATP is net ATP production, Mev is mevalonate production (a measure of bile production), and $w_1 - w_4$ are weights.

2.4.2 Glutathione Supplementation Optimization
Although glutathione (GSH) is used in the UW flush solution prior to SCS and is present in small amounts in the Williams Medium E (WME) nutrient solution used in MP, it can be insufficient to manage ROS generation during hypoxia and reperfusion injury.
   Equation 4 gives the formulation for this optimization problem.

$$\min_{GSH(t)} \sum_{i=1}^{N} GSH \text{ such that } 10^{-9} \text{ M} \leq [H_2O_2] \leq 10^{-8} \text{ M} \tag{4}$$

where $GSH(t)$ is *discrete*, $\{GSH_1, GSH_2, ..., GSH_N\}$.

3. Numerical Results

This section contains results for SCS + mid-thermic machine perfusion (MMP) simulation, temperature policy optimization, and GSH supplementation optimization.

3.1 Static Cold Storage and Machine Perfusion Simulations
Consider 'base case' simulations consisting of (1) flushing the liver with UW solution, (2) placing it on ice for 3 hours and then (3) MP simulations for 4 h. initialized with the SCS concentrations, fluxes, pH, etc. and a fixed (or flat) temperature profile of 16 °C.

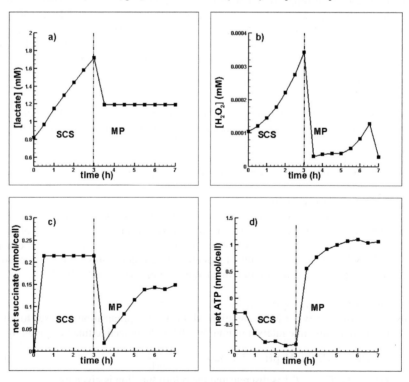

Figure 2. Results for Base Case SCS + MP Simulation. a) Lactate Concentration. b) Hydrogen Peroxide Concentration. c) Net Succinate. d) Net ATP.

Figure 2 shows that there is lactate and hydrogen peroxide synthesis, succinate accumulation, and ATP depletion during SCS. During MMP ATP and succinate are generated, while hydrogen peroxide and lactate are removed from the cell. Although it's difficult to tell from Fig. 2., $[H_2O_2] = 2.867 \times 10^{-8}$ M at the end of MMP is just outside the normal range, a consequence of purine metabolism during SCS and rapid succinate metabolism and ROS generation during MMP. The energy charge and pH for SCS were 0.5011 and 7.52 while the energy state and pH following MMP were 0.6447 and 7.61.

3.2 Temperature Policy Optimization Results

Starting from the base case (flat) temperature policy, 350 MC optimizations of the multi-objective function in Eqs. 2 and 3 were conducted with all weights in Eq, 2 equal to 1.

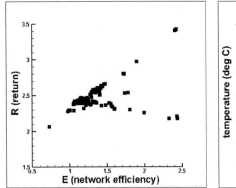 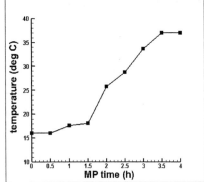

Figure 3: Machine Perfusion Optimal Temperature Policy and Pareto Set/Optimal Front. a) Pareto Set and Optimal Front. b) Optimal Gradual Warming (GW) Temperature Policy.

Figure 3a) shows the Pareto set and optimal front plotted as return, *R*, versus network efficiency, *E* (see Eqs. 2 and 3). The temperature policy in Fig 3b) shows the best gradual warming (GW) policy for the liver from 16 °C to 37 °C (i.e., body temperature) and corresponds to the symbols in Fig. 3a) in the upper righthand corner. Here the energy state and pH for GW MMP were 0.6397 and 7.60 respectively and resulted in almost double the net ATP produced and a 19% increase in net bile precursor (Mev) synthesis.

3.3 Antioxidant Supplementation Results

Using the optimal temperature policy in Fig. 3a), we determined a GSH supplementation protocol (i.e., that adds GSH every 30 minutes) needed to keep $[H_2O_2]$ in the normal range. See Eq. 4. Figure 4a) shows this glutathione protocol. Note that there is significant potential oxidative stress at the end of SCS because $[H_2O_2] = 3.432 \times 10^{-7}$ M.

Figure 4b) shows the ratio of GSH/GSSG during SCS and GW MMP, which is another common metric for oxidative stress (i.e., higher values of GSH/GSSG indicate greater oxidative stress). Note that during MMP with the optimal temperature policy there is a large initial spike in GSH/GSSG as shown in Fig. 4b), which is a clear indication of additional oxidative stress due to rapid succinate metabolism. However, the calculated GSH protocol resolved this issue and resulted in a rapid reduction of GSH/GSSG. In contrast, simulation without GSH supplementation during MMP showed elevated levels of oxidative stress (i.e., $[H_2O_2]$ on the order of 10^{-7} M) that go unresolved.

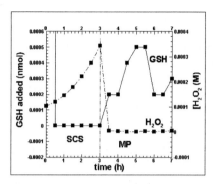 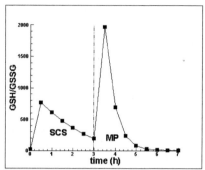

Figure 4: Glutathione Supplementation Effect on Oxidative Stress. a) GSH Protocol with Optimal GW MMP. b) GSH/GSSG Dynamics for GSH Protocol with Optimal GW MMP.

4. Conclusions

A metabolic network model of the liver was presented. SCS +MMP simulations and MMP optimization studies were performed. An optimal gradual warming (GW MMP) policy was determined followed by a glutathione supplementation protocol to keep $[H_2O_2]$ in the normal range. GSH/GSSG ratios were also calculated to monitor oxidative stress. Results showed that the Nash Equilibrium/Monte Carlo framework is capable of successfully modeling SCS and improving net ATP synthesis and ROS mitigation using gradual warming MP and intermittent glutathione supplementation, respectively.

5. References

R.W. Laing, H. Mergental, C. Yap et al. 2017. Viability Testing and Transplantation of Marginal Livers (VITTAL) Using Normothermic Machine Perfusion: Study Protocol for an Open-label, Non-randomised, Prospective, Single Arm Trial. BMJ Open, 7, e017733.

A. Lucia and P.A. DiMaggio. 2016. A Nash Equilibrium Approach to Metabolic Network Analysis. *Lecture Notes in Computer Science 10122*, 45-58.

A. Lucia and P.A. DiMaggio. 2018. Metabolic Network Analysis Using Nash Equilibrium. *J. Global Optim.* 71, 537-550.

A. Lucia and P.A. DiMaggio. 2019. A Multi-Scale Computational Approach to Understanding Cancer Metabolism. in *Data Science for Healthcare: Methodologies and Applications M*, S. Consoli et al. (Eds): Springer, p. 327-345. The Netherlands.

A. Lucia and K. Uygun. 2022. Optimal Temperature Protocols for Liver Machine Perfusion Using a Monte Carlo Method. IFAC PapersOnLine 55-23, 35-40.

J.H. Southard, T.M.., van Gulik, M.S., Ametani, P.K., Vreugdenhil, S.L.., Lindell, B.L., Pienaar, F.O., Belzer. 1990. Important Components of the UW Solution. *Transplantation* 49, 2, 251-257.

H. Sies. 2017. Hydrogen Peroxide as a Central Redox Signaling Molecule in Physiological Oxidative Stress: Oxidative Eustress. *Redox Biology* 11, 613-619.

Acknowledgements. This material is partially based on work supported by the National Science Foundation under Grant No. EEC 1941543. Support from the US National Institutes of Health (Grant R01DK096075 and R01DK114506) and the Shriners Children's Hospital is gratefully acknowledged.

Flavio Manenti, Gintaras V. Reklaitis (Eds.), Proceedings of the 34th European Symposium on Computer Aided Process Engineering / 15th International Symposium on Process Systems Engineering (ESCAPE34/PSE24), June 2-6, 2024, Florence, Italy

Design of a Novel Pass-Through Distillation Process for Bioethanol Recovery

Tamara Janković,[a] Adrie J. J. Straathof,[a] Ian R. McGregor,[b] Anton A. Kiss [a]

[a] *Department of Biotechnology, Delft University of Technology, van der Maasweg 9, 2629 HZ Delft, The Netherlands*
[b] *Drystill Holdings Inc, 3549 Mavis Road, Mississauga, ON, L5C 1T7, Canada*
A.A.Kiss@tudelft.nl

Abstract

Pass-through distillation (PTD) is a novel separation technology that can effectively overcome challenges related to using vacuum distillation in bio-based processes (defined temperature limit for evaporation that might result in very low condensation temperature). This method allows evaporation and condensation to be performed at different pressures by decoupling them using an absorption-desorption loop with an electrolyte absorption fluid. This original paper presents a process design for large-scale bioethanol recovery from fermentation broth (production capacity ~100 ktonne/y) by PTD. The flexibility of the novel PTD technology is expanded by combining it with heat pumps (PTD-HP) and multi-effect distillation (PTD-MED). Total cost and energy requirements for the recovery of high-purity bioethanol (99.8 wt%) are respectively 0.122 \$/kg$_{EtOH}$ and 1.723 kW$_{th}$h/kg$_{EtOH}$ for PTD-HP, and 0.131 \$/kg$_{EtOH}$ and 1.834 kW$_{th}$h/kg$_{EtOH}$ for PTD-MED, proving the effectiveness of the newly designed recovery processes for concurrent alcohol recovery and fermentation.

Keywords: bioethanol, pass-through distillation, industrial fermentation

1. Introduction

The need to transition from fossil fuels to more sustainable alternatives is rapidly gaining significance due to increasing concerns about climate change, environmental pollution and energy security. Biofuels and biochemicals potentially present a renewable replacement for conventional fossil-derived chemicals. In particular, a lot of research emphasis has been put on the fermentative production of lower alcohols, such as ethanol. A major limitation of the industrial production of bioethanol is the low product concentration that can be obtained due to inhibitory effects on microorganisms. Consequently, the downstream processing part of the bioethanol production process is especially challenging. Implementing a concurrent alcohol recovery and fermentation (CARAF) process is one way to improve the competitiveness of the overall bioethanol production process (McGregor and Furlong, 2017).

Conventional vacuum distillation can be used to separate valuable products from the rest of the fermentation broth while maintaining operating conditions appropriate for the present microorganisms. However, the selection of operating pressure in classic distillation determines both the reboiler and the condenser temperatures, and accordingly, the types of external utilities that are needed. Consequently, reducing operating pressure so that evaporation temperature does not exceed a certain limit might easily result in a very low condensation temperature that requires the usage of expensive refrigeration. Described limitations of applying conventional distillation on biobased systems can be conveniently addressed using pass-through distillation (PTD). This relatively new separation technique decouples evaporation and condensation steps with an absorption-desorption loop (McGregor and Furlong, 2017). PTD has already been proven effective by Drystill at lab and pilot scale (Kiss et al., 2014), but further scale-up has not been attempted. Therefore, this original paper contributes to sustainable development by providing an eco-efficient process design for large-scale bioethanol recovery (~100 ktonne/y) from the fermentation broth using a novel PTD technique.

2. Working principle

The working principle of PTD is presented in Figure 1. Firstly, bioethanol product, together with some water, is evaporated from the fermentation broth. Formed vapor is later absorbed by electrolyte absorption fluid, commonly concentrated lithium-bromide (LiBr) solution. The heat released during the exothermic absorption can be transferred to the evaporation part by heat pipes in an integrated process equipment unit called a stripping-absorption module (SAM) (McGregor and Belchers, 2014). Ethanol and water are further desorbed from the diluted brine and condensed. Recovered concentrated electrolyte solution can be recycled and reused in the absorption step. The major benefit of PTD is decoupling the evaporation and condensation steps, allowing operation at different pressures. This means that the evaporator can operate at a lower pressure and a temperature below thermal limits, while the condenser can operate at ambient pressure and a temperature suitable for cheaper cooling utilities (McGregor and Furlong, 2017).

3. Results and discussion

This section contains the main results related to design of large-scale bioethanol recovery process from the fermentation broth by using a novel PTD method. Rigorous simulations for every part of process were designed in Aspen Plus. The main challenges for developing a cost- and energy-effective recovery process are highly diluted feed stream (5 wt% ethanol), presence of living microorganisms, modeling physical properties due to used electrolyte absorption fluid and thermodynamic limitations due to formation of ethanol-water azeotrope (95.57 wt% ethanol).

3.1. Property method development

Aspen Plus and MATLAB were used as CAPE tools to develop a reliable property model employing the electrolyte-NRTL model coupled with the Redlich-Kwong equation of state (ElecNRTL-RK) (Aspen Technology, 2023). Since this model describes complex systems using only binary interactions, experimental data for binary systems (Nasirzadeh et al., 2004; Patil et al., 1990; Perry and Green, 1997) were used to determine the values of binary interaction parameters. The total deviation of the obtained property model from the experimental data is 0.5%, 6.5% and 3.2% respectively for systems water-ethanol, LiBr-water and LiBr-ethanol. Therefore, the property method takes into account the complex interactions between electrolyte and two polar solvents (water and ethanol), as well as interactions among water and ethanol.

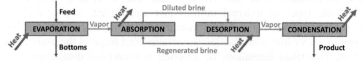

Figure 1. Working principle of pass-through distillation

3.2. Pass-through distillation part of the bioethanol recovery process

A recovery process was designed in Aspen Plus for an industrial-scale bioethanol production process with a production capacity of about 100 ktonne/y. The feed stream for this process is taken from the fermenter (37 °C, 1 bar) and contains about 5 wt% of ethanol and 0.1 wt% of CO_2, while the rest is water with some microorganisms. The first step is removing some of the initially present CO_2 in the degasser unit under reduced pressure. Some of the ethanol is also evaporated together with CO_2 but is later captured in a striping column and recovered.

After the degassing step, the fermentation broth is sent to the SAM unit. As this equipment unit is not available in Aspen Plus, equivalent operations are used (see Figure 2 and Figure 3). The operating pressure for evaporation and absorption parts of PTD (0.054 bar) was chosen such that total vaporization can happen while maintaining temperature below the fermentation temperature. The required flowrate of LiBr absorbent fluid was determined such that the heat content of diluted brine after absorption is sufficient to cover the heat demand of the evaporation part. This led to an absorbent-to-feed ratio of 1.4 on a mass basis. Diluted LiBr after the absorption step is sent to desorption and condensation. The remaining liquid fermentation broth after the evaporation step contains microorganisms and most of the present water, and can be recycled to the fermentation to avoid loss of biomass, allowing the upstream process to operate in a closed loop and to reduce fresh water requirements (Daniell et al., 2012).

Furthermore, the stripping column C1 was included prior to the SAM unit to increase ethanol concentration in formed vapor (from 19 wt% to 30 wt%), reduce ethanol losses in the stream that is being recycled to the fermenter and decrease ethanol concentration in this stream (from 2 wt% to 0.2 wt%). Vapor fraction in the evaporation part of the SAM unit was selected to allow ethanol recovery higher than 90%.

In order to recover and recycle the absorbent fluid, previously absorbed products must be desorbed. Since, this desorption step requires external heating, two process configurations were considered to reduce the overall energy requirements: desorber unit enhanced with heat pumps (PTD-HP) and multi-effect distillation (PTD-MED).

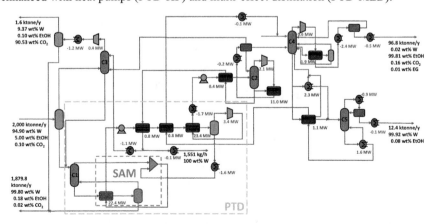

Figure 2. Flowsheet of bioethanol recovery process, PTD-HP configuration

The first process configuration (PTD-HP, see Figure 2) implies using a heat pump system based on vapor recompression to enhance the desorption part of PTD. After the SAM unit, the diluted LiBr needs to be pumped to an appropriate pressure for the following desorption and condensation steps. As the desorption step is very energy-consuming (about 25 MW), heat pumps were implemented to reduce energy requirements. More precisely, the desorbed water-ethanol vapor is compressed and used to provide heat to the diluted LiBr. Consequently, very high amounts of thermal energy are substituted with a much smaller amount of electrical energy. The operating pressure for the desorption and condensation parts (0.2 bar) was determined to minimize total energy requirements, while also allowing condensation with cheaper cooling utilities.

The second process configuration (PTD-MED, see Figure 3) replaces desorption and condensation steps with multi-effect distillation (MED). In this design, diluted brine is separated into high-pressure (HP), medium-pressure (MP) and low-pressure (LP) parts, whereby hot higher-pressure streams provide heat to lower-pressure streams. The split ratio (ratio between flowrates of HP and MP, as well as between MP and LP) determines the required operating pressures needed for efficient heat transfer. The pressure of LP was chosen to allow the following condensation using cheaper cooling utilities. The split ratio of 1.05 was determined to minimize total energy requirements for the PTD part of the bioethanol recovery process while keeping required pressures at reasonable levels. Therefore, pressures of HP, MP and LP are 2.0 bar, 0.5 bar and 0.09 bar, respectively. Replacing desorption and condensation parts with MED results in about 64% reduction in external requirements.

3.3. Further ethanol purification

As a result of PTD, the ethanol concentration increased from 5 wt% to about 30 wt%. However, additional treatment is needed to obtain a high-purity end product. Further processing consists of several steps due to the water-ethanol azeotrope. Firstly, a stream containing separated products from the PTD was preconcentrated, in column C2, to obtain 91 wt% ethanol in distillate since this concentration was determined to minimize total energy requirements (Kiss and Ignat, 2013).

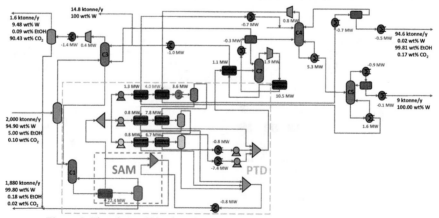

Figure 3. Flowsheet of bioethanol recovery process, PTD-MED configuration

The top product from column C2 is preconcentrated ethanol solution, while the bottom product is pure water that is used to preheat the feed stream for this column. Additionally, since temperatures at top and bottom of the distillation column are relatively close, mechanical vapor recompression (MVR) was applied to reduce energy requirements (Kiss and Infante Ferreira, 2016).

Furthermore, to obtain high-purity ethanol product, more CO_2 needs to be removed in the partial condenser of the column C2. Separated ethanol is captured from two CO_2-rich streams (from the degasser unit and from the partial condenser of column C2) using part of the bottom water from column C2 in an additional stripping column C3. Returning captured ethanol to the recovery process reduces the amount of lost ethanol from 14% to less than 0.002%.

The preconcentrated ethanol-water mixture is further dehydrated, in column C4, using extractive distillation with ethylene glycol since this method was proven to be the best one for large-scale ethanol preconcentration in terms of both investment and operating costs (Kiss et al., 2014). The top product from this column is high-purity (99.8 wt%) ethanol, while the bottom product is ethylene glycol-water mixture that is sent to solvent recovery column C5. Pure water, obtained at the top of column C5, can be cooled and recycled to the upstream process to reduce need for fresh water. Ethylene glycol is obtained as the bottom product and can be reused in extractive distillation column C4.

Additional heat integration opportunities were considered to maximize process performance. Since recovered ethylene glycol requires cooling before being recycled to column C4, it was used in PTD-HP to evaporate part of the bottom liquid from column C4. A side reboiler was added to column C4, whereby compressed top vapor from this column was used to evaporate part of the liquid side stream. These two heat integrations reduced external heating requirements for the extractive distillation part by about 57%. Lastly, water product from column C2 and recovered ethylene glycol were used for heating diluted LiBr in the PTD part, which reduced compressor duty in the heat pump system. In PTD-MED, compressed top vapor from column C2 and recovered ethylene glycol were used to heat HP stream in the MED part. Consequently, external heating requirements for the PTD part decreased by about 60%.

3.4. Analysis of economic and environmental impact

To evaluate the performance of the designed recovery processes, a complete analysis of economic indicators and sustainability metrics was conducted following published recommendations (Humbird et al., 2011; Schwarz et al., 2002). A comparison between the two processes is given in Table 1. Generally, both processes are highly cost- and energy-efficient, and the choice of the optimal downstream process should depend on the exact location site and availability of utilities. In case of lower electricity cost, enhancing PTD with heat pumps (PTD-HP) is preferable solution. Alternatively, if steam is more readily accessible, multi-effect distillation is more favourable choice for desorption and condensation parts of PTD (PTD-MED).

Table 1. Key performance indicators

	PTD-HP	PTD-MED
Economic indicators		
CAPEX (k$)	33,595	28,378
OPEX ($/kg$_{EtOH}$)	0.088	0.101
Total annual costs ($/kg$_{EtOH}$), 10 years payback period	0.122	0.131
Sustainability metrics		
Thermal energy requirements (kW$_{th}$h/kg$_{EtOH}$)	0.320	0.889
Electrical energy requirements (kW$_e$h/kg$_{EtOH}$)	0.561	0.378
Primary energy requirements (kW$_{th}$h/kg$_{EtOH}$)	1.723	1.834
Water consumption (m^3_w/kg$_{EtOH}$)	0.158	0.234
CO$_2$ emissions, grey / green electricity (kg$_{CO2}$/kg$_{EtOH}$)	0.292 / 0.035	0.309 / 0.136

4. Conclusion

This original paper is the first one to develop a complex property model for the ternary system LiBr-ethanol-water and include it in unique process design. The main contribution of this research is the design of recovery process for large-scale bioethanol production using a novel pass-through distillation method (PTD). High-purity bioethanol (99.8 wt%) is obtained by combining PTD with further preconcentration and dehydration steps. Enhancing PTD with heat pumps (PTD-HP) and multi-effect distillation (PTD-MED) resulted in cost- and energy-effective downstream processes (total recovery cost of 0.122 and 0.131 $/kg$_{EtOH}$, and energy requirements of 1.723 and 1.834 kW$_{th}$h/kg$_{EtOH}$ for PTD-HP and PTD-MED, respectively).

References

Daniell, J., Köpke, M., Simpson, S.D. (2012). Commercial Biomass Syngas Fermentation. Energies 5, 5372–5417.

Aspen Technology. (2023). ENRTL-RK. https://knowledgecenter.aspentech.com

Humbird, D., Davis, R., Tao, L., Kinchin, C., Hsu, D., Aden, A., Schoen, P., Lukas, J., Olthof, B., Wordey, M., Sexton, D., Dudgeon, D. (2011). Process Design and Economics for Biochemical Conversion of Lignocellulosic Biomass to Ethanol, National Renewable Energy Laboratory.

Kiss, A.A., Ignat, R.M. (2013). Optimal Economic Design of an Extractive Distillation Process for Bioethanol Dehydration. Energy Technology 1, 166–170.

Kiss, A.A., Ignat, R.M., Bildea, C.S. (2014). Optimal Extractive Distillation Process for Bioethanol Dehydration. Computer Aided Chemical Engineering 33, 1333–1338.

Kiss, A.A., Infante Ferreira, C.A. (2016). Mechanically Driven Heat Pumps, in: Heat Pumps in Chemical Process Industry. CRC Press, Boca Raton, pp. 189–251

Kiss, A.A, McGregor, I.R., Furlong, S. (2014). Pass-through distillation - A new player in separation technology.

McGregor, I., Furlong, S. (2017). Concurrent Alcohol Recovery and Fermentation Using Pass-Through Distillation. Industrial Biotechnology 13, 107–112.

McGregor, I.R., Belchers, C.H. (2014). Stripping absorption module. US 8,757,599 B2.

Nasirzadeh, K., Neueder, R., Kunz, W. (2004). Vapor Pressures, Osmotic and Activity Coefficients of Electrolytes in Protic Solvents at Different Temperatures. 2. Lithium Bromide in Ethanol. Journal of Solution Chemistry 33, 1429–1446.

Patil, K.R., Trlpathi, A.D., Pathak, G., Katti, S.S. (1990). Thermodynamic Properties of Aqueous Electrolyte Solutions. 1. Vapor Pressure of Aqueous Solutions of LiCl, LiBr and LiI. Journal of Chemical and Engineering Data 35, 166–168.

Perry, R.H., Green, D.W. (1997). Distillation, in: Perry's Chemical Engineering Handbook. McGraw-Hill, pp. 13–10.

Schwarz, J., Beloff, B., Beaver, E. (2002). Use Sustainability Metrics to Guide Decision-Making. Chemical Engineering Progress 98, 58–63.

Flavio Manenti, Gintaras V. Reklaitis (Eds.), Proceedings of the 34th European Symposium on Computer Aided Process Engineering / 15th International Symposium on Process Systems Engineering (ESCAPE34/PSE24), June 2-6, 2024, Florence, Italy

From laboratory scale to innovative spruce-based biorefinery. Note I: Conceptual process design and simulation

Filippo Bisotti[a,*], Matteo Gilardi[a,*], Olaf T. Berglihn[a], Roman Tschentscher[b], Line D. Hansen[c], Svein J. Horn[c], Anikó Várnai[c], Bernd Wittgens[a]

[a] SINTEF Industry-Process Technology, Sem Sælands vei 2, Trondheim, 7034, Norway
[b] SINTEF Industry-Process Technology, Forskningsveien 1, Oslo, 0373, Norway
[c] Faculty of Chemistry, Biotechnology and Food Science, NMBU, Chr. Magnus Falsens vei 18, Aas, 1433, Norway
* matteo.gilardi@sintef.no; filippo.bisotti@sintef.no (corresponding authors)

Abstract

This paper presents the conceptual design and simulation of a biorefinery process converting Norway spruce (*Picea abies*) into ethanol, via fermentation of hydrolysed hemicellulose and cellulose sugar fractions, and into bio-oil, via pyrolysis of the lignin fraction. The conceptual design of the biomass pretreatment and fractioning (i.e., steam explosion and enzymatic saccharification) as well as the thermochemical conversion (i.e., fast pyrolysis) was assembled by translating laboratory-scale process steps into industrial unit/series operations. The process design was complemented with downstream processing for both ethanol purification and bio-oil subsequent stabilization and distillation. The experimental observations at the laboratory scale were used to tune the data-driven models for the steam explosion and enzymatic saccharification process units and to validate kinetic models retrieved from existing literature for fast pyrolysis. After establishing flowsheet implementation of the complete model of a wood-to-fuels biorefinery in COFE v3.6 (AmsterCHEM), the CAPE-open simulation environment, we scaled up the process to a relevant industrial scale (treating 100,000 tons of dry wood annually).

Keywords: biorefinery simulation and design, bio-oil, bioethanol, biorefinery scale-up, CAPE-open tool

1. Introduction

Tackling climate change requires decarbonization of fuels, leading to a shift from a fossil- to a bio-based economy. In this context, the biorefinery is a sustainable pathway to produce fuels, such as bioethanol, bio-oil and biochar, and high-added-value bioproducts with properties like the corresponding fossil-based ones, while replacing fossil feedstocks with green sources (Katakojwala and Mohan, 2021). A biorefinery producing bioethanol and bio-oil embraces a complex series of operations where, in our case, the cellulosic fraction is turned into ethanol via enzymatic saccharification and fermentation, while the lignin fraction undergoes pyrolysis to produce bio-oil and, optionally, biochar. Before deployment at scale, scale-up and techno-economic assessments (TEA) of the operations, both individually and in a process concept, are key steps to demonstrate process feasibility and sustainability. Simulation of process units includes the development and validation of process models and is intensified by the complexity of the feedstock and bioproducts. Process steps and process streams often incorporate thousands of reactions and species respectively, which require simplified models to characterize the system reasonably accurately while reducing the enormous computational effort (Vikram et al., 2021). In this work, we present the design, simulation and scale-up of a process to convert Norwegian spruce into bioethanol and bio-oil based on simplified models for the complex reaction schemes using COFE v3.6 (AmsterCHEM), a CAPE-open simulation software.

2. Process layout and implemented sub-models

The simplified layout of the biorefinery is shown in Figure 1. The laboratory-scale experimental setup by Hansen et al. (2022) was used as a basis for upscaling to a plant processing 100,000 tons of spruce/year. We developed dedicated sub-models for each unit operation and then integrated those into the COFE v3.6. The core of the process involves the following steps: (1) steam explosion of the feedstock; (2) saccharification of the pretreated feedstock with lytic polysaccharide monooxygenase (LPMO)-containing cellulase cocktail to break cellulose and hemicellulose into simple sugars; (3) fermentation of those sugars into bioethanol; (4) rectification of bioethanol to 96% (v/v) purity; (5) pyrolysis of the residual lignin-rich fraction from the saccharification step and separation of formed biochar; (6) the stabilization of the crude pyrolysis bio-oil via hydrodeoxygenation (HDO) to reduce oxygenated compounds; with (7) subsequent distillation to recover vacuum gas oil (VGO), diesel-like and gasoline-like fractions. The light tail gas is recovered from the top section and (8) burnt for steam generation.

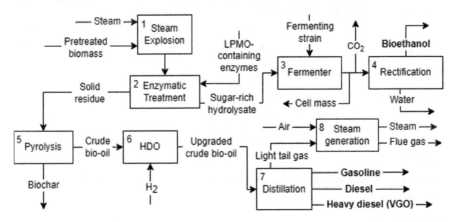

Figure 1: Simplified Block Flow Diagram of the biorefinery.

Biomass composition was defined by Wang et al. (2018). In the model, cellulose and hemicellulose were approximated as dimers, the corresponding monomers as their depolymerization products, and lignin as in Dussan et al. (2019), which considers four "building blocks" for lignin. The optimal linear combination of these four building blocks was determined previously as the best fit for Norway spruce (Bisotti et al., 2023). The main thermodynamic properties needed to close the material and energy balances (i.e., enthalpy of formation, heat capacities, vapour pressure for cellulose, hemicellulose, and lignin constituents) were estimated using the method by Constantinou and Gani (1994). ***Steam explosion:*** Based on the above-mentioned compounds, we set up a simplified kinetics scheme for the steam explosion as proposed by Lam et al. (2009). This model is considered valid for softwood, such as *Picea abies* (spruce). Briefly, the model describes (hemi)cellulose decomposition to its sugar monomers and estimates the partial conversion of these sugars to furfural and 5-hydroxymethylfurfural (HMF) and subsequent polymerization thereof into pseudo-lignin. In addition, the formation of acetic acid, a by-product of steam explosion, was incorporated in the model, based on the work by Chadni et al. (2019). Following the setup by Hansen et al. (2022), operating temperature and residence time were set to 220°C and 10 min, respectively.

Enzymatic saccharification: For the enzymatic saccharification with LPMO-containing enzyme cocktail, a data-driven soft model was tuned to the experimental data published by Hansen et al. (2022). The model estimates the sugar yield as a function of residence time, enzyme concentration and steam explosion temperature. Details are available in Gilardi et al. (2023).

Fermentation and ethanol recovery: The fermentation step was designed according to a technical report by the National Renewable Energy Laboratory (Humbird et al., 2011). The retrieved parameters included the operating temperature (33°C), residence time (48 h), microbial strain consumption (0.1 g/g_{sugar}), glucose and xylose conversions (90% and 85%, respectively), as well as consumables (such as diammonium phosphate and corn steep liquor). Ethanol was recovered using extractive distillation with ethylene glycol using the non-random two-liquid model, as in Li and Bai (2012).

Pyrolysis: The pyrolysis chamber was modelled as a fluidized bed reactor operated isothermally at 550°C. Given the complexity of the system, a lumped kinetic model was adopted. The kinetics for cellulose and hemicellulose conversion were adapted from Ranzi et al. (2008), while the updated model by Dussan et al. (2019) was implemented for lignin conversion. Further details are reported by Bisotti et al. (2023).

Pyrolysis oil stabilization and formulation: The crude bio-oil is stabilized in a two-step HDO treatment. In the first step, at milder conditions (250°C, 100 bar), aldehydes, ketones and carboxylic acids are deoxygenated to prevent coke formation. In the second step, at around 400°C, hydrogen is added to produce a hydrocarbon-rich oil (Xu et al., 2013). Here, paraffines are formed from alcohols, while aromatics are mainly decomposed into phenol, which turns into saturated cyclohexanol and cyclohexane. The kinetic constants for the HDO reactions involving alcohols, carbonyl groups and carboxylic species were retrieved from Grilc et al. (2014); the hydrogenation of aromatics and dehydration of phenols were adopted from Venkatesan et al. (2021) and Yu et al. (2021), respectively. In the subsequent step, the separation of upgraded crude oil into gaseous and liquid fuel fractions by distillation was predicted by the Predictive Redlich-Kwong-Soave equation of state. First, the upgraded crude bio-oil (available at 400°C) is cooled down to 180°C to condense the vacuum gas oil (VGO) in a flash chamber. Then, uncondensed gas is conveyed to a distillation unit with fractions withdrawn at 120°C and 60°C, representing the intermediate and low-boiling point bio-oil fractions. The tail gas leaves at the top of the column and is burnt to produce steam (see Note II for more detail). The above-mentioned sub-models were integrated to build a comprehensive biorefinery flowsheet in COFE v3.6. The simulations gave estimations for ethanol and bio-oil production per unit of biomass and energy requirements, used for the TEA described in Note II.

3. Results

Table 1 summarizes the results of the simulation of the biorefinery sketched in the block flow diagram in Figure 1 in terms of productivity, energy demand and consumables, as well as the main key performance indicators (KPIs) enabling a preliminary feasibility assessment. These results were used for the techno-economic assessment (TEA) in Note II. The intermediate results for the individual process units have been presented earlier by Gilardi et al. (2023) and Bisotti et al. (2023).

Table 1: Simulation results and main KPIs (acronyms – CW: cooling water; BM: biomass)

Entity	Value	Note/comments
Feedstock and products		
Biomass feedstock (5% moisture)	100,000 ton/year	12.5 ton/h assuming 8,000 operating hours per year
Bioethanol	2.68 ton/h	99.9 vol% (fuel grade)
Bio-oil total production	3.03 ton/h	
VGO cut (dry)	0.64 ton/h	Boiling point 180°C
Diesel/naphtha cut (dry)	1.60 ton/h	Boiling point 120°C
Light gasoline cut (dry)	0.79 ton/h	Boiling point 70°C
Biochar	1.69 ton/h	Solid produced during pyrolysis
Light gas	1.35 ton/h	
Utilities and consumables		
Steam for steam explosion	12.5 ton/h	Steam at 220°C and 22.5 bar produced by tail gas combustion
Steam for ethanol purification	17.8 ton/h	External utility
Hydrogen	230 kg/h	Needed in the HDO phase
Cooling water	405 ton/h	Total cooling water demand assuming inlet temperature 20°C and maximum outlet 35°C
2-naphthol	295 kg/h	Biomass impregnation based on (Pielhop et al., 2017)
Cellulase cocktail	57.1 kg/h	For saccharification
Fermenting strain	565 kg/h	For anaerobic fermentation
Energy demand		
Duty for ethanol purification (col-1)	6.55 MW	Column-1 (col-1) is a distillation tower to remove water and get azeotrope at the top stage, column-2 is an absorber, column-3 (col-3) is a distillation column to split ethylene glycol-water. Absorber (col-2) does not need a reboiler and condenser.
Cooling condenser (col-1)	3.43 MW	
Duty for ethanol purification (col-3)	0.57 MW	
Cooling condenser (col-3)	0.57 MW	
Pyrolysis (pre-heating and process)	2.98 MW	Pre-heating heat considers energy to heat up biomass before pyrolysis
H_2 compression (HDO)	0.65 MW	
H_2 compression intercooling (HDO)	0.38 MW	
HDO pre-heating	0.91 MW	Pre-heating before the second HDO reactor
HDO heating	0.66 MW	Re-heating after light gas removal upstream first HDO
HDO pump	0.17 MW	Oil pumping to HDO operating pressure after pyrolysis
HDO cooler	1.45 MW	Cooling system for HDO

Entity	Value	Note/comments
Cooling for crude bio-oil distillation	1.23 MW	
Water pump	0.13 MW	Needed in the steam generation loop when light gas is burnt
KPIs (Key Performance Indicators)		
Process weight yield (including biochar)	59.3% $kg_{product}/kg_{BM}$	Light gas is excluded. The mass yield refers to the treated biomass
Process weight yield (excluding biochar)	45.7% $kg_{product}/kg_{BM}$	Light gas is excluded
Bioethanol yield	0.21 $ton_{ethanol}/ton_{BM}$	Water/moisture is not included in the mass used to calculate these yields
Bio-oil yield	0.24 $ton_{bio\text{-}oil}/ton_{BM}$	
Biochar yield	0.14 $ton_{biochar}/ton_{BM}$	
Light gas yield	0.11 $ton_{tail\,gas}/ton_{BM}$	
Total specific steam demand	2.43 ton_{steam}/ton_{BM}	40% of the steam demand (pre-treatment and ethanol purification) is covered by light gas combustion
Cooling water demand	32.4 ton_{CW}/ton_{BM}	
Pyrolysis specific energy	1.65 $MJ/kg_{dry\,BM}$ 0.46 MWh_{th}/ton_{BM}	In line with Daugaard and Brown (2003)
Total specific thermal duty	0.98 MWh_{th}/ton_{BM}	Includes all the thermal duties (supplied heat)
Specific cooling duty	0.56 MWh_{th}/ton_{BM}	Includes all cooling duties (removed heat)
Specific electricity	1.45 MWh_{el}/ton_{BM}	Simulations assume 70% efficiency for pumps and compressors. Auxiliary pumps are neglected.

4. Conclusions and developments

The present work focuses on a full industrial-scale biorefinery converting softwood into fuel-grade bioethanol and three fuel-grade cuts of the upgraded pyrolysis oil. Here we present the simulation in COCO simulation software (COFE v3.6) of the biochemical and thermochemical conversion steps of the feedstock and product recovery and purification as well as a preliminary assessment of the energy and material balances. The overall product (i.e., biofuel) yield of the process was 46% (w/w; per unit of treated biomass) including ethanol as well as the VGO and gasoline- and diesel-like fractions. This yield reached 60% (w/w) when including biochar as a product. Pyrolysis was the most energy-intensive process, with 47% (0.46 MWh_{th}/t_{BM}) of the total thermal energy demand (0.98 MWh_{th}/t_{BM}). The specific energy demand aligns with the literature, and it confirms the adequacy of the defined/assigned thermodynamic properties and the kinetic model provided as inputs to COFE v3.6. While the product yields are reasonable, to achieve process feasibility at a commercial scale, this simulation needs to be complemented with energy integration, steam generation and minimization of waste streams, which are explored in Note II.

Acknowledgements

This work was supported by the Research Council of Norway through grants no. 257622 (Bio4Fuels) and 268002 (Enzymes4Fuels).

References

F. Bisotti, M. Gilardi, O.T. Berglihn, R. Tschentscher, V.G.H. Eijsink, A. Várnai, B. Wittgens, 2023. Soft modelling of spruce conversion into bio-oil through pyrolysis – Note II: pyrolysis. Computer Aided Chemical Engineering, 52, 769-774.

M. Chadni, N. Grimi, O. Bals, I. Ziegler-Devin, N. Brosse, 2019. Steam explosion process for the selective extraction of hemicelluloses polymers from spruce sawdust. International Crops and Products, 141, 111757.

L. Constantinou and R. Gani, 1994. New group contribution method for estimating properties of pure compounds, AIChE Journal, 40(10), 1697-1710.

D.E. Daugaard and R.C. Brown, 2003. Enthalpy for pyrolysis for several types of biomass. Energy & Fuels, 17(4), 934-939.

K. Dussan S. Dooley, R.F.D. Monaghan, 2019. A model of the chemical decomposition and pyrolysis kinetics of lignin. Proceedings of the Combustion Institute, 37(3), 2697-2704.

M. Gilardi, F. Bisotti, O.T. Berglihn, R. Tschentscher, V.G.H. Eijsink, A. Várnai, B. Wittgens, 2023. Soft modelling of spruce conversion into bio-oil through pyrolysis – Note I: steam explosion and LPMO-activated enzymatic saccharification. Computer Aided Chemical Engineering, 52, 757-762.

M. Grilc, B. Likozar, J. Levec, 2014. Hydrotreatment of solvolytically liquefied lignocellulosic biomass over NiMo/Al$_2$O$_3$ catalyst: Reaction mechanism, hydrodeoxygenation kinetics and mass transfer model based on FTIR. Biomass and Bioenergy, 63, 300-312.

L.D. Hansen, M. Østensen, B. Arstad, R. Tschentscher, V.G.H. Eijsink, S.J. Horn, A. Várnai, 2022. 2-Naphthol impregnation prior to steam explosion promotes LPMO-assisted enzymatic saccharification of spruce and yields high-purity lignin. ACS Sustainable Chemistry & Engineering, 10(16), 5233-5242.

D. Humbird, R. Davis, L. Tao, C. Kinchin, D. Hsu, A. Aden, P. Schoen, J. Lukas, B. Olthof, M. Worley, D. Sexton, D. Dudgeon, 2011. Process design and economics for biochemical conversion of lignocellulosic biomass to ethanol: Dilute-acid pretreatment and enzymatic hydrolysis of corn stover. NREL technical report NREL/TP-5100-47764.

R. Katakojwala, S.V. Mohan, 2012. A critical view on the environmental sustainability of biorefinery systems. Current Opinion in Green Sustainable Chemistry, 27, 100392.

P.S.W. Lam, S. Sokhansanj, C.J. Lim, X. Bi, S. Melin, 2009. Kinetic modeling of pseudolignin formation in steam exploded woody biomass. Conference Proceeding of 8th World Congress of Chemical Engineering, Montreal, August 23-27, 2009

G. Li and P. Bai, 2012. New operation strategy for separation of ethanol–water by extractive distillation. Industrial & Engineering Chemistry Research, 51(6), 2723-2729.

T. Pielhop, J. Amgarten, M.H. Studer, P.R. von Rohr, 2017. Pilot-scale steam explosion pretreatment with 2-naphthol to overcome high softwood recalcitrance. Biotechnology for Biofuels, 10, 130.

E. Ranzi, A. Cuoci, T. Faravelli, A. Frassoldati, G. Migliavacca, S. Pierucci, S. Sommariva, 2008. Chemical kinetics of biomass pyrolysis. Energy & Fuel, 22(6), 4292-4300.

K. Venkatesan, J.V.J. Krishna, S. Anjana, P. Selvam, R.Vinu, 2021. Hydrodeoxygenation kinetics of syringol, guaiacol and phenol over H-ZSM-5. Catalysis Communications, 148, 106164.

S. Vikram, P. Rosha, S. Kumar, 2021. Recent modeling approaches to biomass pyrolysis: A review. Energy and Fuels, 35, 7406-7433.

Z. Wang, S. Winestrand, T. Gillgren, L.J. Jönsson, 2018. Chemical and structural factors influencing enzymatic saccharification of wood from aspen, birch and spruce. Biomass and Bioenergy, 109, 125-134.

X. Xu, C. Zhang, Y. Liu, Y. Zhai, R. Zhang, 2013. Two-step catalytic hydrodeoxygenation of fast pyrolysis oil to hydrocarbon liquid fuels. Chemosphere, 93(4), 652-660.

Z. Yu, K. Yao, Y. Wang, Y. Yao, Z. Sun, Y. Liu, C. Shi, W. Wang, A. Wang, 2021. Kinetic investigation of phenol hydrodeoxygenation over unsupported nickel phosphides. Catalysis Today, 371, 179-188.

Flavio Manenti, Gintaras V. Reklaitis (Eds.), Proceedings of the 34th European Symposium on Computer Aided Process Engineering / 15th International Symposium on Process Systems Engineering (ESCAPE34/PSE24), June 2-6, 2024, Florence, Italy

Utilization of Solid Wastes to Satisfy Energy Requirements of LNG Process

Ahmed AlNouss, Gordon Mckay, Tareq Al-Ansari[*]

College of Science and Engineering, Hamad Bin Khalifa University, Qatar Foundation, Doha 34110, Qatar
Talansari@hbku.edu.qa

Abstract

All across the world, governments struggle to diversify their energy supply with an appropriate and sustainable replacement for fossil fuels while reducing the environmental effects of discharged waste. Due to the potential for increased fuel production and downstream electricity while reducing greenhouse gas emissions, the conversion of industrial wastes has drawn a lot of interest. Solid waste holds the highest potential as a biomass source due to the rapid increase in industrial expansion. The most significant solid waste is oily sludge, a combination of hydrocarbon, sand, clay, and certain metals that is pasty, dense, and semi-solid. However, the solid waste generation specifically from industrial operations possess environmental concerns related to waste management being addressed insufficiently. This study presents an overview on industrial solid waste (ISW) generated from different plant's operation that has the potential to be used as a source of bioenergy in the Liquefied Natural Gas (LNG) process to satisfy energy requirements. Moreover, the study presents additional solids waste that can be potentially utilized to fulfil the power demand of the LNG process. Aspen software is utilized to simulate the gasification of ISW as a biomass feedstock in the power generation flowsheet. Waste-to-energy gasification technology, which recovers energy from discarded and difficult-to-treat ISW and generates electricity and/or steam for heating, is recognized as a renewable energy source and is becoming more and more significant in waste management. Oily sludge is significant solid waste in the LNG process that is produced from multiple units such as; pig receiver, slug catcher, condensate separation, wastewater treatment, tank cleaning and chemical regeneration processes. The power analysis of a 3.12 million metric tons per annum LNG production facility indicates that the gasification of industrial solid waste (ISW) can fulfil only 0.43% of the energy demands within the LNG production process. Nevertheless, this energy integration results in an 18% reduction in utility emissions, thereby decreasing the reliance on plant utilities and associated emissions. Additionally, it addresses the disposal of rejected and challenging-to-treat industrial wastes.

Keywords: Industrial Solid Wastes, LNG, Simulation, Sustainability.

1. Introduction

With each passing day, the need to mitigate the detrimental effects of global climate change becomes more pressing. As a result, a growing number of countries and businesses are declaring to become carbon neutral by 2050, and the supply and demand for fossil fuels, notably oil and gas, are expected to fall. Gas appears to be more resilient in the coming years, particularly liquefied natural gas, although even LNG will eventually be replaced by renewable energy sources or undergo emissions reductions to satisfy the needs of a 1.5-degree trajectory (Agosta et al., 2021). Human activity is primarily responsible for climate change owing to greenhouse gas (GHG) emissions from fossil-fuel consumption according to the Intergovernmental Panel on Climate Change (IPCC). Following the Kyoto Protocol commitment, several climate change mitigation measures were implemented in the EU to reduce anthropogenic GHG emissions, and incentives were provided to develop renewable power plants to reduce reliance on fossil fuels. Renewable energy sources have a variable and intermittent nature, with peak output often falling short of demand. As the use of these sources develops in the energy power source scenario, grid balancing without regulating the RES power plant is required (Morosanu et al., 2018). Globally, access to electricity has grown, from 60 million more users per year in 2000-2012 to 100 million per year in 2012-2016. Despite this expansion, roughly 675 million people will still lack access to power in 2030, showing that demand for energy will continue to rise (Indrawan et al., 2020). As a renewable energy source, biomass for energy provides commercially viable options with high dispatch-ability. Biomass application is only economically viable in locations where biomass resource density is high and there is a demand for both heat and power, allowing combined heat and power (CHP) plants to be used (Pihl et al., 2010). Solid waste holds the highest potential as a biomass source due to the rapid increase in industrial expansion. The most significant solid waste is oily sludge, a combination of hydrocarbon, sand, clay, and certain metals that is pasty, dense, and semi-solid. However, the solid waste generation specifically from industrial operations possess environmental concerns related to waste management being addressed insufficiently (Lahlou et al., 2023). This study presents the potential of solid biomass gasification generated from different plant's operation to be used as a source of bioenergy in the Liquefied Natural Gas (LNG) process to satisfy energy requirements. The aim is to find the potential of industrial solid wastes (ISW) that maximizes the power production and satisfy highest portion of LNG power and heat demands. Scholars in literature have studied power to LNG from different perspectives. Morosanu et al. (2018) created a unique power-to-liquefied-methane design for a 200 kW demonstration plant, completed with process simulations. Water electrolysis to create hydrogen, CO_2 extraction from air using solid adsorption materials, catalytic CO_2 methanation, gas separation, and a single mixed refrigerant (SMR) liquefaction process are all part of the proposed system. The study yielded process efficiency of up to 46.3% (electric to chemical). The findings of the process modeling also demonstrated that the influence of the gas pretreatment and liquefaction process on plant energetics is 4% of total power input. Indrawan et al. (2020) developed a review that focuses on recent technological developments in seven power generation technologies (i.e. fuel cell, organic rankine cycle generator, Stirling engine, steam turbine, micro gas turbine, gas turbine, and internal combustion engine) that are suitable for distributed power applications and can operate independently using syngas derived from biomass and MSW gasification. The major obstacles that these power production technologies face in their future development and commercialization are explored. Pihl et al. (2010) conducted a techno-economical analysis of possibilities for integrating biomass thermal conversion with existing CCGT power facilities. The software Ebsilon Professional and Aspen Plus are used to model simple cycle biomass steam plant, indirect gasification of biomass and hybrid combined cycles (HCC). It was discovered that integrating biomass with CCGT power plants can result in significant efficiency gains and potential cost savings when compared to stand-alone facilities. Recently, Shahbaz et al. (2023) examined three types of waste streams arising from the oil and gas industry: liquids (produced water), flue gases (CO_2 and SO_2), and solid waste (oil sludge). The review addressed their potential emergent prospects current problems, treatment technologies and characterization. There is also information on the resource recovery and reuse possibilities of all three types of wastes studied.

Finally, a case study from the State of Qatar is presented in order to evaluate the theoretical resource recovery and market/economic potential of chosen trash.

2. Methodology and Data

The oil and gas industry produces two types of solid waste: organic and inorganic waste. Inorganic wastes include un-combustible waste, such as sand, drilling fluid and metal scraps from sites, which is also produced during drilling, site construction, petroleum refining industry, and transportation. Organic waste is combustible and includes hydrocarbon waste, such as plastic scrap and oil sludge, which is the most important component for waste to energy conversion. The oil sludge is produced during the washing of equipment, hydrocarbon cracking, reforming section, storage tank and the effluent treatment solution. According to a study, 500 tons of oil produces one ton of OS (Shahbaz et al., 2023). In LNG process, oily sludge is significant solid waste that is produced from multiple units such as; pig receiver, slug catcher, condensate separation, wastewater treatment, tank cleaning and chemical regeneration processes (Coffey, 2022).

In this study, Aspen software is utilized to simulate the gasification of oily sludge as a biomass feedstock in the power generation flowsheet. The characteristics of the oily sludge are summarized in Table1. In addition, Aspen is utilized to simulate the LNG process in order to estimate the requirement of power and heat for each section and match it with relevant production from oily sludge gasification.

Table 1: Characteristics of oily sludge

Att.	Moist	Fixed Carbon	Volatile Matter	Ash	C	H_2	N_2	S	O_2
%	8.3	19.41	8.83	71.76	19.08	2.32	1.1	0.09	5.65

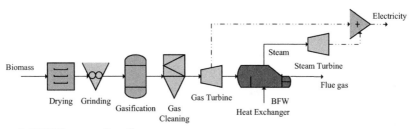

Figure 1: BIGCC process flow diagram

The power generation process from oily sludge is simulated following the Biomass Integrated Gasification Combined Cycle (BIGCC) design illustrated in Figure 1. The assumptions include steady-state conditions, a 13% of overall process efficiency with 1676 kg per MWh biomass to power ratio, and 1620 kg per MWh emissions to power ratio for oxygen-based gasification. The hot effluent syngas from the biomass gasification unit is first cooled to recover the heat, and then enters the combustion reactor. The combustion gases expand in a gas turbine to generate electrical power before it enters the steam generation unit to produce additional power through a series of heat exchangers and steam turbines. The BIGCC design is modelled based on earlier published work on biomass gasification (AlNouss et al., 2023b, 2023a; AlNouss et al., 2022) and BIGCC (Ghiat et al., 2020).

The simulated LNG onshore process illustrated in Figure 2 consist of two main sections: the cold section and the hot section. The hot section encompasses the pre-separation, dehydration, acid gas removal (AGR), and sulfur recovery unit (SRU). In contrast, the cold section comprises units for natural gas liquids (NGL) recovery and fractionation, helium extraction (HeX), gas liquefaction, and nitrogen removal (NR). The process begins with the pre-separation unit, which initially separates sour water and condensate from the sour natural gas (NG) feedstock. The sour NG is then treated to remove dehydration water to prevent hydrate formation and downstream corrosion. The sweetening unit follows, which takes the sour NG and removes undesirable components, including benzene, methylene, xylene (BTX), mercaptans, H_2S, and CO_2, collectively known as acid gases. The SRU unit receives streams from the sweetening unit and utilizes them to produce elemental sulfur allotropes from H_2S. The combustion of acid gas also leads to the creation of SOx. The NGL recovery and fractionation unit play a crucial role in separating residual condensate and providing propane and ethane as refrigerants when needed for liquefaction, while also meeting standard LNG specifications. The primary fractionation plant employs the propane pre-cooled mixed refrigerant (C3MR) liquefaction and cooling process. This process involves compressing vapor in two cycles, which sub-cools, condenses, crushes, and regulates the refrigerants, with the evaporation process providing primary cooling. After liquefaction, the high-pressure LNG undergoes treatment in integrated NR and HeX units to recover helium and meet LNG product purity requirements, such as higher heating value (HHV) and nitrogen content. Subsequently, the LNG can be loaded onto tankers or stored in tanks. The LNG process is modelled based on earlier published work (Fouladi et al., 2023; Al-Yafei et al., 2022; Shaikh et al., 2022).

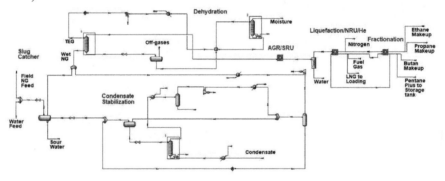

Figure 2: LNG process flow diagram

3. Results

The simulated LNG process produces 3.12 MMTPA of LNG which is associated with around 6250 TPA of oily sludge according to literature (Shahbaz et al., 2023). The results of the Aspen simulation is divided into two parts. The power and heat production from oily sludge gasification and the energy requirement by LNG process. The oxygen-based gasification of oily sludge generates power and heat quantities as illustrated in Table 2.

Table 2: Power and heat production from oily sludge gasification

Oily Sludge (TPA)	Power (kW)	Heat (kW)	Emissions (kg/h CO_2-e)
6250	1900	900	457

The energy requirement of LNG process is illustrated in Figure 3 for each section of the plant along with the associated emissions. The overall requirement of LNG process is 632 MW that is associated with a total of 130,239 kg/h of CO_2-e.

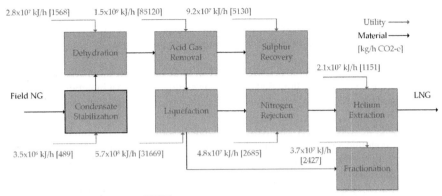

Figure 3: Energy requirement of LNG process

Based on the comparison of oily sludge gasification and LNG process requirement, the power results from biomass gasification demonstrate very small coverage of 0.43% of the energy requirement in the 3.12 MMTPA LNG production facility. However, this small energy integration reduce the associated utility emissions by 18%, hence sustainably reducing the requirement for plant utilities and associated emissions in addition to treating the discarded and difficult-to-treat industrial wastes.

4. Conclusions

Governments all around the globe are struggling to diversify their energy source with a suitable and sustainable substitute for fossil fuels while lowering the environmental impact of discharged trash. The conversion of industrial wastes has sparked a lot of attention because to the possibility for increased fuel output and downstream energy while lowering greenhouse gas emissions. Because of the fast growth in industrial expansion, solid waste has the most potential as a biomass source. The most major solid waste is oily sludge, a pasty, thick, and semi-solid mixture of hydrocarbon, sand, clay, and some metals. However, solid waste creation, particularly from industrial operations, raises environmental issues due to inadequate garbage management.This paper provides an overview of industrial solid waste (ISW) generated from various plant operations that has the potential to be used as a source of bioenergy in the LNG process to meet energy requirements. In the power generation flowsheet, Aspen software is used to simulate the gasification of ISW as a biomass feedstock. Waste-to-energy gasification, which recovers energy from discarded and difficult-to-treat ISW and creates electricity and/or steam for heating, is regarded as a sustainable energy source and is becoming increasingly important in waste management. Oily sludge is a substantial solid waste produced by many units in the LNG process, including the pig receiver, slug catcher, condensate separation, wastewater treatment, tank cleaning, and chemical regeneration operations. The results obtained from the power analysis of a 3.12 MMTPA LNG production facility indicate that the gasification of ISW can fulfill only 0.43% of the energy demands in the LNG production process. Nevertheless, this integration of energy leads to an 18% reduction in emissions from associated utilities. This not only diminishes the necessity for plant utilities and their associated emissions but also addresses the treatment of rejected and challenging-to-treat industrial wastes.

References

A. Agosta, G. Boccara, G. Bresciani, N. Browne, and B. Heringa, 2021, The Impact of Decarbonization on the Gas and LNG Industry, McKinsey & Company, June, 30, 2021.

H. Al-Yafei, A. AlNouss, S. Aseel, M. Kucukvar, N.C. Onat, and T. Al-Ansari, 2022, How sustainable is liquefied natural gas supply chain? An integrated life cycle sustainability assessment model, Energy Conversion and Management: X, 15, 100246.

A. AlNouss, M. Alherbawi, G. McKay, and T. Al-Ansari, 2023a, Integrated Techno-Economic and Sustainability Assessment of Value-Added Products Generated from Biomass Gasification: An Energy–Water–Food Nexus Approach, ACS Sustainable Chemistry & Engineering, 11, 10, 3987-98.

A. AlNouss, M. Alherbawi, G. McKay, and T. Al-Ansari, 2023b, Superstructure optimisation of blended-biomass hybrid poly gasification and utilisation system, Journal of Cleaner Production, 414, 137667.

A. AlNouss, G. McKay, and T. Al-Ansari, 2022, Evaluation of Oxygen and Steam Fed Biomass Gasification Within Energy, Water, and Food Nexus, Springer International Publishing,

Coffey, 2022, Environmental Impact Statement - PNG LNG Project, Coffey Natural Systems,

J. Fouladi, A. AlNouss, and T. Al-Ansari, 2023, Sustainable energy-water-food nexus integration and carbon management in eco-industrial parks, Journal of Cleaner Production, 418, 138071.

I. Ghiat, A. AlNouss, G. McKay, and T. Al-Ansari, 2020, Modelling and simulation of a biomass-based integrated gasification combined cycle with carbon capture: comparison between monoethanolamine and potassium carbonate, IOP Conference Series: Earth and Environmental Science, 463, 1, 012019.

N. Indrawan, A. Kumar, M. Moliere, K.A. Sallam, and R.L. Huhnke, 2020, Distributed power generation via gasification of biomass and municipal solid waste: A review, Journal of the Energy Institute, 93, 6, 2293-313.

F.-Z. Lahlou, A. AlNouss, R. Govindan, B. Hazrat, H.R. Mackey, and T. Al-Ansari, 2023, Water and sludge resource planning for sustainable agriculture: An energy-water-food-waste nexus approach, Sustainable Production and Consumption, 38, 130-48.

E.A. Morosanu, A. Saldivia, M. Antonini, and S. Bensaid, 2018, Process Modeling of an Innovative Power to LNG Demonstration Plant, Energy & Fuels, 32, 8, 8868-79.

E. Pihl, S. Heyne, H. Thunman, and F. Johnsson, 2010, Highly efficient electricity generation from biomass by integration and hybridization with combined cycle gas turbine (CCGT) plants for natural gas, Energy, 35, 10, 4042-52.

M. Shahbaz, N. Rashid, J. Saleem, H. Mackey, G. McKay, and T. Al-Ansari, 2023, A review of waste management approaches to maximise sustainable value of waste from the oil and gas industry and potential for the State of Qatar, Fuel, 332, 126220.

A.A. Shaikh, A. AlNouss, and T. Al-Ansari, 2022, A heat integration case study for the dehydration and condensate stabilization units in LNG plants for economic and energy savings, Computers & Chemical Engineering, 168, 108062.

Flavio Manenti, Gintaras V. Reklaitis (Eds.), Proceedings of the 34th European Symposium on Computer Aided Process Engineering / 15th International Symposium on Process Systems Engineering (ESCAPE34/PSE24), June 2-6, 2024, Florence, Italy

Exploring Biorefinery designs for Agricultural Waste with Stochastic Optimization

Lucas Van der Hauwaert[*a], Alberte Regueira[a,b], Miguel Mauricio Iglesias[a], Edwin Zondervan[c]

[a]CRETUS, Department of Chemical Engineering. Universidade de Santiago de Compostela, Spain. Rúa Lope Gómez de Marzoa, s/n. 15782, Spain
[b]Center for Microbial Ecology and Technology (CMET), Ghent University, Coupure links 653, B-9000 Ghent, Belgium
[c]Sustainable Process Technology (SPT), University of Twente, Enschede 7500, Netherlands.
Email Corresponding Author: lucas.vanderhauwaert@usc.es

Abstract

As the push for designing sustainable processing plants increases, the need for adequate tools to analyze and optimize these plants becomes paramount. Particularly the agricultural sector is in need of new and innovative biorefineries capable of handling the generated waste and transforming them in to added value products. Superstructure optimization offers an elegant solution to explore many alternative processing routes with one or multiple objectives in mind such as, sustainable and financial criteria. Various user friendly and accessible superstructure optimization tools for process design already exist but do not provide the capability to make decisions under uncertainty. This contribution aims to extend the OUTDOOR software package to handle superstructure optimization problems under uncertainty, using a 2-stage approach with fixed recourse. A case study is presented showcasing the extended OUTDOOR application on a processing plant that transforms potato peels into added value products. From the stochastic solution the most beneficial processing route, while considering all the uncertainties, lies in the production of phenolic compounds next to the production of starch, generating an expected revenue of 0.89 million euros per year. The value of perfect information (EVPI) was calculated to be 0.02 million euros, indicating the price of perfect information. The value of the stochastic solution (VSS) was 0 euros, indicating that the produced flowsheet is the most optimal one, across all uncertain scenarios.

Keywords: 2-Stage stochastic problem with fixed recourse, Superstructure optimization, OUTDOOR, optimization under uncertainty

1. Introduction

In the current global scenario, where sustainability is of paramount concern, the agricultural sector is critically situated at the nexus of ensuring food security, preserving environmental integrity, and executing waste management. One of the pressing issues is the management of agricultural waste, with a specific focus on diminishing its environmental impact through reduced methane emissions, while advancing a circular economy paradigm (Gontard et al., 2018).

Biorefineries are pivotal in this context, tasked with the valorization of agricultural waste through the extraction of valuable compounds. However, the development of processing routes to utilize agricultural waste remains a complex challenge. This complexity stems from the rapid emergence of new technologies and the significant unpredictability associated with the efficiencies of processes and the variability of feedstock attributes. Superstructures are mathematical frameworks that encapsulate all potential design pathways and configurations for a given system. Optimization of these superstructures facilitates the identification of the most effective configuration (e.g., in terms of costs, environment or performance) within the bounds of predefined constraints and objectives (Mencarelli et al., 2020). Several user-friendly computational tools, including SUPER-O, O2V, and OUTDOOR, harness the power of superstructure optimization to systematically evaluate process design alternatives (Bertran et al., 2017; Gargalo et al., 2022; Kenkel et al., 2021). However, these tools lack a crucial feature: they do not effectively address uncertainty. Given the variable nature of feedstock properties, process parameters, and market prices, designing bioprocessing plants that can withstand these uncertainties is essential, making optimization under uncertainty a crucial aspect. To address this gap, the OUTDOOR software tool has been extended to incorporate uncertainty into the optimization of superstructures as a 2-stage stochastic linear program with recourse. This enhancement streamlines decision-making for the design of process flowsheets by allowing robust process development under uncertainty, providing a more resilient and user-friendly approach to biorefinery design. The upgraded OUTDOOR tool thus stands to significantly impact the sector by enabling the development of biorefinery configurations that are better equipped to handle the uncertainties inherent in waste management of the agricultural sector.

2. Methods and Materials

2.1. Superstructure design

The configuration of the superstructure in this study largely adheres to the framework established by Kenkel et al. (2021). The software package, developed in Python, employs an Excel wrapper for data aggregation and processing to establish a superstructure model. This model encompasses detailed mass and energy balances, operational (OPEX) and capital expenditures (CAPEX) and provides preliminary estimates of CO_2 emissions and freshwater consumption for each unit operation under consideration. For an in-depth understanding of the mathematical model underpinning OUTDOOR, readers are directed to the detailed exposition in Kenkel et al. (2021).

2.2. 2-Stage stochastic problem with fixed recourse

In this study, a two-stage stochastic program with recourse is proposed to address uncertainties inherent in the superstructure model (Birge and Louveaux, 2011). The uncertain parameters include reactor efficiencies, separation efficiencies, product and substrate prices, reactor yields, and feedstock composition. In a two-stage stochastic program, there are two types of decision variables: In the first stage, decisions regarding the choice of unit operations are made. In other words, a decision of the plant layout needs to be made before the uncertainty manifests, i.e., "here and now". These decisions are irreversible and must be taken without complete knowledge of the future. The second stage involves variables that become apparent post the occurrence of uncertain events or when recourse actions are required to maximize the objective function. In our model, these actions include the diversion of streams to different unit operations, aligning with the "wait and see" principle of optimization. The two-stage stochastic optimization problem can be represented in mathematical notation as follows:

$$\min Z = f(x, y) + \sum_k E_k[q(x, y, \xi_{k,})] \tag{1}$$

$$s.t. \, g_k(\xi_k, x, y) \geq 0 \tag{2}$$
$$h_k(\xi_k, x, y) = 0 \tag{3}$$
$$x^L \leq x \leq x^U \tag{4}$$
$$x \in \mathbb{R} \quad y \in \{0,1\} \tag{5}$$

where the objective function Z is a dependent on decision variables x, y, and the probability E_k of scenario k occurring. The uncertain parameters per scenario are denoted as ξ_k. In our model, equal probability of each scenario k occurring, is assumed. The inequality constraints $g_k(\xi_k, x, y)$ represent operational boundaries, while the equality constraints $h_k(\xi_k, x, y)$ encompass mass and energy balances and logical constraints. The function $f(x, y)$ reflects the costs associated with the first-stage decisions. Conversely, $q(x, y, \xi_k)$ signifies the expected costs of each subsequent action or second-stage decision, in response to the realized uncertainties. The model also includes boundary constraints, ensuring that continuous decision variables remain within realistic limits, such as prohibiting negative flows (Eq. 4).

In the context of our study, Z signifies the Earnings Before Interest and Taxes (EBIT), calculated as the revenue from sales minus the capital (CAPEX) and operating expenses (OPEX). CAPEX, associated with $f(x, y)$, primarily depends on the first-stage integer decision variables y, which indicate the selection of specific technologies and is calculated with linearized economies of scale. The revenue and OPEX, represented by $q(x, y, \xi_k)$, are influenced by the uncertain scenario parameters ξ_k and the continuous variables x, which denote, for example, mass flows and energy consumption. The EBIT is then derived as the expected value from the weighted sum of the revenue and OPEX subtracted by the CAPEX.

In the extended version of the OUTDOOR software, the integration of uncertainties into the optimization framework is efficiently facilitated by the Excel wrapper. Due to the exponential increase in model size with each added uncertain parameter, strategic grouping of certain parameters can be employed to mitigate this growth. For instance, if starch and lipid contents in potato peels exhibit an inverse relationship—high starch content correlating with low lipid percentage—this correlation is consistently reflected across all scenarios. In effect, scenarios featuring above-average lipid and sugar content in potato peels are excluded. This approach not only maintains the model at a feasible scale but also substantially reduces computational time.

2.2.1. VSS and EVPI: Key Metrics in Stochastic Decision-Making

Prior to the optimization, every possible scenario undergoes a feasibility check via deterministic optimization. Scenarios deemed infeasible are excluded, streamlining the stochastic optimization process. This step also helps in determining the feasibility bounds for the process parameters that exhibit uncertainty. Furthermore, the Expected Value of Perfect information (EVPI) can be calculated from these deterministic solutions. EVPI is a measure in stochastic optimization that quantifies the maximum amount a decision-maker would be willing to pay for having perfect information about uncertain parameters, before making a decision. It represents the difference in the expected outcome between the ideal scenario where uncertainty is resolved before the decision and the realistic scenario where decisions are made under uncertainty (Birge and Louveaux, 2011). The EVPI is calculated as followed:

$$EVPI = \text{EVwPI} - \text{EVSS} \tag{6}$$

where EVwPI (Expected Value with Perfect Information) is the average of all the solution of the deterministic optimization problems as if the realizations were known in advance. The EVSS is the Expected Value of the Stochastic Solution.

A second metric that can be calculated is the Value of the Stochastic Solution (VSS). The VSS quantifies the benefit of using a stochastic model over a deterministic model (which uses fixed, often average values of uncertain parameters). In other words, the VSS reflects the improvement in expected performance (e.g., cost reduction, increased efficiency) achieved by accounting for uncertainty in the decision-making process (Birge and Louveaux, 2011). The VSS is calculated as followed:

$$VSS = EVDS - \text{EVSS} \tag{7}$$

where EVDS is the Expected Value of the Deterministic Solution which is the solution from the deterministic equivalent of the problem by replacing the uncertain parameters with their average values.

2.3. Case study description

To demonstrate the capabilities of the updated OUTDOOR framework under uncertainty, a superstructure case study was developed, focusing on the valorization of potato peels (Figure 1). The superstructure begins with the extraction of starch, a relatively straightforward and valuable product derived from potato peels. This process involves grinding the peels into a pulp and then separating the liquid fraction, from which starch is obtained. The remaining pulp fraction, still rich in valuable components, is then considered for further processing into three potential products through different routes: i) Phenolic compounds, targeted as antioxidants for the food industry, ii) bioethanol at 85% volume concentration and iii) polylactic acid (PLA), a type of biopolymer. Moreover, the feasibility of producing methane via anaerobic digestion is also explored. This methane could potentially be utilized to generate electricity and/or heat, necessary for operating the other unit processes. The goal of the optimization problem is to assess which product streams and combination of technologies maximize the total yearly profit defined as the EBIT. Further assumptions made is that the plant is capable of processing 1 ton of potato peels per hour and is operational 8000 hours per year. The complete superstructure with all unit processes can be seen in Figure 1. In this superstructure 4 grouped sources of uncertainty are considered: i) the composition of the potato peels, ii) the conversion efficiency of carbohydrates to ethanol in the fermentation unit, iii) the seperation efficiency of phenolic compounds in the extraction units and iv) the market prices of products.

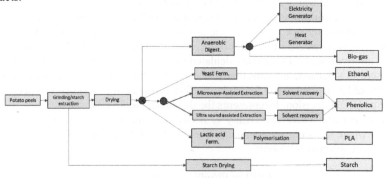

Figure 1: Superstructure of the biorefinery. Green boxes are input streams, yellow boxes are the product outputs, blue boxes represent unit processes and blue circles are where streams can be split.

OUTDOOR automatically creates unique scenarios, where each combination of uncertain parameters is possible. For each parameter in a scenario, three potential values can be represented: the expected value or the expected value adjusted by a predefined standard deviation (either plus or minus). This approach resulted in the creation of 243 distinct scenarios. The stochastic model is then solved where all the unique scenarios are represented. The problem presents itself as a Mixed Integer Linear Problem (MILP) with 131.012 variables, 2220 integer variables and 238.633 constraints and is solved using the Gurobi solver (Gurobi Optimization, 2023) in Python (version 3.10).

3. Results and Discussion

3.1. Stochastic outcome of the case study

The two-stage stochastic optimization problem was integrated into the OUTDOOR framework, as outlined in the methodology section. The case study was executed on a 12th Gen Intel(R) Core(TM) i7-1255U processor, with the solution obtained in 857 seconds. The optimized design of the superstructure, displayed in Figure 2, showcases the minimum, mean, and maximum flow rates through each unit process. The expected EBIT stands at 0.89 million euros per year. Notably, the range of EBIT spans from a minimum of 0.22 million euros to a maximum of 2.57 million euros, underscoring the impact of uncertainties on economic outcomes. A consistent outcome across all scenarios is the co-production of phenolic compounds alongside starch, despite the relatively low production rate of phenolic compounds, averaging at 1.17 kg/h. This decision is largely influenced by the high market value of these compounds. As depicted in Figure 2, the production rate of phenolic compounds is markedly sensitive to the scenario being considered (indicated by the deep red colored line). This sensitivity is attributed to the variability in the efficiency of the extraction process and the fluctuating composition of phenolics, highlighting the significance of incorporating uncertainties in process optimization. Another curious observation is that the generation of electricity or heat, through the combustion of methane, is not considered, suggesting that the savings on energy do not justify the capital investment required to install these unit processes.

3.1.1. Evaluating the stochastic solution

To assess the robustness of the stochastic solution, two key metrics were computed: the Expected Value of Perfect Information (EVPI) and the Value of the Stochastic Solution (VSS). The EVPI was calculated at 0.02 million euros, with the EVwPi being 0.87 million euros. The EVPI indicates the potential benefit of obtaining perfect information about uncertainties before making decisions. In practical terms, this suggests that investing up to this amount in research to improve process reliability or in economic tools for more accurate market price predictions would be justifiable. Conversely, the VSS came out to be 0 euros, implying that under every considered scenario, constructing the refinery as per the stochastic solution is the optimal strategy. This result can primarily be attributed to the fact that, regardless of the efficiency and yield variations in phenolic compound production, the high selling price of these compounds invariably makes their production the most lucrative option.

3.2. Future work

The next step in extending OUTDOOR's capabilities is to include multi-criterion decision-making tools under uncertainty. Such extensions will allow for a more comprehensive understanding and effective balancing of various objectives such as cost, environmental impact, and process reliability, even in the face of uncertainties.

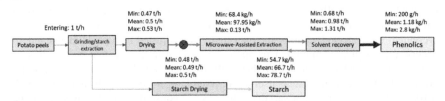

Figure 2: The flowsheet generated by the solution of the stochastic optimization problem. Green boxes are inputs, yellow boxes are outputs, blue boxes are unit operations. The darker red lines represent streams which are more susceptible to uncertainty.

4. Conclusions

OUTDOOR has been successfully updated for superstructure optimization under uncertainty, using a two-stage stochastic optimization with fixed recourse. This solution yields a process flowsheet and adapts stream division according to unfolding uncertain scenarios, alongside metrics for solution assessment. Applied to a case study for valorizing potato peels, OUTDOOR pinpointed an optimal and robust biorefinery design for phenolic compounds and starch production, with an expected EBTI of 0.89 million euros per year. The calculated EVPI is 0.02 million euros, indicating the value of perfect information, while a VSS of 0 euros suggests the flowsheet's optimality under all conditions. With this updated version of OUTDOOR a user-friendly approach integrating uncertainty into process design, is achieved, facilitating the development of biorefinery configurations capable of handling uncertainties.

References

Bertran, M.-O., Frauzem, R., Sanchez-Arcilla, A.-S., Zhang, L., Woodley, J.M., Gani, R., 2017. A generic methodology for processing route synthesis and design based on superstructure optimization. Comput Chem Eng 106, 892–910. https://doi.org/10.1016/j.compchemeng.2017.01.030

Birge, J.R., Louveaux, F., 2011. Introduction to stochastic programming. Springer Science & Business Media.

Gargalo, C.L., Rapazzo, J., Carvalho, A., Gernaey, K. V., 2022. Optimal Conversion of Organic Wastes to Value-Added Products: Toward a Sustainable Integrated Biorefinery in Denmark. Frontiers in Chemical Engineering 4, 54. https://doi.org/10.3389/fceng.2022.837105

Gontard, N., Sonesson, U., Birkved, M., Majone, M., Bolzonella, D., Celli, A., Angellier-Coussy, H., Jang, G.W., Verniquet, A., Broeze, J., Schaer, B., Batista, A.P., Sebok, A., 2018. A research challenge vision regarding management of agricultural waste in a circular bio-based economy. Crit Rev Environ Sci Technol 48, 614–654. https://doi.org/10.1080/10643389.2018.1471957

Gurobi Optimization, L., 2023. Gurobi Optimizer Reference Manual.

Kenkel, P., Wassermann, T., Rose, C., Zondervan, E., 2021. Outdoor–An open-source superstructure construction and optimization tool, in: Computer Aided Chemical Engineering. Elsevier, pp. 413–418.

Mencarelli, L., Chen, Q., Pagot, A., Grossmann, I.E., 2020. A review on superstructure optimization approaches in process system engineering. Comput Chem Eng 136, 106808.

Flavio Manenti, Gintaras V. Reklaitis (Eds.), Proceedings of the 34th European Symposium on Computer Aided Process Engineering / 15th International Symposium on Process Systems Engineering (ESCAPE34/PSE24), June 2-6, 2024, Florence, Italy

Economic Feasibility of Thermochemical Conversion for Woody Biomass-Derived Liquid Fuels in Spain

Usman Khan Jadoon[a,*], Ismael Diaz[a], Manuel Rodriguez[a]

[a]Departamento de Ingeniería Química Industrial Y del Medioambiente, Escuela Superior de Ingenieros Industriales, Universidad Politécnica de Madrid, C/ José Gutiérrez Abascal 2, 28006 Madrid, Spain
*uk.jadoon@upm.es

Abstract

The global shift to renewable biomass resources is crucial for sustainable industrial growth and reducing greenhouse gas emissions. Aligned with the European Green Deal and the Paris Agreement, Spain targets ambitious climate and renewable energy goals for 2030. This study focuses on thermochemical conversion processes, evaluating economic implications within the Spanish context. Using a network optimization framework, we assess technologies like biomass gasification, Fischer–Tropsch synthesis, and methanol-to-gasoline for converting woody biomass into profitable liquid fuels. Economic viability is apparent, with a minimum selling price of 1.506 \$/kg for gasoline and 1.863 \$/kg for ethanol, below current market rates. Gasoline and ethanol meet market demands, emphasizing their profitability. Further research is needed for cost-effective production of other liquid fuels.

Keywords: biomass gasification, economic feasibility, gasification pathways, renewable liquid fuels, linear optimization.

1. Introduction

Shifting society from petroleum to renewable biomass resources is crucial for a sustainable industrial society and energy independence, aligning with global agreements like the Paris Agreement and European Green Deal (Commission, 2019). Spain, within the framework of the European Green Deal, has set ambitious climate and energy targets for 2030, including a renewable energy target of at least 42% of the final gross energy consumption (Carpio Martínez, 2018). The Paris Agreement's goal to cut global GHG emissions by 50% by 2030 has spurred biomass adoption, with Spain's expanding forests providing abundant resources from olive trees, pine, vine residues, and Eucalyptus (*Ministry of Agriculture, Fishery, and Food*, 2019).

Biomass, a low-cost renewable source, plays a key role in a clean energy transition. Incorporating CO_2 capture in biomass systems aims for negative CO_2 emissions, projected to reach 5.5 billion metric tons by 2050 globally (DC, 2020). Biomass is poised to replace part of fossil fuel energy, producing liquid fuels, power, and heat. This study focuses on thermochemical conversion techniques to transform biomass into synthetic liquid fuels (SLFs), contributing to the evolution of a sustainable energy landscape. These SLFs, also known as second-generation fuels, currently face challenges in terms of profitability compared to fossil-based first-generation fuels. However, an integrated approach that combines the co-production of e-fuels with value-added products has the potential to lower production costs and increase the market competitiveness of fuel prices (Stichnothe et al., 2020). The production of SLFs in this study encompasses various thermochemical pathways, including diesel production from fast pyrolysis, aviation fuel production from Fischer-Tropsch (FT) synthesis, and gasoline production from methanol and dimethyl ether. Li et al. (2019) reported the minimum selling price of jet fuel produced from FT synthesis through biomass gasification, which was approximately 0.699 \$/kg, approximately 22% higher than that of traditional fossil-based fuel (M. Li et al., 2019). Another study by Wang et al. (2022) compared the prices of jet fuel produced from FT synthesis and pyrolysis, reporting prices of 2.2 \$/liter and 3.2 \$/liter, respectively (Wang et al., 2022).

Fast pyrolysis is another viable thermochemical route that involves controlled thermal decomposition of biomass at moderate temperatures in the absence of oxygen, resulting in the production of pyrolysis oil and gas (Basu, 2018). Sorunmu et al. (2019) estimated a wide range of minimum selling prices for gasoline derived from pyrolysis, ranging from 2.5 to 4.5 \$/gal (Sorunmu et al., 2020). Another study by Li et al. (2019) examined the relationship between greenhouse gas emissions and the minimum fuel selling price in a pyrolysis-bioenergy-biochar platform, revealing a range of minimum fuel selling prices from 2.2 to 3.5 \$/gal (W. Li et al., 2019). This study employs a robust mixed-integer linear optimization framework developed in Python using the Pyomo library to assess the feasibility of renewable liquid fuel production in Spain through various thermochemical pathways. Notably, our work features a Python-based 2-D network optimization framework, considering factors like capital, operating costs, biomass availability, and specific fuel demand in the dynamic Spanish market. Additionally, our optimization model determines the Minimum Selling Price (MSP) of renewable liquid fuels, contributing to economic viability analysis.

2. Methodology

Our study employs an optimization framework to guide researchers in optimal processing paths, considering sustainability, resource availability, and economics. Technologies vary in advantages, limitations, and feedstock compatibility, with superstructure optimization serving as a key decision-making tool, addressing conversion efficiency, environmental impact, and cost-effectiveness. Drawing upon network optimization models proposed by Kim et al. (2013) our analysis focuses on the Spanish market prices for feedstock and products, as depicted in Figure 1 (Kim et al., 2013). Utilizing Python's Pyomo library, our superstructure involves woody biomass with 47 technologies, 37 intermediates, feedstock, products, and co-products. The optimization framework defines feedstock availability (β_i, kg/year) and costs (PC_i, \$/kg), which incorporates harvesting, and average 100km distance travelled. The final product demand (D_i, kg/year), and corresponding prices (PC_i, \$/kg) Table 1. Within the superstructure, each technology is characterized by the unit technology cost (TC_j, \$/kg), unit energy requirement (TE_j, kWh/kg), energy cost (EC_j, \$/kWh), and mass ratio parameter (mb_i, the product-to-input ratio).

A set of compounds $i \in I$: feedstocks (I^F), intermediates (I^I), and final products (I^P).

$$PCi \neq 0 \quad \forall i \ I^F, I^P \tag{1}$$
$$PC_i = 0 \quad \forall i \ I^I \tag{2}$$
$$D_i = 0 \forall i \in I^F, I^I \tag{3}$$

Unit technology cost $\left(TC_j, \$/kg\right)$ has been disintegrated into three costs, unit product capital cost ($UPCC$), unit product raw material cost ($UPRMC$), and unit product operating cost ($UPOC$). The variables in the set P_i, and S_i are the feedstock purchased and amount of product sold, respectively.

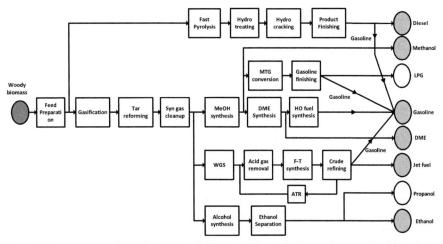

Figure 1: Superstructure depicting feedstock (black node), different processes, and products (grey nodes are main products and white nodes represent by-products).

Table 1: Feedstock availability and product demand with their associated prices*

ID	Name	Availability β_i (Mt/y)	Demand D_i (kt/y)	Market price PC_i ($/kg)
i1	Biomass	57.565		0.065
i13	DME		4.1	0.600
i11	Methanol		932.4	0.488
i14, i18, i28, i34	Gasoline		5759.0	1.620
i17	LPG		2000.0	1.062
i20	Ethanol		283.0	2.447
i23	Diesel		31144.0	1.899
i31	Jet fuel		3280.0	0.817

*The values have been retrieved from literature sources not shown due to paper length limitations.

The constraint of mass balance defines the equation as the amount of feedstock purchased and the product produced must be equal to the amount of any product consumed and sold.

$$P_i + \sum_{j \in JOUT} mb_{ij}X_j = S_i + \sum_{j \in J^{IN}} mb_{ij}X_j \forall \tag{4}$$

However, the products sold must fulfil the market demand, and feedstock is constrained by its availability. In addition, the selling price of all intermediates and feedstock and the purchase price of any product are set to zero.

$$S_i \geq D_i \ \forall_i \in I^P \tag{5}$$
$$P_i \leq \beta_i \ \forall i \in I^F \tag{6}$$
$$S_i = 0 \ \forall i \in I^F, I^I \tag{7}$$
$$P_i = 0 \ \forall i \in I^I \tag{8}$$

The following objective function is enforced to find the optimal processing network for minimum selling price utilizing the raw material cost, capital cost, operating, operating, and energy cost.

$$MSP = \sum_{i \in I^F} PC_i P_i + \sum_j X_j \left(UPCC_j + UPRMC_j + UPOC_j + TE_j EC_j \right) \tag{9}$$

3. Results and Discussion

The study revealed a methanol production cost of 0.725 $/kg, which stands in contrast to the market price of 0.488 $/kg, as shown in Table 2. To contextualize Poluzzi et al., (2022) conducted a comprehensive investigation into various gasification techniques and proposed that indirect gasification could yield methanol at a competitive cost of 0.64 $/kg (Poluzzi et al., 2022). Similarly, Sun et al., (2021) explored methanol production from biomass, conducting a thorough assessment of its thermodynamic and economic performance, with a notably low production cost of 0.479 $/kg (Sun & Aziz, 2021). The MSP of jet fuel, as shown in Table 2, stands at 1.120 $/kg, while the market selling price is notably lower at 0.817 $/kg. Kreutz et al. (2020) and Guimarães et al. (2022) respectively explored the economic viability of 100% biomass-based Fischer-Tropsch jet fuel with a cost of 1.08$/L due to negative greenhouse gas intensity and the comparative advantages of an integrated gasification and Fischer-Tropsch synthesis process, revealing a lower production cost of 0.52 $/L with reduced capital expenditure (Guimarães et al., 2022; Kreutz et al., 2020).

The MSP for diesel, produced through fast pyrolysis of biomass, amounted to 2.865 $/kg. This cost significantly exceeds the market rate, which stands at 1.899 $/kg, as shown in Table 2. On the contrary Hu et al., (2023) explored the production of renewable diesel using fast pyrolysis, employing a combination of algal and straw biomass as feedstock. Their research demonstrated the potential to achieve a highly competitive production cost of only 1.08 $/kg (Hu et al., 2023). In a similar pursuit, Patel et al., (2019) explored fast pyrolysis of Canadian biomass feedstocks, including wheat straw, maize stover, and spruce, finding the potential to produce diesel at a more affordable cost of 1.25 $/kg (Patel et al., 2019).

Figure 2 illustrates the optimized pathway for gasoline production through the methanol-to-gasoline (MtG) process via gasification. According to Table 2, the Minimum Selling Price (MSP) for gasoline is 1.506 $/kg, while the market price is slightly higher at 1.62 $/kg. These numbers reveal a competitive pricing structure for gasoline production in our study. The break-even price of ethanol, as determined by the optimization solver in our study, is 1.863 $/kg. It is worth noting that alternative studies, such as Melin et al. (2022), exploring biomass gasification for ethanol production with syngas purification through a membrane, have reported substantially lower MSP, achieving a levelized cost of 0.88 $/kg (Melin et al., 2022). Similarly, Rigs et al. (2023) proposed that co-utilization of green hydrogen and fermented syngas could achieve an MSP of 0.97 $/kg for ethanol (Regis et al., 2023).

4. Conclusions

The study supplies a thorough exploration of various thermochemical pathways for renewable liquid fuel production in Spain. Using a network optimization framework, technologies like biomass gasification, Fischer–Tropsch synthesis, and methanol-to-gasoline are assessed for converting woody biomass into economically feasible liquid fuels. The economic feasibility of the proposed liquid fuel production pathways is underscored by a compelling MSP of 1.506 $/kg for gasoline and 1.863 $/kg for ethanol, both below current market rates. This underscores their potential to not only meet market demands but also contribute significantly to the renewable energy landscape in Spain. Moreover, a comprehensive evaluation, including detailed supply chain and life cycle analyses, is imperative to assess the environmental impact of any future thermochemical facility within the Spanish territory.

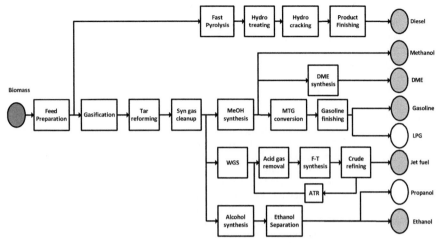

Figure 2: Optimized superstructure

Table 2: Minimum Selling Price (MSP) of each product with feedstock and the associated energy consumed.

Product	Price ($/kg)	MSP ($/kg)	Biomass Consumed	Co-Product	Co-reactant	(kWh/kg)
MeOH	0.488	0.725	2.327	-		1.064
DME	0.600	0.989	2.952	-		1.447
Gasoline	1.620	1.506	8.679	LPG		2.423
Diesel	1.899	2.865	7.739	-	0.2054*	3.542
Jet fuel	0.817	1.120	2.931	Gasoline		1.019
Ethanol	2.447	1.863	4.828	Propanol		6.034

*Hydrogen is consumed as co-reactant in this case.

5. Acknowledgements

This project has received funding from the European Union's Horizon 2020 research innovation and program under the Marie Skłodowska-Curie grant agreement No. 945139

References

Basu, P. (2018). *Biomass gasification, pyrolysis and torrefaction: practical design and theory*. Academic press.

Carpio Martínez, M. (2018). Environmental and economic effects of using renewable energy in residential thermal installations according to 2030 targets: case study in the province of Granada (Spain).

Commission, E. (2019). *The European Green Deal - Striving to be the first climate-neutral continent*. European Commission. Retrieved 22/11/2023 from https://commission.europa.eu/strategy-and-policy/priorities-2019-2024/european-green-deal_enhttps://commission.europa.eu/strategy-and-policy/priorities-2019-2024/european-green-deal_en

DC, A. U. W. (2020). *What is BECCS?* American University Washington DC. Retrieved 29 Nov 2023 from https://www.american.edu/sis/centers/carbon-removal/fact-sheet-bioenergy-with-carbon-capture-and-storage-beccs.cfm

Guimarães, H. R., Bressanin, J. M., Motta, I. L., Chagas, M. F., Bonomi, A., & Barbosa Watanabe, M. D. (2022). Techno-Economic and Environmental Assessments of

Thermochemical Routes Integrated into the Brazilian Sugarcane Industry for the Production of Renewable Jet Fuel. https://doi.org/10.3303/CET2292020

Hu, J., Chen, X., Yang, X., Li, R., & Wu, L. (2023). Co-processing of gas oil and bio-oil derived from algae and straw: Techno-economic analysis. *Fuel, 340*, 127583. https://doi.org/https://doi.org/10.1016/j.fuel.2023.127583

Kim, J., Sen, S. M., & Maravelias, C. T. (2013). An optimization-based assessment framework for biomass-to-fuel conversion strategies [10.1039/C3EE24243A]. *Energy & Environmental Science, 6*(4), 1093-1104. https://doi.org/10.1039/C3EE24243A

Kreutz, T. G., Larson, E. D., Elsido, C., Martelli, E., Greig, C., & Williams, R. H. (2020). Techno-economic prospects for producing Fischer-Tropsch jet fuel and electricity from lignite and woody biomass with CO2 capture for EOR. *Applied Energy, 279*, 115841. https://doi.org/https://doi.org/10.1016/j.apenergy.2020.115841

Li, M., Zhao, W., Xu, Y., Zhao, Y., Yang, K., Tao, W., & Xiao, J. (2019). Comprehensive Life Cycle Evaluation of Jet Fuel from Biomass Gasification and Fischer–Tropsch Synthesis Based on Environmental and Economic Performances. *Industrial & Engineering Chemistry Research, 58*(41), 19179-19188. https://doi.org/10.1021/acs.iecr.9b03468

Li, W., Dumortier, J., Dokoohaki, H., Miguez, F. E., Brown, R. C., Laird, D., & Wright, M. M. (2019). Regional techno-economic and life-cycle analysis of the pyrolysis-bioenergy-biochar platform for carbon-negative energy. *Biofuels, Bioproducts and Biorefining, 13*(6), 1428-1438. https://doi.org/https://doi.org/10.1002/bbb.2043

Melin, K., Nieminen, H., Klüh, D., Laari, A., Koiranen, T., & Gaderer, M. (2022). Techno-Economic Evaluation of Novel Hybrid Biomass and Electricity-Based Ethanol Fuel Production [Original Research]. *Frontiers in Energy Research, 10*. https://doi.org/10.3389/fenrg.2022.796104

Ministry of Agriculture, Fishery, and Food. (2019). La Moncloa. https://www.lamoncloa.gob.es/lang/en/gobierno/news/Paginas/2019/20190320forestheritage.aspx

Patel, M., Oyedun, A. O., Kumar, A., & Gupta, R. (2019). What is the production cost of renewable diesel from woody biomass and agricultural residue based on experimentation? A comparative assessment. *Fuel Processing Technology, 191*, 79-92. https://doi.org/https://doi.org/10.1016/j.fuproc.2019.03.026

Poluzzi, A., Guandalini, G., Guffanti, S., Martinelli, M., Moioli, S., Huttenhuis, P., Rexwinkel, G., Palonen, J., Martelli, E., Groppi, G., & Romano, M. C. (2022). Flexible Power and Biomass-To-Methanol Plants With Different Gasification Technologies [Original Research]. *Frontiers in Energy Research, 9*. https://doi.org/10.3389/fenrg.2021.795673

Regis, F., Monteverde, A. H. A., & Fino, D. (2023). A techno-economic assessment of bioethanol production from switchgrass through biomass gasification and syngas fermentation. *Energy, 274*, 127318. https://doi.org/https://doi.org/10.1016/j.energy.2023.127318

Sorunmu, Y., Billen, P., & Spatari, S. (2020). A review of thermochemical upgrading of pyrolysis bio-oil: Techno-economic analysis, life cycle assessment, and technology readiness. *GCB Bioenergy, 12*(1), 4-18. https://doi.org/https://doi.org/10.1111/gcbb.12658

Stichnothe, H., Bell, G., Jørgensen, H., De Bari, I., Haveren, J., Lindorfer, J., Kepler, J., & de Jong, E. (2020). *Bio-Based Chemicals A 2020 Update Bio-Based Chemicals A 2020 Update With input from: (pdf version) Published by IEA Bioenergy.*

Sun, Z., & Aziz, M. (2021). Comparative thermodynamic and techno-economic assessment of green methanol production from biomass through direct chemical looping processes. *Journal of Cleaner Production, 321*, 129023. https://doi.org/https://doi.org/10.1016/j.jclepro.2021.129023

Wang, W.-C., Liu, Y.-C., & Nugroho, R. A. A. (2022). Techno-economic analysis of renewable jet fuel production: The comparison between Fischer-Tropsch synthesis and pyrolysis. *Energy, 239*, 121970. https://doi.org/https://doi.org/10.1016/j.energy.2021.121970

Flavio Manenti, Gintaras V. Reklaitis (Eds.), Proceedings of the 34th European Symposium on Computer Aided Process Engineering / 15th International Symposium on Process Systems Engineering (ESCAPE34/PSE24), June 2-6, 2024, Florence, Italy

Towards Modelling of an Industrial *Aspergillus oryzae* Aerobic Fed-batch Fermentation Process – Process Characterization Across Scales

Mariana Albino[a], Carina L. Gargalo[a], Ulrich Krühne[a], Mads O. Albæk[b], Gisela Nadal-Rey[b], Krist V. Gernaey[a*]

[a]*Process and Systems Engineering Center (PROSYS), Department of Chemical and Biochemical Engineering, Technical University of Denmark, Building 228A, 2800 Kgs. Lyngby, Denmark*
[b]*Novozymes A/S, Fermentation Pilot Plant, Krogshoejvej 36, 2880 Bagsvaerd, Denmark*
*kvg@kt.dtu.dk

Abstract

In well-established fermentation processes, meaningful improvements in process performance can be achieved through real-time simulation and optimization. Thus, modelling is an essential tool to transform process data towards relevant predictions of variables. This contribution shows the characterization of an *Aspergillus oryzae* fermentation process, marked by significant batch-to-batch variation, both at production and pilot scales. The aim is to understand the impact of process variables and parameters on fermentation process performance for model development. Particularly, since it is a filamentous fungi fermentation, knowledge of biomass concentration and rheology is crucial for successful simulations since the viscosity of the fermentation broth rises due to the organism's morphology, leading to lower mass transfer as biomass concentration increases. Firstly, the biomass concentration and viscosity levels were analysed in the industrial-scale process. Furthermore, the on-line process data were analysed to identify potential sources of batch-to-batch variation in production. Additionally, the process has been scaled down to pilot scale for detailed investigation of important process parameters regarding feeding settings and agitation power. Overall, the data collection and analysis done thus far provides the basis for model development and testing.

Keywords: scale-down, fermentation, *Aspergillus oryzae*, rheology, industrial scale

1. Introduction

The industrial production of enzymes by filamentous fungi (e.g., *Aspergillus oryzae*) is common, due to their highly efficient protein secretion (McIntyre et al., 2001). Protein secretion is associated with hyphal growth, which can influence the broth's rheology by increasing viscosity, causing a negative impact on mixing and mass transfer (McIntyre et al., 2001). For these reasons, understanding the morphology is essential for process productivity; hence the importance of having cell concentration measurements and knowledge of the viscosity of the fermentation broth. Through the years there has been significant effort in characterizing and modelling filamentous fungi fermentation processes, for example by morphological characterization (Spohr et al. 1997), by evaluation of the effects of shear stress on productivity (Amanullah et al. 2002), by modelling of rheological behaviour from biomass concentration (Olsvik and Kristiansen 1994) and by enzyme production with differing agitation and aeration parameters (Albæk et al. 2011).Furthermore, when studying industrial scale processes, a meaningful way to gain process understanding for optimization is through scale-down studies. Running experiments on production scale is not economically feasible, but with an adequate scale-down model, it is possible to study the large-scale process and find leads for improved process performance (Noorman 2011). With a scale-down model, it is also possible to develop relevant process models that can accurately predict process variables from the available data.

2. Methodology

2.1. Sampling at industrial scale

The sampling at industrial scale was done in seven batches that were running simultaneously of the product of interest, all under the same recipe. They were at different stages of the fermentation process. When presenting the data for biomass concentration and apparent viscosity, the data points from the different batches were grouped together to get an overview of the whole fermentation duration.

2.2. Biomass analysis

The biomass content (cell dry weight per litre medium) of the fermentation broth was determined as described in Albæk et al. 2011.

2.3. Rheology

The rheological measurements and description of rheological behaviour were performed as described in Albæk et al. 2012.

2.4. Enzyme activity essay

Enzyme activity was determined using a proprietary enzyme activity assay, and results are reported as arbitrary units per liter of fermentation broth.

2.5. Scale-down experimental plan

For the scale-down experiment, five batches were executed. The fermentation processes were run as fed-batch in 550L fermenters in a process very similar to the one described in Albæk et al. 2011. Batches 1 and 2 had the same inoculation material, while batches 3, 4 and 5 were inoculated from a different seed fermentation process. The seed transfer criterium for batches 1 and 2 was based on seed fermentation duration, and for batches 3, 4 and 5, on a pH drop below a defined threshold. Table 1 summarizes the experimental plan.

Table 1 – Summary of scale-down experimental plan.

Batch number	Seed material	Details
1	A	Reference
2	A	Test of the nutrient feed settings
3	B	Test of pH and temperature settings
4	B	Reference
5	B	Test of higher agitation power

2.6. Statistical data analysis

The statistical data analysis was conducted for 44 production batches executed with the same recipe, using the software SAS JMP 17. An analysis of variation (ANOVA) test was performed of the titre and the product yield on substrate from grouping by tank type and fermenter unit. In the cases where the ANOVA test calculated a significant p-value, a post hoc Tukey's test was performed to identify which groups had statistically different means.

The result is a connecting letters report, where groups identified by the same letter, have the same statistical mean.

3. Results and discussion

3.1. Industrial scale enzyme activity

The activity titre evolution throughout fermentation time was plotted for 44 batches to evaluate the variation. This is shown in Figure 1, where a range of approximately 35% variation is observed for the final activity titre. The coefficient of variation (CV) for this performance metric is 9%.

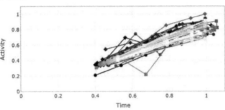

Figure 1 – Enzyme activity evolution over time for 44 industrial batches for an industrial *A. oryzae* aerobic fed-batch fermentation process. The data are normalized.

To understand the sources of variation, the final activity titre and specific yield of product on substrate for each batch were grouped by tank type and fermenter unit. There are three different tank types, A, B and C. There are four fermenter units of type A, and 6 for both types B and C. A statistical analysis was conducted to assess if these variables could explain the variation. The results are presented in Figure 2. Unit B4 was excluded from the analysis, as the group only had one batch.

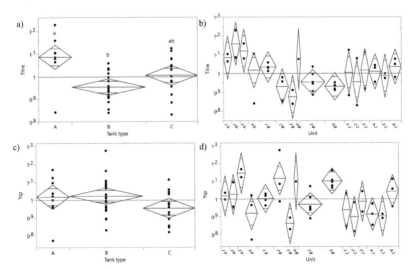

Figure 2 – ANOVA test of a), b) activity titre and c), d) product yield on substrate (Y_{sp}), by tank type (a and c) and fermenter unit (b and c). p-value of the ANOVA test: a) 0.013; b) 0.0444; c) 0.1132; d) 0.0051. A p-value lower than 0.05 indicates that there is a statistically significant difference between group means. The non-capital letters in figure a) refer to the post hoc Tukey's test, for which groups classified with the same letter, have statistically equal means. The data are normalized. The scaling of the data was done by attributing the value 1 to the overall mean.

Regarding titre, both the grouping by tank type and by fermenter unit correspond to a relevant p-value, indicating that both factors are relevant for titre variation. When grouped by fermenter unit, the p-value is higher and thus less significant. Tukey's test shows that tank types A and B have statistically significant different means, whereas type C has the same statistic mean as the other groups. Concerning the grouping by fermenter unit, even though a significant p-value was calculated, Tukey's test did not reveal any pairwise comparison that is significantly different. For this test, the more pairwise comparisons made, the lower the individual significance value, so even if a difference between groups is present, the test might not be able to identify it. On the other hand, the product on substrate yield variation is not explained by tank type, but by fermenter unit, where a relevant p-value is calculated. Once more, the post hoc test did not identify any significantly different pairwise comparison. Summarizing, this analysis indicates that the tank type and unit are relevant for the observed variation, and titre and yield are affected differently. A bigger sample size would provide a more statistically significant conclusion, nonetheless, the analysed data shows a trend. Furthermore, it will be relevant to further investigate the differences between the tanks (e.g., variation in geometry and oxygen transfer among others).

3.2. Scale-down to pilot scale

To further study the process, it was scaled-down to pilot-scale. The focus was 1) to have an accurate scale-down model, that can be later used to study different process conditions (batches 1 and 4) and 2) to have an indication of which process conditions are relevant for performance (batches 2, 3 and 5). Table 1 in the Methodology section details the conditions of each batch.

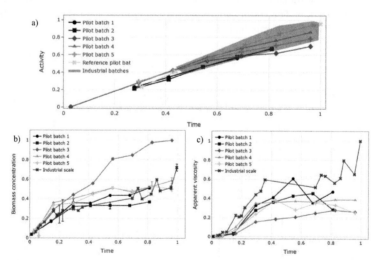

Figure 3 – a) Enzyme activity evolution over time for five pilot-scale batches executed (details in Table 1) and 7 industrial scale batches. The "reference pilot batch" refers to a historical pilot-scale scale-down fermentation process of the same industrial process previously conducted with remarkably high titres. b) Evolution of biomass concentration and c) apparent viscosity for the same batches as in a), except for the "reference pilot batch". The data are normalized.

Batches 1 and 4 had different seed transfer criterium, which led to a titre improvement of approximately 10% for batch 4. Batch 1 had the same transfer criterium as the production batches, and as described in section 2.4, it was different for batch 5. Even though more data are needed to draw statistically significant conclusions, this finding suggests that the seed transfer criterium might be an important factor to investigate further for fermentation process optimization. Batch 3 was an exact copy of the historical reference pilot batch; however, the results were different. Batch 3 had the highest biomass concentration amongst all the analysed, as well as the lowest activity titre, meaning that the carbon was diverted more towards growth rather than enzyme production. Moreover, this batch also presented the lowest apparent viscosity, indicating the possibility of morphological differences from the other batches. Free hyphal growth is generally the preferred morphology when compared to a pelleted growth, as it is associated with higher productivity. However, it is also resulting in higher broth viscosity (Haack et al. 2006). Therefore, a bigger fraction of hyphal elements growing inside pellets could explain both the lower viscosity and titre of batch 3. Nevertheless, there is a lack of biomass and rheological data for the reference pilot batch, as well as no morphological data for either batch. So, it is not possible to conclude, if a different relationship between biomass concentration and rheological behaviour is the driver for performance disparity under the same process conditions.

3.2.1. Power law fit for a viscosity prediction model

The rheological behaviour of each sample can be described by the power law model Eq. (1) (Nienow 1996).

$$\mu_{app} = K\dot{\gamma}_{eff}^{n-1} \tag{1}$$

Where μ_{app} is the apparent viscosity (Pa.s), K the flow consistency index (Pa.s^n), $\dot{\gamma}_{eff}$ the average effective shear rate (s^{-1}) and n the flow behavior index (dimensionless).

The coefficients K and n from Eq. (1) were plotted against the biomass concentration (X). The data were fitted with a power law $K, n = \alpha X^{\beta}$ to investigate the possibility of having a viscosity prediction model based on biomass concentration. This is shown in Figure 4.

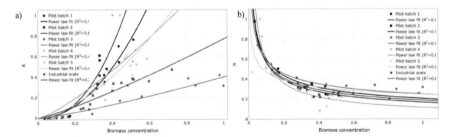

Figure 4 – a) K and b) n coefficients from the viscosity power law (Eq. (1)) against biomass concentration, for the five pilot batches performed (Table 1) and for the 7 industrial batches that were sampled. For each batch, the data points were fitted with a power law, and the regression coefficient was calculated and shown in the legend. The data are normalized.

The regression coefficient value and the shape (values of α and β) of the fits for coefficient K, varied significantly from batch to batch, with the best and worst fits corresponding to batch 3 and 4-5, respectively. As indicated in Table 1, batch 3 had different temperature and pH settings, which could have an impact on the broth's rheological behaviour and thus the fit of the proposed model. This indicates that 1) different equations, such as a logistic regression should be tested to improve the correlation factor (R^2) (Goudar et al. 1999), and that 2) the evolution of coefficient K depends on process conditions. For coefficient n, all batches had very similar power law fit results. These results are in line with the observation by Olsvik and Kristiansen (1992) that K is more sensitive to process conditions than n, thus reflecting to a larger extend the different rheological behaviours. When comparing Fig. 3c) with Fig. 4a), it can be observed that, even though the industrial batches' apparent viscosity values are higher than those of the pilot batches, the values for coefficient K are lower. This can be explained by the lower effective shear rate ($\dot{\gamma}_{eff}$) inside the large-scale reactors since the impellers rotate at a lower speed.

4. Conclusions

This work aimed at studying and understanding the variation of a well-established industrial-scale fungal fermentation process. The main conclusions are the following:

- The use of different tank types/unit has an impact on process performance. Further data collection at industrial scale as well as using a scale-down model to mimic the different tank types should be done to further understand their impact on fermentation process performance.
- Pilot scale experiments highlighted the seed tank transfer criterium as a relevant optimisation parameter. Furthermore, the process conditions that were tested led to different relationships between biomass concentration and the broth's rheological behaviour.
- High variation is observed at both production and pilot scale. Thus, deepening the biological understanding of the process is relevant to study how differences at the cell level can lead to different process performance.

References

McIntyre, M., Müller, C., Dynesen, J., Nielsen, J. (2001), Metabolic Engineering of the Morphology of Aspergillus. Advances in Biochemical Engineering/Biotechnology, vol 73.

Spohr, A., Carlsen, M., Nielsen, J. et al. (1997), Morphological characterization of recombinant strains of Aspergillus oryzae producing alpha-amylase during batch cultivations. Biotechnology Letters 19, 257–262.

Amanullah, A., Christensen, L.H., Hansen, K., Nienow, A.W. and Thomas, C.R. (2002), Dependence of morphology on agitation intensity in fed-batch cultures of Aspergillus oryzae and its implications for recombinant protein production. Biotechnol. Bioeng., 77: 815-826.

E. Olsvik, B. Kristiansen. (1994), Rheology of filamentous fermentations, Biotechnology Advances,12(1): 1-39.

Albaek, M.O., Gernaey, K.V., Hansen, M.S. and Stocks, S.M. (2011), Modeling enzyme production with Aspergillus oryzae in pilot scale vessels with different agitation, aeration, and agitator types. Biotechnol. Bioeng., 108: 1828-1840.

Noorman, H. (2011), An industrial perspective on bioreactor scale-down: What we can learn from combined large-scale bioprocess and model fluid studies. Biotechnology Journal, 6: 934-943.

Albaek, M. O., Gernaey, K. V., Hansen, M. S., & Stocks, S. M. (2012). Evaluation of the energy efficiency of enzyme fermentation by mechanistic modeling. Biotechnol. Bioeng., 109(4), 950–961.

Nienow AW. (1996). Gas–liquid mixing studies: A comparison of Rushton turbines with so modern impellers. Chem Eng Res Des Part A: Trans Inst Chem Eng 74:417–423.

Haack, M.B., Olsson, L., Hansen, K. et al. (2006), Change in hyphal morphology of Aspergillus oryzae during fed-batch cultivation. Appl Microbiol Biotechnol 70, 482–487.

Goudar, C., Strevett, K. & Shah, S. (1999), Influence of microbial concentration on the rheology of non-Newtonian fermentation broths. Appl Microbiol Biotechnol 51, 310–315.

Olsvik, E.S. and Kristiansen, B. (1992), Influence of oxygen tension, biomass concentration, and specific growth rate on the rheological properties of a filamentous fermentation broth. Biotechnol. Bioeng., 40: 1293-1299.

Flavio Manenti, Gintaras V. Reklaitis (Eds.), Proceedings of the 34th European Symposium on Computer Aided Process Engineering / 15th International Symposium on Process Systems Engineering (ESCAPE34/PSE24), June 2-6, 2024, Florence, Italy

Assessment Techniques for Convergence and Degree of Freedom in Biologics Modeling

Tomoyuki Taguchi[a],

[a]*Chiyoda Corporation, 4-6-2 Minatomirai, Yokohama-shi, Kanagawa 220-8765, Japan*
Corresponging author: *taguchi.tomoyuki@chiyodacorp.com*

Abstract

To express the cultivation cell line of recombinant proteins in mathematical models, it is necessary to represent cellular functions such as proliferation and death rate, translation systems, and metabolic systems according to the production purpose. In this process, assuming the mathematical models and validating them through experimental results is extremely crucial. The standardization of these trial-and-error approaches and the minimization of the number of experiments are essential technologies for achieving the rapid establishment of a manufacturing system. In this paper, an antibody producing cell line is assumed, utilizing CHO cells and employing a simplified cell biologics model where protein production is connected to energy production as a mock-up. Through the estimation of system parameters from pseudo-experimental results obtained from the biologics model, the existing parameter estimation methods and a newly proposed approach considering the degrees of freedom are compared. Finally, the paper provides comparative results and a discussion of the characteristics of both methods to address the issue of system parameter estimation in biologics modeling.

Keywords: "Biologics", "Modeling and simulation", "Optimization", "Process design", "Parameter identification", and "Degree of Freedom".

2. Background and purpose

The use of cellular platforms for producing various proteins and substances becomes more popular, especially in the field of biopharmaceutical development (Walsh, 2018). Inside cells, a wide variety of enzymatic reactions and material transport processes take place, modeling the entire system of cell and boundary transportation is extremely challenging. It is crucial to hypothesize models that maintain precision for analyzing the observed phenomena of interest and quickly acquire and analyze experimental data to validate these models (Kitano, 2002).

The requirement for modeling-based system assessment methods is escalated to establish the pharmaceutical manufacturing systems keeping high quality within a short period (Kemmer et. al., 2023). Hence, it is necessary to determine the required minimum experimental data and to identify the parameters in realistic values with the satisfaction of degrees of freedom.

In order to assist in the design of manufacturing systems and the operational procedures, it is advantageous to consider a set of differential-algebraic equations involving critical parameters. This system of equations typically includes simultaneous equations for material transport and Monod-type equations, which depend on state changes and are highly nonlinear (Badr, 2023 and Monteiro, 2023). In other significant aspects, glycolysis and metabolic pathways are crucial for supporting translation work. In recent years, the integration of material and energy production have been considered. The effect of detailed network linking among translation, glycolysis and metabolism further increases the nonlinearity. Therefore, the construction of a model to assess essential cell characteristics from minimal experiments is crucial. (Ramos, 2020).

Parameter identification for such models often falls into the problem of simultaneously determining state variables and parameters multimodality characteristics. Formulating hypothesis-based models and quantitatively verifying them through experiments can significantly contribute to reducing development timelines. Therefore, it is crucial to simplify the above-mentioned nonlinear systems into a linearized form that can be evaluated efficiently.

3. Biologics modeling

2.1 Simplified biologics model

As a mock-up simulation model of antibody production cell line biologics, the following three basic mathematical models are integrated.

- Cell division and death rate linked to the culture media component change

- Oxygen concentration change in a cell regarding the balance between the respiration and energy consumption rate

- Concentration changes of oxygen, glucose and lactose in cultivation media according to the balance between supply and demand amount

The material correlation is shown in Figure 1.

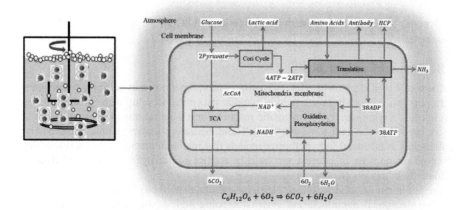

Figure 1.   Conceptual schematic of simplified biologics model for antibody production

Table 1. Symbol definitions for simplified biologics model

Variables and nomenclatures :		Equation categories:

• Initial condition (x)	• Measured variables (y)	A) State and variation of cell properties
$n_{v,0}$ Viable cell density	X_v Viable cell density	$\dot{X}_v = q_v(\hat{\mu}_v, K_m, X_v, X_{Glc}, X_{Lac})$
t Cultivation time	X_d Death cell density	$\dot{X}_d = q_d(\hat{\mu}_d, K_m, X_v, X_d, X_{Glc}, X_{Lac})$
$X_{Glc,0}$ Glucose concentration	Concentration for each component in culture media:	B) State and variation in culture media
	X_{O_2} Oxygen	$\dot{C}_{O_2} = r_{O_2}(\hat{q}_{O_2}, K_m, C_{O_2}, \check{k}_{mtc})$
• Internal Variables (x_k)	X_{Glc} Glucose	$q_{Pyr} = r_{Pyr}(K_m, C_{O_2}, \check{k}_{mtc}, \check{k}_{cor}, p_{Pyr})$
C_{O_2} Oxygen concentration in cell	X_{Lac} Lactose	$q_{ATP} = r_{ATP}(K_m, C_{O_2}, \check{k}_{mtc}, \check{k}_{cor}, p_{Pro})$
q_{Pyr} Rate of pyruvate $\quad p_{Pyr}$ Proportion rate of pyruvate	X_{AB} Antibody	C) State and variation in cell internal
q_{ATP} Rate of ATP $\quad p_{Pro}$ Proportion rate of protein	X_{HCP} Host cell protein	$\dot{X}_{O_2} = s_{O_2}(kla, \dot{X}_{O_2}, X_{O_2}, C_{O_2})$
• System parameters (π)		$\dot{X}_{Glc} = s_{Glc}(q_{Pyr})$
$\hat{\mu}_v$ Maximum cell division rate	σ_{AB} Protein production coefficient	$\dot{X}_{Lac} = s_{Lac}(K_m, \check{k}_{cor}, C_{O_2})$
$\hat{\mu}_d$ Maximum cell death rate	p_{HCP} Proportion rate of host cell protein	$\dot{X}_{AB} = s_{AB}(K_m, \check{k}_{mtc}, \check{k}_{cor}, C_{O_2}, \sigma_{AB}, p_{HCP})$
$\hat{q}_{O_2}$ Maximum respiration rate	$\check{k}_{mtc}$ Maximum mitochondria activation	$\dot{X}_{HCP} = s_{HCP}(K_m, \check{k}_{mtc}, \check{k}_{cor}, C_{O_2}, \sigma_{AB}, p_{HCP})$
K_m Parameters for Monod type equations	$\check{k}_{cor}$ Maximum Cori cycle activation	
(Seven parameters used for this study)	kla Mass transfer rate of Oxygen	

2.2 Constitutive equations, variables and nomenclatures

The simplified biologics model is composed by the equations and variables shown in Table 1. Each symbol is stated with the corresponding nomenclature.

System equations are categorized in three part which are the cell properties, culture media condition and cell internal condition. It is also possible to modify the system modeling to be more complex by adding items to evaluate the behavior of interest. For example, when incorporating more detailed enzyme reaction systems of amino acids or proteins, it is sufficient to add model equations that represent their behavior in the culture medium and inside the cells. The purpose of this study is to identify problems in estimating system parameters from experimental data and its quality. Additionally, as the purpose is to propose a new method for system identification, a preference is given to utilizing as simple a model as possible as minimum.

2.3. Typical simulation results

Some measured variables are shown in Figure 2. These are depending on the set of initial conditions and system parameters.

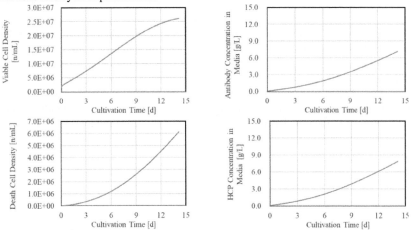

Figure 2.   Model outputs used as pseudo-experimental data.

4. Methodology

In the conventional approach, the minimization of the squared difference between measured and calculated variables is implemented. However, some problems exist.

- The combination of system parameters tends to generate the multimodality.

- The computational cost tends to increase.

- How much system parameters are effective in the hypothesis model.

- How much experimental data are required to determine the system parameters.

- Experimental data includes some types of error such as systematic, random, human and environmental error, which affects the parameter estimation.

Although the biologics model in this study is assumed as a simplified mockup, the fourteen system parameters are incorporated. To verify the conventional system parameter estimation method, the pseudo-experimental results are obtained from the biologics model with the 10% error, followed that the system parameter is reversely estimated. The simulation results are found in Figure 3. The curve features are well traced however the system parameters are different from the original set values due to the effect of multimodality and experimental errors.

To comprehend the characteristics of the system equations, a randomized combination of experimental conditions and system parameters is employed in the case study to generate a dataset of experimental results in integral form. Using this dataset, the verification of the degrees of freedom and the transformation of the equations into a more streamlined form for estimating system parameters are simplified.

Translate the original non-linear differential equations to the regression form using the integral values based on random set of experimental conditions 'x_i' and system parameters 'π_j'.

$$y \sim \zeta(\delta x_i, \delta \pi_j, (\delta x_i)^2, (\delta \pi_j)^2, \delta x_i \delta \pi_j, a, b) \tag{1}$$

$$\delta x_i = x_i - \widetilde{x_i} \tag{2}$$

$$\delta \pi_j = \pi_j - \widetilde{\pi_j} \tag{3}$$

Symbols 'a' and 'b' represent the corrected values to regress the experimental results in a linearized form. Symbol '$\widetilde{x_i}$' and '$\widetilde{\pi_j}$' serve as representative values to express the typical performance of biologics cell line as a center point in the state space of potential cell activation. The equation (1) transforms the original nonlinear differential equation system into a linearized algebraic system. This purpose is to modify the landscape of the parameter space with multimodality in equation (1) to obtain an optimal solution near the global optimum in the broader parameter space of transformed model.

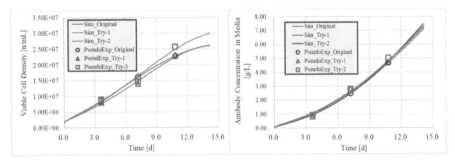

Figure 3. Fitting results for pseudo-experimental data incorporating random errors

5. Results and discussion

Table 2 shows the comparison of estimated results of system parameters. 'SLVR' means the conventional system identification based on the minimization of squared difference. On contrary that 'LPE' means the linearized parameter estimation.

The following aspects are found.

- 'SLVR' results show the different values and large standard deviations. This is the natural features due to the existence of multimodality and strong fitness to the experimental errors.

- 'LPE' results show the different values, however the standard deviations are significantly lower. This is presumed to be due to the evaluation of a linearly approximated solution space, which reduces the sensitivity to assigned experimental errors (10%) in parameter estimation.

To harmonize the characteristics of both estimation methods, the loss function of proposed method is incorporated into that of conventional system identification method, then the parameter optimization is carried out again. Results in the hybridization are presented in Table 3. According to the implementation of hybridization methods, the parameter estimation results become closer to original set values, and the standard deviations are found in mediate.

Table 2. System parameter estimation results incorporating random errors

		Km,1	Km, 2	Km,3	Km,4	Km,5	Km,6	Km,7	μv	μd	σAB	ρq	qO2	kmtc	kcor
	Original	1.00	1.00	1.00	1.00	1.00	1.00	1.00	1.00	1.00	1.00	1.00	1.00	1.00	1.00
SLVR	Try-1	1.07	0.46	1.12	0.53	1.06	0.92	1.06	0.89	1.38	0.91	0.96	0.95	1.12	1.17
SLVR	Try-2	1.01	0.61	1.12	0.69	0.39	0.49	0.77	0.97	1.25	1.07	1.05	1.45	0.62	1.13
SLVR	Try-3	1.10	0.62	1.12	0.51	0.70	1.03	1.05	0.96	1.35	0.82	0.92	1.14	0.94	1.17
SLVR	Try-4	1.30	0.68	0.93	1.25	1.18	0.99	1.10	0.93	1.02	0.87	0.92	0.86	0.82	1.12
SLVR	Try-5	1.15	0.34	0.87	1.04	0.39	0.70	0.92	0.87	1.14	0.86	0.97	1.25	0.66	1.43
LPE	Try-1	0.45	1.47	0.74	1.14	0.87	1.36	0.71	1.78	1.20	1.45	1.07	0.82	0.88	0.97
LPE	Try-2	0.46	1.47	0.74	1.13	0.87	1.36	0.74	1.75	1.20	1.56	1.09	0.84	0.88	0.94
LPE	Try-3	0.41	1.48	0.74	1.13	0.86	1.35	0.72	1.81	1.20	1.50	1.07	0.81	0.87	0.93
LPE	Try-4	0.42	1.48	0.74	1.17	0.87	1.35	0.71	1.82	1.17	1.44	1.06	0.80	0.87	0.95
LPE	Try-5	0.48	1.47	0.75	1.10	0.88	1.36	0.73	1.75	1.18	1.69	1.16	0.85	0.88	0.97
SLVR	Std. Dev.	**0.101**	**0.126**	**0.109**	**0.294**	**0.329**	**0.205**	**0.122**	**0.037**	**0.132**	**0.088**	**0.045**	**0.210**	**0.183**	**0.116**
LPE	Std. Dev.	0.024	0.005	0.004	0.011	0.004	0.003	0.010	0.027	0.015	0.091	0.037	0.020	0.005	0.014

Table 3. System parameter estimation results of hybridization constraints

		Km,1	Km, 2	Km,3	Km,4	Km,5	Km,6	Km,7	μv	μd	σAB	ρq	qO2	kmtc	kcor
	Original	1.00	1.00	1.00	1.00	1.00	1.00	1.00	1.00	1.00	1.00	1.00	1.00	1.00	1.00
SLVR+LPE	Try-1	1.06	0.75	0.81	0.95	1.12	1.15	0.93	0.99	1.17	0.67	0.71	0.94	0.84	1.00
SLVR+LPE	Try-2	1.02	0.76	0.82	0.97	1.12	1.15	0.96	1.01	1.11	0.70	0.72	0.89	0.86	0.94
SLVR+LPE	Try-3	0.99	1.12	0.81	1.06	1.14	1.05	1.02	1.14	1.02	0.89	1.05	1.11	0.98	0.92
SLVR+LPE	Try-4	0.94	1.19	0.82	0.98	1.20	1.04	1.02	1.13	1.16	0.95	1.07	1.15	1.06	1.01
SLVR+LPE	Try-5	0.90	1.08	1.07	1.15	1.07	0.85	1.01	1.10	1.13	0.91	1.07	1.16	1.13	1.05
SLVR+LPE	Std. Dev.	0.053	0.171	0.107	0.067	0.061	0.102	0.031	0.062	0.065	0.124	0.156	0.103	0.104	0.044

6. Conclusion

To conduct cycles of hypothesis and experimental verification, and to construct a model satisfying the degrees of freedom of the target system, robust evaluation of system parameters is essential. In this paper, a method is proposed for estimating the system parameters of the target system, where the prior learning information of the hypothesis model is replaced with an integral solution featuring algebraic input-output relationships. This approach not only enhances the robustness of the estimation results but also facilitates an understanding of the experimental data volume required to satisfy the degrees of freedom of the system parameters. Furthermore, through hybrid estimation with the original nonlinear differential equation system, an improvement in the accuracy of parameter estimation is also confirmed. It becomes possible to quickly obtain a system model for engineering applications such as the performance evaluation of recombinant protein-producing strains, considerations for scaling up cultivation systems based on these strains, and prediction and monitoring of operating conditions adjusted to manufacturing scales.

References

G. Walsh, 2018. Biopharmaceutical benchmarks 2018. *Nature Biotechnology*, 36(12), 1136-1145.

H. Kitano, 2002. Systems Biology: A Brief Overview. *Science*, 295(5560), 1662-1664.

A. Kemmer, et. al., 2022. Nonlinear state estimation as tool for online monitoring and adaptive feed in high throughput cultivations. *Biotechnology and Bioengineering*.

S. Badr, et. al., 2023. Hybrid modeling and data-driven parameterization of monoclonal antibody cultivation processes: Shifts in cell metabolic behavior. In *Computer Aided Chemical Engineering* (Vol. 52, pp. 985-990), Elsevier.

M. Monteiro, & C. Kontoravdi, 2023. Hybrid dynamic model of monoclonal antibody production using CHO cells. In *Computer Aided Chemical Engineering* (Vol. 52, pp. 375-380), Elsevier.

J. R. Ramos, A.G. Rath, Y. Genzai, V. Sandig & U. Reichi, 2020. A dynamic model linking cell growth to intracellular metabolism and extracellular by-product accumulation. *Biotechnology and Bioengineering*, 117(5), 1533-1553.

Flavio Manenti, Gintaras V. Reklaitis (Eds.), Proceedings of the 34th European Symposium on Computer Aided Process Engineering / 15th International Symposium on Process Systems Engineering (ESCAPE34/PSE24), June 2-6, 2024, Florence, Italy

Computer-aided optimization of cooling temperature profiles in slow freezing for human induced pluripotent stem cells

Yusuke Hayashi,[a,*] Yuki Uno,[b] Masahiro Kino-oka,[b] Hirokazu Sugiyama[a]

[a]*Department of Chemical System Engineering, The University of Tokyo, 7-3-1, Hongo, Bunkyo-ku, 113-8656, Tokyo, Japan*
[b]*Department of Biotechnology, Osaka University, 2-1, Yamadaoka, Suita, 565-0871, Osaka, Japan*
[*]y-hayashi@pse.t.u-tokyo.ac.jp

Abstract

Human induced pluripotent stem (hiPS) cells are one of the most promising sources of regenerative medical products. After successful clinical studies of hiPS cells, the demand for these cells is increasing. Thus, establishing the freezing processes of these cells for storage and transportation is necessary. Here, we present a computer-aided optimization of multiobjective optimal temperature profiles in slow freezing for hiPS cells. This study was based on a model that calculates cell survival rates after thawing, and the model was extended to evaluate cell potentials until 24 h after seeding. To estimate the necessary parameter values for this extension, freezing experiments were performed using constant cooling rates. The model was applied to assess 8,705 temperature profiles by quality and productivity indicators, and a promising profile was obtained.

Keywords: Hybrid modeling, Industrialization, Numerical simulation, Optimization, Regenerative medicine

1. Introduction

Human induced pluripotent stem (hiPS) cells are one of the most promising resources for the future industrialization of regenerative medicine. Recently, several clinical studies involving hiPS cells were performed (e.g., Parkinson's disease (Morizane, 2019)), and industrial-scale production of hiPS cells is becoming possible. Thus, establishing slow freezing processes for their preservation and transportation is urgently needed (Carpenter and Rao, 2015).

Several cryobiological studies have investigated the slow freezing of cells. Cell damage mechanisms during slow freezing were explored in Chinese hamster cells by Mazur and colleagues (Mazur et al., 1972). The authors also generated a cell dehydration assessment model and suggested that the extent of cell dehydration and intracellular ice formation was affected by cooling rates. Subsequently, several studies improved on these cell dehydration and intracellular ice nucleation models (Anderson et al., 2019; Traversari and Cincotti, 2021).

Several studies focused on slow freezing processes for hiPS cells. Ntai et al. (2018) applied new CPAs to hiPS cells. Li et al. (2020) measured temperature profile effects on intracellular ice crystals. Most recently, a mechanistic model that can estimate cell damage as a function of process conditions was published previously by the research group of the authors (Hayashi et al., 2020). In addition, a hybrid model that evaluates the cell survival rate after thawing was also published by the same group (Hayashi et al., 2021). Based on the simulation results in this study, it was suggested that a three-zone temperature profile could contribute to quality and productivity improvement. However, a rigorous investigation of the temperature profile is yet to be presented.

Here, we present a computer-aided exploration of multiobjective optimal temperature profiles in slow freezing for hiPS cells. This study was based on a numerical simulation model that evaluated the cell survival rate after thawing, depending on the given conditions (Hayashi et al., 2021). Furthermore, we extended the model using statistical modeling to calculate cell potentials until 24 h after seeding. To estimate required parameter values for extension, freezing experiments were conducted using constant cooling rates. We evaluated 8,705 temperature profiles using the model, and a promising candidate profile was obtained.

2. Experimental Methods

Figure 1 represents an overview of the experimental methods. First, the cells were separated using centrifugation for 3.0 min at $180 \times g$. After removing the supernatant, the cells were resuspended in commercially available cryopreservation solution with 10% dimethyl sulfoxide (STEM-CELLBANKER GMP grade; ZENOGEN PHARMA Co., Ltd, Fukushima, Japan) containing 10 µM Y-27632. Cell counting was performed using an automated cell counting instrument (TC20; Bio-Rad Laboratories, Inc., Hercules, CA, USA) based on the trypan blue exclusion method. Then, the cell suspension was filled into cryotubes at a volume of 0.50 mL each. The cryotubes were placed on an aluminum tube holder in a programmable freezer (Program Deep Freezer FZ-2000; STREX Inc., Osaka, Japan) and maintained for 15 min at 277 K, and then cooled to 193 K using the predetermined cooling temperature profile. During cooling, the temperature of the holder was measured using a temperature sensor built in the freezer, and that of the cell suspension was measured using a platinum resistance thermometer inserted in a cryotube placed at the center position of the holder. After cooling, the cryotubes were stored in the vapor phase of a liquid nitrogen tank for at least 24 h.

To evaluate the cell quality, the cell survival rate after thawing, β [–], was defined using the following equation:

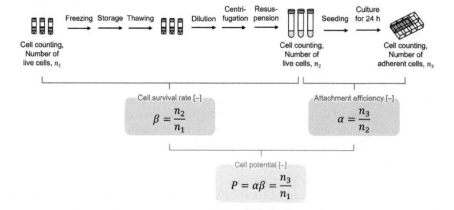

Figure 1. Overview of freezing experiments using hiPS cells

$$\beta = \frac{n_2}{n_1} \tag{1}$$

where n_1 [–] is the number of live cells before freezing and n_2 [–] is the number of live cells after thawing. The attachment efficiency at 24 h after seeding, α [–], was defined as follows:

$$\alpha = \frac{n_3}{n_2} \tag{2}$$

where n_3 [–] is the number of adherent cells on the culture plate at 24 h after seeding. The cell potential until 24 h after seeding, P [–], was obtained using the following equation:

$$P = \alpha\beta = \frac{n_3}{n_1} \tag{3}$$

3. Numerical simulation model

Figure 2 shows an overview of the numerical simulation model. The inputs were defined as the determined cooling rate of the freezer, B [K min^{-1}], and the temperature at which the freezer temperature was changed (changing point hereafter), T^{ch} [K]. The outputs were defined as the required freezing time, t_{freeze} [min], and the cell potential, P, which are the quality and productivity indicators, respectively. The physical part of the model overview consists of the models for heat transfer, mass transfer, and crystallization, which calculates the cell volume change and ice crystal volume. The statistical part connects these two parameters with the cell potential until 24 h after seeding. The overall model can evaluate the quality and productivity indicators given the process conditions.

3.1. Heat Transfer Model
The radial and temporal temperature profiles inside the vial were defined as follows:

$$\frac{\partial T}{\partial t} = \kappa \left(\frac{\partial^2 T}{\partial r^2} + \frac{1}{r}\frac{\partial T}{\partial r} \right) \tag{4}$$

where T [K] is the temperature, t [s] is the time, κ [m^2 s^{-1}] is the thermal diffusion coefficient, and r [m] is the radial distance from the vial center. The productivity indicator, t_{freeze}, was defined using the following equation:

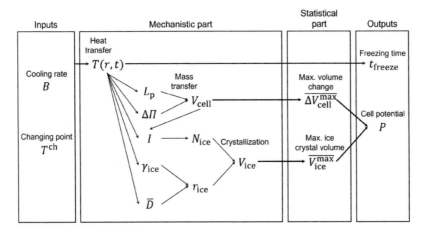

Figure 2. Overview of the numerical simulation model.

$$t_{\text{freeze}} = t|_{T(0,t)=193\,\text{K}} \tag{5}$$

3.2. Mass Transfer Model

The mass transport of water was modeled as follows:

$$\frac{dV_{\text{cell}}}{dt} = L_p A_{\text{cell}} \Delta\Pi \tag{6}$$

where V [m³] is the volume, L_p [m s⁻¹ Pa⁻¹] is the water permeability, A [m²] is the surface area, and $\Delta\Pi$ [Pa] is the pressure difference. The normalized maximum cell volume change, $\overline{\Delta V_{\text{cell}}^{\text{max}}}$ [–], was defined as follows:

$$\overline{\Delta V_{\text{cell}}^{\text{max}}} = \max\left\{ \frac{\left| V_{\text{cell}}^{\text{fin}}(r) - V_{\text{cell}}^{\text{init}} \right|}{V_{\text{cell}}^{\text{init}}} \right\} \tag{7}$$

where the superscripts init and fin represent the initial and final state of freezing, respectively.

3.3. Crystallization Model

In general, ice nucleation in a cell is categorized into two different mechanisms, homogeneous (HOM) and heterogeneous nucleation. The latter is further categorized into two types, namely, surface-catalyzed nucleation (SCN) and volume-catalyzed nucleation (VCN). The ice nucleation rate was estimated using the following equation:

$$J_{\text{ice}} = \begin{cases} 0 \ (T_m < T) \\ I^{\text{HOM}}V_w + I^{\text{SCN}}A + I^{\text{VCN}}V_w \ (T \leq T_m) \end{cases} \tag{8}$$

where J_{ice} [s⁻¹] is the ice nucleation rate, I [s⁻¹ m⁻³ or s⁻¹ m⁻²] is the nucleation rate per volume or area, and the subscript m represents the melting point. The total volume of intracellular ice crystals, $V_{\text{ice}}(r)$ [m³], was obtained from the following equation:

$$V_{\text{ice}}(r) = \sum_{i=1}^{N_{\text{ice}}} \frac{4}{3}\pi r_{\text{ice},i}^3 \tag{9}$$

The normalized maximum ice crystal volume, $\overline{V_{\text{ice}}^{\text{max}}}$ [–], was defined as follows:

$$\overline{V_{\text{ice}}^{\text{max}}} = \max\left\{ \frac{V_{\text{ice}}^{\text{fin}}(r)}{V_{\text{cell}}^{\text{fin}}(r)} \right\} \tag{10}$$

3.4. Cell Potential Model

As the output of the model, the calculated cell potential until 24 h after seeding, P^{cal} [–], was defined using the following equation:

$$P^{\text{cal}} = \omega_1 + \omega_2\overline{\Delta V_{\text{cell}}^{\text{max}}} + \omega_3\overline{V_{\text{ice}}^{\text{max}}} + \omega_4\overline{\Delta V_{\text{cell}}^{\text{max}}} \cdot \overline{V_{\text{ice}}^{\text{max}}} \tag{11}$$

where ω_1 [–], ω_2 [–], ω_3 [–], and ω_4 [–] were the fitting coefficients for the experimental results. The freezing experiments using constant cooling rates provided the necessary values of the cell potential model.

4. Results and Discussion

4.1. Freezing experiments using constant cooling rates

The circles in Figure 3(a) show the cell potentials until 24 h after seeding, P, that were observed in freezing experiments using constant cooling rates. The observed cell potentials were measured at the predetermined cooling rate, $B = 0.10, 1.0, 2.0, 3.0, 4.0,$ and 5.0 K min⁻¹. Three measurements were obtained at each cooling rate ($n = 3$). One-

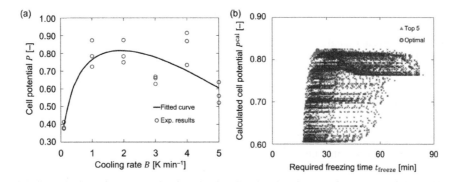

Figure 3. (a) Experimental results of the observed cell potentials and their fitted curve and (b) Model-based assessment result of 8,705 temperature profiles.

way analysis of variance was applied to analyze the experimental results in Figure 3. The p value was found to be 1.9×10^{-6}. Therefore, the relevance of the cooling rate for the cell potential was confirmed. The solid line in Figure 3(a) represents the fitted curve for the experimental results using the determined fitting coefficients.

4.2. Model-based assessment of candidate temperature profiles

For model-based assessment, 8,705 candidate temperature profiles with two temperature-changing points were produced. To determine the optimal temperature profile, a multiobjective optimization problem was formulated, as shown in the following equation:

$$\min S_{\text{total}}\left\{P^{\text{cal}}\left(B_1, B_2, B_3, T_1^{\text{ch}}, T_2^{\text{ch}}\right), t_{\text{freeze}}\left(B_1, B_2, B_3, T_1^{\text{ch}}, T_2^{\text{ch}}\right)\right\} \tag{12}$$

subject to

$$B_i \quad \in \quad \{1.0, 2.0, 3.0, 4.0, 5.0\}$$

$$T_j^{\text{ch}} \quad \in \quad \{198, 203, 208, \ldots, 258, 263, 268\}$$

where S_{total} [–] is the joint objective function, B_1 [K min^{-1}] is the first cooling rate, T_1^{ch} [K] is the first changing point of the freezer temperature, B_2 [K min^{-1}] is the second cooling rate, T_2^{ch} [K] is the second changing point, and B_3 [K min^{-1}] is the third cooling rate. The joint objective function, S_{total}, was defined as follows:

$$S_{\text{total}} = \left(\frac{1 - P^{\text{cal}}}{1 - P_{\text{min}}^{\text{cal}}}\right) + \left(\frac{t_{\text{freeze}}}{t_{\text{freeze}}^{\text{max}}}\right) \tag{13}$$

where P^{cal} [–] is the calculated cell potential until 24 h after seeding, $P_{\text{min}}^{\text{cal}}$ [–] is the minimum calculated cell potential in the considered profiles, and $t_{\text{freeze}}^{\text{max}}$ [min] is the maximum required freezing time.

Table 1. Top 5 temperature profiles judged using the joint objective function.

Rank	B_1 [K min^{-1}]	B_2 [K min^{-1}]	B_3 [K min^{-1}]	T_1^{ch} [K]	T_2^{ch} [K]
1	5.0	1.0	4.0	228	213
2	5.0	1.0	4.0	233	213
3	5.0	1.0	5.0	228	213
4	5.0	1.0	5.0	233	213
5	4.0	1.0	4.0	228	213

The relationship between the calculated cell potential, P^{cal}, and the required freezing time, t_{freeze}, for the 8,705 profiles is shown using cross marks in Figure 3(b). The red circle and green triangles in Figure 3(b) represent the optimal and top 5 profiles, respectively. Table 1 shows the top 5 temperature profiles judged using S_{total}. Fast, slow, and fast cooling was effective for both short freezing time and high cell potential.

5. Conclusions and Outlook

This work presented a computer-aided optimization of multiobjective temperature profiles in slow freezing for hiPS cells. A numerical simulation model was developed to calculate the cell potential until 24 h after seeding using statistical modeling. The model was applied to assess 8,705 temperature profiles by quality and productivity indicators, and a promising profile was obtained. In the field of computer-aided process engineering, cell therapy related studies are becoming relevant, e.g., Triantafyllou et al. (2023). Further model-based studies in this area are encouraged.

Acknowledgements

This research was supported by the Japan Agency for Medical Research and Development under grant number JP20be0704001, the Japan Society for the Promotion of Science under grant numbers 20K21102 and 23K13593, the Suzuki Foundation, and the Fuji Science and Technology Foundation.

References

D. Anderson, J. Benson, A. Kearsley, 2019, Foundations of modeling in cryobiology–II: Heat and mass transport in bulk and at cell membrane and ice-liquid interfaces. Cryobiology, 91, 3–17.

M. Carpenter, M. Rao, 2015, Concise review: making and using clinically compliant pluripotent stem cell lines, Stem Cells Transl. Med., 4, 381–388.

Y. Hayashi, I. Horiguchi, M. Kino-oka, H. Sugiyama, 2021, Model-based assessment of temperature profiles in slow freezing for human induced pluripotent stem cells, Comput. Chem. Eng., 144, 107150.

Y. Hayashi, I. Horiguchi, M. Kino-oka, H. Sugiyama, 2020, Slow freezing process design for human induced pluripotent stem cells by modeling intracontainer variation, Comput. Chem. Eng., 132, 106597.

R. Li, K. Hornberger, J. Dutton, A. Hubel, 2020, Cryopreservation of human iPS cell aggregates in a DMSO-free solution–an optimization and comparative study, Front. Bioeng. Biotechnol., 8, 1.

P. Mazur, S. Leibo, E. Chu, 1972, A two-factor hypothesis of freezing injury: evidence from Chinese hamster tissue-culture cells, Exp. Cell Res., 71, 345–355.

A. Morizane, 2019, Cell therapy for Parkinson's disease with induced pluripotent stem cells, Rinsho Shinkeigaku, 59, 119–124.

A. Ntai, A. La Spada, P. De Blasio, I. Biunno, 2018, Trehalose to cryopreserve human pluripotent stem cells, Stem Cell Res., 31, 102–112.

G. Traversari, A. Cincotti, 2021, Insights into the model of non-perfect osmometer cells for cryopreservation: A parametric sweep analysis, Cryobiology, 100, 193–211.

N, Triantafyllou, S. Papaiakovou, A. Bernardi, M. Lakelin, N. Shah, A. Kokossis, M. Papathanasiou, 2023, Machine learning-based decomposition for complex supply chains, Comput. Aided Chem. Eng., 52, 1653–1658.

Flavio Manenti, Gintaras V. Reklaitis (Eds.), Proceedings of the 34th European Symposium on Computer Aided Process Engineering / 15th International Symposium on Process Systems Engineering (ESCAPE34/PSE24), June 2-6, 2024, Florence, Italy

Bridging Weak Links in Mechanistic Modeling: Approach and Application in CHO Cell Cultivation for mAb Production

Kozue Okamura,[a] Sara Badr,[a] Hirokazu Sugiyama[a]*

[a]*Department of Chemical System Engineering, The University of Tokyo, 7-3-1, Hongo, Bunkyo-ku, 113-8656, Tokyo, Japan*
sugiyama@chemsys.t.u-tokyo.ac.jp

Abstract

Monoclonal antibodies (mAbs) are valuable but expensive pharmaceuticals. Their production involves cell cultivation, often utilizing Chinese hamster ovary (CHO) cells, and purification. Cell cultivation is costly, and various methods have been proposed to enhance efficiency, including improving host cell lines, operating conditions, and modes. Process models are crucial for assessing these alternatives to narrow down the combinations of available options. Recent studies have introduced various models but face challenges in capturing dynamic behavior and biological changes. Lactate is a major system component, which can be affected by metabolic shifts from production to consumption. Accurately modelling such shifts is important because of the potential impacts on cell growth and death, and the subsequent release of process-related impurities. Experimental data from pilot-scale cell cultivation using standard and highly productive CHO cell lines were used. A data-driven investigation was conducted to identify critical factors associated with variations in cell metabolism. The insights gained from the employed principal component analysis and data clustering were used to suggest more representative formulations of metabolism-relevant parameters in the mechanistic models. The updated mechanistic models showed higher robustness and accuracy in modeling lactate shifts. A sensitivity analysis was subsequently carried out to show the impact of changes in process design on drug price flexibility. The developed modeling framework can be used towards achieving more efficient process design and lower production costs.

Keywords: Biopharmaceuticals, Cell cultivation, Hybrid modeling, Sensitivity analysis

1 Introduction

Monoclonal antibodies (mAbs) are important active pharmaceutical ingredients despite their high drug prices. The mAb production process involves cell cultivation, using mainly Chinese hamster ovary (CHO) cells and downstream purification units. Cell cultivation is one of the most expensive steps with many suggested developments to improve process efficiency, including modifying host cell lines, reactor types, operating strategies, and modes. Process models serve as the fundament to screen and evaluate numerous alternatives comprehensively. There have been many modeling works (Reddy et al., 2023) and recent studies include Monod-type mechanistic models (e.g., Badr et al., 2021), CFD-based bioreactor models (e.g., Farzan & Ierapetritou, 2018), and hybrid-modeling with data-driven components (e.g., Okamura et al., 2022). However, these contributions struggle with different aspects of modeling dynamic behavior and changes in the associated biological phenomena. Describing the lactate metabolic shifts from

2492 K. Okamura et al.

production as metabolites to consumption as nutrients is an important modeling challenge. This is because of the potential impacts of lactate on cell growth and death, and the subsequent release of process-related impurities such as host cell protein (HCP), which can affect the final product quality and safety.

This work proposes a modeling approach that makes use of data-driven techniques to compensate for the gap between the experimental data and the process knowledge towards the development of more representative mechanistic models. The focus was to improve the modeling accuracy of lactate concentrations by depicting the changes in cell phases, which led to the lactate metabolic shifts. Principal component analysis (PCA) followed by linear regression (PCR) and clustering techniques were used to identify critical factors contributing to differences in cell phases. Based on the identified phases, the mechanistic cell cultivation model was updated. Then, dynamic simulation of different operating conditions was conducted, and cost of goods (COG) was evaluated based on the performance. The evaluated COG was used to estimate potential impacts of changes in process design on drug price flexibility.

2 Methods

2.1 Experimental data acquisition

CHO cell cultivation data were obtained from the available data pool of the Kobe GMP consolidated laboratory of the Manufacturing Technology Association of Biologics in Japan. Four experiments with different cell lines including CHO-MK 9E-1 cells (Horiuchi, 2019), operating modes, and scales were used for the initial analysis using PCA. Three experimental runs (i.e., Experiments (A)–(C)) with CHO-MK 9E-1 cells in the 50 L fed-batch mode were used for the clustering and mechanistic model update. Experiments (A) and (B) were conducted in orbitally-shaken-tank reactor while Experiment (C) used stirred-tank reactor. Dissolved oxygen (DO) was downshifted from 50% to 10% to maintain cell viability for longer durations. The pH and temperature were controlled and maintained at set values. Daily offline measurements included viable cell density, versatility, concentrations of nutrients and metabolites. DO, pH, temperature, pressure, solution weight, sparging rates of air and oxygen, and agitation rate were measured online every minute. In Experiments (A)–(C), the lactate metabolic shift was observed.

2.2 Mathematical models

2.2.1 Cell cultivation model and simulation

2.2.1.1 Fundamental mechanistic cell cultivation model including impurity generation
The fundamental model to describe cell cultivation including process-related impurity generation developed by Badr et al. (2021) and Okamura et al. (2022) was initially applied. The model involves a set of mass balance equations for system components, including solution volume and density/concentrations of viable cell, mAb, glucose, lactate, dead cell, HCP, and DNA as shown in Eqs. (1)–(8). Specific cell growth and death rates are described in Monod-type equations.

$$\frac{d(VX_v)}{dt} = (\mu - \mu_d)VX_v \tag{1}$$

$$\frac{d(VP)}{dt} = Q_p VX_v \tag{2}$$

$$\frac{d(V[\text{GLC}])}{dt} = -\left(\frac{\mu}{Y_{X_v/\text{glc}}} + m_{\text{glc}}\right) V X_v + F_{\text{in}} c_{\text{in\_glc}} \tag{3}$$

$$\frac{d(V[\text{LAC}])}{dt} = Q_{\text{lac}} V X_v \tag{4}$$

$$\frac{d(V)}{dt} = F_{\text{in}} \tag{5}$$

$$\frac{d(V X_d)}{dt} = \mu_d V X_v - \frac{r_{\text{dcell}} V X_d}{K_{\text{ldcell}} + X_d} \tag{6}$$

$$\frac{d(V[\text{HCP}])}{dt} = Y_{\text{hcp}/X_d}\left(\frac{r_{\text{dcell}} V X_d}{K_{\text{ldcell}} + X_d}\right) - \left(\frac{r_{\text{hcp}} V [\text{HCP}]}{K_{\text{dhcp}} + [\text{HCP}]}\right) \tag{7}$$

$$\frac{d(V[\text{DNA}])}{dt} = Y_{\text{dna}/X_d}\left(\frac{r_{\text{dcell}} V X_d}{K_{\text{ldcell}} + X_d}\right) - \left(\frac{r_{\text{dna}} V [\text{DNA}]}{K_{\text{ddna}} + [\text{DNA}]}\right) \tag{8}$$

where, V [L], X_v [cells L^{-1}], P [g L^{-1}], [GLC] [mmol L^{-1}], [LAC] [mmol L^{-1}], X_d [cells L^{-1}], [HCP] [mg L^{-1}], [DNA] [mg L^{-1}] are the solution volume, density/concentrations of the viable cells, mAb, glucose, lactate, dead cells, HCP, and DNA. F_{in} [L h^{-1}] and $c_{\text{in\_glc}}$ [mmol L^{-1}] are feed flow rate and glucose concentration of fresh media, respectively. μ [h^{-1}] and μ_d [h^{-1}] are specific cell growth and death rates, respectively. Q_p [g cell^{-1} h^{-1}] and Q_{lac} [mmol cell^{-1} h^{-1}] are specific production rates of mAb and lactate, respectively. $Y_{X_v/\text{glc}}$ [cells mmol^{-1}] and m_{glc} [mmol cell^{-1} h^{-1}] are specific glucose consumption for cell growth and cell maintenance, respectively. r and K are the rate constants of the dead cell lyses and the impurity dissolution. Y_{i/X_d} [mg cell^{-1}] is the mass of impurity i released from a lysed dead cell, where i includes HCP and DNA. The previous works used Q_{lac} as a constant which made it difficult to represent the lactate metabolic shifts as cells changed their behavior. Therefore, updating the representation of Q_{lac} was required.

2.2.1.2 Data-driven analysis

To identify critical factors representing changes in Q_{lac} within the experiments under investigation, data-driven modules were introduced. In the analysis, PCR and clustering techniques were used. First, PCR was used to predict changes in lactate concentrations. The PCR module gave updated predictions of lactate concentrations using the input from the fundamental cell metabolism model predictions along with online measurement data. The updated lactate predictions were then used as inputs to the impurity generation module. Analysis of the contribution to variance of each principal component (PC) and the correlations between system components and measurements was used to investigate the variations in cell behavior and the underlying conditions. Second, HDBSCAN clustering (Campello et al., 2013) was applied to offline and online measurement data to automatically identify shifts in phases between different cell behaviors. The sensitivity of the analysis to the minimum cluster size m was investigated. The results of the clustering were used to identify the critical cultivation conditions corresponding to the changes in cell behavior.

2.2.1.3 Updating the mechanistic model

Based on the insights obtained from the data-driven analysis, alternative formulations of Q_{lac} were suggested for each identified cell phase. The updated model was fitted to

Experiments (A) and (C). The estimated parameters in Experiment (A) were used to predict the performance of Experiment (B).

2.2.2   *Dynamic simulation*

Using the developed cell cultivation model, dynamic simulation was conducted. Scenarios with different cell lines, reactor types, and feeding strategies with varying feed flow rates and feed start timing were explored. For CHO-MK 9E-1 cell lines, different timing for DO downshifts was also explored. Scenarios were categorized into five groups depending on the combination of used cell lines, reactor types, and explored variables. The final HCP concentrations $[\text{HCP}]|_{t_{\text{final}}}$ [g L^{-1}] and the total mAb production W_{mAb} [g] were used as indicators of cell cultivation performance, where t_{final} [h] is the duration of cultivation.

2.2.3   *Process evaluation model*

An integrated index I [–] combining the two objectives was defined in Eq. (9). Process options maximizing I were selected for further analysis.

$$I = \frac{W_{\text{mAb}}}{\max(W_{\text{mAb}})} \left(\frac{[\text{HCP}]|_{t_{\text{final}}}}{\max([\text{HCP}]|_{t_{\text{final}}})} \right)^{-1} \tag{9}$$

Then, COG [USD g-mAb^{-1}] was evaluated for operating conditions maximizing I according to Eq. (10). The formulation of COG was based on previous research works (Klutz et al., 2016; Yang et al., 2019). The operating cost of cell cultivation $C_{\text{culture\_op}}$ [USD] was defined as the sum of the annual costs of media C_{media} [USD], single use reactor bag C_{bag} [USD], electricity C_{elec} [USD], labor C_{labor}, [USD] water for injection C_{wfi} [USD], waste water treatment $C_{\text{waste\_water}}$ [USD], and waste plastic treatment $C_{\text{waste\_plastics}}$ [USD]. The operating cost of downstream and capital costs were estimated based on the ratio to cell cultivation operating costs according to previous research works (Yang et al., 2019).

$$COG = \frac{\dfrac{C_{\text{cap}}}{Production\ years} + C_{\text{op}}}{mAb\ production\ demand} \tag{10}$$

2.2.4   *Drug price analysis*

Based on the calculated maximum and minimum COG within the investigated scenarios in each group, the potential drug price flexibility was analysed. In this work, drug price P_{drug} [USD g-mAb^{-1}] was assumed to be a summation of COG and margin to cover other costs and profits P_{margin} [USD g-mAb^{-1}]. Potential drug price flexibility $r_{\text{flexibility}}$ [%] was defined as a ratio of the difference between the cases with maximum and minimum COG to the maximum COG (Eq. (11)). Japanese Yen (JPY) was used in the analysis.

$$r_{\text{flexibility}} = 100 \frac{\max(COG) + P_{\text{margin}} - \left\{ \min(COG) + P_{\text{margin}} \right\}}{\max(COG) + P_{\text{margin}}} \tag{11}$$

3   Results and discussion

Through the PCA, it was identified that the variances in environmental factors such as DO, temperature, and pH were important to explain the variances of specific cell growth and death rates. In the clustering analysis, results showed that DO gave the strongest separation, and similar trends were observed in all the three experiments. The more detailed description is available in the previous paper (Badr et al., 2023). Based on the insights, regions of varying DO levels were analyzed separately in terms of cell metabolism behavior. The impact of changes in nutrient levels were also investigated in combination with changes in DO levels. The observation of glutamine concentration profiles and the experimentally determined Q_{lac} showed that changes in Q_{lac} corresponded well to changes in glutamine concentration, but only under high DO conditions. The hypothesis was that at high DO levels, deficiencies in glutamine could promote the consumption of lactate to keep the TCA cycle running. Accordingly, Q_{lac} was described as a function of glutamine concentration [GLN] at high DO, DO_{high} [%], and as a constant at low DO, DO_{low} [%] (Eq. (12)). Specific cell growth and death rates were updated to reflect the impact of lactate consumption. The modified model was able to predict lactate, mAb, and HCP concentrations in Experiment (B) with high accuracy as shown in **Figure 1**. The average R^2 for all the system components in the model was 0.802.

$$Q_{lac} = \begin{cases} \dfrac{k_{lac11}}{k_{lac12}+\exp\{-k_{lac13}[GLN]\}} + k_{lac14} \Big|_{DO=DO_{high}} \\ \\ k_{lac21}\big|_{DO=DO_{low}} \end{cases} \tag{12}$$

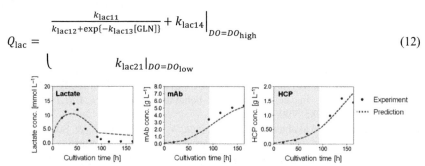

Figure 1. A part of prediction results of Experiment (C). Shaded areas represent high DO levels.

Figure 2 (a) shows a part of COG evaluation results for optimal solutions identified within the investigated scenarios of each group assuming the use of a 2000 L reactor with an overall annual production demand of 50 kg and a downstream yield of 75 %. It was shown that media cost was one of the dominant factors in COG, which was consistent with the previous works (Badr et al., 2021). As an expanded investigation of Group 4 in **Figure 2 (a)**, the potential drug price flexibility was explored as shown in **Figure 2 (b)**. The map can help to quantitatively evaluate the flexibility for the given required margin and mAb production demand. In the explored range with different operating strategies and reactor volumes, the maximum potential price flexibility was 90.6 % while the minimum was 0.0926 %. The figure shows a marked reduction in potential drug price flexibility as annual production demand approaches production capacity limits.

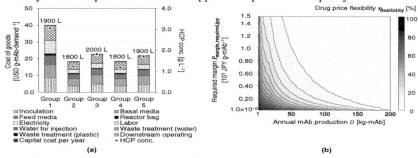

Figure 2. Results of **(a)** COG evaluation and **(b)** potential drug price flexibility for given drug price and annual mAb production.

4   Conclusions

This work demonstrated how data-driven insights were used to update mechanistic cell cultivation models and quantitative assessment of the changes made to cell lines and operating parameters on the potential flexibility of drug pricing. The evaluation findings can help with effective process design using the currently available options and can also be extended to serve as a roadmap for future advancements toward the desired cost flexibility. By using the drug price as a mediating variable connecting different scales, the work would help quantify the effect of improvements in cell and process features on society-level goals like cost-effectiveness and drug accessibility.

Acknowledgements

This work was supported by the Japan Agency for Medical Research and Development (AMED) [grant No. JP21ae0121015, JP21ae0121016].

References

Badr, S., Oishi, K., Okamura, K., Murakami, S., & Sugiyama, H. (2023). Hybrid modelling and data-driven parameterization of monoclonal antibody cultivation processes: Shifts in cell metabolic behavior. *Computer Aided Chemical Engineering, 52*, 985–990.

Badr, S., Okamura, K., Takahashi, N., Ubbenjans, V., Shirahata, H., & Sugiyama, H. (2021). Integrated design of biopharmaceutical manufacturing processes: Operation modes and process configurations for monoclonal antibody production. *Computers and Chemical Engineering, 153*, 107422. https://doi.org/10.1016/j.compchemeng.2021.107422

Campello, R. J. G. B., Moulavi, D., & Sander, J. (2013). Density-based clustering based on hierarchical density estimates. *Advances in Knowledge Discovery and Data Mining*, 160–172. https://doi.org/https://doi.org/10.1007/978-3-642-37456-2_14

Farzan, P., & Ierapetritou, M. G. (2018). A framework for the development of integrated and computationally feasible models of large-scale mammalian cell bioreactors. *Processes, 6*(82). https://doi.org/10.3390/pr6070082

Horiuchi, T. (2019). Establishment of a novel CHO cell line and its application to the production of protein-based pharmaceuticals (In Japanese). *Seibutsu-Kougaku-Kaishi, 97*(6), 328–330.

Klutz, S., Holtmann, L., Lobedann, M., & Schembecker, G. (2016). Cost evaluation of antibody production processes in different operation modes. *Chemical Engineering Science, 141*, 63–74. https://doi.org/10.1016/j.ces.2015.10.029

Okamura, K., Badr, S., Murakami, S., & Sugiyama, H. (2022). Hybrid modeling of CHO cell cultivation in monoclonal antibody production with an impurity generation module. *Industrial and Engineering Chemistry Research, 61*(40), 14898–14909. https://doi.org/10.1021/acs.iecr.2c00736

Reddy, J. V., Raudenbush, K., Papoutsakis, E. T., & Ierapetritou, M. (2023). Cell-culture process optimization via model-based predictions of metabolism and protein glycosylation. *Biotechnology Advances, 67*. https://doi.org/10.1016/j.biotechadv.2023.108179

Yang, O., Prabhu, S., & Ierapetritou, M. (2019). Comparison between batch and continuous monoclonal antibody production and economic analysis. *Industrial and Engineering Chemistry Research, 58*(15), 5851–5863. https://doi.org/10.1021/acs.iecr.8b04717

Flavio Manenti, Gintaras V. Reklaitis (Eds.), Proceedings of the 34th European Symposium on Computer Aided Process Engineering / 15th International Symposium on Process Systems Engineering (ESCAPE34/PSE24), June 2-6, 2024, Florence, Italy

Enhanced kinetic model parameters for xylitol bioproduction from *Candida mogii* ATCC 18364

Julio César Sánchez-Rendón[a], Luis Gerónimo Matallana[b], Ricardo Morales-Rodriguez[c], Oscar Andrés Prado-Rubio[a,d*]

[a]*Departamento de Ingeniería Química, Universidad Nacional de Colombia –Manizales 170003, Colombia*
[b]*Grupo de Investigación en Alimentos y Agroindustria, Universidad de Caldas, Calle 65, No. 26-10, C.P. Manizales 170002, Colombia*
[c]*Departamento de Ingeniería Química, Universidad de Guanajuato, Noria Alta S/N; Guanajuato, Guanajuato, 36050, México.*
[d]*Department of Chemical and Biochemical Engineering, Technical University of Denmark (DTU), Lyngby DK-2800, Denmark*
*oaprador@kt.dtu.dk

Abstract

Xylitol is a common sweetener used in the dental and pharmaceutical industries. This molecule can be obtained from renewable sources and, is also a building block with the potential to produce a wide variety of chemical compounds. However, xylitol bioproduction is still economically unattractive and, there is a need for investigating optimal process design and operation. For that, a mathematical model that accurately predicts the xylitol fermentation is fundamental to reduce uncertainties during process production. In this study, a framework for structural and practical parameter identification is implemented to increase the number of identifiable kinetic parameters, using a mathematical model composed of 5 states and 11 parameters. The methodology uses well-established methods that unfortunately are not commonly used together such as a) experimental data processing, b) structural identifiability analysis, c) enhanced parameters identification using a nested optimization approach for self-tuning stochastic optimization and, d) validation. The employed methodology allows to determine that the full set of parameters is locally identifiable, and the number of identifiable parameters was increased from 4 to 10, also with reduced confidence intervals. The increased confidence in the model parameters brings interesting insights into this fermentation, which might permit peforming further and more certain analysis.

Keywords: xylitol bioproduction, parameter estimation, mathematical modeling, global optimization.

1. Introduction

The European sustainability agenda for 2,050 proposed to achieve up to 38 % of biobased products in the market to migrate to a more balanced future. One of the interesting platform components to be obtained from biomass is xylitol. Xylitol is a sweetener and additive used in food, pharma, dental, cosmetics, and others. Additionally, xylitol could be used to obtain xylaric and xylonic acids, propylene, and ethylene glycol, among others. Xylitol market size is expected to grow up to USD ~1.50 billion at a compound annual growth rate (CAGR) of 6 % (2023-2030) (Custom Market Insights, 2022). Xylitol bioproduction has been investigated, obtaining production cost from 1.59 USD/kg up to 5 USD/kg depending on the raw material and production scheme (Ruales-Salcedo et al., 2022). With a xylitol selling price of ~3.5 USD/kg, it can be said that the bioprocess is economically unattractive and, from the *in silico* process design, predictions could be still lacking of quality especially due to the fermentation model uncertainties. Recently, a xylitol kinetic model from *Candida mogii* ATCC 18364 was investigated, showing that only 4 out of 11 model parameters were identifiable using local optimization (Prado-Rubio et al., 2015). Therefore, there is a need for obtaining a more representative and interpretable xylitol kinetic model that could be reliably used for system understanding, experimental design, and optimal process design/control. This study aims to implement a robust framework for structural and practical parameter identification, which leads to an increase in the number of identifiable parameters. Thus, the quality and interpretability of the improved parameters allows for obtaining new system understanding, evidencing the time-variant nature of the repeated fed-batch fermentations and, the possible intracellular dynamic behavior of the biochemical system during the process.

2. Methodology

The methodology is shown in Fig. 1. As a starting point, both the mathematical model and the experimental data are needed. The data is treated to remove outliers (via signal filters and mobile median analysis) and random noise (via polynomial fitting with 4th order Savitzky-Golay polynomial). Considering the mathematical model and the characteristics of the experimental data (number and type of variables, type of experiments), a structural identifiability analysis is performed to determine if the parameters are identifiable globally/locally or not identifiable (GenSII tollbox). Whether the model is not structurally identifiable, either the experimental design or the mathematical model must be adjusted. When the model is structurally identifiable, an optimization problem is defined and used for optimizer tuning (via the IRACE package in R®). Hyperparameter tuning is an extremely important step that is unfortunately rarely reported, but it is important to mention that only through a specific configuration for a given optimization problem (incorporating experimental data), it possible to guarantee the correct behavior of the optimizer (Wolpert et al., 1997). The tuned hyperparameters are then used to solve the complete parameter estimation problem and calculate the optimal model parameters. As the mathematical model is complete, the practical identifiability (validation) test is performed within several categories as confidence intervals (in parameters and prediction), goodness-of-fit metrics (SSE, MRSE, GoF, R2, etc), and sensibility indexes (standardized regression coefficients method) (Sánchez-Rendón et al., 2020). If the validation process is not satisfactory, modifications in the model or the experimental design are required.

2.1. Case of study: xylitol bioproduction

Xylitol is a C5 alcohol widely used as a sweetener and additive to dental and pharmaceutical products. Xylitol is also a platform chemical fundamental for other chemical compounds production (Ur-Rehman et al., 2015). Xylitol bioproduction experimental data used in this work was taken from Sirisansaneeyakul et al. (2013), who performed a sequential experiment of 22 fed-batch fermentations. The mathematical model of xylitol bioproduction is composed of 5 states (glucose, xylose, biomass, intra and extra xylitol) and 11 parameters that describe complex biological non-linear phenomena such as, inhibition of glucose and xylose uptake, intra- and extracellular transport and reaction stoichiometry (Tochampa et al., 2015, Hernández-Escoto et al., 2016).

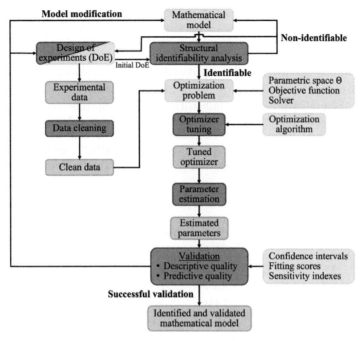

Figure 1. Methodology for robust parameter estimation in bioprocess mathematical models with inputs (Green block), methods (blue block) and results (orange block).

3. Results

After the data preprocessing, outliers and overall random noise were systematically removed. This is beneficial for the solution of the parameter estimation problem, because it reduces the number of possible trajectories that the model can describe. In terms of structural identifiability, the 11 parameters of the mathematical model were found to be locally identifiable as seen in Table 1. For practical identifiability, the nested optimization problem was solved with dataset 1, with the objective of hyperparameter tuning for the Particle Swarm Optimization (PSO) algorithm. This stochastic global optimizer has the desired property of guaranteed theoretical convergence, meaning that with a correct hyperparameter configuration, this algorithm of consistently find points within the neighborhood of the global optimum (Huang et al., 2023). IRACE can calculate the optimizer hyperparameters through a statistical process capable of increasing the reproducibility of the results while decreasing the computational effort. For this case, 96 candidate configurations were found during the tunning process. The best-calculated hyperparameters for the PSO algorithm are inertia range of [0.25, 0.50], MinNeighborsFraction of 0.36, SelfAdjustmentWeight of 1.58, SocialAdjustmentWeight of 1.44, and SwarmSize of 185. The value of the calculated hyperparameters contrasts with those of the default configuration i.e., inertia range of [0.1, 1.1], MinNeighborsFraction of 0.25, SelfAdjustmentWeight of 1.49, SocialAdjustmentWeight of 1.49, and SwarmSize of 100.

In terms of the PSO inner working, the calculated configuration favors local search with slow-moving particles that highly communicate with each other, while the global search is compensated with an increased number of particles. The previously described hyperparameter configuration and a new optimization problem defined with 9 datasets (datasets 1 to 9) led to the estimated parameter values shown in Table 1. However, as shown by the practical identifiability analysis, the estimated values can be classified into different categories in accordance with the confidence levels. First, the parameter $K_{i,glu}$ is practically non-identifiable (xylose uptake inhibition due to glucose). μ_{glu}^{max}, K_r, $K_{S,xil}$ depict high uncertainty and $K_{S,glu}$, q_{glu}^{max}, q_{xil}^{max}, $K_{i,xil}$, P_{xit} have very low uncertainty (less than 1 %). These differences can be attributed to the type of experiments performed where there is only one experiment using diauxic growth (i.e., glucose and xylose). Consequently, there is insufficient information to estimate with high precision the parameters involving glucose behavior and the interaction of both carbon sources within the cell, reflected in the low accuracy of μ_{glu}^{max}, K_r, $K_{S,xil}$ and the non-identifiability of $K_{i,glu}$.

Table 1. Structural identifiability and estimated parameter values.

Parameter	Structural identifiability	Estimated value	Confidence interval	Hernández-Escoto et al., 2016	Variation (%)
μ_{glu}^{max}	Local	6.183×10^{-2}	5.32×10^{-2}	-	-
$K_{S,glu}$	Local	7.5586	3.54×10^{-3}	-	-
q_{glu}^{max}	Local	2.1546	2.78×10^{-2}	-	-
$K_{i,glu}$	Local	9.747×10^{-2}	0.798	-	-
K_r	Local	1.452×10^{-2}	1.39×10^{-2}	-	-
μ_{xit}^{max}	Local	4.458×10^{-3}	2.26×10^{-3}	0.189	4×10^3 %
$K_{S,xil}$	Local	5.909×10^{-3}	4.34×10^{-3}	11.761	198×10^3 %
$K_{S,xit}$	Local	5.116×10^{-5}	1.99×10^{-5}	16.06	31×10^6 %
q_{xil}^{max}	Local	8.284×10^{-2}	3.47×10^{-4}	0.342	312 %
$K_{i,xil}$	Local	19.318	0.28	-	-
P_{xit}	Local	7.823×10^{-11}	2.02×10^{-13}	-	-

Interestingly, comparing these results with previous efforts in kinetic model tuning done by Hernández-Escoto et al. (2016), it can be seen that the parameter values highly depend on how the optimization problem is solved, as shown in Table 1. Specifically, the authors used the full data available with a local optimizer (gradient-based) and determined that only 4 parameters can be reliably estimated. In this work, 9 data sets and a tuned global optimizer were used, increasing the number of identifiable parameters to 10. The substantial differences between the estimated values highlight the importance and need for a carefully chosen setup and solution of the parameter estimation optimization problem.

The parity plot (Fig. 2, left) shows the descriptive quality of the mathematical model after parameter estimation, with a fair fitting in the 9 data sets used for calibration, and a Mean Absolute Percentage Error (MAPE) index of 226.32. Better accuracy can be observed in xylose and xylitol concentrations with most of their points lying between the 10% confidence interval lines in comparison with glucose and biomass. This can be attributed to a higher amount of information present in the data sets for these variables. However, after 150 hours of fermentation discrepancies between the model and the data arise (Fig. 3, top), possibly due to microorganism adaptation to increasing concentrations of xylose.

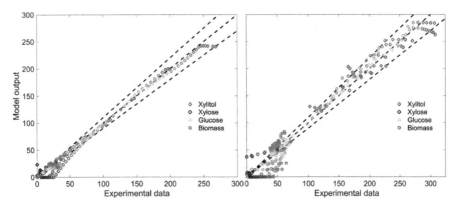

Figure 2. Parity plot for model output. Time progression is shown as darkening color shade. Left: descriptive quality (training datasets). Right: predictive quality (validation datasets).

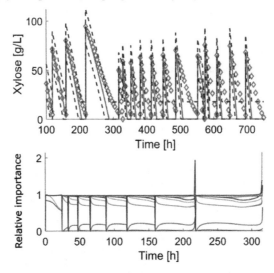

Figure 3. Top: Model prediction for xylose (red line) with 95% confidence intervals (blue dashed line) and experimental data (magenta diamonds). Bottom: Example of standardized regression coefficients for xylose prediction. Each line corresponds to one model parameter.

The parity plot for the predictive quality of the model (Fig. 2, right) shows a lack of accuracy in the prediction of biomass and xylose concentration but a lower MAPE index of 149.31. Specifically, the model predicts a higher xylose uptake rate which increases in the last batches (Fig. 3, top). Then, to keep the cell growth, the model predicts xylitol consumption. These results confirm that the microorganism underwent metabolic adaptation that affect slowing down the growth, xylose uptake, and resulted in higher xylitol accumulation. This adds a complexity layer to the parameter estimation optimization problem given that the system is time-variant.

Finally, a sensitivity analysis was performed with the standardized regression coefficients method for the xylose state (Fig. 3, bottom). As expected, the relevance of the parameters changes dynamically during the fermentation process. The change in the preferred carbon source is shown as a change in the relative importance of parameters related to glucose and xylose. A high parameter interaction is presented during xylose consumption and xylitol production, which highlights the need for an alternative experimental design. In this particular case, the calibration of the mathematical model could be enhanced with more experiments of simultaneous feed of glucose and xylose.

4. Conclusions

Mathematical models comprise a wide range of useful tools for the understanding of complex systems and their practical applications, thus, assessing the quality of the model predictions and the interpretability of the model parameters becomes a fundamental task. In this sense, the present work makes use of previously established, but not combined, methods for experimental data cleaning, structural identifiability, global optimizer tuning, practical identifiability, and model validation with a distinction between the descriptive and predictive quality of model outputs. This methodology allows us to evaluate the adequacy of experimental design (structural identifiability), information quality and relevance (descriptive quality), and fair model prediction of the experimental data (predictive quality). As a result, 10 out of 11 model parameters were reliably estimated which allowed us to provide system insights.

Acknowledgements
This research was partially founded by Novo Nordisk Foundation grant NNF19SA0035474.

References

H. Hernández-Escoto, O. A. Prado-Rubio, R. Morales-Rodriguez, 2016. Model-based framework for enhanced and controlled operation of a fed-batch bioreactor: xylitol production. Computer Aided Chemical Engineering, 38, 301-306.

H. Huang, J. Qiu, K. Riedl, 2023, On the global convergence of particle swarm optimization methods, Applied Mathematics & Optimization, 88, 30.

O. A. Prado-Rubio, H. Hernández-Escoto, R. Rodriguez-Gomez, S. Sirisansaneeyakul, R. Morales-Rodriguez, 2015, Enhancing xylitol bio-production by an optimal feeding policy during fed-batch Operation, Computer-Aided Chemical Engineering, 37, 1757-1762.

A. V. Ruales-Salcedo, V. H. Grisales-Díaz, R. Morales-Rodríguez, J. Fontalvo, O. A. Prado-Rubio, 2022, Production of High-Added Value Compounds from Biomass. Book chapter in: Biofuels and Biorefineries.

J. C. Sánchez-Rendón, R. Morales-Rodriguez, L. G. Matallana-Pérez, O. A. Prado-Rubio. 2020. Assessing Parameter Relative Importance in Bioprocesses Mathematical Models through Dynamic Sensitivity Analysis. Computer Aided Chemical Engineering, 48, 1711-1716.

S. Sirisansaneeyakul, S. Wannawilai, Y. Chisti, 2013. Repeated fed-batch production of xylitol by Candida magnoliae TISTR 5663, Journal of Chemical Technology & Biotechnology, 88, 1121–1129.

W. Tochampa, S. Sirisansaneeyakul, W. Vanichsriratana, P. Srinophakun, H. H. C. Bakker, S. Wannawilai, Y. Chisti, 2015, Optimal Control of Feeding in Fed-Batch Production of Xylitol, Industrial & Engineering Chemistry Research, 54, 1992-2000.

S. Ur-Rehman, Z. Mushtaq, T. Zahoor, A. Jamil, M. A. Murtaza, M.A., 2015, Xylitol: A Review on Bioproduction, Application, Health Benefits, and Related Safety Issues, Critical Reviews in Food Science and Nutrition, 55, 1514-1528.

D. H .Wolpert, W. G. Macready, 1997, No free lunch theorems for optimization, IEEE Transactions on Evolutionary Computation, 1, 1, 67-82

Flavio Manenti, Gintaras V. Reklaitis (Eds.), Proceedings of the 34th European Symposium on Computer Aided Process Engineering / 15th International Symposium on Process Systems Engineering (ESCAPE34/PSE24), June 2-6, 2024, Florence, Italy

Improving the Production of PHBV in *Cupriavidus necator* by Optimal Control

Rudolph L. Kok[a,*], Rolf Findeisen[b], Achim Kienle[a,c], Stefanie Duvigneau[a,c]

[a]*Otto-von-Guericke-University, Universitätsplatz 2, 39106, Magdeburg, Germany*
[b]*TU Darmstadt, Landgraf-Georg-Straße 4, 64283 Darmstadt, Germany*
[c]*Max Planck Institute for Dynamics of Complex Technical Systems, Sandtorstraße 1, 39106 Magdeburg, Germany*
*rudolph.kok@ovgu.de

Abstract

Polyhydroxyalkanoates (PHAs) are biodegradable polymers produced by many microorganisms under growth-limited conditions. Two well-known PHAs are the homopolymer poly(3-hydroxybutyrate) (PHB) and the copolymer poly(3-hydroxybutyrate-co-3-hydroxyvalerate) (PHBV). Both can be produced by *Cupriavidus necator* when grown on specific carbon sources. PHB's rigidity and brittleness limit its application, e.g. in packaging materials or medical drug capsules. Incorporating hydroxyvalerate (HV) into the polymer enhances the flexibility while decreasing the melting point, with these effects becoming more pronounced at higher ratios of HV. Optimising the production is challenging due to an absence of online state measurements. Metabolic models are available to predict the concentration of HB and HV using the outlet CO_2 fraction. This measurement can be affected by changes in the inlet CO_2 fraction as well as the inlet gas flow rate. The metabolic model is extended to address this concern. A Gaussian Process (GP) regression model is developed to predict the outlet CO_2 fraction based on the process inputs. The GP model is integrated into the metabolic model to form a hybrid model that allows for open-loop optimisation to obtain an optimal process input trajectory that maximises the conversion yield and the molar fraction of HV in PHBV.

Keywords: Biopolymer, *Cupriavidus necator*, Poly(3-Hydroxybutyrate-co-3-Hydroxyvalerate), Process Control.

1. Introduction

The importance of biopolymers is increasing due to their favourable properties, especially biodegradability. Poly(3-hydroxybutyrate-co-3-hydroxyvalerate) (PHBV) is considered for various applications due to its flexibility and lower melting point coming from the combination of 3-hydroxybutyrate (HB) and 3-hydroxyvalerate (HV). These properties make it ideal for applications in medicine (Zinn et al. 2003). Optimising PHBV production in view of substrate conversion and product yield is crucial to enhance its economic competitiveness (Duvigneau et al. 2021a).

Duvigneau et al. (2023) developed a metabolic model utilising the outlet CO_2 fraction measurement which correlates to the metabolic activity of the cell. Changes in the gas feed, such as CO_2 content or gas flow rate, can affect this measurement. This concern is addressed by reformulating the correlation to the CO_2 generated by the organism, using the CO_2 fractions in the inlet and outlet as well as the gas flow rate. An inference model, based on the available process measurements and inputs, is required to estimate the outlet CO_2 fractions for optimisation purposes.

Gaussian Process (GP) regression models excel in delivering accurate estimates even with limited data, providing a smooth function that is differentiable (Rasmussen and Williams 2005). Generating experimental data can be time consuming and costly, making GP's an ideal starting model choice. Two independent reactor experiments were performed based on different gas flow rate and agitation speed profiles. A hybrid model consisting of the metabolic model and the GP model, capable of predicting the outlet CO_2 fraction, is used in an open-loop optimisation. An optimal input profile is obtained to increase the substrates conversion yield and increasing the molar fraction of HV in PHBV.

2. Materials and Methods

2.1. Cultivation Conditions

Two distinct reactor experiments were utilised in this work, referred to as Ex1 and Ex2. All experiments were performed using the DASGIP parallel bioreactor system with *Cupriavidus necator* (H16, DSM 428) obtained from DSMZ GmbH Braunschweig. The cultivation conditions for the preculture are described in Duvigneau et al. (2021a). The reactor was controlled using the standard DASware PI controllers as illustrated in Figure 1. The states include the concentrations of fructose (c_F), propionic acid (c_P), ammonium chloride NH$_4$Cl (c_N), residual biomass (c_X), HB (c_{HB}), and HV (c_{HV}). The considered controlled inputs are the gas flow rate in ($\dot{G}_{in}$) and the agitation speed (AG). The CO_2 fractions (x_{CO_2}) are available online measurements. The inlet CO_2 fraction was kept constant. The pH was controlled (pHC) at 6.8 using 20 g/L propionic acid ($\dot{F}_P$) and 2 M sodium hydroxide ($\dot{F}_{NaOH}$). Temperature was controlled (TIC) at 30 °C. Ramped setpoint profiles for AG and G_{in} were used in Ex1 with a run time of 33 hours, as shown in Figure 2. Ex2 had a run time of 14 hours and followed the input profile up to this point.

2.2. Analytics

Propionic acid and NH$_4$Cl concentrations of Ex1 and Ex2 were analysed as described in Duvigneau et al. (2021a). The fructose concentrations were measured using an Agilent 1260 high-performance liquid chromatography (HPLC). After preparation of the supernatant, 10 µL was loaded on an RHM monosaccharide column (Phenomenex, USA) at 80 °C and eluted isocratically with 0.6 mL/min deionised water. The sugar was detected with a refractive index detector (Agilent, Germany) at 60 °C. The determination of the HB and HV components of the PHA was performed as given in Duvigneau et al. (2021b). The biomass concentrations were determined gravimetrically.

2.3. Mathematical Models

The modelling and simulation were done in Python 3.8 using HILO-MPC and CasADi developed by Pohlodek et al. (2022) and Andersson et al. (2019), respectively.

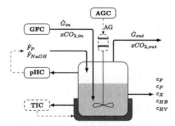

Figure 1: Bioreactor Setup

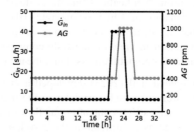

Figure 2: Input Profile

2.3.1. Metabolic Model

The dynamics of the system can be generalised to:

$$\frac{dx}{dt} = f(x, u, \theta) \tag{1}$$

Here, $x \in \mathbb{R}^{n_x}$ represents the states of the system, $u \in \mathbb{R}^{n_u}$ represents the inputs to the system, and $\theta \in \mathbb{R}^{n_\theta}$ represents the parameters in the ordinary differential equations $f: \mathbb{R}^{n_x} \times \mathbb{R}^{n_u} \times \mathbb{R}^{n_\theta} \rightarrow \mathbb{R}^{n_x}$. The full description of the metabolic model can be found in Duvigneau et al. (2023). Eq. (2) expresses the metabolic activity coefficient, b_{CO_2}, as presented in Duvigneau et al. (2023). This coefficient is extended in this study to describe the CO_2 generated by the organism, as presented in Eq. (3), using a mass balance, under the assumptions of negligible CO_2 absorption, constant temperature, and pressure.

$$b_{CO_2} = \frac{xCO_{2,out}}{xCO_{2,in}P_{res}} \tag{2}$$

$$b_{CO_2} = \frac{xCO_{2,out}\dot{G}_{out} - xCO_{2,in}\dot{G}_{in}}{P_{res}} \quad \text{with} \quad P_{res} = \frac{c_X}{c_{HB} + c_{HV} + c_X} \tag{3}$$

Parameter identification is required to update the rate constant values, $k: \{k_1, \ldots, k_8\}$, present in the metabolic model. A weighted least squares optimisation was performed using the root mean square error (RMSE), weighted with the mean standard deviation of the measurements, $\bar{\sigma}^2 \in \mathbb{R}^{n_x}$, to account for measurement noise, as presented in Eq. (4). The predicted values, $\hat{x} \in \mathbb{R}^{n_x}$, are obtained by solving the system in Eq. (1) using a 4th order Runge-Kutta integration method and the IPOPT solver. The inputs are obtained from the experimental data, $D: \{x, u\} \in \mathbb{R}^{(n_x + n_u) \times n_d}$.

$$k^* \triangleq \arg\min_k \sqrt{\sum_{i=1}^{n_x} \frac{\sum_{j=1}^{n_d}(x_{i,j} - \hat{x}_{i,j})^2}{\bar{\sigma}_i^2}} \tag{4}$$

2.3.2. Gaussian Process

Gaussian processes (GPs) use observations to determine a probability distribution over functions, following a normal distribution. This characteristic enables GPs to model complex relationships even with limited data. The observations are assumed to contain additive independent identically distributed Gaussian noise with variance $\sigma_{noise}^2 \in \mathbb{R}$. Based on Rasmussen and Williams (2005), the GP model procedure is given as follows:

$$l = GP(v) + \mathcal{N}(0, \sigma_{noise}) \quad \text{with} \quad GP(v) \sim \mathcal{N}(m(v), k(v, v'))$$

$$k(v_i, v_j) = \sigma_f^2 \exp\left(\frac{-(v_i - v_j)^T(v_i - v_j)}{2d^2}\right) \tag{5}$$

$$\varphi^* \triangleq \arg\max_\varphi \left(-\frac{1}{2}L^T\Sigma^{-1}L - \frac{1}{2}\log(\det(\Sigma)) - \frac{n_d}{2}\log(2\pi)\right)$$

Here $l \in \mathbb{R}$ and $v \in \mathbb{R}^{n_v}$ represents the labels and features respectively, while $m: \in \mathbb{R}^{n_v} \rightarrow \mathbb{R}$ and $k: \in \mathbb{R}^{n_v} \times \mathbb{R}^{n_v} \rightarrow \mathbb{R}$ represents the mean function and covariance function, also referred to as the kernel function. The squared exponential kernel is parameterised by the signal variance $\sigma_f^2 \in \mathbb{R}$ and the length-scale $d \in \mathbb{R}$. The relevance of a feature can be described by its individual length-scale parameter using the automatic relevance determination (ARD) form of the kernel, where $d \in \mathbb{R}^{n_v}$. Large d values indicate a near independency of the covariance. These hyperparameters, $\varphi: \{\sigma_{noise}, \sigma_f, d\}$, are optimised by maximising the log-marginal likelihood objective function using the set of labels L and the covariance matrix Σ.

2.4. Open-loop Optimisation
A hybrid model is formed by integrating of the GP model into the metabolic model. This hybrid model can be used to determine the process inputs that maximise the objective function over the specified horizon. This is achieved by solving an open-loop optimal control problem within a hybrid model framework, as illustrated in Eq. (6) (Morabito et al. 2021). The hybrid model uses the mean function, m, of the GP model to estimate the outlet CO_2 fraction $(\widehat{xCO}_{2,out,k})$ at time $k > 0$.

$$\max_{u_0,\ldots,u_{N-1}} J = \left(\frac{n_{HV}+n_{HB}}{n_F+n_P+n_N}\right)^2 + \left(\frac{n_{HV}}{n_{HV}+n_{HB}}\right)^2$$
$$\text{subject to: } \hat{x}_{k+1} = f\left(\hat{x}_k, u_k, \theta, \widehat{xCO}_{2,out,k}\right) \tag{6}$$
$$\text{with } \hat{x}_0 = x(t_0) \quad \text{and} \quad \widehat{xCO}_{2,out,0} = xCO_{2,out}(t_0)$$
$$\widehat{xCO}_{2,out,k} = m(v_{k-1}, v_{k-2}) \qquad \forall \, k > 0$$

3. Results

3.1. Parameter Identification Results
Both experimental data sets were used to identify the kinetic rate parameters. The performance is summarised in Table 1 based on the coefficient of determination (R^2), the normalised root mean square error (NRMSE), and the Spearman's rho (ρ_S) correlation coefficient. The model exhibits a good fit on the experimental data as indicated by the R^2 and ρ_S values approaching unity. However, challenges arise in accurately capturing the residual biomass concentrations, possibly attributed to high measurement errors or unmodelled phenomenon. The HV production in Ex2 is low, possibly due to the limited experimental time, leading to a suboptimal fit. Negative R^2 values indicate that the model does not account for the variability in the data, which is also indicated by the higher NRMSE values for the residual biomass and HV. Close-to-one ρ_S values suggest strong prediction correlations, indicating that the model effectively captures the monotonic relationship for most of the states, requiring only minor model corrections.

3.2. GP Modelling Results
Training, validation, and test sets were generated by randomly shuffling and splitting the experimental data into a ratio of 80:10:10. Possible feature candidates included all the states, inputs, and the outlet CO_2 fraction measurement, at the current and past time steps. The length-scales for each feature, obtained from the ARD kernel, and ρ_S values were used during feature selection to discard features that were considered irrelevant. The final feature set consisted out of $v: \{xCO_{2,out,\ k-1}, \dot{G}_{in,\ k-1}, AG_{k-1}, c_{N,k-2}\}$: the outlet CO_2 fraction, gas flow rate, and agitation speed at time $k-1$ as well as the NH_4Cl concentration at $k-2$. NH_4Cl is essential for growth and serves as a limiting substrate in these experiments. Including it in the model incorporates information on the bacteria's growth state, while the outlet CO_2 fraction provides insight into its production state.

The simulation results of the hybrid model are summarised in Table 2, with Figure 3 illustrating the predictions specific to Ex1. While the hybrid model provided adequate predictions for most of the states, it struggled to capture the dynamics of the residual biomass in Ex1 and the HV concentrations in Ex2, as discussed in section 3.1. A comparable performance is observed between Table 1 and Table 2, with differences attributed to the random shuffling and splitting of the training data.

Table 1: Parameter Identification Result Summary with k values: k_1: 2.08×10^{-4}, k_2: 1.80×10^{-11}, k_3: 2.91×10^{-2}, k_4: 3.94×10^{-4}, k_5: 4.72×10^{-1}, k_6: 4.31×10^{-1}, k_7: 4.24×10^{-4}, k_8: 1.39×10^{-2}

States	Ex1			Ex2		
	R^2	NRMSE	ρ_S	R^2	NRMSE	ρ_S
Fructose (c_F)	1.00	0.02	1.00	0.95	0.08	0.99
Propionic acid (c_P)	0.88	0.10	0.96	0.89	0.13	0.97
NH$_4$Cl (c_N)	0.97	0.06	0.99	0.94	0.09	0.98
Biomass (c_X)	-0.18	0.25	0.71	0.66	0.18	0.97
HB (c_{HB})	0.99	0.04	1.00	0.94	0.08	0.99
HV (c_{HV})	0.96	0.06	0.99	-0.93	0.49	0.84

Table 2: Hybrid Model Simulation Result Summary

States	Ex1			Ex2		
	R^2	NRMSE	ρ_S	R^2	NRMSE	ρ_S
Fructose (c_F)	0.88	0.12	1.00	0.50	0.24	1.00
Propionic acid (c_P)	0.82	0.13	0.73	0.71	0.22	0.89
NH$_4$Cl (c_N)	0.79	0.17	0.93	0.52	0.25	0.95
Biomass (c_X)	0.18	0.20	0.76	0.80	0.13	0.96
HB (c_{HB})	0.88	0.12	1.00	-0.67	0.41	0.89
HV (c_{HV})	0.86	0.10	0.86	0.09	0.35	0.70

3.3. Optimisation Results

The initial conditions of Ex1 were employed in the open-loop optimisation to obtain optimal process inputs that maximises the substrates-to-PHBV conversion yield and the molar ratio of HV in PHBV. Identical propionic acid and NaOH feed profiles were used, assuming that it will be sufficient to maintain the reactor pH.

The optimisation results in Figure 3 indicate an optimal process input profile, starting with a higher initial gas flow rate and maintaining a near constant agitation rate, resulting in a lower initial outlet CO_2 fraction. The constant agitation profile indicates its limited impact on the production as it mainly contributes to reactor homogeneity. Under this optimal input profile, an increase in the molar fraction of HV in the total polymer from 11 % to 14 % is achieved. A compositional change of the polymer to this extent can lead to a reduction of 15 °C in the melting and 0.5 °C glass transition temperature, as reported by Zinn et al. (2003). This comes with a predicted reduction in the total PHBV molar concentration of 9 %.

4. Conclusions and Recommendations

A hybrid model, using a metabolic model and a GP regression model predicting the outlet CO_2 fraction based on process inputs, was developed. This hybrid model accurately predicted the dynamics of most states. An open-loop optimisation indicated a potential increase of 15 % in HV concentration with a slight decrease in total PHBV. Further investigation and improvement of the metabolic model is recommended, especially for the residual biomass and HV dynamics. The optimal input profiles obtained from open-loop optimisations provide a foundation for designing additional experiments that can improve and validate the hybrid model. The accuracly of the model is important for implementing advanced model-based control methods, such as model predictive control (MPC). MPC enables online control and closed-loop optimisation, holding the potential to significantly enhance the economic competitiveness of the PHBV production process.

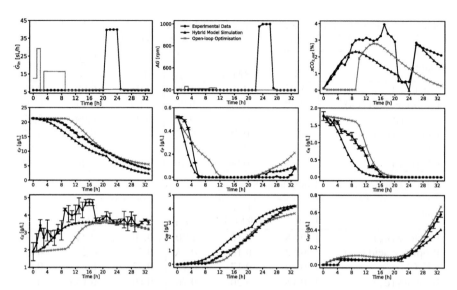

Figure 3: Ex1 Experimental Data, Hybrid Model Simulation, and Optimisation Results

Acknowledgements: The financial support of the Federal State of Saxony-Anhalt within the SmartProSys initiative is greatly acknowledged.

References

J. A. E. Andersson, J. Gillis, G. Horn, J. B. Rawlings, M. Diehl. 2019. "CasADi: a software framework for nonlinear optimization and optimal control". Mathematical Programming Computation, 11(1), 1–36. https://doi.org/10.1007/s12532-018-0139-4

S. Duvigneau, R. Dürr, J. Behrens, A. Kienle. 2021a. "Advanced Kinetic Modeling of Bio-Co-Polymer Poly (3-Hydroxybutyrate-Co-3-Hydroxyvalerate) Production Using Fructose and Propionate as Carbon Sources." Processes 9. doi: https://doi.org/10.3390/pr9081260.

S. Duvigneau, A. Kettner, L. Carius, C. Griehl, R. Findeisen, A. Kienle. 2021b. "Fast , Inexpensive, and Reliable HPLC Method to Determine Monomer Fractions in Poly (3-Hydroxybutyrate-Co-3-Hydroxyvalerate)." Appl. Microbiol. Biotechnol. doi: 10.1007/s00253-021-11265-3.

S. Duvigneau, A. Wilisch-neumann, R. Dürr, A. Kienle. 2023. "Modelling and Experimental Validation of Poly(3- Hydroxybutyrate-co-3-Hydroxyvalerate) Chain Length Distribution," Comput. Aided Chem. Eng.

B. Morabito, J. Pohlodek, J. Matschek, A. Savchenko, L. Carius, R. Findeisen. 2021. "Towards Risk-aware Machine Learning Supported Model Predictive Control and Open-loop Optimization for Repetitive Processes". IFAC-PapersOnLine, 54(6), 321–328. https://doi.org/10.1016/j.ifacol.2021.08.564

J. Pohlodek, B. Morabito, C. Schlauch, P. Zometa, R. Findeisen. 2022. "Flexible development and evaluation of machine-learning-supported optimal control and estimation methods via HILO-MPC". arXiv preprint arXiv:2203.13671. [Online]. Available: http://arxiv.org/abs/2203.13671

C. E. Rasmussen, C. K. I. Williams. 2005. "Gaussian processes for machine learning". MIT Press. Available: http://www.gaussianprocess.org/gpml

M. Zinn, H.-U. Weilenmann, R. Hany, M Schmid and T. Egli. 2003. Tailored Synthesis of Poly([R]-3-Hydroxybutyrate-Co-3-Hydroxyvalerate) (PHB/HV) in Ralstonia eutropha DSM 428. Acta Biotechnol 23 (2–3): 309–16.

Flavio Manenti, Gintaras V. Reklaitis (Eds.), Proceedings of the 34th European Symposium on Computer Aided Process Engineering / 15th International Symposium on Process Systems Engineering (ESCAPE34/PSE24), June 2-6, 2024, Florence, Italy

Mathematical Modelling of a Novel Mineral Carbonation System Based on Biological pH Swing for Atmospheric CO2 Removal

Yukun Zhang,[a] Aidong Yang[a*]

aUniversity of Oxford, Parks Road, Oxford OX1 3PJ, United Kingdom
aidong.yang@eng.ox.ac.uk

Abstract

As an option for removing CO_2 from the atmosphere, this study uses mathematical modelling to explore a novel biological pH swing strategy for mineral carbonation at ambient temperature and pressure. This approach employs microbial processes to modulate pH and then facilitate mineral dissolution and precipitation. The system comprises a sulphur reduction bioreactor and a sulphur oxidation bioreactor utilizing *Desulfovibrio Vulgaris* and *Acidithiobacillus Thiooxidans* respectively. Simulations demonstrate successful pH swing and accelerated CO_2 removal from air, making the sulphur cycle based bioprocess a potential method for cost-efficient atmospheric CO_2 removal.

Keywords: Carbon Capture, Mineral Carbonation, pH Swing, Bacteria, Model.

1. Introduction

The rapid increase in global CO_2 emissions is the primary contributing factor to the current challenges of global climate change. To address this problem, mineral carbonation, one of the representative carbon capture technologies proposed by Seifritz in 1990, is regarded as a promising method for mitigating greenhouse effect (Seifritz, 1990). It involves the chemical reaction between CO_2 and alkaline minerals, such as magnesium, calcium, and iron oxide-based silicates. This reaction results in the formation of carbonate minerals, which can be used to permanently store CO_2. When air is used as the source of CO_2, such a process implements atmospheric CO_2 removal, a measure considered necessary along with carbon capture from point sources to achieve climate goals (Hepburn et al., 2019).

Currently, a significant limitation of many existing mineral carbonation methods is their reliance on high-temperature and high-pressure conditions, which poses practical barriers to large-scale implementation (Olajire, 2013). In response to this constraint, our study explores the potential of biological pH swing, a novel approach designed to achieve more efficient mineral carbonation. Through the adjustment of pH within a biological system, our aim is to enhance the efficiency for both dissolution of alkaline minerals and precipitation of carbonates at ambient temperature and pressure, which could reduce energy consumption and therefore aid the wider adoption of mineral carbonation technology.

2. Method

2.1 Sulphur Cycle Biological pH Swing

In this research, we employ the sulphur cycle biological pH swing strategy, which utilizes metabolic processes of microorganisms to implement the oxidation and reduction of sulphur, and consequently modulates the pH within the process. The idea of using a biological cycle to effect pH swing is based on the proposal by the GGREW project (Lam, 2022). For the alkaline mineral, we have chosen forsterite based on mineral abundance and dissolution rate.

As shown in Figure 1, the overall system is divided into two main components: the reduction bioreactor and the oxidation bioreactor. In the reduction bioreactor, microbes are employed to reduce sulfate ions (SO_4^{2-}) to hydrogen sulfide (H_2S). The generated H_2S is then supplied to the oxidation bioreactor for the regeneration of sulfate. Simultaneously, microbes significantly elevate the pH in the reduction bioreactor, facilitating the reaction between magnesium ions (Mg^{2+}) and atmospheric CO_2, thereby accelerating the precipitation rate of magnesium carbonate ($MgCO_3$).

On the other side, the oxidation bioreactor receives H_2S produced by the reduction bioreactor. Within the oxidation bioreactor, microbes metabolically oxidize H_2S to SO_4^{2-} ions, which supplies energy to sustain microbial activities while significantly reducing the environmental pH. The lowered pH substantially enhances the dissolution rate of forsterite, and then increases the concentration of Mg^{2+} ions in the bioreactor. Mg^{2+} ions and SO_4^{2-} ions produced in the oxidation bioreactor are then transported to the reduction bioreactor, initiating the next cycle of the process.

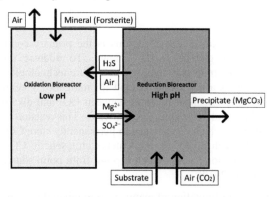

Figure 1. Overall scheme of the sulphur cycle biological pH swing system.

2.2 Modelling of Reduction Bioreactor

The reduction bioreactor serves the purpose of absorbing CO_2 from the air and subsequently precipitate $MgCO_3$. It receives the influent liquid containing Mg^{2+} and SO_4^{2-} ions from the oxidation bioreactor, alongside feed air as the source of CO_2. The optimization for CO_2 removal necessitates an elevated pH environment to foster the formation of $MgCO_3$. To facilitate this, we opt for the utilization of the gram-negative sulfate-reducing bacterium, *Desulfovibrio vulgaris* (*D. vulgaris*), within our model, which enables us to achieve pH swing. Through a series of chemical reactions delineated by the Eq. (1) and (2), both H_2S and $MgCO_3$ are generated (Noguera et al., 1998; Wang, 2013).

$$SO_4{}^{2-} + 5H_2 \rightarrow H_2S + 4H_2O \tag{1}$$

$$Mg^{2+}{}_{(aq)} + CO_3{}^{2-}{}_{(aq)} \rightarrow MgCO_{3(s)} \tag{2}$$

Note that gas-liquid mass transfer exists in the reactor (and the oxidation reactor) was modelled using established correlations for stirred tank reactors. In the following, details of kinetics are presented.

2.2.1 Microbial Kinetics

As shown by Eq. (1), the growth of *D. vulgaris* consumes hydrogen (H_2) (as the energy source) and $SO_4{}^{2-}$ ions to generate H_2S (Badziong et al., 1978). To simulate this process in our model, we use the Monod kinetics equation (Smith et al., 2019):

$$\frac{dS}{dt} = -\frac{\mu_{max,S}*X}{Y_S} * \left(\frac{S}{K_S+S}\right) * \left(\frac{H_{aq}}{K_H+H_{max}}\right) \tag{3}$$

In Eq. (3), $\mu_{max,L}$ (h^{-1}) refers to the maximum growth rate of D. vulgaris, Ys (mg L^{-1} mM^{-1}) refers to the biomass yield of D. vulgaris during sulphate reduction, S (mM) refers to the concentration of sulphate, K_S and K_H (mM) respectively refer to the Monod constants for sulphate and hydrogen, X (mg L^{-1}) refers to the concentration of D. vulgaris, which satisfies the following equation:

$$\frac{dX}{dt} = -Y_S * \frac{dS}{dt} - k_{decay} * X \tag{4}$$

In this equation, k_{decay} (h^{-1}) refers to the decay rate of *D. vulgaris* (Darnajoux et al., 2023).

2.2.2 CO2 Capture and Precipitation

To mitigate the adverse effects of oxygen on the growth and metabolism of *D. vulgaris*, we strategically introduce air into the reduction bioreactor only after the majority of $SO_4{}^{2-}$ ions have been reduced to H_2S. CO_2 introduced with air reacts with Mg^{2+} ions in the solution, leading to the precipitation of $MgCO_3$.

$$\Omega = \frac{a_{Mg^{2+}}*a_{CO_3{}^{2-}}}{K_{MgCO_3}} \tag{5}$$

$$r_{prec} = k * (\Omega - 1)^n \tag{6}$$

We employ Eq. (5) to calculate the saturation index Ω (-), and subsequently use Eq. (6) to calculate the precipitation rate r_{prec} (mol m^{-2} h^{-1}) based on the Ω. Under high-pH conditions, the concentration of carbonate ions in the solution is elevated, resulting in a higher Ω and therefore higher precipitation rate. In these two equations, K_{MgCO_3} (-) refers to the equilibrium constant of $MgCO_3$, a (-) refers to the activities of the participating ions, and k (mol m^{-2} h^{-1}) refers to the specific rate constant.

2.3 Modelling of Oxidation Bioreactor

In this oxidation bioreactor, a relatively low pH environment would be preferred to accelerate the dissolution of forsterite and therefore the release of Mg^{2+} ions. The process of forsterite dissolution can be described by the following chemical Eq. (7):

$$Mg_2SiO_4 + 4H^+ \rightarrow 2Mg^{2+} + Si(OH)_4 \tag{7}$$

$$H_2S + 2O_2 = SO_4^{2-} + 2H^+ \tag{8}$$

Acidithiobacillus thiooxidans (*A. thiooxidans*) is a Gram-negative bacterium known for its ability to facilitate sulphur oxidation and then create an acidic environment, which is shown as Eq. (8). The growth of *A. thiooxidans* is reliant on essential nutrients such as carbon, oxygen and nitrogen, which could be adequately supplied through continuous air feeding into the bioreactor (Waksman and Joffe, 1922).

2.3.1 Forsterite Particle Dissolution

The dissolution of mineral particles is positively related to their surface area. For each mineral particle, the decrease in radius during the process of dissolution would correspondingly decrease their surface area and therefore decrease the overall dissolution rate if no additional mineral added. Eq. (9) is used to estimate the shrinkage of forsterite particles. The rate of change in overall Mg^{2+} ion concentration depends on the dissolution rate $r_{dissolution}$ (m^{-2}h^{-1}), forsterite particle radius $r_{Forsterite}$ (m), and the number of forsterite particles $n_{Forsterite}$ (-).

$$\frac{dMg^{2+}}{dt} = 2 * r_{dissolution} * 4\pi * r_{Forsterite}^2 * n_{Forsterite} \tag{9}$$

To calculate the dissolution rate $r_{dissolution}$ at 298.15 K, the following Eq. (10) and (11) are used (Crundwell, 2014).

$$r_{dissolution} = 2 * 10^{-7} * 10^{-0.5 * pH} \quad if \ pH \leq 6 \tag{10}$$

$$r_{dissolution} = 6.25 * 10^{-9} * 10^{-0.25 * pH} \quad if \ pH > 6 \tag{11}$$

2.3.2 Microbial Kinetics

We adopted the modified Monod-Gompertz kinetic model to simulate the proliferation of *A. thiooxidans* under the environment with varying dissolved oxygen (DO) (Namgung and Song, 2015).

$$R_{bio} = \mu_{max} * V_L * \frac{X}{Y_X} * \gamma_{bio} \tag{12}$$

Eq. (12) shows the method to calculate biodegradation rate R_{bio} (mg/min), where μ_{max} (min^{-1}) is the maximum specific growth rate, Y_X (mg-dry weight/mg-substrate) is the yield coefficient of microorganisms, V_L (litre) is the effective liquid volume of the bioreactor, X (mg-dry weight/L) is the microbial density in the liquid phase, and γ_{bio} (-) is biomass growth rate, which can be calculated by the following Eq. (13) (Namgung and Song, 2015).

$$\gamma_{bio} = \frac{C_{LS}}{K_S + C_{LS}} * \exp[-\exp(\frac{K_O - C_{LO}}{K_O/2})] \tag{13}$$

In this equation, K_S (mg/L) refers to the half saturation constant of H$_2$S, C_{LS} and C_{LO} (mg/L) correspondingly refer to the concentration of H$_2$S and DO.

3. Results and Discussion

The simulations for both the reduction bioreactor and the oxidation bioreactor were completed by using the ode15s solver in MATLAB, and the pH was estimated according to the charge balance in each bioreactor. In both reactors, the temperature was maintained at 25 °C and the pressure were set to1 atm.

3.1 Reduction Bioreactor

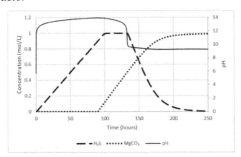

Figure 2. Trends for pH and concentrations of H_2S and $MgCO_3$ in reduction bioreactor.

As shown in Figure 2, within the initial 100 hours, *D. vulgaris* effectively elevated the pH by converting SO_4^{2-} ions to H_2S; around the 90-hour mark, air (containing CO_2) was introduced when the concentration of SO_4^{2-} ions reached a relatively low level, therefore $MgCO_3$ precipitate started to be generated. This precipitation process led to the consumption of Mg^{2+} ions and a subsequent decrease in the overall pH. At about 130 hours, we can observe a decreasing trend for H_2S concentration because the decrease in pH enabled the dissolved H_2S to be transferred to the gaseous phase; the released H_2S gas would be mixed with air and then supplied to the oxidation bioreactor.

3.2 Oxidation Bioreactor

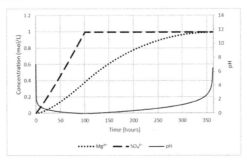

Figure 3. Trends for pH and concentrations of Mg^{2+} ions and SO_4^{2-} ions in oxidation bioreactor.

For the oxidation bioreactor, the concentration and duration of supplied H_2S gas were both set according to the effluent gas of reduction bioreactor. Additionally, gas-liquid mass transfer of H_2S was adjusted through setting agitation such that H_2S concentration in the effluent gas is minimized to avoid harmful leakage. As shown in Figure 3, H_2S gas was supplied by the reduction bioreactor and oxidized by *A. thiooxidans* for the first 100 hours; the rise in concentration of SO_4^{2-} ions significantly lowered the overall pH, thereby expediting the dissolution of forsterite. Until approximately 360 hours, the pH of solution returned to a neutral state, and Mg^{2+} ions reached their maximum concentration while ensuring a reasonable cycle length and operational efficiency.

3.3 Predicted Time Schedule of the Entire Cycle

Based on the simulation results of both reactors, Figure 4 summarises a feasible time schedule of the operation of the entire cycle over 500 hours.

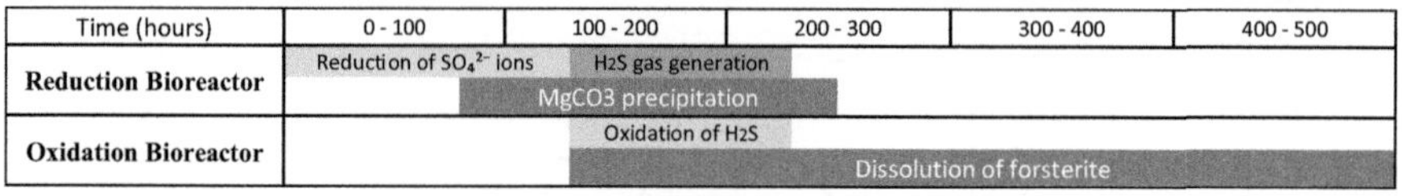

Time (hours)	0 - 100	100 - 200	200 - 300	300 - 400	400 - 500
Reduction Bioreactor	Reduction of SO_4^{2-} ions	H2S gas generation			
		MgCO3 precipitation			
Oxidation Bioreactor		Oxidation of H2S			
		Dissolution of forsterite			

Figure 4. Demonstration of operational cycle for both bioreactors.

4. Conclusions

Based on our simulation results for the reduction bioreactor and the oxidation bioreactor, the implementation of the sulphur cycle pH swing using *A. thiooxidans* and *D. vulgaris* appears to be feasible. This system demonstrates the capability to capture atmospheric CO_2 under ambient conditions. Building on this proof-of-concept modelling study, future work will address experimental validation and system optimisation to reduce energy consumption and operational cycle duration in order to achieve higher efficiencies.

References

W. Badziong, R.K. Thauer, J.G.Zeikus, 1978, Isolation and characterization of Desulfovibrio growing on hydrogen plus sulfate as the sole energy source. Archives of Microbiology 116, 41-49.

F.K. Crundwell, 2014, The mechanism of dissolution of forsterite, olivine and minerals of the orthosilicate group. Hydrometallurgy 150, 68-82.

R. Darnajoux, K. Inomura, X. Zhang, 2023, A diazotrophy-ammoniotrophy dual growth model for the sulfate reducing bacterium Desulfovibrio vulgaris var. Hildenborough. Computational and Structural Biotechnology Journal 21, 3136-3148.

C. Hepburn, E. Adlen, J. Beddington, E.A. Carter, S. Fuss, N. Mac Dowell, J.C. Minx, P. Smith, C.K. Williams, 2019, The technological and economic prospects for CO(2) utilization and removal. Nature 575, 87-97.

P. Lam, 2022. Microbial Enhancement of Alkalinity Release with Mine Tailing. In: GGREW project presentation, UKRI GGR Programme closing event, 10 May 2022, London.

H.K. Namgung, J. Song, 2015, The effect of oxygen supply on the dual growth kinetics of Acidithiobacillus thiooxidans under acidic conditions for biogas desulfurization. Int J Environ Res Public Health 12, 1368-1386.

D.R. Noguera, G.A. Brusseau, B.E. Rittmann, D.A. Stahl, 1998, A unified model describing the role of hydrogen in the growth of desulfovibrio vulgaris under different environmental conditions. Biotechnol Bioeng 59, 732-746.

A.A. Olajire, 2013, A review of mineral carbonation technology in sequestration of CO2. Journal of Petroleum Science and Engineering 109, 364-392.

W. Seifritz, 1990, CO2 disposal by means of silicates. Nature 345, 486-486.

N.W. Smith, P.R. Shorten, E. Altermann, N.C. Roy, W.C. McNabb, 2019, A Mathematical Model for the Hydrogenotrophic Metabolism of Sulphate-Reducing Bacteria. Front Microbiol 10, 1652.

S.A. Waksman, J.S. Joffe, 1922, Microorganisms Concerned in the Oxidation of Sulfur in the Soil: II. Thiobacillus Thiooxidans, a New Sulfur-oxidizing Organism Isolated from the Soil. J Bacteriol 7, 239-256.

F. Wang, 2013, Silicate Mineral Dissolution and Associated Carbonate Precipitation at Conditions Relevant to Geologic Carbon Sequestration. Washington University in St. Louis.

Flavio Manenti, Gintaras V. Reklaitis (Eds.), Proceedings of the 34th European Symposium on Computer Aided Process Engineering / 15th International Symposium on Process Systems Engineering (ESCAPE34/PSE24), June 2-6, 2024, Florence, Italy

Dynamic photo-mechanistic modelling of biomass growth and optical density for the cyanobacterium *Synechococcus* sp. PCC 11901

Bovinille Anye Cho,[a*] José Ángel Moreno-Cabezuelo,[b] Lauren A. Mills,[b] Antonio Del Rio-Chanona,[c] David J. Lea-Smith,[b] Dongda Zhang,[a]

[a]*The University of Manchester, Engineering Building A, Manchester, M13 9PL, UK*
[b]*University of East Anglia, Norwich Research Park, Norwich, NR4 7TJ, UK*
[c]*Imperial College London, South Kensington Campus, London, SW7 2AZ, UK*
*email of the corresponding author: bovinille.anyecho@manchester.ac.uk

Abstract

Fast-growing cyanobacterial species are potential chassis for converting inorganic carbon into biomass and biomolecules for industrial, medical, and herbicidal applications. However, unavailable mechanistic interpretations for the differing bioconversion rates among isolated strains with similar metabolic pathways and transport systems hinders the biotechnological exploitation.

Therefore, this study investigates two strains: *Synechococcus* sp. PCC 11901, the fastest growing cyanobacterium ever isolated, and *Synechocystis* sp. PCC 6803, the benchmark cyanobacterial strain, under a wide range of operational light intensities from 300 – 900 μmol photons m^{-2} s^{-1}. This study reports three original contributions.

Firstly, strain specific photo-mechanistic influences were embedded into dynamic biomass and optical density (OD750nm) models, too sophisticated to be previously achieved in OD750nm. Secondly, bootstrapping parameter estimation methodology with 3-fold cross validations was utilised to simultaneously identify optimal model parameters and associated confidence intervals. This enabled probabilistic simulations and the thorough validation against unseen experimental datasets. For both species, the simulated errors averaged to less than 19 %, thus demonstrating the model reliability for predicting such highly nonlinear bioprocess dynamics. Thirdly, recounted mechanistic interpretations for the over two-folds faster growth of *Synechococcus* sp. PCC 11901 compared to *Synechocystis* sp. PCC 6803 despite the latter's high light utilisation efficiency.

Hence, these models and findings will benefit strain specific photobioreactor design and upscaling of the future cyanobacterial biotechnology applications to produce biomass and biochemicals of industrial importance.

Keywords: Cyanobacterial photobiotechnology, *Synechococcus* sp. PCC 11901, *Synechocystis* sp. PCC 6803, Biomass and Optical density modelling, Bootstraping parameter estimation.

1. Introduction

Cyanobacteria utilises light energy, minimal nutrients, and potentially low-cost waste streams like flue gases (e.g., 4-14 vol% CO_2 from power plants [1]), in technical equipment not requiring arable land, to convert inorganic carbon into biomass and biomolecules for industrial, nutritional, medical, and herbicidal applications [2]. However, commercial viability is dependent on the overall cyanobacterial productivity and product titer being comparable to alternative industrially viable heterotrophic microorganisms. For example, *Escherichia coli* and *Saccharomyces cerevisiae* with doubling times of 20 and 90 minutes, respectively [3]. Therefore, significant research efforts have been invested in isolating faster growing cyanobacterial species featuring *Synechocystis* sp. PCC 6803 (PCC 6803), *Synechococcus elongatus* PCC 7942, *Synechococcus* sp. PCC 7002, *Synechococcus elongatus* UTEX 2973, and *Synechococcus* sp. PCC 11901 (PCC 11901) with the respective doubling times of 6.6 hours, 4.1 hours, 4.0 hours, 2.1 hours, and 2.0 hours [2–4]. PCC 11901 stands out as fastest growing, accumulating biomass concentrations of up to 33 g DCW L^{-1} [4] and therefore most promising species for future biotechnology applications. However, both PCC 11901 and PCC 6803 were shown in the literature [3] to have very similar metabolic pathways and transport systems, contradicting their differing doubling times. Whilst in-depth mechanistic analysis utilising estimated biokinetic model parameters could provide additional insights into the physical, biological, chemical, and interacting aspects, such analysis has not been conducted to the best of our knowledge. Literature approaches either (i) directly compared the obtained final optical densities and/or biomass concentrations [4], (ii) compared experimentally measured oxygen evolution and photoinhibition rates [3], and/or (iii) curve fit for the maximum specific growth rates with the experimentally generated datasets of optical densities and/or biomass concentrations [4]. Therefore, resulting doubling times are grossly estimated without accounting for the impact of (i) process equipment (e.g., photobioreactor path length), (ii) operation (e.g., light intensity and light attenuation), and (iii) growth dynamics (e.g., photolimitation, photosaturation and photoinhibition). Excluding (i) to (iii) makes it challenging to directly compare PCC 11901 to the industrially viable heterotrophic microorganisms whereas embedding (i) to (iii) in dynamic cyanobacterial models has been limited to biomass growth pending optical density models.   Therefore, these limitations were tackled in this study by embedding the impacts of light intensity, light attenuation, photolimitation, photosaturation and photoinhibition mechanisms in dynamic biomass growth and optical density models. The central aim was to reliably assess the growth dynamics and scalability potential of two cyanobacterial species: PCC 11901 and PCC 6803. In addition, providing in-depth mechanistic discussions to support experimental results and identifying the optimal light intensities for cultivation and biotechnological scalabilities of the strains.

2. Methodology

2.1. Photobioreactor operation and analytical techniques
The strains were cultured in a MC-1000 multicultivator bioreactor with an internal diameter of 27 mm, aerated with air/5% CO_2 for inorganic carbon supply and bioreactor mixing, maintained at a temperature of 38 °C and illuminated over 300 - 900 µmol photons m^{-2} s^{-1}. The protocol for photobioreactor operation, analytical equipment and methods for quantifying optical density and biomass concentration has been detailed in our work [2], thus omitted herein.

2.2. Mechanistic modelling of biomass concentration
The constructed dynamic models were to embed the sophisticated influences of (i) incident light intensity, (ii) light attenuation, and (iii) photomechanisms (i.e., photolimitation, photosaturation, and photoinhibition) on the various growth phases of the strains. The lag phase was not pronounced due to the starter cultures being adapted to

the operational light intensity [2], and the remainder phases (namely, primary growth, secondary growth, and stationary phases) showed differing magnitude of light related influences among the cyanobacterial strains. As per PCC 11901's biomass modelling, the light related influences are captured with the first term of Eq. (1) meanwhile the light independent endogenous cellular activities were captured by the second term. The light attenuation (Eq. (2)) and all photomechanisms were noticeably embedded in Eq. (1) as supported by the statistically significant student's t-test (P<0.05) over all the state trajectories. Conversely, PCC 6083's showed statistical significance for only two to three discrete time points on each growth trajectory, thus Eq. (1) was modified to Eq. (3), eliminating light attenuation and photoinhibition.

$$\frac{dX}{dt} = \frac{u_m}{40} \cdot \sum_{n=1}^{19} \left(\frac{I_0}{I_0 + k_s + \frac{I_0^2}{k_i}} + \frac{2 \cdot I_{\frac{n \cdot L}{20}}}{I_{\frac{n \cdot L}{20}} + k_s + \frac{I_{\frac{n \cdot L}{20}}^2}{k_i}} + \frac{I_L}{I_L + k_s + \frac{I_L^2}{k_i}} \right) \cdot X - \mu_d \cdot X^2 \quad (1)$$

$$I_{\frac{n \cdot L}{20}} = I_0 \cdot \exp\left[-(\tau \cdot X + \beta) \cdot \frac{n \cdot L}{20} \right] \quad (2)$$

$$\frac{dX}{dt} = u_m \cdot \frac{I_0}{I_0 + K_s} \cdot X - \mu_d \cdot X^2 \quad (3)$$

where X is the biomass concentration (g L^{-1}), u_m is the maximum specific growth rate (h^{-1}), μ_d is the decay growth rate (h^{-1}), I_0 is the incident light intensity (μmol photons m^{-2} s^{-1}), L is the light path length (mm), k_s, k_i, β and τ are the light saturation (μmol photons m^{-2} s^{-1}), light inhibition (μmol photons m^{-2} s^{-1}), light scattering (mm^{-1}) and light attenuation (mm^2 g^{-1}) coefficients respectively.

2.3. Mechanistic modelling of optical density

The literatures [3,4] presented optical density profiles exhibiting sigmoidal shapes for the *Synechococcus* and *Synechocystis* strains. These sigmoidal shapes are typical of bioprocesses experiencing the three (namely, primary growth, secondary growth, and stationary phases) phases modelled herein. Therefore, the model structures for biomass concentration (i.e., Eq. (1) to (3)) and optical density were assumed to be similar, thus the variable OD_{750} replaces X for the optical density modelling. However, only pigment dominated light absorption influences captured with Eq. (4) were incorporated in the optical density model. As caveat, τ in Eq. (4) has units (mm^{-1}) unlike (mm^2 g^{-1}) in Eq. (2).

$$I_{\frac{n \cdot L}{20}} = I_0 \cdot \exp\left[-(\tau \cdot OD_{750}) \cdot \frac{n \cdot L}{20} \right] \quad (4)$$

where OD_{750} is the optical density at a wavelength of 750 nm (dimensionless).

2.4. Dynamic model parameter estimation

To estimate all model parameters, a weighted non-linear least-square regression problem was formulated. The differential equations were numerically discretised with orthogonal collocation over finite elements in time and transformed into a series of non-linear algebraic equations. These were solved with an interior point-based solver (i.e., IPOPT version 3.11.1) through an open-source interface Pyomo within the Python version 3.9 programming environment [2].

3. Results

3.1. Bootstrapping dynamic parameter estimation results

In addition to identifying all model parameters, the associated confidence intervals were simultaneously estimated with a bootstrapping technique with 3-folds validations. Table 1 shows these optimal parameters to be comparable to those of previous studies [2,5,6], thereby validating the reliability of the presented results. Overall fitting errors (i.e., percentage relative errors (%RE)) were of less than 19.0 %, as presented for PCC 11901's biomass model in Figure 1, thus capturing the complex nonlinear bioprocess behaviour. Similar fittings were observed for the OD and PCC 6083'models, thus not shown herein.

Table 1: Results of bootstrapping dynamic parameter estimation for the biomass and optical density (OD$_{750nm}$) models of the two cyanobacterial strains. Model parameter estimates denote the mean of n=3 bootstrapping partitions ±standard deviations as the parameter confidence intervals. Mean values were comparable to the literature [2,5,6] reported values.

Model parameter	OD$_{750}$ model	Biomass model
PCC 11901		
u_m (h^{-1})	$1.99\times 10^{-1} \pm 2.86\times10^{-3}$	$1.99\times 10^{-1} \pm 5.39\times10^{-4}$
μ_d (h^{-1})	$6.15\times 10^{-4} \pm 8.94\times10^{-6}$	$2.96\times 10^{-3} \pm 2.64\times10^{-4}$
k_s (µmol photons m^{-2} s^{-1})	150.0 ± 4.08	156.67 ± 6.24
k_i (µmol photons m^{-2} s^{-1})	3523.33 ± 24.94	3522.33 ± 23.61
τ (mm^2 g^{-1})	48.57 ± 1.03	208.14 ± 6.62
β (mm^{-1})	na	$3.16\times 10^{-7}\pm 3.07\times10^{-8}$
PCC 6803		
u_m (h^{-1})	$7.9\times 10^{-2} \pm 2.65\times10^{-3}$	$7.9\times 10^{-2} \pm 2.65\times10^{-3}$
μ_d (h^{-1})	$1.57\times 10^{-2} \pm 3.52\times10^{-4}$	$6.54\times 10^{-2} \pm 1.46\times10^{-3}$
K_s (µmol photons m^{-2} s^{-1})	72.84 ± 12.74	72.84 ± 12.74

na: not included in model structure

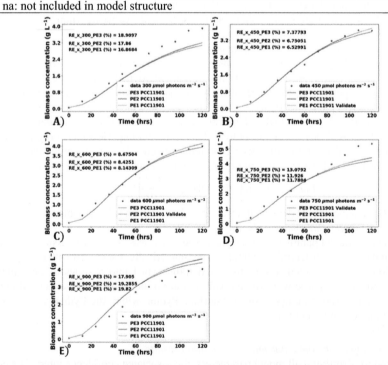

Figure 1: Biomass model fitting results for PCC 11901 at light intensities (µmol photons m^{-2} s^{-1}): (A) 300, (B) 450, (C) 600, (D) 750, (E) 900. The percentage relative error (%RE) of each fitting is as indicated.

3.2. Probabilistic model prediction validations

The performances of the biomass and optical density (OD_{750nm}) models for predicting unseen datasets were deemed necessary to assess their suitability for long-term bioprocess simulation, optimisation, and control. Figure 2 shows the mean model predictions to represent the experimental data points, thereby reliably predicting the complex nonlinear behaviours. Results for optical density (OD_{750nm}) were not presented due to similar trajectories. The uncertainty bands in Figure 2 are observed to grow (i.e., increase of bandwidth size) with time, indicating the models to be responsive to changes of these parameters. However, these parameter changes did not induce large uncertainty bands on the outputs, they are therefore safe for re-estimation during online dynamic bioprocess control [7].

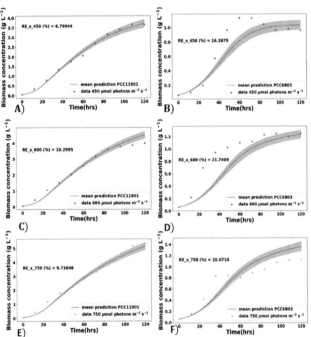

Figure 2: Prediction of biomass models under uncertainty: (A), (C) and (E) for PCC 11901, and (B), (D) and (F) for PCC 6803, at light intensities (μmol photons m^{-2} s^{-1}): 450, 600, and 750 which were unseen datasets during the bootstrapping parameter estimation. The percentage relative error (%RE) of each fitting is as indicated in grey.

3.3. Comparison of the two cyanobacteria strains

Growth characteristics of the two strains in Table 1 showed the maximum specific growth rate of PCC 91101 to be over two-fold higher than that of PCC 6803. The faster growth of PCC 11901 agrees with previous studies [3,4] confirming its superior growth capabilities. PCC 6803's light saturation coefficient was about two-fold lower than that of PCC 11901, indicating superior light affinity and utilisation efficiency. This unexpected observation was deciphered by analysing the maximum specific growth and decay rates in Table 1, showing similar order of magnitudes for PCC 6083 but over 67-fold lower for PCC 11901. This implies that PCC 11901 was experiencing unbalanced growth, the first time of Eq. (1) dominating *(i.e., $u_m \gg \mu_d$)*, whereas that of PCC 6803 was balanced *(i.e., $u_m \sim \mu_d$),* justifying PCC 11901's higher growth *(i.e., $u_{m\_PC11901}$ >* u_{m_PC6803}*)* in Table 1.

4. Conclusion

In this paper, mechanistic models capable of simulating the sophisticated influences of (i) incident light intensity, (ii) light attenuation, and (iii) photomechanisms (i.e., photolimitation, photosaturation, and photoinhibition) on two cyanobacteria strains, namely PCC 11901 and PCC 6083, were investigated for biomass growth and Optical density (OD_{750nm}) accumulation. Dynamic OD_{750nm} models embedding (i) to (iii) were previously unavailable, thus not literature validated. Considerable agreements for biomass models were demonstrated, and both OD_{750nm} and biomass model predictions were within 19 % of simulation error for both strains. PCC 11901's optimal cultivation light intensity was estimated at 735.0 μmol photons m^{-2} s^{-1} whereas that of PCC 6803 was unavailable due to light saturated growth beyond 300 μmol photons m^{-2} s^{-1}. Therefore, fluorometry measurements are recommended in future for confirming the light-stressed photosynthetic activities of PCC 6803 within the 300 to 900 μmol photons m^{-2} s^{-1} range.

5. References

[1]   Collotta M, Champagne P, Mabee W, Tomasoni G. Wastewater and waste CO2 for sustainable biofuels from microalgae. Algal Res 2018;29:12–21. https://doi.org/10.1016/j.algal.2017.11.013.

[2]   Anye Cho B, Moreno-Cabezuelo JÁ, Mills LA, del Río Chanona EA, Lea-Smith DJ, Zhang D. Integrated experimental and photo-mechanistic modelling of biomass and optical density production of fast versus slow growing model cyanobacteria. Algal Res 2023;70. https://doi.org/10.1016/j.algal.2023.102997.

[3]   Mills LA, Moreno-Cabezuelo JÁ, Włodarczyk A, Victoria AJ, Mejías R, Nenninger A, et al. Development of a Biotechnology Platform for the Fast-Growing Cyanobacterium Synechococcus sp. PCC 11901. Biomolecules 2022;12:872. https://doi.org/10.3390/biom12070872.

[4]   Włodarczyk A, Selão TT, Norling B, Nixon PJ. Newly discovered Synechococcus sp. PCC 11901 is a robust cyanobacterial strain for high biomass production. Commun Biol 2020;3. https://doi.org/10.1038/s42003-020-0910-8.

[5]   Balskus EP, Walsh CT. The Genetic and Molecular Basis for Sunscreen Biosynthesis in Cyanobacteria. Science (1979) 2010;329:1653–6. https://doi.org/10.1126/science.1193637.

[6]   Lindberg P, Park S, Melis A. Engineering a platform for photosynthetic isoprene production in cyanobacteria, using Synechocystis as the model organism. Metab Eng 2010;12:70–9. https://doi.org/10.1016/j.ymben.2009.10.001.

[7]   Anye Cho B, Ross BS, du Toit JP, Pott RWMC, del Río Chanona EA, Zhang D. Dynamic modelling of Rhodopseudomonas palustris biohydrogen production: Perturbation analysis and photobioreactor upscaling. Int J Hydrogen Energy 2021;46:36696–708. https://doi.org/10.1016/j.ijhydene.2021.08.162.

Flavio Manenti, Gintaras V. Reklaitis (Eds.), Proceedings of the 34th European Symposium on Computer Aided Process Engineering / 15th International Symposium on Process Systems Engineering (ESCAPE34/PSE24), June 2-6, 2024, Florence, Italy

Adjustable Robust Optimization with Mixed-Integer Recourse for the Synthesis of Continuous Rufinamide Manufacturing Process

Taoyu Qiu,[a] Wenhui Yang,[b] Zhihong Yuan[b*]

[a]*Tanwei College, Tsinghua University, Beijing, 100084,China*
[b]*The State Key Laboratory of Chemical Engineering, Department of Chemical Engineering, Tsinghua University, Beijing, 100084, China*
zhihongyuan@mail.tsinghua.edu.cn

Abstract

Rufinamide, a triazole derivative targeting the cerebral sodium ion channel, provides effective treatment for seizure disorders and has a profitable market prospect. Traditional batch synthesis of rufinamide is subjected to limitations such as depressed yields, complicated procedures, excessive operational expenditure, and high environmental costs. Therefore, a comprehensive scheme for the identification of the best synthesis route and the optimal process design with a systematic evaluation of uncertain factors can accelerate the development and deployment of the pursued advanced manufacturing. In this work, more than 500 possible synthetic routes for continuous rufinamide manufacturing were collected from the existing literature pool and data sources; each route contains a set of design parameters to represent its gains and prices when included in the whole multi-stage synthesis/purification process. Multiple types of uncertainty, such as crucial conversion rate, production goal, running time, and energy consumption, were considered through the two-stage adjustable robust optimization approach represented by the mixed-integer nonlinear programming (MINLP) model. Note that the involved reactions have happened in the flow micro-reactors, which introduces mixed-integer recourse to the robust optimization model. Hence, a nested column-and-constraint generation algorithm was tailored to solve the MINLP model efficiently. The first stage identified the optimal synthetic route, while the optimal number of the flow micro-reactors and the operation conditions were determined in the second stage. The price of the robustness of the adjustable decisions on optimal synthesis of the continuous manufacturing process was finally examined.

Keywords: Adjustable robust optimization, rufinamide, process synthesis, MINLP, mixed-integer recourse

1. Introduction

Computer-aided pharmaceutical process synthesis plays an increasingly decisive role in the disruptive manufacturing of pharmaceutical molecules because it guides the optimal design for molecular construction and topological structure of manufacturing using efficient computational methods (Westerberg, 2004). In recent research, it usually helps engineers optimize the design toward the goal of long-term effectiveness, reduction of overall energy consumption, and control of production cost and hazard (Jørgensen et al., 2019), which typically involves optimization of mixed-integer nonlinear programs (MINLP) based on manufacturing superstructure containing a set of design parameters to represent gains and prices of certain decisions. However, reducing the costs of real-world plants is challenging due to ubiquitous uncertain parameters within the model. Moreover, there is no further investigation into the manufacturing process optimization and design method under uncertainty.

Noticeably, uncertain parameters in models will impede the search for the optimal design and jeopardize the interpretability of optimal solutions to these models. In order to deal with widespread uncertainties, robust optimization (RO) is widely adopted for its inherent simplicity in linear problems, albeit prone to high conservatism under high-dimensional uncertainties. For a better trade-off between conservatism and system robustness, adjustable robust optimization (ARO) is developed by incorporating recourse decision variables, thus avoiding making all decisions all at once (Ben-Tal et al., 2004). However, ARO models are inclined to be computationally intractable faced with nonlinearity and mixed-integer variables. Therefore, it is preferred to formulate a two-stage ARO for complex decision-making tasks, which off-the-shelf solvers can solve by applying strategies, such as the Benders-dual cutting plane algorithm and the column-and-constraint generation (CCG) algorithm (Shi and You, 2016), which both derive equivalent solvable programs for the nested min-max inner subproblem of two-stage ARO (Zeng and Zhao, 2013). However, these methods cannot be directly incorporated into a wide range of superstructure-based modeling of continuous manufacturing processes including number-up amplification of tubular micro-reactors, the presence of which adds to the second stage of ARO recourse variables taking values of positive integer. Instead of applying linear approximation or tolerating the dual gap in the second-stage optimization, we resolve to find an exact algorithm that handles integer variables as recourse variables.

In our work, a tailored two-stage ARO algorithm with mixed-integer recourse is proposed to optimize the process design and solve the problem of identifying the best synthesis route of rufinamide under multiple uncertainties.

2. Methodology

2.1. Synthesis Process of Rufinamide

Rufinamide is a new class of antiepileptic drugs that works by regulating sodium ion channels in the people's brain voltage gate. It can assist in treating a kind of typical epilepsy, Lennox-Gastaut Syndrome (Diab and Gerogiorgis, 2018). The drug Banzel, containing rufinamide as the API, is currently priced at ~ US \$3.75 / mg tablet and ~ US \$3.90 / mL liquid suspension according to its seller. The traditional synthesis process of rufinamide is a batch process with disadvantages such as low yield, complicated procedure, high labor cost, and poor environmental benefit. In recent years, the synthesis routes of rufinamide have been improved and enriched continuously with innovative development of solvent-free synthesis processes and high-efficacy catalysts. However, each production route at different synthesis stages has its advantages and disadvantages. Clearly, it is of great significance to carefully make a comparison of rufinamide synthesis processes and identify optimal production routes.

The synthesis of rufinamide can be roughly divided into three stages (Borukhova et al., 2016): the halogenation reaction of 2,6-difluorobenzyl alcohol, diazotization, and the Huisgen cyclo-addition reaction at last to produce precursors. The superstructure of continuous synthesis of rufinamide shown in Fig. 1 consists of a total of 507 possible process synthesis routes with corresponding parameters attained from the literature pool.

2.2. Deterministic Model of Synthesis Process

Based on the superstructure model, the following assumptions are made in our model:

Adjustable Robust Optimization with Mixed-Integer Recourse for the
Synthesis of Continuous Rufinamide Manufacturing Process

2523

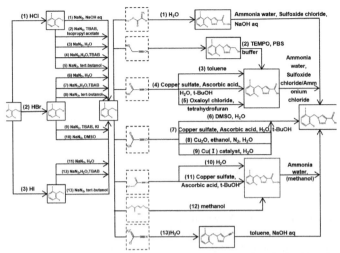

Figure 1 Superstructure of continuous rufinamide synthesis (labeled with subscripts i,j,k) a) Platform chemicals, solvents, and catalysts required in synthesis pathways are purchased at a steady price level all year round with no shipping and storage costs, b) Given the fixed plant implementation and standardized operating schedule, any identified route permitted in the superstructure can be adjusted to meet uncertain demands of production; c) Operation expenses and utility costs are proportionate to a linear function of volumetric scale and energy consumption for preheating material from surrounding temperature.

The following deterministic mathematical model is established. The objective function represented by Eq. (1) is composed of material cost (the first term), capital expenditure (the second term), and operating expenditure (the third term). Eq. (2) defines the continuous variable L as the space velocity of each reaction, i.e. amount of material processed by one single tubular reactor in unit process time. Eq. (3) is the constraint on production goal. Eq. (4) represents the material balance between these three stages. To ensure that the annual production reaches the target within the upper bound of the specified time, the following constraints, Eq. (5) are enforced. Eq. (7) relates binary variables with continuous decision variables via big-M constraint. Eq. (8) defines the indices of this model in which I=3, J=13, K=13.

$$\min_{X_s, N_s, Y_s} \sum_s \left(\frac{c_s X_s}{M_{ruf}} + \varepsilon \frac{CE_0 N_s V_s}{CP_0} + \xi \tau_s (T_s - T_0) N_s L_s + \theta (1 - \eta) N_s L_s V_s \right) \tag{1}$$

$$\text{s.t. } N_s L_s SC_s - X_s M_{ruf} = 0, \forall s \tag{2}$$

$$\sum_{k=1}^{K} X_k M_{ruf} - PT \geq 0 \tag{3}$$

$$\sum_{i=1}^{I} X_0 Y_i r_i - \sum_{i=1}^{I} X_i = \sum_{i=1}^{I} X_i \sum_{j=1}^{J} Y_j r_j - \sum_{j=1}^{J} X_j = \sum_{j=1}^{J} X_j \sum_{k=1}^{k} Y_k r_k - \sum_{k=1}^{K} X_k = 0 \tag{4}$$

$$\max_{i,j,k}\left\{\sum_{i=1}^{I}L_i\tau_i,\sum_{j=1}^{J}L_j\tau_j,\sum_{k=1}^{K}L_k\tau_k,\right\}\leq\tau^U \tag{5}$$

$$\sum_{i=1}^{I}Y_i=1,\sum_{j=1}^{J}Y_j=1,\sum_{k=1}^{K}Y_k=1 \tag{6}$$

$$X_s-MY_s\leq 0,\forall s \tag{7}$$

$$i\in\{1,2,\cdots,I\},j\in\{1,2,\cdots,J\},k\in\{1,2,\cdots,K\},s=i\cup j\cup z \tag{8}$$

2.3 The Uncertainty Set

Global sensitivity analysis (GSA) was performed to recognize and specify the uncertain parameters that are influential to the optimal superstructure design. For instance, results of GSA show that alteration of utility cost coefficient in the nominal deterministic model significantly affects route selection and the objective, where a critical turning point at 0.48 is recognized. Based on our current knowledge of potentially commercialized procedures, the nominal value is predetermined to be 0.40 with a permissible deviation up to 0.2. Besides, Parameter-level uncertainties, including the market demand, the nominal value set at 100 kg and maximum deviation 50 kg) and running time, are modeled.

2.4 ARO Formulation and Solution Strategy

Given the uncertainty set presented in 3.1, we construct ARO to obtain a robust optimal design by distinguishing "here-and-now" variables which are fixed before the realization of uncertainty, and "wait-and-see" variables to be determined after the revelation of uncertainty, hence reformulating a MIP master problem (MP) responsible for the update of superstructure topology and an inner-stage subproblem (SP) for recourse. Here we consider the binary variables aiming at route selection from the superstructure as non-adjustable "here-and-now" variables. The master problem (MP) is responsible for the topology, while in the subproblem (SP), constraints on the other decision variables, including integer variables are incorporated.

It should be noticed that, with the presence of an integer decision variable in the subproblem, the inner-stage problem is again MINLP. Here, we expand the two-stage ARO framework into a tri-level iterative bounding algorithm in pursuit of exact solution for MIP recourse, where a local search for best-so-far integer recourse must be conducted whenever we optimize SP. The mathematical interpretation of bi-level reformed SP is shown below, where z denotes a bounded integer recourse variable, x denotes continuous recourse variables with p dimensions, and u denotes uncertain variables.

$$(\text{SP-Outer})\max_u\mu\ \text{s.t.}\ \mu\leq Az^n+Dx^n,\forall 1\leq n\leq N_S \tag{9}$$

$$E^T\pi^n\leq d^T,\forall 1\leq n\leq N_S,\ x^n\left(d^T-E^T\pi^n\right)=0,\forall 1\leq n\leq N_S \tag{10}$$

$$Ex^n+Ru\geq f-Gz^n,\forall 1\leq n\leq N_S,\ \pi^n\left(Ex^n-f+Ru+Gz^n\right)=0,\forall 1\leq n\leq N_S \tag{11}$$

$$z^n \in \left\{N^n\right\}_{n=1}^{N_S}, u \in \left\{u_0 - \delta_u \Delta u, u_0 + \delta_u \Delta u\right\}, x \in \Re^p \tag{12}$$

The inner-stage optimization of SP follows the procedure:
a) Initialize the lower bound (LB) and the upper bound (UB), starting from Ns=1.
b) Solve (SP-Outer) as an LP with respect to obtain the optimal solution, update

$$UB = \min\left\{UB, \mu\left(z^{N_S*}, x^{N_S*}, u^*\right)\right\}, \text{ terminate if } UB - LB \le \varepsilon_{gap} \tag{13}$$

c) Pass the optimal solution from (SP-Outer) and call an oracle to solve the MINLP:

$$\left(SP - Inner\right) \min_{x,z} dx + gz \tag{14}$$

d) Obtain the optimal recourse variable of the present integer limit.

$$LB = \max\left\{LB, dz^{N_S+1*}, x^{N_S+1*}\right\}, \text{ terminate if } UB - LB \le \varepsilon_{gap} \tag{15}$$

e) Add the following constraints to (SP-Outer), Update Ns and return to step b)

$$\text{s.t. } \mu \le Az^{N_S+1} + Dx^{N_S+1}, \tag{16}$$

$$E^T \pi^{N_S+1} \le d^T, \ x^{N_S+1}\left(d^T - E^T \pi^{N_S+1}\right) = 0 \tag{17}$$

$$Ex^{N_S+1} + Ru \ge f - Gz^{N_S+1}, \ \pi^{N_S+1}\left(Ex^{N_S+1} - f + Ru + Gz^{N_S+1}\right) = 0 \tag{18}$$

3. Results and Discussion

Nominal deterministic optimization suggests the use of HBr as the halogenation agent, TBAB/KI system for diazotization, and DMSO/H_2O for cycloaddition (denoted as 2,6,6). Nevertheless, another route that replaces DMSO with Cu(I) catalyst for cycloaddition (denoted as 2,6,9) is chosen by solving ARO to guarantee that the synthesis process retains optimality under the variation of multiple uncertainties as shown in Tab. 1. Under significant deviation from nominal operation point, the superstructure topology switches to a more tolerable one with relatively low cost. To test the superiority of the new robust topology, as is shown in Fig. 2, 50 scenarios randomly drawn from the uncertain set are optimized with the deterministic model and ARO model with fixed nominal topology. The uncertain variables are sampled uniformly from the polyhedral uncertainty box. The objective cost given by deterministic optimization is averagely higher than that of ARO by over 1.5 % according to the sample, because the (2,6,6) route no longer remains the best design under the variation of uncertainties.

Table 1 The comparison of optimal deterministic design and adjustable robust design.

Model	Chosen Route (subscripts of nonzero Y's)	Number of micro-reactors	Objective ($/a)
Deterministic	2, 6, 6	4, 2, 32	7,594,134
ARO	2, 6, 9	5, 3, 10	12,448,444

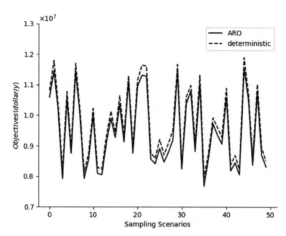

Figure 2 Comparison of deterministic and ARO optimum in 50 random scenarios.

4. Conclusion

The present work investigated a novel ARO approach that effectively hedges against multiple uncertainties in process synthesis and meanwhile deal with mixed-integer decision variable. It can be proven that our methods combining traditional two-stage ARO and exact solution algorithm for second-stage MIP serve with full recourse on operation variables in the uncertainty set. There are at least three incentives for using the proposed strategy: the objective optimality, uncertainty, and control of conservatism of superstructure-based process optimization are simultaneously satisfied. We believe that the continuous manufacturing process of rufinamide is just one of the cases where our conceptual design strategy can apply. This can pave the way for other continuous pharmaceutical manufacturing superstructure design optimization problems.

References

A. Ben-Tal, A. Goryashko, E. Guslitzer, A Nemirovski. 2004, Adjustable Robust Solutions of Uncertain Linear Programs. Mathematical Programming, 99(2), 351–376.

S. Borukhova, T. Noël, B. Metten, E. de Vos, V. Hessel, 2016, From Alcohol to 1,2,3-triazole via a Multi-Step Continuous-Flow Synthesis of a Rufinamide Precursor. Green Chemistry, 18(18), 4947-4953.

S. Diab, D. Gerogiorgis, 2018, Process Modelling, Simulation and Technoeconomic Evaluation of Crystallisation Antisolvents for the Continuous Pharmaceutical Manufacturing of Rufinamide. Computer & Chemical Engineering, 111, 102-114.

S. Jørgensen, M. Lind, N. Jensen, 2019, Functional Modeling View on Product and Process Engineering in Design and Operations. Industrial & Engineering Chemistry Research, 58, 11129–11148.

H. Shi, F. You, 2016, A Computational Framework and Solution Algorithms for Two-Stage Adaptive Robust Scheduling of Batch Manufacturing Processes under Uncertainty, AIChE Journal, 62(3), 687–703.

A. Westerberg, 2004, A Retrospective on Design and Process Synthesis, Computer & Chemical Engineering, 28(4), 447-458.

B. Zeng, L. Zhao, 2013, Solving Two-Stage Robust Optimization Problems Using a Column-and-Constraint Generation Method, Operations Research Letters, 41, 457-461.

Flavio Manenti, Gintaras V. Reklaitis (Eds.), Proceedings of the 34th European Symposium on
Computer Aided Process Engineering / 15th International Symposium on Process Systems
Engineering (ESCAPE34/PSE24), June 2-6, 2024, Florence, Italy

Semi-mechanistic modelling of ionic liquid-based biomass fractionation

Suhaib Nisar[a], Agnieszka Brandt-Talbot[b], Jason P. Hallett[a], Benoit Chachuat[a*]

[a]*Department of Chemical Engineering, South Kensington Campus, Imperial College London, London SW7 2AZ, United Kingdom*
[b]*Department of Chemistry, Molecular Sciences Research Hub, Imperial College London, London W12 0BZ, United Kingdom*
*b.chachuat@imperial.ac.uk

Abstract

Fractionation of lignocellulosic biomass is a crucial step to provide cellulose, lignin, and hemicellulose for further processing. This work focuses on modelling the fractionation of woody biomass using the ionoSolv process, which employs low-cost ionic liquid water mixtures. We model a simple reaction network to describe the solvent-extraction of three main biopolymers from solid lignocellulosic biomass. We estimate the corresponding kinetic parameters and their credibility intervals using Bayesian parameter estimation and then exploit the calibrated model for a multi-criterion analysis employing three process metrics: glucan (cellulose) recovery, hemicellulose removal, and lignin removal (delignification). Specifically, we construct a probabilistic design space by propagating the model parameter uncertainty, with a view to predicting a feasible operating window for key process variables (pretreatment time, temperature and solids loading) to meet certain thresholds for each metric. Overall, the development of semi-mechanistic models provides a novel framework for the analysis and optimisation of ionic liquid-based biomass pretreatment.

Keywords: biomass, ionic liquids, semi-mechanistic models, Bayesian inference

1. Background and Introduction

Climate change and resource scarcity are driving the demand for sustainable alternatives to fossil carbon energy sources and reduced carbon materials such as plastics. Biomass is any renewable organic material coming from plants and animals and has been proposed for both energy and material sources. Specifically, lignocellulosic biomass comprises woody plant parts, including agricultural and food industry residues (Ragauskas et al., 2006, Barbará et al. , 2023). It is mainly composed of three biopolymers: cellulose, hemicellulose, and lignin. The chemistry and spatial arrangement of the components of lignocellulosic biomass hinders the direct conversion to specific products, thereby requiring a chemical transformation to maximise the availability of the biopolymers for specific applications.

Recently, ionic liquids (ILs) have been proposed as effective solvents for biomass fractionation. The ionoSolv process utilises protic ionic liquid-water solutions, with the ILs synthesised by simple combination of an aqueous Bronsted acid with a Bronsted base, to fractionate lignocellulosic biomass into a cellulose-rich pulp and a lignin and hemicellulose rich liquid. Solid lignin can then be separated after increasing the water content in the ionic liquid solution. This is depicted in Figure 1 (Brandt-Talbot et al., 2017). The cellulose pulp is washed after the pretreatment to remove the IL and as much lignin as possible followed by further processing to cellulosic biofuels (after hydrolysis) or biomaterials. The dissolved lignin, recovered from the IL by the addition of an anti-solvent such as water, can be either combusted for process heat or converted to products. Distillation can then be used to regenerate the IL-water solution for recycling.

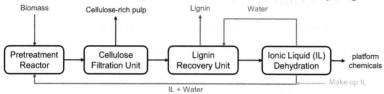

Figure 1: ionoSolv process for lignocellulosic biomass fractionation using protic ionic liquids

Modelling biomass fractionation to predict process behaviour helps design more intelligent experiments to optimise and study the process. Previous studies have considered quadratic response surface modelling of the ionoSolv process (Abouelela et al., 2023). Whilst simple to use, these quadratic models have poor extrapolative capability and require many experiments for wider applicability. This work focuses on the development of semi-empirical chemical models, with the aim of providing a feasible operating region to focus experiments for process optimisation. These models balance the required complexity to adequately model the system with the limited data available. The methodology is detailed in Section 2, followed by results and discussion in Section 3, and conclusions in Section 4.

2. Methodology

2.1. Model Equations

Reaction scheme (R1) was developed to describe the main reactions occurring during lignocellulose fractionation. As the wet-chemical analysis method can only elucidate the compositional structure of the cellulose-rich pulp, the models were trained with the pulp compositions consisting of cellulose, residual hemicellulose, and residual lignin. The compositional analysis method cannot distinguish between glucose derived from cellulose or hemicellulose and as most glucose originates from cellulose; the term *glucan* refers to cellulose. For lignin, the compositional analysis method estimates native and condensed (re-precipitated) lignin as a lumped component as it measures the lignin content gravimetrically. Therefore, when calculating residuals for lignin, the components lignin and condensed lignin were combined.

$$\text{Cellulose}_{(s)} \xrightarrow{k_1} \text{Glucose}_{(diss.)}$$

$$\text{Hemicellulose}_{(s)} \xrightarrow{k_2} \text{Sugars}_{(diss.)} \tag{R1}$$

$$\text{Lignin}_{(s)} \xrightarrow{k_3} \text{Lignin}_{(diss.)} \xrightarrow{k_4} \text{Condensed lignin}_{(s)}$$

Reaction stoichiometries were used to enforce mass balances on the system. For each experiment, the initial composition was set as the raw biomass composition. An Arrhenius power kinetic expression was employed for reactions 2-4 (Eq. (1)), while a Haldane-type kinetic expression was used for reaction 1 (Eq. (2)). Temperature curves (Gschwend et al., 2018) were used to model temperature dependence through the parameters $\theta_{0,i}$ and $\theta_{1,i}$. The solids loading and reaction order effects were described with the parameters a_i and d_i respectively in Eq. (1). The parameter K_i in Eq. (2) primarily describes the inhibition regime in Haldane-style kinetics at high reactant concentrations, while K_m represents the saturation regime, where the reaction rate is maximum at intermediate reactant concentrations.

$$r_i = e^{\left(\theta_{0,i}+\theta_{1,i}\left(1-\frac{298.5}{T(t)}\right)\right)}[\text{solid}]^{a_i} \times n_{\text{reactant}_i}{}^{d_i} \ ; \ i \in \{2,3,4\} \tag{1}$$

$$r_1 = \frac{e^{\left(\theta_{0,1}+\theta_{1,1}\left(1-\frac{298.5}{T(t)}\right)\right)} \times m_{\text{glucan}}}{K_m + m_{\text{glucan}} \times \left(1 + \frac{m_{\text{glucan}}}{K_i}\right)} \ ; \ m_{\text{glucan}} = n_{\text{glucan}} \times [\text{solid}] \tag{2}$$

Ordinary differential equations (ODEs) for each species involved in reaction scheme (R1) were expressed in terms of the reaction rates through the reaction stoichiometry and are shown in Eq. (3). The ODEs were integrated using CasADi (Andersson et al., 2019) in Python.

$$\frac{dn_{\text{glucan}}}{dt} = -r_1 \ ; \ \frac{dn_{\text{hemicellulose}}}{dt} = -r_2 \ ; \ \frac{dn_{\text{lignin}}}{dt} = -r_3$$

$$\frac{dn_{\text{glucose}}}{dt} = r_1 \ ; \ \frac{dn_{\text{sugars}}}{dt} = r_2 \ ; \ \frac{dn_{\text{lignin}_{\text{diss}}}}{dt} = r_3 - r_4 \ ; \ \frac{dn_{Condensed \, \text{lignin}}}{dt} = r_4 \tag{3}$$

The main process metrics used to quantify the performance of lignocellulose fractionation (Eq. (4)) focus on cellulose retention, hemicellulose removal and delignification in the biomass.

$$\text{Glucan Recovery} = \frac{\text{Pulp glucan content} \times \text{Pulp yield}}{\text{Raw biomass glucan content}}$$

$$\text{Hemicellulose Removal} = 1 - \frac{\text{Pulp hemicellulose content} \times \text{Pulp yield}}{\text{Raw biomass hemicellulose content}} \tag{4}$$

$$\text{Delignification} = 1 - \frac{\text{Pulp lignin content} \times \text{Pulp yield}}{\text{Raw biomass lignin content}}$$

2.2. *Bayesian Estimation and Design Space characterisation*

Bayesian parameter inference views the model parameters as random variables and makes use of Bayes' rule to compute a posterior distribution of the parameters by accounting for experimental data through the likelihood function as well as prior knowledge on the parameters. A nested sampling-based method was used with the method outlined in Bernardi et al. (2019) implemented in gPROMS ModelBuilder 7.1.1 (Siemens Industry Software, 2023). The Bayesian estimation returns a set of parameter values with their posterior probabilities, expressing the parametric uncertainty in the estimated system. A flat prior was considered as there was no previous knowledge to suggest where the optimal parameter values may lie. Additionally, a constant variance model was used to represent measurement uncertainty in the likelihood function.

A Bayesian approach was also used to characterise the probabilistic design space using nested sampling with the Python package DEUS as outlined in Kusumo et al. (2020). The design space characterisation yields samples of optimal operating conditions (time, temperature, solids loading) that satisfy desired targets set for the metrics in Eq. (4) at a given feasibility. The design space characterisation considers parametric uncertainty by sampling parameter scenarios from the posterior parameter distribution, which are then considered as uncertainty scenarios for the design space characterisation. As with the parameter estimation, the design space estimation with nested sampling progressively samples in nested contours of increasing likelihood.

3. Results and Discussion

3.1. Bayesian Estimation Results

Figure 2 illustrates the process metric profiles for the maximum a posteriori parameter estimates with the experimental data and actual measurement uncertainty plotted for comparison. Generally, all three components are modelled well. For the glucan recovery (left), the reduction is tracked well even at the highest modelled temperature of 170 °C, where experiments are challenged by the difficulties in washing the sticky pulp after pretreatment. For hemicellulose removal (centre), the models predict the decrease in hemicellulose content across the temperature range. For delignification (right), the combination of lignin extraction and re-deposition of condensed lignin onto the biomass pulp captured the delignification trend well, especially at 150 and 160°C, while anticipating the maximum at 170°C. It has previously been observed that the re-deposited "lignin" is a combination of condensed lignin fragments, and sugars-derived oligomers coined "pseudo-lignin" or humins (Shinde et al., 2018). This is compounded by the inability of the current analysis protocols to quantitatively distinguish water insoluble degradation products from unextracted lignin, complicating the understanding of the re-deposition reaction. As humins formation is expectedly more significant at higher severities, future model refinement should describe reactions involving dissolved sugars.

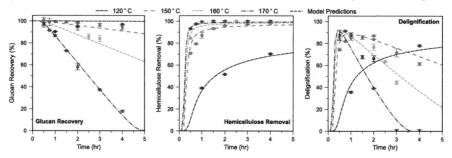

Figure 2: Maximum a posteriori prediction of ionoSolv experiments

Figure 3 illustrates the variability in the model predictions for all three metrics over the 95% credibility region of the estimated parameters at 150°C. In general, the predictive variability is contained within a narrow band through the experimental points. The overall certainty in model predictions provides confidence for using these estimates for further process optimisation and exploitation.

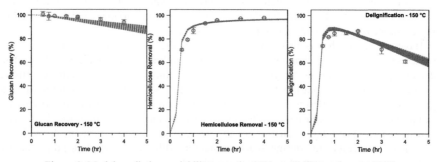

Figure 3: Model prediction variability over the 95% credibility region at 150°C

3.2. Probabilistic Design Space Characterisation

The probabilistic design space characterisation can provide a region for feasible operation of the ionoSolv process. Two scenarios were investigated, one where glucan recovery and hemicellulose removal needed to be greater than 90% and delignification greater than 75%. In the second scenario, the thresholds were tightened to require glucan recovery and hemicellulose removal to be greater than 90% and delignification to be greater than 75%. The probabilistic design spaces were estimated over 1500 parameter uncertainty scenarios obtained from the Bayesian estimation to determine 1000 feasible operating points with at least 85% feasibility.

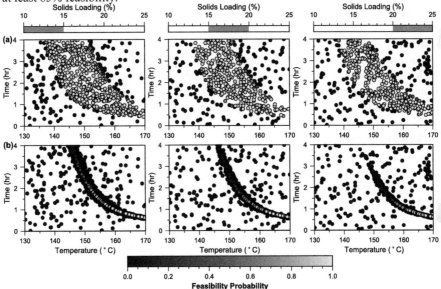

Figure 4: Probabilistic design space for feasible operation of the ionoSolv process for (a) lower and (b) higher quality thresholds

This probabilistic design space in Figure 4 (a) shows that the feasible operating region is sandwiched between regions of low feasibility at higher and lower temperatures of the feasible region. At lower temperatures, there is insufficient hemicellulose and lignin removal from the biomass. At higher temperatures and longer times, the glucan recovery decreases due to hydrolysis of cellulose to water-soluble glucose, cellobiose and short oligomers, while the lignin re-deposition and humin deposition also become dominant. Interestingly, the feasible operating region shrinks with increasing temperature, suggesting a reduced process flexibility and higher risk of error as the temperature increases. This may be traced back to the delignification, with the maximal region becoming narrower with increasing temperature, due to the more pronounced lignin re-deposition. These observations concur with the experimental data in Figure 2, which imply that the ionoSolv process must be operated at low severity for high glucan recoveries and high severity for high hemicellulose removals, with delignification essentially determining the feasible space in this overlapping region. The parametric uncertainty also has a limited impact on the feasibility probability, with most points having a probability of either 0 or 1. This matches the Bayesian estimation results, which implied a limited impact of parametric uncertainty, particularly in high feasibility regions.

For the higher quality thresholds in Figure 4 (b), the more stringent process requirements unsurprisingly limit the range of feasible operation, but the general trends remain unchanged. There is a noticeable shift in the feasible operating region with increasing solids loading, requiring higher temperatures to meet the process constraints. The more constrained design space also requires a balance between conservative and riskier validation experiments to meet process constraints.

4. Conclusions and Future Work

In this work, a semi-mechanistic framework modelling the extraction of the main biopolymers composing lignocellulosic biomass into an ionic liquid water mixture was proposed. Bayesian parameter estimation was employed to estimate the kinetic parameters and their credibility regions. The calibrated model was then exploited for the characterisation of a feasible operating set for different thresholds of the process metrics with high confidence. Further work will require the consideration of humin formation from dissolved sugars for the improvement of the re-deposition model and further experimental validation of the feasible operating set predictions.

Acknowledgements

Suhaib Nisar is grateful to the Department of Chemical Engineering at Imperial College London for a PhD scholarship and to the EPSRC Centre for Doctoral Training in Next Generation Synthesis & Reaction Technology for the PhD studentship under grant EP/S023232/1.

References

A.R. Abouelela, P.Y.S. Nakasu, and J.P. Hallett. 2023. 'Influence of Pretreatment Severity Factor and Hammett Acidity on Softwood Fractionation by an Acidic Protic Ionic Liquid'. *ACS Sustainable Chem. Eng.* 11 (6): 2404–15.

J.A.E. Andersson, et al. 2019. 'CasADi: A Software Framework for Nonlinear Optimization and Optimal Control'. *Math. Program. Comput.* 11 (1): 1–36.

P.V. Barbará, A.A. Rafat, J.P. Hallett, and A. Brandt-Talbot. 2023. 'Purifying cellulose from major waste streams using ionic liquids and deep eutectic solvents'. *Curr. Opin. Green Sustain. Chem.* 41: 100783

A. Bernardi, L. Gomoescu, J. Wang, C.C. Pantelides, D. Chadwick, and B. Chachuat. 2019. 'Kinetic Model Discrimination for Methanol and DME Synthesis Using Bayesian Estimation'. *IFAC-PapersOnLine*, 52 (1): 335–40.

A. Brandt-Talbot, F.J.V. Gschwend, P.S. Fennell, T.M. Lammens, B. Tan, J. Weale and J.P. Hallett, 2017, 'An Economically Viable Ionic Liquid for the Fractionation of Lignocellulosic Biomass', *Green Chem.* 19 (13): 3078–3102.

F.J.V. Gschwend, F. Malaret, S. Shinde, A. Brandt-Talbot, and J.P. Hallett. 2018. 'Rapid Pretreatment of Miscanthus Using the Low-Cost Ionic Liquid Triethylammonium Hydrogen Sulfate at Elevated Temperatures'. *Green Chem.* 20 (15): 3486–98.

K.P. Kusumo, L. Gomoescu, R. Paulen, S.G. Muñoz, C.C. Pantelides, N. Shah, and B. Chachuat. 2020. 'Bayesian Approach to Probabilistic Design Space Characterization: A Nested Sampling Strategy'. *Ind. Eng. Chem. Res.* 59 (6): 2396–2408.

A.J. Ragauskas, et al. 2006. 'The Path Forward for Biofuels and Biomaterials'. *Science* 311 (5760): 484–89.

S.D. Shinde, X. Meng, R. Kumar, and A.J. Ragauskas. 2018. 'Recent Advances in Understanding the Pseudo-Lignin Formation in a Lignocellulosic Biorefinery'. *Green Chem.* 20 (10): 2192–2205.

Siemens Industry Software, 1997–2023. gPROMS

Flavio Manenti, Gintaras V. Reklaitis (Eds.), Proceedings of the 34th European Symposium on Computer Aided Process Engineering / 15th International Symposium on Process Systems Engineering (ESCAPE34/PSE24), June 2-6, 2024, Florence, Italy

Climate Change Effect on Microbial Interactions using Surrogate Modelling of an Individual-Based Model

Lydia Katsini, Jian Wang, Ihab Hashem, Satyajeet S. Bhonsale, Jan F.M. Van Impe*

BioTeC+ - Chemical and Biochemical Process Technology and Control, KU Leuven Ghent, Gebroeders de Smetstraat 1, 9000 Ghent, Belgium
Email: jan.vanimpe@kuleuven.be

Abstract

The climate change effects are numerous, affecting all aspects of life on the planet, including microbes. Bottom-up approaches like Individual-Based Models (IBMs) can describe complex microbial interactions that emerge within a microbial community, at the cost of computational time. To tackle this, surrogate models using data-driven modelling methods are developed. The aim of this paper is to develop a surrogate model of an IBM to assess the effect of increasing temperature on a 3-species community dynamics utilizing the maximum growth rate dependence on temperature. The results show a shift in the bacteria interactions with temperature increases. The importance of the initial population levels on the species prevalence, along with the need to further investigate the influence of temperature on microbial interactions are highlighted.

Keywords: climate change, microbial interactions, growth rate, individual-based modelling, k-nearest neighbour classification

1. Introduction

Climate change is already taking place and is expected to continue in the future. The impact of climate change is wide, from rising sea level to increased incidence of extreme events, like heatwaves, affecting all aspects of life on the planet (Katsini et al., 2022). According to the one health approach, environmental, human, and animal health are interconnected and addressing one means addressing the others as well. Even though microbes are the common denominator between all three pillars of the one health concept, the microbial response to climate change has received limited attention (Cavicchioli et al., 2019).

A major hurdle in tackling this is the misalignment of the scale between the two systems as well as the high complexity that characterizes both. Oftentimes, mathematical modelling facilitates the study of such involved systems. Regarding the microbial system, developed mathematical models have multiple levels of complexity. Although modelling the growth of individual species is straightforward, modelling the spatial growth of multiple species requires more sophisticated tools such as Individual-Based Models (IBMs). In the case of IBMs, the cell is considered as the modelling unit. The cell's individual functions, i.e., cell traits and behavior are modelled utilizing mechanistic knowledge. Thus, such a bottom-up approach allows IBMs to capture the population characteristics related to the complex socio-spatial interactions that emerge within a microbial community (Hashem and Van Impe, 2022).

As the effect of climate change on microbial communities is the result of both the individual species response and the species interactions, the ability of IBMs to model both makes them ideal candidates to assess the temperature shift impact on multispecies bacterial growth (Katsini et al., 2022). Previous research regarding the effect of temperature changes on microbial communities focused on multi-species in marine environments (Abreu et al., 2023). Åkesson et al. (2021) referred to the capability of IBMs to study the species interactions under climate change, however, by highlighting their computational cost. Surrogate modelling can overcome this issue by replacing the IBM and providing model simulations more efficiently (Trucchia et al., 2019). Thus, the aim of this paper is to study the effect of temperature shifts on microbial interactions, focusing on species prevalence, by developing an IBM and utilizing surrogate modelling to extend the predictions.

2. Materials and Methods

The microbial community used as a case study consists of three bacterial species (P, S, V), each with different temperature ranges for growth. The temperature range for P was 10-30 °C, for S 15-35 °C, and for V 20-45 °C. Based on the above, the temperature range, for which all three species can grow is from 20 °C to 30 °C, which is the range for which the IBM and the surrogate model simulations cover. Since the initial population of each species plays a catalytic role in the microbial interactions, several different levels of ratios among the species at the beginning of the simulations are considered.

2.1. Modelling the temperature effect on bacterial growth

The effect of temperature on the individual response is considered as the effect on the maximum growth rate, μ_{max}, (h⁻¹) for each species.. As the food microbiology field provides extensive quantitative research on the effect of temperature, T, on μ_{max}, the model introduced by Zwietering et al. (1991) was used:

$$\mu_{max} = (b(T - T_{min})\{1 - exp[c(T - T_{max})]\})^2 \qquad (1)$$

where T_{min}, T_{max} are the minimum and maximum temperatures for growth (°C), and b, c are Ratkowsky parameters (°C⁻¹), which were the same for all three species. Figure 1 depicts the μ_{max} dependence on temperature based on Eq. (1) for the 3-species system.

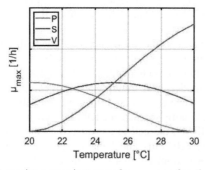

Figure 1: The 3-species system in terms of μ_{max}, as a function of temperature.

2.2. Development of the Individual-Based Model

An IBM simulation consists of two types of entities: the microbial cells and their environment. Each individual cell is defined by its species genre, radius, mass, spatial coordinates, and maximum nutrient uptake rates. For each cell intracellular and diffusion processes, and intercellular and environmental interactions are modeled (Tack et al., 2017, Hashem and Van Impe, 2022). Intracellular processes include cell growth, maintenance, and division, with spatial overlap due to high cell density managed by a cell shoving algorithm (Kreft et al., 2001). The diffusion processes are governed by the second law of Fick modulating nutrient and toxin distribution. IBM simulations are run using MICRODIMS, an in-house IBM modeling platform (Tack et al., 2017), at two time resolutions, one for rapid dynamics, e.g., glucose uptake, and a second one for slower processes, e.g., cell reproduction. The environment is represented as 40 mm × 20 mm section of a 4 mm thick gel, discretized into square units of 10 mm, each characterized by nutrient and toxin concentrations.

2.3. Development of the surrogate model

The species prevalence obtained at the end of the IBM simulation was used as the label with temperature and initial population ratio as predictors. This means that the modelling exercise was a classification task: predict which of the three species prevails under given conditions. Three different algorithms were trained, i.e., decision tree, support vector machine, and k-nearest neighbor, and evaluated in terms of accuracy on unseen data, with the latter achieving the highest performance (87.7 % accuracy). 5-fold cross-validation was used to avoid overfitting and the data were standardized before training to maximize accuracy.

2.3.1. k-Nearest Neighbor (KNN)

The k-Nearest Neighbor (KNN) algorithm is a supervised learning method that facilitates the classification of data based on their distance to each other (Zhang and Zhou, 2007). According to this method, the class for each unseen point is selected by evaluating the classification of its k nearest neighbors with the most common class among them assigned to the unseen point. Following hyperparameter tuning, the number of nearest neighbors was 10, while the distance metric was the squared inverse of the Euclidean distance.

3. Results and Discussion

This section is divided into two main parts: first the results obtained from the IBM, and then the training of the surrogate model along with the predictions for the full set of conditions, i.e., temperature and ratio of initial populations.

3.1. IBM of the 3-species system

The IBM results show that at the end of each simulation only one species out of the three prevails, therefore the results indicate the prevailing one (Figure 2 and 3). Based on Figure 1, there are two temperature levels where two species have equal μ_{max}, which are higher than the third one. Firstly, at 22.62 °C for P and S, and secondly at 25.17 °C for S and V. Considering the stochastic nature of the developed IBM, this is also reflected in the results of the different iterations at those temperature levels. As shown in Figure 4, at 22.62 °C as the ratio of the initial population of P to V increases, the prevailing species interchanges between P and S.

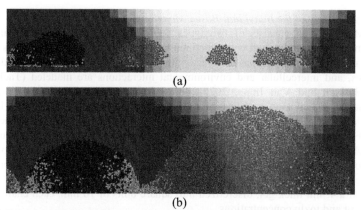

(a)

(b)

Figure 2: Spatial distribution of the 3-species system (P-green, S-blue, V-red) from the IBM at the middle (a) and the end (b) of the simulation for 25.17 °C.

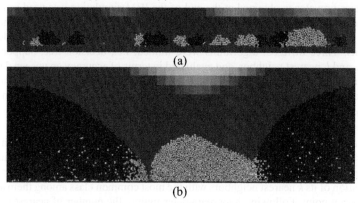

(a)

(b)

Figure 3: Spatial distribution of the 3-species system (P-green, S-blue, V-red) from the IBM at the middle (a) and the end (b) of the simulation for 22.62 °C.

On visually inspecting the prevalence results at 25.17 °C, this distinction is less clear as there is a ratio at which each species prevails at least once through the 10 repetitions. This could be explained by the difference in the μ_{max} values between the two species that have the same μ_{max} and the third one. For 24.13 °C, there is no variation in the prevalent species for the evaluated conditions. This could be attributed to the fact that the tested initial population ratios did not approximate the tipping point for the shift in the prevalence.

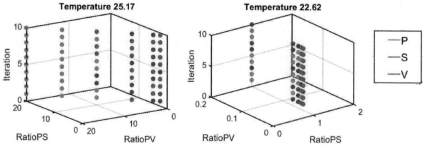

Figure 4: Prevalence results from the developed IBM for selected temperature levels.

3.2. Surrogate model training and application

As mentioned in the previous section, the KNN classification algorithm was the best performing, and thus was selected for the surrogate model. Common practice when building classifiers is to plot the confusion matrix, which provides information on the misclassifications during training. Figure 5 depicts the confusion matrix of the KNN algorithm. The misclassification instances for P and V are lower compared to the misclassification instances for S, which can be explained by inspecting Figure 1. The temperature range where S is prevailing is smaller compared to the other two species and S is the species that has a "conflict" of prevalence with both the other two. Therefore, establishing its clear advantage of prevalence would require additional simulations from the IBM including smaller differences among the initial populations.

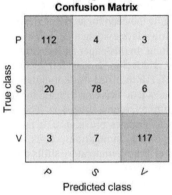

Figure 5: Confusion matrix for the training of the k-nearest neighbor (KNN) classifier.

The developed surrogate model was applied for more coarse initial population fractions by covering the relevant temperature range and the species prevalence results are illustrated in Figure 6. It is important to note that for interpreting the results, the fractions correspond to an increase of the initial population of species P, as the ratios increase. For the temperature range 20-22 °C the prevalent species is constantly P, which is expected as the increasing ratios evaluated are to the benefit of species P. Moreover, for this range based on Figure 1, species P has the highest μ_{max}. At 23 °C, even though species P has the highest μ_{max} value (Figure 1), as the initial population of species S increases (low initial P/S and P/V ratios), the prevalent species becomes species S. Surprisingly this pattern is repeated for 24 °C, although for this temperature it is species S with the highest μ_{max} value (Figure 1).

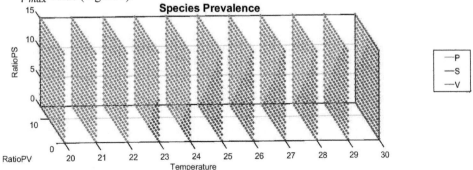

Figure 6: Species prevalence based on the surrogate model for coarser initial population fractions.

One reason for obtaining this result could be the increased misclassification instances of the surrogate model regarding species S. For 25-26 °C, depending on the initial populations, all three species could prevail, which is expected for 25 °C but not for 26 °C. Since at 26 °C, species V has the highest μ_{max} (Figure 1), there are some conditions in which species S prevails, even though the initial population ratios generally correspond to the increase of the initial population of species P. For 27-30 °C, the results are unsurprising, as species V has the highest μ_{max} and the ratios correspond to increase of the initial population of species P.

4. Conclusions

Climate change is an urgent and profound issue owed to the amplitude of its effects. This includes, among other aspects of life, microbial life. Climate change driven biodiversity loss is gaining attention, creating the need for studying the effects of shifting temperatures on microbial communities. Nowadays evidence-based policy making is relying more and more on mathematical modelling. In this paper an Individual-Based Model (IBM) of a 3–species bacterial community is developed considering the effect of temperature on the maximum growth rate (μ_{max}). For the IBM it is computationally expensive to simulate a wide range of conditions, thus, a data-driven surrogate model, by applying the k-Nearest Neighbour algorithm, is built to overcome this issue. The results show that even though the μ_{max} is a good indicator for species prevalence, it fails to take into account species interactions, in contrast to the IBM simulations. Thus, such involved models are the adequate tools to evaluate the effect of temperature shifts on bacterial communities. When isolating the species interaction effect, i.e., where μ_{max} values between species are equal, results show that the initial population ratios are the determinant for prevalence. As the more IBM simulations are used, the more reliable the results of the surrogate model are, future work plans include exploring coarser grids of the temperature-initial populations space. Overall, this work contributes to the understanding of the microbial response to climate change, which can be utilized for future-proofing purposes.

Acknowledgement

This work was supported by the PROTECT and E-MUSE projects funded by the European Union's Horizon 2020 Research and Innovation Programme [MSCA grant 813329 and 956126].

References

Abreu, C.I., Dal Bello M., Bunse C., Pinhassi J., Gore J., 2023. Warmer temperatures favor slower-growing bacteria in natural marine communities. Sci Adv 9(19)

Åkesson, A., Curtsdotter A., Eklöf A., Ebenman B., Norberg, J., Barabás, G., 2021. The importance of species interactions in eco-evolutionary community dynamics under climate change. Nat Commun 12

Cavicchioli, R., Ripple, W.J., Timmis, K.N. et al., 2019. Scientists' warning to humanity: microorganisms and climate change. Nat Rev Microbiol 17

Hashem, I. & Van Impe, J.F.M., 2022. A Game Theoretic Analysis of the Dual Function of Antibiotics. Front Microbiol 12

Katsini, L. Bhonsale S., Akkermans S., Roufou S. Griffin S., Valdramidis V., Misiou O., Koutsoumanis K., Muñoz López C.A., Polanska M., Van Impe J.F.M., 2022. Quantitative methods to predict the effect of climate change on microbial food safety: A needs analysis. Trends Food Sci 126

Kreft, J.U., Picioreanu, C., Wimpenny, J.W. and van Loosdrecht, M.C., 2001. Individual-based modelling of biofilms. Microbiology, 147(11)

Tack, I.L., Nimmegeers, P., Akkermans, S., Hashem, I. and Van Impe, J.F.M., 2017. Simulation of Escherichia coli dynamics in biofilms and submerged colonies with an individual-based model including metabolic network information. Frontiers in microbiology, 8

Truchhia, A., Mattei M.R., Luongo V., Frunzo L., Rochoux M.C., 2019. Surrogate-based uncertainty and sensitivity analysis for bacterial invasion in multi-species biofilm modelling. Commun Nonlinear Sci Numer Simul 73

Zhang, M., Zhou Z., 2007. ML-KNN: A lazy learning approach to multi-label learning. Pattern Recognit 40(7)

Zwietering MH, de Koos JT, Hasenack BE, de Witt JC, van't Riet K. Modeling of bacterial growth as a function of temperature. Appl Environ Microbiol. 1991 Apr;57(4)

Flavio Manenti, Gintaras V. Reklaitis (Eds.), Proceedings of the 34th European Symposium on Computer Aided Process Engineering / 15th International Symposium on Process Systems Engineering (ESCAPE34/PSE24), June 2-6, 2024, Florence, Italy

Stochastic Extreme Pathway generation in view of metabolic network reduction

Wannes Mores, Satyajeet S. Bhonsale, Filip Logist, Jan F.M. Van Impe[*]

BioTeC+ - Chemical and Biochemical Process Technology and Control, KU Leuven Ghent, Gebroeders De Smetstraat 1, 9000 Ghent,
* jan.vanimpe@kuleuven.be

Abstract

Use of metabolic networks for process optimization relies on reducing the network structure. Elementary Flux Modes (EFMs) and Extreme Pathways (EPs) are valuable tools in breaking down the complexity of the network and are extremely effective in reducing small- to medium-scale networks. EP-based reduction relies on generating a large set of candidate EPs and making a sub-selection based on their information content. However, its applicability to larger networks remains infeasible due to the combinatorial explosion of EFM/EP set size. We present a new methodology of generating EP sets using a smart stochastic approach which avoids the combinatorial explosion. Instead of evaluating all possibilities at every iteration of the canonical basis method, a stochastic variable decides which combinations are considered and which aren't. Elementarity tests that normally require the full set to be calculated, are substituted with a matrix rank test resulting in an approach that generates EP subsets. Finally, the applicability of the subsets as a substitute for the full EP matrix is evaluated by SVD analysis for a medium-scale network.

Keywords: Metabolic networks, Extreme Pathways, Model-based Optimisation

1. Introduction

Currently, optimisation of bioprocesses relies on macroscopic models, where kinetic expressions such as Monod and Haldane are used to evaluate the changes in key metabolites. Within these models, the underlying intracellular mechanisms are ignored which can lead to bad predictive performance, especially in a dynamic environment (Hodgson et al., 2004). Large amounts of intracellular information on the host cell is available through their metabolic networks. Exploitation of metabolic networks within dynamic optimisation has already shown significant improvement over macroscopic models (Chang et al. 2016). However, network-based optimisation is currently limited to small-scale networks. Large-scale networks such as genome-scale metabolic networks (GEMs) lead to heavily underdetermined network-based models, which means there are not enough measurements available to estimate all its fluxes. Several techniques exist to deal with or remove the underdeterminacy of the network, an overview is given in (Bogaerts et al., 2021), are not applicable to GEMs due to their size and complexity. Reduction of the complexity of the GEMs is therefore needed as a first step towards their exploitation within dynamic optimisation.

Recently, Maton et al. (2022) showcased a powerful reduction approach based on creating macroscopic bioreactions from EFMs, reducing the medium network to a set of reactions smaller than the number of measurements while retaining satisfactory accuracy towards experimental datasets with just 4-5 macro-bioreactions. This approach removes the problem of underdeterminacy altogether and leads to very simple dynamic models. The downside of this approach lies in the generation of the EFM set. Even though the study presents many ways of reducing the initial EFM set while retaining variety, it still cannot compute EFM sets for GEMs due to the combinatorial explosion (Machado et al., 2012) with network size.

To circumvent this problem, Machado et al. (2012) proposed a random sampling adaptation of the Canonical Basis Approach (CBA). To avoid bias, all candidates have equal probabilities of being chosen. This reduces the candidate sets within each iteration, preventing the exponential growth of combinations during computation. This approach generates a random subset of EFMs within a reasonable timeframe. However, the computation time scaled almost quadratically with filter setting, even for a medium-scale network. High computation time limits the applicability to larger networks, since small filter settings would be needed which lead to very small sets of EFMs. For CBA, the elementarity test is the most computationally intensive. It tests if the candidate is an extreme ray of the flux cone (Figure 2). The most efficient approach to evaluate the elementarity of a candidate is through the combinatorial test, which requires the full EFM set. Alternatively, the rank test was used in its place since the full EFM set is not available.

In this work, we build upon the approach in Machado et al. (2012) and develop a stochastic approach for Extreme Pathways since they represent a more minimal representation of the metabolic capabilities of the network, drastically reducing the size of candidates. This combined with parallelisation of the problem leads to a much more efficient algorithm to analyse a GEM with metabolic network reduction in mind.

2. Materials and methods

In this section, the algorithm for stochastic generation of EPs is presented, together with the SVD analysis used to evaluate the EP subsets obtained. Afterwards, the methods are applied to a case study involving a medium-scale network of *Escherichia Coli*.

2.1. Stochastic Canonical Basis Approach (CBA)

The algorithm for stochastic generation of EPs used in this work is based on CBA, extended with a stochastic filtering step (Machado et al., 2012). However, the selection based on the probability function is evaluated early to avoid unnecessary elementarity testing. The filter setting can then be seen as the maximum amount of candidate testing per iteration. For larger networks where the total amount of combinations can easily surpass hundreds of millions, this early selection is vital to keep computation times reasonable. This is due to the fact that the elementarity test, by far the most computational intensive step, is avoided for many of the candidates. A drawback of this implementation is that the selection could consist mainly of non-elementary candidates, leading to too much loss of information and not enough EPs generated.

Algorithm 1 Stochastic CBA	
Input:	Stoichiometric matrix S of size $m \times n$, filter setting f
Output:	Subset of EPs of the metabolic network defined by S
Step 1:	Augment the stoichiometric matrix with the backwards version of the reversible reactions $S^* = [\, S \;\; -S_{rev}\,]$.
Step 2:	Create a vector μ of intracellular metabolites not directly connected with an exchange reaction
Step 3:	Initialize the tableau $T = [\, I_n \;\; (S^*)^\top \,]$
Step 4:	Iterate over all elements of μ to process the equality constraint defined by $S^*_{[\mu,\,:]} \cdot T_{[:,\,:n]} = 0$

for $i = 1:n_\mu$ (n_μ = number of entries in μ) **do**

$\quad p \,=\, rows\ in\ \boldsymbol{T}$

$\quad \boldsymbol{T^0} = \{x \in 0,1,\dots,p \colon \boldsymbol{T}_{[x,\ n+\mu[i]]} = 0\}$

$\quad \boldsymbol{T^+} = \{x \in 0,1,\dots,p \colon \boldsymbol{T}_{[x,\ n+\mu[i]]} > 0\}$

$\quad \boldsymbol{T^-} = \{x \in 0,1,\dots,p \colon \boldsymbol{T}_{[x,\ n+\mu[i]]} < 0\}$

$\quad$ Initialize new tableau $\boldsymbol{T}_{new} = \boldsymbol{T^0}$

$\quad$ Calculate selection probability $P = \dfrac{f}{size(T^+ \times T^-)+f}$

$\quad$ **for** $(j^+, j^-) \in \boldsymbol{T^+} \times \boldsymbol{T^-}$ **do**

$\qquad$ **if** random variable $X \sim \mathcal{U}(0,1) \le P$

$\qquad\quad$ Candidate $\boldsymbol{c} = \boldsymbol{T}_{[j^-,\ n+\mu]} \times \boldsymbol{T}_{[j^+,:]} + \boldsymbol{T}_{[j^+,\ n+\mu]} \times \boldsymbol{T}_{[j^-,\ :]}$

$\qquad\quad$ **if** $\boldsymbol{c}$ elementary (Eq. 2) **do**

$\qquad\qquad$ Add $\boldsymbol{c}$ to $\boldsymbol{T}_{new}$

$\quad$ **end for**

end for

Step 5:$\qquad$ Add necessary exchange reactions such that $\boldsymbol{T}_{[:,\ n:]} = \boldsymbol{0}$

Step 6:$\qquad$ Create Extreme Pathway matrix $\boldsymbol{P} = \boldsymbol{T}_{[:,\ :n]}$

end

As only a subset of EPs is calculated, the combinatorial elementarity test cannot be employed and is substituted with the matrix rank test, defined as follows:

$$supp(\boldsymbol{c}) = \{i, c_i \ne 0\} \tag{1}$$

$$\boldsymbol{c}\ elementary \equiv rank(\boldsymbol{S}_{[n:,\ supp(c)]}) = |supp(\boldsymbol{c})| - 1 \tag{2}$$

With $supp(\boldsymbol{c})$ the support function of $\boldsymbol{c}$.

2.2. SVD analysis of Extreme Pathway Matrix

Analysis of Extreme Pathway matrices aims to understand the capabilities and characteristics of the original metabolic network. For large sets, it is often difficult to quantify importance of the EPs and analyze their influence on network characteristics. SVD analysis has proven to be effective in breaking down the contribution of EPs to the shape and size of the solution space (Price et al., 2003), enabling insight such as identification of key branchpoints in the network and its effective dimensionality. Analysis of the solution space aids in understanding the key differences in network behaviour of possible steady-state solutions. For an EP matrix $\boldsymbol{P}$ containing only Type I EPs (Price et al., 2002) of size $p \times q$, the SVD analysis is defined as:

$$\boldsymbol{P}^\mathsf{T} = \boldsymbol{U} \cdot \boldsymbol{\Sigma} \cdot \boldsymbol{V}^\mathsf{T} \tag{3}$$

Where $\boldsymbol{U} \in \mathbb{R}^{p \times p}$ contains left singular vectors, $\boldsymbol{\Sigma} \in \mathbb{R}^{p \times q}$ is a diagonal matrix containing the singular values, and $\boldsymbol{V}^\mathsf{T} \in \mathbb{R}^{q \times q}$ contains right singular vectors. The EP matrix $\boldsymbol{P}$ is transposed such that the columns represent the extreme pathways and rows represent the participation of reactions. Normalisation of the columns of $\boldsymbol{P}$ to unit length is done to prevent bias towards EPs with larger coefficients. The matrix $\boldsymbol{U}$ resulting from SVD decomposition defines the eigenpathways or modes of the convex basis of the solution space, which are unit length and gives us the direction of its vector. The magnitude of the mode is defined by the corresponding singular value in $\boldsymbol{\Sigma}$, which helps us evaluate its contribution to the reconstruction of the orthonormal basis. The effective dimensionality of the solution space can therefore be evaluated using the fractional contribution of each singular value. If a high fraction can be reached with a limited amount of the singular values, the solution cone will have a low effective dimensionality.

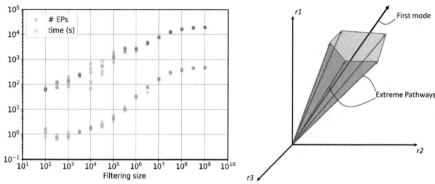

Figure 1: results for different filter settings using the stochastic CBA method

Figure 1: example flux cone

3. Results

In this work, the core *E. coli* model (Orth et al., 2010) is chosen as it allows full enumeration of its EP set which serves as comparison for stochastic CBA. The stochastic CBA algorithm is implemented in Python, with the fourth step parallelised. Different filtering settings are chosen to understand influence on both time and EP subset size.

3.1. Full Extreme Pathway set

The full EP set is calculated by turning off the filtering step and will serve as a benchmark for the EP subsets generated stochastically. Using parallelization, calculation time is reduced from 1725 seconds to 508 seconds, 19580 EPs were obtained in both cases.

3.2. Stochastic generation of Extreme Pathway sets

The stochastic CBA algorithm is implemented for filter settings ranging between 10^2 and 10^9. Five repetitions are done for each filter setting to mitigate the influence of the stochastic variable in the algorithm and shown in Figure 1. Between filter setting 10^4 and 10^7 it is clearly visible that time scales sub-linearly with filter setting, with a slope of around 0.7 on a log-log plot. For a filter setting lower than 10^4, almost all time is used to load in the model, leading to a flatter region, while filter settings higher than 10^8 slowly approach the size full set and thus approach the calculation time of the full set. EP set size also scales sub-linearly until 10^7 with a slope of around 0.7. Even though computational effort per EP stays similar for the filter settings in this case, it is important to keep in mind that this is not necessarily true for other, larger networks.

3.3. SVD analysis

To evaluate the characteristics of the EP matrix, SVD analysis is used. After separating the type I EPs and applying the decomposition, each singular value in Σ is evaluated in terms of their fractional contribution. A more dominant singular value indicates a more significant amount of variance is captured with the corresponding mode in U. Plotting the cumulative fractional dominance of the singular values sorted by decreasing magnitude gives insight into how variance is distributed among the modes. The dimensionality of the EP set can be described with its matrix rank, 27 in case of the full network. However, as seen in Figure 3, the last 7 modes of the full EP matrix contribute to less than 5% of its variance. Hence, the effective dimensionality of the set is defined by the first 20 modes which describe 95% of the variance. Effective dimensionality of the EP set gives insight into the metabolic potential of the network, with lower effective dimensionality signifying a more rigid metabolic network (Price et al., 2003).

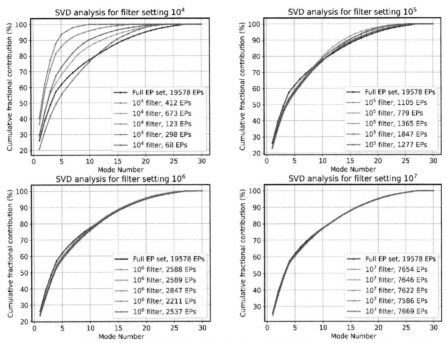

Figure 2: Cumulative fractional distribution of the singular values for full set and different filter settings.

The EP subsets generated are checked in terms of their effective dimensionality and compared to the full set. The cumulative fractional contribution curves for different filter settings are shown in Figure 3. For filter setting of 10^6, a similar effective dimensionality is obtained for all EP subsets, even though the sets are 7 times smaller and the calculation is only 31 seconds on average. Higher filter settings get progressively closer towards the full set. This indicates that the characteristics of the full network are effectively captured with much smaller subsets obtained. However, additional confirmation is needed.

As can be seen in Figure 2, the vector of the first mode is directed down the middle of the flux cone corresponding to the EP set and can be used to describe its general direction. So, using the column vector of U corresponding to the first mode of the EP subsets, the difference in angle compared to the full set can be calculated.

Table 1: Overview of difference in angle for the first mode of a subset and the first mode of the full set.

Filter setting:	10^2	10^3	10^4	10^5	10^6	10^7	10^8	10^9
Run 1	48.8°	19.3°	27.2°	34.7°	21.1°	8.7°	2.2°	0.0°
Run 2	49.4°	13.7°	39.7°	42.5°	10.4°	8.3°	3.6°	0.1°
Run 3	29.8°	27.2°	46.0°	24.7°	16.7°	9.9°	1.2°	0.3°
Run 4	22.9°	23.9°	40.2°	30.1°	14.0°	4.8°	1.5°	0.2°
Run 5	31.1°	45.3°	47.0°	29.5°	17.3°	7.1°	0.8°	0.1°

The angles for the different subsets are shown in Table 1. Even though fractional dominance of the singular values indicated that the metabolic potential of the network is kept with filter setting 10^6, the difference in angle is around 16°. This means there is still a significant loss of information regarding the solution space of the metabolic network. This could be due to the bias towards shorter EPs from stochastic CBA as described in Machado et al. (2012), resulting in an uneven sampling of. The angle differences indicate that a filter setting of at least 10^8 gives good correspondence to the full set, which is to be expected as its subset size approaches the full set. Improving the accuracy of the first mode could be achieved by giving preference to candidates with larger support vectors using the stochastic variable in Step 4 of the algorithm (Machado et al., 2012).

4. Conclusions

Extreme Pathway- or Elementary Flux Mode-based analysis of genome-scale metabolic networks is currently impossible due to the combinatorial explosion of the candidates encountered in Double Description-based enumeration methods. In this work, a novel approach for EP generation is described, relying on stochastic sampling of intermediary candidates using a filter setting in the Canonical Basis Approach. The novel method was parallelised during candidate enumeration, allowing for higher computational efficiency. This could be further exploited using GPU-based calculation, allowing for more efficient parallellisation. The stochastic CBA is then implemented on the core *E. coli* model, investigating the effect of the chosen filter setting on both computational effort and size of the resulting EP subset. Using SVD analysis, the correspondence to the full set was checked for different filter settings. The effective dimensionality of the network, which indicates its rigidity, was captured well with significantly smaller EP sets. This signifies that this approach leads to networks with similar characteristics while needing much less computational effort. However, through analysis of the first mode it was shown that there is still loss of information. This could be due to a bias toward shorter candidates when sampling, as was highlighted in Machado et al. (2012). Changing the selection probability for candidates with larger support vectors could be a way of reducing this bias.

Acknowledgement

This research is co-funded by the Research Foundation Flanders (FWO) through Strategic Basic Project 1SHG124N and the Senior Research Project G0B4121N ("Pharma4S").

References

Bogaerts, P. and Vande Wouwer, A., 2021. How to Tackle Underdeterminacy in Metabolic Flux Analysis? A Tutorial and Critical Review. Processes, 9(9), p.1577.

Chang, L., Liu, X. and Henson, M.A., 2016. Nonlinear model predictive control of fed-batch fermentations using dynamic flux balance models. Journal of Process Control, 42, pp.137-149.

Hodgson, B.J., Taylor, C.N., Ushio, M., Leigh, J.R., Kalganova, T. and Baganz, F., 2004. Intelligent modelling of bioprocesses: a comparison of structured and unstructured approaches. Bioprocess and Biosystems Engineering, 26, pp.353-359.

Machado, D., Soons, Z., Patil, K.R., Ferreira, E.C. and Rocha, I., 2012. Random sampling of elementary flux modes in large-scale metabolic networks. Bioinformatics, 28(18), pp.i515-i521.

Maton, M., Bogaerts, P. and Wouwer, A.V., 2022. A systematic elementary flux mode selection procedure for deriving macroscopic bioreaction models from metabolic networks. Journal of Process Control, 118, pp.170-184.

Orth, J.D., Fleming, R.M. and Palsson, B.Ø., 2010. Reconstruction and use of microbial metabolic networks: the core Escherichia coli metabolic model as an educational guide. EcoSal plus, 4(1), pp.10-1128.

Price, N.D., Famili, I., Beard, D.A. and Palsson, B.Ø., 2002. Extreme pathways and Kirchhoff's second law. Biophysical journal, 83(5), pp.2879-2882.

Price, N.D., Reed, J.L., Papin, J.A., Famili, I. and Palsson, B.O., 2003. Analysis of metabolic capabilities using singular value decomposition of extreme pathway matrices. Biophysical journal, 84(2), pp.794-804.

Flavio Manenti, Gintaras V. Reklaitis (Eds.), Proceedings of the 34th European Symposium on Computer Aided Process Engineering / 15th International Symposium on Process Systems Engineering (ESCAPE34/PSE24), June 2-6, 2024, Florence, Italy

Climate change threatens the food safety of the supply chain

Lydia Katsini[a], Satyajeet S. Bhonsale[a], Styliani Roufou[b], Sholeem Griffin[b], Vasilis Valdramidis[b,c], Simen Akkermans[a], Monika Polanska[a], Jan F.M. Van Impe[a]*

[a]*BioTeC+ - Chemical and Biochemical Process Technology and Control, KU Leuven Ghent, Gebroeders De Smetstraat 1, 9000 Ghent, Belgium*
[b]*Department of Food Sciences and Nutrition, University of Malta, Malta*
[c]*National and Kapodistrian University of Athens, Department of Chemistry, Panepistimiopolis Zografou, Athens, 157 84 Greece*
*Email: jan.vanimpe@kuleuven.be

Abstract

Considering the climate change effect on the food system, there is a growing need for scientific research with the aim of strengthening its resilience. From a food safety perspective, certain foods, like pasteurized milk, rely on low temperature during transportation as barrier to pathogen growth, thus any disturbance in the cold supply chain could result in foodborne illness. This study aimed to evaluate the impact of heatwaves on the cold supply chain of pasteurized milk through mathematical modelling for two European regions, i.e., Greece and Belgium. Based on the results, under heatwave scenarios the cold supply chain was disrupted in both regions. This suggests that heatwaves should not only be a concern for the warmer European south but also for central European regions. The presented framework can be adjusted for other products or enriched with more aspects like the temperature variability at the retail to yield more realistic results. Overall, this study highlights the need for future-proofing the cold supply chain of food.

Keywords: climate change scenarios, supply chain, food safety, dairy, modelling

1. Introduction

With rising global temperatures, altered rainfall patterns, and increased frequency of extreme weather events, climate change is expected to drastically affect the food system (Katsini et al., 2019). The food system, according to FAO (2019), includes, besides the production of food, also its transportation. This means that the supply chain is part of the food system, thus it is expected to be affected by climate change. According to Davis et al. (2021) the food supply is highly susceptible to environmental shocks, extreme rainfall and heatwaves. This underlines the vulnerability of the supply chains to such events, which brings food security at risk. However, especially when dealing with the cold supply chain, also the food safety is jeopardized. As low temperature is used to prevent growth of pathogenic bacteria (Wu et al., 2021), any disruption in the cold supply chain threatens food safety. Usually refrigerated goods are transported with cooling trucks, nevertheless, the cooling capacity of a given truck is dependent on the ambient temperature (Song et al., 2022). One of the numerous effects of climate change is the increased frequency of extreme events such as heatwaves. The European regions, and especially the south, are already experiencing this along with its disastrous consequences.

All the above underline the urgent need to evaluate the effect of heatwave conditions on the cold food supply chain in terms of food safety. There is a growing need to build a future proof and resilient food system, guided by evidence-based decision making. Mathematical modelling is a valuable tool in tackling this. Thus, the aim of this paper is to assess the effect of climate change, in terms of heatwaves, on the cold supply chain with respect to food safety by utilizing mathematical modelling. Pasteurized whole milk is considered as the case study, while data from Greece and Belgium are simulated to include two distinct climatological regions.

2. Materials and Methods

As mentioned in the previous section, this is an *in silico* study, in which three models are utilized: one for describing the temperature of the truck chamber as a function of the ambient temperature, one for describing the milk temperature as a function of the truck chamber temperature, and one for the food safety hazard level as a function of the milk temperature. Four different ambient temperature scenarios are simulated: Greece under summer and heatwave conditions and Belgium under summer and heatwave conditions. The corresponding ambient temperatures for the year 2023 were accessed from the Climate Data Store (CDS) of the Copernicus Climate Change Service (Muñoz Sabater, 2019).

2.1. Cooling truck chamber temperature model

The model introduced by Fallmann et al. (2023) was applied to obtain the cooling truck chamber temperature, T^{cc}[°C], as a function of the ambient temperature, T^{amb}[°C], the heat flow from the milk to the chamber, $\dot{Q}_m$[W], the door openings, $s_{door} \in \{0,1\}$, and the compressor speed, n_c[rpm]:

$$\frac{dT^{cc}}{dt} = f\left(\dot{Q}_m, T^{amb}, s_{door}, n_c, \boldsymbol{\theta}\right) \tag{1}$$

Where $\boldsymbol{\theta}$ corresponds to the parameter vector. A detailed description of the model can be found in Fallman et al. (2023). To capitalize on the door openings functionality of the model, each simulation was broken down into three time steps: one for transporting the milk with closed doors, one for keeping the doors open and reducing the amount of cargo to half, and a last one for transporting the remaining milk. For each step, the heat flow from the milk to the chamber, $\dot{Q}_m$[W], was assumed constant and estimated as:

$$\dot{Q}_m = m c_p \left(T^m_{initial} - T^{cc}_{t_{end}}\right)/t_{total} \tag{2}$$

Where m[kg] is the mass of the milk, c_p[J/kg°C] is the heat capacity of the milk, $T^m_{initial}$[°C] is the initial temperature of the milk, $T^{cc}_{t_{end}}$ [°C] is the temperature of the cooling chamber at the end of the simulated time step, and t_{total} [s] is the total time of the simulated time step. Furthermore, the volume of milk transported was estimated based on the dimensions of the considered cooling truck. Heat transfer was assumed to occur at the vertical sides as well as at the top of the cargo.

2.2. Milk temperature model

A simplistic approach was followed to estimate the milk temperature at time t, T_t^m [°C], based on (Konovalenko et al., 2021):

$$T_t^m = T_t^{cc} + (T_0^m - T_t^{cc}) \exp\left(-\frac{Ah}{mc_p}t\right) \tag{3}$$

Where T_t^{cc} [°C] is the cooling chamber temperature at time t, T_0^m [°C] is the milk temperature at time t, A [m^2] is the heat transfer surface, and h [W/m^2°C] is the heat transfer coefficient for milk. The values of the milk properties were selected from Munir et al. (2016).

2.3. Food safety hazard model

In terms of food safety, one of the major hazards for the milk cold supply chain is *Listeria monocytogenes*, therefore, the growth model and the secondary growth model for this pathogen were applied (Alavi et al., 1999):

$$\frac{dN}{dt} = \mu_{max}\left(\frac{Q}{Q+1}\right)\left(1 - \frac{N}{N_{max}}\right)N \tag{4}$$

$$\frac{dQ}{dt} = \mu_{max} Q \tag{5}$$

$$\mu_{max}(t) = [b(T_t^m - T_{min})]^2\{1 - \exp[c(T_t^m - T_{max})]\} \tag{6}$$

Where N [CFU/ml] is the population level, μ_{max} [h^{-1}] is the maximum growth rate, N_{max} [CFU/ml] is the maximum population level, and Q is a measure of the physiological state of the bacterial cells. Eq. (6) describes the temperature dependence of the μ_{max}, where T_{min}, T_{max} [°C] are the minimum and maximum temperatures for growth, respectively, while b, c are parameters.

3. Results and Discussion

Firstly, the results of the scenarios corresponding to the two temperature models and then the *Listeria monocytogenes* levels are presented. It is important to note that, based on the current regulation, during the storage and transportation of pasteurized milk, the temperature should not exceed 4 °C, as the shelf life of the product is jeopardized if the temperature increases.

3.1. Cooling chamber and milk temperature

The three time steps regarding the door opening mentioned in the previous section were selected as: 1 hour for the transport to the first retailer with closed doors, 10 minutes to unload half of the cargo with open doors, and 1 hour for the transport to the second retailer. The compressor speed was selected at 2000 rpm. Based on recent years' temperature recordings, Belgium, which belongs to the temperate climate based on the Köppen climate classification (Beck et al., 2018), recorded the highest temperature in 2023 on 8 July, at 35 °C based on the downloaded data from the CDS. Therefore, the temperature for the scenarios referring to Belgium was 25 °C for the summer and 35 °C for the heatwave. Figure 1 illustrates the results for these scenarios in terms of temperature evolution for the cooling chamber as well as for the milk.

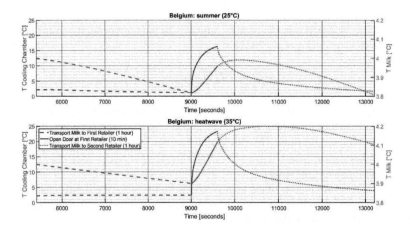

Figure 1: Temperature evolution for the cooling chamber of the truck and the milk for two scenarios (summer and heatwave) referring to Belgium.

Based on these results, the milk temperature did not exceed the 4 °C threshold for the summer scenario, with a maximum milk temperature of 3.99 °C. For the heatwave scenario, nevertheless, the milk temperature reached 4.20 °C, which means that the cold supply chain can be disrupted even for a central European country.

Greece, which belongs to the Mediterranean climate based on the Köppen climate classification (Beck et al., 2018), recorded the highest temperature in 2023 on 23 July, at 45 °C, based on the CDS data. Therefore, the temperature scenarios were 30 °C for the summer and 45 °C for the heatwave, and the results are depicted in Figure 2. In both cases the milk temperature exceeded the 4 °C threshold. For the summer scenario the maximum milk temperature was 4.09 °C, while for the heatwave it was 4.44 °C. These results underline the urgent need for adaptation in the countries that suffer from severe heatwaves. Overall, by comparing Figure 1 with Figure 2, it is clear that as the ambient temperature increased, the maximum milk temperature increased and the time for which the milk had a temperature above 4 °C prolonged.

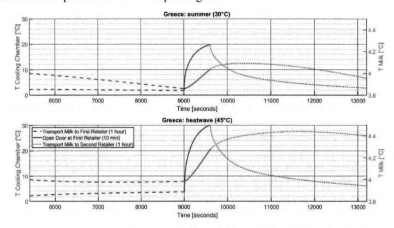

Figure 2: Temperature evolution for the cooling chamber of the truck and the milk for two scenarios (summer and heatwave) referring to Greece.

3.2. Listeria monocytogenes population level

Based on the above, the evaluation of the *Listeria monocytogenes* levels was simulated only for the heatwave scenario in Greece. Considering the effect of temperature on the maximum growth rate of *Listeria monocytogenes*, even though the minimum temperature for growth was below 4 °C, the rate at which the pathogen grew was low. Thus, for the short timeframe of the supply change considered, i.e., about two hours in total, the increase in the population was quite low.

Therefore, for this case, two additional time steps were accounted for: one before the transportation and one after. The first one (1.5 hours) started at the time of contamination, which was assumed to happen at the production facility, until the start of the transportation. For this step, the milk temperature was assumed to be constant at 4 °C. The second one (4 days) started at the end of transportation until the milk purchase, where the milk temperature was considered constant at 4 °C. The reasoning behind this selection was that the shelf life of pasteurized milk in Greece is 5 days by law (Koutsoumanis et al., 2010). The contamination was assumed at 1000 CFU/ml and the resulting population evolution is illustrated in Figure 3. The data were compared with the scenario where the milk temperature is considered constant at 4 °C (no disruption in Figure 3).

As the nature of bacterial growth is exponential, it is expected that at the beginning of the simulation, which corresponded to the cold chain, the population level would be quite low compared to the end of the simulation. By comparing the two cases, the pathogen population at the end of the shelf life was higher for the heatwave scenario, as expected. This shows that an increase in the population of foodborne pathogens is possible due to heatwaves and thus, the food safety of the supply chain is at risk due to climate change.

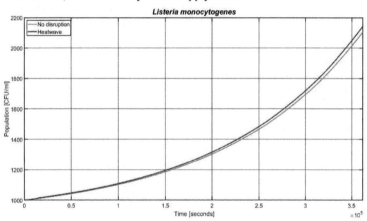

Figure 3: *Listeria monocytogenes* population for heatwave scenario in Greece.

4. Conclusions

There is a growing concern regarding the effect of climate change on food supply chains, as it endangers food security. From a food safety aspect, transporting and storing certain foods, such as pasteurized milk, is utilized as a barrier to pathogen growth. This means that a disruption in the cold supply chain can potentially lead to foodborne illness. The aim of this paper was to evaluate the effect of heatwaves on the cold supply chain of pasteurized milk, both in terms of temperature disruption and pathogen proliferation by utilizing mathematical modelling. Two distinct regions of Europe were selected (Greece and Belgium), and according to the results, for the heatwave scenario the cold supply chain was disrupted in both regions. This means that heatwaves should be a concerning issue not only for the warmer European south, but also for the central European regions. Even though the difference in the final population of the simulated pathogen, i.e., *Listeria monocytogenes*, between the heatwave and the scenario without disruption was low, the applied framework can be used in the context of food safety for other products with longer shelf life, where the corresponding difference will be higher due to the exponential growth of pathogenic bacteria. Taking into account the position of the cargo as well as incorporating the spatial aspect for the milk model would increase the accuracy of the results. Furthermore, in this study the possibility of cold chain disruption at the stage of the retailer, which would highlight the difference between the ideal non-disrupted cold chain and reality, was not considered. Overall, this research shows the need to adapt the operation conditions for the cold supply chain in light of the effect of climate change.

Acknowledgement

This work was supported by the PROTECT project funded by the European Union's Horizon 2020 Research and Innovation Programme [MSCA grant 813329]. Author Simen Akkermans was funded by the Research Foundation Flanders (FWO) under grant number 1224623N.

References

Beck H.E., Zimmermann N.E., McVicar T.R., Vergopolan N., Berg A., Wood E.F., 2018. Present and future Köppen-Geiger climate classification maps at 1-km resolution. Sci Data 5

Davis K.F., Downs S., Gephart J.A., 2021. Towards food supply chain resilience to environmental shocks. Nat Food 2

FAO, 2019. Food systems at risk. New trends and challenges. Rome: FAO-CIRAD-EC

Song H., Cai M., Cen J., Xu C., Zeng Q., 2022. Research on energy saving optimization method of electric refrigerated truck based on genetic algorithm, Int J Refrig 137

Konovalenko I., Ludwig A., Leopold H., 2021. Real-time temperature prediction in a cold supply chain based on Newton's law of cooling. Decis Support Syst 141

Katsini L. Bhonsale S., Akkermans S., Roufou S. Griffin S., Valdramidis V., Misiou O., Koutsoumanis K., Muñoz López C.A., Polanska M., Van Impe J.F.M., 2022. Quantitative methods to predict the effect of climate change on microbial food safety: A needs analysis. Trends Food Sci 126

Koutsoumanis K., Pavlis A., Nychas G.J., Xanthiakos K., 2010. Probabilistic model for *Listeria monocytogenes* growth during distribution, retail storage, and domestic storage of pasteurized milk. Appl Environ Microbiol 76(7)

Munir M.T., Zhang Y., Yu W., Wilson D.I., Young B.R., 2016. Virtual milk for modelling and simulation of dairy processes. J Dairy Sci 99(5)

Fallmann M., Poks A., Kozek M., 2023. Control-oriented hybrid model of a small-scale refrigerated truck chamber. Appl Therm Eng 220

Muñoz Sabater J., 2019. ERA5-Land hourly data from 1950 to present. Copernicus Climate Change Service (C3S) Climate Data Store (CDS), Accessed on 10-11-2023

Alavi S.H., Puri V.M., Knabel S.J., Mohtar R.H., Whiting R.C., 1999. Development and Validation of a Dynamic Growth Model for *Listeria monocytogenes* in Fluid Whole Milk, J Food Prot 62(2)

Wu J., Hsiao H., 2021. Food quality and safety risk diagnosis in the food cold chain through failure mode and effect analysis. Food Control 120

Flavio Manenti, Gintaras V. Reklaitis (Eds.), Proceedings of the 34th European Symposium on Computer Aided Process Engineering / 15th International Symposium on Process Systems Engineering (ESCAPE34/PSE24), June 2-6, 2024, Florence, Italy

A Conceptual Design and Economic Assessment of a Chitin Biorefinery Based on Shrimp Processing Wastes

Ana Carolina Moreira Fonseca,[a*] Bruno Faccini Santoro,[b] Omar José Guerra Fernández,[c] Moisés Teles dos Santos,[a]

[a] Department of Chemical Engineering, Escola Politécnica, Universidade de São Paulo, Av. Prof. Luciano Gualberto, trav. 3, n. 380, São Paulo, 05508-010, Brazil

[b] OP2B - Soluções para Otimização de Negócios Ltda. Avenida Pompeia, 723, São Paulo, 05023-000, Brazil

[c] National Renewable Energy Laboratory, 15013 Denver West Parkway Golden, CO 80401, 303-275-3000

*acmfonseca@usp.br

Abstract

Due to the extensive production of shrimp in captivity, waste generation has increased significantly and has become an environmental problem. The recovery of biomolecules can be an important way to mitigate the environmental problems associated with processing in this sector. In this sense, the present work aimed to evaluate a biorefinery approach for valuing shrimp farming waste to obtain astaxanthin, chitin and chitosan. Stoichiometric segmentation was used as a tool to identify the process steps, whose information on process variables (fresh water consumption, flow rate and reaction conditions) was adapted from the literature. A biorefinery coupled to a shrimp processing plant was proposed for the immediate use of highly perishable biomass, to guarantee the quality of the extracted products and reduce storage and transportation costs. In practice, the biomass treatment sequence adopted (demineralization followed by deproteinization) eliminates the depigmentation step, as the chitin obtained has a lighter tone. The proposed route was evaluated for four scenarios based on two indicators: gross economic potential (EGP) and metrics for inspection of sales and reagents (MISR). The results indicate that economic viability is achieved only for the production of chitosan, resulting in a gross revenue of US$832.50/cycle and a MISR value > 1. The sale of astaxanthin promotes an increase of US$3.73/cycle in the EGP, considered too low for the inclusion of another stage in the process.

Keywords: chitin, chitosan, astaxanthin, biorefinery, shrimp waste.

1. Introduction

Shrimp farming is a kind of aquaculture in which shrimp are raised in a confined and controlled space. The risk of extinction of marine species captured in the wild has stood out as one of the main reasons for the increase in consumption of species cultivated in captivity, in addition to controlling production costs, standardizing products, and consistency in supply (Veríssimo et al., 2021). However, the amount of waste generated is significant, representing 30-60 % of the animal's total weight, and is disposed in landfills or inappropriate locations, causing environmental problems and risks to human health. The recovery of this waste presents itself as a promising alternative since this biomass is a source of bioactive compounds such as astaxanthin, chitin, proteins, and minerals (Aneesh et al., 2020).

Chitin, which makes up about 15-40 % of shrimp shells, is the product of greatest interest. It is the second most abundant biopolymer in nature after cellulose, with similar molecular structures. The chitin extraction process involves three steps: i) depigmentation, ii) demineralization, and iii) deproteinization. Chitosan, obtained from the deacetylation of chitin, is a biopolymer of industrial interest as it has properties such as biodegradability, biocompatibility, low levels of toxicity, and allergenicity, forms gels easily and inhibits growth of microorganisms (Verardi et al., 2023). Despite the potential for application in several areas, chitosan production on a commercial scale is still under investigation. The chemical method is the most commercially used to obtain this biopolymer. However, it results in acidic and alkaline residues that are toxic to the environment and difficult to treat. Furthermore, it requires the consumption of large amounts of water to wash the biomass between the stages, which limits the sustainability of the process on an industrial scale.

Process Systems Engineering (PSE) deals with the development of systematic techniques to identify an optimal topology of processes, raw materials, and products (Bertran et al., 2022). Recent studies have employed simulation tools (Gómez-Ríos et al., 2019), life cycle assessment (Yang et al., 2019), technical, economic, and environmental assessments (TEA) (Zuorro et al., 2021), and exergetic techniques (Muñoz et al., 2023) to estimate the impact of biorefineries based on chitinous biomass. In this sense, the present work aims to develop a conceptual design for a chitin biorefinery based on shrimp farming waste. A preliminary economic analysis was carried out to identify the feasibility of recovering astaxanthin, chitin, and chitosan-based on product sales prices, reagent costs, and effluent treatment costs generated in the process.

2. Methodology

2.1. Process description

Three possible products are considered: astaxanthin, chitin and chitosan. The design was made considering that the plant is installed close to a shrimp processing plant with a batch processing capacity of 1 t/cycle of fresh shrimp, and each section is briefly described.

2.1.1. Shrimp Fishing, Processing and Waste Pre-treatment

Shrimp is removed from the ponds and immersed in tanks with ice and sodium metabisulfite solution (MBS) 9 % (w/w). Damaged and stained shrimp is separated in the sorting unit. The heads and shells are removed in the decapitation and peeling steps, respectively. The main output stream corresponds to shrimp meat. The output streams containing the shrimp heads and shells are washed, dried and ground. The composition of the incoming dry biomass stream in the depigmentation section was considered the experimental characterization of the *Penaeus vannamei* shrimp shell, as presented in Table 1, with the set of reactions used for stoichiometric segmentation.

Table 1. Average composition of *Penaeus vannamei* shrimp shells and stoichiometric reactions for processing shrimp farming waste.

Component	Composition (%)	Process Step	Reaction Set
Astaxanthin	0.41	Depigmentation	
Calcium carbonate	5.13		$CaCO_3 + 2\ HCl \rightarrow CaCl_2 + H_2O + CO_2$
Sodium carbonate	2.62	Demineralization	$Na_2CO3 + 2\ HCl \rightarrow 2\ NaCl + H_2O + CO_2$
Magnesium carbonate	1.52		$MgCO_3 + 2\ HCl \rightarrow MgCl_2 + H_2O + CO_2$
Calcium phosphate	12.90		$Ca_3(PO4)_2 + 6\ HCl \rightarrow 3\ CaCl_2 + 2\ H_3PO_4$
Total protein	36.60	Deproteinization	Dipeptide + 2NaOH→ 2Aminoacid·Na$^+$ + H_2O
Total fat	6.40	Saponification	$C_{17}H_{34}O_2 + NaOH \rightarrow C_{16}H_{31}0_2Na + CH_3OH$
Chitin	29.97	Deacetilation	$C_8H_{15}NO_6 + NaOH \rightarrow C_6H_{13}NO_5 + C_2H_3NaO_2$
Moisture	4.45		

2.1.2. Chitin Recovery

Depigmentation is carried out by suspending the material in an 80 % ethanol-water solution (w/w), in a solid-liquid ratio of 1:5. With the material dried and discolored, acid demineralization of inorganic salts is carried out using 5.2 % (w/w) HCl solution, in a solid-liquid ratio of 1:5, at room temperature, under constant agitation for approximately 50 min. Then, the stream is filtered and the demineralized biomass is washed with water until neutral pH is achieved. For the deproteinization step, the chitin-rich stream is separated from proteins using 4 % (w/w) NaOH solution, in a solid-liquid ratio of 1:10. The output stream is filtered and the resulting solid fraction is washed with water until pH neutrality. Then, the product can be sold as a raw material for the synthesis of chitosan. This step also hydrolyzes and removes lipids which can then be separated from the protein. A fraction of fats presented in the raw material was assumed to be methyl palmitate.

2.1.3. Chitosan Recovery

The deacetylation reaction produces chitosan from the hydrolysis of acetamide groups of chitin molecules with 50 % (w/w) NaOH solution, in a ratio of 1:10. The chitosan-rich stream is washed until pH neutral and dried.

2.2. Economic viability

Revenue was the economic metric used to preliminarily assess the viability of the shrimp biorefinery based on four scenarios: 1) chitin recovery; 2) recovery of chitin and astaxanthin; 3) conversion of chitin to chitosan, and 4) conversion of chitin to chitosan and recovery of astaxanthin. The indicators economic gross potential (EGP) and metric for inspecting sales and reactants (MISR) were adapted from El-Halwagi (2017), as described in Eqs. (1) and (2). EGP provides an upper limit for process revenue without considering operational and fixed costs. For the process to be viable, the EGP must be greater than zero. However, positive EGP values do not guarantee the viability of the process. Therefore, MISR is used as an indicator analogous to EGP, with values greater than one being desirable for a more detailed analysis of the approach. Table 2 shows the prices of reagents and products, as well as the costs of treating effluents.

$$\text{EGP} = \left(\sum_{p=1}^{N_{products}} \text{Production rate of product } p * \text{Selling price of product } p\right) - \left[\left(\sum_{r=1}^{N_{reactants}} \text{Feed rate of reactant } r * \text{Purchase cost of reactant } r\right) + \left(\sum_{e=1}^{N_{effluents}} \text{Effluent generation rate } e * \text{cost for effluent treatment } e\right)\right] \quad (1)$$

$$\text{MISR} = \frac{\sum_{p=1}^{N_{products}} \text{Production rate of product } p * \text{Selling price of product } p}{\left(\begin{array}{c}\sum_{r=1}^{N_{reactants}} \text{Feed rate of reactant } r * \text{Purchase cost of reactant } r + \\ \sum_{e=1}^{N_{effluents}} \text{Effluent generation rate } e * \text{cost for effluent treatment } e\end{array}\right)} \quad (2)$$

Table 2. Prices of feedstock, products, and effluent treatment costs.

Feedstock	Price (Moreno-Sader et al., 2021)
Sodium metabisulfite	$ 0,50/kg
Ethanol	$ 0,85/kg
HCl	$ 0,30/kg
NaOH	$ 0,20/kg
Freshwater (Turton et al., 2018)	$0,26/1000kg
Product	**Price (Moreno-Sader et al., 2021)**
Astaxanthin	$ 40,00/kg
Chitin	$ 17,00/kg
Chitosan	$ 35,00/kg
Effluents	**Costs (Turton et al., 2018)**
Wastewater treatment	(filtration+activated sludge+chemical processing): $ 56/1000 m^3

3. Results and Discussion

The conceptual design for the shrimp farming waste biorefinery is based on material recycling and reuse flows. The limited data available on industrial-scale crustacean biorefinery justifies the use of the stoichiometric segmentation technique to comprehensively evaluate the chosen routes. Based on the reactions involved in each stage of the process, the input and output flow rates per component were identified, as well as the points where fresh water is used and where effluents are discarded. The flowsheet diagram of the shrimp shell biorefinery is shown in Figure 1.

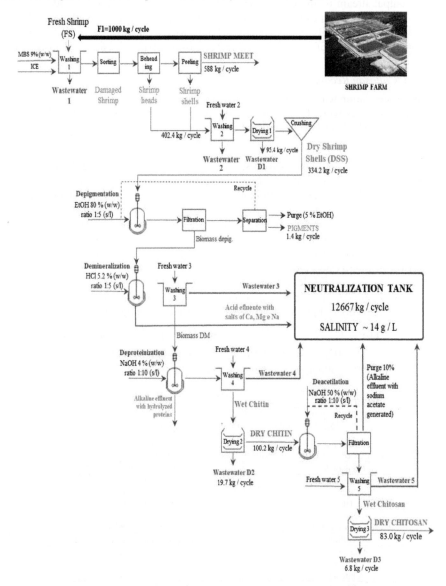

Figure 1. Process flowsheet of a biorefinery for valorizing shrimp farming waste.

In the waste processing stage, peel flour is produced, which has a high nutritional value and can be used as a protein source in animal diets, in addition to containing astaxanthin and chitin, considered the components with the highest added value. This approach considered the recycling strategy in the depigmentation and deacetylation stages to minimize production costs. The ethanol used to extract the pigment is evaporated and the vapor must be condensed and purged by 5 % by mass. The NaOH solution used for chitin deacetylation must be recycled and purged by 10%. Adjusting the concentration of recycled solutions is done by adding fresh reagents according to the purge (Gómez-Ríos et al., 2017). Given the acidic and basic nature of the effluents generated in the process, the streams from washing stages 3, 4, and 5, the effluent generated in the demineralization stage, and the purge of the deacetylation stage are neutralized in a mixing tank to reuse this water for irrigation or shrimp farming in artificial waters (Moura et al., 2023). In the case of integrating wastewater without prior treatment, the output streams from drying stages 1, 2 and 3 would be able to meet the demand for ice in the shrimp fishing process, generating savings of $ 0.03/cycle, representing a value insignificant.

By changing the order of steps and reaction parameters in the pretreatment and conversion of shrimp biomass, chitin and chitosan with variable physicochemical properties can be produced. It is advisable to first extract the pigments to guarantee the integrity of the product. This case study considered the hypothesis that demineralization occurs before deproteinization. This sequence of operations does not require the biomass depigmentation step, as the chitin obtained has a lighter tone when compared to the reverse sequence. In this sense, a preliminary economic analysis was carried out to assess whether it would be worthwhile to include the pigment recovery stage. According to the prices of raw materials, products, and wastewater treatment costs provided by Table 2, the values for EGP and MIRS were estimated for four scenarios, as shown in Table 3.

Table 3. EGP and MIRS indicators before and after water mass integration.

SCENARIO	REVENUE ($/cycle)	COSTS ($/cycle)	EGP ($)	MISR
1) Chitin recovery	1702,73	1731,07	-28,34	0,98
2) Chitin recovery + Astaxanthin	1765,95	1782,15	-16,20	0,99
3) Chitosan recovery	2906,01	2073,51	832,50	1,40
4) Chitosan recovery + Astaxanthin	2960,82	2124,59	836,23	1,39

The process did not prove to be economically viable for Scenarios 1 and 2, as shown by the negative EGP values. The revenue obtained from the sale of pigments promoted a slight increase in gross profit ($ 3.73), as indicated by positive values for EGP and greater than 1 for MIRS in scenario 4. However, it is worth highlighting that the recovery of the solvent used to extract the pigments requires high energy consumption, which directly impacts revenue. This study only considered the costs of reagents and, therefore, the proposed approach presents attractive economic potential only for scenario 3.

Decolorization becomes an important step if a highly purified product is required, for example in application as a biomaterial where residual pigments can cause side effects. In this case, high-quality chitosan is more expensive, offsetting the costs of implementing more steps in the process. The price of astaxanthin must be adjusted so that the inclusion of the pigment recovery step is profitable. It is worth noting that the EGP and MIRS values are linked to the sales prices of the products and may undergo changes, requiring a sensitivity analysis. Furthermore, the use of enzymatic and fermentative processes must be considered as they enable the recovery of protein hydrolysates and mineral salts, diversifying the products to be obtained from the shrimp wastes.

4. Conclusions

This work aimed at applying stoichiometric segmentation to determine the performance of shrimp farming waste processing to obtain chitin, chitosan, and astaxanthin by the chemical method without considering detailed project calculations. According to the parameters adopted, the conceptual approach of the biorefinery was viable only for obtaining chitosan (Scenario 3), resulting in a gross revenue of $ 832.50/cycle. The slight increase in revenue obtained from the sale of astaxanthin did not compensate for the inclusion of another step in the process. In this study, economic indicators were considered that provide an upper limit to the process revenue. However, it is important to consider other sustainability assessment tools when making decisions regarding the implementation of large-scale facilities.

Acknowledgements. The authors thank FAPESP agency for the financial support (project number 2022/02809-0 and 2023/07775-0).

References

P. A. Aneesh, R. Anandan, L. R. G. Kumar, K. K. Ajeeshkumar, K. A. Kumar, S. Mathew. 2020. A step to shell biorefinery-Extraction of astaxanthin-rich oil, protein, chitin, and chitosan from shrimp processing waste. Biomass Conversion and Biorefinery, 13, 205-214.

M. Bertran, A. K. Tulac, R. Gan. 2022. Sustainable biorefinery process synthesis, design, and simulation: Systematic computer-aided methods and tools. *In*: N. Thongchul, A. Kokossis, S. Assabumrungrat, A-Z of Biorefinery, Elsevier, 2022, 559-605.

M. M. El-Halwagi. 2017. Benchmarking Process Performance Through Overall Mass Targeting. *In:* Sustainable Design through Process Integration, 2nd edition, Elsevier, 73-125.

D. Gómez-Ríos, R. Barrera-Zapata, R. Ríos-Estepa. 2017. Comparison of process technologies for chitosan production from shrimp shell waste: A techno-economic approach using Aspen Plus®. Food and Bioproducts Processing, 103, 49-57.

D. Gómez-Ríos, G. Navarro, P. Monsalve, R. Barrera-Zapata, R. Ríos-Estepa. 2019. Aspen Plus® Simulation Strategies Applied to the Study of Chitin Bioextraction from Shrimp Waste. Food Technology and Biotechnology, 57, 2, 238-248.

K. A. Moreno-Sader, J. D. Martinez-Consuegra, A. D. González-Delgado. 2021. Development of a biorefinery approach for shrimp processing in North-Colombia: Process simulation and sustainability assessment. Environmental Technology and Innovation, 22,1-14.

P. Moura, I. A. Neto, H. Brandão, P. Furtado, L. Poersch, W. Wasielesky Jr. 2023. Effects of magnesium reduction in artificial low-salinity water on the growth of Pacific white shrimp Litopenaeus vannamei in a biofloc system. Aquaculture, 577, 1-9.

F. L. Muñoz, S. Meramo, L. Ricardez-Sandoval, A. D. Gonzalez, B. C. Castillo, A. G. Quiroga, B. L. G. Baptiste, J. León-Pulido. 2023. Insights from an exergy analysis of a green chemistry chitosan biorefinery. Chemical Engineering Research and Design, 194, 666-677.

A. Verardi, P. Sangiorgio, S. Moliterni, S. Errico, A. Spagnoletta, S. Dimatteo. 2023. Advanced technologies for chitin recovery from crustacean waste. Clean Technologies and Recycling, 3, 1, 4-43.

R. Turton, R. Bailie, W. Whiting, J. Shaeiwitz, D. Bhattacharyya. 2018. Analysis, Synthesis, and Design of Chemical Processes, 4th edition, Pearson, 212-213.

N. V. Veríssimo, C. U. Mussagy, A. A. Oshiro, C. M. N. Mendonça, V. C. Santos-Ebinuma, A. P. Júnior, R. P. S. Oliveira, J. F. B. Pereira. 2021. From green to blue economy: Marine biorefineries for a sustainable ocean-based economy. Green Chemistry, 23, 9377-9400.

H. Yang, G. Gözaydın, R. R. Nasaruddin, J. R. G. Har, X. Chen, X. Wang, N. Yan. 2019. Toward the Shell Biorefinery: Processing Crustacean Shell Waste Using Hot Water and Carbonic Acid. ACS Sustainable Chemistry and Engineering, 7, 5, 5532-5542.

A. Zuorro, K. A. Moreno-Sader, A. D. Gonzalez-Delgado. 2021. Evaluating the feasibility of a pilot-scale shrimp biorefinery via techno-economic analysis. Journal of Cleaner Production, 320, 1-11.

Flavio Manenti, Gintaras V. Reklaitis (Eds.), Proceedings of the 34th European Symposium on Computer Aided Process Engineering / 15th International Symposium on Process Systems Engineering (ESCAPE34/PSE24), June 2-6, 2024, Florence, Italy

Parameter estimation of multi-substrate biokinetic models of lignocellulosic microbial protein systems

Mason Banks,[a] Mark Taylor,[b] Miao Guo[a*]

*a*King's College London, Strand, London WC2R 2LS, United Kingdom
*b*Marlow Ingredients Ltd, Nelson Ave, Billingham TS23 4HA, United Kingdom
*miao.guo@kcl.ac.uk

Abstract

The current global food system faces significant challenges related to waste production, carbon emissions, and resource inefficiency. This work aims to address these issues by focusing on the application of microbial protein technology for sustainable protein production from organic waste, thereby promoting a circular economy. The study focuses on a critical bottleneck in bioprocess development, specifically in waste carbon utilisation, emphasising the need for precise biokinetic models. Unstructured models are to be employed for their simplicity and widespread applicability, but challenges in parameter estimation persist, especially for multi-substrate systems. The research introduces an experimental-computational methodology for high-throughput screening, utilising absorbance spectroscopy and HPLC analysis from batch 96 well plate fermentations. The study expands parameter estimation techniques towards multi-substrate biokinetic models for the conversion of lignocellulosic hydrolysates to mycoprotein (*Fusarium venenatum* A3/5). Various experimental designs explore the influence of sugar composition, pre-culture environment, and substrate-to-biomass ratio on model performance. The ultimate goal is to inform decision-making for the viable scale-up of industrial waste-to-mycoprotein processes, considering sustainability and technoeconomic constraints.

Keywords: Lignocellulose, Microbial Protein, Parameter Estimation, Waste-to-Protein

1. Introduction

1.1. Background

The current global food system produces substantial waste and carbon emissions and relies on excessive use of arable land and freshwater supplies (Holden et al., 2018). These factors not only result in environmental degradation but also exacerbate the issues of increasing global hunger and protein deficiency according to a recent meta-analysis by Van Dijk et al. (2021). A potential solution to this global challenge was explored by Durkin et al. (2022) who demonstrated high potential for recovery of carbon and nutrients from global by-product streams (i.e. organic waste) using microbial protein technology to produce sustainable, high-quality protein while promoting a circular economy. However, despite increasing research attention in waste valorisation and microbial protein technologies, several critical bottlenecks exist at each stage of bioprocess development that hinder rapid and viable scale-up (Piercy et al., 2023). In the context of waste carbon utilisation, the development of precise and accurate biokinetic models is critical to informing decision makers in fermentation process design (Narayanan et al., 2019) but remains a challenging task due to compositional variation of feedstock substrates utilised via complex gene regulatory pathways which are experimentally demanding to characterise particularly for non-model microorganisms (Panikov, 2021), in addition to outstanding challenges in model identification and parameter estimation of microbial processes (Wieland et al., 2021).

1.2. Parameter estimation of biokinetic models

Biokinetic models describe the behaviour of a biological system, such as cell growth, substrate consumption, and product formation. Unstructured models predict microbial growth and metabolism without considering detailed intracellular processes or population structures (Muloiwa et al., 2020). Eq. (1) is the model empirically determined by Monod (1949), a hyperbolic expression relating specific growth rate (μ) to the concentration of the limiting substrate (S) defined by two parameters, the maximum specific growth rate (μ_{max}) and the half-saturation constant (K_s).

$$\mu = \mu_{max} \frac{S}{S + K_s} \tag{1}$$

For a single substrate system, growth of biomass (X) and substrate depletion can be described by a pair of ODEs, Eq. (2). A yield coefficient ($Y_{X/S}$) is introduced as a third parameter to define the conversion efficiency from substrate to biomass.

$$\frac{dX}{dt} = \mu X \qquad \frac{dS}{dt} = -\frac{\mu X}{Y_{X/S}} \tag{2}$$

This unstructured model is predominantly employed for design and simulation of industrial bioprocesses due to its simplicity and good performance when applied to a wide range of microorganisms and environmental conditions. Previous research has focused on incorporating the influence of other variables into unstructured models, including pH and temperature (Infantes et al., 2012), cell maintenance (van Bodegom, 2007), endogenous decay (Bahar & Ciggin, 2016), substrate/product inhibition (Tan et al., 2000), and extending models to describe multi-substrate utilisation (Amrane et al., 2005; Chohji et al., 1984) and microbial consortia interactions (Hanly & Henson, 2013) to accurately model more complex systems. However, despite the advantages provided by unstructured models, several challenges hinder their effective implementation. Firstly, a long-standing research problem is the ability to determine unique estimates of

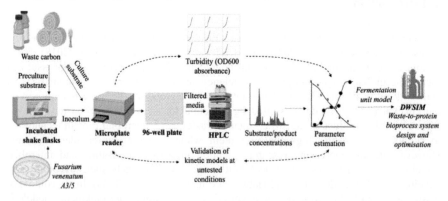

Figure 1: Experimental-computational methodology workflow (Solid arrows = Material flows; Dashed arrows = Data flows).

μ_{max}, K_s, and $Y_{X/S}$ parameters. An excellent review by Kovárová-Kovar & Egli (1998) highlighted how parameter estimates with high goodness-of-fit from E. coli growth experiments varied greatly between different publications, the result of differing experimental designs and parameter estimation methods. Furthermore, a ubiquitous method for reliably obtaining uncorrelated estimates of μ_{max} and K_s has not yet been developed (Liu & Zachara, 2001). Furthermore, despite their relevance to sustainable bioprocesses using complex sugar feedstocks, the development of rigorous unstructured multi-substrate models remains relatively underexplored compared to structured modelling approaches such as flux balance analysis, the development of which can be experimentally expensive and highly strain-dependent and therefore not always generalisable across processes (Qiu et al., 2023). Recent work by Manheim et al. (2019) in unstructured modelling of microbial kinetics have attempted to create a generalised methodology for parameter estimation and have demonstrated improved accuracy, predictive capacity and lower estimator bias when utilising global non-linear regression routines, particularly when employing metaheuristic optimisation algorithms (e.g. particle swarm optimisation), compared to local non-linear regression. However, only single-substrate models were investigated using this approach, leaving scope for future work exploring multi-substrate systems of key relevance to waste-recovery fermentation processes.

1.3. Extension of parameter estimation methodology towards multi-substrate biokinetic models of microbial protein production from lignocellulosic hydrolysates
This work aims to expand upon research efforts into accurate and precise parameter estimation techniques towards predictive modelling of multi-substrate systems. Our specific focus is to develop high fidelity mathematical models that describe the fermentation kinetics underpinning the conversion of synthetic lignocellulosic hydrolysate (containing primary monomeric sugars D-glucose and D-xylose) to mycoprotein using generally recognised as safe (GRAS) certified fungal strain *Fusarium venenatum* A3/5. To achieve this, we have implemented a hybrid experimental-computational methodology for high-throughput screening of biomass and substrate/by-product time-series profiles through on-line absorbance spectroscopy and off-line high performance liquid chromatography (HPLC) analysis respectively.

2. Materials and Methods

2.1. Biokinetic model parameter estimation methodology and experimental design
Experimental data will be used within a parameter estimation framework applied to an array of candidate unstructured biokinetic models describing dual-substrate depletion and biomass growth. One example system is given by Eq. (3-4), which models consumption of substrates through semi-independent metabolic pathways using distinct growth parameters for each substrate, including constants k_{s1} and k_{s2} to capture transcriptomic inhibition effects of substrate pairs such as carbon catabolite repression.

$$\mu_1 = \mu_{max,1} \frac{S_1}{S_1 + K_{s1} + k_{s2}S_2} \qquad \mu_2 = \mu_{max,2} \frac{S_2}{S_2 + K_{s2} + k_{s1}S_1} \qquad (3)$$

$$\frac{dX}{dt} = (\mu_1 + \mu_2)X \qquad \frac{dS}{dt} = -\mu_1 \frac{X}{Y_{X/s1}} - \mu_2 \frac{X}{Y_{X/s2}} \qquad (4)$$

Different experimental designs covering the space of lignocellulosic sugar composition of agricultural residues will be explored to determine the range of parameter values associated with waste resources of variable batch-to-batch valorisation potentials. In addition, the pre-culture environment and initial substrate to biomass ratio will also be varied to determine the influence of culture history and adaptation on the values of parameter estimates and model performance. The use of high-throughput 96-well plates provides a significant advantage when investigating several influencing factors. For example, using a full-factorial design, the three aforementioned factors can be investigated at three levels in triplicate in a six-point time series, the total number of experiments (wells) required can be calculated as the total number of conditions multiplied by the number of time points and replicates respectively (i.e. $3^3 \times 6 \times 3 = 486$), thereby requiring only five 96-well plates in total to investigate the design space. Different non-linear regression methods including the Levenberg-Marquardt algorithm, particle swarm optimisation, and differential evolution algorithms and will be compared in their ability to provide unbiased, accurate and precise parameter estimates, in addition to model goodness of fit and convergence speed. The open-source platform Pyomo will be used to optimise the objective function to minimise the sum of square errors between observed experimental data and the predicted values of the candidate biokinetic model systems as stated in Eq. (5), where n is the number of data points, y_i and x_i are the output response and input at point i respectively, and $f(x_i, \theta)$ is the non-linear system evaluated at point x_i with the vector of parameter values θ.

$$\text{minimise} \sum_{i=1}^{n} [y_i - f(x_i, \theta)]^2 \tag{5}$$

Subsequently, the predictive accuracies of the candidate models and best parameter estimates are then evaluated through cross-validation with testing data partitioned from the original experimental dataset.

2.2. Experimental materials and methods

50 mL Erlenmeyer flasks containing 3 w/v% of carbon substrate in minimal salts media are inoculated with *F. venenatum* A3/5 from agar plates and incubated at 28 °C with a shaking speed of 130 rpm. After 72 h, spores are harvested using a 100 μm cell strainer and spore concentration is determined using a hemocytometer and optical microscope, and subsequently diluted with sterile media to the desired concentration. Aliquots of stock solutions containing 300 g/L D-glucose and D-xylose are then added to minimal salts media to make up 5 mL vials containing 3 w/v% total substrate with varying ratios of the two sugars. The prepared dilution is then used to inoculate each of the vials with a predefined spore concentration. Wells of a clear, flat-bottom, non-treated 96 well plate are then filled with 200 μL of the vial contents. Each vial is used to make up 6 wells of the plate which are sequentially harvested at 6 time points over the course of 96 hours of batch fermentation. Each of the time points are repeated in triplicate. A microplate reader is used to measure the well absorbance at a wavelength of 600 nm at 28 °C and 100 rpm using a double-orbital shaking mode. Optical density (OD) readings are taken every 20 min and subsequently converted to biomass concentrations using a predetermined calibration function. Extracellular media of the harvested wells is separated from cell material using Sartorius Claristep 0.2 μm filters into 2 mL vials. The liquid media from each well is analysed following a protocol for residual sugars and sugar alcohols. The column used for separation of compounds is the Biorad Aminex HPX-87H (300 x 7.8 mm) with mobile phase of dilute sulphuric acid (5 mM) at a flowrate of 0.6 mLmin⁻¹ and temperature of 50 °C. The separated compounds are then detected by an in-line refractive index detector (RID) with absorbance wavelength of 210 nm to generate spectra, from which time-series concentrations are to be determined.

3. Results & Discussion

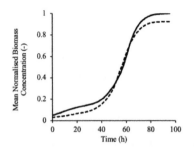 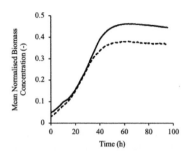

Figure 2: Mean biomass growth curves normalised relative to positive control using D-glucose (left panel) and D-xylose (right panel). Solid curves represent identical pre-culture substrate (e.g. glucose/glucose), while dashes lines represent alternate pre-culture substrate (e.g. xylose/glucose).

Preliminary research aimed to investigate the relative growth of *F. venenatum* A3/5 utilising D-glucose and D-xylose as sole substrates and the effect of preculture (inoculation) substrate environment on subsequent growth. The results demonstrate that the final biomass concentration achieved when utilising D-xylose is less than half of that of D-glucose, suggesting a lower substrate-to-biomass conversion efficiency (yield) despite a longer initial lag time when utilising D-glucose. Furthermore, results suggest that glucose is the preferred pre-culture substrate for this mixed sugar cultivation when the objective is to maximise the overall biomass yield, suggesting that D-xylose preculture potentially enhances production of by-products (e.g. ethanol) throughout the fermentation. However, upcoming work implementing HPLC analysis of media composition and rigorous model-based parameter estimation (as discussed in the previous sections) is required to test these hypotheses. Nevertheless, the initial results provide parameter intervals for $\mu_{max,1}$ and $\mu_{max,2}$ calculated from tangential approximation of the biomass curves to narrow the solution space of parameters thereby increasing the likelihood of locating the global optimum solution to the non-linear regression problem.

4. Conclusion

In conclusion, this research lays the groundwork for advancing microbial protein technology and waste valorisation. The ongoing work involves rigorous parameter estimation for multi-substrate systems, specifically focusing on lignocellulosic hydrolysate fermentation by fungal strain *Fusarium venenatum* A3/5 to produce microbial protein (mycoprotein). The proposed methodology integrates experimental data with computational models, aiming to enhance accuracy in predicting fermentation kinetics. Results from this ongoing research will contribute to the optimisation of bioprocess flowsheets, guiding decision-making for the sustainable and economically viable scale-up of waste-to-mycoprotein systems. Preliminary results demonstrate the feasibility of utilising lignocellulosic sugars for the growth of F. venenatum A3/5 biomass, including pentose substrates despite demonstrating lower overall growth yields. Future work will build upon this knowledge by investigating sugar consumption and by-product concentration throughout the fermentation for implementation within a parameter estimation framework to more comprehensively characterise and model the lignocellulosic fermentation system.

References

Amrane, A., Adour, L., & Couriol, C. (2005). An unstructured model for the diauxic growth of Penicillium camembertii on glucose and arginine. Biochemical Engineering Journal, 24(2), 125–133.

Bahar, S., & Ciggin, A. S. (2016). A simple kinetic modeling approach for aerobic stabilization of real waste activated sludge. Chemical Engineering Journal, 303, 194–201.

Chohji, T., Sawada, T., Nakamura, Y., & Kuno, S. (1984). Mathematical model for diauxic growth of microorganisms in mixed substrate medium. Journal of Chemical Engineering of Japan, 17(5), 478–485.

Durkin, A., Finnigan, T., Johnson, R., Kazer, J., Yu, J., Stuckey, D., & Guo, M. (2022). Can closed-loop microbial protein provide sustainable protein security against the hunger pandemic? Current Research in Biotechnology, 4, 365–376.

Hanly, T. J., & Henson, M. A. (2013). Unstructured Modeling of a Synthetic Microbial Consortium for Consolidated Production of Ethanol. IFAC Proceedings Volumes, 46(31), 157–162.

Holden, N. M., White, E. P., Lange, M. C., & Oldfield, T. L. (2018). Review of the sustainability of food systems and transition using the Internet of Food. Npj Sci Food, 2(18).

Infantes, D., González del Campo, A., Villaseñor, J., & Fernández, F. J. (2012). Kinetic model and study of the influence of pH, temperature and undissociated acids on acidogenic fermentation. Biochemical Engineering Journal, 66, 66–72.

Kovárová-Kovar, K., & Egli, T. (1998). Growth Kinetics of Suspended Microbial Cells: From Single-Substrate-Controlled Growth to Mixed-Substrate Kinetics. Microbiology and Molecular Biology Reviews, 62(3), 646–666.

Liu, C., & Zachara, J. M. (2001). Uncertainties of Monod Kinetic Parameters Nonlinearly Estimated from Batch Experiments. Environmental Science & Technology, 35(1), 133–141.

Manheim, D. C., Detwiler, R. L., & Jiang, S. C. (2019). Application of unstructured kinetic models to predict microcystin biodegradation: Towards a practical approach for drinking water treatment. Water Research, 149, 617–631.

Monod, J. (1949). The Growth of Bacterial Cultures. Annual Review of Microbiology, 3(1), 371–394.

Muloiwa, M., Nyende-Byakika, S., & Dinka, M. (2020). Comparison of unstructured kinetic bacterial growth models. South African Journal of Chemical Engineering, 33, 141–150.

Narayanan, H., Luna, M. F., von Stosch, M., Cruz Bournazou, M. N., Polotti, G., Morbidelli, M., Butté, A., & Sokolov, M. (2020). Bioprocessing in the Digital Age: The Role of Process Models. Biotechnology Journal, 15(1).

Panikov, N. S. (2021). Genome-Scale Reconstruction of Microbial Dynamic Phenotype: Successes and Challenges. Microorganisms, 9(11).

Piercy, E., Verstraete, W., Ellis, P. R., Banks, M., Rockström, J., Smith, P., Witard, O. C., Hallett, J., Hogstrand, C., Knott, G., Karwati, A., Rasoarahona, H. F., Leslie, A., He, Y., & Guo, M. (2023). A sustainable waste-to-protein system to maximise waste resource utilisation for developing food- and feed-grade protein solutions. Green Chemistry, 25(3), 808–832.

Qiu, S., Yang, A., & Zeng, H. (2023). Flux balance analysis-based metabolic modeling of microbial secondary metabolism: Current status and outlook. PLOS Computational Biology, 19(8), e1011391.

Tan, Y., Wang, Z.-X., & Marshall, K. C. (2000). Modeling Substrate Inhibition of Microbial Growth. Biotechnology and Bioengineering, 52(5), 602–608.

van Bodegom, P. (2007). Microbial Maintenance: A Critical Review on Its Quantification. Microbial Ecology, 53(4), 513–523.

Van Dijk, M., Morley, T., Rau, M. L., & Saghai, Y. (2021). A meta-analysis of projected global food demand and population at risk of hunger for the period 2010-2050. Nature Food, 2, 494–501.

Wieland, F.-G., Hauber, A. L., Rosenblatt, M., Tönsing, C., & Timmer, J. (2021). On structural and practical identifiability. Current Opinion in Systems Biology, 25, 60–69.

Flavio Manenti, Gintaras V. Reklaitis (Eds.), Proceedings of the 34th European Symposium on Computer Aided Process Engineering / 15th International Symposium on Process Systems Engineering (ESCAPE34/PSE24), June 2-6, 2024, Florence, Italy

Sustainable Production and Scale-Up of Succinic Acid from Cyanobacteria

Roja K.,[a] Yogendra Shastri[a*]

[a]*Department of Chemical Engineering, Indian Institute of Technology, Mumbai, 400076, India*
yshastri@iitb.ac.in

Abstract

Cyanobacteria, owing to their high growth rates, are considered promising candidates for CO_2 capture and its conversion to value-added chemicals and fuels. This work deals with the design of the cyanobacterial systems' sustainable process for succinic acid production. The downstream process involving separation and purification of succinic acid was designed based on the experimental data of disodium succinate productivity of 2 g/L from cyanobacteria. Two processes were considered for the purification of succinic acid: high and low temperature crystallization of succinic acid (Process I) and purification using methanol addition (Process II). The detailed commercial scale downstream process was designed and simulated in ASPEN Plus® for 100 t/y succinic acid production capacity. Cradle to gate life cycle assessment was also conducted using the experimental and simulation data in combination with Ecoinvent® 3.9 database. Environmental impacts are high for process I due to the large amount of feed requirement indicating that process II is more efficient than process I.

Keywords: cyanobacteria, succinic acid, life cycle assessment, crystallization

1. Introduction

With the growing population, there is an increase in the demand for energy, food, and other resources such as commodity materials, construction materials, and medicines. Humans mainly depend on fossil fuel-derived products to meet their daily requirements, such as fuel, clothing, plastic products, etc. On average, global energy consumption increases by 1-2 % yearly. The increasing consumption of fossil fuels has led to CO_2 emissions and impacted the environment and human health. Global emissions have rapidly grown, and 36.8 Gt of CO_2 was emitted in 2022 (IEA, 2023). Most fuels and chemicals such as ethanol, succinate, and fatty acids are obtained from petroleum-based chemical processes. In order to meet the energy demands of the growing population and to tackle the ongoing environmental issues, eco-friendly, renewable, and sustainable forms of energy sources and chemical production processes must be developed.

Presently, many feedstocks such as palm oil, sugarcane, corn, grass, and agricultural residue are being studied for the producing biofuels and value-added chemicals. Some of these feedstocks may impact food availability, while others are not viable as the pretreatment cost is very high (Hossain et al., 2019). Cyanobacteria are identified as a potential source to resolve the issue. These microorganisms can capture up to 10 % of solar energy (Niederholtmeyer et al., 2010). There is an increasing attraction towards these organisms because of their ability to produce biofuels and chemicals via genetic modification. Due to the ease of genetic modification and substantial stress tolerance, they are considered as potential cell factories. Several research studies show that various chemicals such as ethylene, succinate, ethanol, butanol, and hydrogen, are produced in a significant amount from genetically modified cyanobacteria. However, limited work has been done on studying the environmental impacts and economic feasibility of chemical production from cyanobacteria, even though a lot of experimental studies are being conducted on laboratory scale. This work focuses on the design of succinic acid production from cyanobacteria as well as to determine the environmental feasibility of the developed process.

2. Methodology

2.1 Process Description

The engineered cyanobacteria are cultured in a photo bio-reactor (PBR) using energy from a light source, nutrient (BG-11 medium), and air (CO_2) supply with a growth condition of 7.5 pH and 38 °C. At the end of the fifth day, growth of cyanobacteria and production of succinate is completed and the culture is harvested and the succinate salt is separated. The filtrated disodium succinate solution is preheated to 99 °C. Two methods are considered for the recovery of succinic acid from disodium succinate and purification of succinic acid. Process I uses high and low temperature crystallization, while process II uses purification via methanol addition.

2.1.1 Process I: High and Low Temperature Crystallization

Preheated feed is fed to a triple-effect evaporator in which feed is concentrated to 16 %. The concentrated solution is cooled down to 70°C and reacted with sulfuric acid producing succinic acid and sodium sulfate. The solution is concentrated and heated to obtain sodium sulfate concentration so that the sodium sulfate crystals are precipitated selectively. The precipitated sodium sulfate is filtrated. Succinic acid and uncrystallized sodium sulfate solution are cooled to 35 °C to precipitate succinic acid crystals (Fujita et al., 2009). Succinic acid crystals are filtrated and dissolved in water to remove the impurities. Pure succinic acid crystals are obtained by crystallization.

2.1.2 Process II: Purification using Methanol

Preheated feed is fed to a triple-effect evaporator in which feed is concentrated to 50 % (Berglund et al., 1999). The concentrated solution is cooled down to 40 °C and is fed to the reactor with sulfuric acid to obtain succinic acid and sodium sulfate. The pH is maintained at 1.5 – 1.8 to precipitate succinic acid. Succinic acid crystals are separated and the liquid stream containing sodium sulfate is processed to separate sodium sulfate. Methanol is added to the succinic acid crystals for further purification. Methanol is evaporated from the succinic acid stream and finally, succinic acid crystals are obtained. The methanol is recovered and recycled.

2.2 Design and Simulation of Succinic Acid Downstream Production Process

The detailed commercial scale downstream process is designed and simulated in ASPEN Plus® using Wilson vol. as the thermodynamic property package. The simulation provides the material and energy balances and equipment sizing details using the economic analyzer tool. The flowsheet's basis is 2 g/L of succinate productivity level from cyanobacteria. The production capacity of the plant based on current succinate productivity is 100 t/y of succinic acid. The evaporator is modeled using Aspen flash and heater. Filters given in the flow sheet are component separator's based on split fractions. Steam flow for triple-effect evaporator system is calculated based on varying the steam flow rate to obtain the concentration in the last effect.

2.3. Life Cycle Assessment

2.3.1. Goal and Scope Definition

The present work focuses on studying the environmental impacts of succinic acid production from cyanobacteria via two purification processes. The impact assessment is conducted using OpenLCA 1.11 software with the EcoInvent® 3.9 database and data collected from the literature. Cradle to gate approach is used where the impact analysis from the extraction of raw materials to the production stage is determined. ReCiPe (H) midpoint using physical allocation is used as the impact assessment method as ReCiPe offers characterization elements that are representative for the global scale. The functional unit of this study is 1 kg of succinic acid. Cyanobacteria cultivation, feed preheating and evaporation, reaction, succinic acid separation, and purification is considered in the system boundary in both processes. The energy requirement in the evaporation process is calculated in terms of natural gas quantity for the boiler operation. Pure CO_2 is considered in the study with 0.135 vvm for the cultivation of cyanobacteria. The heating operations' energy is met through the energy recovered from the vapor from multi-effect evaporator. Cooling water and chilled water is considered as the source of cooling. The electricity source is from a conventional plant with production mix in India. Machinery manufacturing is not considered as a part of system boundary. The condensate from the boiler is recycled back with 5 % loss. The system boundaries for process I and process II are shown in Figure 1 and 2.

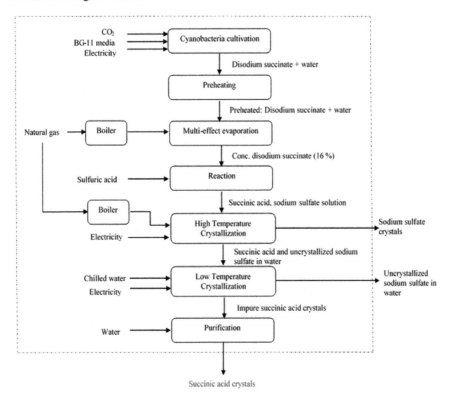

Figure 1. System boundary for succinic acid production via process I

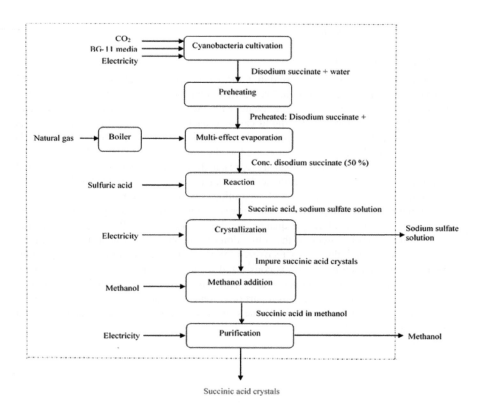

Figure 2. System boundary for succinic acid production via process II

3. Life Cycle Impact Analysis

The impact analysis is conducted for 1 kg of succinic acid production based on two downstream methods and is shown in Table 1.

Table 1. Life cycle impact analysis of succinic acid production from cyanobacteria

Impact category	Reference unit	Process I	Process II
terrestrial acidification potential (TAP)	kg SO$_2$-Eq	0.013	0.006
global warming potential (GWP100)	kg CO$_2$-Eq	6.540	2.835
freshwater ecotoxicity potential (FETP)	kg 1,4-DCB-Eq	0.170	0.074
marine ecotoxicity potential (METP)	kg 1,4-DCB-Eq	0.221	0.096
terrestrial ecotoxicity potential (TETP)	kg 1,4-DCB-Eq	6.888	3.312
fossil fuel potential (FFP)	kg oil-Eq	12.301	5.116
human toxicity potential (HTPc)	kg 1,4-DCB-Eq	0.116	0.055
human toxicity potential (HTPnc)	kg 1,4-DCB-Eq	5.631	2.351

The total energy consumption for processes I and II are 2.88 MJ and 2.05 MJ per kg of succinic acid respectively as heat recovery is incorporated in the both processes. It is observed that the environmental impacts of process I are more than that of process II. The initial feed requirement for process I is higher than process II. There are two evaporation processes in process I, which resulted in higher energy consumption compared to process II. The water potential is high for process I as the process requires a higher amount of water for steam generation and for the cultivation of cyanobacteria. GWP of fossil-based succinic acid production process is 1.94 kg CO_2 eq/ kg of succinic acid which is lower than the processes considered in this study. The impacts of the both methods can be further reduced by improving the process operating conditions.

Figure 3 provides the impact contribution of Process I. 73 % of GWP100 and 94 % of FFP is due to the feed evaporation. Natural gas is the source of energy for evaporation. 45 % of the WCP and 77 % of TETP contributed by the cyanobacterial cultivation due to the use of chemicals for BG-11 media preparation.

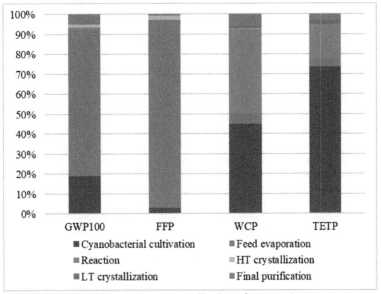

Figure 3. Impact contribution of Process I

The impact contribution of process II is provided in Figure 4. The highest contributor towards GWP100 (69 %), FFP (92 %) is the feed evaporation stage due to the use of natural gas as fuel source. The cultivation of cyanobacteria contributed towards WCP (44 %) and TETP (73 %) as similar to Process I. The cultivation stage requires huge amount of water and nutrients for the growth of cyanobacteria.

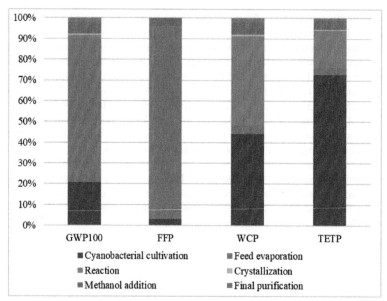

Figure 4. Impact contribution of Process II

4. Conclusions

In this work, the downstream processes for the production of succinic acid from the cyanobacterial system have been designed and simulated in ASPEN Plus software. Cradle to gate life cycle assessment of cyanobacterial succinic acid production has conducted. Energy consumption is highest for the feed evaporation process, and it contributed most to the total impacts in process I and II. FFP is highest for the feed evaporation stage for both processes as natural gas is used as fuel for steam generation. Environmental impacts are high for process I due to the large feed requirement, indicating that process II is more efficient than process I. The climate change impact for both processes are high when compared with the conventional petroleum route succinic acid production.

The work is being extended to perform techno-economic feasibility for the two processes which will provide concrete recommendations for scale-up. Opportunities to improve the economic and environmental performance are also being identified.

References

Berglund, K. A., Yedur, S., and Dunuwila, D. D., 1999, US Patent 5958744.

Hossain, N., Zaini, J., Mahlia, T.M.I., & Azad, A.K., 2019, Elemental, morphological and thermal analysis of mixed microalgae species from drain water, Renewable Energy, 131, 617-624.

Ichiro Fujita and Kouichi Wada, 2009, US Patent 7915447.

International Energy Agency, 2023, CO_2 Emmisons in 2022.

Niederholtmeyer H., Wolfstadter B.T., Savage, D.F, 2010, Engineering cyanobacteria to synthesize and export hydrophilic products, Applied and Environmental Microbiology, 76, 3462-3466.

Flavio Manenti, Gintaras V. Reklaitis (Eds.), Proceedings of the 34th European Symposium on Computer Aided Process Engineering / 15th International Symposium on Process Systems Engineering (ESCAPE34/PSE24), June 2-6, 2024, Florence, Italy

Minimal Target Indices for Cyanobacteria-Based Biorefineries and Optimal Design of the Metabolic Network

Matías Ramos[a,b], Fernando Ramos[a,b], Romina Lasry Testa[a,b], Vanina Estrada[a,b], Maria Soledad Diaz[a,b,*]

[a]*Planta Piloto de Ingeniería Química (PLAPIQUI CONICET-UNS), Camino La Carrindanga km. 7, Bahía Blanca, Argentina*
[b]*Departamento de Ingeniería Química, Universidad Nacional del Sur (UNS), Bahía Blanca, Argentina*
Corresponding Author's E-mail: sdiaz@plapiqui.edu.ar

Abstract

In this work we propose a mixed integer nonlinear programming multiobjective (MOO) model for the determination of minimal target indices for the sustainable design of an integrated cyanobacteria-based biorefinery and its heat exchanger network (HEN), for the production of phycocyanin and zeaxanthin, PHB, fourth-generation bioethanol, biogas, hydrogen and diethyl ether. The main objective is to determine *Synechocystis* sp's minimal target indices (productivity, yield, titer) that should be reached in order to achieve a sustainable biorefinery design by imposing lower bounds on a multi-criteria sustainability metric (Sustainability Net Present Value, SNPV). In the case of strain *in-silico* design, a bilevel programming problem that identifies gene knockouts in a genome scale *Synechocystis* sp. PCC6803 metabolic model (GEM) to couple growth and product synthesis has been formulated. Through this approach, the target indices of alternative *in-silico* strains are compared to their minimum required values. Numerical results show that minimal targets are largely surpassed, for the case of a *Synechocystis* wild-type strain modelled through the GEM and a tailored strain designed for ethanol production. These results offer promising insights into cyanobacteria biorefineries.

Keywords: MINLP, *Synechocystis* sp. PCC 6803, Cyanobacteria-based biorefinery, *In-silico* cyanobacteria

1. Introduction

Biofuels have emerged as an alternative to complement renewable energy sources to increasingly complement fossil fuels paving the way to CO_2 emissions reduction and mitigation of the environmental impact. At present, commercial biofuels are derived from agricultural crops (first-generation) and lignocellulosic biomass (second-generation) but both have disadvantages like the known controversy of competing with food for the first-generation case, or not being economically feasible for the second case (Sarwer *et al.*, 2022). Biofuels produced from algae biomass are considered third-generation, but are not yet commercially produced due to the high production costs, leading to the need of improving production rates and separation processes efficiency. Recent studies have been reported for macroalgae-based integrated biorefineries (Pedrozo *et al.*, 2022) showing that they can be economically feasible. In this sense, fourth-generation biofuels, which are produced directly by genetically modified microorganisms, constitute a more recently studied alternative (Ramos et al., 2023).

In this context, photoautotrophic microorganisms like cyanobacteria, stand out as potential cell factories, thriving on atmospheric/industrial CO_2, inorganic phosphorus (P), and nitrogen (N), using solar and/or artificial light as energy source. Among its value-added products is phycocyanin, an intense blue pigment sought after by food and nutraceutical industries. Additionally, certain cyanobacteria store carbon as PHB, a biopolymer similar to polypropylene with a wide range of applications.

In this work, we aim to assess the viability of three *in-silico* strains of *Synechocystis* sp. PCC6803, developed in previous work (Lasry Testa *et al.,* 2019, 2022), in a large scale biorefinery. We propose a mixed-integer nonlinear programming (MINLP) multiobjective model for the simultaneous optimal plant design and heat exchanger network synthesis (HEN) of a cyanobacteria-based integrated biorefinery for pigments (phycocyanin and zeaxanthin), PHB, biofuels, hydrogen, diethyl ether (DEE) and biofertilizers. The objective is to minimize the target indices of the *in-silico* strains, productivity-titer-yield, in order to achieve a sustainable biorefinery design, measured by the SNPV metric (Zore *et al.*, 2018). The idea behind obtaining the minimal targets is to evaluate the performance of the developed *in-silico* strains and determine if it is worth the effort to design them *in-vivo* based on metabolic engineering strategies in the laboratory.

2. Process description

2.1. Synechocystis strains

In this study, three different *Synechocystis* strains constitute the main "cell factories" for the biorefinery superstructure, as we aim at assessing *in-silico* developed strains' efficiency within the frame of an integrated biorefinery. S1 is a wild type strain (no ethanol production) represented by its genome-scale metabolic model (GEM). The GEM comprises 784 reactions and 535 metabolites, with 80 exchange reactions that include cytoplasm, carboxisome, tillacoidal lumen, tillacoidal membrane, cytoplasmatic membrane, periplasm and extracellular space. S2 includes the reactions codified by the genes *pdc* and *adh* from *Zymomonas mobilis*, and produces ethanol coupled to growth, and S3 produces PHB coupled to growth (Lasry Testa *et al.*, 2019, 2022). The coupled strains were designed by formulating a bilevel optimization problem that identifies gene deletions to achieve the desired coupling. Coupling production to growth has the objective of turning the desired product's production into a subproduct of growth, so that it becomes necessary for the microorganism's metabolic function. In the bilevel optimization problem, the outer objective function is to maximize product synthesis rate, while setting an upper bound to the number of gene deletions (represented through binary variables), and the inner optimization problem minimizes product synthesis rate subject to the metabolic network model (LP). The problem has been reformulated as a single level optimization problem by applying duality theory; i.e., replacing the inner LP by a set of equations comprising the primal LP constraints, its dual problem constraints and imposing the strong duality condition (primal LP objective function equal to dual problem objective function). The resulting Mixed Integer Linear Programming (MILP) problem solution renders a genetically engineered strain that couples ethanol production to cell growth through fourteen genetic intervention in the case of S2 and with sixteen genetic interventions for PHB production in the case of S3 (Lasry Testa *et al.*, 2019, 2022).

2.2. Process superstructure

The proposed superstructure of a cyanobacteria-based biorefinery for the potential production of pigments (phycocyanin and zeaxanthin), PHB, bioethanol, biogas, hydrogen, DEE and biofertilizers is shown in Fig. 1. It includes three main continuous processing stages: production, separation and purification. These processing stages comprise the cultivation in open ponds and harvesting through microfiltration membranes (S2 strain only) or centrifugation (S1 and S3), are described in detail in Ramos *et al.* (2023). Ethanol separation and purification section (S2 strain only), carried out with PDMS membranes for pervaporation, a vapor compression distillation system and ceramic membranes, follows the technologic route proposed by Lopes *et al.* (2019). Pigments extraction and purification section (S1 and S2), also refers to the same author, and includes a detailed description of the technological pathway. Regarding the residual biomass outlet from the cell disruption process in the pigment extraction section, for the three strains, the main stream of harvested biomass can be directly fed to an anaerobic digestor for the production of fertilizers and biogas, and also to recycle nutrient streams to the cultivation stage at the Open Pond system (García Prieto *et al.*, 2017). The PHB extraction and purification section (S3 strain only) is described in detail in Ramos *et al.* (2017). Fuel-grade bioethanol with a concentration of 99.5 % obtained from the purification stage can be directly sold or further processed. The superstructure considers two different alternatives: the conversion of bioethanol into DEE or into green Hydrogen. The first case contemplates the production of DEE in an isothermal tubular packed-bed reactor, using Ru-HBZ as catalyst. Equations for this section have been taken from Charoensuppanimit *et al.* (2021) and included in the process superstructure. The second case considers a steam reforming process in the biorefinery. This technological route model equations have been taken from those proposed by Khamhaeng *et al.* (2021).

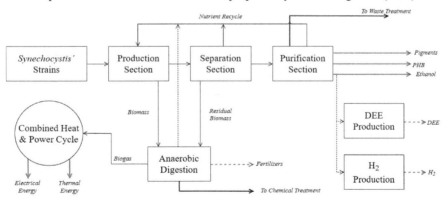

Figure 1. Cyanobacteria-based integrated biorefinery simplified superstructure

3. Mathematical model

The proposed superstructure is formulated as a mixed-integer nonlinear programming (MINLP) problem and implemented in GAMS 35.2.0 (McCarl *et al.*, 2022) in order to determine the optimal design of an integrated cyanobacteria-based biorefinery and its

HEN as presented in Pedrozo *et al.* (2022). The problem is formulated as a multiobjective MINLP, whose objective functions include minimization of the different target indices to be reached to ensure a sustainable biorefinery design, by imposing a lower bound on the sustainability metric SNPV. It is worth noting that, for scenarios where two indices are minimized, like biomass and bioethanol productivities, the epsilon constraint method is used to solve the multiobjective optimization problem (MOO). The proposed superstructure includes mass and energy balances for the integrated biorefinery process, as well as its HEN design and connection equations to link process design variables with HEN variables. Binary variables are associated to potential units and to heat exchanger matches.

4. Numerical results

The MINLP multiobjective model formulated for minimal target indices determination in terms of sustainability optimization and simultaneous process and HEN design includes 9,131 discrete variables, 52,521 continuous variables and 71,854 constraints. It was solved with the epsilon constraint methodology, for alternative scenarios *A*, *B* and *C*, which correspond to minimal biomass productivity for strain S1, minimal biomass and ethanol productivities for strain S2, and minimal biomass productivity for strain S1 and minimal PHB productivity for strain S3, respectively. The solver used was DICOPT, with CONOPT and CPLEX as nonlinear and linear subsolvers, respectively (Grossmann *et al.*, 2003). Table 1 shows the alternative strain indices obtained by a bioreactor model that takes into account light limitation due to the increase in cellular density of the culture that is simulated with a dFBA (Dynamic Flux Balance Analysis) model, considering the growth and production rates of each of the strains. For a more detailed description of the GEM, the resolution of the bilevel optimization problems and an analysis of the *in-silico* mutant strains refer to Lasry Testa *et al.* (2019, 2022).

Table 1. S1, S2 and S3 strain indices obtained by dFBA simulations based on *in-silico* design (Lasry Testa *et al.*, 2019, 2022)

Index	S1	S2	S3
Biomass productivity (g/L/d)	1.375	0.669	0.224
Ethanol productivity (g/L/d)	0	0.875	0
PHB productivity (g/L/d)	0	0	0.116
Biomass titer (g/L)	5.580	2.753	0.535
Ethanol titer (g/L)	0	3.498	0
PHB titer (g/L)	0	0	0.238
Biomass yield (g Product/g CO_2)	0.471	0.229	0.078
Ethanol yield (g Product/g CO_2)	0	0.300	0
PHB yield (g Product/g CO_2)	0	0	0.041

In scenario A, a required production of 180 t/y of phycocyanin (industrial level) was fixed. The minimal target indices of S1 strain that led to a positive SNPV value (SNPV > 0 lower bound), resulted in a biomass productivity of 0.0762 $g_{biomass}$/L/d, titer of 0.383 $g_{biomass}$/L and a yield of 0.0261 $g_{biomass}$/g_{CO2}. The indices achieved through metabolic mathematical modelling for strain S1 (1.375 $g_{biomass}$/L/d, 5.580 $g_{biomass}$/L and 0.471 $g_{biomass}$/g_{CO2}, for biomass productivity, titer and yield, respectively, Table 1), are considerably higher compared to those obtained by solving the superstructure MINLP problem in this work, demonstrating the industrial potential of this *Synechocystis* strain. In scenario *B*, a minimum bioethanol production of 1,750 t/y was considered along with a fixed production of 180 t/y of phycocyanin. In this scenario, the MINLP multiobjective model was solved implementing the epsilon constraint method to consider the minimization of two objective functions, S2 biomass and ethanol productivity. In Figure 2 (a) the Pareto frontier for a positive SNVP value is presented. It is noteworthy that there are four solutions from the Pareto frontier (0.462, 0.583, 0.703, 0.823 $g_{ethanol}$/L/d) that resulted in a lower ethanol productivity when compared to the one reported in Table 1 (0.875 $g_{ethanol}$/L/d). Similar results were obtained regarding the minimal biomass productivity for any solution, as it can be seen in the Pareto frontier. The maximum bioethanol that could be produced for an ethanol productivity of 0.823 g/L/d, is 3,293 t/y. The biorefinery optimal design for each solution, considers directly selling the bioethanol, instead of further processing it into DEE or green hydrogen conversion. Finally, in scenario *C* a fixed production of 180 t/y of phycocyanin and 10,000 t/y of PHB, cultivating strains S1 and S3 at the open pond system, were considered. In this case, the MINLP multiobjective model was solved with the epsilon constraint method to minimize biomass and PHB productivity for strains S1 and S3, respectively. Figure 2 (b) presents the Pareto frontier with these two objectives, for a positive SNVP value. For each nondominated solution, it was observed that it was necessary to reach a PHB productivity of 0.757 g/L/d, 550 % higher than the determined by solving the bilevel optimization problem for *in-silico* design (0.116 g_{PHB}/L/d, Table 1). This result is in agreement with Price *et al.* (2022), where they concluded that there are still significant technical and economic barriers to be solved before PHB production from cyanobacteria can be economically feasible. It is worth mentioning that, although a sensitivity analysis should be performed in order to evaluate the impact of uncertainty in model parameters, similar biorefineries studies (García Prieto *et al.*, 2017) underscore that pigments selling price, such as phycocyanin, exert the main influence on the objective function.

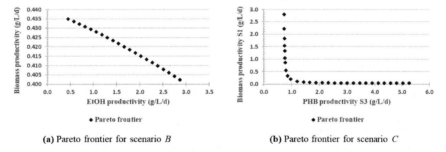

(a) Pareto frontier for scenario *B*   **(b)** Pareto frontier for scenario *C*

Figure 2. (a) Nondominated solutions (Pareto front) for scenario *B* for minimization of biomass and ethanol productivity (S2 strain), (b) Scenario *C* for minimization of biomass and PHB productivity of strains S1 and S3

5. Conclusions

In this work, we have addressed minimal target indices of alternative *Synechocystis* sp. PCC 6803 strains, required to be surpassed in order to obtain sustainable biorefinery designs, for the production of pigments, biofuels, PHB, DEE, green hydrogen and biofertilizers, by a mixed integer nonlinear programming (MINLP) multiobjective model including HEN design. A sustainable biorefinery design that produces pigments and biogas was attainable by cultivating strain S1, where the minimal target indices were significantly lower than those achieved by the *in-silico* proposal. Similarly, by a multiobjective optimization (MOO) approach, the model was solved to minimal biomass and bioethanol productivities for strain S2, that were achievable and outperformed by the productivities resulting from the previously designed *in-silico* strain. Conversely, for the case of a biorefinery that produces pigments (S1) and PHB (S3), it was found that it is necessary to further improve the considered strains in order to achieve a minimal PHB productivity required for any of the solutions obtained through the MOO problem. Overall, numerical results are encouraging into *in-vivo* testing for *Synechocystis* sp. strains S1 and S2, and further improving the strategies for identification of gene knockouts, aiming for optimal metabolic pathways for PHB production.

References

P. Charoensuppanimit, B. Chaiapha, S. Assabumrungrat, B. Jongsomjit, 2021. Incorporation of Diethyl Ether Production to Existing Bioethanol Process: Techno-Economic Analysis. J. Clean. Prod. 327 (May), 129438.

C. V. García Prieto, F. D. Ramos, V. Estrada, M. A. Villar, M. S. Diaz, 2017. Optimization of an integrated algae-based biorefinery for the production of biodiesel astaxanthin and PHB. Energy. 139, 1159-1172.

I. E. Grossmann, J. Viswanathan, A. Vecchietti, R. Raman, E. Kalvelagen, 2003. GAMS/DICOPT: A discrete continuous optimization package. Washington, DC, USA.

P. Khamhaeng, N. Laosiripojana, S. Assabumrungrat, P. Kim-Lohsoontorn, 2021. Techno-Economic Analysis of Hydrogen Production from Dehydrogenation and Steam Reforming of Ethanol for Carbon Dioxide Conversion to Methanol. Int. J. Hydrog. Energy, 46 (60), 30891–30902.

R. Lasry Testa, C. Delpino, V. Estrada, M. S. Diaz, 2019. Bioethanol Production with Cyanobacteria by a Two-Stage Fermentation Strategy. Comp. Aided Chem. Eng. 46, 499-504.

R. Lasry Testa, C. Delpino, V. Estrada, M. S. Diaz, 2022. Development of *in silico* strategies to photoautotrophically produce poly-β-hydroxybutyrate (PHB) by cyanobacteria. Algal Res. 62, 102621.

T. F. Lopes, C. Cabanas, A. Silva, D. Fonseca, E. Santos, T. L. Guerra, C. Sheahan, A. Reis, F. Girio, 2019. Process simulation and techno-economic assessment for direct production of advanced bioethanol using a genetically modified *Synechocystis* sp. Bioresour. Technol. 6, 113-122.

B. A. McCarl, A. Meeraus, P. van der Eijk, M. Bussieck, S. Dirkse, P. Steacy, F. Nelissen, 2022. McCarl Expanded GAMS user guide, Washington, DC, USA.

H. A. Pedrozo, A. I. Casoni, F. D. Ramos, V. Estrada, M. S. Diaz, 2022. Simultaneous design of macroalgae-based integrated biorefineries and their heat exchanger network. Comp. Chem. Eng. 164, 107885.

S. Price, U. Kuzhiumparambil, M. Pernice, P. Ralph, 2022. Techno-economic analysis of cyanobacterial PHB bioplastic production. J. Environ. Chem. Eng., 10, 107502.

M. Ramos, R. Lasry Testa, F. D. Ramos, V. Estrada, M. S. Diaz, 2023. Simultaneous design of integrated cyanobacteria-based biorefinery and its heat exchanger network. Comput. Aided Chem. Eng. 52, 2075-2080.

F. D. Ramos, M. A. Villar, M. S. Diaz, 2017. Optimal Design of Poly(3-hydroxybutyrate) Production using alternative Carbon Sources. Comput. Aided Chem. Eng. 40, 877-882.

A. Sarwer, M. Hussain, A. H. Al-Muhtaseb, A. Inayat, S. Rafiq, M. S. Khurram, N. Ul-Haq, N. S. Shah, A. Alaud Din, I. Ahmad, F. Jamil, 2022. Suitability of Biofuels Production on Commercial Scale from Various Feedstocks: A Critical Review. ChemBioEng Rev. 9 (5), 423–441.

Ž. Zore, L. Čuček, D. Širovnik, Z. Novak Pintarič, Z. Kravanja, 2018. Maximizing the Sustainability Net Present Value of Renewable Energy Supply Networks. Comp. Chem. Eng. 131, 245–265.

Flavio Manenti, Gintaras V. Reklaitis (Eds.), Proceedings of the 34th European Symposium on Computer Aided Process Engineering / 15th International Symposium on Process Systems Engineering (ESCAPE34/PSE24), June 2-6, 2024, Florence, Italy

Use of Bioremediation System to Regenerate Wastewater from Shale Gas Production.

Ariadna Armendáriz-Ortega,[a*] Antonio Espuña,[b] Sergio Medina-González [a*]

[a] Tecnológico de Monterrey, School of Engineering and Sciences
[b] Chemical Engineering Department, Universitat Politècnica de Catalunya, EEBE. Av. Eduard Maristany, 10-14, Edifici I, Planta 6, 08019 Barcelona, Spain
A01568486@tec.mx; sergio.medina@tec.mx

Abstract

This study addresses the growing environmental and health concerns arising from wastewater generated by the shale gas industry, focusing specifically on the toxic BTEX compounds. In response to the global energy crisis, shale gas extraction, primarily through hydraulic fracturing, has experienced exponential growth, leading to the production of contaminated effluents known as Flowback and Produced Water (FPW). Among its various contaminants, BTEX compounds stand out for their significant toxicity. The study investigates the potential of a Biological Membrane Bioreactor (BRM) with a halophilic bacterial consortium, providing a sustainable solution for FPW treatment. It develops a modelling framework to optimise the biological treatment process, specifically targeting the removal of BTEX compounds. The findings reveal that the BRM process effectively removes BTEX compounds, bringing them below Maximum Contaminant Levels (MCLs). Furthermore, the study highlights the superiority of external membranes over submerged membrane configurations, achieving maximum flows of 24.477 m³/s and 21.169 m³/s at an initial pressure of 1 Pa, while maintaining a consistent final pressure at 30 % for optimal performance. This integrated approach offers a biotechnological alternative to mitigate the environmental and health implications associated with shale gas extraction activities.

Keywords: shale gas, FPW, BTEX, BRM, optimization model.

1. Introduction

In recent years, there has been a global energy shortage and increasing energy demand worldwide, which has led to exploring unconventional natural gas sources from academia and industrial perspective. A promising alternative for highly energy-efficient gas is shale gas. Currently, shale gas production has been exponentially growing and it is expected to continue increasing and by 2040 shale gas and tight oil will supply 69 % of all-natural gas produced in the United States (Dou et al., 2021).

Shale gas extraction consists of hydraulic fracturing. When fracking a well, millions of litres of fresh water (7000–21,000 m^3/well) are mixed with sand and chemicals and injected into the well at high pressure to break up the shale and release oil and gas, producing high volumes of polluted effluents (8–70 % of the injected water) (He et al., 2019). Flowback and Produced Water (FPW) encompass the water that resurfaces, known as flowback, and the water originating underground, termed produced water. Throughout different stages, the wastewater generated is collectively referred to as FPW.

FPW resulting from shale gas operations is known for its diverse composition, typically containing elevated concentrations of total dissolved solids (TDS), which encompass salts and metals, as well as hydrocarbons, organic compounds, production chemicals, and other substances. This composition varies significantly based on factors such as the shale play, well location, well depth, and other contributing factors (Dou et al., 2021). Based on Ma et al. (2023), among the myriad components found in FPW, toxic compounds like BTEX (benzene, toluene, ethylbenzene, and xylenes) are particularly concerning due to their documented toxicity. These compounds are frequently detected in FPW above regulatory limits, underscoring the environmental and health implications associated with shale gas extraction activities. Effective treatment is crucial, however it is technologically challenging.

Wastewater treatment involves four levels: pre-treatment and primary treatment for physical removal of suspended solids, oil, and grease; secondary treatment for ion removal with physical-chemical methods; and tertiary treatment for fracking reuse or surface discharge which require biological methods and membrane filtration (Dou et al., 2021).

Acharya et al. (2020), have shown the potential of using a biological membrane bioreactor (BRM) with a halophilic bacterial consortium. This biological process consists of an aerated tank containing conventional activated sludge fed with wastewater and an external or submersible micro or ultrafiltration membrane module for filtering the treated effluent. In high-salinity wastewaters, such as FPW, where bacterial flocculation is compromised, BRM can overcome the flocculation requirements and retain biomass in the reactor. Noteworthy advantages of this system include the production of high-quality effluent suitable for reuse, a compact physical footprint, and a substantial reduction in excess sludge production.

This study focuses on the wastewater coming out of the shale gas industry operations, specifically addressing BTEX compounds. A literature review was undertaken to improve understanding and optimise the biological treatment of FPW. We develop a modelling framework to facilitate understanding of the use of a BRM for the removal of BTEX compounds. This integration seeks optimal operating conditions to maximise regenerated wastewater, providing a more sustainable alternative based on biotechnology for treating water extracted from shale gas.

2. Compounds of Concern

As reported by Ma et al. (2023), groundwater samples collected from spill-affected areas reveal elevated concentrations of BTEX compounds surpassing their Maximum Contaminant Levels (MCLs). Specifically, benzene exceeded the MCL in 90 %, toluene in 30 %, ethylbenzene in 12 %, and xylenes in 8 %. The regulatory Maximum Contaminant Levels (MCLs) for these BTEX compounds are set at 5, 1,000, 700, and 10,000 µg/litre (ppb) for benzene, toluene, ethylbenzene, and xylenes, respectively.

3. Methods

3.1. BMR Configurations

Various BRM configurations offer flexibility in design, involving the placement of membranes either submerged in the bioreactor (BMS) or externally in a side-stream setup (BME). These variations induce shear stress, affecting the size of flocs, mass transfer resistance, bacterial access to pollutants, and altering apparent biokinetic parameters. Depending on the type of contaminant to be treated, the choice of BRM is influenced because the membrane's location can impact how filtration is applied and how flocculation formation is controlled (Sari et al., 2018).

3.2. Mathematical Modelling

To enable the passage of filtrate through the membrane, a force must be exerted to drive fluids through it. The two most crucial transport mechanisms in BRM are diffusion and convection. The force used for membrane filtration in BRMs is a pressure gradient known as transmembrane pressure (TMP). Since flow and pressure are closely interconnected in the process, the series resistance model results from applying Darcy's law. According to the model, this relationship is expressed by the following equation:

$$J = \frac{\Delta P}{\mu \sum_{i=1}^{n} R_i} \tag{1}$$

Where J represents the filtrate flux (m^3/s), μ the filtrate viscosity (Pa $\cdot$ s), P the operating pressure (Pa), R_i the individual resistance component (m^{-1}), and n total number of resistances considered in the system. Within the individual components of resistance, membrane resistance (R_m), cake resistance (R_t), or polarisation gel resistance (R_{pol}) are typically considered, along with resistance due to pore blockage, whether reversible or irreversible (R_{col}). In this case, μ from water was employed, if the removal of large compounds had already occurred. Additionally, it is assumed that the removal of BTEX does not have a significant impact on the filtrate's viscosity.

As reported by González-Hernández et al. (2013), depending on the chosen BRM configuration, distinct resistance types are associated with each, as outlined in Table 1. It is noteworthy that the R values may, in some instances, indicate a range of validity. In our application, we specifically utilise an average value for R to characterise the resistance within the system.

Table 1. Resistance values reported depending on the system utilised.

BRM type	Membrane type	Resistance ($10^{11} m^{-1}$)
BMS	Tubular, microfiltration (0.5 µm), ceramic	R_m= 3-5, R_{col} = 10, R_t = 3-48
BME	Tubular, microfiltration (0.05 µm), ceramic	R_m = 3,6, R_t = 29

Another way to generally describe the filtrate flow, according to McCabe et al. (2007), is through the relationship between the feed composition (x) and the permeate composition at an axial position (y). Here, x and y refer to the molar fractions of the most permeable species, which is A in a binary $A - B$ mixture. This depends on the relative permeabilities Q_A and Q_B and differences in partial pressure. This relationship is expressed by the following equation:

$$J_A = Q_A(P_1 x - P_2 y) \tag{2}$$
$$J_B = Q_B[P_1(1 - x) - P_2(1 - y)] \tag{3}$$

Where P_1 represents the feed pressure, P_2 the permeate pressure, x the feed composition, and y represents the permeate composition.

The relationship of absolute pressures K is introduced into Eq. (2) and (3), making it possible to reduce the number of variables and eliminate P_2 :

$$K = \frac{P_2}{P_1} \tag{4}$$
$$J_A = Q_A P_1(x - Ky) \tag{5}$$
$$J_B = Q_B P_1[1 - x - K(1 - y)] \tag{6}$$

On the other hand, the relationship of permeabilities for a binary mixture is the membrane selectivity α (also known as the ideal separation factor):

$$\alpha = \frac{Q_A}{Q_B} = \frac{D_A S_A}{D_B S_B} \tag{7}$$

In this case, we are considering the relationship $S_A/S_B = 1$, as the impact of selectivity may be negligible compared to the effect of D_A/D_B. However, in instances where $S_A/S_B \neq 1$, the model demonstrates flexibility in addressing these variable scenarios.

Diffusivities for solutes can be predicted using the Wilke-Chang correlation (Geankoplis, 2018):

$$D_{AB} = 1.173x10^{-16}(\varphi M_B)^{\frac{1}{2}}\frac{T}{\mu_B V_A^{0.6}} \tag{8}$$

Where M_B is the molecular weight of solvent B, in this case, water; μ_B is the viscosity of B (Pa·s), V_A is the molar volume of the solute at the boiling point (m³/kg mol), and $\varphi = 2.6$ for water.

Even though diffusivities calculated using Eq. 8 are for liquid phase, we are using this equation to estimate each element diffusion and using Eq. 7, estimate the multicomponent diffusion through the membrane. It is possible to estimate the molar volume for each BTEX compound based on its respective molecular formula at its normal boiling point. Simultaneously, the diffusivity coefficient of the ceramic membrane is influenced by various characteristics such as porosity, structure, and specific affinity for each compound. Therefore, an average was calculated using the values obtained by Kim et al. (2020). The resulting calculations are detailed in Table 2.

Table 2. D_{AB} calculated for each BTEX compound.

Compound	Molar volume (m³/kg mol)	Diffusivity BTEX $(D_A)(m^2/s)*$	Diffusivity membrane $(D_B)(m^2/s)**$
Benzene	0.24511	647,453.014	1.1
Toluene	0.27769	571,479.309	1.32
Ethylbenzene	0.30790	515,407.498	1.30
Xylenes	0.30790	515,407.498	1.29

*Predicted using the Wilke-Chang correlation **(Kim et al., 2020).

An increase in x always leads to an increase in y because the flow of A increases while that of B decreases; additionally, a decrease in K increases y, as shown in Fig 1. By reducing K from 0.5 to 0.2, it is observed that, with a highly selective membrane, nearly pure permeate can be obtained for component A. This suggests that a lower K is more effective in obtaining permeate highly enriched in the desired component. Without loss of generality, we worked based on $K = 0.2$ based on its wide operation range for both composition and membrane selectivity.

Therefore, by utilising the permeability ratio α and incorporating experimental data from literature curves, as shown in Fig. 1, we derived an empirical equation linked to the composition variable y. Subsequently, we can calculate the permeate flow by considering the interplay of pressures, selectivity, and the composition of the feed, denoted as J_A. This approach enables us to ascertain the volume of wastewater flow without BTEX contaminants.

$$y = 0.1207 \ln(\alpha) + 0.2558 \tag{9}$$

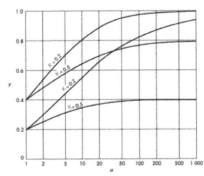

Figure 1. Effects of selectivity (α, x-axis) and pressure ratio (k's iso-lines) on permeates composition (y-axis). (McCabe, et al., 2007)

3.3 Objective Function

In summary, the form of the nlp model BRM-BTEX is max $J_A(xn)$ st (1-7), (9); $xn \in \mathbb{R}$ are all variables K, y, x, α.

4. Results and Discussion

4.1 Operation Flux

The model results depict specific flows for each type of reactor considered in the filtration process, whether submerged membrane or external membrane, considering the associated resistances for each, and considering an initial operating pressure of 1 Pa. It was observed that the BME exhibits a superior maximum flow compared to the BMS, reaching values of 24.477 m³/s and 21.169 m³/s respectively. Similar findings were obtained by (Sari et al. (2018), where the choice of an external (side stream) membrane is supported by its comparable performance in deposit formation, superior efficiency at higher flow rates, and the positive influence of the slug flow regime in improving permeability compared to the BMS configuration. On the other hand, it was determined that the final pressure always tends to be 30 % of the initial pressure to optimise process performance. To validate this pressure relationship, a sensitivity analysis was conducted, varying initial operating pressures in increments of 0.01, 0.1, and 1, confirming the consistency and robustness of choosing BME as the preferred option in terms of flow through a porous medium, regardless of variations in magnitude under different operating conditions. These results are presented in Table 3.

4.2 Separation Efficiency

The permeate flow (y) obtained for each BTEX component, considering the interplay of pressures (K), selectivity and diffusivity of both the membrane and each BTEX compound (α), as well as the feed composition (x), is illustrated in Fig. 2. On the left side of the figure, the elevated initial concentrations of each BTEX compound found in the reactor effluent before entering the membrane (BME) are observed, while on the right side, their corresponding MCLs are depicted along with the required flow to achieve them. As can be observed, in all cases, there is a decrease in the concentration of the compounds: benzene (B), toluene (T), ethylbenzene (E), and xylene (X), demonstrating that with a BME their removal is possible at a relatively low total flow of 3.60x10^-9 m3/s, which has an impact on the required energy cost of the entire system. These results support those obtained by Mozo et al. (2021), where two types of BRMs based on crossflow and semi-dead-end filtration systems were experimentally used for the efficient removal of up to 90 - 99.9 % of hazardous aromatic compounds (BTEX and PAH) from wastewater.

Table 3. Flows at different initial pressure
for each type of BMR.

Pressure (Pa)		Permeate flow (m3/s)	
Initial	Final	BMS	BME
$P_i 1 = 0.01$	$P_f 1 = 0.003$	0.212	0.245
$P_i 2 = 0.1$	$P_f 2 = 0.03$	2.117	2.448
$P_i 3 = 1$	$P_f 3 = 0.3$	21.169	24.477

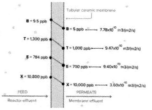

Figure 2. Equilibrium concentrations and flows for BTEX compounds.

5. Conclusions

This study underscores the pressing environmental and health challenges posed by wastewater from the expanding shale gas industry, with a specific focus on the toxic BTEX compounds. The research reveals the promising potential of BRM with a halophilic bacterial consortium, presenting a sustainable solution for FPW treatment. The developed modelling framework demonstrates the efficacy of the BRM in removing BTEX compounds and aligning concentrations with MCLs. Furthermore, the study highlights the superiority of external membrane configurations over submerged counterparts, achieving optimal flows at an initial pressure of 1 Pa and maintaining a consistent final pressure at 30 %. This underscores the critical role of optimising energy-efficient processes, offering a biotechnological alternative that addresses the multifaceted challenges associated with shale gas extraction activities. This integrated approach not only enhances wastewater treatment efficiency but also contributes to achieving a sustainable balance between escalating energy demands and environmental responsibility, marking a significant step towards mitigating the environmental and health implications of the shale gas industry. As future work it is proposed to integrate this bioremediation wastewater model using the BRM system focused on the removal of BTEX compounds into a shale gas extraction model, as well as run experimental validation of the model.

References

Acharya, S. M., Chakraborty, R., & Tringe, S. G. (2020). Emerging Trends in Biological Treatment of Wastewater from Unconventional Oil and Gas Extraction.

Dou, Z., Liu, Y., Zhang, J., Xu, X., Zhang, W., & Zhu, J. (2021). Optimization of Well Factory Platform Mode Considering Optimal Allocation of Water Resources.

Geankoplis, C. J. (2018). Transport Process and Separation Process Principles. 5th. Pg. 448-449.

González-Hernández, Y., Zarragoitia-González, A., Jáuregui-Haza, U., Alliet, M., and Albasi, C. (2013). Modelling and optimization of bioreactors with membranes for wastewater treatment.

He, M., Chen, W. J., Tian, L., Shao, B., & Lin, Y. (2019). Plant-microbial synergism: An effective approach for the remediation of shale-gas fracturing flowback and produced water..

Kim, I., Yoon, J., & Kim, S. D. (2020). Application of a solid ceramic membrane for monitoring volatile organic compounds in industrial wastewater.

Ma, L., Hurtado, A., Eguilior, S., & Llamas Borrajo, J. F. (2023). Acute and chronic risk assessment of BTEX in the return water of hydraulic fracturing operations in Marcellus Shale.

McCabe, W., Smith, J., & Harriot, P. (2007). *Operaciones Unitarias en Ingenieria Quimica Mcabe 7th. Pg. 925-935.*

Mozo, I., Stricot, M., Lesage, N., & Spérandio, M. (2021). Fate of hazardous aromatic substances in membrane bioreactors.

Sari Erkan, H., Bakaraki Turan, N., & Önkal Engin, G. (2018). Membrane Bioreactors for Wastewater Treatment.

Flavio Manenti, Gintaras V. Reklaitis (Eds.), Proceedings of the 34th European Symposium on Computer Aided Process Engineering / 15th International Symposium on Process Systems Engineering (ESCAPE34/PSE24), June 2-6, 2024, Florence, Italy

Onboard or Onsite Hydrogen Production: A Comparative Investigation

Bruna Gava Floriam[a*], Aulus R. Romão Bineli[a], Rubens Maciel Filho[a]

[a]*VALPET, Scholl of Chemical Engineering, Universidade Estadual de Campinas. R. Josiah Willard Gibbs, s/n, Cidade Universitária, Campinas, SP, Zip code 13417-780, Brazil*

brunna.gfl@gmail.com, b219361@dac.unicamp.br

Abstract

The search for measures to deal with problems of greenhouse gas emissions and the energy transition has led to alternatives for cleaner energy production, including the use of hydrogen for transportation and industrial applications. This investigation conducts a comparative analysis of two noticeable hydrogen production methods by process simulation on AspenPlus® software: onboard hydrogen production from ethanol steam reforming and onsite production for high-pressure hydrogen commercialization. The first approach is gaining attention for its potential to allow vehicles with hydrogen fuel cells to generate hydrogen onboard, reducing the need for centralized hydrogen refuelling infrastructures. Through this process, hydrogen and carbon dioxide are formed in a reformer inside the vehicle so that hydrogen is produced locally and fed directly into the fuel cell to produce electricity. In the second approach a dedicated stationary plant produces hydrogen utilizing Ethanol Steam Reforming (ERS) in a centralized, fixed manner. The fuel is liquefied, compressed and transported to stations, where it is stored in a pressurized manner and made available for purchase, usually 700-900 bar for mobility applications. Thus, this investigation compares the two strategies using process simulation, considering their energy efficiency and economic viability. In general, both approaches depend on the context and objectives of hydrogen use, but by focusing the analysis on use in the transport sector in a country like Brazil, where the existing infrastructure and logistics associated with the commercialization of ethanol as a fuel, onboard production stands out and proves to be viable in energy, economic, and environmental terms.

Keywords: Steam Reforming, Hydrogen Production, Comparative Analysis, Process Simulation.

1. Introduction

Producing cleaner energy is an important goal, and hydrogen is being explored as an alternative for industrial and transportation use since it has a great potential as an energy carrier with high energy content (Ruth *et al.*, 2009; Ehteshami and Chan, 2014; IEA, 2023). In the mobility field, hydrogen is used as a raw material for fuel cells, which convert the chemical energy of fuels like hydrogen into electrical energy through electrochemical devices (Du *et al.*, 2021).

However, when considering a new path in the energy transition, one must consider the factors of economic and environmental impact, as well as the maturity of the technology. Presently, the majority of globally produced hydrogen originates from fossil fuels; with only 0.7 % derived from low-emission sources, constituting 1 million metric tons out of the total 95 million metric tons produced in 2022 (IEA, 2023). On the other hand, though water electrolysis is a clean and environmentally friendly pathway, there are improvements in development to it be feasible for commercialization (IEA, 2023), and a cost reduction in its production is an issue. Therefore, one alternative is the use of biofuels, like ethanol, as an interesting strategy with a low carbon footprint. Indeed, US Energy Efficiency and Renewable Energy Office has incorporated biofuels reforming as a mid-term strategy to produce renewable hydrogen while solar conversion technology is in development (Ruth *et al.*, 2009; U.S. Department of Energy, 2020).

From a commercialization perspective, the question arises of how to market and distribute the hydrogen produced by biofuels. Onsite, centralized production for later distribution is a method that has proven to be effective, especially when advanced carbon capture and emissions control technologies are implemented, reducing the environmental footprint of hydrogen production. However, this process requires high energy costs for pressurization and cooling operations for storage and transport, since hydrogen molecule has a relatively low volumetric energy density and low liquefaction temperature (IEA, 2023). Additionally, the use of this approach to transportation requires the vehicle to have storage cylinders able to couple with high pressure and associated problems related to material embrittlement. Onboard hydrogen production from ethanol seems a viable alternative though, with greater efficiency by reducing the energy losses associated with long-distance hydrogen distribution, especially with the advances in fuel cells to accept a lower purity of hydrogen (Du *et al.*, 2021). In fact, in this approach the hydrogen does not need to be storage at high pressure since it is produced on demand.

Bearing this in mind, this study carries out a comparative analysis of two hydrogen production methods using process simulation in AspenPlus® software: onboard hydrogen production from the steam reforming of ethanol and onsite production for the commercialization of high-pressure hydrogen. The study aims to assess the feasibility of producing hydrogen from bioethanol as a way of justifying the development of a technology that meets the demands for cleaner and safer energy.

2. Methodology

In this study, Aspen Plus software was employed to compare a centralized Ethanol Steam Reforming (ESR) plant with onboard production of the same process. The emphasis was on the entire process, encompassing the conversion of ethanol raw material into hydrogen, its purification in accordance with current ISO 14687-2:2012 and SAE J2719-201511 regulations, and the compression of hydrogen for distribution. In general, when ethanol reacts with steam, it forms hydrogen (H_2) and by-products, primarily carbon monoxide (CO), carbon dioxide (CO_2), and methane (CH_4). The first stage of the reaction involves the conversion of ethanol and water into CO and H_2, as shown in Eq. (1). This is followed by the water gas shift reaction (WGS), described in Eq. (2), in which CO reacts with more steam and is converted into hydrogen and CO_2. However, other parallel reactions, such as the methanation of CO and CO_2, as shown in Eq. (3) and (4), can also occur in the reactor.

$$C_2H_5OH(g) + H_2O \rightleftharpoons 2CO(g) + 4H_2(g) \qquad \Delta H = 256 \text{ kJ/mol} \qquad (1)$$

$$CO_{(g)} + H_2O_{(g)} \rightleftharpoons CO_{2(g)} + H_{2(g)} \qquad \Delta H = -41 \text{ kJ/mol} \qquad (2)$$

$$CO_{(g)} + 3H_2(g) \rightleftharpoons CH_4(g) + H_2O(g) \qquad \Delta H = -206 \text{ kJ/mol} \qquad (3)$$

$$CO_{2(g)} + 4 H_2(g) \rightleftharpoons CH_4(g) + 2 H_2O(g) \qquad \Delta H = -164,9 \text{ kJ/mol} \qquad (4)$$

To use hydrogen in fuel cells, it needs to be purified through additional processes such as membrane separation, pressure swing adsorption (PSA), or other methods to ensure high purity. All simulations are conducted under the following conditions, as assumed by Ehteshami and Chan (2014) and Compagnoni *et al.* (2017):

- Water and ethanol enter the reforming reactor at a temperature of 25 °C and pressure of 1 atm, with a molar ratio of 1:6 for steam:ethanol.
- The inlet flow temperature for the ERS reactor is 600 °C.
- The hydrogen-rich gas final temperature is 70°C, and its composition meets the international H_2 quality requirements for H_2 PEMFCs: ISO 14687-2:2012 and SAE J2719-201511, with H_2 purity of 99.97 %, CO_2 at 2 ppm, and CO at 0.2 ppm.

2.1. Process design and modeling

The Peng Robinson equation of state was used as a thermodynamic model to provide satisfactory predictions at high temperature and pressure. The simulation is extended to include downstream processes such as purification and compression, ensuring a holistic understanding of the entire hydrogen production and distribution chain.

2.1.1. SR model for onsite production

In the case of the plant with centralized production, the system consisted of series equilibrium reactors for hydrogen production (ESR), followed by the high-temperature water gas shift reactor (HTWGS) and the low-temperature water gas shift reactor (LTWGS). The operating temperatures were 600 °C, 350 °C and 280 °C, respectively (Compagnoni *et al.*, 2017). For purification, a pressure swing adsorption unit is used to separate hydrogen from the other components of the displaced gas stream, mainly unreacted CO_2 and CO, CH_4 and other hydrocarbons (Ruth *et al.*, 2009). After the production and purification of hydrogen, it needs to be liquefied to enable its transportation to filling stations. The compression and cooling process is facilitated using liquid nitrogen until the hydrogen reaches its critical temperature of -253 °C and a pressure of up to 2 bar. In this study, the Linde-Sankey process, as described by Aziz (2021), was simulated for the liquefaction process. Once liquefied, the hydrogen can be transported using appropriate trucks, although losses may occur during transportation, which were not considered in this study. At the hydrogen refueling unit, the fuel is vaporized, compressed again, and stored in tanks of up to 700 bar to comply with the prevailing refueling standards for vehicles (Ruth *et al.*, 2009). Figure 1.a. represents the scheme for an onsite hydrogen production.

2.1.2. ERS model for onboard production

In the onboard production process, ethanol is directly fed into the vehicle, avoiding the hydrogen liquefaction and compression stages. The process involves a single reformer that carries out the necessary reactions. However, to meet the fuel cell's specifications, the hydrogen purification stage needs to be incorporated into the process. This requires replacing the PSA with a filter membrane that has hydrogen permeability. With the latest advancements in purification systems and the improved flexibility of PEMFCs, it is now possible to consider adapting the process (Lu *et al.*, 2021; Du *et al.*, 2021).

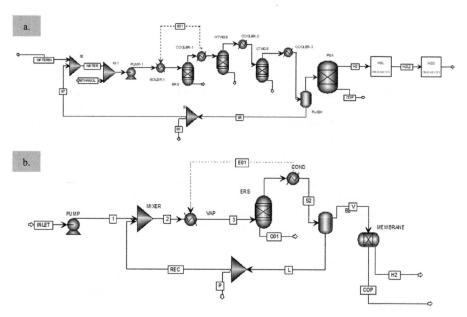

Figure 1: Simulation process scheme a. onsite hydrogen production; b. onboard hydrogen production

2.2. Energy Analysis

A general energy balance was carried out, considering the energy demand of each operation. The energy demands in each production unit, compression and delivery, and distribution for both processes were compared, as well as the feed and product streams at each stage.

2.3. Economic Analysis

The aim of the economic study is to compare the viability of the processes studied for the generation and distribution of hydrogen. Thus, the costs related to raw materials and the utilities used in the processes are considered.

3. Results and discussion

Centralized or onsite hydrogen production often involves large-scale processes that are energy intensive. On the other hand, onsite production provides an opportunity for economies of scale. Larger facilities usually can take advantage of more efficient processes, which results in lower energy consumption per unit of hydrogen produced. However, the efficiency gain is counterbalanced by the energy required for liquefaction and pressurization processes, as depicted in Figure 2.

The comparison of the energy efficiency of local and embargoed hydrogen production reveals that the latter offers significant advantages. Embargoed production obviates the need for compression processes, resulting in a lower energy demand of 2.36 kWh/kg H_2, compared to 12.9 kWh/kg H_2 for local production. This represents a tenfold increase in energy efficiency that significantly enhances the feasibility of hydrogen production. The results demonstrate the importance of considering the energy demands of different production methods and the need to prioritize the most energy-efficient options.

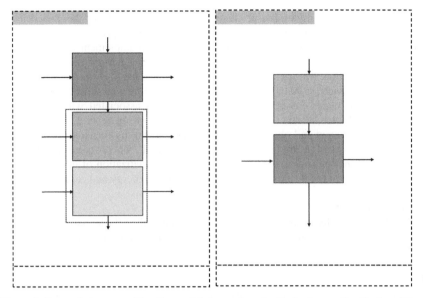

Figure 2: Energy balance resulting from a 6:1steam:ethanol ratio feed normalized by kg of H_2 produced a. onsite; b. onboard.

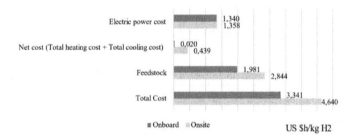

Figure 3: Cost comparison considering utility and feedstock cost.

When examining the costs associated with energy and raw materials, as shown in Figure 3, the process of onboard production holds an advantage as it reduces costs of utilities, and compression and liquefaction operations. Given the recent advances in purification systems for PEMFCs and the intensified processes of microreactors in onboard production, this process appears to be a promising alternative. This is particularly true in countries that have an established distribution and supply network and economy for the production and marketing of ethanol, such as Brazil. Onboard production's viability and competitiveness as an alternative solution depend on its cost-effectiveness compared to other alternatives.

4. Conclusions

Considering the hydrogen production and distribution chain, liquefaction, pressurization and cooling for hydrogen storage and transport are operations with a high energy cost and, consequently, a high associated economic cost. The high cost of infrastructure and maintenance to guarantee stations with large quantities of safely stored hydrogen is another problem that has been pointed out about high-pressure commercialization. Furthermore, with the development of technologies that address the challenges in terms of the capacity of the hydrogen produced onsite and its purity in the fuel cell feed, onboard production has become an even more attractive process. Concerning the environmental aspect, although centralized facilities can implement advanced carbon capture and emissions control technologies, reducing the environmental footprint of hydrogen production, when a renewable source such as ethanol is used, greenhouse gas emissions are reduced in both processes. In addition, the increased efficiency generated by onboard production, by reducing the energy losses associated with long-distance hydrogen distribution, has an impact on the overall balance. In general, both approaches depend on the context and objectives of hydrogen use, but by focusing the analysis on use in the transport sector in a country like Brazil, where there is already an infrastructure and logistics associated with the commercialization of ethanol as a fuel, onboard production stands out and proves to be viable in energy and economic terms.

Acknowledgments
The authors gratefully acknowledge the support from FAPESP (the Sao Paulo Research Foundation, Project Number 2022/10644-1, Grant Numbers 2021/08940-9 and 2023/14455-1).

References
H. T. Lu, W. Li, E. S. Miandoab, S. Kanehashi, G. Hu, 2021, The opportunity of membrane technology for hydrogen purification in the power to hydrogen (P2H) roadmap: a review. Front. Chem. Sci. Eng., 15, 464–482.

IEA, 2023, Global Hydrogen Review 2023, IEA, Paris https://www.iea.org/reports/global-hydrogen-review-2023, License: CC BY 4.0

M. Aziz, 2021, Liquid Hydrogen: A Review on Liquefaction, Storage, Transportation, and Safety, Energies, 14, 5917.

M. Compagnoni, E. Mostafavi, A. Tripodi, N. Mahinpey, I. Rossetti, 2017, Techno-economic analysis of a bioethanol to hydrogen centralized plant, *Energy & Fuels*, 31(11), 12988–12996.

M. Ruth, M. Laffen, TA.Timbario, 2009, Hydrogen Pathways: Cost, Well-to-Wheels Energy Use, and Emissions for the Current Technology Status of Seven Hydrogen Production, Delivery, and Distribution Scenarios. Springfield, VA: U.S. Department of Energy, 1–277.

S. M. M. Ehteshami, S.H. Chan, 2014, Techno-Economic Study of Hydrogen Production via Steam Reforming of Methanol, Ethanol, andDiesel, Energy *Technology & Policy*, 1(1), 15-22.

U.S. Department of Energy, Office of Fossil Energy, 2020, Hydrogen Strategy: Enabling a Low-Carbon Economy, DC 20585, 1-24.

Z. Du, C. Liu, J. Zhai, X. Guo, Y. Xiong, W. Su, G. He, 2021, A Review of Hydrogen Purification Technologies for Fuel Cell Vehicles. Catalysts, 11, 393.

Flavio Manenti, Gintaras V. Reklaitis (Eds.), Proceedings of the 34th European Symposium on Computer Aided Process Engineering / 15th International Symposium on Process Systems Engineering (ESCAPE34/PSE24), June 2-6, 2024, Florence, Italy

Continuous Production of Recombinant Adeno-associated Viral Vectors via Transient Transfection of HEK293 Cells in Perfusion Bioreactor

Damdae Park[a][†], Tam N.T. Nguyen[a][†], José Sangerman[b], Prasanna Srinivasan[b], Rui Wen Ou[b], Georgios Katsikis[c], Moo Sun Hong[a], Paul W. Barone[b], Caleb Neufeld[b], Jacqueline M. Wolfrum[b], Stacy L. Springs[b], Anthony J. Sinskey[b,d], Richard D. Braatz[a,b*]

[a]*Department of Chemical Engineering, Massachusetts Institute of Technology, Cambridge, MA 02139, United States*

[b]*Centre for Biomedical Innovations, Massachusetts Institute of Technology, Cambridge, MA 02139, United States*

[c]*Koch Institute for Integrative Cancer Research, Massachusetts Institute of Technology, Cambridge, MA 02139, United States*

[d]*Department of Biology, Massachusetts Institute of Technology, Cambridge, MA 02139, United States*

braatz@mit.edu | [†]*These authors contributed equally.*

Abstract

Gene therapy offers a promising approach to remedy genetic deficiencies by introducing missing genes into the patient's body. Recombinant adeno-associated virus (rAAV) is one of the most widely used gene carriers, whose therapeutic doses reach up to ~10^{15} viral genomes (vg) per patient. However, existing technology imposes limitations on rAAV production, necessitating a large-scale and cost-effective manufacturing process. In this paper, we propose a continuous manufacturing process and a model-based control strategy for transient transfection of HEK293 cells. A dynamic model of the system is developed and utilized for soft sensing of the component concentrations in cell culture. Based on which, key operational decisions including transfection timing, plasmid dosages, and perfusion rates are made. We demonstrate that the proposed system and control strategy efficiently produce rAAV at a scale comparable to the conventional batch process of the same volume. Recommendations and insights are provided for further process intensifications and optimizations of the proposed system.

Keywords: continuous production, gene therapy, transient transfection.

1. Introduction

In recent decades, extensive investigations on the human genome have unveiled numerous genes associated with genetic diseases and consequently led to the emergence of a therapeutic approach called gene therapy. In gene therapy, genetic disorders are cured by introducing missing genetic material (e.g., DNA or RNA) directly into a human body. Recombinant adeno-associated virus (rAAV) is one of the most widely used gene carriers, where its exponential reproducing nature is exploited to amplify the cure genes.

However, the yield from conventional batch-type rAAV manufacturing processes falls short of the required dosages for clinical and commercial applications, mainly due to their low productivity, difficulties in system scale-up, and high-level impurity in products (Shupe et al., 2022). These challenges directly influence the market price of gene therapy medicine, limiting access to gene therapy.

A potential breakthrough for this is to develop a continuous process that provides mass production with higher flexibility and thereby reduces operating costs (Hong et al., 2018). Our previous research on repeated transfections of rAAV in shake-flask cultures (Nguyen et al., 2023) shows the possibility of improving the process through continual waste removal and plasmid feeding. Such a repeated transfection strategy has been explored in a few previous studies, with applications for recombinant protein production and virus-like particle production (Cervera et al., 2015). However, a continuous manufacturing system for rAAV and the transfection protocol for leveraging high-cell density culture have not yet been proposed.

To this end, we propose a continuous manufacturing system including a perfusion system and build protocols for rAAV production via high-density HEK-293 cell transfection, that results in increased efficiency and productivity of viral vectors at scale. A dynamic model for the system is developed and used to estimate the concentrations of the key components in cell culture. Based on which key operational decisions are made, such as transfection timing, plasmid dosages, and perfusion rates, while balancing the trade-offs existing in the system.

2. Materials and Methods

2.1. Materials

FreeStyle™ 293-F cells, culture medium FreeStyle™ F17 Expression Medium, and Gibco™ l-glutamine (200 mM) were purchased from Thermo Fisher Scientific (Waltham, MA, USA). A set of plasmids for AAV5 production, including pAAV-GFP (Part No. AAV-400), pRC5 (Part No. VPK-425) and pHelper (Part No. 340202), were purchased from Cell Biolabs (San Diego, CA. USA). The transfection reagent PEI Max™ is the transfection grade linear polyethylenimine hydrochloride with a molecular weight of 40,000 and was purchased from Polysciences (Warrington, PA, USA). The detailed preparation procedure can be found in our previous work (Nguyen et al., 2023).

2.2. Development of continuous manufacturing process

2.2.1. Bioreactor setup and operating conditions

Cell cultivation, transient transfection, and viral production were performed in a 500 mL stirred-tank bioreactor (Getinge, Rochester, NY, USA) with a 300 mL working volume. The reactor was equipped with a three-blade marine impeller and a micro-sparger. The Operating conditions were maintained using *my-Control* console (Getinge, Rochester, NY, USA) where the controller settings are described in Table 1. Antifoam C from MilliporeSigma (Burlington, MA, USA) was used to break the foam when the foam was detected. FreeStyle™ 293-F cells were used, which were stored in liquid nitrogen, thawed in a 37°C water bath, and then transferred to 30 mL FreeStyle™ 293 expression medium in a 125 mL shake flask. The cells were inoculated to the bioreactor after they reached a total density of 3×10^5 cells/mL, and then grown to reach the cell density of 1×10^6 cells/mL before the first transfection.

Continuous Production of Recombinant Adeno-associated Viral Vectors via
Transient Transfection of HEK293 Cells in Perfusion Bioreactor
2589

Table 1. Operating conditions and controller settings made.

Control loop	Setpoint / bounds	Actuator (-)	Actuator (+)
pH	7 ± 0.1	CO_2	0.5M NaHCO$_3$
Agitation rate	125 rpm		
Temperature	$37 \pm 1°C$	Condenser	Heating jacket
dO$_2$	40% saturated air		Air, O$_2$

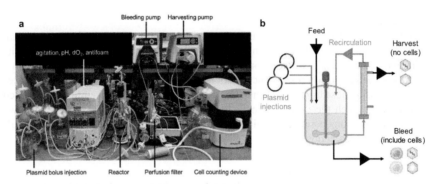

Figure 1. (a) Bioreactor system developed and **(b)** its schematic.

2.2.2. Perfusion system

The schematic of the perfusion system developed is shown in Figure 1. It includes a tangential flow filtration (TFF) system consisting of a 0.2 μm hollow membrane filter (Artemis Biosystems, Quincy, MA, USA) driven by a magnetic pump (Levitronix, Framingham, MA, USA). The working volume, which includes the volume inside the vessel, a perfusion system, and the recirculation tubing, was 370 mL. The cell-free harvest line is connected to the filter and driven by a controllable peristaltic pump (Masterflex, Radnor, PA, USA). The cell-containing bleed line is drawn through a dip tube directly from inside the vessel via a controllable peristaltic pump (Masterflex, Radnor, PA, USA). Through bleeding, the desired cell health and culture environment can be maintained. During the perfusion operation, the flow rates of harvest and bleed lines were controlled to achieve the desired cellular density and maintain steady and non-limiting nutrient levels. The feed media flow rate is controlled to maintain a constant volume via a level sensor. The perfusion rate was maintained at 1–3 vvd during the perfusion operation.

2.3. Mathematical modeling of bioreactor

A dynamic model consisting of 44 state variables is developed and utilized to trace the concentration profiles of key components in the cell culture.

$$\frac{dX}{dt} = \frac{X_i}{V}\left(F_i + \frac{V_b(t)}{dt}\right) - \frac{X}{V}\left(F_b + \delta F_h + \frac{V_s(t)}{dt}\right) + r_X \tag{1}$$

$$\frac{dV}{dt} = F_i - F_b - F_h + \frac{V_b(t) - V_s(t)}{dt} \tag{2}$$

where X and X_i are the concentrations of the interest inside the reactor and inlet feed media, V is the working volume of the system, V_b and V_s are the bolus injection and sampling volumes, and F_i, F_h, and F_b are the flowrates of feed line, harvest line, and bleed line, respectively. δ is a component-specific factor where $\delta = 1$ if a given component can penetrate the membrane (e.g., plasmids and metabolites), otherwise $\delta = 0$ (cells). The volumetric reaction rate r_X is given by the kinetic model developed in our previous work (Nguyen et al., 2023), with some adjustments in parameter values: $k_{Rep\,syn} = 5.2 \times 10^4$, $k_{Cap\,syn} = 1.2 \times 10^2$, $k_{secrete,cyto} = 3.6$, $k_{secrete,media} = 2 \times 10^{-2}$, $k_{rep,licaiton,DNA} = 5.7 \times 10^2$, and $k_{pack,DNA} = 1.24 \times 10^{-1}$.

2.4. Transient transfection

The cells were transfected by discrete injections of transfection boluses, where the amount of plasmids is determined based on the cell density at the time of each transfection. The detailed procedures can be found in our previous work (Nguyen et al., 2023). The transfection was performed when the concentrations of extracellular PEI/plasmid complexes dipped to zeros or close to zeros. At each point of transfection, the cell culture was diluted by bleeding to reach the desired transfection cell density. After each transfection, we stopped the perfusion operation (no bleeding/harvest) and incubated the cells to give sufficient time for transfection.

2.5. Sampling and analytical methods

The samples were taken from the culture by 6 mL every 24 hours, where 1 mL sample with smaller intervals were additionally collected to monitor the health of cell culture. Detailed procedures for the quantification of cell counts, metabolites, AAV5 capsids, and genome titers can be found in our previous work (Nguyen et al., 2023).

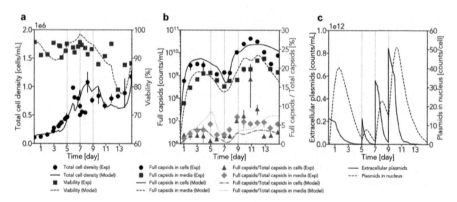

Figure 2. Trajectories of **(a)** total cell density and viability, **(b)** full capsids and the fractions over total capsids, and **(c)** plasmids outsides the cells and inside the nucleus.

3. Results

3.1. Model-based transfection design and continuous production of rAAV

The developed dynamic model of the system was able to predict the trends of key components inside the cell culture, including the cell density (Figure 2a) and capsid concentrations (Figure 2b). Based on the estimated extracellular concentration profiles (Figure 1c), timings for subsequent transfection after the first transfection were determined as day

5, 7, and 9. The plasmid dosages and incubation periods were manually set as in Table 3. With the developed system and transfection strategy, we were able to maintain cell viability more than 90% up to day 11. Furthermore, the system shows the ability of recovery from low viability caused by high plasmid dosage of fourth transfection, demonstrating its potential in continuous and stable production of rAAV. It is observed that, compared to the third transfection, the fourth transfection, which has the same plasmid dosage per cells but 50% larger in terms of volumetric concentration, gave detrimental effects on cells (Table 2). This emphasizes the significance of transfection design and suggests the potential benefits of employing dynamic optimization to achieve optimal transfection timing and dosages.

Table 2. Designed transfection scheme. The volume [mL] in denominator is working volume.

Time [day]	Culture cell density [M cells/mL]	Plasmid dosage [μg/mL]	Plasmid dosage [μg/M cells]	Incubation period [h]
0	1.1	2	2	24
5	4.7	2	0.43	0
7	5.1	5.1	1	12
9	7.6	7.6	1	24

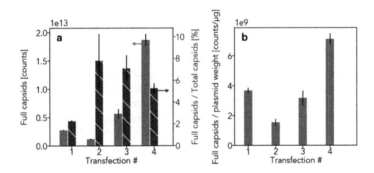

Figure 3. Total titer obtained from each transfection. **(a)** Full capsid yields and the fractions of full capsids over total capsids. **(b)** Full capsids yield per plasmid weight.

3.2. Mass production of rAAV

It is found that transfections at high densities can yield over a magnitude order more product than the conventional design (Figure 2b). The total amount of full/total capsids produced over the operation are estimated using the system model, by assuming that the TFF system allows 100% of the viral particles to pass through to the harvest system. The total yield of the first transfection was 2.7×10^{12} vg, which is comparable to the yield from batch production in a suspension bioreactor that typically yields 10^9–10^{10} vg/mL [12, 9, 13] – 3.7×10^{11}–3.7×10^{12} when 370 mL reactor volume is assumed. The total yield obtained from the second transfection was half the yield of the first transfection.

The plasmid concentration profiles in Figure 1 suggests that the low yield may be attributed to low plasmid uptake resulting from a lower plasmid dosage per cell and the absence of an incubation time. Remarkably, the third and fourth transfections yielded more than two and six times more vector genomes than the first transfection, respectively, (Figure 3a) which is equivalent to a batch production. This result demonstrates that the developed system and protocols enable the transfection at high cell density in the same amount of time, and potentially enable mass production of rAAV. Moreover, as shown in Figure 3b, the fourth transfection had almost twice the productivity than the first transfection. Together with the third transfection, the back-to-back transfections at high cell density resulted in 32% higher plasmid usage efficiency, lowering the development cost and therapeutic cost. The calculation of total product purity shows that the third and fourth transfection product at high cell density transfection had three times as high of full capsid in harvest than the first transfection, which is comparable to a conventional batch transfection (Figure 3c).

4. Conclusions

This study pioneers the development of a continuous manufacturing system for rAAV, strategically designed to surmount the productivity limitations of conventional batch-type processes. We propose a model-guided continuous manufacturing approach, and demonstrate its efficiency and productivity against the batch process. Notably, our findings underscore the substantial potential of the developed model in informing crucial operational decisions, including transfection timing and plasmid dosages. This unveils the potential for dynamic optimization, where the optimal trajectories of the operation variables are systematically evaluated. The proposed continuous processing system and control strategy are anticipated to be applicable to manufacturing processes for other virus-based gene therapy products.

Acknowledgement

This work was supported by the Korea Institute for Advancement of Technology (KIAT) with a grant funded by the Korean Government (MOTIE) (P0017304, Human Resource Development Program for Industrial Innovation) and the U.S. Food and Drug Administration (Grant ID: 1R01FD006584-02, Continuous Viral Vector Manufacturing based on Mechanistic Modeling and Novel Process Analytics). T.N.T.N. was partially supported by a MathWorks Engineering Fellowship. A.J.M. was partially supported by the National Science Foundation (NSF) Graduate Research Fellowship Program under grant number 1122374. This research was also supported by a grant from the Massachusetts Life Sciences Center as part of the Building Breakthroughs Program.

References

L. Cervera, S. Gutiérrez-Granados, N.S. Berrow, M.M. Segura, F. Gòdia, 2015, Extended gene expression by medium exchange and repeated transient transfection for recombinant protein production enhancement, Biotechnol. Bioeng., 112, 934–946, https://doi.org/10.1002/bit.25503.

M.S. Hong, K.A. Severson, M. Jiang, A.E. Lu, J.C. Love, R.D. Braatz, 2018, Challenges and opportunities in biopharmaceutical manufacturing control, Comput. Chem. Eng., 110, 106–114.

T.N.T. Nguyen, S. Sha, J. Sangerman, G. Katsikis, M.S. Hong, J. Ng, P.W. Barone, C. Neufeld, J.M. Wolfrum, S.L. Springs, A.J. Sinskey, R.D. Braatz, (submitted), Multi-stage transfection increases full capsid ratio in rAAV viral vector production via triple transfection in HEK293 cells Multi-stage transfection for rAAV production, Mol. Ther. - Methods Clin. Dev.

J. Shupe, A. Zhang, D.C. Odenwelder, T. Dobrowsky, 2022, Gene therapy: challenges in cell culture scale-up, Curr. Opin. Biotechnol., 75, 102721.

Flavio Manenti, Gintaras V. Reklaitis (Eds.), Proceedings of the 34th European Symposium on Computer Aided Process Engineering / 15th International Symposium on Process Systems Engineering (ESCAPE34/PSE24), June 2-6, 2024, Florence, Italy

Life cycle design of bioprocess system applying simulation-based approach

Satoshi Ohara,[a,b*] Yuichiro Kanematsu,[c] Shoma Fujii,[a,b] Yasunori Kikuchi[a,b,c]

[a]*Institute for Future Initiatives, The University of Tokyo, 7-3-1 Hongo, Bunkyo-ku, Tokyo 113-8654, Japan*
[b]*Department of Chemical System Engineering, The University of Tokyo, 7-3-1 Hongo, Bunkyo-ku, Tokyo 113-8656, Japan*
[c]*Presidential Endowed Chair for "Platinum Society", The University of Tokyo, 7-3-1 Hongo, Bunkyo-ku, Tokyo 113-8656, Japan*
ohara@ifi.u-tokyo.ac.jp

Abstract

In this study, we are tackling the development of a simple dynamic model of bioprocesses that enables life cycle design through computer-aided simulation. The material and energy balances of bioprocesses are significantly affected by scale. The dynamic model considers changes in microbial growth and metabolic production over time and the associated energy balance, such as heating and cooling, as the fermenter is scaled up. The dynamic model developed in this study will theoretically enable efficient bioprocess design by predicting future productivity and environmental impacts and their hotspots and bottlenecks on a commercial scale from early-stage research data and feeding them back to basic laboratory-scale research. As a case study, we simulated the ethanol fermentation process using a prototype of the dynamic model developed in this study. As a result, we confirmed no significant differences in the rates of yeast growth or ethanol production depending on the scale of the fermenter. Still, there were substantial differences in the heat balance. Furthermore, a gate-to-gate LCA limited to the ethanol fermentation process revealed that scaling up from a 5 L jar fermenter to a 50 kL commercial-scale fermenter reduced Greenhouse gas (GHG) emissions per product by 88 % and visualized the impact of fermenter scale on GHG emissions hot spots.

Keywords: microorganism, scale up, prospective life cycle assessment

1. Introduction

The global decarbonization trend accelerates research and development on plant-derived products using bioprocesses (Yaashikaa *et al.,* 2023). Bioprocesses utilize enzymatic reactions and other biochemical reactions by microorganisms. They are widely used in various industries, such as pharmaceuticals (Jones and Gerogiorgis, 2022), foods (Shimada *et al.,* 2021), bioplastics (Kikuchi *et al.,* 2022), and biofuels (Ohara *et al.,* 2012). The life cycle design of bioprocesses often differs from that of the chemical industry because it deals with plant-derived raw materials and complex reactions by microorganisms. In particular, the process's scale significantly affects the material and energy balance of a process such as fermentation, in which microbial growth and metabolite production occur simultaneously (Imamoglu and Sukan, 2013). For example, the processes of media preparation, sterilization, incubation, separation, and purification at the laboratory scale (flasks, jars) significantly differ from the plant scale regarding energy, utility use, and productivity. Therefore, it is common in bioprocess technology development to conduct primary research at the lab scale followed by scale-up to the plant scale for validation. However, there is a concern with this conventional method of developing bioprocesses. If environmental or economic problems are found during the demonstration stage in a large-scale plant, the process will revert to the primary research level. In chemical processes, models have been proposed that can quantitatively forecast the material balance, energy balance, and environmental impact of future scale-up in the lab-scale phase of research (Piccinno *et al.*, 2016). Quantitative models of microbial growth and metabolite productivity have been reported for the bioprocesses (Luong *et al.*, 1988). Still, no models have been reported, including energy consumption at each scale and its hot spots.

In this study, we develop a simple dynamic model that enables computer-aided simulation of bioprocesses' material and energy balance. This dynamic model would allow efficient bioprocess design by forecasting future productivity, environmental impacts, and costs on a commercial scale, as well as their hotspots and bottlenecks, from early-stage research data and feeding them back into basic laboratory-scale research. First, we will develop a model for each culture tank from jar fermenter scale (5 L) to pilot plant scale (500 L) and commercial scale (50 kL), taking as an example the ethanol production process, which is a typical bioprocess. Furthermore, as a case study, a gate-to-gate LCA (Lifecycle Assessment) is performed to clarify the influence of the scale of the culture tank on the environmental load per product and its hotspot and the usefulness of dynamic models in bioprocess life cycle design is discussed.

2. Materials and methodologies

2.1. Modeling of fermenter in bioprocess

Depending on the strain type, microbial reactions differ in conditions (e.g., growth rate, fermentation rate, resistance to fermentation inhibitors, optimum temperature, etc.). This study selected ethanol fermentation by general yeast (ex. *Saccharomyces cerevisiae*), which has been reported at various scales (Ouchida *et al.*, 2017), as the first model. Simulations were performed in an Excel-based in-house code based on the microbial kinetics model, in which the medium was heated after the start of incubation, yeast growth started at 35 °C, and the total fermentation time was set to 100 h. The initial glucose concentration of the medium was set at 100 g/L, and it was assumed that all glucose was consumed by yeast growth and ethanol fermentation. The final yeast yield was set at 90 g-dry/mol-glucose. The Monod equation shown by Eq. (1) determined the yeast growth rate and ethanol productivity from the concentration of yeast and glucose in the medium (Nosrati-Ghods *et al.*, 2020).

$$\mu = \mu_{max}\left(\frac{S}{K_s+S}\right), \quad v = v_{max}\left(\frac{S}{K_p+S}\right) \tag{1}$$

where μ is the specific yeast growth rate [h^{-1}], μ_{max} is the maximum yeast growth rate [h^{-1}], S is the substrate concentration [g/L], v is the specific ethanol productivity [h^{-1}], v_{max} is the maximum ethanol productivity [h^{-1}], K_s and K_p are substrate utilization constant [g/L] equal to substrate concentration when μ and v are half of μ_{max} and v_{max}, respectively. The heat balance considered direct heating and cooling of the fermenter, fermentation heat, heat dissipation from the walls, and heat loss due to ventilation. Heating and cooling conditions were different for each scale. The fermentation heat was calculated by Eq. (2).

$$\Delta H_c = \Delta H_r - \Delta H_\alpha \Delta X - \Delta H_p \Delta P \tag{2}$$

where ΔH_c is fermentation heat [J], ΔH_r is glucose consumption heat [J], ΔH_a is the heat of yeast combustion [J/g], ΔX is yeast growth [g], ΔH_p is the heat of products combustion [J/g], and ΔP is products amount [g].

Heat dissipation from the fermenter wall was calculated assuming natural convection from the wall. Heat loss due to aeration was calculated assuming cooling by evaporative latent heat based on the saturated vapor pressure at the medium temperature and the assumption that 90 % of the saturated vapor content of the aerated air evaporates.

2.2. Scale-up fermenter configuration

The ethanol fermenter was step-wise scaled up from a 5 L jar fermenter to a 500 L pilot-scale and 50 kL commercial-scale fermenter, as shown in Table 1 and Fig. 1. The 5 L jar fermenter was modeled after the Middle Scale Bioreactor BMS-P manufactured by ABLE Corporation. An electric heater (capacity: 0.15 kW) was wrapped around the glass vessel, and the heater surface temperature was calculated by considering the heat transfer between the heater and the outside air, and the net heat added to the liquid medium in the vessel was calculated. The liquid and vessel were assumed to be heated by heat transfer between the heater and the glass, and the heater was assumed to be controlled to maintain the target temperature by on/off control. For cooling, a chiller (0.05 kW) was constantly operated to maintain the target temperature by on/off control. 500 L and 50 kL fermenters were modeled as stainless-steel tanks with jackets attached to the outer walls. The fermenters were maintained at the target temperature by on/off control of heating with 60 °C hot water passing through the jacket and cooling with 20 °C cold water passing through the jacket. The flow rate of hot and cold water was set at 60 kg/h. The minimum flow rate of hot water was literately determined to raise the liquid temperature to the target temperature based on the heat balance. Also, assuming that yeast growth is completed in 40 h after the liquid reaches the target temperature, in the 500 L and 50 kL scale, the aeration was assumed to be stopped when yeast growth was saturated.

Table 1. Fermenter configurations modeled at each scale

| | 5 L | 500 L | 50 kL |
	Jar fermenter	Pilot plant	Commercial plant
Vessel type	Glass	Stainless-steel	Stainless-steel
Working volume [m³]	0.004	0.4	40
Height of fermenter (H) [m]	0.34	1.38	6.35
Diameter of fermenter (D) [m]	0.14	0.68	3.17
Aspect ratio (H/D)	2.4	2.0	2.0
Heater	Electrical heating (50 W)	Jacket heating with hot water (60°C)	Jacket heating with hot water (60°C)
Chiller	Chiller with water	Jacket cooling with hot water (20°C)	Jacket cooling with hot water (20°C)
Aeration flow [Nm³/min]	0.05	0.5	50

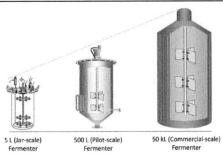

5 L (Jar-scale) Fermenter 500 L (Pilot-scale) Fermenter 50 kL (Commercial-scale) Fermenter

Fig.1 Overview of fermenter scale-up

2.3. Setting for gate-to-gate LCA

Gate-to-gate LCA was performed to determine the environmental load per product at each fermenter scale and the impact of its hot spots. The system boundary is from the start to the end of the fermentation process, and only the energy-derived environmental impact input to the fermentation process is considered, excluding the environmental impact related to the production of raw and auxiliary materials, disposal of by-products, etc. The environmental load item was the Global Warming Potential (GWP), calculated as CO_2-equivalent. The functional unit was 1 kg of ethanol contained in the fermentation liquid. Foreground data for ethanol fermentation were taken from Ouchida *et al.* (2017), and background data were taken from IDEA v2.2, a Japanese LCA database.

3. Results and discussion

3.1. Simulation of fermenter at each scale

Simulated fermentation profiles showing relative values for glucose consumption, yeast growth, ethanol production, and medium temperature at 5 L, 500 L, and 50 kL scales are shown in Fig. 2. Starting from a medium temperature of 20 °C, there was a difference in scale in the rate at which the medium reached the target temperature of 35 °C. This was attributed to differences in heating method and heating capacity. Since the heating capacity depends on the model settings, for example, at plant scale, the time to reach the target temperature can be easily reduced by increasing the amount of hot water passed through the jacket or by raising the hot water temperature. In terms of kinetics, ethanol production started after 3.3 h in the 5 L jar and after 11.0 h in the 500 L and 50 kL fermenters. This is due to the time required to reach the target temperature. The 500 L and 50 kL scales designed under the same conditions of heating and cooling showed the same performance as expected. The slight temperature increase after about 50 h in the 500 L and 50 kL was due to disappearing the latent heat of vaporization loss by stopping aeration after yeast growth saturation, and it took time for cooling.

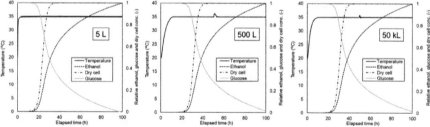

Fig.2 Simulated fermentation profiles at each scale of fermenter

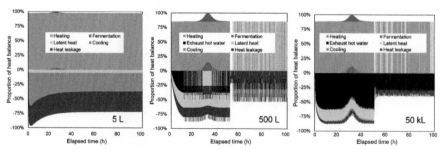

Fig.3 Simulated heat balance at each scale of fermenter

Figure 3 shows the results of the heat balance at each scale. The graph's vertical axis is expressed as relative values, with the maximum heating value as 100 and negative values for cooling. In the 5 L scale, heating, cooling, and heat dissipation from the glass vessel were relatively large. In contrast, heat loss from fermentation and latent heat of evaporation due to aeration were slight. In the 500 L and 50 kL scales, heating, heat loss due to hot water discharge, and latent heat loss due to aeration were relatively significant in the early fermentation stage. In the late stages of fermentation, heat loss decreased because aeration was set to stop when yeast growth was saturated.

3.2. Greenhouse gas emissions from fermentation process at each scale

The results of the gate-to-gate LCA limited to the ethanol fermentation process are shown in Fig. 4. The results are shown as relative emissions values at each scale, with the total emissions at the 5 L scale as 100 %. The Greenhouse gas (GHG) emissions per weight of ethanol were reduced by 87.0 % and 88.5 % for the 500 L and 50 kL scales, respectively, compared to the 5 L scale. In other words, GHG emissions were reduced by scale-up.

In the 5 L jar scale, GHG emissions from electricity consumption in the chiller accounted for 42.5 % of the total GHG emissions. In contrast, emissions from electricity consumption in the compressor for aeration, heater, and agitation were 19.5 %, 19.0 %, and 19.1 %, respectively. Since the chiller of the jar fermenter is in constant operation, its electricity consumption is significant. Furthermore, the heater was controlled on/off while the cooling chiller was constantly running, resulting in higher emissions from the heater power. The 500 L and 50 kL stainless steel fermenters have a larger diameter than the glass 5 L jar fermenter, resulting in lower heat dissipation. Therefore, once the target temperature is reached, energy consumption for heating and cooling is lower, resulting in lower GHG emissions derived from heating and cooling. In the scale-up from 500 L to 50 kL, the environmental impact from heating is slightly lower because the heat dissipation is reduced due to the larger body diameter. In the 500 L and 50 kL scales, GHG emissions were mainly attributable to compressor power consumption for aeration. This amount was equivalent to that of the 5 L jar scale. This is because the model was set up assuming that the ratio of dissolved oxygen required for yeast growth and ethanol production would be the same regardless of scale. GHG emissions derived from stirring power decreased with scale-up. This is because the mechanical loss of the stirring device becomes relatively smaller with a larger capacity, resulting in smaller stirring power per liquid volume [kW/m^3] (Murakami *et al.*, 2000).

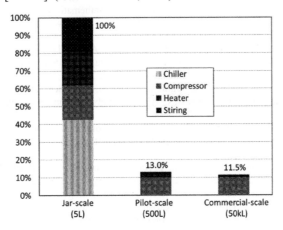

Fig.4 Relative greenhouse gas emissions and their breakdown at each scale of fermenter

In this case study, the simulation-based scale-up enabled visualization of the total GHG emissions and hot spots as shown in Fig. 4. Scale-up prediction in the early stages of the study can provide feedback on improvement points from environmental and economic aspects at the commercial scale, which will enable appropriate process design.

4. Conclusions

This study developed a prototype of a fermenter model that contributes to the bioprocesses' simulation-based prospective life cycle design. Further improvement of the accuracy of the dynamic model will enable simulation of the material and energy balance of the fermenter from laboratory-scale to commercial scale. It will help design bioprocesses for higher productivity and lower environmental impact requirements.

Acknowledgement

This work was supported by New Energy and Industrial Technology Development Organization (NEDO, Grant number JPNP20011), JSPS KAKENHI (Grant Number JP23K11521), JST COI-NEXT (Grant Number JPMJPF2003). The activities of the Presidential Endowed Chair for "Platinum Society" at the University of Tokyo are supported by Mitsui Fudosan Corporation, Sekisui House, Ltd., East Japan Railway Company, and Toyota Tsusho Corporation.

References

E. Imamoglu and F. Sukan. 2013. Scale-up and kinetic modeling for bioethanol production, Biores. Technol., 144, 311–320.

W. Jones and D. Gerogiorgis. 2022. Dynamic optimisation and comparative analysis of fed-batch and perfusion bioreactor performance for monoclonal antibody (mAb) manufacturing, Comput. Aided Chem. Eng., 51, 1117–1122.

Y. Kikuchi, N. Torizaki, L. Tahkamo, A. Enstrom, S. Kuusisto. 2022. Life cycle greenhouse gas emissions of biomass- and waste-derived hydrocarbons considering uncertainties in available feedstocks, Proc. Saf. Environ. Protec., 166, 693–703.

J. Luong, A. Mulchandani, A. Leduy. 1988. Kinetics of biopolymer synthesis: a revisit, Enzyme microbial Technology, 10, 326–332.

S. Murakami, R. Nakano, T. Matsuoka. 2000. Scale-up of fermenter: Survey of industrial fermenter specifications (in Japanese), Kagaku Kogaku Ronbunsyu. 26(4), 557–562.

N. Nosrati-Ghods, S. Harrison, A. Isafiade, S. Tai. 2020. Mathematical modelling of bioethanol fermentation from glucose, xylose or their combination - a review, ChemBioEng. Rev., 7(3), 68–88.

S. Ohara, Y. Fukushima, A. Sugimoto, Y. Terajma, T. Ishida, A. Sakoda. 2012. Rethinking the cane sugar mill by using selective fermentation of reducing sugars by Saccharomyces dairenensis, prior to sugar ctystallization, Biomass and Bioenergy, 42, 78–85.

K. Ouchida, Y. Fukushima, S. Ohara, A. Sugimoto, M. Hirao, Y. Kikuchi. 2017. Integrated Design of Agricultural and Industrial Processes: A Case Study of Combined Sugar and Ethanol Production, AIChE J., 63(2), 560–581.

F. Piccino, R. Hischier, S. Seeger, C. Som. 2016. From laboratory to industrial scale: a scale-up framework for chemical processes in life cycle assessment studies. J. Clean. Prod., 135, 1085–1097.

Y. Shimada, T. Ishida, Y. Kato, H. Uwagami, Y. Kato, Y. Kanematsu, Y. Kikuchi, S. Ohara. 2021. Material balance and energy consumption in the factory-scale coproduction of glucan and mannan from yeast extract residue, Food Science and Technology Research, 27(6), 871–880.

P. Yaashikaa, P. Kumar, A. Saravabab, S. Karishma, g. Rangasamy. 2023. A biotechnologicall roadmap for decarbonization systems combined into bioenergy production: Prelude of environmental life-cycle assessment, Chemosphere, 329. 1338670.

Flavio Manenti, Gintaras V. Reklaitis (Eds.), Proceedings of the 34th European Symposium on Computer Aided Process Engineering / 15th International Symposium on Process Systems Engineering (ESCAPE34/PSE24), June 2-6, 2024, Florence, Italy

Use of dynamic Flux Balance Analysis for evaluation of the poly-3-hydroxybutyrate production potential of recombinant *Escherichia coli*

Willians O. Santos,[a] Rafael David de Oliveira,[b] José Gregorio Cabrera Gomez,[c] Galo A. C. Le Roux[a]

[a]*Department of Chemical Engineering Polytechnic School University of São Paulo, Av. Prof. Lineu Prestes 580, São Paulo 05508-220, Brazil*
[b]*Department of Chemical Engineering Norwegian University of Science and Technology (NTNU), Torgarden 7491, Trondheim 8900, Norway*
[c]*Institute of Biomedical Sciences University of São Paulo, Av. Prof. Lineu Prestes 2415, São Paulo 05508-000, Brazil*
Galoroux@usp.br

Abstract

Environmental problems due to plastic disposal have been a major concern. Bioplastics are considered as possible alternatives because of their biodegradability, but given their high production cost, optimization is required. For this purpose, many works have been done with the intention of engineering strains capable of greater product yields. But for certain products, there is a trade-off between biomass and product formation. Not only the yield but also titer and productivity have to be considered. A method known as dynamic Flux Balance Analysis (dFBA) allows computation of the final yield, titer and productivity, through simulations. This work presents an approach using dFBA simulations together with an economic metric for the analysis of the bioplastic production potential of recombinant *Escherichia coli* using glucose, xylose and glycerol as carbon sources. The proposed economic metric calculates the monthly gross profit based on the estimation of the production costs as a function of the product yield, biomass yield, titer and productivity. By estimating the monthly profit of each simulated scenario, the set of yield, titer, and productivity that would maximize profitability in the case of growth associated bioplastic production, and the ideal point to shift from the growth phase to the bioplastic production phase in the case of non-growth associated bioplastic production were found, setting potential targets for future synthetic biology and metabolic engineering strategies.

Keywords: Dynamic Flux Balance Analysis, bioplastics, *Escherichia coli*, monthly gross profit.

1. Introduction

In the last decades, bioprocesses have seen great developments, due to increasing concerns with environmental impacts. For instance, the search for more sustainable processes led to an increase of interest in the production of bioplastics as potential replacement for conventional plastics in some applications (Dürr et al., 2021; Ioannidou et al., 2020). But the economic viability remains a problem for bioprocesses (Wang et al., 2023), such as in the production of bioplastics like the well-known poly-3-

hydroxybutyrate (PHB) (Amadu et al., 2021; Duvigneau et al., 2021). In order to make bioprocesses more economically viable, many studies have used mathematical models (Wang et al., 2023) and metabolic engineering techniques to build strains capable of greater yields, or capable of using cheaper carbon sources (Bodor et al., 2019; Sen et al., 2019). The use of genome-scale metabolic models of microorganisms and mathematical methods like flux balance analysis (FBA) is validated in the literature and very common in metabolic engineering strategies, and provides relevant information that can assist in the strain design process (Hohenschuh et al., 2015). However, most of these studies focus on improving product yield, without much regard for other important bioprocess parameters, such as the titer and productivity (Zhuang et al., 2013). Since there can be a trade-off between product and biomass formation in the case of products that share a common precursor with biomass and products that accumulate inside the cell, methods that can keep track of both yield, titer and productivity are better suitable for evaluation of bioprocesses of industrial interest, and this can be done using the mathematical method known as dynamic Flow Balance Analysis (dFBA) (Zhuang et al., 2013), which expands upon classic FBA by using uptake kinetic expressions, and mass balance equations for the external metabolites. By introducing a suitable economic metric that takes into consideration the impact of the yield, titer and productivity, this study expands upon the literature (Zhuang et al., 2013) and presents an approach that allows pre-assessment of the production potential and optimization of bioprocesses of industrial interest through dFBA simulations. Using the production of PHB by recombinant *Escherichia coli* as a case study, the proposed approach estimated the monthly gross profit of each scenario simulated and identified the set of yield, titer and productivity that would lead to the theoretical maximum PHB production profitability with each carbon source tested, thus setting potential goals for metabolic engineering and synthetic biology strategies.

2. Material and Methods

The series of dFBA simulations were carried out in a program written in MATLAB. The *E. coli* K-12 MG1655 model iML1515 (Monk et al., 2017) with addition of the PHB synthesis pathway from the bacteria *Cupriavidus necator* (Duvigneau et al., 2021) was used in the simulations. Figure 1 illustrates how a dFBA simulation works.

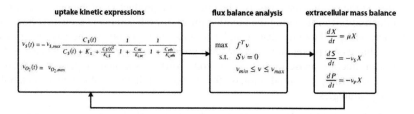

Figure 1: dynamic flux balance analysis framework. Kinetic expressions determine the substrate uptake at each time step, as a function of substrate and inhibiting products concentration. The uptake rate is used as input for the flux balance analysis, which is essentially a linear optimization problem with constraints based on available genome-scale models of microorganisms, such as *E. coli*. The result of the flux balance analysis, the growth rate, is then fed into the mass balance equations, which updates the concentration of the external metabolites. The external metabolites concentrations are then used in the next time step to recalculate the uptake rate.

Based on data available in the literature, a maximum glucose uptake rate of 10.5, maximum glycerol uptake rate of 13, maximum xylose uptake rate of 7.5, and maximum oxygen uptake rate of 15 mmol/gCDW.h were used in the simulations (Varma and

Palsson, 1994). Both the growth associated and the non-growth associated set of simulations were run as batch processes with volume of 200 m^3 and initial conditions of 25 g/L of carbon source (glucose, or glycerol or xylose) and 0.25 g/L biomass. Figure 1 illustrates the procedure used for the simulations of each PHB production type.

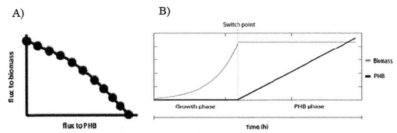

Figure 1: A) Growth associated PHB production simulations, each point is a different yield and its respective set of titer and productivity, that was simulated in order to explore the trade-off between biomass and product formation. B) Non-associated PHB production simulations, each simulation varied the point to switch from growth to PHB production phase.

In the case of growth associated PHB production, the compromise between biomass and product formation was explored by carrying out a series of simulations with growth as the objective function, but with each subsequent simulation also fixing an increasingly higher flow to the PHB synthesis reaction, thus ranging from a flow for PHB synthesis of zero all the way up to the maximum flow possible predicted by the microorganism model, given the carbon source consumption rate used. For the case of non-growth associated PHB production, sets of two-phase simulations were carried out. The first phase of each set had growth as the objective function, representing a phase where ideal conditions for growth are provided for the bacteria. The second phase of each set had PHB synthesis as objective function, representing the point where the ideal conditions for PHB synthesis, such as nitrogen limitation and excess carbon (Kaur, 2015), are provided for the bacteria. Working with the same total amount of carbon source as used in the growth associated simulations, each two-phase simulation varied the fraction of this total amount that was given to the growth phase and to the PHB production phase.

The proposed metric used to evaluate the simulations was the monthly gross profit. To obtain the monthly gross profit, the upstream and downstream costs and the revenue with PHB sales were estimated as a function of the product yield, titer, cultivation time, and final biomass obtained in each simulation. Prices of USD 0.77/kg (Alvarez Chavez et al., 2022), USD 0.53/kg (Alvarez Chavez et al., 2022) and USD 0.44/kg (Manker et al., 2022) were used for glucose, glycerol and xylose, respectively, and a PHB selling price of USD 5.5/kg (Pavan et al., 2019).

3. Results and Discussion

As a result of the simulation, sets of biomass, yield, titer, productivity and monthly gross profit were obtained for each carbon source. As an example, the set of results obtained for growth associated PHB production with glucose as a carbon source are presented in Table 1. Table 1 indicates that the scenario that would result in the highest monthly gross profit, taking into consideration the maximum PHB accumulation in microorganisms of around 85% (wt) shown experimentally in the literature (Chen and Jiang, 2018; Raza et al., 2018), is obtained when reaching a yield of around 0.47 g PHB/g glu, and its set of titer of 11.74 g/L and productivity of 0.88 g PHB/L.h, leading to a monthly gross profit of about 22 thousand USD/month, for the conditions used in the simulations. It can be noted from Table 1 that the highest theoretical monthly gross profit is not achieved in the scenario with the highest possible yield, but rather in the scenario where the set of yield, titer and productivity, when analysed in terms of upstream and downstream costs, and revenue with the product, actually results in the best performance, something that can be identified mathematically with the proposed approach, setting therefore better targets for future metabolic engineering strategies. The results for non-growth associated PHB production with glucose are shown in Table 2.

Table1: Growth associated PHB production with *Escherichia coli* using glucose as the carbon source

flux to PHB mmol/gCDW.h	Final biomass g/L	Final yield g PHB/g glc	Final titer g PHB/L	Final productivity g PHB/L.h	PHB content %	monthly gross profit USD/month
0	11.15	0.01	0.25	0.04	2.19	-371903
1	10.45	0.06	1.43	0.24	12.02	-347917
2	9.83	0.11	2.68	0.46	21.42	-306451
3	9.28	0.15	3.78	0.65	28.95	-267775
4	8.79	0.19	4.76	0.82	35.13	-229540
5	8.04	0.23	5.87	0.94	42.22	-184936
6	7.09	0.28	7.05	1.02	49.85	-140087
7	6.12	0.33	8.22	1.07	57.31	-92963
8	5.07	0.38	9.39	1.06	64.96	-50374
9	4.00	0.42	10.57	1.00	72.54	-10931
10	2.93	0.47	11.74	0.88	80.02	22058
11	1.86	0.52	12.91	0.70	87.38	44239
12	0.79	0.56	14.07	0.41	94.71	46163
12.909	0.25	0.59	14.67	0.28	98.32	40313

Table 2: Non-growth associated PHB production with *Escherichia coli* using glucose as the carbon source

percentage of glucose to growth phase %	Final biomass g/L	Final yield g PHB/g glc	Final titer g PHB/L	Final productivity g PHB/L.h	PHB content %	monthly gross profit USD/month
100	11.15	0.01	0.25	0.04	2.19	-372407
90	9.99	0.06	1.47	0.25	12.81	-352383
80	8.83	0.12	2.93	0.50	24.93	-305433
70	7.69	0.18	4.40	0.76	36.40	-252287
60	6.55	0.23	5.87	1.00	47.23	-198498
50	5.44	0.29	7.33	1.24	57.41	-141296
40	4.34	0.35	8.80	1.42	66.96	-83338
30	3.27	0.41	10.27	1.52	75.85	-26502
20	2.23	0.47	11.73	1.44	84.06	25666
10	1.22	0.53	13.20	1.07	91.55	63421
0	0.25	0.59	14.67	0.28	98.32	40174

It can be seen in Table 2 that, for the maximum PHB content of around 85% (wt) (Chen and Jiang, 2018; Raza et al., 2018), the best performance is obtained when using 20%

(mol) of the total available glucose for growth and the remaining 80% (mol) for PHB synthesis, resulting in a final yield of also 0.47 g PHB/g glu, but with a respective titer of 11.73 g/L and productivity of 1.44 g PHB/L.h. This scenario indicates what would be potentially the ideal moment to switch from the growth phase to the production phase, pointing therefore, targets for future bioprocess optimization and synthetic biology strategies. This switch is often accomplished with limitation of nutrients such as phosphorus or nitrogen (Kaur, 2015), but can also be accomplished with the use of genetic toggle-switches (Batianis et al., 2023). The simulations also mathematically show that, by having a dedicated growth phase and production phase, less total time is required to achieve the same yield and titer, resulting then in higher productivity.

Summarizing the results obtained for all carbon sources, Figure 3 illustrates the maximum theoretical performance that can be obtained for both growth and non-growth associated PHB production in the conditions of the simulations.

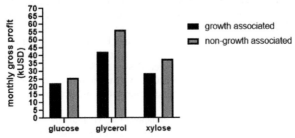

Figure 3: Maximum monthly gross profit for growth and non-growth associated PHB production with different carbon sources

It can be seen in Figure 3 that both glycerol and xylose lead to a higher maximum production potential than glucose, where glycerol displayed the best potential, especially on non-growth associated production, in the conditions of the simulations.

4. Conclusions

Using the growth associated and non-growth associated PHB production with recombinant *E. coli* on different carbon sources as a case study, this work shows how the proposed approach can be used for pre-assessment of bioprocesses in different scenarios and to find the conditions that would lead to the maximum theoretical profit possible, thus establishing potential goals for metabolic engineering and synthetic biology techniques, as well as bioprocess optimization strategies. The approach also pointed glycerol has the highest production potential between the carbon sources tested, for PHB production with *E coli* in the conditions simulated.

Acknowledges

This research was financially supported by the Coordination of Superior Level Staff Improvement (CAPES) grant no. 88887.464619/2019-00, PROEX program and RCGI/FAPESP (2020/15230-5). The following productivity fellowships from National Council for Scientific and Technological Development CNPq are also acknowledged: J. Gregorio C. G. (308714/2019-9) and Galo A.C. L. R. (311550/2022-3).

References

B. Alvarez Chavez, V. Raghavan, B. Tartakovsky, 2022. A comparative analysis of biopolymer production by microbial and bioelectrochemical technologies. RSC Advances 12 (25), 16105–16118.

A. A. Amadu, S. Qiu, S. Ge, G. N. D. Addico, G. K. Ameka, Z. Yu, W. Xia, A.-W. Abbew, D. Shao, P. Champagne, S. Wang, feb 2021. A review of biopolymer (Poly-β -hydroxybutyrate) synthesis in microbes cultivated on wastewater. Science of The Total Environment 756, 143729.

C. Batianis, R. P. van Rosmalen, M. Major, C. van Ee, A. Kasiotakis, R. A. Weusthuis, V. A. Martins dos Santos, jan 2023. A tunable metabolic valve for precise growth control and increased product formation in *Pseudomonas putida*. Metabolic Engineering 75, 47–57.

Z. Bodor, S. Lanyi, B. Albert, K. Bodor, A. C. Nechifor, I. Miklossy, dec 2019. Model Driven Analysis of the Biosynthesis of 1,4-butanediol from Renewable Feedstocks in *Escherichia coli*. Revista de Chimie 70 (11), 3808–3817.

G. Q. Chen, X.-R. Jiang, oct 2018. Engineering microorganisms for improving polyhydroxyalkanoate biosynthesis. Current Opinion in Biotechnology 53, 20–25.

R. Dürr, S. Duvigneau, A. Kienle, 2021. Microbial Production of Polyhydroxyalkanoates – Modeling of Chain Length Distribution. Vol. 50. Elsevier Masson SAS.

S. Duvigneau, R. Dürr, L. Kranert, A. Wilisch-Neumann, L. Carius, R. Findeisen, A. Kienle, 2021. Hybrid Cybernetic Modeling of the Microbial Production of Polyhydroxyalkanoates Using Two Carbon Sources. Vol. 50. Elsevier Masson SAS.

W. Hohenschuh, R. Hector, G. S. Murthy, jul 2015. A dynamic flux balance model and bottleneck identification of glucose, xylose, xylulose co-fermentation in Saccharomyces cerevisiae. Bioresource Technology 188, 153–160.

S. M. Ioannidou, C. Pateraki, D. Ladakis, H. Papapostolou, M. Tsakona, A. Vlysidis, I. K. Kookos, A. Koutinas, jul 2020. Sustainable production of bio-based chemicals and polymers via integrated biomass refining and bioprocessing in a circular bioeconomy context. Bioresource Technology 307 (November 2019), 123093.

G. Kaur, jul 2015. Strategies for Large-scale Production of Polyhydroxyalkanoates. Chemical and Biochemical Engineering Quarterly 29 (2), 157–172.

L. P. Manker, G. R. Dick, A. Demongeot, M. A. Hedou, C. Rayroud, T. Rambert, M. J. Jones, I. Sulaeva, M. Vieli, Y. Leterrier, A. Potthast, F. Maréchal, V. Michaud, H. A. Klok, J. S. Luterbacher, 2022. Sustainable polyesters via direct functionalization of lignocellulosic sugars. Nature Chemistry 14 (9), 976–984.

J. M. Monk, C. J. Lloyd, E. Brunk, N. Mih, A. Sastry, Z. King, R. Takeuchi, W. Nomura, Z. Zhang, H. Mori, A. M. Feist, B. O. Palsson, oct 2017. iML1515, a knowledgebase that computes *Escherichia coli* traits. Nature Biotechnology 35 (10), 904–908.

F. A. Pavan, T. L. Junqueira, M. D. Watanabe, A. Bonomi, L. K. Quines, W. Schmidell, G. M. de Aragao, jun 2019. Economic analysis of polyhydroxybutyrate production by *Cupriavidus necator* using different routes for product recovery. Biochemical Engineering Journal 146 (November 2018), 97–104.

Z. A. Raza, S. Abid, I. M. Banat, jan 2018. Polyhydroxyalkanoates: Characteristics, production, recent developments and applications. International Biodeterioration Biodegradation 126 (September 2017), 45–56.

K. Y. Sen, M. H. Hussin, S. Baidurah, 2019. Biosynthesis of poly(3-hydroxybutyrate) (PHB) by *Cupriavidus necator* from various pretreated molasses as carbon source. Biocatalysis and Agricultural Biotechnology 17, 51–59.

A. Varma, B. O. Palsson, oct 1994. Stoichiometric flux balance models quantitatively predict growth and metabolic by-product secretion in wild-type *Escherichia coli* W3110. Applied and Environmental Microbiology 60 (10), 3724–3731.

H. Wang, C. Kontoravdi, E. A. del Rio Chanona, 2023. A Hybrid Modelling Framework for Dynamic Modelling of Bioprocesses. Vol. 52. Elsevier Masson SAS.

K. Zhuang, B. R. Bakshi, M. J. Herrgård, sep 2013. Multi-scale modeling for sustainable chemical production. Biotechnology Journal 8 (9), 973–984.

Flavio Manenti, Gintaras V. Reklaitis (Eds.), Proceedings of the 34th European Symposium on Computer Aided Process Engineering / 15th International Symposium on Process Systems Engineering (ESCAPE34/PSE24), June 2-6, 2024, Florence, Italy

Flow Phenomena in Renal Arteries with Partial Coverage after Aneurysm

Dhurjati Chakrabarti,[a] Laura D. Edwards[b]

[a,b]*Chemical Engineering, The University of the West Indies, St. Augustine, Trinidad and Tobago*
laura.edwards@sta.uwi.edu

Abstract

Since endovascular aortic repair (EVAR) has a lower death rate and a shorter recovery period, it is being used more often to treat abdominal aortic aneurysms (AAA). Renal artery coverage complications, however, continued to be a serious worry. The flow pattern, wall shear stress distribution, and blood perfusion during a cardiac cycle were all numerically investigated here using three different renal orientations and three different partial renal coverage degrees. According to the findings, the renal artery with a downward orientation experienced more blood perfusion and less unfavourable wall shear stress (WSS) distribution at the mild partial coverage. Notably, the renal artery exhibiting a horizontal orientation experienced a more unfavourable distribution of WSS. All of the renal arteries showed highly disturbed wall shear distribution in terms of severe coverage (approximately 45–50 %), which significantly reduced blood perfusion. It's interesting to note that the artery oriented upward experienced a lower rate of blood perfusion reduction. In summary, renal arteries oriented downward may reduce the risk of renal occlusion in cases of mild renal coverage following EVAR, whereas renal arteries oriented horizontally may increase the unfavourable wall shear distribution. However, for serious coverage (>50 %), regardless of renal orientation, there is a significant increase in the risk of renal ischemia.

Keywords: Flow phenomena, hemodynamics, orientation, CFD, renal artery

1. Introduction

Surgeons have generally accepted endovascular aneurysm repair (EVAR) as a treatment for abdominal aortic aneurysms (AAAs) since it was first presented by Parodi et al. in the early 1990s. While EVAR offers some advantages over open AAA surgical repair, including a shorter recovery period and a lower 30-day mortality rate (Paravastu et al., 2014), it has drawbacks. Using a computational fluid dynamics approach, Liu et al. investigated the impact of partial renal coverage on hemodynamics and discovered that partial coverage to the renal branch office causes flow recirculation and vortices with an unfavourable wall shear stress distribution (Edwards et al., 2018) around the renal ostium. As a result, the degree of obstruction increased in the renal arteries' oscillatory shear index (OSI) and relative resistance time (RRT) (Liu et al., 2018). Additionally, in an in vitro study, Van de Velde et al. examined the impact of partial renal coverage on flow patterns and wall shear stress (WSS). They discovered that the proximal cranial wall of the renal artery exhibits low and oscillating WSS, indicating the development of renal artery stenosis and atherosclerosis in the future. It should be mentioned that the study only used

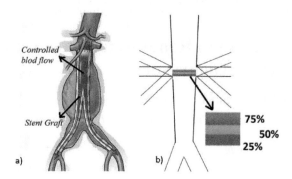

Figure 1 a) abdominal aortic aneurysms (AAAs) and Stent; b) Construction of the idealized abdominal artery (AA) with visceral branches, three typical take-off angles

two-dimensional velocity measurement to identify hemodynamic parameters, despite the fact that the renal arteries' true flow pattern was three-dimensional. The purpose of the present study was to numerically evaluate the effect of partial renal coverage on hemodynamics based on the influence of renal orientation. This study will help to understand the potential risk of progressive renal disease in relation to renal artery anatomy for EVAR. As indicated by Martínez et al. (2012), the use of simulation will provide better insight into the phenomena. Kerst et al. (2015) noted that the utilisation of CFD provided useful results for observation.

2. Methods

Jun Wen et al. (2023) provided the inspiration for this study, which was basically the same simulation and varification. Figure 1a shows AAAs and stent. Figure 1b depicts the construction of the idealized abdominal artery (AA) with visceral branches. The AA portion of the artery extends uniformly from a 24 mm diameter circular cross-section at the descending aorta's inlet to a 17 mm diameter circular cross-section at the AA bifurcation. Renal arteries (RAs) have a diameter of 5 mm. Next, the covered-stent partial renal coverage was constructed and its thickness of 0.2 mm was set based on the postoperative computer tomography angiography (CTA) of a patient whose AAA was repaired by EVAR using infrarenal fixation. Three typical take-off angles, 110 degrees (upward), 90 degrees (horizontal), and 50 degrees (downward) were chosen for analysis to more thoroughly investigate the effect of renal artery take-off angle on renal artery occlusion after EVAR. The blood was thought to be incompressible, homogenous, and non-Newtonian. The following were the matching governing equations:

$$\rho \frac{\partial \bar{u}}{\partial t} + \rho(\bar{u}.\nabla)\bar{u} + \nabla p - \mu \Delta \bar{u} = 0 \qquad (1)$$

$$\nabla.\bar{u} = 0 \qquad (2)$$

$\bar{u}$ and p stand for the velocity vector and pressure value, respectively, ρ is the density (1050 kgm^{-3}).

The Carreau-Yasuda model in this study describes the dynamic viscosity (μ), which can be useful to reflect the relationship between viscosity and shear rate $\dot{\gamma}$:

$$\frac{\mu - \mu_\infty}{\mu_0 - \mu_\infty} = [1 + (k\dot{\gamma})^a]^{\frac{n-1}{a}} \tag{3}$$

Using the values given by Cho and Kensey (1991) as well as Jun Wen et al. (2023), at low shear rates, $\mu_0 = 0.056$, and at large shear rates, $\mu_\infty = 0.0035$, the blood flow is observed. 1.9, 0.2, and 1.3 were the values assigned to the material coefficients k, n, and a, respectively. The total shear stress applied to the wall throughout a cardiac cycle can be determined using the time-average WSS (TAWSS) (Jun Wen et al., 2023), which is defined as follows:

$$TAWSS = \frac{1}{t}\int_0^t |WSS(s,t)| dt \tag{4}$$

A popular metric for assessing the axial directional shift of WSS during a cardiac cycle is the oscillatory shear index (OSI), which is defined as (Ku et al., 1995). A low OSI value shows unidirectional shear flow, whereas a high OSI value suggests oscillatory shear distribution on the vessel wall during a cardiac cycle. The OSI scale runs from 0 to 0.5.

$$OSI = 0.5 \left[1 - \frac{\left| \int_0^t WSS(s,t) dt \right|}{\int_0^t |WSS(s,t)| dt} \right] \tag{5}$$

Another often used indicator is the relative residence time (RRT), which calculates the length of time the particles spend close to the vessel wall. It falls between 0 and infinity. Regions with low and oscillating WSS are indicated by high RRT (Lee et al., 2009), which is defined as (Himburg et al., 2004):

$$RRT = \frac{1}{(1 - 2.OSI).TAWSS} \tag{6}$$

Velocity profile (VP) with shear stress distribution is defined as:

$$v = \frac{b^2}{2\mu} \left[\left(\frac{y}{b}\right)^2 - \frac{y}{b} \right] \frac{d}{dx}(p + \rho gh) \tag{7}$$

b is the distance between Caudal and cranial wall, μ is the fluid viscosity and h is the vertical distance of the flow point from the datum line.

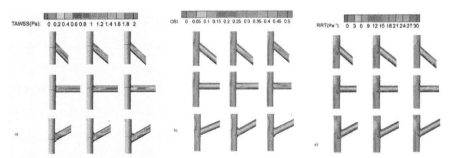

Figure 2: Unsteady WSS fluctuations on the left renal arteries. Three types of renal orientation (downward, horizontal, upward) and three types of partial renal coverage (25%, 50%, 75%) were taken into account. a) TAWSS; b) OSI; c) RRT.

The hemodynamic parameters based on the finite volume approach were visualized and analyzed using commercial computational fluid dynamics software, ANSYS FLUENT. In this investigation, an implicit 3D solver with default segregation was used. To adjust the pressure and velocity, the Semi-Implicit approach for Pressure Linked Equations (SIMPLE) approach was applied. Each pulse cycle in pulsatile simulations was divided into 300 time-steps, each measuring 2.5 ms (the simulated cycle period was T = 0.75 s). For each simulation, four cardiac cycles were chosen in order to get consistent outcomes.

3. Results and Discussions

The TAWSS contour map on the left renal arteries is displayed in Figure 2a. Regarding the renal arteries oriented horizontally and downwardly, areas on the cranial and caudal walls exhibit high (>2 Pa) and low (0.4 Pa) TAWSS, respectively. These regions are particularly noticeable near the branch orifice and become more pronounced as coverage deteriorates. Downstream in the renal arteries, the total WSS level progressively dropped, particularly as the partial coverage worsened. It should be mentioned that, in addition to the exacerbation of the partial coverage, there is a negligible decrease in the overall WSS distribution downstream in the renal arteries with an upward inclination.

However, the contour maps of OSI and RRT, which have a similar distribution, are shown in Figures 2 b and c. Regarding the moderate degree of coverage (~25 %), it is rare to find high RRT (>30 Pa^{-1}) and OSI (>0.4) in any renal artery. Concerning the significant level of coverage (less than 50 %), there were evident variations in the OSI and RRT distributions, which were influenced by the distinct orientations. Regarding the downward-oriented renal arteries, the caudal wall near the covered stent or away from the branch orifice is where elevated OSI and RRT are most commonly seen.

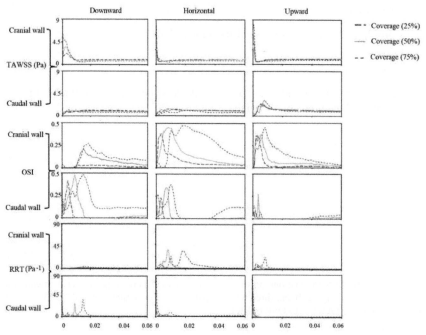

Figure 3: TAWSS, OSI and RRT on left renal artery for renal orientations and degrees of coverage.

Regarding the horizontally oriented renal arteries, high OSI and RRT distribution can be detected in both the caudal wall (near the covered-stent) and cranial wall (far from the branch orifice). Even though the partial coverage of the renal arteries with the upward-oriented artery reached 75 %, there was no discernible high OSI and RRT distribution. As seen in Figure 3, TAWSS, OSI, and RRT were examined along the caudal and cranial walls of left renal arteries. First, because to renal branching and incomplete coverage, high and low TAWSS typically developed near the branch orifice. It is noteworthy that the renal arteries with horizontal orientation on their caudal wall exhibit the highest areas rate of low TAWSS, particularly when the partial coverage reaches 75 %, whereas the arteries oriented upward exhibit the lowest areas rate. Conversely, the cranial wall of the renal arteries oriented horizontally also had the highest WSS value, whereas the arteries oriented downwardly had a comparatively lower WSS in the same area. Regarding the OSI distribution on the renal arteries, it was discovered that the cranial wall of the arteries had the highest OSI, and that the aggravation of partial coverage was correlated with an increase in the average OSI value. OSI distribution can be found on the cranial wall of real arteries with horizontal orientation, even if the coverage was mild (horizontal) with respect to 25 % coverage as for the area-averaged OSI on cranial wall. Regarding the distribution of RRT within the renal arteries.

In general, the renal arteries oriented downward on the cranial wall had the lowest RRT distribution when compared to the other two artery types (downward vs. horizontal and upward) with regard to 25 % coverage. The highest RRT value recorded on the cranial wall was only 3.8 Pa^{-1} when the partial coverage reached 75 %. But in this area, the renal arteries oriented horizontally distributed. The instantaneous flow rate of left renal arteries with varying orientations and partial coverage levels during a cardiac cycle is depicted in Figure 4. In general, the renal arteries with downward and horizontal orientations did not significantly differ in terms of instantaneous flow rate. Similar reversed flow rates of approximately 4% (downward) versus horizontal occurred in both types of renal arteries during the diastolic phase, when partial coverage reached 75 %. It is surprising, though, that the upward-oriented renal arteries, which may have resulted from the retrograde flow pattern, eliminated the reversed flow during the diastolic period and increased the flow rate during the systolic period with regard to the 75 % partial coverage.

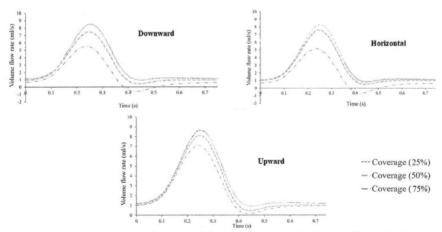

Figure 4: Instantaneous volume flow rate of the left renal artery during a cardiac cycle, the renal arteries with downward, horizontal and upward orientation

The renal arteries oriented downward had the highest blood perfusion, while the arteries oriented upward had the lowest, concerning the mild coverage (~25 %). In contrast, the cumulative flow rate in the upward renal arteries had the least reduction in blood perfusion with respect to 75 % coverage during a cardiac cycle for the serious coverage (~50 %). In relation to the TAWSS or RRT on the vessel wall, the renal artery with a downward orientation exhibited a less unfavourable WSS distribution for the mild partial coverage (~25 %). When mild partial coverage developed, the downward renal artery may be at lower risk of thrombosis. On the caudal and cranial walls of all three types of renal arteries, however, unfavorable WSS distribution progressively increased in tandem with the worsening of coverage (~50 %).

4. Conclusions

For mild renal coverage following EVAR, renal arteries oriented downward may have the advantage of lowering the risk of renal occlusion. The main concern for all types of renal arteries remains the high risk of renal complications due to highly disturbed wall shear distribution, which would increase significantly if serious renal coverage appeared regardless of renal orientation. Since renal arteries oriented horizontally continue to suffer from more unfavourable wall shear distribution than renal arteries with upward or downward orientation, it may be necessary to accept longer follow-up even in cases of mild partial renal coverage.

5. References

Y. Cho, K. Kensey, 1991, Effects of the non-Newtonian viscosity of blood on flows in a diseased arterial vessel. Part 1: steady flows. Biorheology, 28, 241–62

L. Edwards, D. Dhanpat, D. Chakrabarti, 2018, Hydrodynamics of three phase flow in upstream pipes, Cogent Engineering, 5, 1433983

H. Himburg, D. Grzybowski, A. Hazel, J. LaMack, X. Li, M. Friedman, 2004, Spatial comparison between wall shear stress measures and porcine arterial endothelial permeability, Am J Physiol Heart Circ Physiol, 286, H1916–22

J. Jun Wen, X. Liu, J. Lei, J. Wang, X. Chen, T. Zheng, D. Yuan, 2023, Hemodynamics in renal arteries with partial coverage after endovascularaneurysm repair affected by renal orientations. Medicine in Novel Technology and Devices, 18, 100224

K. Kerst, L. de Souza, A. Bartz, A. Seidel-Morgenstern, G. Janiga, 2015, CFD-DEM simulation of a fluidized bed crystallization reactor, CACE, 37, 263-268

D. Ku, D. Giddens, C. Zarins, S. Glagov, 1985, Pulsatile flow and atherosclerosis in the human carotid bifurcation. Positive correlation between plaque location and low oscillating shear stress, Arteriosclerosis, 5, 293

S. Lee, L. Antiga, D. Steinman, 2009, Correlations among indicators of disturbed flow at the normal carotid bifurcation, J Biomech Eng, 131, 61013

M. Liu, A. Sun, X. Deng, 2018, Hemodynamic effect of obstruction to renal arteries caused by stent grafts in patients with abdominal aortic aneurysms, J Mech Med Biol, 18, 1–14

E. Martínez, R. Jaimes, J. Gomez, R. Maciel Filho, 2012, CFD simulation of three-dimensional multiphase flow in a rotating packed bed, CACE, 30, 1158-1162

S. Paravastu, R. Jayarajasingam, R. Cottam, S. Palfreyman, J. Michaels, S. Thomas, 2014, Endovascular repair of abdominal aortic aneurysm, Cochrane Database Syst Rev, CD004178

J. Parodi, J. Palmaz, H. Barone, 1991, Transfemoral intraluminal graft implantation for abdominal aortic aneurysms, Ann Vasc Surg, 5, 491–9

L. van de Velde, E. Donselaar, E. Groot Jebbink, J. Boersen, G. Lajoinie, J. de Vries, C. Zeebregts, M. Versluis, M. Reijnen, 2018, Partial renal coverage in endovascular aneurysm repair causes unfavorable renal flow patterns in an infrarenal aneurysm model, J Vasc Surg, 67, 1585–94

Flavio Manenti, Gintaras V. Reklaitis (Eds.), Proceedings of the 34th European Symposium on Computer Aided Process Engineering / 15th International Symposium on Process Systems Engineering (ESCAPE34/PSE24), June 2-6, 2024, Florence, Italy

Thermodynamic approach to simulate the HydroDeOxygenation process of Lignin

Aristide Giuliano[a], Aniello Di Giacomo[b], Nicola Pierro[a], Isabella De Bari[a], Diego Barletta[b*]

[a]ENEA, Italian National Agency for New Technologies, Energy and Sustainable Economic Development, S.S. 106 Ionica, km 419+500, Rotondella, MT, Italy
[b]Dipartimento di Ingegneria Industriale, Universitá degli Studi di Salerno, Via Giovanni Paolo II 132, I-84084 Fisciano SA, Italy
dbarletta@unisa.it

Abstract

The high availability of lignin as a renewable carbon source, coupled with its chemical structure rich in aromatic compounds, offers a potential opportunity to convert lignin into chemicals, fuels and other valuable building blocks. Within this context, the hydrogenation process was considered a good pathway to obtain profitable compounds converting lignin. In the present work, a novel thermodynamic approach was carried out by lignin hydrogenation simulation. First, a lignin property model was developed in the process simulation software Aspen Plus® and based on its chemical structure and thermodynamic properties. Subsequently, a set of reactions was considered for the hydrogenation process, and the "*temperature approach*" was used to fit the reactor's yield experimental data available in the literature with the reaction network model predictions. This procedure enabled the replication of the results obtained in the reactor without the need to directly consider the reaction kinetics. The results showed that there is a good approximation between experimental and modelling results for each of the four different catalysts tested in the literature works data. The main potential utilization of the model consists in the forecasting of the lignin HDO process individuating the hydrogen needs and the best pressure to use to maximize the yields to aromatics also testing several kinds of lignin sources.

Keywords: lignocellulosic biomass, HDO, temperature approach, lignin modelling, aromatics

1. Introduction

Lignin is the most abundant natural resource among the aromatics yet, it is largely unexploited for this purpose. It has a lower oxygen content compared with cellulose and hemicellulose (Mastrolitti et al., 2021). These properties make lignin an attractive feedstock for chemicals and fuels. The lignin matrix is bound together through a variety of carbon-carbon and ether linkages, unlike most natural polymers, which consist of single inter-monomeric bondings. Lignin's polymer network consists of p-hydroxyphenyl (H), guaiacyl (G), and syringyl (S) units, derived from the dehydrogenation and polymerization of three different hydroxycinnamyl alcohols (monolignols) (Yang et al., 2023). Among the substructures, the β-O-4 (8-O-4, aryl ether) inter-unit linkage is the most predominant and readily cleaved one, either chemically or biochemically, providing a basis for the deconstruction of the polymeric framework in various industrial processes and several analytical methods. Other linkages, such as β–5, β–β, 5–5, 5–O–4, and β–1, are more resistant to both kinds of degradation processes. Many different conversion technologies have been proposed for the depolymerization of lignin into its derived aromatic compounds (Robinson et al., 2022). In particular, reductive depolymerization can break the β-O-4 and α-O-4 bonds and the hydroxyl groups of the side chain (Laskar et al., 2014). The function of the catalyst is to prevent polymerization reactions and condensation of alkenes and carbonyl groups. On the other hand, reductive catalysts are unable to break C-C bonds and the efficiency of depolymerization depends only on the number of ether bonds that can be broken. Nowadays, lignin is only modeled as an inert solid, and therefore, does nothing more than absorb or provide heat. The main approach can be found in the work of (Wooley and Putsche, 1996), which is relevant because it describes a database for all lignocellulosic biomass compounds and defines them in Aspen Plus using their physical properties. In particular, lignin is considered as a solid and its molecular weight, enthalpy of formation at 298 K, density and heat capacity are used to describe it. In the work of Mabrouk et al. (2018), the data given by Wooley and Putsche (1996) were employed to define lignin and experimental data was used for the design of a yield reactor. Finally, in the work by (Shahbaz et al., 2022) lignin was defined as a non-conventional solid and "proximate and ultimate" analysis is used. Nevertheless, non-conventional solids defined in Aspen Plus cannot participate directly in chemical reactions and therefore this approach is not used for reactor design. The possibility of developing models able to predict the behavior of lignin under specific reaction conditions stands as a major challenge in current research, finalized to perform a process simulation and design strategies (Giuliano et al., 2015). In this work, a novel thermodynamic approach will be carried out by lignin hydrogenation simulation based on experimental data and a temperature approach procedure. Hydrogen partial pressure, hydrogen-to-carbon ratio and lignin moisture will be evaluated as main process parameters influencing the lignin hydrogenation.

2. Lignin modelling by thermodynamics approach

2.1. Lignin Modelling in Aspen Plus
In this work, the modelling of lignin using Aspen Plus, its chemical structure was studied in detail, in terms of the monomer's composition, the linkages present in the polymer and the probability of breaking each of these bonds. On the other hand, experimental data on the thermodynamic properties of the biopolymer was collected.

Table 1. Oligomers description (MR, monomers ratios; LR, linkages ratios)

	Lig1	Lig2	Lig3	Lig4	Lig5	Lig6	Lig7
Formula	$C_{30}H_{36}O_{11}$	$C_{40}H_{48}O_{15}$	$C_{27}H_{32}O_{10}$	$C_{39}H_{44}O_{14}$	$C_{38}H_{44}O_{14}$	$C_{30}H_{36}O_{11}$	$C_{31}H_{38}O_{12}$
MW (g/mol)	572	768	516	772	724	572	602
MR (H/G/S)	(1/1/1)	(1/2/1)	(1/1/1)	(0/2/2)	(0/3/1)	(0/3/0)	(0/2/1)
LR (β-O-4/β-1/5-5)	(2/0/0)	(3/0/0)	(1/1/0)	(2/1/0)	(1/1/1)	(2/0/0)	(2/0/0)

Laskar et al. (2014) studied the distribution types of linkages in different types of lignin. With this information, it is possible to state that the aryl-ether linkage (β-O-4) is the most abundant bond in the polymer structure, followed by the β-1 linkage. On the other hand, given the lignin depolymerization processes, it can be assumed that the β-O-4 bond is the weakest since it is likely to be attacked by the different depolymerizing agents. Hence, known the variable composition of lignin and, to introduce its chemical structure into the software, a battery of oligomers of between 3 and 4 monolignols with different kinds of linkages are used. As depicted in the figure below, seven different oligomers were designed with different monomer ratios (MR) and linkages ratios (LR). Each one of these is described in Table 1. The main advantage of using a battery of oligomers instead of a single molecule lies in the fact that there are hundreds of different lignins, with diverse monomers ratio and linkages ratio. Thus, representing lignin by employing different types of oligomers allows us to define certain mixtures during the design phase, enabling us to carry out approximation processes to obtain models in line with the kind of lignin desired. To determine the correct thermodynamic properties that represent lignin, it is necessary to assign accurate characteristics to each oligomer. To begin with, oligomers are defined as solids in Aspen Plus, hence, for temperature-sensitive properties such as heat capacity and density, the values reported in the article by Wooley and Putsche (1996) are employed. Finally, for the definition of the solid enthalpy of formation at 298 K and the standard Gibbs free energy, the values obtained by Azad et al. (2020), are employed. In this paper, authors modeled a lignin oligomer consisting of ten coniferyl units linked through nine β-O-4 bonds. In addition, they calculated standard thermodynamic properties, including enthalpy of formation, entropy, and Gibbs free energy for a wide range of temperatures from 25 K to 1000 K and for oligomers ranging from one to ten monomer units. Thermodynamic properties are obtained through experimental techniques, classical approaches (i.e., equation of state and GE model) and computational approaches (Azad et al., 2020).

2.2. Hydrogenation of lignin in an equilibrium reactor
Following the modelling of lignin, the design of a set of reactions to carry out the depolymerization and hydrogenation of the oligomers has to be performed. For this purpose, two equilibrium reactors were used. The stoichiometric matrix was employed to calculate the number of independent reactions required for each reactor. The main objective of this reactor is to produce the depolymerization of the oligomers so that the complete hydrogenation process can be carried out in the next reactor. It should be noted that all the reactions present in this first set are exothermic. Between the first and the second reactor, the non-depolymerized oligomers are separated, while the products and the unreacted hydrogen encounter are subject to a second set of reactions, shown in Figure 1, to finally obtain the ultimate hydrogenation products. Subsequently, another 15 reactions are added, leading to a total of 25 reactions and 28 possible products. Among the added reactions, the most remarkable ones are the production of alkyl phenolics, such as Cresol, and the generation of various types of cyclic and linear alkanes, which are products of interest in the hydrogenation of lignin. In addition, reactions for the generation of aromatic aldehydes, such as p-hydroxybenzaldehyde, vanillin and syringaldehyde, were also included. Finally, there is also the generation of oxygenated gaseous products (CO and CO_2) and organic acids, such as acetic acid and formic acid.

2.3. Experimental data fitting
Given the set of reactions and their known behavior inside the equilibrium reactor, it is possible to use the "temperature approach" to take into account non-equilibrium conditions. This method enables modification of the temperature at which the equilibrium constants of each reaction are calculated with the objective of fitting the results obtained in the second reactor to the experimental data available in the literature. In particular, in the present project, the approximation has been carried out by employing the data obtained in Kumar et al. (2015). The investigation mentioned uses a known type of Kraft lignin, called "Indulin-AT", and carries out its hydrogenation process by making use of different kinds of catalysts and supports.

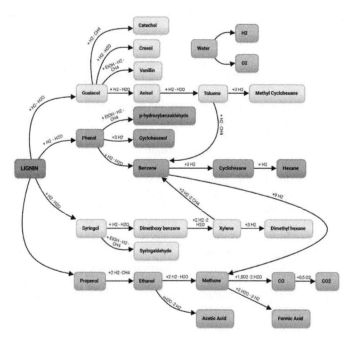

Figure 1. The set of reactions considered in the first reactor

2.4. Optimization method for the Temperature approach parameter fitting

As has already been mentioned, the system is constituted by 25 reactions and 28 species, which are initially assumed at chemical equilibrium inside the reactor. Within this project, the strategy followed consists of altering that equilibrium by employing the Temperature approach, to obtain yield values that are close to the ones reported in the literature. In addition, this approach does not require to consider the kinetics involved in this complex reaction network. The procedure described above entails the need to vary the temperature of all 25 reactions present in the system. However, being able to determine the temperature shifts for each reaction is not an easy task. For that reason, the following optimization method was developed. The temperature of 22 out of the 25 reactions was varied, excluding the reactions with O_2. Provided that the oxidation reaction equilibrium is shifted towards the products, the variation of the temperature approach should not have a significant impact on the yield.

Table 2. Lignin and a mixture of oligomers considered in this work

		Kumar et al. (2015)	This work
Lignin		Indulin-AT, Kraft Lignin, Softwood	33.3 % Lig5 – 66.7% Lig6
Composition	H	0 %	0 %
	G	90-95 %	90 %
	S	5-10 %	10 %
Linkages	β-O-4	74 %	71 %
	β-1	11 %	14 %
	5-5	15 %	14 %

On the other hand, O_2 is produced through the hydrolysis of water and as the reactor works with an excess of H_2, this reaction practically does not take place. To define the objective function, the quadratic errors of the product's yields obtained in Aspen Plus concerning the product's yields given in the literature were calculated. Finally, the objective function is defined as the sum of all the errors.

3. Thermodynamics approach modeling results

Before the temperature approach application, the equilibrium reactor was performed the lignin was converted into gas products (i.e., Methane, CO and CO_2) and water. The total yield to products greater than 100 % is because this is calculated only considering the weight of lignin. Using the optimization procedure described in the previous section, comparison results shown in Figure 2 were obtained. The model is a good fit for Kumar et al. (2015) experimental data, especially when the catalyst favors the production of alkyl phenolics and aromatics. However, excessive water production can cause problems for the fit when it is not followed by the simultaneous generation of other compounds. This is observed in the case of $CoMo/Al_2O_3$, for which the adjustment shows appreciable errors in the amount of water produced. In the case of $NiMo/MgO-La_2O_3$, the best fit can be observed, which has a production of alkyl phenolics as the main product and water and aromatics as by-products. This also occurs in the case of NiMo/ZSM-5. This could indicate that using catalysts more selective towards the generation of some product such as alkyl phenolics or aromatics, improves the performance of the model.

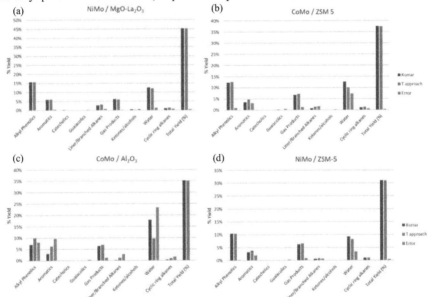

Figure 2. Adjustment of the equilibrium reactor using as catalysts: (a) $NiMo/MgO-La_2O_3$, (b) CoMo/ZSM-5, (c) $CoMo/Al_2O_3$, (d) NiMo/ZSM-5

4. Conclusions and Future Perspectives

The lignin modelling procedure described in this work can well simulate the HydroDeOxygenation process in determined conditions and using specific literature catalysts. The model allows to vary both the intrinsic composition of the lignin entering the reactor and the operating parameters of the hydrogenation process. In the future, through a dedicated optimization analysis will be possible to determine the optimal conditions of pressure and H/C ratio, as well as the moisture content and the optimal chemical structure that the lignin should present to increase the production of target products, such as aromatic monomers. It could be determined that the increase of the H/C ratio enhances the conversion of lignin and consequently, the production of alkyl phenolics increases.

Acknowledgments

The authors deeply acknowledge the current national representatives of IEA task 42 'Biorefining in a Circular Economy' from Austria, Denmark Germany, Ireland, the Netherlands and USA for useful debate and discussions. Prepared by Aristide Giuliano, Nicola Pierro, Isabella De Bari (ENEA, Italy), on behalf of IEA Bioenergy Task42.

References

Azad, T., Schuler, J.D., Auad, M.L., Elder, T., Adamczyk, A.J., 2020. Model Lignin Oligomer Pyrolysis: Coupled Conformational and Thermodynamic Analysis of β-O-4′ Bond Cleavage. Energy Fuels 34, 9709–9724. https://doi.org/10.1021/acs.energyfuels.0c01573

Giuliano, A., Poletto, M., Barletta, D., 2015. Process Design of a Multi-Product Lignocellulosic Biorefinery, in: Computer Aided Chemical Engineering. Elsevier B.V., pp. 1313–1318. https://doi.org/10.1016/B978-0-444-63577-8.50064-4

Kumar, C.R., Anand, N., Kloekhorst, A., Cannilla, C., Bonura, G., Frusteri, F., Barta, K., Heeres, H.J., 2015. Solvent free depolymerization of Kraft lignin to alkyl-phenolics using supported NiMo and CoMo catalysts. Green Chem. 17, 4921–4930. https://doi.org/10.1039/C5GC01641J

Laskar, D.D., Tucker, M.P., Chen, X., Helms, G.L., Yang, B., 2014. Noble-metal catalyzed hydrodeoxygenation of biomass-derived lignin to aromatic hydrocarbons. Green Chemistry 16, 897–910. https://doi.org/10.1039/c3gc42041h

Mabrouk, A., Erdocia, X., Alriols, M.G., Labidi, J., 2018. Economic analysis of a biorefinery process for catechol production from lignin. Journal of Cleaner Production 198, 133–142. https://doi.org/10.1016/j.jclepro.2018.06.294

Mastrolitti, S., Borsella, E., Giuliano, A., Petrone, M.T., Bari, I.D., Gosselink, R., van Erven, G., Annevelink, E., Triantafyllidis, K.S., Stichnothe, H., 2021. Sustainable lignin valorization 194.

Robinson, A.J., Giuliano, A., Abdelaziz, O.Y., Hulteberg, C.P., Koutinas, A., Triantafyllidis, K.S., Barletta, D., De Bari, I., 2022. Techno-economic optimization of a process superstructure for lignin valorization. Bioresource Technology 364, 128004. https://doi.org/10.1016/j.biortech.2022.128004

Shahbaz, M., AlNouss, A., Parthasarathy, P., Abdelaal, A.H., Mackey, H., McKay, G., Al-Ansari, T., 2022. Investigation of biomass components on the slow pyrolysis products yield using Aspen Plus for techno-economic analysis. Biomass Conv. Bioref. 12, 669–681. https://doi.org/10.1007/s13399-020-01040-1

Wooley, R.J., Putsche, V., 1996. Development of an ASPEN PLUS Physical Property Database for Biofuels Components. Victoria 1–38.

Yang, X., Zhang, Y., Ye, M., Tang, Y., Wen, Z., Liu, X., Li, C.C., 2023. Renewable lignin and its macromolecule derivatives: an emerging platform toward sustainable electrochemical energy storage. Green Chem. 25, 4154–4179. https://doi.org/10.1039/D3GC00565H

Flavio Manenti, Gintaras V. Reklaitis (Eds.), Proceedings of the 34th European Symposium on Computer Aided Process Engineering / 15th International Symposium on Process Systems Engineering (ESCAPE34/PSE24), June 2-6, 2024, Florence, Italy

Second-generation biorefinery location selection in Europe using satellite data and crop calendars

Varun Punnathanam[a], Raunak Bardia[a], Shirish Potu[a], Nicole Elliott[b], Jose Maria Gonzalez Martinez[c]

[a]*Shell India Markets Private Limited, Bengaluru 562149*
[b]*Shell International Petroleum Company Limited, London SE17NA*
[c]*Shell Global Solutions International B.V., Amsterdam 1031HW*
Varun.Punnathanam@shell.com

Abstract

The feasibility of large-scale second-generation biofuel production is largely dependent on feedstock availability. Agricultural residue based feedstock have temporal variation in addition to regional variation, as these residues are primarily available during the harvesting season. This work utilizes the open-source database EUCROPMAP to generate a map of biomass availability throughout the 27 EU countries by down-sampling from the original 1.75×10^{11} pixels of resolution 10 m to 2.7×10^6 pixels of resolution 2.56 km without loss of land use information. The residue generated per pixel is then calculated as a function of the crop yield using the residue-to-product ratio formula. This is followed by accounting for collectability and availability of the residues using crop-specific factors from literature. Lastly, heatmaps are generated that showcase the total quantity of biomass that can be procured within a specified collection radius. The seasonal variation in feedstock is incorporated by utilizing European crop calendars. Each crop in each country is assigned a harvesting season using this database. The biomass availability hotspots and the seasonality data are then utilized to recommend biorefinery locations that minimize feedstock storage and transport. A case study of France is presented, considering barley, maize, rapeseed, sunflower, and wheat to be crops of interest. Using seasonality information was shown to drastically change the recommended biorefinery location and reduce inventory capacity requirement and average feedstock storage by 9.7% and 20%, respectively. The presented information and methodology can help biofuel producers to de-risk upstream supply chains for biorefinery investments.

Keywords: Second generation biofuels, feedstock mapping, biorefinery location

1. Introduction

Renewable fuels of biological origin offer the most immediate and achievable pathway to decarbonize hard-to-abate transport sectors such aviation and marine. Of these, biomass-derived fuels such as cellulosic ethanol, biodiesel, and sustainable aviation fuel have the highest gap to potential, but have challenges due to uncertainties in feedstock availability and supply chain cost. Reducing this cost and the risk associated with procuring feedstock from thinly distributed sources will help stimulate global biorefinery investments needed to meet companies' and governments' climate targets and associated biofuel demand. A primary challenge in addressing this risk lies in reliable information on agricultural feedstock availability in a region of interest.

In this paper, we consider the European Union (EU) as the region of interest and present a methodology to generate a map of biomass availability at a resolution of 2.56 km² using open source EUCROPMAP (d'Andrimont, et al., 2021) data and provide a case study of biorefinery site recommendation for France from a feedstock availability point of view. Section 2 discusses a data assimilation methodology for bio-feedstock mapping without loss of land use information and provides the estimated residue available for collection in the EU along with heatmaps to identify feedstock hotspots. Section 3 provides a framework to recommend optimal biorefinery location taking seasonal variation of feedstock, harvesting cycle, feedstock collection radius, storage, and transport into consideration. Section 4 presents details on the case study of France, followed by results and conclusions in Section 5 and Section 6, respectively.

2. Biomass feedstock mapping

Mapping of residue requires an understanding of the geospatial distribution of the crops grown in the EU region. This distribution is available as an open-source database from the European Commission at a spatial resolution of 10 m (d'Andrimont, et al., 2021). This implies that data is available for over 175 billion data points for the European region. The land use pattern information is classified into forest, wasteland, arable land, agricultural land, and urban land categories. Relevant to this work the agricultural land is further sub-categorized to specify the type of crop grown.

2.1. Crop area mapping

While information is available at the fine resolution of 10 m, it is not practically relevant to assess agricultural residue grown within a country or in a region at that scale. To make the database more tractable for practical use, the information is aggregated over an area of 2.56 km x 2.56 km. Each coarse pixel aggregates information of 65,536 original 10 m pixels by summing up the number of 10 m land parcels for each classification presented above. After aggregation, the total number of coarse pixels for the EU region is ~2.7 million. Area under each crop (j) for each coarse pixel (i) is given by Equation 1.

$$A_{i,j} = 10 \times 10 \times N_{ij} \ m^2, \tag{1}$$

Where, N_{ij} refers to the number of 10 m pixels that correspond to the jth crop classification in i^{th} coarse pixel. A representation of the most prominent common wheat crop in the EU region is show in Figure 1. Each pixel position is identified by its latitude and longitude position. However, to make the analysis comprehensible, this information is also translated into geographical nomenclature used for statistics, often termed as NUTS regions (NUTS - GISCO - Eurostat, n.d.). This translation is done by locating each [lat, long] position in individual NUTS shapes.

2.2. Estimating biomass available for biorefineries

The raw data for area under a crop available at each pixel can be converted to available biomass at each pixel from each crop in the following manner *(Chakraborty, et al., 2022)*:

$$\alpha = A \times Y \times RPR \times CF \times AF, \tag{2}$$

Where α refers to the available biomass, A is the area under cultivation, Y is the yield of crop, RPR is the residue production ratio, CF is the collection factor, and AF is the availability factor of the biomass. Note that the evaluation of α can only be an estimate and is dependent on highly variable climatic and agricultural factors that cannot be precisely controlled or predicted. Area information for each pixel is defined from Section

2.1 for individual crops separately. Yield is crop and region specific and was taken from the Food and Agriculture Organization database (FAOSTAT, 2019). The key component

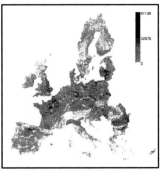

Fig. 1. Geospatial distribution of wheat cropping area in the EU region at $2.56 \times 2.56\ km^2$ resolution. Colour bar represents the number of 10 m pixels.

to convert crop information to biomass is an estimation of the amount of residue generated, which is highly variable and dependent on plant variety, climate conditions, farming practices, and cutting height. This data is often reported as a ratio compared to the crop yield and is referred as RPR. An approximate estimate of RPR has been defined as an exponential relationship with crop yield by (Karan & Hamelin, 2021). Appropriate assumptions are made in case of mismatches in crop categorizations. While RPR converts crop information to the amount of generated residue, about 50% to 60% residues cannot be collected due to equipment and terrain limitations (Monforti, Bódis, Scarlat, & Dallemand, 2013). Additionally, of the collected residues, about 10% to 20% is usually utilized in-situ for applications such as animal bedding or mulching (Monforti, Bódis, Scarlat, & Dallemand, 2013). Although these numbers may have significant regional and temporal variations, they are incorporated to provide a more realistic estimate of available biomass.

The available biomass is then utilized to a generate heatmap of the feedstock collectable within a collection radius, assumed to be 80 km for this study. For each of pixel in Figure 2 (a), the neighboring pixels within this collection radius is identified. This search is conducted smartly and is sped-up by GPU-based parallelization. Next, the total biomass procurable at each point is calculated as the summation of the biomass available at each neighboring point. As a result, each point from Figure 2 (a) now has an associated biomass availability within the collection radius. This value can be utilized to visualize the biomass hotspots, as shown in Figure 2 (b).

3. Location selection and optimization

For the present study, the only criterion on selection of biorefinery location is assumed to be the feedstock collectable within the collection radius. For this purpose, the first step is to identify the points that meet a threshold on the feedstock available at each harvest season. The amount of feedstock procured in each harvest should be at least enough to sustain the biorefinery production till the subsequent harvest. For instance, for a region with two harvests a year in July and October, the annual requirement of feedstock is divided such that the procurement in July sustains for at least 3 months and the procurement in October sustains for at least nine months. All points that satisfy these thresholds have the possibility of having a balanced feedstock inventory profile at the biorefinery. Among these points, the point with the most biomass available is the recommended biorefinery location.

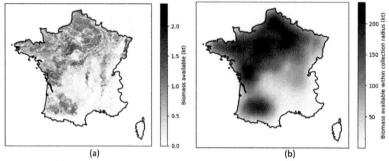

Fig. 2. Annual biomass availability (a) at each pixel and (b) collectable within a radius of 80 km

The impact of selecting the biorefinery location in this manner is studied by solving a simple optimization problem with the objective of minimizing the transport and inventory costs while meeting the demand for feedstock at the biorefinery. The time periods are defined based on harvest seasons. The objective function is shown in Equation 3.

$$\text{Min } z = w^{tr} \sum_{p,t} D_p f_{p,t} + w^{inv-c} C_{in} + w^{inv-o} \sum_t i_t \qquad (3)$$

Where, w^{tr}, w^{inv-c} and w^{inv-o} are the weights associated with transportation and CAPEX and OPEX associated with feedstock storage. Note that the weights may be replaced with costs as applicable. D_p is the distance from biomass source p to biorefinery, $f_{p,t}$ is the feedstock procured from biomass source p at time t, C_{in} is the capacity of inventory required, obtained as the maximum feedstock stored at any time period, and i_t is the feedstock in the inventory at time t. Here, all pixels within the collection radius of the biorefinery location are biomass sources.

The constraints to the optimization problem are the limit of feedstock available from each biomass source, the inventory balance at each biorefinery, and the demand for feedstock at each time period, and are given in Equation 4, Equation 5, and Equation 6. respectively.

$$f_{p,t} \leq F_{p,t} \qquad (4)$$

$$i_t = k_{t-1} i_{t-1} + \sum_p f_{p,t} - d_t \qquad (5)$$

$$d_t = D_t \qquad (6)$$

Where, $F_{p,t}$ is the feedstock available in biomass source p at time t, k_{t-1} is the feedstock loss factor at time t-1, d_t is the feedstock processed the biorefinery at time t, and D_t is the demand for feedstock at time t. Note that the intention of the optimization problem is primarily to demonstrate the implications of the biorefinery selection and not to perform economic analysis of biofuel production.

4. Case study

The data and method proposed in this work is demonstrated for France. Residues from barley, maize, rapeseed, sunflower, and wheat are considered in this work as they account for about 98% production in the country. Based on the cropping calendars (U.S. Department of Agriculture, 2023), the harvest periods of these crops were assumed to be as follows: July for wheat, barley and rapeseed, and October for corn and sunflower. The feed requirement at the biorefinery is assumed to be 160 ktpa of agricultural residues with a minimum 15 kt feedstock in storage at any time period and a storage loss of 12% pa. To provide a comparative study, two cases are presented in this work: an annual case and a seasonal case where the recommendations are based on the annual and seasonal availability data, respectively. For the annual case, the point with the highest biomass available within the collection radius is recommended for setting up the biorefinery.

5. Results and discussion

Figure 3 (a) represents the feedstock availability heatmap on enforcing a minimum threshold of 160 ktpa for the annual case. For the seasonal case, the thresholds were 40 kt and 120 kt for July and October, respectively, and the heatmap is presented in Figure 3 (b). For the annual case, the heatmap is primarily spread across a large region in the north-west of France. On the other hand, the hotspot is a relatively small region in the south-west of France for the seasonal case. As a result, the recommended biorefinery location is significantly different for both these cases.

The implications of the biorefinery location selection are obtained by solving the optimization problem. Figure 4 showcases the expected feedstock inventory for both cases. In the annual case, seasonality was not considered, and hence, the biorefinery was located in a region that had very high feedstock availability in July, but less so in October. In order to meet the demand for feedstock throughout the year, the biorefinery would require to procure large quantities of feedstock in the July that would be carried forward throughout the year, resulting in a requirement of inventory of capacity 154 kt, annual average storage of 99 kt of feedstock, and peak procurement of about 135 kt in July. On the other hand, the biorefinery location in the seasonality case is such that it would procure similar quantities of feedstock in both months, with larger procurement in October to account for monthly production till the next harvest season in July. As a result, the inventory capacity requirement would be 139 kt (9.7% lower), annual average storage would be 79 kt (20% lower), and peak procurement would be around 100 kt in October (26% lower). Thus, the seasonal case solution would incur lesser inventory CAPEX and OPEX, lesser feedstock lost at storage, and easier logistics in terms of peak procurement.

6. Conclusions

This work presents a methodology to recommend biorefinery locations considering the regional and temporal variation in agricultural residue availability using publicly available data. The 10 m resolution information from EUCROPMAP was aggregated to a courser resolution of 2.56 km to improve tractability of mapping feedstock in the EU.

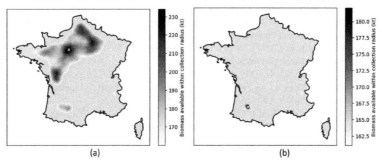

Fig. 3. Heatmap for regions that meet the threshold on (a) annual and (b) seasonal availability and resulting biorefinery location shown as a white cross.

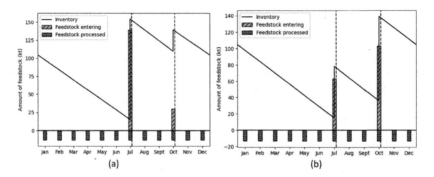

Fig. 4. Feedstock inventory at biorefinery for (a) annual and (b) seasonal case. Positive bars represent the feed entering (at harvest season), negative bars represent the feed processed at each month, and the solid line is the inventory level.

A case study of France is presented considering residues from barley, maize, rapeseed, sunflower, and wheat to provide feedstock for a biorefinery. Two solutions are presented, using annual and seasonal feedstock availability information. The recommended biorefinery location was observed to be different for both cases, with the annual and seasonal case recommending north-west and south-west of France, respectively. The seasonal case was observed to result in a better inventory profile, with 9.7% lower inventory capacity requirement and 20% lower average inventory storage as compared to the annual case. Hence, accounting for seasonality was shown to be critical for agricultural residue-based biofuel production and should be considered while deciding asset locations. The data utilized and the methods presented in this work can be replicated for any other country or combination of countries in the EU. Moreover, for designing a large-scale multi-echelon supply chain, the presented method can be used to locate pre-processing facilities rather than biorefineries.

References

Chakraborty, A., Biswal, A., Pandey, V., Shadab, S., Kalyandeep, K., Murthy, C. S., . . . Chowdhury, S. (2022). Developing a spatial information system of biomass potential from crop residues over India: A decision support for planning and establishment of biofuel/biomass power plant. *Renewable and Sustainable Energy Reviews, 165*, 112575.

d'Andrimont, R., Verhegghen, A., Lemoine, G., Kempeneers, P., Meroni, M., & Van der Velde, M. (2021). From parcel to continental scale–A first European crop type map based on Sentinel-1 and LUCAS Copernicus in-situ observations. *Remote sensing of environment*, 112708.

FAOSTAT. (2019). (Food and Agriculture Organization fo the United Nations) Retrieved from https://www.fao.org/faostat/en/#data/QCL

Karan, S. K., & Hamelin, L. (2021). Crop residues may be a key feedstock to bioeconomy but how reliable are current estimation methods? *Resources, Conservation and Recycling, 164*, 105211.

Monforti, F., Bódis, K., Scarlat, N., & Dallemand, J.-F. (2013). The possible contribution of agricultural crop residues to renewable energy targets in Europe: A spatially explicit study. *Renewable and Sustainable Energy Reviews, 19*, 666-677.

NUTS - GISCO - Eurostat. (n.d.). (European Commission – Eurostat/GISCO) Retrieved from https://ec.europa.eu/eurostat/web/gisco/geodata/reference-data/administrative-units-statistical-units/nuts

Flavio Manenti, Gintaras V. Reklaitis (Eds.), Proceedings of the 34th European Symposium on Computer Aided Process Engineering / 15th International Symposium on Process Systems Engineering (ESCAPE34/PSE24), June 2-6, 2024, Florence, Italy

Exergoeconomical and Ecological Analysis of Biogas Valorization Pathways – Comparing a Combined Heat & Power Plant with a Pressurized Water Process

Fizza Tahir[a,d], Burcu Aker[b], Sven Nater[c], Keren Djuffo Jiofack[a], Jens-Uwe Repke[d], Jan Schöneberger[a]

[a]Berliner Hochschule für Technik, 13353 Berlin, Germany
[b]Chemstations, 11000 Richmond, Houston
[c]DAH Guppe, 16515 Oranienburg, Germany
[d]Technische Universität Berlin, 10623 Berlin, Germany
Jan.Schoeneberger@bht-berlin.de

Abstract

The production of biogas is an important stepstone on the pathway to a climate neutral economy and society. This paper conducts a thorough investigation about comparative analysis of two distinct biogas valorization pathways: cogeneration (A) and production of biomethane in a Pressurized Water Process (B). The investigation is based on a careful examination of three linked aspects: thermodynamic efficiency (exergy), economic feasibility, and environmental effect. This Exergoeconomical and Ecological Analysis (EEEA) is performed by combining rigorous first-principle flowsheet simulation and empirical insights gained from operational biogas facilities. The resulting validated and consistent mass and energy balances serve as the foundation for a comprehensive life cycle assessment (LCA) focusing climate change category. The findings showed that exergetic efficiency of scenario A is 34% and for scenario B it is 76%, the economic benefit of A is 168 €/h and for B it is 296 €/h. The upgrading of the biogas (B) is thermodynamically favorable. Moreover, LCA analysis showed that upgrading (B) has less impact on the climate change as compared to cogeneration (A). The proposed method proved to be a comprehensive procedure to analytically evaluate the viability of biogas plants.

Keywords: Biomethane, Cogeneration, Thermodynamic analysis, Economic analysis, Life cycle assessment

Introduction

In recent years, the rising need for environmentally friendly and sustainable energy sources has boosted interest in biogas and biomethane production as feasible options for both energy generation and waste management. Biogas, obtained from the anaerobic digestion of organic materials, and biomethane, its purified equivalent can be pumped into natural gas pipelines, utilized as a transportation fuel, or to generate power contributing to cleaner and more sustainable energy options.

Several studies have emerged focusing on the exergy and energy concept. Sevinchan et al. (2019) examined a biogas-powered multigeneration system and concluded energy efficiency of 72.5% and a maximum exergy efficiency of 30.44%, with considerable exergy destruction in the combustion chamber. Gong and Lunelli (2023) investigated agro-industrial and urban organic waste for energy production via anaerobic digestion, with an emphasis on biogas generation. The continuous stirred tank reactor (CSTR) biodigester was responsible for 57.2% of the overall exergy destruction, while the heat exchanger exhibited the highest exergy efficiency at 99.95%. Siefert et al. (2014) studied exergy and economics of a power plant that uses biogas from a thermophilic anaerobic digester (AD) to power a solid oxide fuel cell (SOFC). Vilardi et al. (2020) analyzed three biogas upgrading systems (amine scrubbing, water scrubbing, and membrane separation) for exergy and energy performance. These technologies converted biogas into biomethane. The authors concluded that water scrubbing had the highest exergy efficiency (94.5%) and methane recovery (99%), membrane separation had the lowest efficiency (90.8%) and the highest specific energy usage (0.94 kWh/m3 STP). Amine scrubbing used a lower amount of energy (0.204 kWh/m3 STP) and had a high exergy efficiency (91.1%). Xiao et al. (2019) compared untreated, hydrothermally pretreated, and solar-driven hydrothermally pretreated biogas generation techniques. Solar-driven hydrothermal pretreatment had the highest exergy efficiency of 40.85%, outperforming untreated (26.2%) and hydrothermally pretreated (35.98%) procedures. Notably, biogas residue contributed considerably to exergy losses, ranging from 35.13% to 60.58% of total exergy input in the various processes. Therefore, as per our knowledge, no literature has cumulatively focused on exergy analysis, cost analysis and life cycle assessment for upgrading and cogeneration process of biogas plant. This study bridges the gap by providing comparative analysis on two biogas valorization pathways: cogeneration and upgrading through Pressurized Water Process. The objectives of the research are investigation of thermodynamic efficiency, economic cost and life cycle assessment of biogas plant focusing climate change impact category.

2. Methodological approach

The biogas facility under consideration is at the DAH plant in Vehlefanz, Germany. Primary data from the site were collected, including design specifications, operating conditions, feedstock kinds, and production rates. A combined Exergoeconomical and Ecological Analysis (EEEA) is performed as proposed by Schöneberger et al. (2011), using the above-mentioned plant data and rigorous flowsheet simulation. For the latter the flowsheet simulator CHEMCAD from Chemstations Inc. is used. Two scenarios have been identified for the analysis; (A): all biogas is fed to a combined heat and power plant (CHP) and upgradation is switched off and (B): 65% of the biogas is send to a pressurized water plant while the rest is fed to a CHP.

2.1. Economic analysis
A simplified economic analysis is used, considering only product income and feed cost flows. The depreciation of investment costs is neglected because the scenarios compare different operation modes of an existing plant. Operation and maintenance costs are assumed to be small compared to the feed costs. The revenues for the fermentation residues are not calculated explicitly, but lower feedstock costs are considered assuming that the residues are used company internally as fertilizer.

2.2. Thermodynamic analysis
Thermodynamic analysis concentrated on energy conversion efficiency for electricity generation as well as exergetic efficiency, which included heat as a valued output. To compare the efficiency of the electricity production it is assumed that the biomethane is sent to a combined cycle power plant (CCPP) with an electric efficiency of 55 % (higher

heating value - HHV based). The exergies are calculated from enthalpies and entropies at process and at ambient conditions using the the Volume Translated Peng Robinson (VTPR) equation of state to calculate phase equilibria and physical properties, see Tsai & Chen (1998) for details. Chemical exergies must also be considered because chemical reactions take place in the CHP.

2.3. Eco-balance analysis

LCA is a comprehensive approach for assessing the environmental implications of a product, process, or system over the course of its life cycle. In this analysis, Gabi LCA software has been utilized for the modeling and calculation processes. The goal of the study is to evaluate the environmental impacts generated from the biogas plant focusing the defined scenarios. The functional unit selected for the study is $1 Nm^3$ of biogas produced from feedstock. The system boundary selected for the study is "cradle to gate", which encompasses activities related to biogas production and its subsequent conversion into biomethane, electricity and heat as shown in Fig.1.

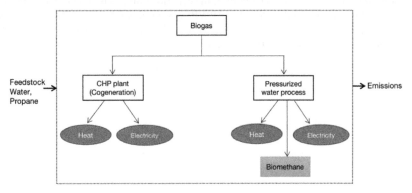

Fig. 1 Schematic flow chart of the chosen system boundary

It does not extend to consider any downstream applications. It's important to note that the initial stage of biogas production is a shared component between both investigated pathways (pressurized water upgrading and cogeneration). The processes are modelled using Ecoinvent databases. A system boundaries expansion (or avoided burden approach) is also applied: the avoided production of natural gas that can be substituted from biomethane is accounted for. For this study, the global warming potential has been evaluated.

3. Process description and model assumptions

The process flowsheet is depicted in Fig. 2. An amount of 12.2 t/h of biomass are fed to the fermenter (U1), which requires 100 kW of electricity and 500 kW of heat for operation. The biomass is composed of 50% maize silage and 50% gras silage by weight. This feed leads to a dry gas production of 2020 Nm^3/h while the remaining 7.3 t/h give the fermentation residues. The dry biogas composition is 53.6% CH_4 46.4% CO_2 with 90 ppm H_2S by mol. The gas is saturated at the fermenter conditions (50°C, 1 bar abs.) which gives an additional water flowrate of 230 kg/h. A part of the biogas (S4) is cooled down and sent to the CHP plant, where H_2S is removed with activated carbon before it is used in the combustion engine to produce heat and electricity. The engine is modelled as a combination of compressors, expanders, and an equilibrium reactor. The model gives an electric efficiency around 38% (HHV based), which fits well with the empirical values for CHP plants.

The gas that is sent to the upgrading process (S13) is compressed in three stages to the absorber pressure of 8 bar abs. For the compressors (U8, U10, and U13) an adiabatic efficiency of 75% is assumed. The coolers (U3, U9 and U11) are modelled as compression machines with a COP of 3. The absorber (U14) is set-up with 8 equilibrium stages. Before the biomethane can be injected into the natural gas grid it is dried and its heating value is adjusted by adding propane (S22). The loaded wash water (S24) is flashed in order to recover absorbed methane (S25) before it is sent to the stripper column (U17). Ambient air (S27) is used for stripping the loaded water in 8 equilibrium stages. The stripping air (S28) contains the H_2S and rests of CH_4 and is transported to a regenerative thermal oxidation unit (RTO, U19) with blower U18, where all residues are oxidized to H_2O, CO_2, and SO_2. The regenerated wash water (S31) is cooled, compressed, and sent back to the absorber. The chiller (U23) must reach lower temperatures than the coolers and therefore is modelled with a COP of 2. In scenario A all gas is send to the CHP plant (S4=S2) and the pressurized water plant (PWP) is shut down. In scenario B 65% of the biogas is fed to the PWP (S13 = 1500 Nm³/h wet). In Table 1 the main production and consumption data for both scenarios are summarized.

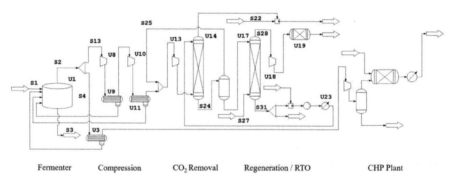

Fig. 2 Process flowsheet of the biogas production and valorization process as implemented at the DAH plant site in Vehlefanz.

Table 1. Main production and consumption data for both scenarios

	Electricity consumption	Electricity production	Net electricity production	Biomethane production	Biomethane production	Economic benefit
A	0.7 MW	4.5 MW	3.8 MW	0 Nm³/h	0.0 MW (HHV)	168 €/h
B	0.6 MW	1.6 MW	1.0 MW	740 Nm³/h	7.7 MW (HHV)	296 €/h

5. Results and Discussion

5.1 Economic analysis

In scenario A, 3.8 MW of electricity are produced which leads to an income of 760 €/h. The income for scenario A is 528 €/h. In scenario B 1 MW of electricity and 7.7 MW of biomethane (HHV base) are produced, which generate an income of 969 €/h. This income is reduced by the costs for propane, which is used to adjust the heating value of the biomethane. 60 kg/h propane are added resulting in an additional cost flow of 18 €/h. In both scenarios the feed costs of 360 €/h must be subtracted. With these parameters, the benefit for scenario A is 168 €/h and for scenario B 296 €/h. At an electricity to gas price ratio of 2.5 scenario A becomes economically more attractive than scenario B, because under these conditions selling the electric power creates a larger benefit than using it for the biogas upgrading process.

5.2 Thermodynamic analysis
This gives an electric efficiency of 38% for scenario A and of 44% for scenario B. The upgrading of the biogas is thermodynamically favorable because electricity can be produced more efficiently in a CCPP than in a CHP, which predominates the losses during the upgrading process. In order to avoid the assumption of the usage of the biomethane in a CCPP the exergetic efficiency of both processes can be compared.

Table 2 has depicted the main exergy flows. The flows are summarized into inputs, outputs, and losses. The difference of these values gives the exergy destruction that occurs during the specific scenarios. The exergetic efficiency of scenario A is 34% and of scenario B 76%. This confirms the result based on the electric efficiency. Furthermore, it points out that the losses related to the CHP off gas have a considerable effect on the exergetic efficiency of the process.

Table 2. Main exergy flows summarized into inputs, outputs, and losses.

	Input			Output			Loss
	Biogas	Electricity	Propane	Biomethane	Electricity	Heat	Off gas
A	11.2 MW	0.7 MW	0.0 MW	0.0 MW	4.5 MW	26 kW	2.8 MW
B	11.2 MW	0.6 MW	0.8 MW	8.0 MW	1.6 MW	26 kW	0.9 MW

5.3 Eco-balance analysis
Table 3 shows the life cycle inventory table used for calculating the life cycle impact assessment.

Table 3. Life cycle inventory

	Scenario A	Scenario B
	CHP	PWP and CHP
Inputs		
Biogas	2,850 kg/h (wet)	2,850 kg/h (wet)
Active carbon	0.62 kg/h	0.22 kg/h
Water	-	5 m³/d
Propane	-	30 Nm³/h
Outputs		
Carbon dioxide	3,966 kg/h	2,578 kg/h
Nitrogen	32,457 kg/h	12,368 kg/h
Nitric oxide	15.7 kg/h	5.6 kg/h
Sulphur dioxide	-	0.3 kg/h
Electricity	3,800 kW	1,002 kW
Heat	500 kW	500 kW
Biomethane	-	581 kg/h (8.5 MW HHV)

The upgrading process produces less impact on climate change whereas cogeneration produces a higher amount of electricity. This is due to the fact that upgrading leads to the production of biomethane, a clean and renewable fuel with reduced CO_2 emissions when compared to the combustion of raw biogas in cogeneration.

Considering mean CO_2 emissions of 0.4 kg/kWh for electricity production and 2.75 kg CO_2 emissions for utilizing 1 kg of natural gas, net CO_2 reductions of 1,520 kg/h in scenario A and 1,999 kg/h in scenario B are achieved.

6. Conclusion and way forward

This study has performed a thorough Exergoeconomical and Ecological Analysis comparing cogeneration (scenario A) and biomethane production via pressurized water scrubbing (scenario B) for biogas valorization. The analysis includes thermodynamic efficiency, economic feasibility, and life cycle assessment. The results indicate that scenario A exhibited an exergetic efficiency of 34% and an economic benefit of 168 €/h, while scenario B demonstrated higher exergetic efficiency at 76% and generates a higher economic benefit of 296 €/h. For an electricity price to gas price ratio of higher than 2.5 scenario A becomes economically more attractive. Upgrading the biogas is thermodynamically advantageous and has a higher CO_2 reduction potential than cogeneration. The market prices for natural gas and electricity can still force owners and operators of biogas plants to go for the cogeneration.

These results develop an insight towards policy making and implement scientific and empirical research to achieve environmental and energy sustainability through biogas generation. Future research can be carried out on the sustainable feedstock scoring, comprehensive life cycle assessment considering multiple environmental and social factors and conducting analysis on different upgrading technologies to know which is better in terms of sustainability.

References

Gong, R., & Lunelli, B. H. (2023). Exergy Analysis of Biogas Production from Sugarcane Vinasse. *BioEnergy Research*.

Nsair, A., Onen Cinar, S., Alassali, A., Abu Qdais, H., & Kuchta, K. (2020). Operational parameters of biogas plants: A review and evaluation study. *Energies, 13(15)*.

Schöneberger, J., Arellano-Garcia, H. and Wozny, G. (2011), Inverse exergo-ökologisch-ökonomische Prozessanalyse von Abgasbehandlungsprozessen. *Chemie Ingenieur Technik, 83*.

Siefert, N. S., & Litster, S. (2014). Exergy & economic analysis of biogas fueled solid oxide fuel cell systems. *Journal of Power Sources, 272*.

Sevinchan, E., Dincer, I., & Lang, H. (2019). Energy and exergy analyses of a biogas driven multigenerational system. *Energy, 166*.

Thrän, D., Schaubach, K., Majer, S., & Horschig, T. (2020). Governance of sustainability in the German biogas sector—adaptive management of the Renewable Energy Act between agriculture and the energy sector. *Energy, Sustainability and Society, 10*.

Theuerl, S., Herrmann, C., Heiermann, M., Grundmann, P., Landwehr, N., Kreidenweis, U., & Prochnow, A. (2019). The future agricultural biogas plant in Germany: A vision. *Energies, 12(3)*.

Tsai, J.-C., Chen, Y-P. (1998) Application of a volume-translated Peng-Robinson equation of state on vapor-liquid equilibrium calculations, *Fluid Phase Equilibria, 145(2)*.

Vilardi, G., Bassano, C., Deiana, P., & Verdone, N. (2020). Exergy and energy analysis of three biogas upgrading processes. *Energy Conversion and Management, 224*.

Xiao, C., Liao, Q., Fu, Q., Huang, Y., Xia, A., Shen, W., ... & Zhu, X. (2019). Exergy analyses of biogas production from microalgae biomass via anaerobic digestion. *Bioresource technology, 289*.

Flavio Manenti, Gintaras V. Reklaitis (Eds.), Proceedings of the 34th European Symposium on Computer Aided Process Engineering / 15th International Symposium on Process Systems Engineering (ESCAPE34/PSE24), June 2-6, 2024, Florence, Italy

Improving Butanol and Acetone Production by Two-Stage Fermentation Coupled with Flash Distillation

Juan C. Barreiro[a], Paula A. Tapias[a], Nicolas Muñoz[a], Karoll M. Rubiano[a], Jose M. Bernal[b], Carlos A.M. Riascos[a,b]*

[a]Chemical and Environmental Engineering Dpt., Universidad Nacional de Colombia, Bogotá 111321, Colombia
[b]Institute of Biotechnology, Universidad Nacional de Colombia, Bogotá 111321, Colombia.
camartinezri@unal.edu.co

Abstract

Bio-butanol and bio-acetone are alternatives to develop sustainable products and processes. The competitiveness of biotechnological processes depends on raw materials and operational costs, as well as on the productivity of the process. In the present work, butanol and acetone production by ABE fermentation coupled with an initial recovery stage by flash distillation is proposed. For the fermentation, a spontaneous mutant of *Clostridium acetobutylicum* DSM 1732, obtained at the Institute of Biotechnology of Universidad Nacional de Colombia, was employed. To increase productivity, a two-stage fermentation is proposed: the first stage, the acidogenesis phase, runs as a cyclic fed-batch, while the second one, the solventogenesis, runs as a batch; for this strain, ethanol production is practically negligible. This strategy allows to maintain high metabolic rates in both phases. On the other way, in the flash distillation, water-butanol azeotrope and the low boiling point of acetone allow to generate a solvent-concentrated vapor phase with high recovery (48 to 80 %). To generate a proposal for fermentation coupled with flash distillation, fed-batch fermentation and vapor-liquid equilibrium were studied, it allows to define operational conditions for each system unit. Results show that the operation in a cascade with two stages increases the combined productivity (acetone plus butanol) by 15 %, from 1.21 g L^{-1} h^{-1} in batch operation to 1.40 g L^{-1} h^{-1} in the proposed system, with no reduction in yield and reducing inoculum preparation, which is an advance for the development of a competitive process.

Keywords: ABE fermentation, cascade fermentation, flash distillation.

1. Introduction

Acetone-Butanol-Ethanol (ABE) fermentation has had a boom during the last 10 years due to the variability of production, price, the energy crisis and environmental problems of fossil fuels. It is one of the most ancient fermentation processes as it was important for obtaining the acetone necessary for the synthesis of cordite which was employed for gunpowder production in the First World War. With the rise of biofuels, interest in this fermentation has resumed, generating strains resistant to toxic metabolites and butanol hyperproducers (Patakova et al., 2013).

Butanol is mainly used in the surface coatings sector. 1-butyl esters of phthalic, adipic, sebacic, oleic, azelaic, stearic, and phosphoric acids are produced from butanol, serving as plasticizers and additives for surface coatings. In Addition, butanol is used as biofuel, proving to be even more effective than ethanol for gasoline replacement, due to its higher energy content and lower corrosiveness owing to its low miscibility with water (Bîldea et al., 2016). On the other hand, acetone is a key industrial solvent for cleaning purposes, given its complete miscibility with water and most organic solvents and oils. Furthermore, acetone serves as a precursor for large-scale products such as bisphenol A and methyl isobutyl ketone. Other uses of acetone as a solvent include dilution of fiberglass resin, paint formulations, ink, resin, and varnish (Morales-Rodriguez et al., 2014).

ABE fermentation has been developed by using strict-anaerobic bacteria from the *Clostridiae* family. Although there are different species capable of ABE production, *C. Acetobutylicum* and *C. Beijerinckii* are the most employed (Qureshi et al., 2001). The first fermentation stage –known as acidogenesis– occurs simultaneously with bacterial growth, this stage considers production of ethanol, and butyric and acetic acids, using glucose as substrate, which generates an important pH decrease. Acidogenesis ends when the concentration of acids reaches the maximum tolerance; at this point, a metabolic switch activates the set of reactions that allow acids to be transformed into solvents, the consumption of acid increases the pH and the final metabolic inhibition is generated by high concentration of solvents. The solventogenesis stage is a non-growth period.

Commercial butanol production through ABE fermentation considers challenges in solvent purification, as they are highly diluted in fermentation broth, due to the toxicity of the products. Recent research has generated new options for the separating of these solvents using techniques such as gas extraction, distillation, extractive distillation, pervaporation, and liquid-liquid extraction, among others. Moreover, it has been observed that combining fermentation and separation increases process productivity due to the reduction of butanol inhibition. However, these methods have disadvantages, such as the loss of micronutrients and intermediate products, as well as their lack of industrial implementation. Nevertheless, good performance and a high potential have been observed with the integration of fermentation plus separation (Zetty Arenas, 2019).

At the Institute of Biotechnology of Universidad National de Colombia (IBUN), spontaneous mutants of *Clostridium acetobutylicum* DSM 1732, resistant to high butanol concentrations, have been isolated (Sierra et al., 1996). For these mutants, the production of total solvents is between 6 and 18 g/L, with yields ($Y_{P/S}$) between 0.2 and 0.5 and productivities between 0.09 and 0.27 g of solvents/L·h. In the present work, alternatives to increase the productivity of butanol and acetone through ABE fermentation are evaluated.

2. Material and Methods

2.1. Strain

ABE Fermentation studies started with vial fermentation for strain selection, and batch bioreactor experiments to develop a mathematical model, details of this previous research are presented in a complementary work (Tapias et al., 2024). IBUN IV, a spontaneous mutant of *Clostridium acetobutylicum* DSM 1732 strain, obtained at the Institute of Biotechnology of Universidad Nacional de Colombia, was selected due to its productivity and solvent tolerance. Tapias et al. confirmed the main characteristic of ABE fermentation: metabolism is carried out in two phases. The first phase employs sugars to generate acids (butyric and acetic) and biomass; whereas, in the second one sugars and acids are metabolized to generate solvents (butanol and acetone) without biomass generation. In that way, the switch between the metabolic phases generates changes in pH evolution. The best results were obtained with 40 g/L of glucose, which generates 36.3 g/L of solvents ($Y_{P/S} = 0.908$). Table 1 presents the key fermentation characteristics.

Table 1. Key batch fermentation characteristics with IBUN-IV strain.

	Acidogenesis phase	Solventogenesis phase
Lag phase	6 h	N.A.
Process time	9 h	15 h
Glucose Evolution	From 40.0 to 27.0 g/L	From 27.0 to 0.0 g/L
Biomass Evolution	From 1.0 to 3.2 g/L	Non-growing
Acids Evolution	From 4.5 to 10 g/L	From 10 to 4.5 g/L
pH Evolution	From 6.0 to 4.6	From 4.6 to 5.2
Average acids generation rate	0.611 g/L h	N.A.
Solvents Evolution	No-generated	From 0.0 to 36.3 g/L
Average solvents generation rate	N.A.	2.42 g/L·h

2.2. Analytics

Concentrations of glucose, butanol, acetone, butyric and acetic acids from fermentation were measured by HPLC, in a Shimadzu chromatograph, using a 300 x 4 mm Eurokat H column, 5 mM H_2SO_4, at 0.5 mL/min and 85 °C, using a refractive index detector RID 10A. Biomass was quantified by dry weight (Tapias et al., 2024).

2.3. Fed-batch Fermentation

As other authors observed (Guo et al., 2018), metabolic differences between both phases and the non-growing production in the solventogenesis phase generate complexities for a single-stage process with feeding, whether continuous or fed-batch; considering that, two strategies for improving butanol and acetone production were considered. The first one includes two cyclic fed-batch bioreactors, the acidogenesis would begin with batch operation and, when it is at 2/3 of evolution, 2/3 of its volume is replaced with the original media to put on glucose and other spent nutrients, and to reduce the concentration of acids and other products. Meanwhile, the solventogenesis bioreactor would be fed with the volume harvested from acidogenesis, this feeding puts on spent acids, replaces biomass that is removed with the products, and reduces solvent concentration.

The second strategy considers a two-stage (cyclic fed-batch + batch) fermentation: the acidogenesis stage works like in the first strategy, meanwhile, the solventogenesis bioreactor would operate at batch regime.

To evaluate the viability of implementing a cyclic fed-batch solventogenesis process, a fed-batch fermentation was performed, this fermentation considers a 1:1 volumetric feeding of a synthetic acidogenesis broth at 36 h (approximately 2/3 of the solventogenesis phase). The concentration of the main components in the feeding was: glucose: 40.0 g/L, acetic acid: 7.5 g/L, butyric acid: 4.5 g/L, and other components: equal to the original media. This fermentation was performed in a 1 L BIOSTAT A with no pH control, details of equipment and procedures are presented in our previous work (Tapias et al., 2024).

2.4. Vapor-Liquid Equilibrium

To assess VLLE, simulations in ASPEN PLUS® with NRTL model were performed. Due to the possibility of partial solubility, simulations were contrasted with experimental results from Lee et al. (2021). Results from Lee et al. confirmed that the NRTL model generates accurate predictions for this system. The simulations were employed to estimate butanol fraction and recovery in the vapor generated from a flash distillation of a mixture with the compositions of the broth after solventogenesis. Pressure between 260 and 560 mmHg was considered.

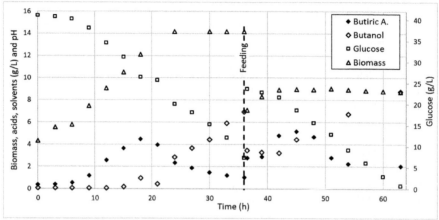

Figure 1. Concentration profiles for fed-batch fermentation.

3. Results and Analysis

3.1. Fed-Batch Fermentation

Results from this fermentation suggest that it is very complex to maintain the fermentation in solventogenesis phase by cyclic feeding. That is supported by the evolution of the fermentation after the feeding: biomass grew again, acids were produced again, and solvent production stagnated, as observed in Figure 1; this suggests that feeding changed the metabolic state leading it to return to the acidogenesis phase.

3.2. Vapor-Liquid Equilibrium

For the fermentation broth (butanol: 10 g/L and acetone: 26 g/L), VLE experiments did not show partial solubility (methodology presented in Chasoy et al., 2012), it agrees with the results from the simulations. On the other hand, mass fraction and recovery of butanol in distillate as functions of pressure and temperature (Figure 2), obtained from simulations, showed that 560 mmHg and 88 °C is a good set for the operation of the flash separation (dotted vertical line), at these conditions butanol mass titer in vapor is 8.35 % (an eight-fold increase compared to the fermentation broth) and the recovery is 47.8 %, which is a satisfactory separation. Another option for the flash condition is 560mmHg and 90 °C which generates vapor with 5.0 % butanol and recovery of 79.5 %. To rigorously define the flash operational conditions, an optimization analysis is suggested.

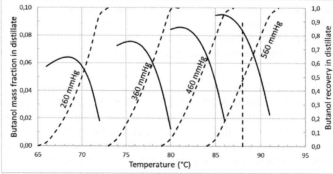

Figure 2. Mass fraction and recovery of butanol in flash distillation. Continuous lines are mass fraction, dotted lines are fractional recovery.

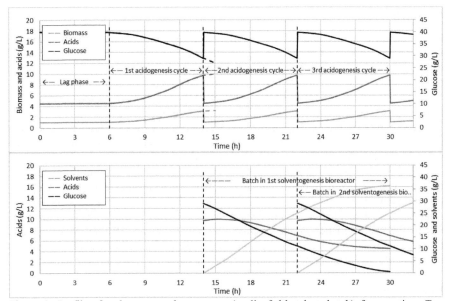

Figure 3. Profiles for the proposed two-stage (cyclic fed-batch + batch) fermentation. Top, acidogenesis cyclic reactor; down, solventogenesis batch reactors.

3.3. Proposed Production System.

From the fermentation results, the proposed butanol + acetone production system considers a cyclic fed-batch bioreactor for acids production and two batch bioreactors for solvents production, estimated profiles for these reactors are presented in Figure 3.

Considering the time for each fermentation stage (9 and 15 h), the processing lasting in each bioreactor can be adjusted for highly efficient scheduling (8 and 16 h) with two solventogenesis bioreactors operating alternately: the first solventogenesis reactor receives the broth from the odd (first, third, etc.) cycles, while the second one receives from the even (second, fourth, etc.) cycles. The product from solventogenesis reactors takes turns to feed the separation system which begins with a flash distillation (Figure 4).

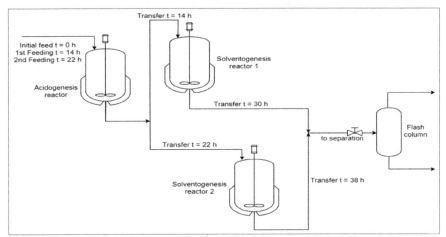

Figure 4. System configuration with cyclic fed-batch acidogenesis, batch solventogenesis and flash separation.

4. Conclusions

Due to the metabolic complexity of the ABE fermentation, a single-stage continuous or fed-batch fermentation is not viable. As an alternative, two-stage fermentation systems were evaluated. The best alternative includes a fed-batch cyclic bioreactor for acidogenesis and two batch bioreactors for solventogenesis, this configuration allows to eliminate idle time for all the bioreactors as well as the lag phase in the acidogenesis (lag phase reduces productivity in traditional batch operation).

The proposed configuration increases productivity from 1.21 g L^{-1} h^{-1} in batch operation to 1.40 g L^{-1} h^{-1} in the proposed system. Due to the solventogenesis phase being performed in batches, glucose is used until complete consumption, which allows to reach a high yield (0.91 g of solvents / g of glucose). Additionally, the cyclic operation in the first phase reduces the necessity of inoculum preparation, which is an advance for the development of a competitive process.

Analysis of flash distillation, as a first stage for the recovery of the products, shows that, due to the characteristics of the mixture obtained from the ABE fermentation, this operation allows to recover a high fraction of the solvents (between 48 and 80 %) with an important increase in concentration (from approximately 1 %, 10 g/L, to between 5 to 8 %).

References

C.S. Bîldea, I. Patraşcu, J.G. Segovia Hernandez, A.A. Kiss, 2016, Enhanced Down-Stream Processing of Biobutanol in the ABE Fermentation Process. Computer Aided Chemical Engineering, 38, 979-984. DOI: 10.1016/B978-0-444-63428-3.50168-5

W.A. Chasoy, 2012, Determinación experimental del equilibrio líquido-vapor del sistema etanol-agua-glicerina, M.Sc. Thesis, Universidad Nacional de Colombia, Colombia. https://repositorio.unal.edu.co/handle/unal/55058

D.D. Guo, X.J. Ji, L.J. Ren, F.W. Yin, X.M. Sun, H. Huang, G. Zhen, 2018, Development of a multi-stage continuous fermentation strategy for docosahexaenoic acid production by *Schizochytrium sp*. Bioresource Technology, 269, 32-39. DOI: 10.1016/j.biortech.2018.08.066

H.Y. Lee, T.S. You, C.L. Chen, 2021, Energy efficient design of bio-butanol purification process from acetone butanol etanol fermentation, J. Taiwan Institute of Chemical Engineers. DOI: 10.1016/j.jtice.2021.08.003

R. Morales-Rodriguez, D. Rodriguez-Gomez, M. Sales-Cruz, J.A. de los Reyes-Heredia, E.S. Pérez C., 2014, Model-Based Analysis for Acetone-Butanol-Ethanol Production Process through a Dynamic Simulation, Computer Aided Chemical Engineering, 33, 133-138. DOI: 10.1016/B978-0-444-63456-6.50023-5

P. Patakova, M. Linhova, M. Rychtera, L. Paulova, K. Melzoch, 2013, Novel and neglected issues of acetone–butanol–ethanol (ABE) fermentation by clostridia: *Clostridium* metabolic diversity, tools for process mapping and continuous fermentation systems, Biotechnology Advances, 31, 1, 58-67, DOI: 10.1016/j.biotechadv.2012.01.010.

N. Qureshi, H.P. Blaschek, 2000, Recent advances in ABE fermentation: hyper-butanol producing *Clostridium beijerinckii* BA101, Journal of Industrial Microbiology & Biotechnology, 27, 287-291.

P.A. Tapias, 2024, A Two Phases Model for ABE Fermentation with a Modified *Clostridium acetobutylicum* Strain, Computer Aided Chemical Engineering,

J. Sierra, R. Acosta, D. Montoya, G. Buitrago, E. Silva, Edelberto, 1996, Obtention of spontaneous mutant of *Clostridium acetobutylicum* of butanol resistant, Rev. Colomb. Ciencias Quim. Farm, 25, 26-35

A.M. Zetty Arenas, 2019, Towards enhanced second-generation n-butanol production from sugarcane, Ph.D. Thesis, TU Delft. DOI: 10.4233/uuid:7e5a2017-e3ef-4224-bdd2-e8a970c4fed9

Flavio Manenti, Gintaras V. Reklaitis (Eds.), Proceedings of the 34th European Symposium on Computer Aided Process Engineering / 15th International Symposium on Process Systems Engineering (ESCAPE34/PSE24), June 2-6, 2024, Florence, Italy

Economic optimization of intensified processes to produce bioethanol from lignocellulosic biomass.

Yulissa M. Espinoza-Vázquez, [a] Fernando Israel Gómez-Castro, [a*] Eduardo Sánchez-Ramírez, [a] Araceli Guadalupe Romero-Izquierdo, [b]

[a] *Departamento de Ingeniería Química, División de Ciencias Naturales y Exactas, Universidad de Guanajuato, Noria Alta S/N, Guanajuato, Guanajuato 36050, México. fgomez@ugto.mx*
[b] *Facultad de Ingeniería, Universidad Autónoma de Querétaro, Campus Amazcala, Carretera a Chichimequillas S/N km. 1, Amazcala, El Marqués, Querétaro, Querétaro 76010, México.*

Abstract

In this work, the optimization of a conventional and two intensified processes to produce bioethanol from sorghum residues is developed. The intensification of the production process is applied to the separation zone and includes the whole biomass transformation process in a biorefinery scheme. The process was simulated in the software Aspen Plus, using thermally coupled columns. Then, the optimization is carried out using the total annual cost (TAC) as the objective function, with differential evolution with tabu list (DETL) as the optimization algorithm. DETL was coded in Python and linked with Aspen Plus using the PyWin32 library. The developed tool allows obtaining the optimal design for each process after iterating during approximately 30 hours, with a population of 120 and 200 generations as parameters of the optimization algorithm. It has been found that the optimized conventional system has slightly lower total annual costs than the intensified systems, but the intensified schemes require less equipment.

Keywords: bioethanol, optimization, differential evolution, process intensification.

1. Introduction

In 2021, the use of fossil fuels represented 77% of the world energy system, the same percentage as 30 years ago (Ritchie et al., 2022). These resources are non-renewable, and their deposits are depleted daily, generating greenhouse gases' emissions. To address this situation, the concept of biofuels stands up, which are renewable fuels generated by processing biomass, reducing CO_2 emissions in the transportation sector (Alam and Tanveer, 2020). They can be used in blends with conventional fuels. Bioethanol is a fuel that can be obtained from biomass; it can be mixed with gasoline in proportions up to 10 vol% to run internal combustion engines. It is important to mention that lignocellulosic residues are usually burned after the grain has been harvested (Law Corner, 2021), therefore it is important to consider routes of use and valorization for these residues. The production of bioethanol from biomass requires pretreatment, hydrolysis, and fermentation processes. Of the possible routes, Conde-Mejía et al. (2012) have shown that acid hydrolysis with H_2SO_4 followed by separate hydrolysis and fermentation achieve higher yields and lower costs.

The production of biofuels from biomass is not fully profitable. Particularly, bioethanol production costs are too high compared to the current prices of fossil fuels (Reboredo et al., 2017). In this context, process intensification (PI) plays a key role as it could help to have more compact, energy efficient, safer, and environmentally friendly processes. With respect to the intensification of the conversion process, several proposals have been presented (Hernández, 2022). In this work, we will focus on the purification zone. Regarding bioethanol purification, various intensification proposals have been reported. Torres-Ortega and Rong (2016) studied the separation of a fermentation broth with a dividing wall system, generating a 21.42% reduction in total annual cost compared to the conventional separation train. On the other hand, Espinoza-Vázquez et al. (2023) proposed intensified schemes for bioethanol purification, including thermally coupled columns and column bonding, performing an analysis of heat duty and key product recoveries, concluding that using a thermally coupled column could enhance the process. However, this comparison is made on non-optimized schemes, with no evaluation of economic indices. Therefore, in this work the rigorous optimization of intensified bioethanol purification schemes is proposed, including the design of the biomass conversion step. The proposed schemes in this work are optimized through the hybrid stochastic algorithm differential evolution with tabu list (DETL), taking as objective function the total annual cost (TAC).

2. Case study

The case study is based on the work of Espinoza-Vázquez et al. (2023), where a feed stream of 87, 539 kg/h of sorghum residues has been considered. The mass composition for the feed stream is 27.56% cellulose, 15.37 % hemicellulose, 14.11 % lignin and 42.93 % carbohydrates (Conde-Mejía et al., 2013). The reactions and conditions for the pretreatment process, hydrolysis and fermentation process have been defined according to Espinoza-Vázquez et al. (2023). All the proposed configurations have been simulated using Aspen Plus. The NRTL equation has been selected as the thermodynamic model to represent the phase equilibrium. In Figure 1, the equipment that can be optimized is marked in blue, corresponding either to the heat exchangers or the separation columns; such units have degrees of freedom. This study analyzes three configurations for the purification section: one conventional (CS) and two intensified schemes (TCC and CTC). All the schemes are evaluated using economic indexes. The two intensified schemes were proposed following the systematic procedure to generate intensified configurations from simple column sequences proposed by Errico and Rong (2016), and their configuration is described next.

2.1. Conventional Scheme (CS)

This scheme consists of four columns in the separation train, shown in Figure 1 A). C-1 is a distillation column for the separation of volatile gases and heavy compounds. A side stream with bioethanol, water and other products is fed to an additional distillation column (C-2), where non desired products are removed at the bottom. A stream consisting of a mixture of bioethanol and water in the azeotropic point is fed to an extractive distillation column (C-3), using glycerol as solvent in a mass ratio 1:1 regarding the amount of bioethanol in the feed stream. C-4 is a glycerol recovery column.

2.2. Thermally Coupled Column (TCC)

This scheme proposes a thermally coupled column to replace the glycerol recovery column (C-4), as shown in Figure 1 B).

2.3. Coupling of two columns (CTC)

This scheme consists of merging column 2 and 3 of the conventional scheme into a single column to reduce the number of equipment; this new column is labeled as C-2. In addition, a column labeled as C-3 is proposed for the recovery of the solvent, as shown in Figure 1 C).

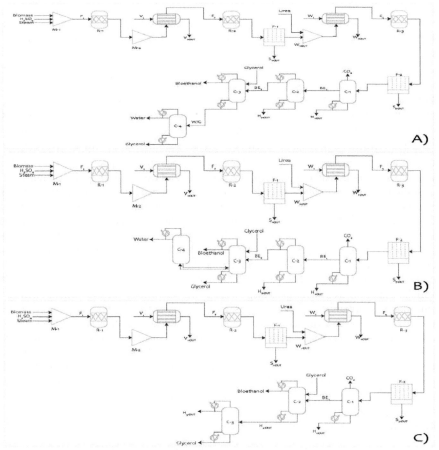

Figure 1: Process flowsheet for: A) CS, B) TCC, C) CTC.

3. Methodology

The objective function considered for this analysis is the TAC, this involves capital and operating costs related to the construction and operation of a chemical process (Turton et al., 2008). The Guthrie method was used to calculate the TAC (Guthrie, 1969), estimating the cost per unit of the process, as shown in Eq. 1.

$$TAC = CO + \frac{CC}{PP} \tag{1}$$

where CO is the cost of the services, CC is the capital cost of the plant and PP is the payback period, assumed as 5 years (Susmozas et al., 2018). The minimization of this objective is constrained by the temperatures, recoveries and purities required in each equipment and process stream:

$$Min(TAC) = f(TH_{in}, FH, N_s, N_f, B_R, N_{ss}, F_{ss}, D_R, R_R, F_L, F_V) \qquad (2)$$

Subject to: $y_b \geq x_b \qquad w_b \geq u_b \qquad y_g \geq x_g \qquad w_g \geq u_g$

where TH_{in} is the inlet temperature of the utility's stream of the heat exchangers used, FH is the mass flow rate for the exchangers, N_s is the number of stages of each distillation column, N_f is the column feed stage, B_R is the bottoms flow rate, N_{ss} is the side outlet or inlet stage (in the case of the extractive columns), F_{ss} is the mass flow for each side outlet or inlet, D_R is the distillate flow rate, R_R is the reflux ratio, F_L is the interconnection liquid flow rate and F_V is the interconnection vapor flow rate. In addition, the optimization problem is constrained by the purities of bioethanol (y_b) and glycerol (y_g), that must be equal to or greater than x_b and x_g, respectively. Moreover, the recoveries of bioethanol (w_b) and glycerol (w_g), must be equal to or greater than u_b and u_g, respectively. Due to the large number of local solutions and the nonlinearity of the model of the process, the use of a stochastic search algorithm is proposed. DETL was used as the optimization algorithm since it has demonstrated its ability to solve constrained optimization problems common in chemical engineering (Sánchez-Ramírez et al., 2015). To implement the optimization algorithm, Aspen Plus was linked to Python with data storage in Excel. The DETL algorithm was coded in Python with the PyWin32 library, allowing the access to the Windows Component Object Model (COM). Pandas' library was used for the analysis and storage of data in Excel. Therefore, in this work the proposed schemes were optimized using DETL method through a link using Python and Aspen Plus. The decision variables are sent from Python to Aspen via COM technology for evaluation. After the simulation is performed, Aspen returns the values needed for the calculation of the objective function to Python and new decision variables are proposed according to the optimization method used. Finally, the data of the variables and objective functions are saved in a vector and sent to an Excel file for analysis. For the optimization of the process, the following parameters are used for the DETL method: 120 individuals, 200 generations, a taboo list of 50% of the total individuals, a Taboo radius of 0.0001, 0.3 of amplification factor and 0.9 of crossover rate (Alcocer-García et al., 2019).

4. Results

This section presents the main results of the economic optimization for all the schemes. For the three cases, the first heat exchanger operates with a flow rate of 122,621.1 kg/h at 233 °C, while the second heat exchanger operates with a flow rate of 397,702.6 kg/h at 24 °C. In the case of the first column, it has 25 stages with a feed flow rate of 1,157,377.6 kg/h, having the side outlet located in stage 7 with a flow rate of 28,000.2 kg/h. The configurations for the other columns are shown in Table 1. Figure 2 shows the results regarding the total heat duty of the optimized equipment for each scheme as well as the total TAC in thousands of dollars per year. In the three cases, the highest cost is derived from the capital cost, representing 85% of the total TAC, due to the magnitude of the process, which can recover up to 12,242.4 kg/h of bioethanol. In the two intensified schemes, 99% bioethanol purity and 99% glycerol recovery and purity are achieved. However, in the case of bioethanol recovery, it is observed that with respect to the total amount that leaves the conversion process, the CTC scheme only has a 96.5% recovery, while the other two schemes have a recovery of 97%. The conventional scheme has the lowest thermal load with a value of 38.5 kW/kg of bioethanol, in defiance of the efforts to reduce the load in the proposed schemes. Concerning the TAC, the TCC scheme is the closest to the CS, with a TAC increase of 0.18 % but reducing the use of a column and a cost of 2.91 USD/kg of bioethanol.

Table 1: Comparison of schemes.

	Variable	CS	TCC	CTC
Column 2	Number of stages	19	19	22
	Distillate rate (kg/h)	13,215.1	13,215.1	-
	Reflux ratio	3.03	3.03	3.54
	Feed stage	12	12	18
	Bottoms rate (kg/h)	-	-	28,121.9
	Feed Stage Glycerol	-	-	2
Column 3	Number of stages	17	21	10
	Distillate rate (kg/h)	12,050	11,924.3	-
	Feed stage	5	14	3
	Reflux ratio	0.30	0.30	0.30
	Feed Stage Glycerol	2	4	-
	Bottoms rate (kg/h)	-	-	12,185
	Liquid flow stage	-	19	-
	Vapor flow stage	-	19	-
	Mass flow of vapor	-	1,176.1	-
Column 4	Number of stages	29	10	-
	Bottoms rate (kg/h)	12,125.8	1,171.9	-
	Feed stage	2	-	-
	Reflux ratio	0.30	24.1	-

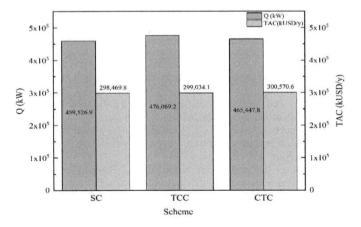

Figure 2: Comparation of heat duty and TAC of schemes.

5. Conclusions

The optimization of a conventional scheme and two intensified schemes to produce bioethanol from lignocellulosic wastes has been carried out using the DETL method. It has been observed that the conventional scheme is the one that has shown the lowest total annual cost as well as the lowest heat duty with a cost of 2.91 USD/kg of bioethanol and

38.5 kW/kg of bioethanol, respectively; however, the TCC scheme is the one that has shown a similarity in cost and thermal load with the advantage of reducing one processing equipment. During this study, an attempt has been made to reflect the benefits of process intensification in economic terms, however, it is interesting that process intensification does not always produce large savings. This means that through process intensification it is not always possible to design schemes that can reduce the cost and heat duty of the process. For future work, it is proposed to implement alternative intensification schemes to achieve a minimization of the TAC with respect to the conventional scheme. Likewise, it is proposed to use another objective function such as the environmental aspect, to obtain information not only related to costs but also on which configuration has less environmental impact, therefore having a more detailed comparison.

References

M. S. Allan and M. S. Tanveer (2020). Conversion of biomass into biofuel: a cutting-edge technology. In Bioreactors, 55–74.

H. Alcocer-García, J. G. Segovia-Hernández, O. A. Prado-Rubio, E. Sánchez-Ramírez and J. J. Quiroz-Ramírez (2019). Multi-objective optimization of intensified processes for the purification of levulinic acid involving economic and environmental objectives. Chem Eng Process, 136, 123-137.

C. Conde-Mejía, A. Jimenez-Gutiérrez and M. El-Halwagi (2012). A comparison of pretreatment methods for bioethanol production from lignocellulosic materials. PSEP, 90, 189–202.

C. Conde-Mejía, A. Jimenez-Gutiérrez and M. El-Halwagi (2013). Assessment of combinations between pretreatment and conversion configurations for bioethanol production. ACS Sustain. Chem. Eng., 1(8), 956–965.

M. Errico and B.G. Rong (2016). Systematic synthesis of intensified distillation systems. In Process Intensificacion in Chemical Engineering: Desing, Optimization and Control, 35-64.

Y. M. Espinoza-Vázquez, F.I. Gómez-Castro, E. Sánchez-Ramírez and A. G. Romero-Izquierdo (2023). Development and assessment of intensification alternatives on the lignocellulosic bioethanol production process. Comput. Aided Chem. Eng.. 52, 2735-2740.

K. M. Guthrie (1969). Capital cost estimation. Chemical Engineering, 24, 114–142.

S. Hernández (2022). Process intensification in biofuels production. In Biofuels and Biorefining, 2, 1-40. Elsevier.

Law Corner (2021). Stubble burning – a trouble to the environment. https://lawcorner.in/stubble-burning-a-trouble-to-the-environment/, last consulted on November, 2023.

F. H. Reboredo, F. C. Lidon, J. C. Ramalho and M. F. Pessoa (2017). The forgotten implications of low oil prices on biofuels. Biofpr, 11(4), 625–632.

H. Ritchie, M. Roser and P. Rosado (2020). CO_2 and greenhouse gas emissions. Our World in Data. https://ourworldindata.org/co2-and-greenhouse-gas-emissions, last consulted on November, 2023.

E. Sanchez-Ramírez, J. G. Segovia-Hernandez and A. Bonilla-Petriciolet (2015). Process alternatives for biobutanol purification: design and optimization. Ind. Eng. Chem. Res., 54(1), 351–358.

A. Susmozas, A. D. Moreno, J. M. Romero-García, P. Manzanares and M. Ballesteros (2018). Designing an olive tree pruning biorefinery for the production of bioethanol, xylitol an antioxidants: A techno-economic assessment. Holzforschung, 73(1), 15–23.

C. E. Torres-Ortega and B. G. Rong (2016). Intensified separation processes for the recovery and dehydration of bioethanol from an actual lignocellulosic fermentation broth. In Comput. Aided Chem. Eng., 38, 727-732. Elsevier.

R. Turton, R. C. Bailie, W. B. Whiting and J. A. Shaeiwitz (2008). Analysis, synthesis and design of chemical processes. Pearson Education.

Flavio Manenti, Gintaras V. Reklaitis (Eds.), Proceedings of the 34th European Symposium on Computer Aided Process Engineering / 15th International Symposium on Process Systems Engineering (ESCAPE34/PSE24), June 2-6, 2024, Florence, Italy

Dynamic simulation and evaluation of integrated chromatography-ultrafiltration in mAb production

Wil Jones, Dimitrios I. Gerogiorgis*

Institute for Materials and Processes (IMP), School of Engineering, University of Edinburgh, EH9 3FB, UK
*D.Gerogiorgis@ed.ac.uk

Abstract

Dynamic simulation and optimisation offer the opportunity to identify process operating strategies for rapid-scale up of production platforms from benchtop to industrial scale. The challenge of process scalability is especially critical for downstream separation units, as the latter account for ca. 60% of total mAb manufacturing costs (DiLeo et al., 2017). Two key operations of interest are polishing chromatography and ultrafiltration which are typically operated sequentially in flowsheets. This paper addresses how robust simulation and optimisation of polishing-ultrafilter systems can elucidate key operating decisions (pH, elution and pressure drop manipulation strategies), as well as key design decisions (ultrafilter configuration) in pursuit of lower capital and operational expenditure for monoclonal antibody (mAb) separation. Moreover, mAb yield and titer specification constraints are simultaneously considered with the CapEx and OpEx reduction objective.

Keywords: Dynamic simulation; polishing chromatography; ultrafiltration; mAbs.

1. Introduction

Bioprocess systems engineering has capitalised on benefits from dynamic modelling, simulation, and optimisation: the latter facilitate rapid scale-up of mAb production, from laboratory and pilot scales all the way to industrial platforms (Badr and Sugiyama, 2020). Despite significant developments in upstream unit operations over the past few decades, leading to titers as high as 3–5 g L^{-1} (Chon and Zarbis-Papastoitsis, 2011), major downstream separation breakthroughs only emerged in the last one (DiLeo et al., 2017). Two key downstream separation pillars are *polishing chromatography* and *ultrafiltration*. Polishing chromatography is used to remove undesirable by-products, e.g. misfolded and charge variant proteins (Rathore et al., 2018), whilst ultrafiltration is routinely used with diafiltration post polishing, to purify the mAbrug excipient formulation (Baek et al., 2017). The operating strategies of polishing chromatography columns and ultrafilters must ensure industrial specifications of mAb quality and throughput are met. Achieving these set targets can be challenging, given the inherent variability of bioprocess platforms.

This paper employs dynamic simulation for a wide array of integrated polishing-ultrafilter flowsheet operating strategies, to visualise and comparatively assess their effectiveness at obtaining products meeting industrial specifications for mAb recovery yield and titer. Our comparative analysis relies on published studies: a pH-dependent steric mass action model is used for polishing chromatography (Saleh et al., 2020), and a Darcy's law flow resistance (gel layer) model is employed for ultrafiltration (Thakur and Rathore, 2021). Dynamic simulation of 23 distinct polishing chromatography elution profiles enables a comparative analysis of each of the best six operating strategies combined with three ultrafilter configurations, to identify the elution-filter combination of max. performance.

2. Design of Integrated Polishing Chromatography-Ultrafiltration Systems

2.1. Polishing Chromatography Model and Operating Strategy

The complete system of partial differential (PDE) and algebraic equations employed for polishing chromatography dynamic simulations is given in Eqs. (1-8) below; detailed descriptions of all model states and parameters are already published (Saleh et al., 2020). All polishing steps are considered in the context of a Poros HS 50 resin in BPG 140 columns, 14 cm in diameter and 20.5 cm in length (GE Healthcare, Uppsala, Sweden). Model parameters are estimated via the Yamamoto correlation and the inverse method.

The inlet feed concentration has not been specified in the said model publication, in which the inlet has been assumed to consist of three species (main mAb variant, acidic charge variant, and basic charge variant; the aggregate mAb concentration is deemed negligible). Therefore, we hereby estimate an inlet feed concentration to the polishing column using data by Zhang et al. (2023), in which two acidic and two basic variants are considered. The given percentage contents for acidic and basic variants are summed separately, and the largest of the coefficients of variation of the variants is taken to be that of entire inlet.

The polishing chromatography elution strategies screened here are by Saleh et al. (2020). To ensure that the elution step is our exclusive focus here, we consider the operational template of loading, washing and re-equilibrium steps given in Müller-Späth et al. (2011): their cation exchange chromatography (CEX) cycle is followed here for every simulation. The pH is taken as constant throughout all steps, set to the value at which elution occurs.

$$\frac{\partial c_i(x,t)}{\partial t} = -\frac{u}{\varepsilon_{col}}\frac{\partial c_i(x,t)}{\partial x} + D_{ax}\frac{\partial^2 c_i(x,t)}{\partial x^2} - \frac{(1-\varepsilon_{col})}{\varepsilon_{col}}\left(\frac{3}{r_p}k_{eff,i}(c_i(x,t)-c_{p,i}(x,t))\right) \quad (1)$$

$$\frac{\partial c_{p,i}(x,t)}{\partial t} = \frac{3}{r_p}\frac{k_{eff,i}}{\varepsilon_p}(c_i(x,t)-c_{p,i}(x,t)) - \frac{(1-\varepsilon_p)}{\varepsilon_p}\frac{\partial q_i(x,t)}{\partial t} \quad (2)$$

$$\frac{\partial c_i(0,t)}{\partial x} = \frac{u(t)}{D_{ax}}(c_i(0,t)-c_{in,i}(t)) \quad (3)$$

$$\frac{\partial c_i(L,t)}{\partial x} = 0 \quad (4)$$

$$k_{kin,i}\frac{\partial q_i(x,t)}{\partial t} = k_{eq,i}(pH)\left(\Lambda - \sum_{j=1}^{k}\left(v(pH)_j+\sigma_j\right)q_j\right)^{v(pH)_i}c_{p,i} - q_i c_s^{v(pH)_i} \quad (5)$$

$$q_{salt} = \Lambda - \sum_{j=1}^{k} v_j q_j \quad (6)$$

$$k_{eq,i}(pH) = k_{eq0,i}e^{k_{eq1,i}pH+k_{eq2,i}pH^2} \quad (7)$$

$$v_i(pH) = v_{0,i} + pH\, v_{1,i} \quad (8)$$

2.2. Single-Pass Tangential Flow Filtration (TFF) Model and Operating Strategy

The semi-empirical dynamic model for the ultrafiltration system is given in Eqs. (9-16). Darcy's law therein underpins the flow dynamics through membrane filters, whilst Graetz-Laveque correlations define the gel thickness growth (Thakur and Rathore, 2021). Therein and here, only negligible mAb amounts may permeate the membranes (losses). Combinations of membrane modules in parallel and in series yield tree configurations: this is essential in mAb scale-up, to handle la/rge inlets for industrial production capacity.

$$K = C2 \cdot \log\left(C_o^2 \cdot e^{\frac{\Delta P}{u^{C1}}} + C3\right) \tag{9}$$

$$M_d^* = C4 \cdot \log\left(C_o^2 \cdot e^{\frac{\Delta P}{u^{C1}}} + C5\right) \tag{10}$$

$$R_b = C8 \cdot C7 \cdot \left(\frac{u}{(\Delta P \cdot C_o)}\right)^{C6} \tag{11}$$

$$R_d = \alpha_d \cdot M_d \tag{12}$$

$$J = \frac{\Delta P}{\mu(R_b + R_m + R_d)} \tag{13}$$

$$F_{RET} = u - (J \cdot XSA) \tag{14}$$

$$V_{CF} = \frac{u}{F_{RET}} \tag{15}$$

$$\frac{dM_d}{dt} = K(M_d^* - M_d) \tag{16}$$

3. Results

3.1. Polishing Chromatography Column Outputs Evaluation

The detailed specifications of all 23 elution strategies simulated here are listed in Table 1 below: these distinct operational options include 16 gradient elutions and 7 step elutions. The total protein feed concentration to the column is taken as 2 g L^{-1} (the mAb variant content is 0.300, 1.442 and 0.258 g.L^{-1} for acidic, main and basic variants, respectively). A minimum recovery yield level (90%) is taken as required for industrial implementation: this specification is only achieved by 12 gradient elutions and 3 step elutions (Figure 1).

Table 1: Polishing chromatography elution strategies considered (Saleh et al., 2020).

Elution Number	Code	pH	Strategy	Elution Number	Code	pH	Strategy
1	C3a	5.5	Gradient	13	C5a	6.1	Gradient
2	C3b	5.5	Gradient	14	C5b	6.1	Gradient
3	C3c	5.5	Gradient	15	C5c	6.1	Gradient
4	V7	5.5	Gradient	16	V10	6.1	Gradient
5	C1	5.8	Gradient	17	V8	5.5	Step
6	C4a	5.8	Gradient	18	V9	5.5	Step
7	C4b	5.8	Gradient	19	C2	5.8	Step
8	C4c	5.8	Gradient	20	V3	5.8	Step
9	V1	5.8	Gradient	21	V4	5.8	Step
10	V2	5.8	Gradient	22	V11	6.1	Step
11	V5	5.8	Gradient	23	V12	6.1	Step
12	V6	5.8	Gradient				

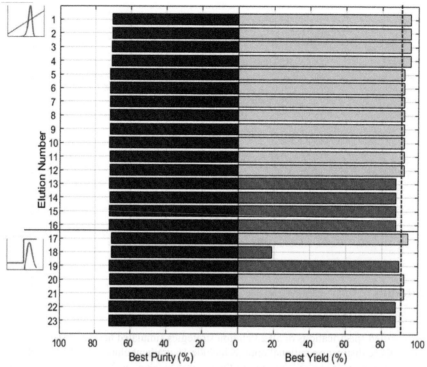

Figure 1: Purity and yield values for all polishing chromatography elution strategies.

3.2. Ultrafiltration Tangential Flow Filter (TFF) Cascade Outputs Evaluation

Each of the 23 polishing column outputs seen in Figure 1 are integrated with a reputable, commercial 7-stage Pall Corporation filter design. The Cadence Single-Pass TFF modular membrane units are 93 cm^2 in cross sectional area and configured as 3-3-2-2-1-1-1, where the '-' denotes a series connection and the number value of parallel modules at each stage.

The corresponding 23 outputs for the polishing-ultrafilter systems are shown in Figure 2. The outlet product flow from a polishing column is 1577.82 mLmin^{-1}: for the said 7-stage ultrafiltration, an inlet flow of 525.94 mLmin^{-1} must thus be fed to each of the three units. A target concentration of ultrafilter design of 100 g L^{-1} has been set (Kollár et al., 2020).

Figure 2 shows the few operational strategies which have achieved this effluent target, as only 6 of the 23 flowsheets succeed in achieving 100 g L^{-1} (namely 1, 2, 6, 11, 20, 21). All designs failing the 90% polishing recovery yield also fail the said ultrafiltration target. Key flowsheet success factors include a low pH, a short elution time domain and a salt concentration that is high enough to elute large quantities of the main mAb variant, fast.

Clearly, there is a correlation between purified stream concentration and pressure drop. In every ultrafiltration case simulated here, a fixed pressure drop operation is considered. Every ultrafiltration has an upper limit of pressure drop; if this value is exceeded it causes negative fluxes to arise within the final set of filters, thus clearly leading to system failure. The wide variation of pressure drops is because every flowsheet is operated just below the upper pressure drop limit, to elucidate the maximum outlet final mAb concentration.

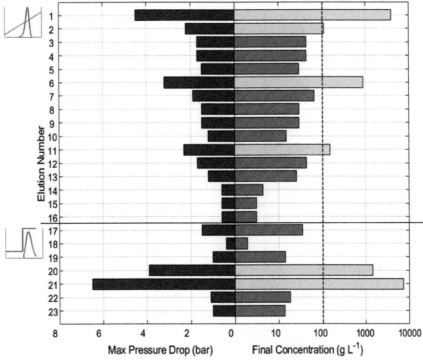

Figure 2: Maximum pressure drop and final concentration of the ultrafilter designs.

3.3. Ultrafiltration Configuration Performance Analysis

The ultrafilter configuration used in the foregoing flowsheets we consider is arbitrary, but the number of its stages and units per stage can be optimised (Thakur and Rathore, 2021). Figure 3 shows how two other configurations (5-5-3, 5-4-4), also with 13 filters in total, perform in purifying the polishing chromatography outlet stream: none of the two 3-stage cascades matches the high purity of the 7-stage one, indicating system design is critical.

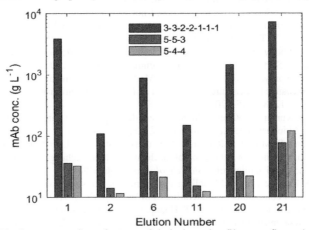

Figure 3: Final concentration of successful elution-ultrafilter configuration systems.

4. Conclusions

Dynamic simulation of polishing chromatography-ultrafilter systems for industrial mAb production has great value in comparative visualisation of design and operating strategies. A pH-dependent steric mass action model for polishing chromatography and a semi-empirical (Darcy and Graetz-Laveque) model for ultrafiltration have been combined here. A series of 23 (either gradient- or step-based) elution strategies (Saleh at el., 2020) have been analysed for performance vs. a target recovery yield of 90% in mAb manufacturing. A 7-stage (3-3-2-2-1-1-1) ultrafiltration system (Cadence Single Pass, Pall Corporation) has been subsequently considered to receive and purify the outlet of each of these elutions, and assessed vs. achieving a target (purified effluent) mAb concentration of 100 g L^{-1}. Only 6 of the 23 integrated polishing chromatography-ultrafiltration flowsheets proposed are shown as successful vs. both specifications. Finally, two new ultrafilter configurations are computationally implemented, to probe whether shorter series (fewer stages, but using the same number of total membrane units, 13) can achieve matching mAb performance. The original 7-stage (3-3-2-2-1-1-1) configuration outperforms by far both 3-stage ones, showing that structural optimisation can tremendously benefit mAb flowsheet efficiency.

Acknowledgements

The authors gratefully acknowledge UKRI and the Engineering and Physical Sciences Research Council (EPSRC) Doctoral Training Partnership (DTP) PhD Scholarship awarded to W.J., and a Royal Society Industrial Fellowship (2020-22) awarded to D.I.G. Financial support via another UKRI-EPSRC grant (*RAPID: ReAltime Process ModellIng & Diagnostics–Powering Digital Factories EP/V028618/1*) is also hereby acknowledged.

References

S. Badr, & H. Sugiyama. (2020). A PSE perspective for the efficient production of monoclonal antibodies: integration of process, cell, and product design aspects. *Curr. Opin. Chem. Eng.*, 27, 121-128.

Y. Baek, N. Singh, A. Arunkumar, M. Borys, Z. J. Li, & A. L. Zydney. (2017). Ultrafiltration behavior of monoclonal antibodies and Fc-fusion proteins: Effects of physical properties. *Biotechnol. Bioeng.*, 114, 2057-2065.

J. H. Chon, G. Zarbis-Papastoitsis. (2011). Advances in the production and downstream processing of antibodies. *New Biotechnol.*, 28, 458-463.

M. DiLeo, A. Ley, A. E. Nixon, J. Chen. (2017). Choices of capture chromatography technology in antibody manufacturing processes. *J. Chromatogr. B*, 1068, 136-148.

É. Kollár, B. Balázs, T. Tari, I. Siró. (2020). Development challenges of high concentration monoclonal antibody formulations. *Drug Discov. Today: Technologies*, 37, 31-40.

T. Müller-Späth, G. Ströhlein, L. Aumann, H. Kornmann, P. Valax, L. Delegrange, E. Charbaut, G. Baer, A. Lamproye, & M. Jöhnck. (2011). Model simulation and experimental verification of a cation-exchange IgG capture step in batch and continuous chromatography. *J. Chromatogr. A*, 1218, 5195-5204.

A. S. Rathore, D. Kumar,, N. Kateja. (2018). Recent developments in chromatographic purification of biopharmaceuticals. *Biotechnol. Lett.*, 40, 895-905.

D. Saleh, G. Wang, B. Müller, F. Rischawy, S. Kluters, J. Studts, & J. Hubbuch. (2020). Straightforward method for calibration of mechanistic cation exchange chromatography models for industrial applications. *Biotechnol. Progr.*, 36, e2984.

G. Thakur, A.S. Rathore. (2021). Modelling and optimization of single-pass tangential flow ultrafiltration for continuous manufacturing of mAbs. *Sep. Purif. Technol.*, 276, 119341.

X. Zhang, T. Chen, V. Li, T. Bo, M. Du, T. Huang. (2023). Cutting-edge mass spectrometry strategy based on imaged capillary isoelectric focusing (icIEF) technology for characterizing charge heterogeneity of monoclonal antibody. *Anal. Biochem.*, 660, 114961.

Flavio Manenti, Gintaras V. Reklaitis (Eds.), Proceedings of the 34th European Symposium on Computer Aided Process Engineering / 15th International Symposium on Process Systems Engineering (ESCAPE34/PSE24), June 2-6, 2024, Florence, Italy

Multi-objective optimisation of an integrated cultivation-aggregation model for mAb production

Wil Jones, Dimitrios I. Gerogiorgis*

Institute for Materials and Processes (IMP), School of Engineering, University of Edinburgh, EH9 3FB, UK
*D.Gerogiorgis@ed.ac.uk

Abstract

The proteinaceous structure of mAbs imply susceptibility to irreversible aggregation, shown to seriously impact drug efficacy and patient safety (van der Kant et al., 2017). Dynamic simulation and optimisation are widely employed in order to drive and visualise the effect of manipulating cell culture inputs (temperature, pH, media composition) on bioreactor performance for mAbs (Jones & Gerogiorgis, 2022) and many other biologics. This study presents an integrated dynamic model accounting for both mAb cultivation and aggregation phenomena, combining a temperature-dependent Chinese Hamster Ovary (CHO) cell cultivation model (Kumar et al., 2022) and a Smoluchowski Population Balance Model (PBM) describing aggregation behaviour in detail (Bansal et al., 2020). The integrated model is first employed for dynamic simulation and visualisation of the temperature manipulation and feeding control strategies, leading to a series of plots which demonstrate the clear trade-off between the two conflicting objectives, namely mAb throughput maximisation and aggregation minimisation. A series of multi-objective optimisations are conducted in order to obtain bioreactor operating strategies which can simultaneously maximise mAb mass and minimise the degree of irreversible aggregation.

Keywords: Multi-objective optimisation; CHO cultivation; Protein aggregation; mAbs.

1. Introduction

Monoclonal antibodies (mAbs) are genetically engineered proteins acting as therapeutics against numerous ailments (Haidar and Mellors, 2021): their high demand accounts for USD 217 billion of the biopharmaceutical market, as mAb therapies are now approved for treating Alzheimer's disease and certain cancer types (Sirasitthichoke et al., 2023). Nevertheless, mAbs have an inherent tendency to aggregate into clusters which have no therapeutic value, seriously hindering drug efficacy and possibly affecting patient safety. Current good manufacturing practice (cGMP) aims to overcome production challenges by Design of Experiments (DOE), to achieve operating strategies reducing aggregation without compromising plant throughput (Bollin et al., 2011; Millán-Martín et al., 2023).

Dynamic evolution of mAb aggregation can be studied via Population Balance Models, relying on well-calibrated aggregation sensing and parameterisation over a wide design space, to thus quantify how operation affects irreversible clustering (Bansal et al., 2020). This study presents an integrated mAb cultivation-aggregation model based on literature precedents, analysing how temperature and culture feed manipulation affect aggregation. An initial dynamic simulation analysis for an array of operating strategies is followed by multi-objective optimisation cases (with variable weights) to trace the Pareto front (mAb mass maximisation vs. aggregate minimisation) and identify superior operating strategies.

2. Integrated Dynamic Model for mAb Cultivation-Aggregation

2.1. Differential-Algebraic Equation (DAE) System

A complete overview of the integrated system of equations is given below in Eqs. (1-21). The temperature-dependent Chinese Hamster Ovary (CHO) cultivation model is the basis for mAb production simulation in batch and fed-batch bioreactors (Kumar et al., 2022). Our assumption here is that all mAbs secreted from the culture are monomer molecules, and aggregation of monomers, dimers and higher can only occur after the mAb secretion. Aggregation has been assumed to take place as a result of Brownian motion, shown to be an accurate representation of small molecule cluster interactions (Bansal et al., 2020). The published Population Balance Modelling (PBM) framework of Bansal et al. (2020) assumes reversible aggregation occurs for monomer-monomer and monomer-oligomer interactions, whilst irreversible aggregation occurs for oligomer-oligomer interactions. Pentamer data are for tetramers, due to the absence of the latter in Bansal et al. (2020). This assumption is valid for analysing small oligomer interactions (Brummitt et al., 2011) and model parameter values have been estimated again via MATLAB (*fminsearchbnd*).

$$\frac{k_a}{W}(T) = \frac{k_a}{W} \cdot \frac{T}{298} \tag{1}$$

$$\lambda = 1 - \left(\frac{1}{D_f}\right) \tag{2}$$

$$P_{i,j} = (ij)^\lambda \tag{3}$$

$$B_{i,j} = \frac{\left(i^{1/D_f} + j^{1/D_f}\right)\left(\frac{1}{i^{1/D_f}} + \frac{1}{j^{1/D_f}}\right)}{4} \tag{4}$$

$$k_{i,j} = \frac{k_a}{W}(T) \cdot P_{i,j} \cdot B_{i,j} \tag{5}$$

$$f_{lim} = \frac{GLC}{GLC + (K_{GLC} \cdot X_V)} \tag{6}$$

$$f_{inh} = \frac{KI_{LAC}}{LAC + KI_{LAC}} \cdot (1 - KI_{mAb} \cdot N_1^*) \tag{7}$$

$$\mu = \mu_{max} \cdot f_{lim} \cdot f_{inh} \tag{8}$$

$$\mu_d = \mu_{d,max} \tag{9}$$

$$q_{GLC} = -\frac{\mu}{Y_{\frac{X}{GLC}}} - m_{GLC} \tag{10}$$

$$q_{LAC} = \left(\frac{\mu}{Y_{\frac{X}{LAC}}} + (Y_{LAC} \cdot q_{GLC})\right) \cdot \left(\frac{LAC_{max1} - LAC}{LAC_{max1}}\right) + m_{LAC} \cdot \left(\frac{LAC_{max2} - LAC}{LAC_{max2}}\right) \tag{11}$$

$$q_{mAb} = Y_{mAb/x} \cdot \mu + m_{mAb} \tag{12}$$

$$\frac{dV}{dt} = Q_i + Q_k - Q_{os} - Q_{or} \tag{13}$$

$$\frac{dX_V}{dt} = \left(\mu \cdot e^{\frac{-K_1}{T}} - \mu_d e^{\frac{-K_2}{T}}\right)X_V - Q_{os}\frac{X_V}{V} - \frac{dV}{dt}\frac{X_V}{V} \tag{14}$$

$$\frac{dX_D}{dt} = \left(\mu_d e^{\frac{-K_2}{T}}\right)X_V - Q_{os}\frac{X_D}{V} - \frac{dV}{dt}\frac{X_D}{V} \tag{15}$$

$$\frac{dGLC}{dt} = \left(Q_i \frac{GLC_i}{V}\right) + \left(Q_k \frac{GLC_k}{V}\right) - \left((Q_{os} + Q_{or})\frac{GLC}{V}\right) + (q_{GLC} \cdot X_V) - \left(\frac{dV}{dt}\frac{GLC}{V}\right) \tag{16}$$

$$\frac{dLAC}{dt} = \left(Q_i \frac{LAC_i}{V}\right) + \left(Q_k \frac{LAC_k}{V}\right) - \left((Q_{os} + Q_{or})\frac{LAC}{V}\right) + (q_{LAC} \cdot X_V) - \left(\frac{dV}{dt}\frac{LAC}{V}\right) \tag{17}$$

$$\frac{dN_1^*}{dt} = \left(-Q_{os}\frac{N_1^*}{V}\right) + (q_{mAb} \cdot X_V) + 2k_1 N_1^{*2} + 2k_{-1}N_2^* - k_2 N_1^*(N_2^* + N_3^*) + k_{-2}(N_3^* + N_4^*) - \frac{dV}{dt}\frac{N_1^*}{V} \tag{18}$$

$$\frac{dN_2^*}{dt} = k_1 N_1^{*2} - k_{-1}N_2^* - k_2 N_1^* N_2^* + k_{-2}N_3^* - k_{2,2}N_2^{*2} - \frac{dV}{dt}\frac{N_2^*}{V} \tag{19}$$

$$\frac{dN_3^*}{dt} = k_2 N_1^* N_2^* - k_{-2}N_3^* - k_2 N_1^* N_3^* + k_{-2}N_4^* - \frac{dV}{dt}\frac{N_3^*}{V} \tag{20}$$

$$\frac{dN_4^*}{dt} = k_2 N_1^* N_3^* - k_{-2}N_4^* + k_{2,2}N_2^{*2} - \frac{dV}{dt}\frac{N_4^*}{V} \tag{21}$$

The CHO cultivation model is temperature-dependent, but the aggregation model is not. An Arrhenius relationship (Eq. 22) is used to generalise it: we use data from two acetate buffer experiments of Bansal et al. (2020), to perform a linear (Eq. 23) regression for each of the reversible and irreversible aggregation kinetic constants (: k_1, k_{-1}, k_2, k_{-2}, $k_{2,2}$).

$$K = k_0 e^{\frac{-E_a}{RT}} \tag{22}$$

$$\ln(K) = \ln(k_0) - \frac{E_a}{RT} \tag{23}$$

2.2. Multi-Objective Dynamic Optimisation Methodology

Exploring trade-offs between mAb product maximisation and aggregation minimisation can be tackled via multi-objective dynamic optimisation (Jones and Gerogiorgis, 2022), where varying weight factors can be used to assess the relative importance of each of the objectives: normalised values of the latter must be used (Rodman and Gerogiorgis, 2016). This is done by scaling both objective function values by dividing each of the two by the average values for monomer and tetramer masses seen in the dynamic simulation analysis. The weights for our objectives take 3 values: $\alpha, \beta = \{0.25, 0.5, 0.75\}$ (sum is always 1). The resulting Nonlinear Programming (NLP) problem is solved using the IPOPT solver (APMonitor web environment) due to its great robustness (Jones and Gerogiorgis, 2022).

3. Results

3.1. Dynamic Simulation for Varying Temperature and Feeding Strategies

Culture productivity for protein manufacturing is shown to benefit from hypothermic conditions (Kumar et al., 2022): the temperature range tested here is hence 303–306 K. To match experimental conditions therein, the initial bioreactor volume is 5.65 L, with an upper volume bound of 10 L. A typical fed-batch operating time (15 days) is employed. The upper flowrate bound is fixed at $4 \cdot 10^{-4}$ L.day^{-1}, as operating continuously with the 0-4 midpoint ($2 \cdot 10^{-4}$ L.day^{-1}) yields a final volume of 9.97 L, respecting the upper bound.

The CHO culture must never be glucose-starved at any point during bioreactor operation, as this compromises mAb quality (Fan et al., 2015). For our dynamic simulation analysis, bioreactor temperature and feed flowrates are manipulated simultaneously at given times. Table 1 presents all set points, with all possible combinations used in this initial analysis (the set point values can be be manipulated at three time points: day 0, day 5 and day 10).

Table 1: All set points for dynamic analysis of the cultivation-aggregation system.

Set point	Inlet flowrate (L day^{-1})	Temperature (K)
1	$0 \cdot 10^{-4}$	303.0
2	$2 \cdot 10^{-4}$	304.5
3	$4 \cdot 10^{-4}$	306.0

The ensemble of initial/mid-course set points comprises 729 distinct operation strategies, to visualise cultivation-aggregation phenomena with acceptable computational demand.

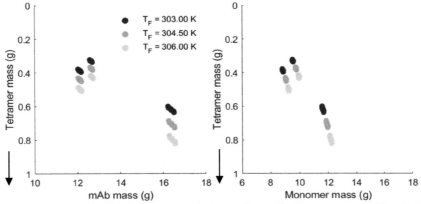

Figure 1: Dynamic simulation results (colour refers to final temperature shift value).

Only 81 of the said 729 strategies tracked are shown as successful: the rest fail since the volume is exceeded, the culture becomes glucose-starved, or both constraints are violated. Figure 1 depicts these 81 points, their colour denoting the final temperature shift values. A low (or decreasing) temperature value at the final time point (day 10) induces less irreversible aggregation, with almost negligible consequence on total mAb concentration. The monomer (desirable for manufacturing) mAb fraction (Fig. 1 right) is distinctly lower than the total mAb mass (Fig. 1 left), without great benefit from temperature reduction (for each plot cluster, monomer mass is actually reduced for decreasing final temperature, a small price to pay for the clear tetramer reduction signifying aggregation mitigation).

The preliminary conclusion emerging is that for any given feeding strategy, a final stage shift to a lower temperature leads to lower monomer and lower tetramer concentrations with no major consequence on total mAb throughput, thus more reversible aggregation. The industrial potential for process intensification in mAb manufacturing must however be examined by means of a more theoretically comprehensive and computationally robust method: we thus use multi-objective dynamic optimisation to address aggregation issues.

3.2. Multi-Objective Dynamic Optimisation

All said constraints probed during dynamic simulation are implemented here as well, and the complete dynamic optimisation NLP problem formulation is illustrated in Table 2. Bioreactor temperature and inlet flow are now continuous manipulation variables, but their levels can change only at specific time points discussed previously (days 0, 5, 10). More elaborate (fully continuous) temporal manipulations are possible, but our purpose here is to facilitate meaningful comparisons vs. the operational space shown in Figure 1.

Our goal here is to improve on NLP problem outputs for mAb and tetramer throughputs in comparison to those depicted in Figure 1 from our exploratory dynamic simulations. To host both operational goals (mAb mass maximisation and tetramer minimisation) within the same objective function, we consider the weight factors α and β, respectively.

Table 2: A summary of the multi-objective optimisation problem for mAb production.

Multi-objective optim. function:	$\displaystyle \max_{u(t),t_f=15\text{ days}} \left(\alpha \frac{[mAb](t_f)\cdot V(t_f)}{13.7295} - \beta \frac{600\cdot 10^6 N_4(t_f)\cdot V(t_f)}{0.5098} \right)$
s.t.:	
Process model:	$X_i = f_i(X_j(t), u(t), t)$ $\qquad\qquad i,j = 1 \dots 10$
Inequality constraints:	$5.65\text{ L} \le V \le 10\text{ L}$ $[GLC] > 0$
Manipulation (control) vector:	$u(t) = [Q_i(t), T(t)]$ with $\quad 0\text{ L min}^{-1} \le Q_i \le 4\cdot 10^{-4}\text{ L min}^{-1}$ and $\qquad 303\text{ K} \le T \le 306\text{ K}$
Initial state variable conditions:	$V_0 = 5.65\text{ L}; \ X_{V,0} = 0.7 \times 10^6 \text{ cells mL}^{-1};$ $X_{D,0} = 0.07 \times 10^6 \text{ cells mL}^{-1}; \ [GLC]_0 = 5.36\text{ g L}^{-1};$ $[LAC]_0 = 0.12\text{ g L}^{-1}; \ [mAb]_0 = [N_1]_0 = [N_2]_0 = [N_3]_0 = [N_4]_0 = 0$

The NLP problem is solved for all three α-β weight factor combinations that sum up to 1. Both manipulation (temperature, flowrate) trajectories for all cases are given in Figure 2. Clearly, optimal strategies for $\{\alpha = 0.25, \beta = 0.75\}$, and $\{\alpha = 0.5, \beta = 0.5\}$ are identical. For $\{\alpha = 0.75, \beta = 0.25\}$, i.e. mAb mass prioritised, the feed peaks at day 10 (not day 5), but tetramers rise. The final temperature in all cases emerges as T=303 K, agreeing with our observation that irreversible aggregation decreases with decreasing final temperature.

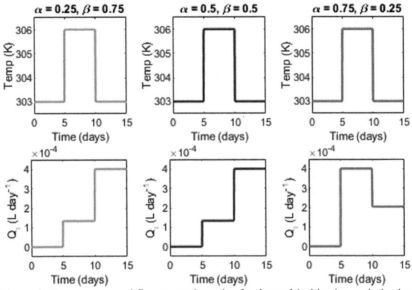

Figure 2: Temperature and flowrate trajectories for the multi-objective optimisations.

Multi-objective optimisation results are compared to early simulation results in Figure 3. Both $\{\alpha = 0.25, \beta = 0.75\}$ and $\{\alpha = 0.5, \beta = 0.5\}$ cases are both successful in achieving a strategy with a lower tetramer concentration than those seen in our exploratory analysis. The $\{\alpha = 0.75, \beta = 0.25\}$ optimisation case, which prioritises total mAb mass throughput and penalises aggregation (tetramer production) much less than the other two cases, only manages a minor performance improvement vs. the 303 K plot clusters seen in Figure 1. Multiobjective dynamic optimisation clearly shows that priorities (weights) matter a lot, but also that higher-DOF (fully continuous) manipulation signals may improve outcomes.

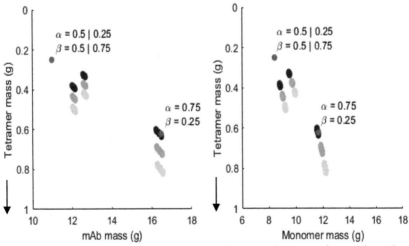

Figure 3: Multi-objective optimisation results (red points) superimposed on Fig. 1.

4. Conclusions

An integrated mAb cultivation-aggregation model has been formulated on the basis of two papers describing each of the phenomena (Kumar, 2022; Bansal, 2020; respectively); An Arrhenius relationship is used to generalise the population balance model of the latter. The DAE system model is first tested via an array of dynamic simulations in which manipulation strategies (feed-temperature combinations) are screened to elucidate their potential to simultaneously improve mAb throughput and reduce irreversible aggregation. Multi-objective optimisation is also employed to the same end, considering continuous temperature and flowrate manipulations but only at specific times of a 15-day operation: three $\{a,\beta\}$ weight combinations are used to vary the importance of the two objectives. Two of the said three weight sets yield the same operation protocol which successfully reduces tetramer output to a value much lower than all previous (at mAb mass penalty); the third (prioritising mAb mass) only manages a very minor tetramer output reduction. A more detailed multi-objective optimisation with more freedom degrees (e.g. fully continuous manipulation signals) can further improve optimal mAb bioreactor operations.

Acknowledgements

The authors gratefully acknowledge UKRI and the Engineering and Physical Sciences Research Council (EPSRC) Doctoral Training Partnership (DTP) PhD Scholarship awarded to W.J., and a Royal Society Industrial Fellowship (2020-22) awarded to D.I.G. Financial support via another UKRI-EPSRC grant (*RAPID: ReAltime Process ModellIng & Diagnostics–Powering Digital Factories EP/V028618/1*) is also hereby acknowledged.

References

R. Bansal, P. Srivastava, A. S. Rathore, P. Chokshi. (2020). Population balance modelling of aggregation of monoclonal antibody based therapeutic proteins. *Chem. Eng. Sci.*, 216, 115479.

F. Bollin, V. Dechavanne, L. Chevalet. (2011). Design of Experiment in CHO and HEK transient transfection condition optimization. *Protein Expres. Purif.*, 78, 61-68.

R.K. Brummitt, D.P. Nesta, L. Chang, A.M. Kroetsch, C.J. Roberts. (2011). Nonnative aggregation of an IgG1 antibody in acidic conditions, part 2: nucleation and growth kinetics with competing growth mechanisms. *J. Pharm. Sci.*, 100, 2104-2119.

Y. Fan, I. Jimenez Del Val, C. Müller, A.M. Lund, J.W. Sen, S.K. Rasmussen, C. Kontoravdi et al. (2015). A multi-pronged investigation into the effect of glucose starvation and culture duration on fed-batch CHO cell culture. *Biotechnol. Bioeng.*, 112, 2172-2184.

G. Haidar, J.W. Mellors. (2021). Improving the outcomes of immunocompromised patients with coronavirus disease 2019. *Clin. Infect. Dis.*, 73, e1397-e1401.

W. Jones, D.I. Gerogiorgis. (2022). Dynamic simulation, optimisation and economic analysis of fed-batch vs. perfusion bioreactors for advanced mAb manufacturing. *Comput. Chem. Eng.*, 165, 107855.

D. Kumar, N. Gangwar, A.S. Rathore, M. Ramteke. (2022). Multi-objective optimization of monoclonal antibody production in bioreactor. *Chem. Eng. Proc.-Proc. Intensif.*, 180, 108720.

A.D. Rodman, D.I. Gerogiorgis. (2016). Multi-objective process optimisation of beer fermentation via dynamic simulation. *Food Bioprod. Proc.*, 100, 255-274.

S. Millán-Martín, C. Jakes, S. Carillo, R. Rogers, D. Ren, J. Bones. (2023). Comprehensive multi-attribute method workflow for biotherapeutic characterization and current good manufacturing practices testing. *Nature Protocols*, 18, 1056-1089.

C. Sirasitthichoke, D. Hoang, P. Phalak, P.M. Armenante, B.I. Barnoon, I. Shandil. (2023). Computational prediction of blend time in a large-scale viral inactivation process for monoclonal antibodies biomanufacturing. *Biotechnol. Bioeng.*, 120, 169-183.

R. van der Kant, A.R. Karow-Zwick, J. van Durme, M. Blech, R. Gallardo, D. Seeliger, K. Aßfalg, P. Baatsen, G. Compernolle, A. Gils. (2017). Prediction and reduction of the aggregation of monoclonal antibodies. *J. Mol. Biol.*, 429, 1244-1261.

Flavio Manenti, Gintaras V. Reklaitis (Eds.), Proceedings of the 34th European Symposium on Computer Aided Process Engineering / 15th International Symposium on Process Systems Engineering (ESCAPE34/PSE24), June 2-6, 2024, Florence, Italy

From laboratory scale to innovative spruce-based biorefinery. Note II: Preliminary techno-economic assessment

Matteo Gilardi[a,*], Filippo Bisotti[a,*], Olaf T. Berglihn[a], Roman Tschentscher[b], Line D. Hansen[c], Svein J. Horn[c], Anikó Várnai[c], Bernd Wittgens[a]

[a] *SINTEF Industry-Process Technology, Sem Sælands vei 2, Trondheim, 7034, Norway*
[b] *SINTEF Industry-Process Technology, Forskningsveien 1, Oslo, 0373, Norway*
[c] *Faculty of Chemistry, Biotechnology and Food Science, NMBU, Chr. Magnus Falsens vei 18, Aas, 1433, Norway*
* *matteo.gilardi@sintef.no; filippo.bisotti@sintef.no (corresponding authors)*

Abstract

This work shows a preliminary techno-economic assessment (TEA) of a biorefinery co-producing ethanol, pyrolysis oil and char from Norway spruce (*Picea abies*) via steam explosion and enzymatic saccharification followed by anaerobic fermentation of the sugars, and fast pyrolysis of the lignin-rich saccharification residue. The capacity of the modelled biorefinery was set to treat 100,000 tons of dry wood per year. The input for the assessment of the facility was retrieved from process simulations carried out in COFE v3.6 (AmsterCHEM), see Note I. Here, we propose different strategies to minimize the total costs of the biorefinery. The results indicate that the studied biorefinery process is economically feasible, while its profitability depends considerably on the source of hydrogen, oscillation in the market price of the generated products and utility costs.

Keywords: biorefinery, techno-economic assessment, energy integration, hydrogen, bio-oil and bioethanol production, biorefinery optimization

1. Introduction

The need for decarbonization drives a shift from fossil fuel- to bio-based economy. In this scenario, bio-products (bulk biochemicals such as methanol, ethanol, and biofuels) are expected to replace the conventional ones produced from crude oil (Cherubini et al., 2010). While the concept of biorefinery is not new, designing a process that is economically feasible at a commercial scale is a challenge, partly due to the low cost of fossil resources, the high O-content of biomass and the high complexity of operations (Bisotti et al., 2023; Gilardi et al., 2023). Despite the sustainability aspect, the marginal profitability, competition against highly optimized traditional oil refineries and suboptimal use of on-site resources exacerbate the struggle of biorefineries for competitiveness (Cherubini, 2010). Here, we provide a preliminary techno-economic assessment (TEA) of spruce-to-fuel biorefinery that is based on a combined biochemical and thermochemical conversion to produce ethanol and bio-oil-derived fuel fractions, as described in Note I. We adjusted the process layout to minimize the energy demand, waste generation and carbon footprint. Furthermore, we considered using alternative hydrogen sources (i.e., green, blue and grey). The TEA shows that a profitable implementation of the proposed biorefinery is realistic; however, the costs of utilities, raw materials and source of hydrogen deeply affect the breakeven point and pay-back time.

2. Improvements to the biorefinery baseline

To improve the feasibility of the spruce-to-fuel biorefinery process depicted in Figure 1, we introduced the following improvements (also highlighted in green in Figure 1).

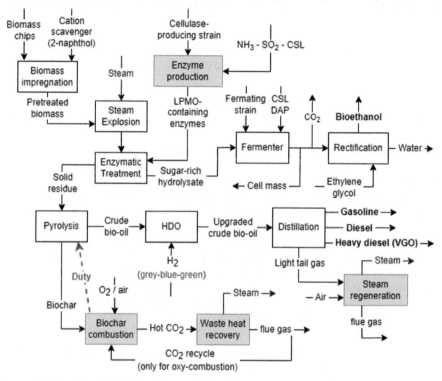

Figure 1: Biorefinery block flow diagram (only main streams are reported).

On-site enzyme production: Since enzymes (when purchased from external producers) can make up about one-third of the total operating costs, we included enzyme production on-site based on the setup by Humbird et al. (2011) using cheap raw materials, e.g., corn steep liquor (CSL, C-source), ammonia (N-source), SO_2 (S-source), and a cellulase-producing strain.

Fermentation: Regarding bioethanol production, the fermenting strain was added together in solution with corn steep liquor (CSL) and diammonium phosphate (DAP) as suggested by Humbird et al. (2011).

Heat integration: Biochar, the side product of pyrolysis, has many potential applications. As the market is not stable, we chose to recover its high heating value by burning it. We compared oxy-combustion, which requires pure oxygen, and air combustion as alternatives. For the oxy-combustion, we adjusted the CO_2 recycle to achieve the desired flame temperature (1100°C). To achieve the same temperature in the air combustion, we regulated the airflow to the combustor. The resulting hot flue gas supplies thermal heat for the pyrolysis reactions and, subsequently, to a steam generation unit. This unit generates steam by burning the light tail gas recovered from the top of the distillation column fractionating the upgraded crude bio-oil. The total produced steam could cover the steam demand for biomass pretreatment (i.e., steam explosion) completely and ethanol purification partially. The difference was covered with natural gas combustion.

3. Materials and methods

After closing the energy and material balances in Note I, here, we prepared a techno-economic assessment (TEA) for the spruce-to-fuel biorefinery sketched in Figure 1 (process design) and Note I (operating conditions). For that, we made the following assumptions (Section 3.1) and analysed the impact of the hydrogen source on process feasibility and profitability (Section 3.2).

3.1 Assumptions

3.1.1 Capital Investments (CAPEX)

The CAPEX was estimated based on Guthrie's work (1978) and updated to 2021 using the Chemical Engineering Plant Cost Index (CEPCI). This year was selected to evaluate feasibility under stable market conditions as it predates the war in Ukraine in 2022, which created turmoil for the economic indexes. The purchase base cost of each piece of equipment was turned into the corresponding bare module cost, where expenditure for materials, actual operating pressure, and installation were included. The size of reactors was based on the residence time and inlet volumetric flow. The diameter and height of separation columns and the number of trays were estimated for achieving adequate vapor–liquid contact (i.e., 70% flooding conditions) and global separation efficiency (70% efficiency). The reactors were designed as simple vessels since correlations for tube bundles are not available. The analysis neglects the costs of filters and cyclones. Furthermore, we assumed that combustion technology (air or oxy-combustion) does not affect investment costs for the waste heat boiler. This assumption considers that compact volumes for oxy-combustion compensate for the need for more expensive materials. The final value for the CAPEX reflects the grass-roots cost, meaning that the biorefinery is built as a greenfield plant. The lifetime of the plant was assumed to be 20 years.

3.1.2 Operating costs (OPEX)

The OPEX (Costs of Manufacturing – COM) were calculated based on Turton's work (2018), as given in Equation 1, where FCI is the total investment cost, C_{OL} is the operating labour cost, C_{UT}, C_{RM} and C_{WT} are the total utility, raw material and waste treatment costs. For simplicity, the C_{WT} term was neglected.

$$\text{COM} = 0.28 \cdot \text{FCI} + 2.73 \cdot C_{OL} + 1.23 \cdot (C_{UT} + C_{RM} + C_{WT}) \tag{1}$$

The costs of the consumables and utilities were retrieved from prior literature for hydrogen (Arcos and Santos, 2023) and part of the consumables (Bbosa et al., 2018). The remaining values were retrieved from databases (https://ceskdata.com/).

3.1.3 Cash flow and internal rate of return (IRR)

For the discounted cash flow, we assumed a minimum acceptable target value of 12% for the internal rate of return (IRR) and 30% taxation on the revenues. IRR is a discount rate that makes the net present value (NPV) of all cash flows equal to zero.

3.2 Sensitivity analysis

A sensitivity analysis was performed to gain insight into the biorefinery's performance under various case studies (CS). We defined the process with air combustion of biochar as the baseline scenario (CS1). For biochar combustion, either air or oxy-combustion was considered. For oxy-combustion, the pure O_2 was either co-produced with green-H_2, via water splitting with electrolysis, or obtained from an Air Separation Unit (ASU) when using grey- or blue-H_2. When using green-H_2, oxy-combustion was considered only since oxygen is a vented by-product of green-H_2 and hence is free (0 \$/kg$_{O2}$). For the cases CS1 to CS5, the calculated profitability indexes were the IRR and payback time, considering a lifetime of 20 years for the biorefinery:

- CS1: baseline biorefinery (with air combustion and grey-H_2)
- CS2: biorefinery with oxy-combustion (O_2 from ASU) and grey-H_2
- CS3: biorefinery with air combustion and blue-H_2
- CS4: biorefinery with oxy-combustion (O_2 from ASU) and blue-H_2
- CS5: biorefinery with oxy-combustion and green-H_2

Based on the biorefinery layout of CS5, we assessed the impact of the bioethanol selling price on the overall economics. CS6 to CS8 were set up to find the minimum ethanol selling price (MESP) to achieve an IRR of 12%.

- CS6: MESP for the biorefinery as in CS5
- CS7: MESP for a biorefinery as in CS5, but when green-H_2 price equals blue-H_2 one
- CS8: MESP for a biorefinery as in CS5, but when green-H_2 price equals grey-H_2 one

Finally, we assessed the impact of using green-H_2 on the economics (CS9 to CS11). These last cases were designed to determine the maximum affordable green-H_2 price (MGHP) considering market price oscillations and different countries, e.g., 0.60 in the US and 1.20 \$/litre in Sweden; thus, 0.80 \$/litre is a time-weighted average worldwide. The target value for the IRR was kept fixed at 12%.

- CS9: MGHP at the current market price of bioethanol (0.80 \$/litre, fuel-grade spec)
- CS10: MGHP when bioethanol price is set at 0.60 \$/litre (i.e., US price)
- CS11: MGHP when bioethanol price is set at 1.20 \$/litre (i.e., Sweden price)

4. Results

Table 1 highlights the contributions of the single-unit operations to the investment cost (CAPEX) of the biorefinery. Table 2 gathers the prices of raw materials, utilities and end products used for the calculation of operating costs and revenues reported in Table 3.

Table 1: CAPEX for biorefinery plant: characteristic size, base purchase cost, and bare module cost of each piece of equipment. Costs are reported in millions of USD (M\$).

Unit	Size	Purchase cost	Bare module cost
Steam explosion reactor chamber	8 m^3	0.02	0.60
Saccharification reactor chamber	600.3 m^3	0.67	2.71
Pyrolysis chamber	455.6 m^3	0.50	2.04
Fermenter (all units)	689 m^3	1.64	6.67
HDO mild	91.8 m^3	0.11	0.45
HDO severe	15.7 m^3	0.03	0.11
Enzyme production	524.5 m^3	0.58	2.35
Ethanol purification columns (total)	37.0 m^3	0.07	0.27
Bio-oil distillation columns (total)	14.5 m^3	0.02	0.10
Steam boiler	6290 kW	3.83	9.38
Char combustion boiler	5160 kW	2.85	6.97
Compressors (all 4 units)	650 kW	0.58	1.25
Heat recovery exchanger-1	85.1 m^2	0.16	0.34
Heat recovery exchanger-2	258.2 m^2	0.28	0.60
Heat recovery exchanger-3	113.1 m^2	0.18	0.39
Water coolers (all 8 units)	276.7 m^2	1.12	3.69

Table 2: Costs of consumables (light blue), utilities (red) and products (grey background).

Chemical	Price ($/ton)	Value (M$/year)	Chemical	Price	Value (M$/year)
Spruce chips	43.23	4.34	Oxygen (ASU)	2.50 $/kg	7.02
2-naphthol	3500	6.25	Grey H_2	1.50 $/kg	2.64
			Blue H_2	3.50 $/kg	6.16
			Green H_2	7.25 $/kg	12.76
NH_3	410	1.48	Natural gas for steam generation	20 $/MWh	0.99 (oxy-comb.) 1.09 (air comb.)
SO_2	276	1.46	Electricity	80 $/MWh	0.77
Sodium acetate	20	0.99	Cooling water	0.02 $/m^3	0.08
Fermen strain	100	0.45	Bioethanol	0.80 $/litre	17.1
DAP	895	1.44	Gasoline	2.10 $/litre	17.9
CSL	50	1.10	Light diesel	1.72 $/litre	25.9
Ethylene glycol	860	0.01	Heavy diesel	0.37 $/litre	2.0

In addition to CAPEX, OPEX and revenues, Table 3 indicates the profitability indexes, i.e., the internal rate of return (IRR), payback time (PBT) and MESP/MGHP, resulting from the sensitivity analysis described in Section 3.2. For PBT, "Never" means that the investment cannot be recovered by 20 years (i.e., the assumed biorefinery's lifetime).

Table 3: Results of the sensitivity analysis. Colored cell(s) report the main outcome(s) of the corresponding case study (CS). Different colors cluster the cases as reported in Section 3.2.

Case	IRR (%)	MESP ($/litre)	MGHP ($/kg$_{H2}$)	CAPEX (M$)	OPEX (M$)	Revenues (M$)	PBT (year)
CS1	17.5	0.80[1]	1.50[1]	71.62	49.24	67.90	9.5
CS2	9.40	0.80[1]	1.50[1]	71.62	57.75	67.90	Never
CS3	12.7	0.80[1]	3.50[1]	71.62	53.57	67.90	17
CS4	3.50	0.80[1]	3.50[1]	71.62	62.08	67.90	Never
CS5	4.40	0.80[1]	7.25[1]	71.62	61.45	67.90	Never
CS6	12.0	1.06	7.25	71.62	61.45	75.15	20 (fixed)
CS7	12.0	0.77	3.50	71.62	61.45	67.14	20 (fixed)
CS8	12.0	0.62	1.50	71.62	61.45	62.81	20 (fixed)
CS9	12.0	0.80	3.85	71.62	54.20	67.90	20 (fixed)
CS10	12.0	1.20	8.93	71.62	65.20	78.90	20 (fixed)
CS11	12.0	0.60	1.31	71.62	48.69	62.39	20 (fixed)

[1] Bioethanol and hydrogen average prices as in Table 2.

5. Conclusions

Here we report the TEA of a spruce-to-fuel biorefinery. Our sensitivity analysis estimates the biorefinery's economics when accounting for the hydrogen source, strategies to burn the formed biochar (CS1 to CS5), the selling price of the fuel-grade bioethanol (CS6 to CS8) and the price for green-H_2 (CS9 to CS11). Our calculations indicate that, with the current market price values, only CS1 and CS3 (using air for biochar combustion and grey- or blue-H_2 for HDO of the crude bio-oil) are economically feasible for the proposed cases. The price of bioethanol (product) and hydrogen (consumable) strongly affects the profitability of the proposed biorefinery. In CS6 to CS11, we focused on green-H_2 because of the growing importance of renewable energy with a reduced carbon footprint and of current regulations and fuel blending mandates requiring "green" alternative fuels with the lowest carbon footprint. If the price of green-H_2 decreases from the current 7.25 (CS6) to 3.50 (blue-H_2; CS7) or 1.50 $/kg$_{H2}$ (grey-H_2; CS8), the MESP will decrease correspondingly. CS6 reveals that the MESP should be at least 1.06 $/litre (against the current average of 0.80 $/litre) to make the biorefinery profitable when using green-H_2. However, if the MESP rises to 1.20 $/litre (CS10), the biorefinery can reach a break-even point and it can tolerate a much higher MGHP of 8.93 $/kg$_{H2}$. CS6 indicates that incentives on bioethanol of at least 0.26 $/litre, i.e., 33% of the current bioethanol average price (0.80 $/litre), or even higher, e.g., 0.40 $/litre as assumed in CS10 (Sweden case), can support the "greenest" option. At the current average selling price of bioethanol, the MGHP is expected to almost halve to get a profitable green-H_2-based process as shown in CS9. In the worst scenario (i.e., the US average price of 0.60 $/litre; CS11), the MGHP must drop to 1.31 $/kg$_{H2}$, i.e., below the current price of grey-H_2 (1.50 $/kg$_{H2}$). Although to date this case is not feasible, technological developments will likely make the production of green-H_2 competitive with that of grey-H_2 in the next decade. The carbon footprint of the proposed case studies and the incorporation of a carbon capture system will be done in the next studies. Further strategies to reduce the costs, such as internal recycling of phenols as cation scavengers for feedstock pretreatment, will be assessed.

Acknowledgements

The Research Council of Norway supported this work through grant no. 257622 (Bio4Fuels) and 268002 (Enzymes4Fuels).

References

J.M.M. Arcos and D.M.F. Santos, 2023. The hydrogen color spectrum: Techno-economic analysis of the available technologies for hydrogen production. Gases, 3(1), 25-46.

D. Bbosa, M. Mba-Wright, R.C. Brown, 2018. More than ethanol: a techno-economic analysis of a corn stover-ethanol biorefinery integrated with a hydrothermal liquefaction process to convert lignin into biochemicals. Biofuels, Bioproducts & Biorefining, 12(3), 497-509.

F. Bisotti, M. Gilardi, O. T. Berglihn, R. Tschentscher, V.G.H. Eijsink, A. Várnai, B. Wittgens, 2023. Soft modelling of spruce conversion into bio-oil through pyrolysis – Note II: pyrolysis. Computer Aided Chemical Engineering, 52, 769-774.

F. Cherubini, 2010. The biorefinery concept: Using biomass instead of oil for producing energy and chemicals. Energy Conversion and Management, 51(7), 1412-1421.

M. Gilardi, F. Bisotti, O. T. Berglihn, R. Tschentscher, V.G.H. Eijsink, A.Várnai, B. Wittgens, 2023. Soft modelling of spruce conversion into bio-oil through pyrolysis – Note I: steam explosion and LPMO-activated enzymatic saccharification. Computer Aided Chemical Engineering, 52, 757-762.

K.M. Guthrie, 1974. Process plant estimating, evaluation and control. ISBN: 9780910460224, Craftsman Book Company of America, Solana Beach, CA.

L.D. Hansen, M. Østensen, B. Arstad, R. Tschentscher, V.G.H. Eijsink, S.J. Horn, A. Várnai, 2022. 2-Naphthol impregnation prior to steam explosion promotes LPMO-assisted enzymatic saccharification of spruce and yields high-purity lignin. ACS Sustainable Chemistry & Engineering, 10(16), 5233-5242.

D. Humbird, R. Davis, L. Tao, C. Kinchin, D. Hsu, A. Aden, P. Schoen, J. Lukas, B. Olthof, M. Worley, D. Sexton, D. Dudgeon, 2011, Process design and economics for biochemical conversion of lignocellulosic biomass to ethanol: Dilute-acid pretreatment and enzymatic hydrolysis of corn stover. NREL technical report NREL/TP-5100-47764.

R. Turton, J.A. Shaeiwitz, D. Bhattacharyya, W.B. Whiting, 2018. Analysis, synthesis, and design of chemical processes (International Series in the Physical and Chemical Engineering Sciences). 5th Edition, ISBN-13: 9780134177403, Pearson Education Inc.

Webpage: https://ceskdata.com/ (accessed September 2023)

Flavio Manenti, Gintaras V. Reklaitis (Eds.), Proceedings of the 34th European Symposium on Computer Aided Process Engineering / 15th International Symposium on Process Systems Engineering (ESCAPE34/PSE24), June 2-6, 2024, Florence, Italy

Novel process for eco-efficient production of formic acid by CO$_2$ hydrogenation

Maximiliano Taube,[a#] Amsalia Barus,[a#] Nikolaos Kalmoukidis,[a#]

Savvas Staikos,[a#] Farzad Mousazadeh,[a] Anton A. Kiss [a*]

[a] *Department of Chemical Engineering, Delft University of Technology, Van der Maasweg 9, 2629 HZ, Delft, the Netherlands*
[#] *These authors have equal contribution*
[*] *Corresponding author e-mail: a.a.kiss@tudelft.nl*

Abstract

Valorization of carbon dioxide towards value added chemicals can drastically mitigate the increased CO$_2$ levels in the atmosphere. In this context, formic acid is a versatile bulk chemical with promising market potential. The novel process design proposed in this work involves a sustainable thermochemical synthesis of formic acid from CO$_2$, which is rigorously simulated using Aspen Plus V12 as a CAPE tool. The process relies on the reverse water-gas shift reaction (RWGS) to synthesize CO from green H$_2$ and CO$_2$. The purified CO is used for the synthesis of methyl formate, which is then hydrolyzed to produce formic acid. To address downstream processing energy intensity, a distillation column with a dividing wall (DWC) is employed. The designed process achieves high molar yields of 95% for CO$_2$ and 96% for H$_2$ with a specific energy intensity of 21.8 MJ/kg of formic acid. The new process achieves a substantial reduction of 51% in the CO$_2$ emissions, 64% in electricity consumption and 20% in steam usage as compared to conventional fossil fuel-based FA production plants (reference case).

Keywords: carbon dioxide; formic acid; process design; process intensification

1. Introduction

To mitigate the ever-increasing CO$_2$ emissions, efforts have been directed toward the conversion of CO$_2$ into valuable chemicals and fuels. Formic acid is considered a versatile bulk chemical with various applications in food and tanning industry. Moreover, its potential as hydrogen carrier has been recently evaluated. However, direct thermochemical synthesis of formic acid from CO$_2$ encounters challenges due to the endergonic nature of the reaction ($\Delta G° = 32.9$ kJ·mol^{-1}). To overcome the key thermodynamic challenge of the direct reaction, intermediates have been introduced to the synthesis pathway. The most common commercial route to produce formic acid is from the hydrolysis of methyl formate derived from the reaction of fossil-fuel-based CO with methanol. This route is exergonic ($\Delta G° = -5.28$ kJ·mol^{-1}), rendering formic acid synthesis feasible. The CO needed for this design is provided from the reverse water-gas shift reaction (RWGS) of CO$_2$ and green hydrogen (Hietala et al 2016).

To the best of our knowledge, a detailed design of an energy efficient, sustainable and novel chemical process for formic acid production has not been extensively exploited in the open literature. The case study proposed combines readily available technologies, which enable the faster integration of this design into existing industries, with process intensification. The latter addresses the energy-intensive downstream processing of formic acid, involving the separation of a four-component solution with azeotrope.

2. Methodology

2.1. Properties database and thermodynamic models

The properties of the compounds employed in this design have been obtained from the Aspen Plus V12 database and additional literature (Novita et al., 2015), including the thermodynamic binary parameters necessary for describing the mixtures within the design. For the CO synthesis, given the low polarity of the compounds involved, the Peng-Robinson model has been selected as the most suitable. The NRTL model is used for the ethylene glycol/water mixture that serves as a thermal fluid with low freezing point. For the formic acid synthesis, the UNIQUAC with Hayden O' Connell equation of state for vapor phase (UNIQUAC-HOC) best describes this system. Both vapour-liquid and liquid-liquid interactions are involved resulting in a non-ideal system with polar compounds. The HOC variance of the method accounts for the vapor phase dimerization of carboxylic acids, such as formic acid. Moreover, Henry's law was used to consider the dissolved CO in liquid phase, which is the most appropriate model in temperatures well above the critical temperature.

2.2. Technology selection and operating conditions

The first step for the synthesis of formic acid involves the endothermic RWGS reaction:

$$CO_2 + H_2 \rightleftharpoons CO + H_2O \qquad \Delta H_{300K} = 41.2 \text{ kJ/mol}$$

For CO_2, a temperature of 25 °C, and a pressure of 35 bar and two compositions (typical and limit for post-combustion capture quality) were considered, while pure green H_2 was used at 70 °C and 30 bar. High temperature, high H/C ratio, and low-pressure favor selectivity (against methanation and methanol formation) and conversion towards CO formation. A solid transition metal carbide catalyst (1K-Cu/Mo$_2$C) is chosen due to its improved selectivity (100%), stability and capability of preventing sintering of the fine copper particles at the elevated temperatures required. Based on this catalyst, the reaction takes place at near atmospheric pressure (1-1.5 bar), at a temperature range of 573-600 °C and H_2/CO_2 molar ratio of 2.5. At the chosen conditions, this catalyst achieves 48% single-pass conversion with WHSV of 84000 mL/g/h (Xu et al., 2021). The RWGS reactor would ideally operate isothermally to maximize conversion. However, the elevated temperatures needed are not easy to control, and in practice adiabatic stages with inter-heating (using a fired heater) are preferred. Five stages are used to limit the adiabatic temperature fall.

The produced CO is separated using the COPure™ technology, consisting in the selective chemisorption of CO with a CuAlCl$_4$ salt dissolved in toluene. This selection was based on the achieved purity (> 99%) and CO recovery (98%) and its ability to separate N_2 from CO where cryogenic distillation or membranes fail. Operating conditions in the absorption column were selected based on the pilot plant data (Go et al., 2019), adjusting the pressure to 27 bar to compensate for the slightly lower CO concentration in the feed. After CO is chemically bound to CuAlCl$_4$ at low temperature (12-52 °C), other gases dissolved in the toluene are desorbed in a flash vessel at 90 °C and atmospheric pressure. Finally, the CO-CuAlCl$_4$ complex is dissociated in a stripper operating at 2 bar and 135 °C in the reboiler (Bierhals, 2001). Taking advantage of the relatively high pressure of the raw materials and recycle stream, and low pressure of the RWGS reaction, turbines are installed to generate power. Additionally, this pressure difference is also exploited to recover hydrogen from the inert purge by means of a polymeric membrane, suited to reject the main impurities such as CH$_4$ and N$_2$.

Methyl formate synthesis involves catalytic methanol carbonylation with CO to produce methyl formate, typically utilizing sodium methoxide as a homogeneous catalyst with a concentration of 2.5 wt. %. The reaction is the following:

$$CH_3OH + CO \rightleftharpoons HCOOCH_3 \qquad \Delta H_{300K} = -29.3 \text{ kJ/mol}$$

Anhydrous environment is essential to avoid fouling since the catalyst is sensitive to moisture. Increased pressure favours methyl formate synthesis, with optimal conditions at 80 °C and 40 bar. Excess methanol (CH$_3$OH/CO molar ratio of 5) guarantees an almost complete carbon monoxide conversion. The reaction is conducted in a CSTR equipped with cooling coil to actively remove the heat generated. After the reaction, the unreacted CO is flashed and recycled back. Then distillation follows, where the excess of methanol is retrieved at the bottom and recycled back to the carbonylation reactor (BASF, 2006).

The last step is the hydrolysis of methyl formate towards formic acid:

$$HCOOCH_3 + H_2O \rightleftharpoons CH_3OH + HCOOH \qquad \Delta H_{300K} = 16.3 \text{ kJ/mol}$$

This reaction poses challenges due to formic acid decomposition being favoured. The equilibrium constant for hydrolysis depends on the water:ester ratio, with a molar ratio of 1.8 being recommended to diminish downstream processing energy requirements. Thermal decomposition of formic acid and azeotrope presence were considered for the selected conditions. The main reaction should ideally occur at 120°C at 18 bar. PFR reactor with L/D = 30 is employed to ensure turbulent flow. For both methyl formate and formic acid synthesis, kinetic reactor type in Aspen was utilized with kinetic equation obtained from Chua et al's work (Chua et al., 2019).

The downstream processing involves decompression of the reactor outlet and cooling to prevent re-esterification. Methyl formate and methanol are separated from formic acid and water, and recycled back to the hydrolysis and carbonylation reactors, respectively. The final stage involves formic acid dehydration using distillation, carried out at 2.7 bar to yield a concentration of 85% wt. in formic acid while avoiding thermal decomposition in the bottom stream. Water distillate is recycled to the hydrolysis reactor (Chua et al., 2019).

2.3. Process Intensification

Process intensification has been introduced as a novelty to this design to reduce the energy needs of the process, namely reactive distillation (RD) and divided wall column (DWC) configurations have been considered. RD cannot be implemented to methyl formate synthesis, since the elevated pressure requirement (40 bar) of the reaction is incompatible with the operating pressure of the distillation (da Cunha et al, 2018). Several works have mentioned the utilization of RD and RDWC in formic acid synthesis. Despite the good results reported, narrow overlap between reaction and separation conditions and vapor recompression makes the process control challenging and hard to be retrofitted in existing plants (Ge et al, 2020).

On the contrary, the DWC configuration is deemed suitable for formic acid downstream processing. The separation of methyl formate, methanol, and the formic acid/water mixture can be achieved at the same pressure and is crucial to prevent the reverse decomposition of formic acid. In the Aspen Plus simulation, the DWC configuration is modeled using the Petlyuk configuration, which is its thermodynamic equivalent. The DWC design was initiated with constructing the V_{min} diagram which shows a graphical representation of the minimum vapor flow rate required at the column for proper separation (Figure 1). The minimum energy needed to separate a multicomponent mixture using a three-product Petlyuk arrangement is equivalent to the minimum energy required for the most challenging separation between the top/middle or middle/bottom products in a conventional single column (Halvorsen and Skogestad, 2003).

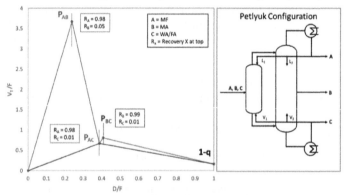

Figure 1. V_{min} diagram in FA separation

2.4. Heat Integration

Aligned with the energy-saving objective, heat integration was also performed. Firstly, the medium-pressure steam generation from the hot outlet stream of the CO synthesis reactor (573 °C) was valorized to fully cover the duty of the reboiler in the stripper. Moreover, the refrigerant generation through the turbines during the feedstock depressurization was also incorporated; thus, eliminating the need for chilled water.

3. Results and discussion

The simplified process diagram of the proposed concept is shown in Figure 2. This process renders 50.2 kta of formic acid with a process yield of 95% for CO_2 and 96% for H_2 (mass-based). Formic acid separation is the most energy intensive step in the whole process due to high energy demand for water and formic acid separation. Implementation of a DWC substantially contributes to achieving 20% energy saving compared to conventional distillation column arrangements. After applying heat integration, the overall heating duty is 31.8 MW, the cooling duty is 36.4 MW, and the power consumption equals 3.5 MW. This integrated approach not only enhances overall energy efficiency but also mitigates indirect CO_2 emissions within the proposed system.

Table 1. Comparison of this work with the reference case

Parameters	Unit	Reference Case*	This Work	Savings
Electricity	MWh/t FA	1.55	0.56	64%
Steam usage	MJ/kg FA	19.25	15.34	20%
Cooling water usage	t H_2O/t FA	375.50	501.59	-34%
Process water usage	t H_2O/t FA	0.60	0.50	17%
Total CO_2 emissions	t CO_2/t FA	2.18	1.07	51%

*Obtained from European Commission - JRC Science for Policy Report (Perez-Fortes, 2016)

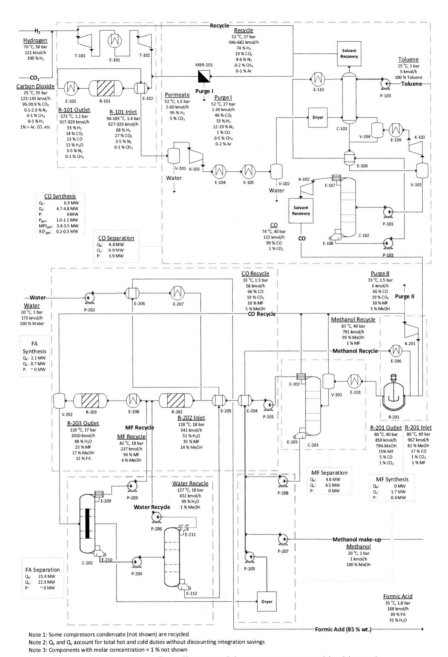

Note 1: Some compressors condensate (not shown) are recycled
Note 2: Q_h and Q_c account for total hot and cold duties without discounting integration savings
Note 3: Components with molar concentration < 1 % not shown

Figure 2. Process flow diagram of the concept proposed in this work

To evaluate the performance of the proposed design, a comprehensive comparison was conducted with conventional formic acid production with CO produced from heavy-fuel oil partial oxidation, serving as the reference case for this work (Perez-Fores, 2016). Table 1 lists the main results which prove significant advantages across various key performance indicators (KPIs), such as 64% reduction in electricity consumption and a substantial 51% reduction in total CO_2 emissions. From a sustainability point of view, the waste generated from this process comes from the purge streams (rich in CO_2) and waste water. The waste water is almost pure and could be recycled again to the methyl formate hydrolysis which accounts for 73% process water savings.

4. Conclusions

This work successfully showcased a novel process design with a capacity of 50.2 kta of formic acid produced from captured CO_2. Significant energy savings were achieved through process intensification (namely a DWC configuration) and heat integration, CO_2(eq) emissions were effectively halved as compared to the conventional method. One suggested approach for additional energy efficiency involves employing a membrane reactor for a simultaneous reaction and selective separation of the CO. Continuous removal of the product shifts the equilibrium towards higher CO yield. The electrification of the fire heater could assist in to accomplishing net-zero emissions. Another area of improvement involves refining the modeling of the process. Specifically, the CO separation the system was analyzed with a combination of pilot plant data and physical absorption simulations. Using a custom model in Aspen Plus which incorporates the chemisorption reaction would render more accurate results. The same principle applies to the CO synthesis reactor, where it is essential to incorporate a kinetic-based reactor.

The success of this work lies on the utilization of readily available technologies in which innovative adaptations were incorporated to enable a swift integration of this design into a more sustainable and energy efficient formic acid production plant.

References

BASF SE, 2006, Method for producing metyl formate, 10/511088, 5

J. Biehals, 2001, Carbon Monoxide, Ullmann's Encyclopedia of Industrial Chemistry,

W. X. Chua, S. da Cunha, G. P.Rangaiah, K.Hidajat, 2019, Design and optimization of Kemira-Leonard process for formic acid production, Chemical Engineering Science: X, 2, 100021 Halvorsen, I.J. and S. Skogestad, 2003, Minimum Energy Consumption in Multicomponent Distillation. 2. Three-Product Petlyuk Arrangements. Industrial & Engineering Chemistry Research, 42(3): p. 605-615

Y.Go, Y.Yoon,Y. Lee, S.Y. Lee, 2019, Mathematical Modeling and Simulation of Carbon Monoxide Absorption Column for Blast Furnace Gas and Linz–Donawitz Gas Separation by COSORB Process, Journal of Chemical Engineering of Japan, 52, 439-446

J. Hietala, Jukka, V.Antti, J. Pekka, P. Ilkka, R. Werner, K.Heinz, 2016, Formic Acid, Ullmann's Encyclopedia of Industrial Chemistry,1-22

F. Novita, H. Lee, M. Lee, 2015, Self-heat recuperative dividing wall column for enhancing the energy efficiency of the reactive distillation process in the formic acid production process, Chemical Engineering and Processing: Process Intensification, 97, 144-152

J. Xu, X. Gong, R. Hu, Z. Liu, Z. Liu, 2021, Highly active K-promoted Cu/β-Mo2C catalysts for reverse water gas shift reaction: Effect of potassium, Molecular Catalysis, 516, 111954

Mar Perez-Fores, E.T., 2016, Techno-economic and environmental evaluation of CO_2 utilisation for fuel production: Publications Office of the European Union, JRC99380

Flavio Manenti, Gintaras V. Reklaitis (Eds.), Proceedings of the 34th European Symposium on Computer Aided Process Engineering / 15th International Symposium on Process Systems Engineering (ESCAPE34/PSE24), June 2-6, 2024, Florence, Italy

Extracting and Ranking Metabolic Pathways from Large Metabolic Networks using Graph Theory and Metabolic Flux Analysis

Konstantinos Mexis[a], Stefanos Xenios[a], Nikos Trokanas[a], Antonis Kokossis[a*]

[a]*Department of Process Engineering, NTUA, Iroon Politechniou 6 Zografou, Athens, 157 80, Greece*

[*]*Corresponding author: akokossis@mail.ntua.gr*

Abstract

Efficiently deriving biosynthetic pathways from complex biochemical networks is crucial for advancing metabolic engineering. However, efficient analysis and navigation of big biochemical networks remain a challenge. Moreover, ranking the constructed pathways introduces further complexities. We propose a novel graph-based method for extracting biologically relevant metabolic pathways within large metabolic networks. The graph links metabolites as nodes via edges, representing reactant-product connections. Edges are assigned weights defining relations between two connected nodes. By incorporating further constraints based on compounds' molecular similarity, network connectivity and the availability of metabolites in the selected microorganism, we facilitate the rapid and reliable extraction of feasible metabolic pathways from large biochemical networks. Our method not only identifies pathways as a series of metabolites from source to target, but also delineates the specific enzymatic reactions for each step of the heterologous pathway. To illustrate the effectiveness of our approach, we provide a case study involving the bioproduction of butanol from E. coli.

Keywords: Metabolic Pathways, Pathway Discovery, Bioproduction, Retrobiosynthesis

1. Introduction

Metabolic pathways play a fundamental role in various applications, guiding the intricate conversion of source molecules into target molecules through a series of consecutive reactions. Extracting biologically relevant metabolic pathways from large biochemical networks which encompass thousands of metabolites interconnected by tens of thousands of enzymatic reactions remains a substantial challenge. Additionally, ranking the constructed pathways introduces further complexities. Historically, these pathways were crafted by hand, derived directly from experimental evidence. However, the omics era and the proliferation of computational resources have revolutionized the landscape of biochemistry research. The continuous expansion of biochemical databases not only supports fundamental research and metabolic engineering but also enables the design of non-canonical pathways not found in nature. While intuition and manual design once dominated non-natural pathway creation, the wealth of available biochemical data suggests that more efficient alternatives may be overlooked. Consequently, the development of systematic and automated pathway extraction tools has become essential to meet this challenge. These computational tools are designed to extract metabolic pathways from biochemical databases, with the primary goal of ensuring the pathways extracted are biologically relevant. They differ in how they build and search the available biochemical space, weight individual steps and complete pathways (Haffner et al., 2021). In this context, we tackle the challenge of efficiently exploring and analyzing extensive biochemical networks. We introduce a graph-based approach designed to prioritize the search for pathways featuring similar molecules in terms of molecular weight and molecular similarity, leveraging the SMILES representation. Notably, our method excels not only in extracting biologically meaningful pathways from these networks, but also in identifying the specific enzymatic reactions required for integration into a chosen host microorganism, enabling the production of a desired target molecule.

2. Pilot study: Butanol production form *Escherichia Coli*

The global butanol is on the rise, owing to its expanding applications and role as a chemical precursor of several other compounds. Recently, *n-butanol*, with its superior biofuel characteristics compared to *ethanol*, have stimulated even more interest. Clostridium species naturally produce (bio)butanol. To enhance butanol production, various pathways have been transplanted into the more accessible host, *Escherichia coli* (Atsumi, et al.). In our pilot study, we utilized a Genome-Scale model for the core metabolism of *E. coli*. Our method was tested on a vast biochemical network, comprising 30,081 enzymatic reactions sourced

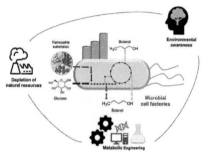

Figure 1: Microbial cell factories can convert renewable substrates into target metabolites replacing chemical-based

from the KEGG database. Our aim was to highlight our method's proficiency in extracting biologically relevant pathways from complex networks and its support for efficient navigation using our proposed network structure. Through the application of our method, we successfully rediscovered a previously experimentally validated novel pathway for biobutanol production in E. coli. Furthermore, our approach uncovered additional pathways by initiating the search with metabolites from E. coli's metabolism, showcasing the robustness and effectiveness of our method in identifying pathways of interest withing the metabolic network.

3. Materials and Methods

3.1. Biochemistry: Finding a retrosynthetic route through metabolism

In metabolic engineering, retrosynthesis aims to identify enzymatic reaction paths linking a target molecule to a cellular precursor. This process differs from organic chemistry retrosynthesis as it operates within a concurrent, system-level biochemical context, often involving heterologous pathways with shared reaction conditions and enzyme promiscuity. These characteristics create interconnected networks with unknown reactions and multiple potential carbon flow paths, affecting product yield, a critical economic metric (Geng-Min Lin, et al.).

3.2. Metabolic Network construction

We constructed an undirected graph using reactions sourced from the KEGG database, where each enzymatic reaction was decomposed into pairs of reactants and products. This graph links metabolites as nodes via edges, representing reactant-product connections. Edges are assigned a weight that defines the relation between two connected nodes. Out of the 30,081 enzymatic reactions sourced from the KEGG database, we extracted 55,979 substrate-product pairs. Among these pairs, 10,747 had associated information from

KEGG RPAIR. Within this subset, 5,148 pairs were categorized as *'main'* KEGG RPAIRs. A *'main'* KEGG RPAIR signifies the primary biotransformation occurring in a specific enzymatic reaction.

3.2.1. RPAIR Prediction using Machine Learning

To complete reactant-product pairs with missing RPAIR data, we implemented a machine learning (ML) pipeline incorporating the SMILES representation of the reactants and products as inputs. SMILES strings offer a linear representation of molecules and can be further transformed into molecular fingerprints, which serve as mathematical representations of molecules. In our study, we utilized the Morgan Fingerprint, a fixed-length binary vector representing molecular structure. Both reactants and products in each pair were converted into binary vectors of equal length. These vectors were then combined into a unified vector for each pair, serving as input for the ML model. The model's output determined whether the pair was a *main* pair or not. We divided pairs with known RPAIR data into an 80:20 training-validation split and used these sets to train a *Random Forest Classifier*, which was subsequently employed to predict missing RPAIR values for the entire dataset.

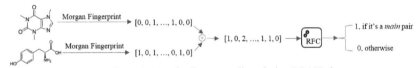

Figure 2: ML pipeline to predict missing RPAIR data

3.3. Calculation of weighted reactant-product pairs

In our approach, edges in the graph are assigned weights that define the relationship between the connected nodes. To enable the utilization of state-of-the-art shortest-path graph search algorithms, reactants of similar molecular weight should be close to each other, while pairs with significantly different weights are distanced further apart. This arrangement is based on the atom-conserving nature of reactants with similar molecular weights, enhancing the likelihood of reactions, a key aspect in pathway analysis optimization. Shorter paths typically represent more biologically feasible and efficient pathways. As a retrosynthetic path gets longer, each added enzyme is likely to decrease the amount of product made from the precursor. To achieve this, we transformed the difference in molecular weights into a distance metric:

$$W_{S \to P} = \frac{|MW_s - MW_P|}{MW_s + MW_P}$$

where MW_S and MW_P are the molecular weight of the substrate and product of a reaction pair respectively.

3.4. Pruning the Metabolic Network

3.4.1. Pruning for core pathway focus

The general picture of a metabolic network is that of a highly connected complex network of metabolites and reactions, sharing many features with other large-scale biological networks. To distill the network into biologically meaningful pathways, we employed a pruning strategy by retaining solely the *main* reactant-product pairs. The removal of *non-main* pairs led to a significantly reduces, more focused network, concentrated on the core biotransformations. The pruned network comprises 7,997 nodes and 11,783 edges.

3.4.2. Currency metabolites

Metabolic networks feature metabolites like ATP and NAD, commonly known as "currency" or "hub" metabolites, as they participate in numerous reactions. These hub metabolites, while essential for the metabolism, present a challenge in metabolic network analysis. Their prevalence in the network often obscures the underlying pathway-like structure. To clarify the network's actual properties, it is common to exclude these metabolites during analysis. However, no consensus exists on what constitutes a currency metabolite. In our study, we opted to remove 209 well-known hub metabolites (e.g., H_2O, ATP, NAD) from the network.

Figure 3: Metabolic network pruning

3.5. Pathway refinement via molecular similarity

In addition to employing a weighted-shortest path approach with weights determined by the molecular weights of reactant-product pairs, we incorporated an additional constraint to refine the resulting metabolic pathways. This constraint involved evaluating the molecular similarity of every reactant-product intermediate pair within the metabolic pathway. We calculated molecular similarity using Fingerprint Similarity, extracted from the SMILES representation of the molecules. In our analysis pipeline, we took a step further by sorting the top-10 weighted shortest paths based on the average similarity between these intermediate metabolites. This step allowed us to prioritize pathways that not only exhibited efficient weight-based connections but also demonstrated a higher degree of molecular similarity among the metabolites involved, thus enhancing the biological relevance of the identified metabolic pathways.

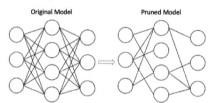

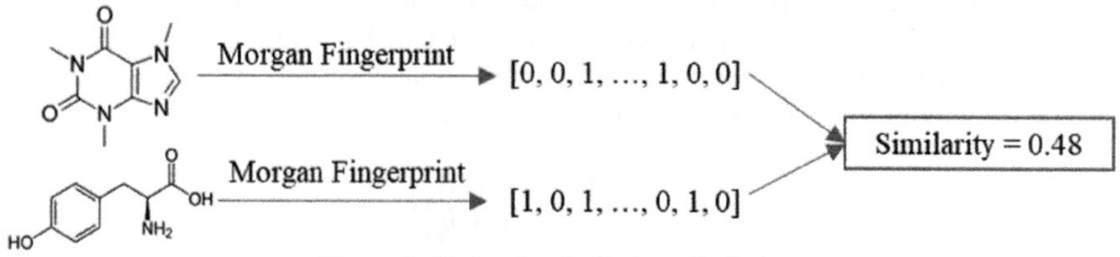

Figure 4: Molecular similarity calculation

3.6. Selecting specific enzymatic reactions

To successfully integrate a heterologous pathway into a chosen microorganism, it is imperative to specify not only the precursor metabolites starting from a given molecule but also the precise enzymatic reaction to introduce to the host cell. Complicating matters, a single reactant-product pair extracted from a large metabolic network, can belong to multiple enzymatic reactions, necessitating the careful selection of the most suitable reaction for incorporation. To address this challenge, we examine the metabolites available within the selected microorganism. Subsequently, we focus on selecting reactions that exclusively utilize the already present metabolites to generate a new metabolite. This new metabolite then serves as the starting point for subsequent reactions, ultimately culminating in the synthesis of the desired target molecule. This strategic approach ensures the compatibility of the introduced pathway with the host microorganism and paves the way for successful heterologous pathway integration.

3.7. Finding metabolic pathways with graph search

Our method employs Yen's k-shortest loop-less path algorithm, utilizing the Python package *NetworkX*, to extract the shortest pathways from the weighted network of reactant-product pairs (Haffner et al., 2021). This algorithm takes as input a weighted graph representing the network, a source compound, a target compound, and a specified maximum number of shortest paths (k) to be identified. After identifying the specified number of k-shortest paths, the algorithm ceases its search and makes these pathways available for analysis. The algorithm then ranks these k-shortest paths according to the average molecular similarity at each reaction step. This ranking prioritizes pathways with the highest overall similarity, ensuring the selection of metabolic routes that are both biologically relevant and chemically consistent for our analysis.

4. Results

4.1. Extracting biologically relevant pathways

To demonstrate the effectiveness of our approach, we present two illustrative pathway searches. In the first instance, our goal was to establish a biochemical connection between *tyrosine* and *caffeate*. The resulting pathway, with a length of just two steps, indicates its high quality, as it involves only a minimal number of intermediate reactions. Furthermore, the pathway we extracted aligns with KEGG's phenylpropanoid biosynthesis map, underscoring its biological relevance and validity.

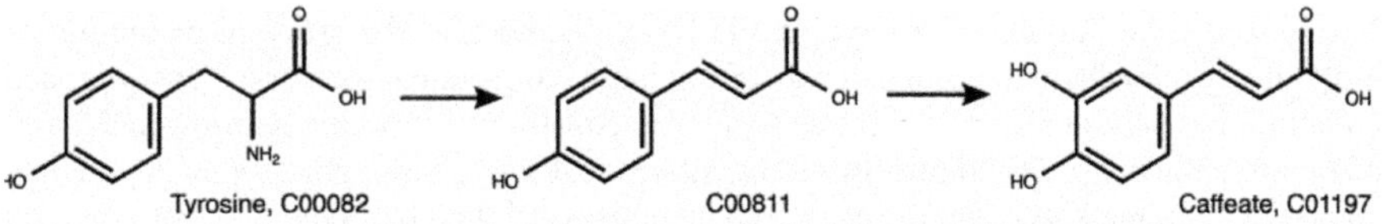

Figure 5: Extracted pathway connecting tyrosine and caffeate

In the second example, we searched for a pathway connecting the compounds *tyrosine* and *syringin*. The extracted pathway is part of the KEGG pathway map for phenylpropanoid biosynthesis, and it can therefore be called a confirmed, biologically meaningful pathway. These two examples of pathway search problems illustrate the capacity of our method to efficiently extract biologically relevant pathways from large biochemical networks. The algorithm robustly handled searches for long pathways of eight and more biotransformation steps, as they are usually present in secondary metabolism.

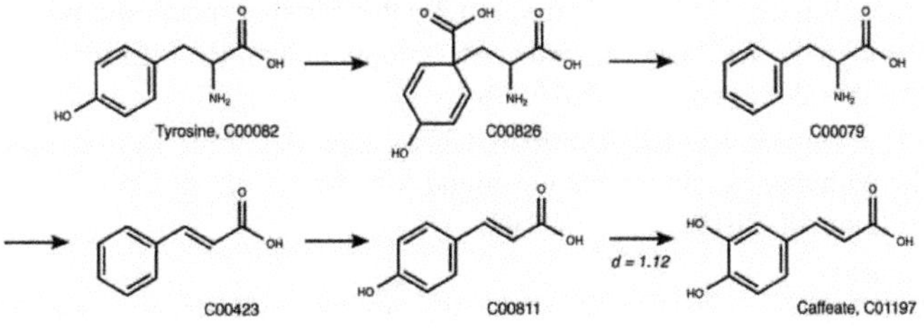

Figure 6: Extracted pathway connecting tyrosine and syringin

4.1. Pathway discovery and host integration

To demonstrate our approach's efficacy, we conducted a case study on butanol bioproduction in E. coli. E. coli, a well-studied microorganism with versatile genetic tools, lacks the natural capacity for 1-butanol production. Our method rediscovered a six-step metabolic pathway, starting from acetyl-CoA, to enable 1-butanol production in this host organism. To construct our host organism representation, we utilized the *E. coli* core metabolism Genome-scale metabolic model, from which we extracted the metabolites assessable for participation in

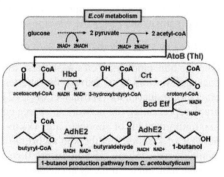

Figure 7: Schematic representation of 1-butanol production in engineered E. coli

the enzymatic reactions required for the heterologous metabolic pathway. Employing the methodology outlined in *Section 3*, our algorithm successfully determined the precise enzymatic reactions to incorporate into the host organism, enabling the production of 1-butanol. To assess the biological significance of the extracted pathway, we integrated it into the host organism's genome-scale model and conducted Flux Balance Analysis (FBA). Within this analysis, we imposed anaerobic conditions and we set the biomass production as the optimization function. The FBA algorithm subsequently calculated the flux for the biomass reaction, indicating the pathway's biological relevance and feasibility within the host organism.

5. Conclusions

In this study, we introduced a novel graph-based method for the efficient extraction of biologically relevant metabolic pathways from large biochemical networks. Our approach combines network analysis, molecular similarity constraints, machine learning and state-of-the-art pathway search algorithms to facilitate the discovery of pathways with practical applications in metabolic engineering. We demonstrated the effectiveness of our method through a case study focusing on 1-butanol bioproduction in E. coli, highlighting its potential to develop valuable bioproduction processes in microorganisms. Our approach streamlines pathway discovery, enhances the likelihood of success in practical bioproduction processes, and offers a valuable asset for metabolic engineers, bridging the gap between theory and application in the field of metabolic engineering.

References

Atsumi, S., Cann, A. F., Connor, M. R., Shen, C. R., Smith, K. M., Brynildsen, M. P., Chou, K., Hanai, T., & Liao, J. C. (2008). Metabolic engineering of Escherichia coli for 1-butanol production. Metabolic Engineering, 10(6), 305–311

Jasmin Hafner, Vassily Hatzimanikatis, NICEpath: Finding metabolic pathways in large networks through atom-conserving substrate–product pairs, Bioinformatics, Volume 37, Issue 20, October 2021, Pages 3560–3568

Geng-Min Lin, Robert Warden-Rothman, Christopher A. Voigt, Retrosynthetic design of metabolic pathways to chemicals not found in nature, Current Opinion in Systems Biology, Volume 14, 2019, Pages 82-107

Acknowledgments

The research project was supported by the Hellenic Foundation for Research and Innovation (H.F.R.I.) under the 2nd Call for H.F.R.I. Research Projects to support Faculty Members & Researchers (Project Number: 3817).

Flavio Manenti, Gintaras V. Reklaitis (Eds.), Proceedings of the 34th European Symposium on Computer Aided Process Engineering / 15th International Symposium on Process Systems Engineering (ESCAPE34/PSE24), June 2-6, 2024, Florence, Italy

Intimately Coupled Photocatalysis and Biodegradation Hybrid Systems in Tetracycline Removal

Rachel Mugumo,[a] Shepherd M. Tichapondwa,[a] Evans M.N. Chirwa[a]

[a]*Water Utilisation and Environmental Engineering Division, Department of Chemical Engineering, University of Pretoria, South Africa*
Email: rachel.mugumo@tuks.co.za

Abstract

The presence of tetracycline in wastewater is a global concern due to its pervasive nature, persistence, and harmful effects on both humans and aquatic ecosystems, even at extremely low concentrations. The shortcomings of traditional wastewater treatment methods have prompted the exploration of Advanced Oxidation Processes such as photocatalysis. However, these processes are often hindered by their inability to completely mineralise wastewater pollutants. Hence, this study aims to introduce and implement an innovative, environmentally friendly, cost-effective, and sustainable solution through an intimately coupled photocatalysis and biodegradation (ICPB) hybrid system. The primary objective is to enhance the removal and achieve complete mineralisation of recalcitrant pollutants. The metal-sulphide/ZnO photobiodegradation system, when subjected to visible irradiation, demonstrated a remarkably impressive 100 % tetracycline removal. This study therefore presents a groundbreaking effective approach to establish a robust ICPB system that combines cost effectiveness with superior degradation efficiency, offering potential applications at a large scale.

Keywords: photocatalysis, biodegradation, tetracycline, photo-biodegradation, visible light irradiation.

1. Introduction

Antibiotics have become prominent pollutants in natural aquatic environments globally, primarily driven by the escalating misuse of these drugs. This misuse is a consequence of the growing demand for pharmaceuticals and the swift advancements in the drug and medical industry, and animal husbandry (He et al., 2021). Tetracycline is a broad-spectrum antibiotic that has frequently been identified in landfills, sludge, sediments, groundwater, drinking water, surface water and wastewater (Shao and Wu, 2020).

The presence of tetracycline hinders the growth and development of aquatic species and has the potential to accumulate in the food chain, posing a risk to human health. This can result in various health issues such as central nervous system defects, nephropathy, joint disease, endocrine disruption and mutagenicity (Xu et al., 2021). Hence, it is imperative to identify a practical and efficient technology for the degradation of tetracycline in water environments.

Photocatalysis as an advanced oxidation process (AOP) has garnered significant interest for the degradation of antibiotics as an eco-friendly green technology due to its cost-effectiveness and environmental friendliness (Wu et al., 2020). While numerous noteworthy strides have been taken in the field of photocatalysis, it suffers many limitations such as wide band gaps that can be activated by UV-light that only accounts for 5 % of the solar spectrum, and it has fast recombination rates of the photoinduced charge carriers (He et al., 2021). Moreover, although photocatalysis has the ability to convert antibiotics into easily biodegradable compounds or less toxic organic molecules, it fails to completely mineralise organic compounds (Wu et al., 2020).

This compels the need to further treat the photodegraded effluent with bacteria adaptable to feed on the generated products. Li et al. (2022) investigated the degradation of tetracycline using 0.3 gL^{-1} recyclable cellulose nanofibrils/polyvinyl alcohol/Fe_3O_4 hybrid hydrogel as a photo-Fenton catalyst (PVA/CNF/Fe_3O_4) and achieved 98 % removal in 120 min. Another study conducted by Gopal et al. (2019) reported photo-assisted removal of tetracycline using bio-nanocomposite-immobilised alginate beads (Fe_3O_4 and TiO_2 nanoparticles along with dead biomass of *Acinetobacter sp.*) and measured 98 % 10 mgL^{-1} tetracycline removal.

In this study, visible-light-active Ag_2S/ZnO nanocomposites were synthesised using a solid-phase combustion method. The physicochemical properties of the synthesised material were characterised using XRD, SEM, TEM and BET. Tetracycline, a notorious antibiotic resistant to degradation was employed as a target pollutant and its photodegradation tested under visible light irradiation. Herein, to the best of our knowledge a microbial consortium predominantly *Clostridium bifermentans* and *Klebsiella pneumoniae* have never been reported for this purpose were adopted for subsequent biodegradation. The two-step hybrid photo-biodegradation technique was interestingly effective in the removal of tetracycline and holds significant potential in wastewater treatment applications.

2. Materials and method

2.1. Materials

Silver (II) nitrate hexahydrate [$Ag(NO_3)_2.6H_2O$] and zinc oxide (ZnO) were purchased from Glassworld (Johannesburg, South Africa). Thiourea [$(NH_2)_2CS$] (sulphur precursor and oxidant fuel) were purchased from Sigma-Aldrich (St Louis, MO, United States). Silver (II) nitrate hexahydrate was used as the silver precursor in the synthesis of the photocatalyst. Tetracycline ≥ 95 % HPLC (the model organic pollutant) was purchased from Sigma-Aldrich South Africa. Methanol and acetonitrile used as mobile phases for the HPLC were purchased from VWR BDH chemicals (France), and phosphoric acid and persulphate used as mobile phase for the TOC-V analyser were purchased from Merck Schuchardt (Germany) and ACE (Johannesburg) respectively. All reagents were used without further purification. Deionised water (DI) was used as a solvent throughout this study.

2.2. Photocatalyst synthesis

According to the one-pot synthesis method reported by Mugumo et al. (2023), ZnO, $Ag(NO_3)_2.6H_2O$ and $(NH_2)_2CS$ were respectively weighed in a 2:1:0.25 ratio and transferred to a clean crucible. The mixture was subsequently calcined for 30 min at 400 °C. A pastel and mortar was used to grind the obtained product into a powdery photocatalyst.

2.3. Bacterial preculture

Chimhundi et al. (2021) prepared preculture cultured from a contaminated soil sample from an automotive battery recycling plant borehole situated in Gauteng, South Africa. *Clostridium bifermentans* and *Klebsiella pneumoniae* were the primary predominant bacterial species identified from the conducted cultured microbial consortium analysis and characterisation.

2.4. Material characterisation

The X-ray diffraction (XRD) spectra of the prepared sample was analysed using the PANalytical X'Pert Pro powder diffractometer in θ–θ configuration with an X'Celerator detector and variable divergence- and fixed receiving slits with Fe filtered Co-Kα radiation (λ=1.789Å). Scanning electron microscope (SEM) images were captured on a Zeiss Ultra PLUS FEG SEM and the optical absorption spectra of the synthesised nanomaterials was measured using a Hitachi U-3900 single monochromatic double-beam system. Transmission electron microscopy (TEM) imaging was captured using a JOEL JEM 2100F, 200 kV analytical electron microscope. The Brunuaer-Emmett-Teller (BET) surface areas of the prepared material was determined using a micrometrics TriStar II 3020 Version 3.02 BET system. A Shimadzu TOC-V analyser was used to measure (total organic carbon) TOC removal rate.

2.5. Photocatalytic studies

The synthesised Ag$_2$S/ZnO nanocomposite photocatalytic performance was investigated by measuring the removal of 100 mgL^{-1} tetracycline under visible light irradiation. The experimental set-up was conducted in a Lelesil Innovative Systems photoreactor connected to a 450 W visible light lamp controller. The photodegradation tests were conducted using a 1 gL^{-1} Ag$_2$S/ZnO catalyst loading. The suspension was stirred for 60 min in the dark to allow for adsorption-desorption equilibrium prior to 2 h of visible light irradiation. Aliquot samples of 2 mL were extracted every half hour for centrifugation at 9,000 rpm for 10 min. 0.45 µm Millipore microfilters were used to filter the collected solution which was subsequently analysed using a High-Performance Liquid Chromatography (HPLC – waters 2695 separation module, 2996 Photodiode Array detector), with Empower software. The parameters for detection of tetracycline were PAH C18 (4.6 x 250 mm, 5 µm) column, injection volume of 10 µL, a flow rate of 1.0 mLmin^{-1}, a wavelength of 360 nm, and a mobile phase of 100 % methanol and 100 % acetonitrile. The photodegradation efficiency was calculated using Eq. (1) below.

$$\% \, Degradation = \frac{(C_o - C_t)}{C_o} \times 100 \tag{1}$$

where C_o is the initial tetracycline concentration and C_t is tetracycline concentration at time, t.

2.6. Biodegradation studies

TOC was measured initially before photodegradation and after the conducted photocatalysis. Microbial consortium (*Clostridium bifermentans and Klebsiella pneumoniae*) was fed into the photodegraded solution to investigate the efficiency of bacteria in the reduction of carbon content present in solution. This solution was further analysed after 24 h of biodegradation using a Shimadzu TOC-V analyser. An HPLC was subsequently used to measure tetracycline removal after bacteria was fed into the system.

3. Characterisations

3.1. XRD

Figure 1 depicts the crystalline phases of the synthesised nanomaterials (ZnO and Ag$_2$S/ZnO). The narrow intense sharp peaks are indicative of high crystallinity and purity of the synthesised materials. The intense diffraction peaks at 37°, 40°, 42° and 56° correspond to (100), (002), (101), and (110) planes of hexagonal wurtzite ZnO (JCPDS 36-1451). The observed highest peak (101) suggests anisotropic growth, an indication of preferred crystallites orientation. Additional peaks on the Ag$_2$S/ZnO spectra noted at 2Θ values of 44° and 52° correspond to Ag$_2$S which confirms successful doping of Ag$_2$S onto ZnO (Subash et al., 2012).

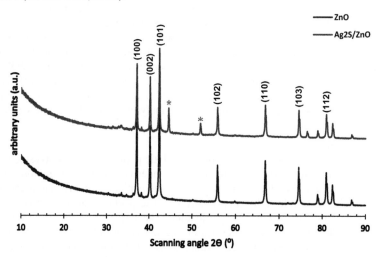

Figure 1: XRD spectra of ZnO and Ag$_2$S/ZnO.

3.2. SEM and TEM

The composite synthesis method determines the morphological and structural properties of the synthesised material. The structure and morphology of ZnO modified with Ag$_2$S is depicted in Figure 2. The SEM image Figure 2(a) depicts a combination of nanorods and porous spherical sheets exhibiting a wide distribution of particle sizes. Furthermore, the TEM image Figure 2(b) confirms the presence of hexagonal rod-like and well-defined spherical structures observed in the SEM analysis.

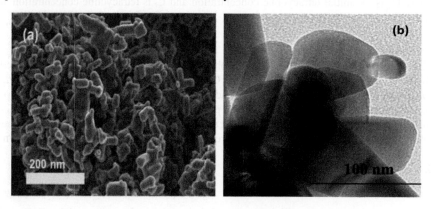

Figure 2: (a) SEM image and (b) TEM image of the synthesised Ag$_2$S/ZnO.

3.3. BET

The material surface area is a crucial parameter that influences photocatalytic activity. Specific surface area of ZnO and Ag$_2$S/ZnO was measured using BET analysis and reported as 50 m^2/g and 46 m^2/g, respectively. The noted slight surface area reduction can be attributed to the coating of Ag$_2$S particles onto ZnO surface. This leads to the collapse in pores and subsequently agglomeration of particles.

4. Photo-biodegradation studies

Photocatalysis was conducted as a pre-treatment method followed by biodegradation as a post-treatment method and the results shown in Figure 3. The photocatalytic performance of the synthesised Ag$_2$S/ZnO was investigated a 100 mgL^{-1} tetracycline solution using 1 gL^{-1} catalysts loading in a 500 ml volume under visible light irradiation. The prepared solution was left stirring in the dark for 60 min to achieve adsorption_ desorption equilibrium. The reactor was then subjected to visible light illumination for 120 min and an outstanding 96 % tetracycline removal was measured. An anaerobic microbial consortium was then fed into the system for biodegradation to occur. The solution after biodegradation was reanalysed using the HPLC and measured an excellent 100 % tetracycline removal. A TOC analysis was subsequently conducted to determine the carbon content present before photodegradation, after photodegradation and after biodegradation and reported carbon content of 5140 mgL^{-1} (100 %), 2310 mgL^{-1} (45 %) and 1050 mgL^{-1} (20 %), respectively. This confirms that although photocatalysis is a promising water treatment technique, it suffers drawbacks of incomplete mineralisation which can be postulated to the formation of intermediates during treatment. Therefore, biodegradation as post-treatment method proved efficient in complete tetracycline removal and the reduction of the measured carbon content.

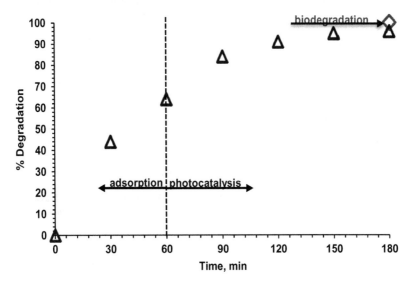

Figure 3: Hybrid photo-biodegradation efficiency in tetracycline removal.

5. Conclusions

Tetracycline removal was investigated using a two-step treatment technique. Photocatalysis was adopted as a pre-treatment method where a visible-light-active Ag_2S/ZnO photocatalyst was applied in the removal of tetracycline. A microbial consortium was then fed into the reactor for biodegradation which was employed as post-treatment method. It is interesting to note that although 96 % tetracycline removal was noted after photocatalysis and 55 % carbon content reduction, a post-treatment technique is therefore crucial to further lower the carbon content. The achieved results promote further research into identifying and testing bacteria efficient enough to completely remove any remaining carbon content after photocatalysis, and this study shows the potential implementation of a hybrid photo-biodegradation system for commercial use.

6. Acknowledgements

This study is based on research financially supported by the National Research Foundation (NRF) through Grant No. EQP180503325881 and Rand Water Company, through Grant No. RW01413/18 awarded to Prof E.M.N. Chirwa, and The NRF Thuthuka Fund Grant No. TTK18024324064 awarded to Prof S.M. Tichapondwa at the University of Pretoria.

References

J. Chimhundi, C. Hörstmann, E.M. Chirwa, H.G. Brink, 2021, Microbial Removal of Pb (II) Using an Upflow Anaerobic Sludge Blanket (UASB) Reactor, *Catalysts,* 11, 512.

G. Gopal, N. Roy, N. Chandrasekaran, A. Mukherjee, 2019, Photo-assisted removal of tetracycline using bio-nanocomposite-immobilized alginate beads, *ACS omega,* 4, 17504-17510.

X. He, T. Kai, P. Ding, 2021, Heterojunction photocatalysts for degradation of the tetracycline antibiotic: a review, *Environmental Chemistry Letters,* 19, 4563-4601.

Y. Li, H. Cao, W. Liu, P. Liu, 2022, Effective degradation of tetracycline via recyclable cellulose nanofibrils/polyvinyl alcohol/Fe_3O_4 hybrid hydrogel as a photo-Fenton catalyst, *Chemosphere,* 307, 135665.

R. Mugumo, E.O. Ichipi, S.M. Tichapondwa, E.M. Chirwa, 2023, Bandgap tailoring of ZnO using metallic sulphides for enhanced visible-light-active photocatalytic water treatment, *Chemical Engineering Transactions,* 103, 829-834.

S. Shao, and X. Wu, 2020, Microbial degradation of tetracycline in the aquatic environment: a review, *Critical reviews in biotechnology,* 40, 1010-1018.

B. Subash, B. Krishnakumar, V. Pandiyan, M. Swaminathan, M. Shanthi, 2012, An efficient nanostructured Ag_2S–ZnO for degradation of Acid Black 1 dye under day light illumination, *Separation and Purification Technology,* 96, 204-213.

S. Wu, H. Hu, Y. Lin, J. Zhang, Y.H. Hu, 2020, Visible light photocatalytic degradation of tetracycline over TiO_2, *Chemical Engineering Journal,* 382, 122842.

L. Xu, H. Zhang, P. Xiong, Q. Zhu, C. Liao, G. Jiang, 2021, Occurrence, fate, and risk assessment of typical tetracycline antibiotics in the aquatic environment: A review, *Science of the total Environment,* 753, 141975.

Flavio Manenti, Gintaras V. Reklaitis (Eds.), Proceedings of the 34th European Symposium on Computer Aided Process Engineering / 15th International Symposium on Process Systems Engineering (ESCAPE34/PSE24), June 2-6, 2024, Florence, Italy

Data-driven Process Variable Prediction Using Augmented Orthogonal Autoencoder

Junqing Xia*, Yoshiyuki Yamashita

*Department of Applied Physical and Chemical Engineering,
Tokyo University of Agriculture and Technology,
2-24-16, Naka-cho, Koganei City, Tokyo 184-8588, Japan*
xiajunqing@m2.tuat.ac.jp

Abstract

In recent years, data-driven soft sensors have grown in popularity as a means of measuring hard-to-obtain variables. However, many modelling methods for soft sensors encounter difficulties when dealing with highly correlated and nonlinear data found in chemical plants. This paper presents a simple and effective soft sensor modelling method based on orthogonal autoencoder neural network augmented with regression network structure. This configuration allows the findings of a low-dimensional latent space suitable for constructing a regression model for a process response variable. The Tennessee Eastman Process and Benchmark Simulation Model no.2 were used to evaluate the predictive performances of our proposed method, and the results demonstrated that our proposed method can provide benefits over conventional data-driven techniques for soft sensor modelling.

Keywords: Machine learning, variable prediction, soft sensor modelling.

1. Introduction

Reliable and timely measurement is a crucial aspect of ensuring plant-wide control and product quality managements. While modern hardware sensors can effectively cover a wide range of measurement tasks, measuring variables such as product concentrations in a chemical process still demands a substantial investment in equipment, not to mention the significant delay caused by the measurement. Software sensor (or soft sensor), utilising mathematical models and existing measurements, offers an alternative means of measurement alongside hardware sensors. Soft sensors based on first-principle models have been developed and deployed over the past few decades. Nevertheless, developing such a soft sensor requires a profound comprehension of the target process, as well as a large amount of time and efforts.

A preferable alternative to first-principle soft sensor is data-driven soft sensor constructed using collected process historical operation data. However, it has been widely recognised that data obtained from a typical chemical plant exhibits high correlations among its process variables. Therefore, direct application of regression techniques for soft sensor construction would result undesirable predictive results. Moreover, nonlinear characteristics of process data, as well as the correlations between latent variables and response variables, must be taken into consideration as well (Ching, et al., 2021).

In this study, we propose regression network structure based on an augmented orthogonal autoencoder architecture to address the aforementioned challenges of modelling soft sensors for chemical processes. Section 2 introduces some fundamental concepts, while section 3 describes our proposed modelling method in detail. In section 4, we examine the prediction performance of our approach using two industrial benchmarks.

2. Preliminaries

2.1. PCR and PLSR

Principal component analysis (PCA) is undoubtedly one of the most employed data compression techniques. A data matrix, consisting of n samples with m features, is projected onto a low-dimensional subspace $\mathbf{T}$, formed by p ($p < m$) principal components:

$$\mathbf{X} = \mathbf{TP}^{\mathrm{T}} + \mathbf{E} \tag{1}$$

These principal components can be further utilised as explanatory variables in constructing regression models. This technique is referred to as principal component regression (PCR), and it has been widely used for soft sensor modelling (Ebrahimi, et al., 2017). However, as the explanatory principal components are obtained solely from the decomposition of the process variable matrix $\mathbf{X}$, necessary correlations with the response variables might be absent, thus adequate predictive performance of PCR cannot be assured.

Partial least squares regression (PLSR) was developed from the idea of compressing data akin to PCA and PCR. But instead of focusing on $\mathbf{X}$ alone, PLSR projects both explanatory and response variables onto two different low-dimensional subspaces (Eqs. 1 and 2). The decomposition of the two matrices is performed to maximize the covariance between the two projection matrices $\mathbf{T}$ and $\mathbf{U}$.

$$\mathbf{Y} = \mathbf{UQ}^{\mathrm{T}} + \mathbf{F} \tag{2}$$

2.2. Autoencoder and Orthogonal Autoencoder

Autoencoder (AE) is another well-known machine learning technique that can be used as a tool for data compression. A typical AE comprises an encoder and a decoder. If the dimensionality of the middle layer formed between encoder and decoder is smaller than that of the input, then the input data will be forcedly compressed using the encoder before being reconstructed again by the decoder. This procedure creates a bottleneck, leading to the capture of the underlying data features. Such features captured by the bottleneck layer can be referred to as latent features. In a typical AE with only one hidden layer (i.e. the bottleneck layer), the latent features can be obtained as:

$$\mathbf{h} = f(\mathbf{W}_{en}\mathbf{x} + \mathbf{b}_{en}) \tag{3}$$

where $\mathbf{x}$ and $\mathbf{h}$ are the vectors for input and the latent layers, $\mathbf{W}_{en}$ is the weight matrix of the encoder, $\mathbf{b}_{en}$ is the bias term, and f is the activation function for the neurons. One of the significant advantages of AE over PCA is its capability of obtaining nonlinear underlying data features via the use of nonlinear activation functions.

Recently, a modified version of AE called orthogonal autoencoder (OAE) has been utilised for the purpose of process fault detection and diagnosis (Davide and Kulahci, 2022). It was discovered that without the enforcement of the orthogonality regularisation L_O, there will be no warranty on the correlation issue, thus high-level correlation was observed among the extracted features from AE. As a solution to this issue, an additional regularisation term was added into the data reconstruction cost of AE training as the "cost of correlation" in Eq. 4.

$$L_{OAE} = L_O + L_{AE} \tag{4}$$

where L_O and L_{AE} are cost for latent feature correlation and AE data reconstruction, respectively.

3. Proposed Method

Although the elimination of multi-collinearity among latent features can be guaranteed using OAE, similar to the limitation of PCR, the latent features of a regular OAE are obtained only through mapping of the process data matrix alone, without any feedback from response variable. Thus it is conceivable that a regression model constructed with such latent features as explanatory variables will not attain acceptable predictive accuracy for soft sensors.

Inspired by the concept of PLSR and its relation with PCR, this study presents a modified OAE network to model soft sensors. As shown in Figure 1, an additional network structure, starts from the bottleneck layer and ends at a single node, is integrated into a regular OAE network. Using this architecture, high dimensional data is firstly compressed into uncorrelated latent features by the OAE. Then through the newly added network, these latent features are utilised as explanatory variables to construct a regression model for the response variable. To ensure the correlations between latent features and the response variable, as well as optimal predictive capability of the entire model, an additional regularisation term L_{RG} is integrated into Eq. 4 as "the cost of regression performance:"

$$L_{NN} = L_{RG} + L_O + L_{AE} \tag{5}$$

In this research, we employed the squared error between the measured value of response variable and its prediction as L_{RG}, and thus Eq. 5 can be written in details as:

$$L_{NN} = \lambda_{RG}(y - \hat{y})^2 + \lambda_O \left\| \mathbf{h}^T \mathbf{h} - \mathbf{I} \right\|^2 + \lambda_{AE} \left\| \mathbf{x} - \hat{\mathbf{x}} \right\|^2 \tag{6}$$

where λ_{RG}, λ_O, and λ_{AE} are the predetermined weights of regression performance, orthogonality, and data reconstruction cost, respectively. y and $\hat{y}$ denote the measured response variable and its prediction. $\mathbf{h}$ denotes the vector consisted of m explanatory latent features. $\mathbf{I}$ is a $k \times k$ identity matrix. $\mathbf{x}$ and $\hat{\mathbf{x}}$ are the sample vector and its reconstruction.

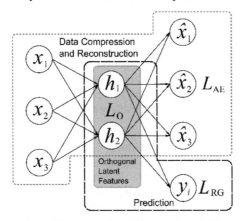

Figure 1   The architecture of our proposed modelling approach

Our proposed approach shares many similarities with PLSR, consequently benefiting from the numerous advantages offered by PLSR. The OAE section of our network is the equivalent to $\mathbf{X} = \mathbf{TP}^T + \mathbf{E}$ (Eq. 1) for compressing data, while the regression section resembles $\mathbf{Y} = \mathbf{UQ}^T + \mathbf{F}$ (Eq. 2). And the total training cost function has similar role to the manner of how data is decomposed in PLSR, which regulates OAE data compression in favour of finding uncorrelated explanatory latent features that have decent capabilities of modelling and predicting a response variable.

Beyond these similarities, our proposed approach provides two more advantages over PLSR and its nonlinear variants, therefore provides more flexibility for process engineers and operators: firstly, by choosing nonlinear activation functions such as ReLU and tanh for OAE and regression sections of the network, nonlinear mappings can be established with ease; secondly, the nature of neural network further allows our structure to be modified in needs of handling process data of various types and forms.

4. Case Studies

In order to assess the predictive performance of our proposed approach, case studies were conducted on two industrial benchmarks: the Tennessee Eastman Process (TEP) and the Benchmark Simulation Model No.2 (BSM-2). The TEP study primarily focused on the predictive performances under near-steady-state operations, whereas the BSM-2 study examined the predictions under nonlinear operating conditions. The weights of each regularisation term was set to $\lambda_{RG} : \lambda_O : \lambda_{AE} = 1 : 1 : 1$ for both studies. The predictive performances were evaluated by rooted mean squared error (RMSE) as well as coefficient of determination (R^2), and the results were compared with PCR, PLSR, and linear regression utilising latent features from a regular OAE (OAE-LLR).

4.1. Tennessee Eastman Process and Case Study Results

The Tennessee Eastman Process (Downs and Vogel, 1993) is a widely recognised chemical process benchmark simulator with a total of 52 process variables. In this study, 33 variables (xmeas 1 ~ 22 and xmv 1 ~ 11) were used as model inputs, while the remaining variables (xmeas 23 ~ 41) were considered as response variables. The dataset under normal operating condition (Rieth, et al., 2017) acquired from an upgraded version of TEP (Reinartz, et al., 2021) were partitioned into two potions with an 80:20 ratio for training and testing. The number of latent features was set to 15 according to Davide and Kulahci's work (2022) for all involved test methods.

The OAE section of our proposed approach consisted of an input layer (33 nodes), three encoder layers (75-50-30 nodes), a bottleneck layer (15 nodes), as well as the mirroring decoder and output layers. The augmented regression section started from the OAE bottleneck layer and concluded at the prediction output layer (1 node) with no hidden layer. For each of the 19 response variables, a neural network model was constructed. The linear activation function was selected based on preliminary tests. Due to spatial constraints, only a subsets of prediction results are presented in Table 1 and Figure 2.

4.2. Benchmark Simulation Model No.2 and Case Study Results

Benchmark Simulation Model No.2 (BSM-2) is another commonly utilised process simulator, that models a wastewater treatment plant featuring non-linear and long-term process dynamics (Gernaey, et al., 2014). In this research, 19 variables were used as model inputs (Table 2). Total nitrogen amount and dissolved nitrogen in the effluent were chosen as response variables due to their significant contributions to water pollution (Takeuchi and Yamashita, 2023). The dataset encompasses one year of operation with

Table 1 RMSE and R^2 scores using various modelling approaches for TEP

Response Variable	PCR		PLSR		OAE-LLR		Proposed Method	
	RMSE	R^2	RMSE	R^2	RMSE	R^2	RMSE	R^2
xmeas 23	0.665	0.572	0.633	0.672	0.662	0.575	0.578	0.676
xmeas 25	0.720	0.533	0.665	0.623	0.703	0.553	0.637	0.631
xmeas 26	0.827	0.331	0.795	0.473	0.813	0.379	0.733	0.474
xmeas 29	0.704	0.518	0.613	0.703	0.664	0.554	0.551	0.704
xmeas 38	0.719	0.511	0.709	0.637	0.721	0.511	0.606	0.650

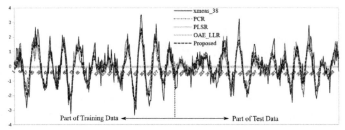

Figure 2   Part of predictions with various approaches for TEP *xmeas-38*

Table 2   Process variables of BSM-2 used for modelling

Flow rate (Influent)	Flow rate (Reactor 1)	Total suspended solid (Reactor 5)	Flow rate (Dewater inflow)
Temperature (Influent)	Temperature (Reactor 1)	Flow rate (Reject)	Temperature (Dewater inflow)
Flow rate (Primary clarifier overflow)	Dissolved O_2 (Reactor 3)	Temperature (Thickener inlet)	Flow rate (Sludge)
Temperature (Primary clarifier overflow)	Dissolved O_2 (Reactor 4)	Flow rate (Thickener overflow)	Temperature (Sludge)
Flow rate (Primary clarifier underflow)	Dissolved O_2 (Reactor 5)	Flow rate (Thickener underflow)	

15-minute sampling interval and has been partitioned into training and test portions with an 80:20 ratio. The number of latent features has been set to five for all involved test methods, since it was found by preliminary tests that 85% of total data information can be preserved with five principle components using PCA. The nodes of each layer in the OAE section of our proposed approach have been set to 19-36-24-12-5-12-24-36-19 using ReLU activation functions. The nodes in regression section has been set to 5-1 using linear activation functions. The predictive performances were listed in Table 3.

4.3. Overall Discussions

From the results of both studies, it can be observed that modelling using the latent variables from OAE generally performed better than using these from PCA, possibly due to the improved capture of process data pattern by utilising OAE rather than PCA. Furthermore, it can be observed from Figure 3 that our proposed approach was able to predict the overall trend of response variable better than PCR, OAE-LLR, and PLS. These studies clearly demonstrated that by integrating the evaluation of regression performances into the procedure of finding uncorrelated latent features, not only the linear and non-linear latent features of processes can be captured during the training of network, correlations between these latent features and response variables can also be identified simultaneously, thus enabling better modelling of soft sensors with improved predictive performances.

Table 3 RMSE and R^2 scores using various modelling approaches for BSM-2

	Response Variable	PCR	PLSR	OAE-LLR	Proposed Method
RMSE	Total nitrogen in effluent	0.998	0.956	0.940	0.848
	Dissolved nitrogen in effluent	0.697	0.652	0.671	0.562
R^2	Total nitrogen in effluent	0.002	0.148	0.07	0.335
	Dissolved nitrogen in effluent	0.232	0.346	0.117	0.575

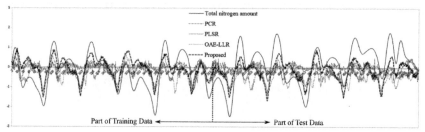

Figure 3 Part of predictions with various approaches for BSM-2 *Total Nitrogen*

5. Conclusions

In this study, we presented a simple, flexible, and effective approach for modelling data-driven soft sensors. An additional network structure was attached to the bottleneck layer of an orthogonal autoencoder for the purpose of predicting response variable. This proposed concept was tested by two industrial process benchmarks, demonstrating its capability of modelling soft sensors regardless of steady-state or nonlinear operation data. The results from the case studies illustrate the potential of our proposed method for modelling soft sensors, and we firmly believe that it can be further developed to fulfil various needs in process monitoring and operation.

References

P.M.L. Ching, R.H.Y. So, T. Morck, 2021, Advances in soft sensors for wastewater treatment plants: A systematic review, J. Water Proces. Eng., 44, 102367

C. Davide, M. Kulahci, 2022, A novel fault detection and diagnosis approach based on orthogonal auto-encoders, Compu. Chem. Eng., 163, 107853

J.J. Downs, E.F. Vogel, 1993, A plant-wide industrial process control problem. Comput. Chem. Eng., 17, 245 – 255

M. Ebrahimi, E.L. Gerber, T.D. Rockaway, 2017, Temporal performance assessment of wastewater treatment plants by using multi-variate statistical analysis, J. Environ. Manage., 193, 234 – 246

K.V. Gernaey, U. Jeppsson, P.A. Vanrolleghern, J.B. Copp, 2014, Benchmark of Control Strategies for Waste Water Treatment Plants, IWA Publishing, London, U.K.

C. Reinartz, M. Kulahci, O. Ravn, 2021, An extended Tennessee Eastman simulation dataset for fault-detection and decision support systems. Comput. Chem. Eng., 149, 107281

C.A. Rieth, B.D. Amsel, R. Tran, M.B. Cook, 2017, Additional Tennessee Eastman process simulation data for anomaly detection evaluation, Harvard Dataverse

A. Takeuchi, Y. Yamashita, Prediction of nitrogen content in effluent from waste water treatment plants using a data-driven model, 2023, The 66th Japan Joint Automatic Control Conference, October 7-8, 2023, Sendai, Japan

Flavio Manenti, Gintaras V. Reklaitis (Eds.), Proceedings of the 34th European Symposium on Computer Aided Process Engineering / 15th International Symposium on Process Systems Engineering (ESCAPE34/PSE24), June 2-6, 2024, Florence, Italy

Combining automated machine learning and molecular simulation to advance the discovery of COF-based membranes for acid gas separation

Bingru Xin[a], Minggao Feng[b], Min Cheng[c], Zhongde Dai[d], Li Zhou[a], Yiyang Dai[a]*, Xu Ji[a]*

[a]*College of Chemical Engineering, Sichuan University, Chengdu 610065, China*
[b]*Department of Chemistry and Materials Innovation Factory, University of Liverpool, Liverpool L7 3NY, UK*
[c]*BYD Company Ltd, No 5. Xiusha Road, Kenzie Town, Pingshan District, Shenzhen, Guangdong, 518122, P.R China*
[d]*College of Carbon Neutrality Future Technology, Sichuan University, Chengdu 610065, China*
* Corresponding Authors:Yiyang Dai: daiyy@scu.edu.cn ; *Xu Ji: jxhhpb@163.com

Abstract

Due to the rapid increase in the number of covalent organic frameworks (COFs), there is a need for efficient methods to quickly assess the properties of these materials. In this study, we used a combination of automated machine learning (ML) and molecular simulations to investigate the membrane permeability and selectivity of 811 curated COFs for acid gas (H_2S and CO_2) separation. An automated ML model was developed to directly predict membrane permeability based on 20 features obtained through fast computation. Next, we analysed the feature weights using SHAP and found that pore size and structural features had the highest correlation with gas permeability. Based on the feature knowledge and ML model we screened 69,840 hypothetical COFs (hCOFs) to obtain high-performance COFs without the need for expensive molecular simulations. Finally, the separation performance of COF/polymer mixed matrix membranes (MMMs) was evaluated under a ternary gas mixture system. This integrated approach of artificial intelligence and molecular simulations accurately and efficiently advances the discovery of high-performance COF membrane materials for acid gas separation and provides valuable insights for experimental and computational work.

Keywords: Covalent organic framework (COF), Machine learning, Molecular simulation, Acid gas separation, Membranes separation

1. Introduction

In the realm of fossil fuels, natural gas is widely recognized as the most environmentally beneficial alternative due to its minimal emission of pollutants during the combustion process. However, to optimize the efficiency of methane utilization, it is crucial to eliminate acid gas (H_2S, CO_2) from natural gas. Membrane separation method is a promising technology with the advantages of small footprint, low energy consumption and easy operation. The choice of membrane material is crucial to the performance of membrane separation. Covalent organic frameworks(COFs) are widely used in gas membrane separation applications as popular porous materials in recent years (Yuan et al., 2019).

For the study and characterization of material properties, traditional experimental methods are time-consuming and labor-intensive. In recent years, with the rapid development of computer technology, high-throughput computational screening (HTCS) methods for rapid study of large-scale material properties through molecular simulation (MS) can overcome the limitations of traditional experimental methods to a certain extent. In our previous work, the helium purification properties of 688 COFs were investigated by molecular simulation, and five high-performance COFs were finally obtained by the synergistic screening strategy of both He/CH$_4$ and He/N$_2$ systems (Feng et al., 2022).With the increasing amount of material in the database, traditional MS-based high-throughput methods require expensive computational costs. As an alternative, machine learning (ML) is increasingly popular for understanding complex structure-property relationships, predicting material properties, and expediting material discovery. Many researchers are now utilizing ML and molecular simulation (MS) to assess the performance of new materials. Cheng et al. screened adsorbents with high iodine adsorption performance from more than 12,020 MOFs by MS and constructed structure-property relationships by ML(Cheng et al., 2023). On the other hand, Onder Aksu and Keskin used ML and MS to explore the CH$_4$/H$_2$ separation performance of COFs(Onder Aksu and Keskin, 2023).

Although there are already several approaches on combining ML and MS for material screening, combining the interpretability of the models to quickly screen large amounts of data is a challenge. To the best of our knowledge, no systematic methodology has been developed to integrate model interpretability into the screening process of COFs. Therefore, the main goal of this study is to combine an automated ML and MS approach while integrating the chemical insights obtained from model interpretability for the rapid screening of COF materials in a large amount of chemical space, and ultimately to investigate and obtain high-performance COFs for acid gas membrane separation.

2. Methodology

This section describes the proposed workflow combining interpretable ML and MS for COF membrane discovery for acid gas separation in natural gas, as shown in Figure. 1.

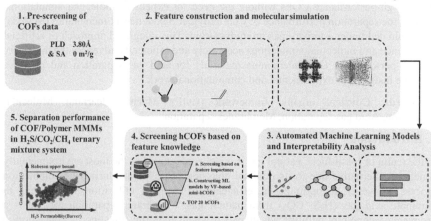

Figure 1. Workflow for interpretable ML-assisted discovery of innovative COF-based membranes with high performance.

The workflow is (1) Structural pre-screening of the CURATED-COFs database to exclude COFs with pore limiting diameter smaller than 3.80 Å (CH$_4$ kinetics diameter).

(2) Extract pore size, structural, atomic, and chemical property descriptors from COFs to be used as feature inputs for ML models. The feature dimension was 20 dimensions. The results of GCMC and MD simulations at 10 bar and 298 k were used as predictive properties. (3) The regression and tree models for predicting gas permeability were trained using the automated machine learning tool TPOT. Chemical insights were obtained by calculating SHAP values. (4) High-throughput permeability prediction using feature knowledge and machine learning for a large number of hCOFs. (5) Finally, molecular simulation of ternary gas mixtures under real conditions is performed for high-performance COFs to obtain optimal COF materials.

2.1. Datasets and Features

In this work, we choose two databases, CUTARED-COFs (Ongari et al., 2019) and hCOFs,(Mercado et al., 2018) as candidate materials. The former is an automatic recognition grabbing of the current experimentally synthesized COFs with several 788. The latter is the computer-virtual synthesized COFs with number up to 69654. COFs with PLD less than 3.8Å were excluded from the calculation. All features are listed in Table 1.

Table 1. List of features of COFs used for ML model

Descriptor type	Feature		Unit
Pore size descriptors	Largest cavity diameter (LCD)		Å
	Pore limiting diameter (PLD)		Å
Structure descriptors	Density (ρ)		g/cm^3
	Surface area (SA)		m^2/g
	Pore volume (PV)		cm^3/g
	Void fraction (VF)		-
	Dimensions (D)		
Atomic descriptors	C%	H%	
	N%	O%	
	S%	Halogen %	-
	Metalloid %	Metal %	
	Nitrogen-to-Oxygen (N-to-O)		
Chemical property descriptor	Total degree of unsaturation (TDU)		
	Degree of unsaturation per carbon (DUC)		-
	Total electronegativity (TE)		
	Atomic weighted electronegativity (AWE)		

2.2. Molecular Simulation & Calculation of Membrane

The adsorption (N_i) and diffusion (D_i) characteristics of all CURATED-COFs were evaluated by GCMC with MD for three single-component gases (H_2S, CO_2, CH_4) at 298k, 10 bar. Along with the N_i properties, the D_i of gas molecules through the COFs' pores are calculated for membrane-based gas separations. After obtaining the molecular simulation data on the permeability of COFs, the gas permeability of the mixed matrix membrane can be calculated by combining it with the permeability data of the experimental polymers based on Maxwell's theoretical permeation model. Detailed computational parameters for molecular simulations and membrane calculations can be found in our previous work. (Feng et al., 2022)

2.3. Automated Machine Learning and Interpretable Analysis

Four sets of descriptors are used as input features to construct a ML model. The Tree-based Pipeline Optimization Tool (TPOT), an automated machine learning tool, is employed for this purpose.(Olson and Moore, 2019) To ensure reliable results, the data is divided into an 80% training set and a 20% test set, with stratified sampling implemented to maintain consistent feature distribution. To prevent overfitting, a 50% discount cross-validation is utilized. The effectiveness of the model is evaluated using four metrics: coefficient of determination (R^2), root mean square error (RMSE), mean absolute error (MAE), and Spearman's rank correlation coefficient (SRCC). Shapley additive explanations(SHAP) analysis is an effective tool for machine learning model interpretability(Yang et al., 2022). In this model, all features are regarded as "contributors" to the predicted value, leading to the computation of SHAP values. The selection of the best machine learning algorithm, as determined by TPOT, varies depending on the prediction tasks at hand. For each ML model, we utilize the corresponding SHAP interpreter, specifically the tree-based explainer and the linear-based explainer.

3. Results

3.1. Structure-Performance Analysis

Based on the data obtained from GCMC and MD simulations, the gas permeability of the COF membrane was calculated. Figure 2. shows the separation performance of H_2S/CH_4 (a.) and CO_2/CH_4 (b.) for COF membranes at 298k and 10 bar, respectively. The color gradient in the figure represents the size of the void fraction. Like polymers, COF membranes exhibit a trade-off between permeability and selectivity, with only a few COFs approaching the Robeson upper bound. The classification of COF gradients based on void fraction demonstrates the positive impact of high VF on membrane performance. This finding can be further validated through subsequent interpretable ML techniques.

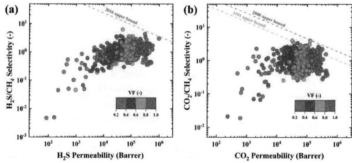

Figure 2. H_2S permeability and H_2S/CH_4 selectivity (a), CO_2 permeability and CO_2/CH_4 selectivity (b) of COF membranes at 10bar, 298K. The VF indicates void fraction.

3.2. ML Model Prediction

The model input comprised 19-dimensional features by excluding features with a Pearson correlation coefficient exceeding 0.9. Figure 3a demonstrates the direct construction of ML model for predicting H_2S permeability, which is superior to predicting adsorption and diffusion first and then calculating gas permeability. Subsequently, we explored the extent to which features contribute to the prediction model. Figure 3b shows the order of importance of the features used to predict H_2S permeability (displaying only the top six). Pore size and structure descriptors are the most important descriptor types, while atomic and chemical descriptors contribute to a lesser extent. Void fraction is the most contributing feature in all models. Consistent findings were observed in experimental studies on the effect of porosity and pore size on the membrane effectiveness of porous materials (Ying et al., 2022).

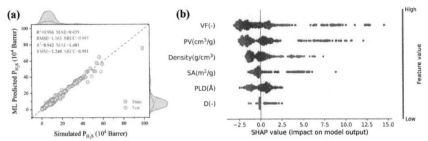

Figure 3. Marginal distribution scatter plots of H2S permeability predicted by ML compared with molecular simulation results and SHAP feature importance distribution.

3.3. Rapid screening of hCOFs

Using the previously acquired key features, we have successfully pre-screened hCOFs, resulting in the identification of 14,956 potential candidate COFs (cCOFs). We then uniformly sampled cCOFs based on VF to obtain 500 mini-cCOFs for molecular simulation calculations and merged them with the data of CURATED-COFs for a total of 1300 data points to construct ML models. The MSE of the H2S permeability prediction test is 2.45, and the R^2 is 0.953, which indicates the high prediction accuracy of the ML models. Figure 4 shows the "permeability-selectivity" distribution of hCOFs obtained for training and prediction, where the orange data represents the data used to participate in training the model in cCOFs, and the blue data points represent the COFs data obtained from ML prediction.

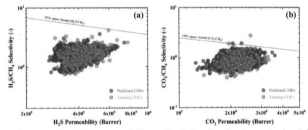

Figure 4. H2S/CH4 & CO2/CH4 permeability-selectivity distributions obtained from hCOFs database after ML projection.

3.4. TOP COFs

Finally, we selected 20 advanced COFs designed for single-component gas separation and evaluated their performance under real operating conditions with ternary mixtures. Our research revealed that JUC-551-2 was the top-performing COF and other TOP COFs are shown in Table 2 and Figure 5.

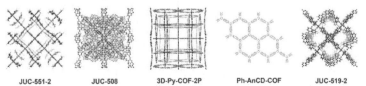

JUC-551-2   JUC-508   3D-Py-COF-2P   Ph-AnCD-COF   JUC-519-2

Figure 5. Structure of TOP-5 CURATED-COFs for acid gas separation of the membrane.

Table.2 Separation performances of the Top-5 CURATED-COFs

COFs	PLD (Å)	VF (-)	Di (-)	P_{H_2S} (Barrer)	P_{CO_2} (Barrer)	S_{H_2S/CH_4} (-)	S_{CO_2/CH_4} (-)
JUC-551-2	10.1	0.91	3D	4.19×10^5	3.02×10^5	5.46	3.93
JUC-508	8.9	0.87	3D	6.01×10^5	1.85×10^5	5.19	1.60
3D-Py-COF-2P	12.3	0.91	3D	5.31×10^5	2.88×10^5	4.23	2.29
Ph-AnCD-COF	21.1	0.91	2D	3.70×10^5	2.30×10^5	4.70	2.92
JUC-519-2	8.9	0.89	3D	3.83×10^5	3.12×10^5	3.54	2.90

To further enhance separation performance, we explored the potential of combining the top five COFs with six different polymers, resulting in the development of MMMs. This approach successfully boosted the permeability of the polymer membranes, without compromising their selectivity.

Conclusions

In this work, the performance of COF-based membranes for acid gas separation is systematically investigated. The workflow combining automated ML and MS shows well the exploration process of high-performance COF materials. Interpretability helps to extract the necessary feature knowledge helping us to quickly explore the material space in the unknown chemical space. The method provides an integrated working idea for future experimental discovery and design of optimal COF-based membranes.

References

Cheng, M., Zhang, Z., Wang, S., Bi, K., Hu, K., Dai, Z., Dai, Y., Liu, C., Zhou, L., Ji, X., Shi, W., 2023. A large-scale screening of metal-organic frameworks for iodine capture combining molecular simulation and machine learning. Front. Environ. Sci. Eng. 17, 148.

Feng, M., Cheng, M., Deng, J., Ji, X., Zhou, L., Dang, Y., Bi, K., Dai, Z., Dai, Y., 2022. High-throughput computational screening of Covalent−Organic framework membranes for helium purification. Results Eng. 15, 100538.

Li, H., Chang, J., Li, S., Guan, X., Li, D., Li, C., Tang, L., Xue, M., Yan, Y., Valtchev, V., Qiu, S., Fang, Q., 2019. Three-Dimensional Tetrathiafulvalene-Based Covalent Organic Frameworks for Tunable Electrical Conductivity. J. Am. Chem. Soc. 141, 13324–13329.

Mercado, R., Fu, R.-S., Yakutovich, A.V., Talirz, L., Haranczyk, M., Smit, B., 2018. In Silico Design of 2D and 3D Covalent Organic Frameworks for Methane Storage Applications. Chem. Mater. 30, 5069–5086.

Olson, R.S., Moore, J.H., 2019. TPOT: A Tree-Based Pipeline Optimization Tool for Automating Machine Learning, in: Hutter, F., Kotthoff, L., Vanschoren, J. (Eds.), Automated Machine Learning, The Springer Series on Challenges in Machine Learning. Springer International Publishing, Cham, pp. 151–160.

Onder Aksu, G., Keskin, S., 2023. Advancing CH 4 /H 2 separation with covalent organic frameworks by combining molecular simulations and machine learning. J. Mater. Chem. A.

Ongari, D., Yakutovich, A.V., Talirz, L., Smit, B., 2019. Building a Consistent and Reproducible Database for Adsorption Evaluation in Covalent–Organic Frameworks. ACS Cent. Sci. 5, 1663–1675.

Yang, J., Tao, L., He, J., McCutcheon, J.R., Li, Y., 2022. Machine learning enables interpretable discovery of innovative polymers for gas separation membranes. Sci. Adv. 8, eabn9545.

Ying, Y., Peh, S.B., Yang, H., Yang, Z., Zhao, D., 2022. Ultrathin Covalent Organic Framework Membranes via a Multi-Interfacial Engineering Strategy for Gas Separation. Adv. Mater. 34, 2104946.

Yuan, S., Li, X., Zhu, J., Zhang, G., Van Puyvelde, P., Van Der Bruggen, B., 2019. Covalent organic frameworks for membrane separation. Chem. Soc. Rev. 48, 2665–2681.

Flavio Manenti, Gintaras V. Reklaitis (Eds.), Proceedings of the 34th European Symposium on Computer Aided Process Engineering / 15th International Symposium on Process Systems Engineering (ESCAPE34/PSE24), June 2-6, 2024, Florence, Italy

Prediction Method for Reaction Yield of Deuteration of Polyfluoroperylene using Generative AI Techniques

Kazuhiro Takeda,[a*] Naoya Ohtsuka,[b,c] Toshiyasu Suzuki,[b] and Norie Momiyama[b,c]

[a]*Department of Applied Chemistry and Biochemical Engineering, Shizuoka University, Hamamatsu, Shizuoka, 4328561, Japan*
[b]*Institute for Molecular Science, Okazaki, Aichi, 4448787, Japan*
[c]*Molecular Science Program, Graduate Institute for Advanced Studies, SOKENDAI, Okazaki, Aichi, 4448787, Japan*
takeda.kazuhiro@shizuoka.ac.jp

Abstract

Deuterated organic electroluminescent materials are gaining interest due to their enhanced luminous efficiency and durability with applications spanning academia and industry (Saito et al., 1994). Perylene is a typical organic molecule for organic light-emitting devices. Deuterated polyfluoroperylene (PFDPR), in which the hydrogen of the polyfluoroperylene is replaced by a deuterium, has potential as a new luminescent material. However, synthesizing PFDPR is challenging due to the complexity and scale of the required deuteration processes. On the other hand, in machine learning, large amounts of data are required to improve the estimation accuracy. Takeda et al. (2023) has proposed the virtual variables-enabled generation of datasets for the prediction of the yield of the iodination reactions of the polyfluoronaphthalenes. Using this method, this study proposes a model to estimate the non-experimental yield of PFDPR with a high accuracy from a small amount of data. The experimental conditions investigated in this study were two variables; i.e., temperature and time, across 16 conditions. While comprehensive data for the polyfluoronaphthalenes were fully available, the polyfluoroperylene data were limited to only 8 conditions. the experimental data from polyfluoronaphthalenes determined the yield prediction of the polyfluoroperylene under untested conditions. This process involved optimization using virtual variables to maximize the coefficient of determination between the actual and predicted yields of PFDPR. The model's efficacy is highlighted by the close alignment of the predicted and actual yields, offering a promising tool for accelerating the PFDPR synthesis research.
Keywords: generative artificial intelligence; small data; prediction of reaction conditions; in-silico data generation; digitalization of organic molecules.

1. Introduction

Deuterated organic electroluminescent materials have been reported to improve the luminous efficiency and durability, thus are attracting attention in industry (Saito et al., 1994). Perylene is a typical organic molecule for organic light-emitting devices. We have recently developed an efficient synthesis of polyfluoronaphthalene (Ohtsuka et al., 2023, Takeda et al., 2023). Furthermore, the synthetic method has been successfully applied and developed to synthesize polyfluoroperylene (F8), a fluorine-modified in eight positions (in preparation for submission). Deuterated F8 (deuterated polyfluoroperylene;

PFDPR), in which the hydrogen of F8 is replaced by a deuterium, has the potential as a new luminescent material. However, the synthesis of F8 requires multiple steps and it is difficult to synthesize large quantities of F8 as it requires numerous deuteration experiments. When assessing the luminescence properties, it is necessary to fully scrutinize whether all four of the hydrogen atoms are deuterated or partially deuterated in the organic material.

On the other hand, machine learning has been used to try to determine the conditions for a chemical reaction (Struble et al., 2020). Many algorithms for machine learning have been proposed. PyCaret (2020) can treat 26 algorithms, such as 'Linear Regression', 'Lasso Regression', 'Ridge Regression', 'Elastic Net', 'Least Angle Regression', 'Lasso Least Angle Regression', 'Orthogonal Matching Pursuit', 'Bayesian Ridge', 'Automatic Relevance Determination', 'Passive Aggressive Regressor', 'Random Sample Consensus', 'TheilSen Regressor', 'Huber Regressor', 'Kernel Ridge', 'Support Vector Regression', 'K Neighbors Regressor', 'Decision Tree Regressor', 'Random Forest Regressor', 'Extra Trees Regressor', 'AdaBoost Regressor', 'Gradient Boosting Regressor', 'MLP Regressor', 'Extreme Gradient Boosting', 'Light Gradient Boosting Machine', 'CatBoost Regressor', and 'Dummy Regressor'. When the experimental data for F8 is limited, the algorithm employing Bayesian optimization can effectively identify the optimal conditions using limited data (Kondo et al., 2023). However, this algorithm does not offer explainable insights into the reaction mechanisms as it primarily processes data through a statistical analysis. Takeda et al. (2023) has proposed a generative machine learning method with virtual variables (GMLV) to predict results under non-experimental conditions (Figure 1). The GMLV can also contribute to the understanding of the reaction mechanism as the virtual variables represent the relationships between the reactants. In this study, we report the development of a predictive model for the deuteration of F8 using the GMLV.

2. Generative Machine Learning Method with Virtual Variables

The algorithm of GMLV (Takeda et al., 2023) is illustrated in Figure 1. This algorithm is based on a dual-loop structure. To express the relationship between the objective reactants, virtual variables were assumed in the outer loop. The optimal value of each virtual variable was investigated in the inner loop by maximizing the evaluation value. The Bayesian optimization method, which can determine the optimal value even with a small number of trials (Kondo et al., 2023), was used for the investigations. Therefore, in the outer loop, the explanatory variables were virtual variables, and the objective function was the optimizing inner loop. In the inner loop, the non-experimental yields were assumed and the coefficient of determination R^2 for the experimental and assumed non-experimental yields was maximized. As there were multiple assumed yields in the investigation, a dual-annealing optimization method, which is less likely to fall into local solutions (Xiang et al. 1997), was used, and the minimum value obtained after three trials was adopted. The yield surface was predicted using SVR (Vapnik, 1995), which is most suitable for predicting experimental yields. This study developed a more precise regression model by incorporating additional appropriate samples. A reaction space model was constructed, representing yield as a function of time and temperature. This involved using assumed yield data for conditions not experimentally tested. The model's explanatory variables included both the experimented time and temperature, and virtual variables representing the relationship between the reactants. The inner loop's objective function aimed to maximize the R-squared (R^2) value, enhancing the predictive accuracy for both the experimental and assumed non-experimental yields. Consequently, the non-experimental yield that optimizes R^2 is considered most fitting for this model. Additionally, the optimized virtual variables establish a more accurate relationship between the objective reactants.

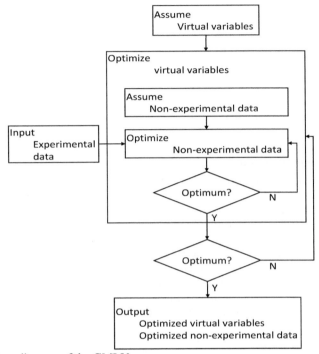

Figure 1: Flow diagram of the GMLV.

3. Objective Reactants and Conditions

Figure 2 illustrates the various fluorinated naphthalenes and perylenes used in the study. 1,2,3,4,5,6,8-Heptafluoronaphthalene, a naphthalene derivative with seven fluorine atoms, is denoted as 'F7'. There are two types of hexafluoronaphthalenes, modified with six fluorine atoms; i.e., 1,2,4,5,7,8-hexafluoronaphthalene ('3,6H-F6') and 1,2,4,5,6,8-hexafluoronaphthalene ('3,7H-F6'). Similarly, 1,3,4,6,7,9,10,12-octafluoroperylene, a perylene variant with eight fluorine atoms, was labeled as 'F8'.

In the magnesiation process, polyfluoronaphthalene and polyfluoroperylene were treated with $Mg(TMP)_2 \cdot 2LiBr$ in 0.13 M THF solvent and subsequently deuterated using 0.5 mL D_2O. The $Mg(TMP)_2 \cdot 2LiBr$ equivalents used were 1.2 for F7, 2.4 for F6, and 4.8 for F8. In our experiments, both hydrogens in F6 were fully deuterated. For F8, depending on whether one, two, three, or all four hydrogens are deuterated, the compounds were referred to as D1, D2, D3, and D4, respectively. The reactions were conducted at temperatures of -78 °C, -40 °C, 0 °C, and 25 °C, and for durations of 0.5 h, 1.0 h, 2.0 h, or 4.0 h.

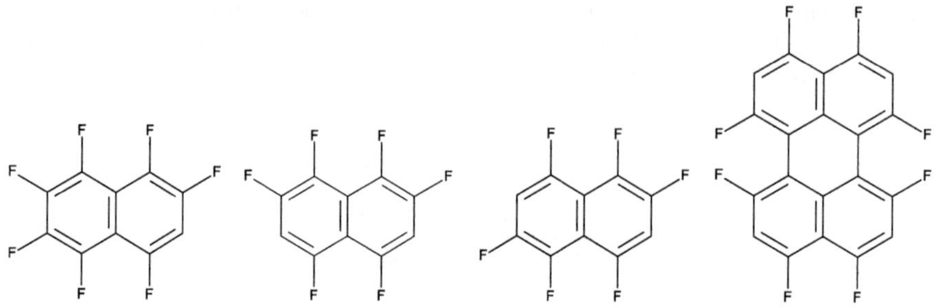

F7   3,6H-F6   3,7H-F6   F8

Figure 2 Structures of polyfluoronaphthalenes and polyfluoroperylene.

4. Results and Discussion

For F6 (both 3,6H-F6 and 3,7H-F6) and F7, the deuteration yields were determined across 16 different conditions, varying in 4 reaction temperatures and 4 reaction times. In contrast, for F8, the deuteration yields were obtained under eight specific conditions: (-78 °C, 4.0 h), (-40 °C, 4.0 h), (-40 °C, 0.5 h), (0 °C, 4.0 h), (0 °C, 2.0 h), (0 °C, 1.0 h), (0 °C, 0.5 h), and (25 °C, 0.5 h). Average yields from multiple experiments under identical conditions are presented in Table 1. While D4 was identifiable, D1, D2, and D3 were not; thus, the products were categorized into D1-D3, D4, and D1-D4 groups. The yield for D1-D4 is the cumulative yield of D1-D3 and D4. These datasets were then utilized for model training. The model's predicted yields were subsequently validated against new experimental data, as detailed in Table 2.

Table 1: Mean yields for training regarding the various reaction temperatures and times.

Temperature (°C)	Time (h)	Deuteration yield (%)				
		F7	F6		F8	
			3,6H-F6	3,7H-F6	D1-D3	D4
-78.0	0.5	85.5	83.5	81.0	-	-
-78.0	1.0	86.0	83.0	85.0	-	-
-78.0	2.0	83.5	82.5	86.0	-	-
-78.0	4.0	86.0	85.0	86.0	78.0	7.0
-40.0	0.5	87.0	85.5	86.0	74.0	10.0
-40.0	1.0	86.5	84.5	85.0	-	-
-40.0	2.0	83.0	83.5	88.0	-	-
-40.0	4.0	76.0	84.5	89.0	65.0	16.0
0.0	0.5	85.0	81.5	87.0	76.0	13.0
0.0	1.0	85.0	82.5	88.0	58.0	35.0
0.0	2.0	46.0	83.0	89.0	50.0	46.0
0.0	4.0	12.5	70.5	89.0	36.0	53.0
25.0	0.5	2.0	83.5	86.0	18.0	25.0
25.0	1.0	0.0	77.5	88.0	-	-
25.0	2.0	0.0	63.0	86.0	-	-
25.0	4.0	0.0	54.5	83.0	-	-

Table 2: Mean yields for validating the various reaction temperatures and times.

Temperature (°C)	Time (h)	Deuteration yield of F8 (%)	
		D1-D3	D4
25.0	1.5	8.0	15.0
25.0	3.5	0.0	0.0
-40.0	2.0	70.0	15.0
15.0	3.0	9.0	24.0
30.0	3.0	0.0	0.0
0.0	3.0	38.0	52.0
40.0	3.0	0.0	0.0
-20.0	2.0	63.0	27.0
50.0	3.0	0.0	0.0

Table 3 displays the predictive performance of the various models for the studied products. To compare with the proposed models, 26 different models from PyCaret (2020) were assessed. These models were evaluated based on the temperature, time, and yields of D1-D3, D4, and D1-D4 from the training datasets. The evaluation criteria focused on the R-squared (R^2) value as the objective function, utilizing a 2-fold (k=2) cross-validation algorithm. The best models for D1-D3, D4, and D1-D4 were 'Light Gradient Boosting Machine: LGBM', 'Multi Layer Perceptron Regressor: MLP', and 'Gradient Boosting Regressor: GBR' respectively. The predicted results for F8 were evaluated with the mean absolute error (MAE), root mean squared error (RMSE), and R^2 for training and validating datasets. Although the proposed models had less performance than the other models for the training datasets without D1-D3, the proposed models had more performance than the other models for all the validating datasets. Therefore, the proposed models can accurately predict the yields for the non-experimental conditions.

Table 3: Predicting performance of various models for products.

Product	Model	Training			Validation		
		MAE	RMSE	R^2	MAE	RMSE	R^2
D1-D3	Proposed model	12.984	19.850	0.005	10.068	10.274	0.855
	LGBM	20.675	22.968	-0.333	33.889	36.420	-0.828
D4	Proposed model	15.723	21.296	-0.731	13.819	17.653	-0.125
	MLP	10.330	13.934	0.259	35.791	41.788	-5.303
D1-D4	Proposed model	14.789	19.170	-0.509	15.902	18.948	0.762
	GBR	5.457	10.016	0.588	39.833	48.608	-0.564

The optimized virtual variable ratios were established as (1:2:-2.6:-2.6) for (3,6HF6:3,7HF6:F7:F8) in the case of the D1-D3 yields. For D4, the ratio was set as (2:1:0.01) for (3,7HF6:F7:F8), and for the D1-D4 yields, it was (2:1:1.36) for (3,6HF6:F7:F8). The nearest descriptors by the standard scaled distance to the optimized variables were IC3 or SIC1 for D1-D3, AATSC6s or SM1_Dzv for D4, and Psi_i_0d or GATS6v for D1-D4. Based on these optimized variables and the nearest descriptors, the F8 yields were inferred as follows: the D1-D3 yields were mainly affected by the variety of atoms within 1 or 3 bonds of 3,6HF6, 3,7HF6, F7, and F8. For the D4 yields, the major influences were autocorrelation of the nearest 6 atoms weighted by the intrinsic state or spectral moment weighted by Van-der-Waals volume of 3,7HF6, F7, and F8. Lastly, the D1-D4 yields were primarily determined by the intrinsic state of atoms or autocorrelation of the nearest 6 atoms weighted by Van-der-Waals volume associated with 3,6HF6, F7, and F8. These results indicated that the yields of D1-D3 and D4 were, respectively, affected by atoms within 1 or 3 bonds and atoms within 6 bonds.

Conclusions

This study introduces a novel predictive model for the deuteration yield of polyfluoroperylene, leveraging advanced generative AI techniques. This model stands out in its ability to provide dependable and plausible yield estimates for experimental conditions that have not yet been tested. Key to this model's effectiveness is the virtual variables, which serve as ideal descriptors to represent the relationships between the reactants. Through this approach, we offer a significant tool for streamlining and guiding future experimental research in the field of organic electroluminescent materials.

Acknowledgments

This work was financially supported by a Grant-in-Aid for Transformative Research Areas (A) (Grant Number JP21H05222 and JP21H05218) for Digitalization-driven Transformative Organic Synthesis (Digi-TOS) from the Ministry of Education, Culture, Sports, Science, and Technology (MEXT), Japan. Part of this study was conducted at the Institute for Molecular Science and supported by the Advanced Research Infrastructure for Materials and Nanotechnology in Japan (Organic Synthesis DX No. JPMXP1222MS5042 and No. JPMXP1223MS5005) from MEXT, Japan.

References

M. Kondo, H. D. P. Wathsala, K. Ishikawa, D. Yamashita, T. Miyazaki, Y. Ohno, H. Sasai, T. Washio, and S. Takizawa, 2023, Bayesian Optimization-Assisted Screening to Identify Improved Reaction Conditions for Spiro-Dithiolane Synthesis, Molecules, 28, 13, 5180

N. Ohtsuka, H. Ota, S. Sugiura, S. Kakinuma, H. Sugiyama, T. Suzuki, and N. Momiyama, 2023, Perfluorohalogenated Naphthalenes: Synthesis, Crystal Structure, and Intermolecular Interaction, ChemRxiv. Cambridge: Cambridge Open Engage

PyCaret: An open source, low-code machine learning library in Python, 2020, https://www.pycaret.org

S. Saito, M. Nagaoka, T. Nagatomo, and O. Omoto, 1994, Color Variations in Light Emission from Perylene Doped Organic EL Device, The Institute of Image Information and Television Engineers, 18, 2, 65–70

T. J. Struble, T.J., Alvarez, J.C., Brown, S.P., Chytil, M., Cisar, J., DesJarlais, R.L., Engkvist, O., Frank, S.A., Greve, D.R., Griffin, D.J., et al., 2020, Current and Future Roles of Artificial Intelligence in Medicinal Chemistry Synthesis, J. Med. Chem., 63, 8667–8682

K. Takeda, N. Ohtsuka, T. Suzuki, and N. Momiyama, 2023, Virtual Variables-Enabled Generation of Datasets for Prediction in Organic Synthesis: Digitalization of Small Molecules and Its Application to Functional Molecule Syntheses, ChemRxiv. Cambridge: Cambridge Open Engage

V. Vapnik, 1995, The Nature of Statistical Learning Theory, Springer, New York

Y. Xiang, D. Y. Sun, W. Fan, and X. G. Gong, 1997, Generalized Simulated Annealing Algorithm and its Application to the Thomson Model, Physics Letters A, 233, 3, 216–220

Flavio Manenti, Gintaras V. Reklaitis (Eds.), Proceedings of the 34th European Symposium on Computer Aided Process Engineering / 15th International Symposium on Process Systems Engineering (ESCAPE34/PSE24), June 2-6, 2024, Florence, Italy

Enhancing Fault Identification in Chemical Plants: A Multimodal Approach Combining CNN and Continuous Wavelet Transform

Chinatsu Ukawa[a], Yoshiyuki Yamashita[a*]

[a]*Tokyo University of Agriculture and Technology, 2-24-16 Naka-cho, Koganei, Tokyo 184-8588, JAPAN*
*yama_pse@cc.tuat.ac.jp

Abstract

Fault detection and identification is a crucial task to ensure safe and stable operation of chemical plants. This study introduces a novel multimodal model that incorporates a continuous wavelet transform (CWT) along with two distinct convolutional neural networks (CNN): a two-dimensional CNN (2DCNN) and a three-dimensional CNN (3DCNN). Utilizing a time-shifting window, multivariate time series data from chemical plants are segmented, with the resulting segments combined into two-dimensional input data. Prior to the combination, the data were transformed into scalograms using CWT. The multimodal model processes these 2D and 3D input data, producing outputs that indicate the occurrence of faults in the chemical plant processes. We applied the proposed method to the Tennessee Eastman process (TEP) dataset. The proposed method showed superior accuracy in fault identification compared to existing methods.

Keywords: Fault Identification, Continuous Wavelet Transform, Three-dimensional convolutional neural network

1. Introduction

Fault detection and identification is one of the most important steps in chemical process monitoring to ensure safe, stable, and efficient operation. Up to now, numerous studies have been conducted due to the aforementioned fact that fault detection and identification are essential for chemical process monitoring. In recent years, a variety of deep learning methods have been applied to this field due to the exponential growth of computer technology. There are a lot of types of deep learning methods. For instance, CNN, deep belief network, autoencoder, long short-term memory, and recurrent neural network (Chen et al., 2022).

In our previous work, we introduced the fault detection and identification model using CWT and 3DCNN (Ukawa et al., 2023). Although the model showed good performance on about half of the process conditions of the TEP datasets, the accuracy of the normal operating condition and some of the faulty condition showed lower accuracy than other comparative models. We had assumed that this was due to the lack of information about the absolute values of the chemical process data, which occurs when CWT is used to pre-process the original data. Therefore, in this paper, we propose a novel multimodal model using CWT and two types of CNN: 2DCNN and 3DCNN, to retain and effectively use the absolute values of chemical process data.

2. Method

2.1. CWT

CWT is one of the wavelet transforms which is used for signal and image processing. The wavelet function is shown in equation 1. The parameter a represents the scale index which determines the center frequency of the function ψ (a^{-1}(t-b)). The parameter b indicates the time shifting.

$$W_x(a, b) = \frac{1}{\sqrt{a}} \int_{-\infty}^{\infty} x(t)\psi^* \left(\frac{t-b}{a}\right) dt \tag{1}$$

CWT generates scalograms from original signal data. Scalograms are the plot of the CWT coefficient and show the feature on the time-frequency domain. The application of spectrograms has been reported in various fields.

2.2. 2DCNN and 3DCNN

The CNN has been widely used for various types of research. Especially, 2DCNN has gotten attention because of its high ability in the fields of image recognition, action recognition, medical imaging, and machinery. It is also used for research on process systems engineering and demonstrated good performance (Zhu et al., 2019) (Wu et al., 2018) (Chen et al., 2022).

3DCNN has garnered attention in the fields of action recognition (Liu et al., 2019) and 3D image analysis (Riahi et al., 2022). It is the logical extension of 2DCNN. The 2DCNN uses 2D convolution filter to extract the features of the 2D images. This process will be conducted for each channel of the input images. On the other hand, 3DCNN uses 3D filters and extracts the features of all channels or all dimensions simultaneously. Due to this characteristic, 3DCNNs enable feature extraction from data while preserving relationships across channels or dimensions. In this study, 3DCNN was used to deal with 3 dimensions: time, frequency, and process variables.

2.3. Proposed method

The approach involves the following steps: initially, the process data is divided by applying a moving time window to each process variable. This segmentation process results in 2D input data derived from segments of each process variable, which is subsequently prepared for the 2DCNN model. These segments transform into spectrograms through CWT, capturing the unique features of chemical process data in the time-frequency domain. After this preprocessing, 3D input data is generated for the 3DCNN. A multimodal model is then trained, integrating both 2D and 3D data, with the output representing various process states, encompassing normal operation and fault conditions.

3. Case study

The proposed model was evaluated using TEP datasets introduced by Rieth et al. (2017). This process consists of five main units: a reactor, a condenser, a stripper, a separator, and a compressor. There are 52 process variables including 41 measured variables and 11 manipulated variables. In this study, we used 33 variables including 22 measured variables and all manipulated variables.

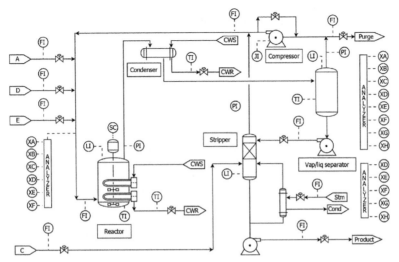

Figure 1 The TEP flow sheet

4. Result

4.1. Evaluation metrics

We assessed the suggested approach and analyzed its effectiveness by examining the fault detection rate (FDR) and false positive rate (FPR). In this context, *TP* denotes true positive, while *FN* signifies false negative.

$$\text{Fault Detection Rate (FDR)} = \frac{TP}{TP + FP} \tag{2}$$

$$\text{False Positive Rate (FPR)} = \frac{FP}{FP + TP} \tag{3}$$

4.2. Comparison of the application result

Table 1 shows a comparison of model accuracies of 2DCNN, CWT-3DCNN, and Multimodal CWT-3DCNN. The accuracy average of CWT-3DCNN is lower than the 2DCNN model although it demonstrated better performance on half of the faults. On the other hand, multimodal CWT-3DCNN accomplished the best performance comparing the accuracy average. The accuracy of the normal operation condition is still not high, but it is improved compared with the previous CWT-3DCNN model. In the case When 2DCNN and CWT-3DCNN have scores of 0.8 or higher, the score of multimodal CWT-3DCNN becomes higher than that of 2DCNN and CWT-3DCNN. The average of FDR shows the best score among the three models. It indicates that using the time-frequency information with absolute values is possible to further improve and enhance the ability of the CNN model for fault detection and identification.

Table 1 Comparison of model accuracies

	2DCNN		CWT-3DCNN-W20		Multimodal	
Fault	FDR	FPR	FDR	FPR	FDR	FPR
0	0.935	0.222	0.166	0.031	0.342	0.031
1	0.825	0.000	0.979	0.004	0.988	0.002
2	0.826	0.000	0.974	0.001	0.983	0.000
3	0.392	0.014	0.479	0.064	0.629	0.042
4	0.950	0.000	0.969	0.001	0.990	0.000
5	0.825	0.000	0.964	0.002	0.987	0.012
6	0.815	0.000	0.988	0.002	0.712	0.002
7	0.825	0.000	0.951	0.005	0.999	0.001
8	0.831	0.000	0.789	0.009	0.887	0.003
9	0.026	0.004	0.183	0.061	0.288	0.055
10	0.811	0.002	0.596	0.033	0.819	0.005
11	0.932	0.000	0.702	0.020	0.979	0.001
12	0.803	0.001	0.739	0.004	0.769	0.007
13	0.805	0.000	0.864	0.006	0.901	0.005
14	0.967	0.000	0.879	0.018	0.995	0.000
15	0.083	0.009	0.193	0.052	0.392	0.087
16	0.784	0.001	0.675	0.015	0.859	0.005
17	0.936	0.000	0.906	0.005	0.953	0.001
18	0.829	0.001	0.771	0.010	0.808	0.007
19	0.937	0.000	0.483	0.033	0.955	0.003
20	0.883	0.000	0.894	0.006	0.934	0.002
AVERAGE	0.763	0.012	0.721	0.018	0.817	0.013
MEDIAN	0.825	0.000	0.789	0.009	0.901	0.003
VARIANCE	0.0660	0.0022	0.0715	0.0004	0.0480	0.0005

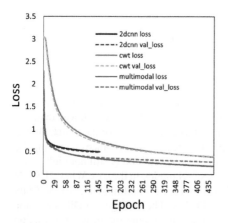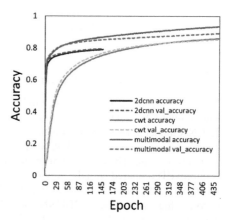

Figure 2 Training history of the accuracy and the loss

5. Discussion

5.1. Model Training

Figure 2 shows the learning history of the models. CWT-3DCNN models can achieve higher accuracy than the 2DCNN model in exchange for the long training time. The proposed Multimodal model demonstrates the highest accuracy among the comparing models. CWT-3DCNN models are found to be less prone to overfitting even when trained for extended periods, as compared to other models.

5.2. Batch size

Batch size affects the learning speed and model accuracy. We investigated the difference in the accuracy between the models which have different batch sizes. We selected 64, 128, 256, 512, and 1024 for batch size. Table 2 shows the result comparison. The best batch size is 512. The optimized batch size can contribute to shorten model training time.

Table 2 Result comparison of the models with different batch sizes.

	Batch size									
	64		128		256		512		1024	
Fault	FDR	FPR	FDR	FPR	FDR	FPR	FDR	FPR	FDR	FPR
0	0.342	0.031	0.344	0.035	0.299	0.032	0.422	0.046	0.316	0.037
1	0.988	0.002	0.990	0.000	0.987	0.000	0.992	0.000	0.992	0.000
2	0.983	0.000	0.983	0.000	0.981	0.000	0.982	0.000	0.982	0.000
3	0.629	0.042	0.652	0.049	0.652	0.057	0.614	0.049	0.636	0.067
4	0.990	0.000	0.991	0.000	0.990	0.000	0.990	0.000	0.991	0.000
5	0.987	0.012	0.991	0.003	0.991	0.007	0.989	0.001	0.987	0.001
6	0.712	0.002	0.871	0.005	0.778	0.005	0.997	0.004	0.957	0.005
7	0.999	0.001	0.999	0.002	0.999	0.000	0.999	0.000	0.999	0.000
8	0.887	0.003	0.863	0.002	0.889	0.002	0.861	0.002	0.883	0.002
9	0.288	0.055	0.215	0.057	0.179	0.050	0.215	0.057	0.228	0.059
10	0.819	0.005	0.839	0.007	0.833	0.007	0.837	0.007	0.833	0.005
11	0.979	0.001	0.975	0.001	0.982	0.001	0.977	0.000	0.978	0.000
12	0.769	0.007	0.757	0.003	0.744	0.002	0.763	0.003	0.741	0.003
13	0.901	0.005	0.897	0.005	0.894	0.007	0.893	0.004	0.862	0.001
14	0.995	0.000	0.996	0.000	0.996	0.000	0.996	0.000	0.996	0.000
15	0.392	0.087	0.342	0.074	0.374	0.084	0.285	0.060	0.316	0.075
16	0.859	0.005	0.844	0.004	0.851	0.006	0.802	0.003	0.758	0.005
17	0.953	0.001	0.952	0.002	0.952	0.000	0.952	0.000	0.950	0.000
18	0.808	0.007	0.940	0.007	0.939	0.007	0.933	0.006	0.932	0.008
19	0.955	0.003	0.976	0.003	0.974	0.004	0.975	0.003	0.976	0.001
20	0.934	0.002	0.938	0.003	0.933	0.001	0.933	0.002	0.918	0.001
AVERAGE	0.817	0.013	0.826	0.012	0.820	0.013	0.829	0.012	0.820	0.013

6. Conclusion

In prior studies, the fault detection and identification model proposed using CWT and 3DCNN demonstrated notable effectiveness on benchmark process datasets. However, it failed to achieve a higher accuracy score compared to previous models, especially 2DCNN, particularly under normal operating conditions in TEP datasets. The preprocessing with CWT resulted in a lack of information from absolute values of chemical process data, as opposed to the abundance of time-frequency information.

Therefore, in this study, a model capable of handling both data types: time-frequency scalograms and absolute values of chemical processes is introduced. The incorporation of these data types is expected to enhance the model's performance in fault detection and identification. The proposed model is a multimodal CNN with 2D and 3D input layers, utilizing both 2DCNN and 3DCNN.

The model is evaluated on TEP datasets. The multimodal CWT-3DCNN achieves the best overall performance, surpassing the accuracy average of the other models although the model training time is longer than 2DCNN. Batch size is one of the important hyper-parameters of deep learning. We investigated the effects of the different batch sizes. In this case, the best batch size is 512. The bigger batch sizes can contribute to shortening model training time.

References

C. Ukawa, Y. Yamashita, Fault Detection and Diagnosis for Chemical Processes based on Deep Neural Networks with Continuous Wavelet Transform, Computer Aided Chemical Engineering, Elsevier (2023), https://doi.org/10.1016/B978-0-443-15274-0.50267-5

C. A. Rieth, B. D. Amsel, R. Tran, M. B. Cook, Additional Tennessee Eastman Process Simulation Data for Anomaly Detection Evaluation, Harvard Dataverse (2017), V1, https://doi.org/10.7910/DVN/6C3JR1

H. Chen, Jian. C, Z. Yang, W. Si, H. Cheng, Fault diagnosis of the dynamic chemical process based on the optimized CNN-LSTM network. ACS Omega (2022), https://doi.org/10.1021/acsomega.2c04017

G. Zhu, L. Zhang, P. Shen, J. Song, S. A. A. Shah, M. Bennamoun, Continuous Gesture Segmentation and Recognition Using 3DCNN and Convolutional LSTM, IEEE Trans. Multimedia (2019), https://doi.org/10.1109/TMM.2018.2869278

H. Wu, J. Zhao, Deep convolutional neural network model based chemical process fault diagnosis, Computers & Chemical Engineering (2018), https://doi.org/10.1016/j.compchemeng.2018.04.009

A. Riahi, O. Elharrouss, S. A. Maadeed, BEMD-3DCNN-based method for COVID-19 detection, Computers in Biology and Medicine (2022), https://doi.org/10.1016/j.compbiomed.2021.105188

Y. Liu, T. Zhang, Z. Li, 3DCNN-Based Real-Time Driver Fatigue Behavior Detection in Urban Rail Transit, IEEE Access (2019), https://doi.org/10.1109/ACCESS.2019.2945136

S. Shikhar, K. Kumar. ASL-3DCNN: American sign language recognition technique using 3-D convolutional neural networks, Multimedia Tools and Applications (2021), https://doi.org/10.1007/s11042-021-10768-5

S, Qian. *Introduction to time-frequency and wavelet transform.* 2002. Prentice Hall, New Jersey

Printed and bound by CPI Group (UK) Ltd, Croydon, CR0 4YY

03/10/2024

01040328-0005